D1069042

Safety Symbols

These safety symbols are used in laboratory and field investigations in this book to indicate possible hazards. Learn the meaning of each symbol and refer to this page often. *Remember to wash your hands thoroughly after completing lab procedures.*

Safety Symbols	Hazard	Examples	Precaution	Remedy
Disposal	Special disposal procedures need to be followed.	certain chemicals, living organisms	Do not dispose of these materials in the sink or trash can.	Dispose of wastes as directed by your teacher.
Biological	Organisms or other biological materials that might be harmful to humans	bacteria, fungi, blood, unpreserved tissues, plant materials	Avoid skin contact with these materials. Wear mask or gloves.	Notify your teacher if you suspect contact with material. Wash hands thoroughly.
Extreme Temperature	Objects that can burn skin by being too cold or too hot	boiling liquids, hot plates, dry ice, liquid nitrogen	Use proper protection when handling.	Go to your teacher for first aid.
Sharp Object	Use of tools or glassware that can easily puncture or slice skin	razor blades, pins, scalpels, pointed tools, dissecting probes, broken glass	Practice common-sense behavior and follow guidelines for use of the tool.	Go to your teacher for first aid.
Fume	Possible danger to respiratory tract from fumes	ammonia, acetone, nail polish remover, heated sulfur, moth balls	Make sure there is good ventilation. Never smell fumes directly. Wear a mask.	Leave foul area and notify your teacher immediately.
Electrical	Possible danger from electrical shock or burn	improper grounding, liquid spills, short circuits, exposed wires	Double-check setup with teacher. Check condition of wires and apparatus. Use GFI-protected outlets.	Do not attempt to fix electrical problems. Notify your teacher immediately.
Irritant	Substances that can irritate the skin or mucous membranes of the respiratory tract	pollen, moth balls, steel wool, fiberglass, potassium permanganate	Wear dust mask and gloves. Practice extra care when handling these materials.	Go to your teacher for first aid.
Chemical	Chemicals that can react with and destroy tissue and other materials	bleaches such as hydrogen peroxide; acids such as sulfuric acid, hydrochloric acid; bases such as ammonia, sodium hydroxide	Wear goggles, gloves, and an apron.	Immediately flush the affected area with water and notify your teacher.
Toxic	Substance may be poisonous if touched, inhaled, or swallowed.	mercury, many metal compounds, iodine, poinsettia plant parts	Follow your teacher's instructions.	Always wash hands thoroughly after use. Go to your teacher for first aid.
Flammable	Open flame may ignite flammable chemicals, loose clothing, or hair.	alcohol, kerosene, potassium permanganate, hair, clothing	Avoid open flames and heat when using flammable chemicals.	Notify your teacher immediately. Use fire safety equipment if applicable.
Open Flame	Open flame in use, may cause fire.	hair, clothing, paper, synthetic materials	Tie back hair and loose clothing. Follow teacher's instructions on lighting and extinguishing flames.	Always wash hands thoroughly after use. Go to your teacher for first aid.

Eye Safety
Proper eye protection should be worn at all times by anyone performing or observing science activities.

Clothing Protection
This symbol appears when substances could stain or burn clothing.

Animal Safety
This symbol appears when safety of animals and students must be ensured.

Radioactivity
This symbol appears when radioactive materials are used.

Handwashing
After the lab, wash hands with soap and water before removing goggles.

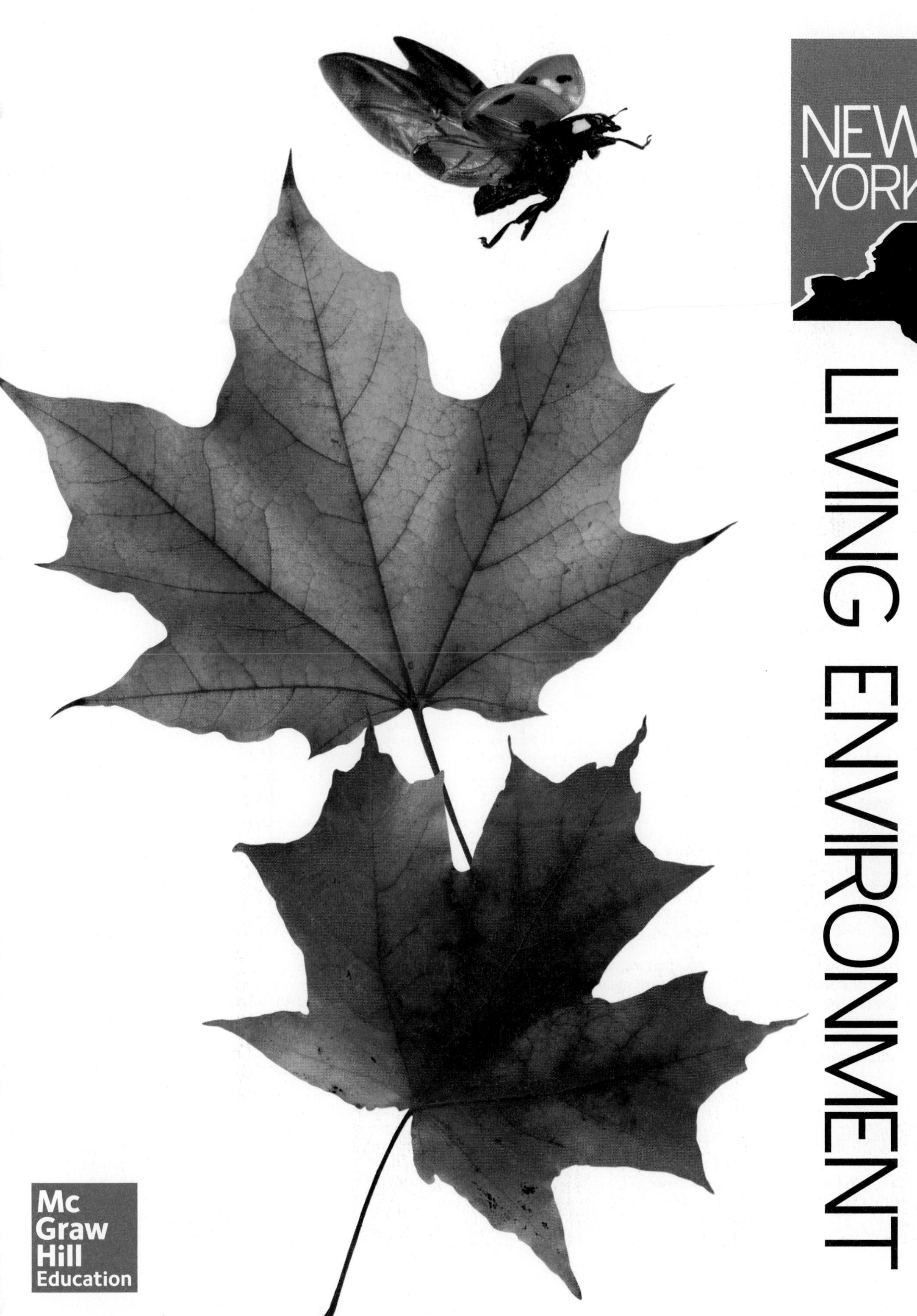
NEW YORK
LIVING ENVIRONMENT
Mc
Graw
Hill
Education

COVER CREDIT: (t)John Foxx/Getty Images; (b)Siede Preis/Getty Images

MHEonline.com

Send all inquiries to:
McGraw-Hill Education
8787 Orion Place
Columbus, OH 43240

ISBN: 978-0-02-144791-6
MHID: 0-02-144791-8

Printed in the United States of America.

1 2 3 4 5 6 7 8 9 QVS 20 19 18 17 16 15

Authors

The authors of *New York Biology* used their content knowledge and teaching expertise to craft manuscript that is accessible and accurate, geared toward student achievement.

Alton Biggs

has been a biology educator in Texas public schools for more than 30 years. He has a BS and an MS in biology from Texas A & M University—Commerce. Mr. Biggs was the founding president of the Texas Association of Biology Teachers in 1985, received the National Association of Biology Teachers' (NABT) Outstanding Biology Teacher Award for Texas in 1982 and 1995, and in 1992 was the president of the NABT.

Whitney Crispen Hagins

teaches biology at Lexington High School in Lexington, Massachusetts. She has a BA and an MA in biological sciences from Mount Holyoke College and an MAT from Duke University. In 1998, she received NSF funding for the development of molecular biology activities. In 1999, she was a Massachusetts NABT Outstanding Biology Teacher Award recipient. In 2005, she was awarded the Siemens Foundation AP Award for Math and Science Teachers for Massachusetts. She works with the Wisconsin Fast Plant Program to develop curriculum, and she enjoys sharing ideas and activities at national meetings.

William G. Holliday

is a science education professor at the University of Maryland (College Park), and before 1986, a professor at the University of Calgary (Alberta, Canada). He served as president of the National Association for Research in Science Teaching and later as an elected board member to the National Science Teachers Association. He has an MS in biological sciences and a PhD in science education. Dr. Holliday's multifaceted teaching experience totals more than 40 years.

Chris L. Kapicka

is a retired faculty member from Northwest Nazarene University in Nampa, Idaho. She has a BS in biology from Boise State University, an MS in bacteriology and public health from Washington State University, and a PhD in cell and molecular physiology and pharmacology from the University of Nevada Medical School. In 1986, she received the Presidential Award for Science Teaching, and in 1988, she was awarded NABT's Outstanding Biology Teacher Award.

Margaret Kilgo

has 30 years of experience in the Houston Independent School District as a teacher and campus principal. After leaving the school system, Ms. Kilgo founded Kilgo Consulting, Inc., which provides innovative models, strategies, and data-driven decisions based on the Kilgo Research Model for studying state and national standards from the viewpoint of standardized assessments.

(t)Alton Biggs, (tc)Whitney Hagins, (c)William G. Holliday, (bc)Chris L. Kapicka, (b)Courtesy Margaret Kilgo

Linda Lundgren

has more than 25 years of experience teaching science at the middle school, high school, and college levels, including ten years at Bear Creek High School in Lakewood, Colorado. For eight years, she was a research associate in the Department of Science and Technology at the University of Colorado at Denver. Ms. Lundgren has a BA in journalism and zoology from the University of Massachusetts and an MS in zoology from The Ohio State University. In 1991, she was named Colorado Science Teacher of the Year.

Ann Haley MacKenzie

currently teaches at Miami University in Oxford, Ohio, where she works with future high school science teachers and teaches a life science inquiry course. She is the editor of *The American Biology Teacher* for the National Association of Biology Teachers. Dr. MacKenzie has a BS in biology from Purdue University, an MEd in secondary education from the University of Cincinnati, and an EdD in curriculum and instruction from the University of Cincinnati. She is a former Ohio Teacher of the Year and Presidential Award Winner for Secondary School Science.

William D. Rogers

is a faculty member in the Department of Biology at Ball State University in Muncie, Indiana. He has a BA and an MA in biology from Drake University and a Doctor of Arts in biology from Idaho State University. He has received teaching awards for outstanding contributions to general education, and he has also received funding from the American Association of Colleges and Universities to study different approaches to science teaching.

Marion B. Sewer

is an assistant professor at the Georgia Institute of Technology and a Georgia Cancer Coalition Distinguished Scholar. She received a BS in biochemistry from Spelman College in 1993 and a PhD in pharmacology from Emory University in 1998. Dr. Sewer studies how the integration of various signaling pathways controls steroid hormone biosynthesis.

Dinah Zike

is an international curriculum consultant and inventor who has developed educational products and three-dimensional, interactive graphic organizers for more than 30 years. As president and founder of Dinah-Might Adventures, L.P., Ms. Zike is the author of more than 100 award-winning educational publications, including *The Big Book of Science.* She has a BS and an MS in educational curriculum and instruction from Texas A & M University. Dinah Zike's *Foldables* are an exclusive feature of McGraw-Hill textbooks.

(t)Linda Lundgren, (tc)Ann Haley MacKenzie, (c)Dr. William Rogers, (bc)Dr. Marion Sewer, (b)Dinah Zike

Contributing Writer

Thomas Matthiesen
Tissue Engineer
Chicago, IL

Thomas Matthiesen wrote, consulted, and provided photographs for Chapter 20's Cutting Edge Biology feature.

A² DEVELOPMENT PROCESS

Why A²?

Accuracy Assurance is central to McGraw-Hill's commitment to high-quality, learner-oriented, real-world, and error-free products. Also at the heart of our A² Development Process is a commitment to make the text **Accessible** and **Approachable** for both students and teachers. A collaboration among authors, content editors, academic advisors, and classroom teachers, the A² Development Process provides opportunities for continual improvement through customer feedback and thorough content review.

The A² Development Process begins with a review of the previous edition and a look forward to state and national standards. The authors combine expertise in teacher training and education with a mastery of biology content knowledge. As manuscript is created and edited, consultants review the accuracy of the content while our Teacher Reviewers examine the program from the points of view of both teacher and student. Student labs and teacher demonstrations are reviewed for both accuracy of content and safety. As design elements are applied, chapter content is again reviewed, as are photos and diagrams.

Throughout the life of the program, McGraw-Hill continues to troubleshoot and incorporate improvements. Our goal is to deliver to you a program that has been created, refined, tested, and validated as a successful tool for your continued **Academic Achievement.**

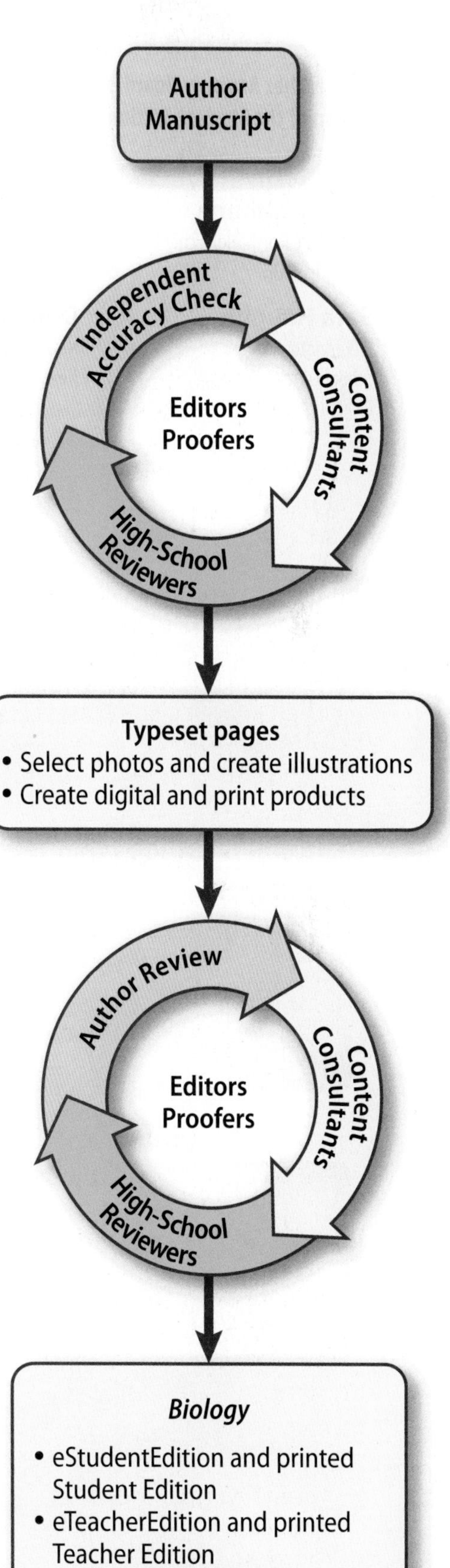

(t)Eye of Science/Science Source, (b)K. Kjeldsen/Science Source, (bkgd)©George McCarthy/Corbis

Teacher Advisory Board

The Teacher Advisory Board gave the authors, editorial staff, and design team feedback on the content and design of the Student Edition. We thank these teachers for their hard work and creative suggestions.

Chuck Cambria
Springfield North High School
Springfield, OH

Sara Haughn
Pickerington High
School Central
Pickerington, OH

Michelle M. Lewis
Lancaster High School
Lancaster, OH

Daniel J. Regelski
New Albany High School
New Albany, OH

Pamela J. Schumm
Wawasee High School
Syracuse, IN

Danielle S. Scrase
Sycamore High School
Cincinnati, OH

Sharon Seckel
Canal Winchester High School
Canal Winchester, OH

Paula Weaver
Seymour High School
Seymour, IN

Reviewers

Each teacher reviewed selected chapters of *Glencoe Biology* and provided feedback and suggestions for improving the effectiveness of the instruction.

Beth Adams, EdS
Cartersville High School
Cartersville, GA

Michele Wonser Altavilla
Elk River High School
Elk River, MN

Elaine Asmus
Snake River High School
Blackfoot, ID

Shelley Barker
Danville High School
Danville, IL

Stephanie L. Baron
Patrick Henry High School
San Diego, CA

Rochelle Battersby
Sanford F. Calhoun High School
Merrick, NY

Ann Blackwell
Travelers Rest High School
Travelers Rest, SC

Fran S. Bouknight
Brookland-Cayce High School
Cayce, SC

Kimberly A. Brown
East Ridge High School
Chattanooga, TN

John H. C. Chipley
Palma High School
Salinas, CA

Melissa C. Donham
Little Rock Central High School
Little Rock, AR

William A. Donovan, Jr.
Amesbury High School
Amesbury, MA

Erica Dosch, BSN, MEd
Connetquot High School
Bohemia, NY

Julie Ertmann
University City High School
University City, MO

Mark Fife
Centerville High School
Centerville, OH

Sasha Hammond
Yakima School District
Yakima, WA

Kenneth L. Harms
Tigard High School
Tigard, OR

David Iott
Holden High School
Holden, MO

Rebecca Jackson
Summerville High School
Summerville, SC

Clinton A. Kennedy
Cascade JR/SR High School
Cascade, ID

Kristen Holly Kent
Pioneer Valley High School
Santa Maria, CA

Deborah L. Krause, EdD
West Orange Public Schools
West Orange, NJ

Kimberly Lane-Hinton
Whitney Young Magnet High School
Chicago, IL

Samantha A. Long
Carlisle High School
Carlisle, PA

Charlotte Parnell
Sullivan High School
Sullivan, MO

Cynthia A. Pousman
Davidson Fine Arts Magnet School
Augusta, GA

Rebekah R. Ravgiala, EdD
Merrimack High School
Merrimack, NH

Gail Raymond
Anchorage School District
Anchorage, AK

Kathryn A. Roberts
Lakeside Public High Schools
Hot Springs, AR

Tracy Rojo
Tucker High School
Tucker, GA

Pamela D. Sherley
Chicago Public Schools
Chicago, IL

Gary R. Smith
Pinelands Regional High School
Tuckerton, NJ

Sue Whitsett
Fond du Lac High School
Fond du Lac, WI

Karen Ann Wickersham
Troy High School
Troy, MI

A² DEVELOPMENT PROCESS

Lead Consultants

Lisa K Felske
Science Specialist
Harris County Department of Education
Houston, Texas

Ann C. Mulvihill
PK-12 Science Coordinator
Irving ISD
Irving, Texas

Content Consultants

Content consultants each reviewed selected chapters of *Glencoe Biology* for content accuracy and clarity.

Larry Baresi, PhD
Associate Professor of Biology
California State
University, Northridge
Northridge, CA

Janice E. Bonner, PhD
Associate Professor of Biology
College of Notre Dame
of Maryland
Baltimore, MD

Renea J. Brodie, PhD
Assistant Professor of
Biological Sciences
University of South Carolina
Columbia, SC

Luis A Cañas, PhD
Assistant Professor
Department of
Entomology/OARDC
The Ohio State University
Wooster, OH

John S. Choinski, Jr., PhD
Professor of Biology
Department of Biology
University of Central Arkansas
Conway, AR

Dr. Lewis B. Coons, PhD
Professor of Biology
The University of Memphis
Memphis, TN

Cara Lea Council-Garcia, MS
Biology Lab Coordinator
The University of New Mexico
Albuquerque, NM

Dr. Donald S. Emmeluth, PhD
Department of Biology
Armstrong Atlantic State University
Savannah, GA

Diana L. Engle, PhD
Ecology Consultant
University of California Santa Barbara
Santa Barbara, CA

John Gatz, PhD
Professor of Zoology
Ohio Wesleyan University
Delaware, OH

Alan D. Gishlick, PhD
National Center for
Science Education
Oakland, CA

Yourha Kang, PhD
Assistant Professor of Biology
Iona College
New Rochelle, NY

Mark E. Lee, PhD
Assistant Professor of Biology
Spelman College
Atlanta, GA

Judy M. Nesmith, MS
Lecturer—Biology
University of Michigan—
Dearborn
Dearborn, MI

Hay-Oak Park, PhD
Associate Professor
Department of
Molecular Genetics
The Ohio State University
Columbus, OH

Carolyn F. Randolph, PhD
President NSTA
2001–2002
Assistant Executive Director
The SCEA
Columbia, SC

David A. Rubin, PhD
Assistant Professor of
Physiology
Illinois State University
Normal, IL

Malathi Srivatsan, PhD
Assistant Professor of Biology
State University of Arkansas
Jonesboro, AR

Laura Vogel, PhD
Associate Professor of
Biological Sciences
Illinois State University
Normal, IL

VivianLee Ward, MS
Director of CyberEducation; Codirector of Fellows
Program; Project Director
Access Excellence @ the
National Health Museum
Washington, DC

Safety Consultants

Safety Consultants reviewed labs and lab materials for safety and implementation.

Jack Gerlovich
School of Education
Department of
Teaching and Learning
Drake University
Des Moines, IA

Dennis McElroy
Director of Curriculum
Assistant Director
for Technology
School of Education
Graceland University
Lamoni, IA

Reading Consultant

Dr. Douglas Fisher provided expert guidance on prototypes, Real-World Reading Links, and the reading strand.

Douglas Fisher, PhD
Professor of Language and Literacy Education
San Diego State University
San Diego, CA

Standardized Test Practice Consultant

Dr. Ralph Feather provided expert guidance on effective standardized test practice questions.

Ralph Feather, PhD
Assistant Professor of Education
Bloomsburg University of Pennsylvania
Bloomsburg, PA

Lab Tester

Science Kit performed and evaluated the Student Edition labs and additional Teacher Edition material, providing suggestions for improving the effectiveness of student instructions and teacher support.

Science Kit and Boreal Laboratories
Tonawanda, NY

Your assignment's due tomorrow...
but your book is in your locker!
James Woodson/Digital Vision/Getty Images

Even in crunch time, with ConnectED, we've got you covered!

With ConnectED, you have instant access to all of your study materials—anytime, anywhere. From homework materials to study guides—it's all in one place and just a click away. ConnectED even allows you to collaborate with your classmates and use mobile apps to make studying easy.

Resources built for you—available 24/7:

- Your eBook available wherever you are
- Personal Tutors and Self-Check Quizzes to help your learning
- An Online Calendar with all of your due dates
- eFlashcard App to make studying easy
- A message center to stay in touch

Reimagine Learning

Go Online!
MHEonline.com

Vocab

Learn about new vocabulary words.

Watch

Watch animations and videos.

Tutor

See and hear a teacher explain science concepts

Tools

Find tools to help you study.

Check

Check your progress.

Lab

Get all of your labs and lab worksheets.

Resources

Access practice worksheets.

eGames

Play interactive games to reinforce lessons.

TABLE OF CONTENTS

Ecology

CHAPTER 1

Go Online!

Concepts in Motion Visualizing Scientific Methods
Characteristics of Living Organisms

Video Scientific Methods
A Shark's Story

Virtual Lab Biotechnology—Dependent and Independent Variables

WebQuest Medical Research Technology

Go Online!
MHEonline.com

Go Online!

Ecology

CHAPTER 2

Principles of Ecology 30

Go Online!

CHAPTER 3

Communities, Biomes, and Ecosystems 58

Go Online!

Ecology

Go Online!
MHEonline.com

Go Online!

Unit 2 Webquest Snake Venom

The Cell

CHAPTER 6

Go Online!

Concepts in Motion Ionic Bonds
Personal Tutor How Monomers Bond, Types of Bonds
Video Atomic Model, Visualizing Properties of Water, Isotopes, Biological Macromolecules
Video Lab Does Temperature Affect an Enzyme Reaction
Virtual Lab Enzyme-Controlled Reactions
WebQuest The Perfect Substitute?

CHAPTER 7

Go Online!

Concepts in Motion Plasma Membrane Summary of Cell Structures, Visualizing Cells, Facilitated Transport, Sodium-Potassium Pump, Isotonic, Hypertonic, and Hypotonic Solutions
Personal Tutor Na/K Pump
Video Cell Structures, Cell Specialization
Video Lab Observing and Comparing Different Cell Types
Virtual Lab Cell Pursuit Game
WebQuest Snake Venom

The Cell

CHAPTER 8

CHAPTER 9

Go Online!
MHEonline.com

Genetics

Go Online!

Unit 3 **Webquest** Livestock Genetics

CHAPTER 10

Go Online!

Concepts in Motion	Visualizing Meiosis
	Mitosis and Meiosis
	Homozygous-Homozygous Cross
Personal Tutor	Producing Variation
	Punnett Squares
Video	Heredity
Virtual Lab	Punnett Squares
WebQuest	A Foundation of Hope

CHAPTER 11

Go Online!

Concepts in Motion	Review of Terms
	Recessive Genetic Disorders in Humans
	Dominant Genetic Disorders in Humans
	Visualizing Nondisjunction
	Nondisjunction in Sex Chromosomes
	Fetal Tests
Personal Tutor	Pedigrees
	Complex Patterns of Inheritance
Virtual Lab	Sex-Linked Traits
WebQuest	Livestock Genetics

Genetics

CHAPTER 12

CHAPTER 13

Go Online!
MHEonline.com

Go Online!

Unit 4 **Webquest** Texas During the Cretaceous Period

History of Biological Diversity

CHAPTER 14

Go Online!

Concepts in Motion Categories of Fossil Types
Visualizing the Geologic Time Scale
Continental Drift
Miller-Urey Experiment
Margulis's Theory
Personal Tutor Making Proteins
Video Digging Through Science
Video Lab Fossils
Virtual Lab Dino Dig
WebQuest Texas During the Cretaceous Period

CHAPTER 15

Go Online!

Concepts in Motion Visualizing Natural Selection
Basic Principles of Natural Selection
Vestigial Structures
Hardy-Weinberg Principle
Convergent Evolution
Gradualism and Punctuated Equilibrium
Personal Tutor Comparison of Selection
Virtual Lab Natural Selection
Webquest Biodiversity Hotspots

History of Biological Diversity

CHAPTER 16

CHAPTER 17

Go Online!

The Human Body

CHAPTER 18

Go Online!

CHAPTER 19

Go Online!

The Human Body

CHAPTER 20

Go Online!

Concepts in Motion From Cadavers to Artificial Hearts Timeline
Blood Vessel Structure
Circulatory System
Blood Types
Visualizing Gas Exchange
Common Respiratory Disorders
Kidney Filtration
Common Excretory Disorders
Personal Tutor ABO Blood Groups
Dialysis
Video Circulatory System
Respiratory System
Virtual Lab Blood Pressure
WebQuest An Eye for an Eye

The Human Body

CHAPTER 21

Go Online!

Concepts in Motion: The Digestive System, Smooth Muscle Contraction, Time for Digestion, Steroid Hormone Stimulation, Activities and Average Calorie Usage, Major Roles of Some Vitamins and Minerals, Amino Acid Hormone Stimulation, Visualizing the Endocrine System
Personal Tutor: Glucagon and Insulin Feedback
Video: Digestion
Video Lab: The Action of the Enzyme Amylase on Breakfast Cereals
Virtual Lab: The Digestive and Endocrine Systems
WebQuest: Chemicals Tell the Story

CHAPTER 22

Go Online!

Concepts in Motion: Ovulation, Preventable Causes of Birth Defects, Menstrual Cycle Phases, Visualizing a Placenta
Personal Tutor: Sperm and Egg Formation
Video: Fertilization and Birth
WebQuest: Sizing Up the Situation

The Human Body

CHAPTER 23

Go Online!

Concepts in Motion	Human Infectious Diseases
	Immunology Through Time Timeline
	Complement System
	Cells of the Immune System
	Visualizing Specific Immune Responses
	Common Immunizations
	Common Allergens
Personal Tutor	Primary and Secondary Responses
Video	Immune System
Virtual Lab	Virtual Pathology
WebQuest	Relief in Small Packages

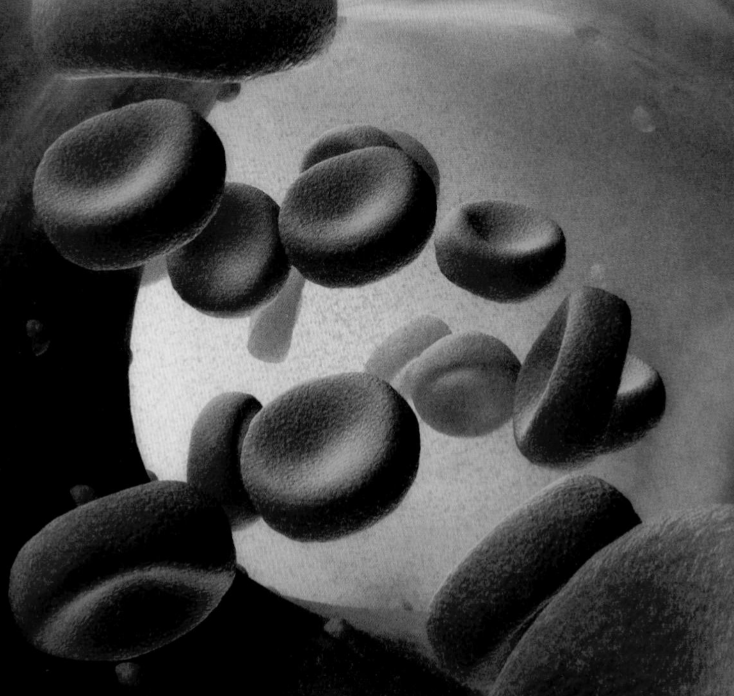

MedicalRF.com

STUDENT RESOURCES

Investigation and Experimentation

Laboratory Guidelines

Data Collection

Laboratory Equipment and Techniques

Skillbuilder Handbook

Problem-Solving Skills

Math Skills

Reference Handbook

Rubberball/Getty Images

by Dinah Zike

Folding Instructions

The following pages offer step-by-step instructions to make the Foldables study guides.

Layered-Look Book

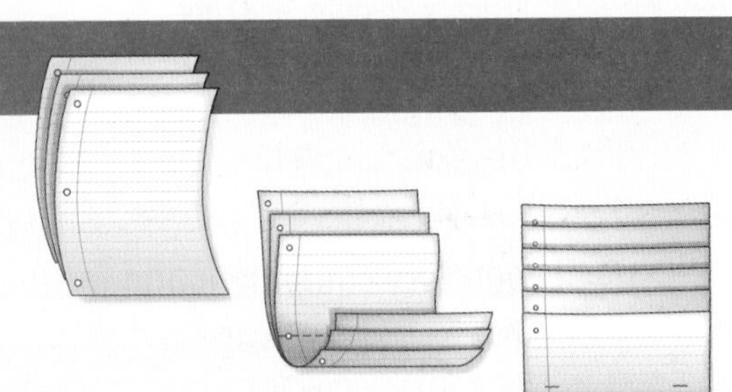

1. Collect three sheets of paper and layer them about ½ inch apart vertically. Keep the edges level.
2. Fold up the bottom edges of the paper to form six equal tabs.
3. Fold the papers and crease well to hold the tabs in place. Staple along the fold. Label each tab.

Trifold Book

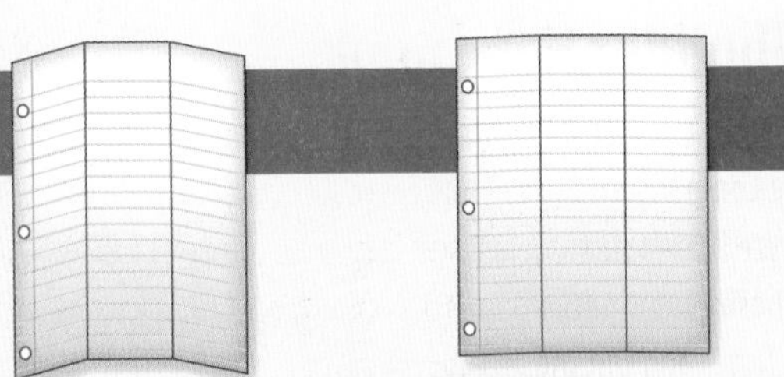

1. Fold a vertical sheet of paper into thirds.
2. Unfold and label each row.

Three-Tab Book

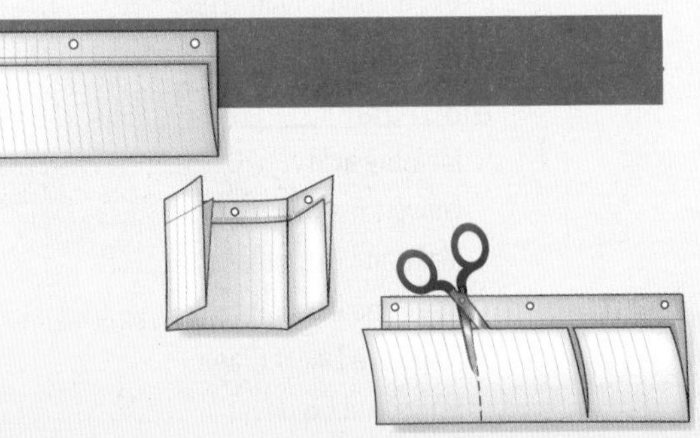

1. Fold a vertical sheet of paper from side to side. Make the front edge about 2 cm shorter than the back edge.
2. Turn lengthwise and fold into thirds.
3. Unfold and cut only the top layer along both folds to make three tabs. Label each tab.

Two- and Four-Tab Books

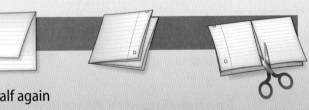

1. Fold a sheet of paper in half.
2. Fold in half again. If making a four-tab book, then fold in half again to make three folds.
3. Unfold and cut only the top layer along the folds to make two or four tabs. Label each tab.

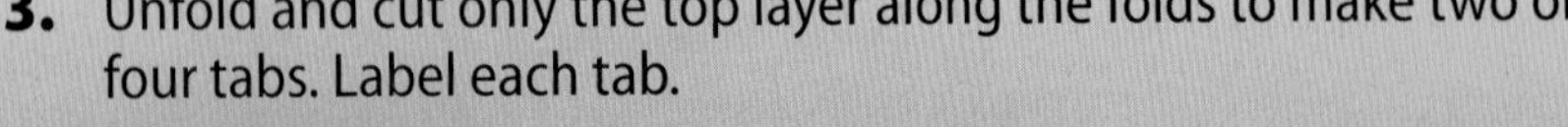

Four-Door Book

1. Find the middle of a horizontal sheet of paper. Fold both edges to the middle and crease the folds.
2. Fold the folded paper in half, from top to bottom.
3. Unfold and cut along the fold lines of the top layers to make four tabs. Label each tab.

Concept-Map Book

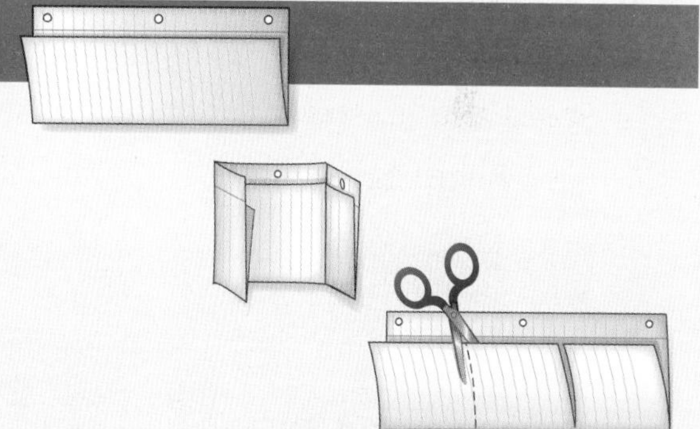

1. Fold a vertical sheet of paper from top to bottom. Make the top edge about 2 cm shorter than the bottom edge.
2. Turn lengthwise and fold into thirds.
3. Unfold and cut only the top layer along both folds to make three tabs. Label the top and each tab

Vocabulary Book

1. Fold a vertical sheet of notebook paper in half.
2. Cut along every third line of only the top layer to form tabs. Label each tab.

Folded Chart

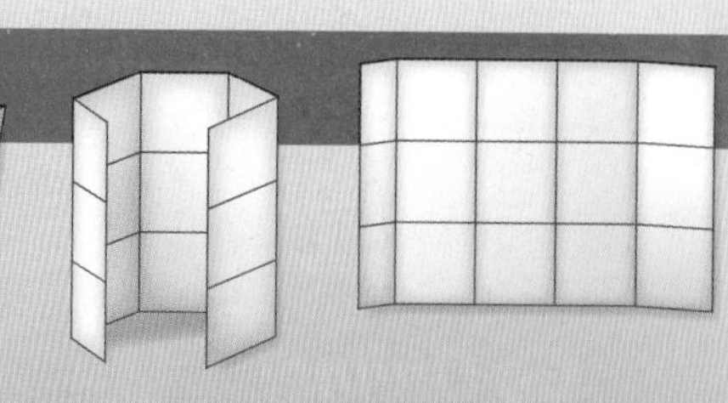

1. Fold a sheet of paper lengthwise into thirds.
2. Fold the paper widthwise into fifths.
3. Unfold, lay the paper lengthwise, and draw lines along the folds. Label the table.

Biologists study organisms from the depths of the ocean to the upper reaches of Earth's atmosphere. Humans are just one species out of an estimated 100 million species.

LaunchLAB 

Why is observation important?

Scientists use a planned, organized approach to solving problems. A key element of this approach is gathering information through detailed observations. Scientists extend their ability to observe by using scientific tools and techniques.

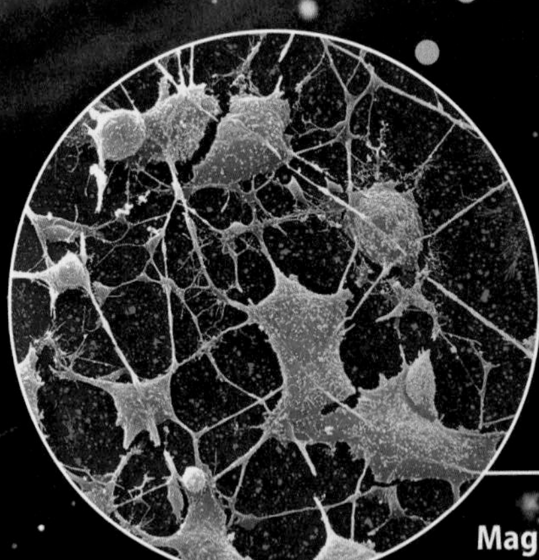

Human neurons
Color-Enhanced SEM
Magnification: unavailable

Go Online!
MHEonline.com

Watch  Resources  Vocab  Tutor  IWB  Check  Lab  Tools  Science Notebook 

CHAPTER 1

The Study of Life

1 Introduction to Biology

1.1.1b, 1.1.3b, 4.1.2a, 4.1.2b, 4.1.2c, 4.1.2d, 4.1.2e, 4.1.3a, 4.3.1g, 4.3.1h, 4.4.1a, 4.5.2a, 4.7.3a, ¥e, ¥n

2 The Nature of Science

1.1.1a, 1.1.1b, 1.1.1c, 1.1.2a, 1.1.2b, 1.1.3a, 1.1.4a, 1.2.2a, 1.2.3a, 1.2.3b, 1.2.3c, 1.3.1a, 1.3.2, 1.3.3, 1.3.4a, 1.3.4b, 1.3.4c, 1.3.5a, 1.3.5b, ¥a, ¥e, ¥I, ¥j, ¥k, ¥l, ¥n, ¥o, ¥p, ¥q

THEMEFOCUS

Structure and function **All living things have structures and functions that help them maintain homeostasis.**

BIGIDEA

Biology is the study of life.

FOLDABLES® Study Organizer

Some Roles of Biologists

Make a layered-look book using the titles shown. Use it to organize your notes on the roles of biologists.

Some Roles of Biologists

Study the diversity of life

Research diseases

Develop technology

Improve agriculture

Preserve the environment

 USE IT! Science Notebook

1 Introduction to Biology

1.1.1b, 1.1.3b, 4.1.2a, 4.1.2b, 4.1.2c, 4.1.2d, 4.1.2e, 4.1.3a, 4.3.1g, 4.3.1h, 4.4.1a, 4.5.2a, 4.7.3a, ¥e, ¥n

BIOLOGY 4U

Think of as many living things as you can. What do oak trees, cheetahs, grass, snakes, planaria, and sharks have in common? What makes them unique? How do we know?

Review Vocabulary

environment: the living and nonliving things that surround an organism and with which the organism interacts

New Vocabulary

biology
organism
organization
growth
development
reproduction
species
stimulus
response
homeostasis
adaptation

Multilingual eGlossary

MAINIDEA

All living things share the characteristics of life.

Essential Questions

- What is biology?
- What are possible benefits of studying biology?
- What are the characteristics of living things?

The Science of Life

Before Jane Goodall, pictured in **Figure 1,** arrived in Gombe Stream National Park in Tanzania, Africa, in 1960 to study chimpanzees, the world of chimpanzees was a mystery. Jane's curiosity, determination, and patience over a long period of time resulted in the chimpanzee troop's acceptance of her presence so that she was able to observe their behavior closely.

When people study living things or pose questions about how living things interact with the environment, they are learning about **biology,** the study of life. Biology comes from the Greek word *bio,* meaning *life,* and from *logos,* meaning *study.*

In biology, you will study the origins and history of life and once-living things, the structures of living things, how living things interact with one another, and how living things function. This will help you understand how humans have a vital role in preserving the natural environment and sustaining life on Earth.

Have you ever hiked in a forest and wondered why different trees have leaves with different shapes? Maybe you have watched an ant quickly cross the sidewalk toward a breadcrumb and wondered how the ant knew that the breadcrumb was there. When you ask these questions, you are observing, and you are asking questions about life.

■ **Figure 1** Jane Goodall conducted field research for many years to observe chimpanzee behavior.

Predict ***the types of questions you would ask if you observed chimpanzee behavior.***

What do biologists do?

Imagine being the first person to look into a microscope and discover cells. What do you think it was like to find the first dinosaur fossils that indicated feathers? Who studies how organisms, including the marbled stargazer fish in **Figure 2,** obtain food? Will the AIDS virus be defeated? Is there life on other planets or anywhere else in the universe? Biologists are people who study biology. They make discoveries and seek explanations by performing laboratory and field investigations. Throughout this textbook, you will discover what biologists in the real world do and you will learn about careers in biology.

■ **Figure 2** The marbled stargazer fish lives beneath the ocean floor off the coast of Indonesia. It explodes upward from beneath the sand to grab its food.

Observe ***How does this fish hide from its food?***

Study the diversity of life Jane Goodall, shown in **Figure 1,** traveled to Africa for the first time in the summer of 1960 to study chimpanzees in their natural environment. By studying chimps in the wild, Goodall witnessed behaviors that had not been observed before. For example, she saw chimps pulling leaves off twigs and using the twigs to retrieve termites from a mound. Before this observation, scientists thought only humans used tools. From her detailed notes, sketches, and maps of chimpanzees' daily travels, Goodall learned how chimpanzees grow and develop and how they gather food. Through Goodall's research we better understand chimpanzees and how to protect them.

FOLDABLES®
Incorporate information from this section into your Foldable.

Research disease Mary-Claire King started studying the link between genes and disease in the 1970s. In 1990, she found that a gene on human chromosome 17, later named BRCA1, was related to the development of breast and ovarian cancers. King's work in genetics has helped us to better understand why some people or families are more likely to develop particular types of cancers.

Many biologists research diseases. Questions such as "What causes the disease?", "How does the body fight the disease?", and "How does the disease spread?" often guide biologists' research. Biologists have developed vaccines for smallpox, chicken pox, and diphtheria, and currently, some biologists are researching the development of a vaccine for HIV. Biologists worldwide are researching new treatments for such things as lowering cholesterol levels, fighting obesity, reducing the risk of heart attacks, and preventing Alzheimer's disease.

Develop technologies When you hear the word *technology,* you might think of high-speed computers, cell phones, and DVD players. However, technology has a broader definition. Technology is defined as the application of scientific knowledge to solve human needs and to extend human capabilities. **Figure 3** shows how "bionic" hand technology can help someone who has lost an arm.

■ **Figure 3** A prosthetic "bionic" hand is new technology that can help extend human capabilities.

Other examples of technology include the work of Charles Drew, a doctor who pioneered methods to separate blood plasma from blood cells and safely store and transport blood plasma for transfusions. His research led to blood banks that saved soldiers during World War II and helps countless patients today.

Biologists today continue to discover new ways to improve and save lives. For example, the field of bioengineering applies knowledge gained from studying the function of living systems to the design of mechanical devices such as artificial limbs. In addition, biologists in the field of biotechnology research cells, DNA, and living systems to discover new medicines and medical treatments.

■ **Figure 4** Research into how mustard plants respond to light may contribute to improvements in agriculture.

Improve agriculture Some biologists study the possibilities of genetically engineering plants to grow in poor soils or to resist insects, fungal infections, or frost damage. Other biologists research agricultural issues to improve food production to feed the world's growing human population.

Plant biologist Joanne Chory studies mustard plants, such as the one shown in **Figure 4**, to better understand their sensitivity to light and responses when exposed to different light sources, different times of exposure, and other conditions. Because of her work with plant growth hormones and light, agriculturists might be able to increase the amount of food produced from crops or to grow crops in areas where they normally would not grow.

Preserve the environment Environmental biologists seek to prevent the extinction of animals and plants by developing ways to protect them. Some biologists study the reproductive strategies of endangered species while they are in captivity. Other biologists work in nature preserves that provide safe places for endangered species to live, reproduce, and have protection against poachers.

Lee Anne Martinez is an ecologist who worked to protect the environment where outdoor toilets are common. She helped people in rural Africa construct composting toilets that use no water. The composted waste from the toilets can be added to soil to improve it for agricultural use.

The Characteristics of Life

Have you ever tried to define the word *alive?* If you were to watch a grizzly bear catch a salmon from a river, you obviously would conclude that the bear and salmon are both alive. Is fire alive? Fire moves, increases in size, has energy, and seems to reproduce, but how does fire differ from the bear and salmon?

Over time and after many observations, biologists concluded that all living things have certain characteristics, as listed in **Table 1.** An **organism** is anything that has or once had all these characteristics.

■ **Figure 5** *Streptococcus pyogenes* is a unicellular organism. It can infect the throat, sinuses, or middle ear.

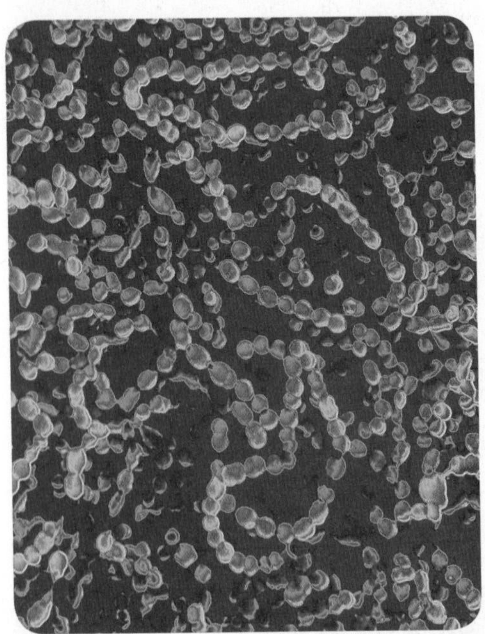

SEM Magnification: 7300×

Made of one or more cells Have you ever had strep throat? It probably was caused by a group A streptococcal bacteria, such as the *Streptococcus pyogenes* shown in **Figure 5.** A bacterium is unicellular—it has just one cell—yet it displays all the characteristics of life just like a skin cell on your body or a cell in a plant's leaf. Humans and plants are multicellular—they have many cells.

Table 1 Characteristics of Living Organisms		Interactive Table
Characteristic of Life	**Example**	**Description**
Made of one or more cells	Magnification: 160×	All organisms are made of one or more cells. The cell is the basic unit of life. Some organisms, such as the *Paramecium sp.*, are unicellular.
Displays organization		The levels of organization in biological systems begin with atoms and molecules and increase in complexity. Each organized structure in an organism has a specific function. The structure of an anteater's snout relates to one of its functions—a container for the anteater's long tongue.
Grows and develops		Growth results in an increase in mass. Development results in different abilities. A frog tadpole grows and develops into an adult frog.
Reproduces		Organisms reproduce and pass along traits from one generation to the next. For a species like the koala to continue to exist, reproduction must occur.
Responds to stimuli		Reactions to internal and external stimuli are called responses. This cheetah responds to the need for food by chasing a gazelle. The gazelle responds by running away.
Requires energy		Energy is required for all life processes. Many organisms, like this mouse, must take in food. Other organisms make their own food.
Maintains homeostasis		All organisms keep internal conditions stable by a process called homeostasis. For example, humans perspire to prevent their body temperature from rising too high.
Adaptations evolve over time		Adaptations are inherited changes that occur over time that help the species survive. Tropical orchids have roots that are adapted to life in a soil-less environment.

Figure 6 In less than a month, these robin chicks grow and develop from helpless chicks to birds capable of flying.

Infer ***how the robins have developed in other ways.***

Cells are the basic units of structure and function in all living things. For example, each heart cell has a structure that enables it to contribute to the heart's function—continually pumping blood throughout the body. Likewise, each cell in a tree's roots has a structure that enables it to help anchor the tree in the ground and to take in water and dissolved minerals from the surrounding soil.

Displays organization Think of all the people in your high school building each day. Students, faculty, counselors, administrators, building service personnel, and food service personnel are organized based on the different tasks they perform and the characteristics they share. For example, the students are designated freshmen, sophomores, juniors, and seniors based on age and coursework.

Living things also display **organization,** which means they are arranged in an orderly way. The *Paramecium* in **Table 1** is made up of one cell, yet that cell is a collection of organized structures that carries on life functions. Each of those structures is composed of atoms and molecules. The many cells that make up the robin chicks in **Figure 6** also contain structures made of atoms and molecules. However, in multicellular organisms, specialized cells are organized into groups that work together called tissues. These tissues are organized into organs, which carry on functions such as digestion and reproduction. Organ systems work together to support an organism.

MiniLAB 1

Observe Characteristics of Life

Is it living or nonliving? In this lab, you will observe several objects to determine if they are living or nonliving.

Procedure

1. Read and complete the lab safety form.
2. Create a data table with four columns titled *Object, Prediction, Characteristic of Life,* and *Evidence.*
3. Your teacher will provide several objects for observation. List each **object** in your table. Predict whether each object is living or nonliving.
4. Carefully observe each object. Discuss with your lab partner what characteristics of life it might exhibit.
5. Use **Table 1** to determine whether each object is living or nonliving. List the evidence in your data table.

Analysis

1. **Compare and contrast** your predictions and observations.
2. **Explain** why it was difficult to classify some objects as living or nonliving.

Grows and develops Most organisms begin as one cell. **Growth** results in the addition of mass to an organism and, in many organisms, the formation of new cells and new structures. Even a bacterium grows. Think about how you have grown throughout your life.

Robin chicks, like those in **Figure 6,** cannot fly for the first few weeks of their lives. Like most organisms, robins develop structures that give them specific abilities, such as flying. **Development** is the process of natural changes that take place during the life of an organism.

Reproduces Most living things are the result of **reproduction**—the production of offspring. Reproduction is not an essential characteristic for individual organisms. Many pets are spayed or neutered to prevent unwanted births. Obviously, these pets can still live even though they cannot reproduce. However, if a species is to continue to exist, then members of that species must reproduce. A **species** is a group of organisms that can breed with one another and produce fertile offspring. If the individuals of a species do not reproduce, then when the last individual of that species dies, the species becomes extinct.

Responds to stimuli An organism's external environment includes all things that surround it, such as air, water, soil, rocks, and other organisms. An organism's internal environment is all things inside it. Anything that is part of either environment and causes some sort of reaction by the organism is called a **stimulus** (plural, stimuli). The reaction to a stimulus is a **response.** For example, if a shark smells blood in the ocean, it will respond quickly by moving toward the blood and attacking any organism present. Plants also respond to their environments, but they do so more slowly than most other organisms. If you have a houseplant and you place it near a sunny window, it will grow toward the window in response to the light. How does the Venus flytrap in **Figure 7** respond to stimuli?

Being able to respond to the environment is critical for an organism's safety and survival. If an organism is unable to respond to danger or to react to potential enemies, it might not live long enough to reproduce.

CAREERS IN
BIOLOGY

Biology Teacher An enthusiasm for biology is one of the many reasons people become biology teachers. Other than courses in biological sciences, prospective biology teachers might take classroom management, teaching methods, and other courses needed to develop teaching skills.

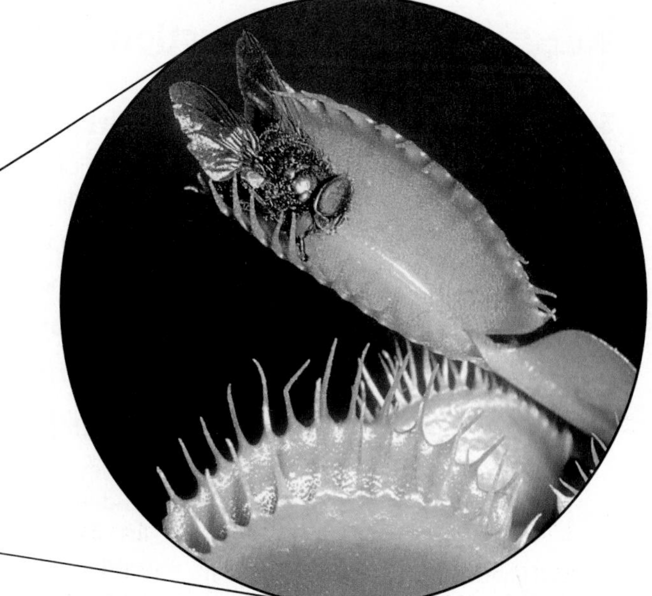

Figure 7 In nature, this Venus flytrap grows in soils that lack certain nutrients. The plant captures and digests insects and takes in needed nutrients.

Explain ***how this plant responds to stimuli to obtain food.***

■ **Figure 8** The structure of a drip-tip leaf is an adaptation to rainy environments.

Requires energy Living things need sources of energy to fuel their life functions. Living things get their energy from food. Most plants and some unicellular organisms use light energy from the Sun to make their own food and fuel their activities. Other unicellular organisms can transform the energy in chemical compounds to make their food.

Organisms that cannot make their own food, such as animals and fungi, get energy by consuming other organisms. Some of the energy that an organism takes in is used for growth, development, and maintaining homeostasis. However, most of the energy is transformed into thermal energy and is radiated to the environment as heat.

Maintains homeostasis Regulation of an organism's internal conditions to maintain life is called **homeostasis** (hoh mee oh STAY sus). Homeostasis occurs in all living things. If anything happens within or to an organism that affects its normal state, processes to restore the normal state begin. If homeostasis is not restored, death might occur.

Connection to Earth Science When athletes travel to a location that is at a higher altitude than where they live, they generally arrive long before the competition so that their bodies have time to adjust to the thinner air. At higher altitudes, air has fewer molecules of gases, including oxygen, per unit of volume. Therefore, there is less oxygen available for an athlete's red blood cells to deliver to the cells and tissues, which disrupts his or her body's homeostasis. To restore homeostasis, the athlete's body produces more red blood cells. Having more red blood cells results in an adequate amount of oxygen delivered to the athlete's cells.

Adaptations evolve over time Many trees in rain forests have leaves with drip tips, like the one shown in **Figure 8.** Water runs off more easily and quickly from leaves with drip tips. Harmful molds and mildews will not grow on dry leaves. This means a plant with dry leaves is healthier and has a better chance to survive. Drip tips are an adaptation to the rain forest environment. An **adaptation** is any inherited characteristic that results from changes to a species over time. Adaptations like rain forest trees with drip tips enable species to survive and, therefore, they are better able to pass their genes to their offspring.

REVIEW IT! Introduction to Biology

Section Summary

- Biologists study the structure and function of living things, their history, their interactions with the environment, and many other aspects of life.
- All organisms have characteristics that scientists use to determine whether the organisms are alive. All living organisms share these certain characteristics.

Self Check

Understand Main Ideas

1. MAINIDEA **Describe** four characteristics used to identify whether something is alive.
2. **Explain** why cells are considered the basic units of living things.
3. **Define** homeostasis and evaluate its importance to an organism.
4. **Differentiate** between response and adaptation.

Think Critically

MATH IN ▶ Biology

5. Survey students in your school—biology students and nonbiology students—and adults. Have participants choose characteristics of life from a list of various characteristics and rank their choices from most important to least important. Record, tabulate, average, and graph your results. Prepare a report that summarizes your findings.

 USE IT! Science Notebook

2 The Nature of Science

1.1.1a, 1.1.1b, 1.1.1c, 1.1.2a, 1.1.2b, 1.1.3a, 1.1.4a, 1.2.2a, 1.2.3a, 1.2.3b, 1.2.3c, 1.3.1a, 1.3.2, 1.3.3, 1.3.4a, 1.3.4b, 1.3.4c, 1.3.5a, 1.3.5b, ¥a, ¥e, ¥i, ¥j, ¥k, ¥l, ¥n, ¥o, ¥p, ¥q

BIOLOGY 4U

What do you do to find answers to questions? Do you ask other people, read, investigate, or observe? Are your methods haphazard or methodical? Over time, scientists have established standard procedures to find answers to questions.

Review Vocabulary

investigation: a careful search or examination to uncover facts

New Vocabulary

science
hypothesis
scientific inquiry
peer review
observation
inference
scientific methods
experiment
control group
experimental group
independent variable
dependent variable
constant
scientific theory
scientific law

Multilingual eGlossary

MAIN IDEA

Science is a process based on inquiry that develops explanations.

Essential Questions

- What are the characteristics of scientific inquiry?
- What are the differences between science and pseudoscience?
- What are the scientific methods scientists used in scientific inquiry?

What is science?

You probably have taken science classes since you were in elementary school, but what is science? **Science** is the use of evidence to construct testable explanations and predictions of natural phenomena, as well as, the knowledge generated through this process. A testable explanation of a situation or phenomena is called a **hypothesis.**

Science is a vast body of knowledge that is described in many ways, including the use of physical, mathematical, and conceptual models. A model is a visual tool that is used to help understand a scientific concept. A physical model important in the history of biology is shown in **Figure 9.** Some models can be described by complex mathematical equations. Watson and Crick also drew conceptual models of DNA, as also shown in **Figure 9.** These simple drawings also represent scientific explanations about the structure of DNA.

The models of DNA represent one tiny segment of the vast amount of scientific knowledge that exists today. It is the nature of science that scientific explanations change as more information is discovered. As a result, science, or the explanations of natural phenomena, also changes.

It is important to remember that science cannot answer all questions. Science only answers questions that are testable by a process called scientific inquiry. **Scientific inquiry** is the planned and deliberate investigation of the natural world. Scientific inquiry is both a creative process and a process rooted in unbiased observations and experimentation.

■ **Figure 9** Watson and Crick made physical models and drew conceptual models based on experimental results to determine the structure of DNA.

A. Barrington Brown/Science Source

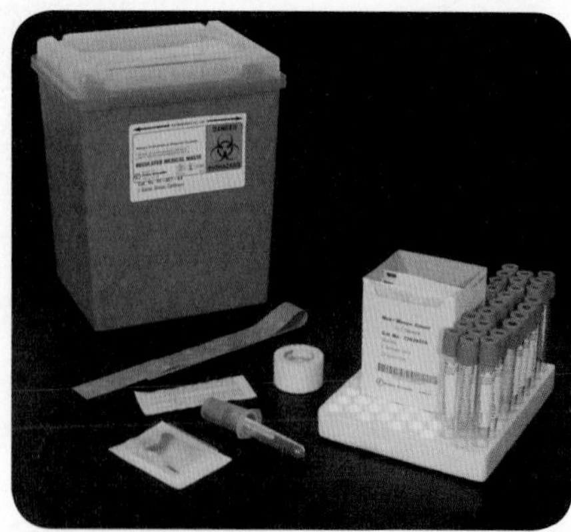

Blood draw kit

Tape measure

Caliper

■ **Figure 10** Dr. Buell and her team used supplies like these to collect data for her study. Blood was collected and tested by using sterile needles and syringes. Her team used a tape measure to measure waist circumference, and they used a caliper to determine body mass composition.

Relies on evidence Scientists ask many kinds of well-defined testable questions. One scientist asked questions about athletes and sports nutrition. The following text describes how this scientist used scientific inquiry to gather evidence and answer her questions.

Dr. Jackie Buell is a scientist who conducts research at The Ohio State University in Columbus, Ohio. One of Dr. Buell's focuses is sports nutrition. Do you think a marathon runner, a college football player, and a golfer all need the same types of food and the same number of calories every day? Through the work of many scientists, we know how to calculate the number of calories a person needs every day. We also know what types of nutrients, vitamins, and minerals are needed, as well as other information about nutrition.

Subject selection Dr. Buell conducted a study on college football linemen to help further the understanding of sports nutrition. Dr. Buell investigated the presence of a condition called metabolic syndrome. A person with metabolic syndrome has risk factors such as abdominal obesity and elevated blood pressure. These risk factors are known to lead to heart disease, stroke, and diabetes.

Why do you think Dr. Buell studied college athletes to gather evidence in her study? Many people assume that all athletes are healthy because they exercise and do many of the things doctors recommend for a healthy lifestyle. For this reason, an athlete with metabolic syndrome might not be aware that they are at risk for things such as heart disease or stroke.

Dr. Buell's research, however, showed that 34 of the 70 college linemen studied were at risk for metabolic syndrome. This information can be used to treat the athletes in the study. It can also be used to increase awareness. Athletes and doctors might be more likely to take health concerns in athletes more seriously. In addition, athletes can be given access to information regarding diet and exercise to help them decrease their risk factors.

Data collection What sort of data do you think Dr. Buell and her team gathered to study metabolic syndrome in her subjects? First, they measured the subjects' height, mass, blood pressure, upper-body skin folds, and waist circumference. Dr. Buell and her team also collected blood samples, family health histories, and information about exercise routines and nutrition habits. They used tools like the ones shown in **Figure 10** to collect the data.

Once all of these data were collected, they were analyzed to determine which athletes were at risk. Dr. Buell identified five risk factors for metabolic syndrome. For one of the data sets, blood work, athletes that were found to have three, four, or all five risk factors were determined to have metabolic syndrome. Dr. Buell used this evidence to conclude that college athletes, specifically college football linemen, should not be assumed to be in good health simply because they are athletes.

Expands knowledge How can you know what information is science-based? Scientific explanations combine what is already known with evidence from additional observations and experiments. Most scientific fields are guided by research that results in a constant reevaluation of what is known. This reevaluation often leads to new knowledge that scientists then evaluate. The search for new knowledge is the driving force that moves science forward.

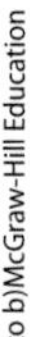

Pseudosciences are those areas of study that try to imitate science, often driven by cultural or commercial goals. Astrology, horoscopes, psychic reading, tarot card reading, face reading, and palmistry are pseudosciences. They do not provide science-based explanations about the natural world.

In pseudoscience, little research is done. If research is done, then often it is simply to justify existing knowledge rather than to extend the knowledge base. Pseudoscientific ideas generally do not ask new questions or welcome more research.

Scientists have done the research to identify metabolic syndrome. They know why the risk factors associated with it can lead to heart disease and other health concerns. Dr. Buell applied this information to athletes, specifically college football linemen. She expanded knowledge by showing that athletes, those often assumed to be healthy, might have metabolic syndrome. What do you think scientists might study next?

Challenges accepted theories Scientists welcome debate about one another's ideas. They regularly attend conferences and meetings where they discuss new developments and findings. Often, disagreements occur among scientists. When disagreements occur, more research is done to find which ideas are supported by research.

Sciences advance by accommodating new information as it is discovered. For example, athletes are often assumed to be at low risk for cardiovascular disease and other health concerns because they exercise regularly and often live what is considered to be a healthy lifestyle. However, Dr. Buell challenged this idea. Her research showed that there was a high incidence of metabolic syndrome in the athletes studied, putting them at risk for cardiovascular disease, diabetes, and stroke.

Questions results Observations or data that are not consistent with current scientific understanding are of interest to scientists. These inconsistencies often lead to further investigations. For example, early biologists grouped bats with birds because both had wings. Further study showed that bat wings are more similar to mammalian limbs than they are to bird wings, as shown in **Figure 11.** This led to an examination of the anatomy, genes, and proteins of rats and bats. The relationship was confirmed, and scientists established that bats were more closely related to mammals than birds. In pseudoscience, observations or data that are not consistent with beliefs are discarded or ignored.

GET IT? **Describe** how observations that are not consistent with current scientific understanding should be treated.

CAREERS IN
BIOLOGY

Science Writer Communicating scientific information to the public is one of the goals of a science writer. He or she might write news stories, manuals, or press releases, or edit and summarize the written materials of scientists.

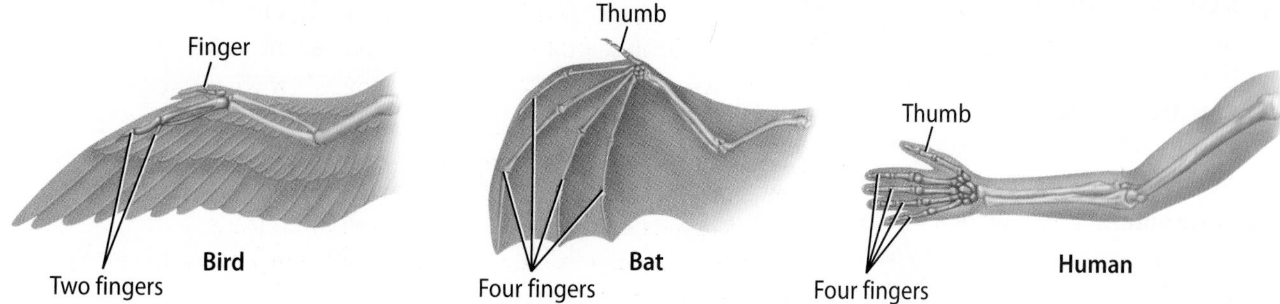

Figure 11 The structure of a bat's wing is more like that of a human arm than a bird's wing.

VOCABULARY

ACADEMIC VOCABULARY

Unbiased
to be objective, impartial, or fair
The judges were unbiased in choosing the winner.

Tests claims Scientists use standard experimental procedures in their research. They make claims and draw conclusions based on a large amount of data and observations obtained from unbiased investigations and carefully controlled experimentation. Bias can occur when a scientist unfairly influences the results or conclusions of an investigation or experiment. Pseudoscientists often make claims that cannot be tested. These claims are often mixtures of fact and opinion and are heavily biased.

Dr. Buell made claims based on 14 data points for all the athletes in the study. The data were analyzed before any conclusions were drawn. The use of data to test and support claims is one way to differentiate science from pseudoscience.

Peer review Finally, before Dr. Buell's study was made public, it was reviewed by peers—scientists who are working in the same field of study. **Peer review** is a process by which the procedures and results of an experiment are evaluated by other scientists who are in the same field or who are conducting similar research. Peer review gives credibility to research papers and prevents false information from being printed in scientific journals.

When scientists publish their work, they make it available for other scientists to examine. You can examine data from Dr. Buell's study in Data Analysis Lab 1.

GET IT? **Summarize** why scientists utilize peer reviews.

Data Analysis LAB 1

Based on Real Data*

Make and Use Graphs

How can graphs help us interpret data? The table shows the number of risk factors for metabolic syndrome college linemen exhibited. The more factors a player exhibited, the greater the chance they had metabolic syndrome. The data are separated into players that play at a college identified as Division I, II, or III, according to the NCAA.

Think Critically

1. **Identify** which division had the largest sample size.
2. **Determine** which division had the largest percentage of participants with three or more risk factors.
3. **Construct** a line graph that shows the number of risk factors and the number of athletes that possess these risk factors.
4. **Extrapolate** If you were a doctor treating these athletes, what would your advice to them be?

Number of Risk Factors for Metabolic Syndrome

Number of Risk Factors	Division			
	I	II	III	Total
0	0	1	0	1
1	3	5	5	13
2	10	6	6	22
3	7	8	10	25
4	2	6	0	8
5	0	1	0	1

*Data obtained from: Buell, Jackie L., et al. 2008. Presence of Metabolic Syndrome in Football Linemen. *Journal of Athletic Training* 43(6):608-616

Scientific Methods

Imagine that you saw an unfamiliar bird in your neighborhood. You might develop a plan to observe the bird for a period of time. Scientific inquiry begins with **observation,** a direct method of gathering information in an orderly way. Often, observation involves recording information. In the example of your newly discovered bird, you might take photographs or draw a picture of it. You might write detailed notes about its behavior, including when and what it ate.

Scientific inquiry involves asking questions and processing information from a variety of reliable sources. The process of combining what you know with what you have learned to draw logical conclusions is called inferring; the conclusions themselves are called **inferences.** For instance, if you saw a photo of a bird similar to the unfamiliar bird in your neighborhood, you might infer that your bird and the bird in the photo are related. **Figure 12** illustrates how a field guide might be helpful in making inferences.

Biologists work in different places to answer their questions. For example, some biologists work in laboratories, perhaps developing new medicines, while others work outdoors in natural settings. No matter where they work, biologists all use similar methods to gather information and to answer questions. These methods sometimes are referred to as **scientific methods,** illustrated in **Figure 13** on the next page. Even though scientists do not use scientific methods in the same way each time they conduct an experiment, they observe and infer throughout the entire process.

Forming a Hypothesis

Imagination, curiosity, creativity, and logic are key elements of the way biologists approach their research. In 1969, the U.S. Air Force asked Dr. Ronald Wiley to investigate how to enhance a pilot's ability to endure the effects of an increase in gravity (*g*-force) while traveling at high speed in an F-16 aircraft. It was known that isometrics, which is a form of exercise in which muscles are held in a contracted position, raised blood pressure. Wiley formed the hypothesis that the use of isometric exercise to raise blood pressure during maneuvers might increase tolerance to *g*-force and prevent blackouts.

Before Wiley formed his hypothesis, he made inferences based on his experience as a physiologist, what he read, discussions with Air Force personnel, and previous investigations. He did find that increasing a pilot's blood pressure could help the pilot withstand *g*-forces.

■ **Figure 12** Scientists might use a field guide to help them identify or draw conclusions about things they observe in nature, such as this peregrine falcon.

VISUALIZING Scientific Methods

Figure 13 The way that scientists answer questions is through an organized series of events called scientific methods. There are no wrong answers to questions, only answers that provide scientists with more information about those questions. Questions and collected information help scientists form hypotheses. As experiments are conducted, hypotheses might or might not be supported.

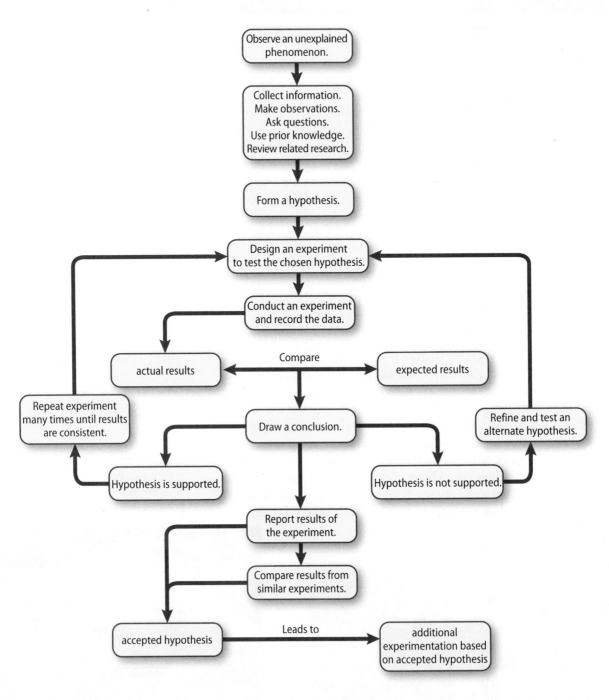

Observe an unexplained phenomenon.

Collect information.
Make observations.
Ask questions.
Use prior knowledge.
Review related research.

Form a hypothesis.

Design an experiment to test the chosen hypothesis.

Conduct an experiment and record the data.

actual results

Compare

expected results

Repeat experiment many times until results are consistent.

Draw a conclusion.

Refine and test an alternate hypothesis.

Hypothesis is supported.

Hypothesis is not supported.

Report results of the experiment.

Compare results from similar experiments.

accepted hypothesis

Leads to

additional experimentation based on accepted hypothesis

Wiley also made a serendipitous discovery. Serendipity is the occurrence of accidental or unexpected but fortunate results. He discovered that isometric exercise decreased the resting blood pressure of the pilots. As a result, weight lifting and muscle-strengthening exercises are recommended today to help people lower blood pressure. Wiley's serendipitous discovery is one of many such discoveries in science.

When a hypothesis is supported by data from multiple investigations, the hypothesis is usually considered valid and is accepted by the scientific community. If the hypothesis is not supported by scientific investigations, the hypothesis is revised, and additional investigations are conducted. Even when a hypothesis is not supported by an investigation, additional scientific information is usually learned. This additional information helps scientists refine their future hypotheses and scientific progress is made.

Launch Lab

Review Based on what you've read about observing and inferring, how would you now answer the analysis questions?

Data Collection

Imagine that while in Alaska on vacation, you noticed various kinds of gulls. You saw them nesting high in the cliffs, and you wondered how they maintain their energy levels during their breeding season. A group of biologists wondered the same thing and conducted a controlled experiment using gulls known as black-legged kittiwakes shown in **Figure 14.** When a scientist conducts an **experiment,** he or she investigates a phenomenon in a controlled setting to test a hypothesis. During investigations, scientists not only formulate hypotheses, they also ask questions, and select appropriate equipment and technology.

Virtual Lab

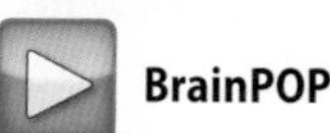
BrainPOP

Controlled experiments The biologists inferred that the kittiwakes would have more energy if they were given extra feedings while nesting. The biologists' hypothesis was that the kittiwakes would use the extra energy to lay more eggs and raise more chicks. A **control group** in an experiment is used for comparison. The kittiwakes not given the supplemental feedings were the control group. The **experimental group** is the group exposed to the factor being tested. The kittiwakes getting the supplemental feedings were the experimental group.

Experimental design When scientists design a controlled experiment, only one factor can change at a time. It is called the **independent variable** because it is the tested factor and it might affect the outcome of the experiment. In the kittiwakes experiment, the supplemental feeding was the independent variable. During an experiment, scientists measure a second factor called the **dependent variable.** It results from or depends on changes to the independent variable. The change in the kittiwakes' energy levels was the dependent variable. A **constant** is a factor that remains fixed during an experiment while the independent and dependent variables change.

Data gathering As scientists test their hypotheses, they gather data—information gained from observations. The data can be quantitative or qualitative. Data collected as numbers are called quantitative data. Numerical data can be measurements of time, temperature, length, mass, area, volume, or density. Qualitative data are descriptions of what our senses detect. Often, qualitative data are interpreted differently because everyone does not sense things in the same way.

Figure 14 This colony of black-legged kittiwakes along the Alaskan coast includes nesting pairs.

MiniLAB

Manipulate Variables

How does a biologist establish experimental conditions? In a controlled experiment, a biologist develops an experimental procedure designed to investigate a question or problem. By manipulating variables and observing results, a biologist learns about relationships among factors in the experiment.

Procedure

1. Read and complete the lab safety form.
2. Create a data table with the columns labeled *Control, Independent Variable, Constants, Hypothesis,* and *Dependent Variable.*
3. Obtain a **printed maze.** Seated at your desk, have a classmate time how long it takes you to complete the maze. Record this time on the chart. This is the control in the experiment.
4. Choose a way to alter experimental conditions while completing the same maze. Record this as the independent variable.
5. In the column labeled *Constants,* list factors that will stay the same each time the experiment is performed.
6. Form a hypothesis about how the independent variable will affect the time it takes to complete the maze.
7. After your teacher approves your plan, carry out the experiment. Record the time required to complete the maze as the dependent variable.
8. Repeat Steps 3–7 as time allows.
9. Graph the data. Use the graph to analyze the relationship between the independent and dependent variables.

Analysis

1. **Explain** the importance of the control in this experiment.
2. **Error Analysis** By completing the maze more than once, you introduced another variable, which likely affected the time required to complete the maze. Would eliminating this variable solve the problem? Explain.

Accuracy and precision When numerical data is collected, there is always some amount of error. Error is the difference between the measured value and the real value. The amount of error depends on the tools and techniques used to make the measurements. When collecting data, precision refers to how close a group of measurements are to one another. Accuracy refers to how close a group of measurements are to the real or accepted value. For more information about Accuracy, Precision, and Error refer to the Investigation and Experimentation section in Student Resources.

Data organization During an investigation, organizing data is very important. Science notebooks are often used to record experimental observations. Data tables in the science notebook are used to record numerical data and observations. Keeping data together and organized helps keep information from getting lost.

Investigations Scientists conduct other kinds of scientific inquiry. Biologists can investigate the behavior of organisms or spend their careers discovering and identifying new species. In investigations such as these, the procedure involves observation and collection of data rather than controlled manipulation of variables. Investigations include descriptive investigations, comparative investigations, and experimental investigations.

Consider the use of resources during investigations When conducting investigations, it is important to conserve resources, to prevent waste, and to dispose of waste in a responsible manner. Recycle materials as much as is reasonable to reduce the amount of resources used.

Use reusable equipment and tools One way to conserve resources is to use reusable equipment and tools. For example, using plastic disposable cups instead of washable glass beakers creates unnecessary trash. This trash must be collected, transported to a landfill, and buried. This creates unnecessary cost and uses up valuable landfill space.

Consider a school that has 200 students in 10 classes repeating the same lab during one lab day at school. If each two-member lab team used one disposable cup for their lab, that is 100 cups that must be disposed of. If the same students used 10 reusable beakers, the amount of trash generated on that one lab day would be significantly reduced. Recycling materials conserves many kinds of resources, such as the resources used to make the lab equipment and tools and the resources used to dispose of trash and other waste.

Use small quantities When conducting investigations in all fields of science, the smallest reasonable quantity of all resources should be used. The reason for this practice is especially apparent in chemistry experiments. Using large amounts of chemicals is costly in many ways. More chemicals must be purchased and more chemical waste must be disposed of in landfills, by wastewater treatment plants, or by hazardous waste treatment facilities.

Use responsible waste disposal methods The proper disposal of lab waste reduces land, water, and air pollution. It also conserves space in landfills and at other disposal sites. There are many local, state, and national governmental agencies that can help with waste disposal issues. Following governmental guidelines for waste disposal is a good way to make sure that the land, water, and air pollution is minimized and disposals sites are not depleted sooner than necessary.

SI and the metric system To make communication easier, most scientists use the SI system of units in their investigations and publications. SI is the International System of Units that was devised in 1960 by the General Conference of Weights and Measures. SI is based on the metric system, which uses units with divisions that are powers of ten. The SI units you will use most often are meter (to measure length), gram (to measure mass), liter (to measure volume), and second (to measure time).

Data Analysis

After analyzing the data from an investigation, a scientist usually asks, "Has my hypothesis been supported?" He or she then might ask, "Are more data needed?" or "Are different procedures needed?" Often, the investigation must be repeated many times to obtain consistent results.

As scientists look for explanations, patterns generally are noted that help to explain the data. A simple way to display the data is in a table or on a graph, such as the ones in **Figure 15,** which describe the change in mass over time of a lizard called an anole. The graph of the data makes the pattern easier to grasp. In this case, there is a regular pattern. Notice that the mass increases over a three-day period and then levels off for three days before increasing again. For more review about making graphs, refer to the Skillbuilder Handbook, pp. 719–722.

Because scientists often work in teams, meetings are held to discuss ongoing investigations, to analyze the data, and to interpret the results. The teams continue to examine their research plans to be certain they avoid bias, repeat their trials, and collect a large enough sample size. Analysis of the data might lead to a conclusion that the hypothesis has been supported. It also could lead to additional hypotheses, to further experimentation, or to general explanations of nature. Even when a hypothesis has not been supported, it is valuable.

Conclusions

Scientists report their findings and conclusions in scientific journals. Before a scientist can publish in a journal, the work is reviewed by peers. The reviewers examine the paper for originality, competence of the scientific method used, and accuracy. They might find fault with the reasoning or procedure, or suggest other explanations or conclusions. If the reviewers agree on the merit of the paper, then the paper is published for review by the public and use by other scientists.

GET IT? **Infer** How does the hypothesis guide data collection and interpretation?

Figure 15 After plotting the data points from the table on graph paper, draw a line that fits the pattern of the data rather than connects the dots.
Extrapolate ***What do you think the mass of the anole will be at 21 days?***

Anole

Change in Mass of Anole	
Date	**Mass (g)**
April 11	2.4
April 14	2.5
April 17	2.5
April 20	2.6
April 23	2.6
April 26	2.7
April 29	2.7

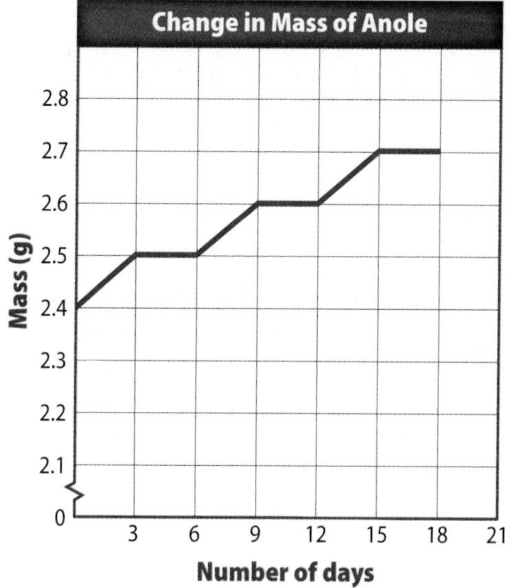

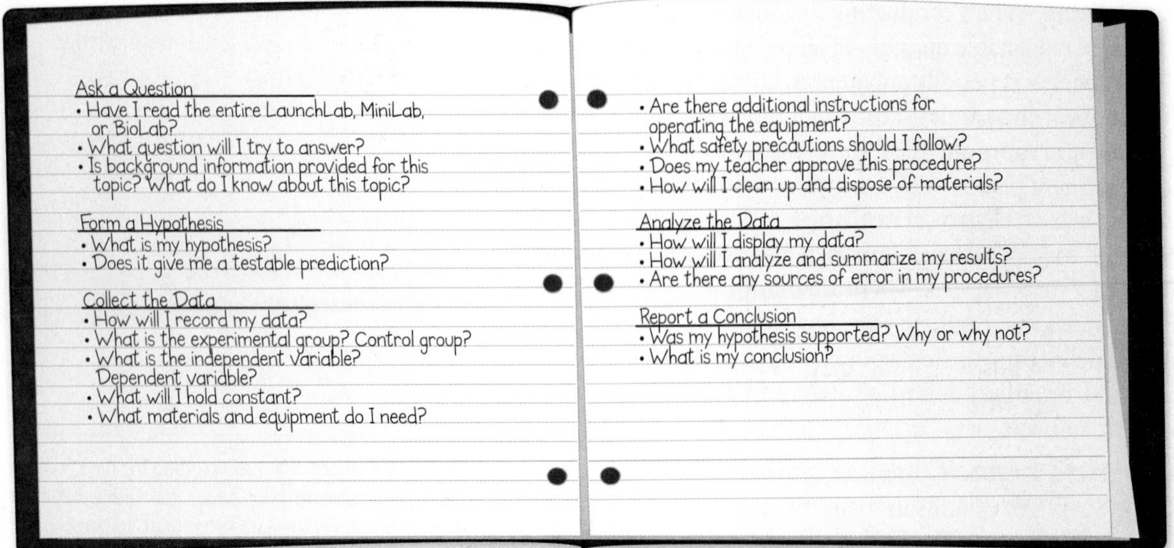

■ **Figure 16** To ask meaningful questions, form hypotheses, and conduct careful experiments, develop research plans based on scientific methods. Use your lab report to list your procedure, record your data, and report your conclusions.

Student Scientific Inquiry

You will be given many opportunities during your study of biology to do your own investigations and experiments. You might also receive a lab assignment that spells out a series of steps to follow or you might design your own procedure. Whether you are planning a lab report or an entire procedure and its lab report, be sure to ask yourself questions like those in **Figure 16.** For additional help with setting up experiments and using equipment, go to Investigation and Experimentation in the Student Handbook of this textbook.

Lab safety During biology labs, you will be alerted of possible safety hazards by warning statements and safety symbols. A safety symbol is a logo designed to alert you about a specific danger. Always refer to the safety symbols chart at the front of this book before beginning any field investigation or lab activity. Carefully read the meaning of each lab's safety symbols. Also, learn the location in the classroom of all safety equipment and how and when to use it. You are responsible for being safe at all times to protect yourself and your classmates.

Safe practices help keep you, your classmates, and your teacher from harm during laboratory and field investigations. Your teacher will show you the safety equipment and teach you how to properly use them in case of an emergency.

Lab safety form Before each lab activity, carefully read the entire procedure. Examine any safety symbols and warnings. Include additional information from MSDS, if applicable. Answer all of the questions on the form and have it approved by your teacher.

MSDS When you use chemicals in the laboratory or you are in contact with substances in the field, you should learn about the safe use and handling of the materials. Students and teachers should review the Material Safety Data Sheets (MSDS) for all substances to learn specific hazards, such as flammability, corrosiveness, and toxicity. Every chemical manufacturer is required by law to supply a recent MSDS with each chemical it produces. These sheets should be sent with each chemical that is purchased by a school or school district. If MSDS forms are not available, they can be requested from the chemical manufacturer or found on the Internet.

Scientific Theories, Laws, and Hypotheses

You have read about various scientific theories, or simply theories, hypotheses, and scientific laws in previous science courses. These terms have very specific definitions in science and the terms are not interchangeable.

Scientific theory A **scientific theory** is an explanation of natural or physical phenomenon supported by many observations and experiments over time. Scientific theories are tested by multiple independent researchers. They are considered valid until new areas of study are developed or until new technologies are developed and new evidence is found. In biology, one highly regarded theory is the cell theory. In chemistry, one important theory is the atomic theory. In physics, an important theory is the theory of general relativity. These theories are based on countless observations and investigations, and they have extensive supporting evidence.

Scientific law A **scientific law** describes relationships under certain conditions in nature. For example, the law of conservation of matter indicates that before and after a chemical change the same amount of matter exists. The law does not explain why this occurs, but it describes the relationship between matter before a change and matter after a change. It is important to note that because they are fundamentally different, theories do not become laws and laws do not become theories.

Scientific theory vs. hypothesis Recall that a hypothesis is a testable explanation of a situation or phenomena. A hypothesis is not necessarily a well-established explanation in the scientific community. Scientific investigations often start with a hypothesis and the hypothesis is refined as more and more evidence is collected. When a hypothesis is tested many times and the explanation is durable, the hypothesis can be incorporated into a theory. Unlike a hypothesis, a scientific theory is a well-established and highly reliable explanation.

VOCABULARY

SCIENCE USAGE V. COMMON USAGE

Conclusion

Science usage: judgment, decision, or opinion formed after an investigation
The researcher formed the conclusion that the hypothesis was not supported.

Common usage: the end or last part
The audience left at the conclusion of the movie.

REVIEW IT! The Nature of Science

Section Summary

- Science is the study of the natural world and is rooted in scientific inquiry.
- Careful observation involves an orderly way of gathering information.
- Controlled experiments involve a control group and an experimental group.
- Scientific theories do not become scientific laws; scientific laws do not become scientific theories.

Understand Main Ideas

1. MAINIDEA **Describe** how a biologist's research can proceed from an idea to a published article.
2. **Describe** the characteristics of scientific inquiry.
3. **Compare and contrast** science and pseudoscience.
4. **State** why an observation cannot be an inference.
5. **Differentiate** between controls, independent variables, and dependent variables.
6. **Explain** why the metric system and SI are important.
7. **Compare and contrast** scientific theory, scientific law, and hypothesis.

Think Critically

8. **Design** a controlled experiment to determine whether earthworms are more attracted to perfume or to vinegar.

MATH IN Biology

9. One kilogram equals 1000 grams. One milligram equals 0.001 grams. How many milligrams are in one kilogram?

BIOLOGY & society

1.1.2a, 1.1.2b, 1.3.5b, 4.7.3b

Science Literacy

Many issues in our world every day relate to biology. Drugs, alcohol, tobacco, AIDS, mental illness, cancer, heart disease, and eating disorders provide subjects for biological research worldwide. Environmental issues such as global climate change, pollution, alternate energy sources, genetically modified foods, and conserving biodiversity are issues that you and future generations will face. In addition, topics such as genetic engineering, cloning, euthanasia, and cryonics all involve ethics, which is a set of moral principles or values. Ethical issues must be addressed by society based on the values it holds important.

How can you be scientifically literate? To evaluate the vast amount of information available and to participate in the fast-paced world of the twenty-first century, each of us must be scientifically literate. A person who is scientifically literate combines basic understanding of science and its processes with critical thinking skills. As a scientifically literate individual, you will be an educated consumer who can participate in discussions about important issues and support policies that reflect your views.

Develop critical thinking skills All scientists analyze, evaluate, and critique scientific explanations. Recall it is the nature of science to be dynamic—it is a body of knowledge that is always growing and changing. Scientists studying the same natural process do not always ask the same questions, use the same procedures, or produce the same results. As a result, their conclusions and explanations might differ. Therefore, each scientific explanation must be closely examined and the explanations are often debated. Disagreements among scientists can lead to new research and discoveries.

Think about the amount of information you can find in the media. Add to that what you learn in your science classes. How do you make informed decisions? You must also analyze, evaluate, and critique scientific explanations. What does this mean?

- **Analyze**—break down the scientific explanation into its essential parts.
- **Evaluate**—study closely the parts of the scientific explanation; consider what you know about the topic; look at the scientific methods used to support the explanation.
- **Critique**—review and consider the merits and faults of the explanation and its parts.

Examine the evidence In your study of science, you will have opportunities to read about how scientists developed some scientific explanations. When you read these explanations or carry out your own laboratory and field investigations, ask yourself "How were these conclusions reached?"

- **Empirical evidence**—the process of verifying explanations by using experience or by using investigations and collecting data
- **Logical reasoning**—the process of evaluating an explanation using reasoning to draw conclusions
- **Experimental testing**—the process of gathering data based on controlled investigations
- **Observational testing**—the process of gathering data based on observations
- **Examining all sides of scientific evidence** that are used to support scientific explanations looking for unsupported conclusions or bias

Evaluating Promotional Materials When you read promotional materials that make scientific claims, you can use the same skills that you use when you read published scientific information. First, you must extract the scientific claims from the promotional information. Then, analyze, evaluate, and critique the scientific claims. Do the claims make sense or do the claims seem biased or outright false? Then consider the evidence on which the claims are based.

WRITING IN ▶ Biology

Collaborate Plan a class project in which you analyze, evaluate, and critique a promotional claim. Prepare a presentation to inform others of your findings.

WebQuest

BioLAB DESIGN YOUR OWN

1.1.1c, 1.1.2b, 1.2.1, 1.2.2a, 1.2.4, 1.3.3, 1.3.5b, ¥a, ¥e, ¥i, ¥j, ¥n, ¥o, ¥p

How can you keep cut flowers fresh?

Background: When first cut from the garden, a bouquet of flowers looks healthy and has a pleasant aroma. Over time, the flowers droop and lose their petals. Leaves and stems below the water line begin to decay.

Question: *What steps can I take to extend the freshness of cut flowers?*

Possible Materials

Choose materials that would be appropriate for this lab.

fresh cut flowers
vases
water
scissors

Safety Precautions

Plan and Perform the Experiment

1. Read and complete the lab safety form.
2. Research strategies for extending the life of cut flowers. During your research, look for possible reasons why a specific strategy might be effective.
3. Form a hypothesis based on your research. It must be possible to test the hypothesis by gathering and analyzing specific data.
4. Design an experiment to test the hypothesis. Remember, the experiment must include an independent and dependent variable. Identify a control sample. List all factors that will be held constant.
5. Design and construct a data table.
6. Make sure your teacher approves your plan before you proceed.
7. Implement the experimental design. Organize the data you collect using a graph or chart.
8. **Cleanup and Disposal** Properly dispose of plant material. Wash hands thoroughly after handling plant material. Clean and return all lab equipment to the designated locations.

Analyze and Conclude

1. **Describe** the strategy tested by your hypothesis. Why did you choose this strategy to examine?
2. **Explain** how you established the control sample.
3. **Interpret Data** What trends or patterns do the data show?
4. **Analyze** What is the relationship between your independent and dependent variables?
5. **Draw Conclusions** Based on your data, describe one way to extend the freshness of cut flowers.
6. **Error Analysis** Critique your experimental design. Is it possible that any other variables were introduced? Explain. How could these variables be controlled?

WRITING IN ▶ Biology

Brochure Compare the strategy for extending the freshness of cut flowers your group examined with strategies tested by other groups. Based on class results, create a brochure with the title "Make Cut Flowers Stay Beautiful Longer." Include tips for extending the life of cut flowers. Share the brochure with community members who might benefit from this information.

CHAPTER 1 STUDY GUIDE

BIGIDEA **Biology is the study of life.**

SECTION 1 Introduction to Biology

MAINIDEA All living things share the characteristics of life.

- Biologists study the structure and function of living things, their history, their interactions with the environment, and many other aspects of life.
- All organisms have characteristics that scientists use to determine whether the organisms are alive. All living organisms share these certain characteristics.

VOCABULARY

- **biology**
- **organism**
- **organization**
- **development**
- **growth**
- **reproduction**
- **response**
- **species**
- **stimulus**
- **adaptation**
- **homeostasis**

SECTION 2 The Nature of Science

MAINIDEA Science is a process based on inquiry that develops explanations.

- Science is the study of the natural world and is rooted in scientific inquiry.
- Careful observation involves an orderly way of gathering information.
- Controlled experiments involve a control group and an experimental group.
- Scientific theories do not become scientific laws; scientific laws do not become scientific theories.

VOCABULARY

- **science**
- **hypothesis**
- **scientific inquiry**
- **peer review**
- **inference**
- **observation**
- **scientific methods**
- **experiment**
- **constant**
- **control group**
- **dependent variable**
- **experimental group**
- **independent variable**
- **scientific theory**
- **scientific law**

CHAPTER 1 ASSESSMENT

SECTION 1

Vocabulary Review

Replace the underlined phrase with the correct vocabulary term from the Study Guide page.

1. The production of offspring is a characteristic of life that enables the continuation of a species.
2. The internal control of mechanisms allows for an organism's systems to remain in balance.
3. The study of life involves learning about the natural world.

Understand Main Ideas

Use the graph below to answer question 4.

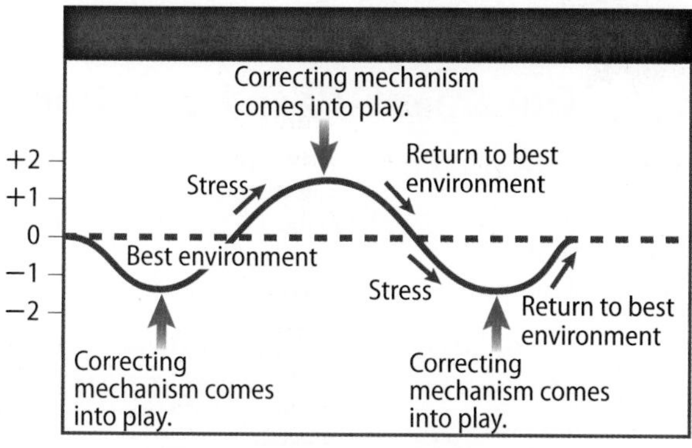

4. Which characteristic of life should be the title of this graph?
   A. Cellular Basis
   B. Growth
   C. Homeostasis
   D. Reproduction
5. Which best describes adaptation?
   A. reproducing as a species
   B. a short-term change in behavior in response to a stimuli
   C. inherited changes in response to environmental factors
   D. change in size as an organism ages

Constructed Response

6. **Open Ended** What is the role of energy in living organisms? Is it a more or less important role than other characteristics of life? Defend your response.

Think Critically

7. **MAIN**IDEA Evaluate how the contributions made by Goodall, Chory, and Drew reinforce our understanding of the characteristics of life.
8. **Compare and contrast** a response and an adaptation. Use examples from your everyday world in your answer.

SECTION 2

Vocabulary Review

Explain the differences between the terms in the following sets.

9. observation, data
10. control group, experimental group
11. independent variable, dependent variable

Understand Main Ideas

12. Which describes this statement, "The frog is 4 cm long"?
    A. quantitative data
    B. inference
    C. control group
    D. qualitative data
13. Which is a testable explanation?
    A. dependent variable
    B. independent variable
    C. hypothesis
    D. observation
14. Which best describes a scientific theory?
    A. a possible explanation of an event
    B. a set of moral values or principles
    C. a description of the relationship between objects
    D. an explanation supported by many experiments over time

15. Which is true about scientific inquiry?
    A. It poses questions about astrology.
    B. It can be done only by one person.
    C. It is resistant to change and not open to criticism.
    D. It is testable.

Constructed Response

16. **Short Answer** Differentiate between pseudoscience and science.

Think Critically

17. **MAIN**IDEA Evaluate the statement: "Scientists just perform experiments to prove what they already believe."

Constructed Response

Use the table below to answer question 18.

Mean Body Mass and Field Metabolic Rate (FMR) of Black-Legged Kittiwakes

	Number	Mean body mass (g)	FMR
Fed females	14	426.8	2.04
Control females	14	351.1	3.08
Fed males	16	475.4	2.31
Control males	18	397.6	2.85

18. **Short Answer** Examine the data shown above. Describe the effects of feedings on the energy expenditure, FMR, of male and female kittiwakes.

Think Critically

19. **Short Answer** Defend the metric system to a scientist who does not want to use it.

20. **MAIN**IDEA Design a survey to investigate students' opinions about current movies. Use 10 questions and survey 50 students. Graph the data. Report the findings to the class.

Summative Assessment

21. **BIG**IDEA Biology is the study of life. Write a paragraph about one area of biology that interests you. Include information about what the area is, what you already know about it, and what you would like to know.

22. **MATH**IN ▶ **Biology** Which metric unit of measurement would you use to measure the distance from your home to your school?

23. **WRITING**IN ▶ **Biology** Prepare a letter to the editor of your school newspaper that encourages citizens to be scientifically literate about topics such as cancer, the environment, ethical issues, AIDS, smoking, lung diseases, cloning, genetic diseases, and eating disorders.

DBQ Document–Based Questions

Use the data below to answer questions 24 and 25.

Data obtained from: U.S. Geological Survey. *Seabirds, forage fish, and marine ecosystems.* http://alaska.usgs.gov/science/biology/seabirds_foragefish/index.php

Relative Fish Biomass of Three Seabird Colonies in Lower Cook Inlet

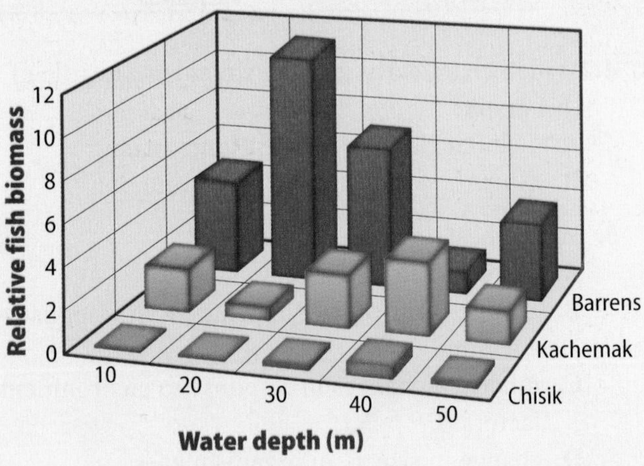

24. Identify the water depth with the highest relative fish biomass.

25. Determine which seabird colony has access to the highest fish biomass at a depth of 40 m.

TEST PRACTICE

1 Many scientific discoveries begin with direct observations. Which could be a direct observation?

A Ants communicate by airborne chemicals.

B Birds navigate by using magnetic fields.

C Butterflies eat nectar from flowers.

D Fish feel vibrations through special sensors.

Use this experimental description and data table to answer question 2.

A student reads that some seeds must be exposed to cold before they germinate. She wants to test seeds from one kind of plant to see if they germinate better after freezing. The student put the seeds in the freezer, took samples out at certain times, and tried to germinate them. Then she recorded her results in the table.

Germination Rate for Seeds Stored in a Freezer

Time in Freezer at −15°C	Germination Rate
30 days	48%
60 days	56%
90 days	66%
120 days	52%

2 Infer, how many days should seeds be stored in the freezer before planting for best germination.

A 30

B 60

C 90

D 120

EXTENDED RESPONSE

Use this drawing to answer question 3.

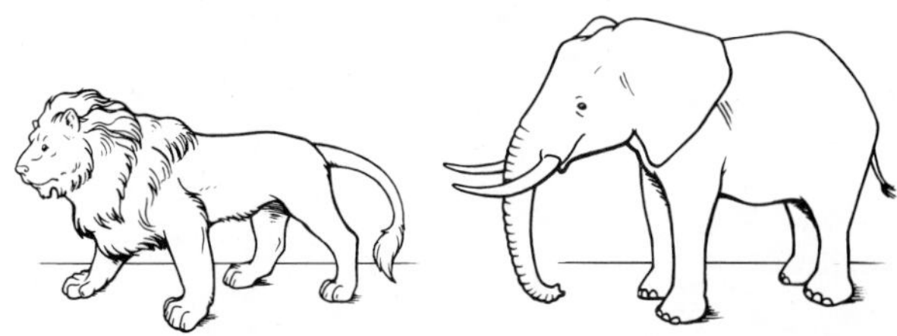

3 Look at the drawing and write five specific questions about the organisms shown that a biologist might try to investigate. Explain your choices.

4 Compare and contrast a scientific hypothesis and a scientific theory. How do they differ from a scientific law?

ESSAY QUESTION

A researcher experimented with adhesives and glues to find new and stronger adhesives. In 1968, he discovered an adhesive that was very weak rather than strong. The adhesive would stick to paper but it could be removed easily without leaving a trace of adhesive. Because he was trying to find stronger adhesives, the results of that experiment were considered a failure. Several years later, he had the idea of coating paper with the weak adhesive. This meant that notes could be stuck to paper and easily removed at a later time. Today, these removable notes are used by millions of people.

Using the information in the paragraph above, answer the following question in essay format.

5 The original adhesive experiment was considered a failure. Appraise the importance of evaluating the results of an experiment with an open mind.

NEED EXTRA HELP?					
If You Missed Question . . .	1	2	3	4	5
Review Section . . .	1.2	1.2	1.1	1.2	1.2

UNIT 1

WHAT'S THAT? The Congress Avenue Bridge in Austin, Texas is more than just a bridge. It is also a home—to 1.5 million Mexican free-tailed bats. The bats roost under the bridge during the summer and emerge each night to fly around the city and nearby countryside. The bats consume between 10,000 and 30,000 pounds of insects every night, greatly reducing the need for pesticides in the Austin area.

CAREERS USING BIOLOGY

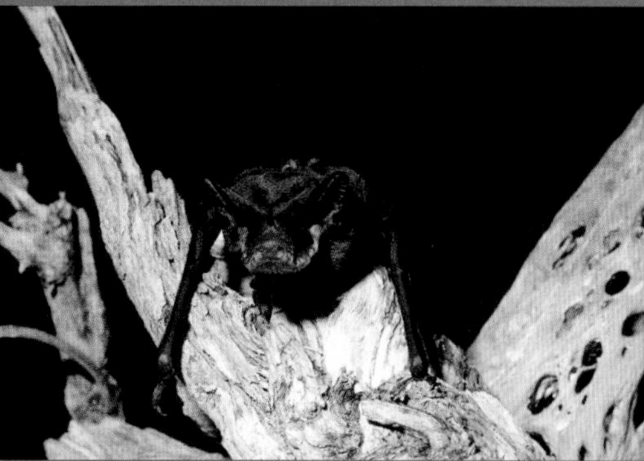

A Closer Look The Mexican free-tailed bats that arrive in Austin each spring are all pregnant females. The colony doubles in size when each mother gives birth in June or July.

IN THE FIELD

See **page 82** for more information about the history of the Mexican free-tailed bats.

ECOTOUR GUIDE

Ecotourism is a form of tourism meant to educate travelers about natural areas and natural phenomena. At least 100,000 people come to the Congress Avenue Bridge to view the bat emergence each year. Different companies provide kayaking and boat tours of the bat emergence. Ecotour guides strive to minimize the impact on fragile areas and local cultures, as well as promote conservation. Ecotour guides must have good communication skills, a love of nature, and knowledge about local ecology and environmental issues.

Related Careers

wildlife educator

conservation biologist

environmental consultant

bridge engineer

Career Resources

Investigate

Evaluate How has bat research and conservation affected Austin? What effect does bat conservation have on the economy of Austin? How does bat conservation affect local farmers?

An ecosystem is made up of many living and nonliving things. Scientists observe the interactions among organisms and between organisms and their environment.

LaunchLAB

Problems in *Drosophila* world?

What we understand to be the world is many smaller worlds combined to form one large world. Within the large world, there are groups of creatures interacting with each other and their environment. In this lab, you will observe an example of a small part of the world.

Go Online! MHEonline.com

Watch | Resources | Vocab | Tutor | IWB | Check | Lab | Tools | Science Notebook

CHAPTER 2

Principles of Ecology

1 Organisms and Their Relationships

1.1.1b, 1.1.3b, 1.1.4a, 4.5.3a, 4.6.1g, 4.6.3a

2 Flow of Energy in an Ecosystem

4.1.1a, 4.5.1a, 4.6.1g

3 Cycling of Matter

4.1.1d, 4.5.3a, 4.6.1c, 4.6.1d, 4.6.3a, ¥a, ¥e, ¥o

THEMEFOCUS

Energy and matter Energy from the Sun flows through all levels of biological organization and cycles.

BIGIDEA

Energy is required to cycle materials through living and nonliving systems.

Water and Carbon Cycle

Make a three-tab book using the labels shown. Use it to organize your notes about the water and carbon cycles.

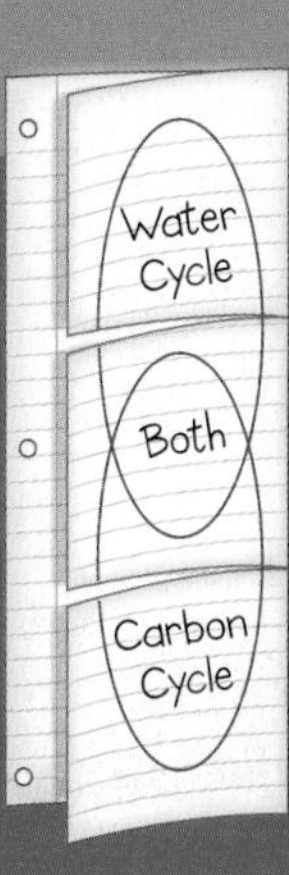

USE IT! Science Notebook

1 Organisms and Their Relationships

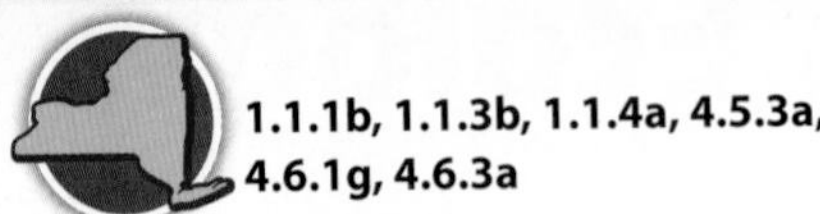

MAINIDEA

Biotic and abiotic factors interact in complex ways in communities and ecosystems.

Essential Questions

- What is the difference between abiotic factors and biotic factors?
- What are the interactions between the levels of biological communities?
- What is the difference between an organism's habitat and its niche?

BIOLOGY 4U

On whom do you depend for your basic needs such as food, shelter, and clothing? Humans are not the only organisms that depend on others for their needs. All living things are interdependent. Their relationships are important to their survival.

Review Vocabulary

species: group of organisms that can interbreed and produce fertile offspring in nature

New Vocabulary

ecology
biosphere
biotic factor
abiotic factor
population
biological community
ecosystem
biome
habitat
niche
predation
symbiosis
mutualism
commensalism
parasitism

Multilingual eGlossary

Ecology

Scientists can gain valuable insight about the interactions between organisms and their environments and between different species of organisms by observing them in their natural environments. Each organism, regardless of where it lives, depends on nonliving factors found in its environment and on other organisms living in the same environment for survival. For example, green plants provide a source of food for many organisms as well as a place to live. The animals that eat the plants provide a source of food for other animals. The interactions and interdependence of organisms with each other and their environments are not unique. The same type of dependency occurs whether the environment is a barren desert, a tropical rain forest, or a grassy meadow. **Ecology** is the scientific discipline in which the relationships among living organisms and the interaction the organisms have with their environments are studied.

■ **Figure 1** Milestones in Ecology

1900 — 1960 — 1970

1905 Theodore Roosevelt urges the U.S. Congress to set aside over 70 million hectares of land to protect the natural resources found on them.

1962 Rachel Carson publishes a best-selling book warning of the environmental danger of pollution and pesticides.

1967 The government of Rwanda and international conservation groups begin efforts to protect mountain gorillas, due in a large part to the work of Dian Fossey.

1971 Marjorie Carr stops the construction of the Cross Florida Barge Canal because of the environmental damage the project would cause.

■ **Figure 2** Ecologists work in the field and in laboratories. This ecologist is enduring harsh conditions to examine a seal.

The study of organisms and their environments is not new. The word *ecology* was first introduced in 1866 by Ernst Haeckel, a German biologist. Since that time, there have been many significant milestones in ecology, as shown in **Figure 1.**

Scientists who study ecology are called ecologists. Ecologists observe, experiment, and model using a variety of tools and methods. For example, ecologists, like the one shown in **Figure 2,** perform tests in organisms' environments. Results from these tests might give clues as to why organisms are able to survive in the water, why organisms become ill or die from drinking the water, or what organisms could live in or near the water. Ecologists also observe organisms to understand the interactions among them.

Science models are a way of creating a visual representation of a hypothesis to test in a lab setting. A model allows a scientist to simulate a process or system. Studying organisms in the field can be difficult because there often are too many variables to study at one time. Models allow ecologists to control the number of variables present and to slowly introduce new variables in order to fully understand the effect of each variable.

VOCABULARY

WORD ORIGIN

Ecology
comes from the Greek words *oikos,* meaning *house,* and *ology,* meaning *to study.*

GET IT? **Describe** a collection of organisms and their environment that an ecologist might study in your community.

1990 The Indigenous Environmental Network (IEN), directed by Tom Goldtooth, is formed by Native Americans to protect their tribal lands and communities from environmental damage.

2004 Wangari Maathai wins a Nobel Prize. She began the Green Belt Movement in Africa, which hires women to plant trees to slow the process of deforestation and desertification.

1980 — 1990 — 2000

1987 The United States and other countries sign the Montreal Protocol, an agreement to phase out the use of chemical compounds that destroy atmospheric ozone.

1996 Completing a phase-out that was begun in 1973, the U.S. Environmental Protection Agency bans the sale of leaded gasoline for vehicle use.

2007 The American Bald Eagle is removed from the Endangered Species list with the successful population of 10,000 mating pairs.

■ **Figure 3** This color-enhanced satellite photo of Earth taken from space shows a large portion of the biosphere.

The Biosphere

Because ecologists study organisms and their environments, their studies take place in the biosphere. The **biosphere** (BI uh sfihr) is the portion of Earth that supports life. The photo of Earth taken from space shown in **Figure 3** shows why the meaning of the term *biosphere* should be easy to remember. The term *bio* means "life," and a sphere is a geometric shape that looks like a ball. When you look at Earth from this vantage point, you can see how it is considered to be "a ball of life."

Although "ball of life" is the literal meaning of the word *biosphere,* this is somewhat misleading. The biosphere includes only the portion of Earth that includes life. The biosphere forms a thin layer around Earth. It extends several kilometers above Earth's surface into the atmosphere and extends several kilometers below the ocean's surface to the deep-ocean vents. It includes landmasses, bodies of freshwater and saltwater, and all locations below Earth's surface that support life.

Figure 4 shows a glimpse into the vast amount of diversity contained within Earth's biosphere. From rainforests to deserts to coral reefs, diverse organisms populate diverse locations. The biosphere's diverse locations contain organisms that are able to survive in the unique conditions found in their particular environment. Ecologists study these organisms, their adaptations, and the factors in their environment. These factors are divided into two large groups—the living factors and the nonliving factors.

GET IT? **Define** the term *biosphere.*

■ **Figure 4** Rainforests, deserts, and coral reefs are all home to unique organisms. The plants, animals, and microorganisms that live in each of these parts of the biosphere are adapted to the living and nonliving factors there.

(t)NASA, (b)©Stockbyte/PunchStock, (bl)Glen Allison/Getty Images, (r)Steve Allen/Getty Images

■ **Figure 5** The salmon swimming upstream are biotic factors in the stream community. Other organisms in the water, such as frogs and algae, also are biotic factors.

Explain ***how organisms are dependent on other organisms.***

Biotic factors The living factors in an organism's environment are called the **biotic** (by AH tihk) **factors.** Consider the biotic factors in the habitat of salmon shown in **Figure 5.** These biotic factors include all of the organisms that live in the water, such as other fish, algae, frogs, and microscopic organisms. In addition, organisms that live on the land adjacent to the water might be biotic factors for the salmon. Migratory animals, such as birds that pass through the area, also are biotic factors. The interactions among organisms are necessary for the health of all species in the same geographic location. For example, the salmon need other members of their species to reproduce. Salmon also depend on other organisms for food and, in turn, are a food source for other organisms.

Abiotic factors The nonliving factors in an organism's environment are called **abiotic** (ay bi AH tihk) **factors.** The abiotic factors for different organisms vary across the biosphere, but organisms that live in the same geographic area might share the same abiotic factors. These factors might include temperature, air or water currents, sunlight, soil type, rainfall, or available nutrients. Organisms depend on abiotic factors for survival. For example, the abiotic factors important to a particular plant might be the amount of rainfall, the amount of sunlight, the type of soil, the range of temperature, and the nutrients available in the soil. The abiotic factors for the salmon in **Figure 5** might be the temperature range of the water, the pH of the water, and the salt concentration of the water.

Organisms are adapted to surviving in the abiotic factors that are present in their natural environments. If an organism moves to another location with a different set of abiotic factors, the organism might die if it cannot adjust quickly to its new surroundings. For example, if a lush green plant that normally grows in a swampy area is transplanted to a dry desert, the plant likely will die because it cannot adjust to abiotic factors present in the desert.

GET IT? **Compare and contrast** abiotic and biotic factors for a plant or animal in your community.

CAREERS IN BIOLOGY

Ecologist The field of ecology is vast. Ecologists study the organisms in the world and the environments in which they live. Many ecologists specialize in a particular area such as marine ecology.

Levels of Organization

Virtual Lab 

BrainPOP 

The biosphere is too large and complex for most ecological studies. To study relationships within the biosphere, ecologists look at different levels of organization or smaller pieces of the biosphere. The levels increase in complexity as the numbers and interactions between organisms increase. The levels of organization are

- organism;
- population;
- biological community;
- ecosystem;
- biome;
- biosphere.

Refer to **Figure 6** as you read about each level.

STUDY TIP

QUESTION SESSION Study the levels of organization illustrated in **Figure 6** with a partner. Question each other about the topic to deepen your knowledge. Take notes by writing down your partner's answers in your own words.

Organisms, populations, and biological communities

The lowest level of organization is the individual organism itself. In **Figure 6,** the organism is represented by a single fish. Individual organisms of a single species that share the same geographic location at the same time make up a **population.** The school of fish represents a population of organisms. Individual organisms often compete for the same resources, and if resources are plentiful, the population can grow. However, usually there are factors that prevent populations from becoming extremely large. For example, when the population has grown beyond what the available resources can support, the population size begins to decline until it reaches the number of individuals that the available resources can support.

The next level of organization is the biological community. A **biological community** is a group of interacting populations that occupy the same geographic area at the same time. Organisms might or might not compete for the same resources in a biological community. The collection of plant and animal populations, including the school of fish, represents a biological community.

 Launch Lab

Review Based on what you've read about populations, how would you now answer the analysis questions?

Ecosystems, biomes, and the biosphere The next level of organization after a biological community is an ecosystem. An **ecosystem** is a biological community and all of the abiotic factors that affect it. As you can see in **Figure 6,** an ecosystem might contain an even larger collection of organisms than a biological community. In addition, it contains the abiotic factors present, such as water temperature and light availability. Although **Figure 6** represents an ecosystem as a large area, an ecosystem also can be small, such as an aquarium or tiny puddle. The boundaries of an ecosystem are somewhat flexible and can change, and ecosystems even might overlap.

The next level of organization is the biome. A **biome** is a large group of ecosystems that share the same climate and have similar types of communities. The biome shown in **Figure 6** is a marine biome. All of the biomes on Earth combine to form the highest level of organization—the biosphere.

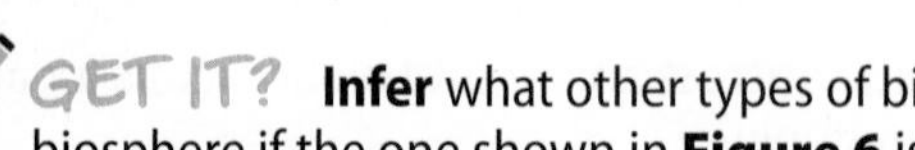

GET IT? **Infer** what other types of biomes might be found in the biosphere if the one shown in **Figure 6** is called a marine biome.

VISUALIZING
VISUALIZING

VISUALIZING Levels of Organization

Figure 6 In order to study relationships within the biosphere, it is divided into smaller levels of organization. The simplest level of organization is the organism, with increasing organization shown in the population, biological community, ecosystem, and biome until reaching the most complex level of biosphere.

Biosphere The highest level of organization is the biosphere, which is the layer of Earth—from high in the atmosphere to deep in the ocean—that supports life.

Biome A biome is a group of ecosystems, such as the coral reefs off the coast of the Florida Keys, that share the same climate and have similar types of communities.

Ecosystem A biological community, such as the coral reef, and all of the abiotic factors, such as the sea water, that affect it make up an ecosystem.

Biological Community All of the populations of species—fishes, coral, and marine plants—that live in the same place at the same time make up a biological community.

Population A group of organisms of the same species that interbreed and live in the same place at the same time, such as the school of striped fish, is a population.

Organism An individual living thing, such as one striped fish, is an organism.

Photo Library International/Science Source

■ **Figure 7** These trees are the habitat for the community of organisms that live there.

Ecosystem Interactions

The interactions between organisms are important in an ecosystem. A community of organisms increases the chances for survival of any one species by using the available resources in different ways. If you look closely at a tree in the forest, like the one shown in **Figure 7,** you will find a community of different birds using the resources of the tree in different ways. For example, one bird species might eat insects on the leaves while another species of bird eats the insects found on the bark. The chance of survival for the birds increases because they are using different resources.

The trees shown in **Figure 7** also are habitats. A **habitat** is an area where an organism lives. A habitat might be a single tree for an organism that spends its life on one tree. If the organism moves from tree to tree, its habitat would be a grove of trees.

Organisms not only have a habitat—they have a niche as well. A **niche** (NIHCH) is the role or position that an organism has in its environment. An organism's niche is how it meets its needs for food, shelter, and reproduction. The niche might be described in terms of requirements for living space, temperature, moisture, or in terms of appropriate mating or reproduction conditions.

GET IT? **Compare and contrast** a habitat and a niche.

Community Interactions

Organisms that live together in a biological community constantly interact. These interactions, along with the abiotic factors, shape an ecosystem. Interactions include competition for basic needs such as food, shelter, and mates, as well as relationships in which organisms depend on each other for survival.

Competition Competition occurs when more than one organism uses a resource at the same time. Resources are necessary for life and might include food, water, space, and light. For example, during a drought, as shown in **Figure 8,** water might be scarce for many organisms. The strong organisms directly compete with the weak organisms for survival. Usually the strong survive and the weak die. Some organisms might move to another location where water is available. At times when water is plentiful, all organisms share the resources and competition is not as fierce.

Predation Many species get their food by eating other organisms. The act of one organism pursuing and consuming another organism for food is **predation** (prih DAY shun). The organism that pursues another organism is the predator, and the organism that is pursued is the prey. If you have watched a cat catch a bird or mouse, you have witnessed a predator catch its prey.

■ **Figure 8** During droughts, animals compete for water; when water is plentiful, organisms share this resource.

Some insects also prey on other insects. Ladybugs and praying mantises are two examples of insects that are predators. Insect predators, such as these two, also are called beneficial insects because they are used by organic gardeners for insect control. Instead of using insecticides, organic gardeners use beneficial insects to control other insect populations.

Animals are not the only organisms that are predators. The Venus flytrap, a plant native to some regions of North and South Carolina, has modified leaves that form small traps for insects and other small animals. The plant emits a sweet, sticky substance that attracts insects. When the insect lands on the leaf, the leaf trap snaps shut. Then, the plant secretes a substance that digests the insect over several days.

Symbiotic relationships Some species survive because of relationships they have developed with other species. The close relationship that exists when two or more species live together is **symbiosis** (sihm bee OH sus). There are three different kinds of symbiosis: mutualism, commensalism, and parasitism.

Mutualism The relationship between two or more organisms that live closely together and benefit from each other is **mutualism** (MYEW chuh wuh lih zum). Lichens, shown in **Figure 9,** display an example of a mutualistic relationship between fungi and algae. The tree merely provides a habitat for lichens, allowing it to receive ample sunlight. The algae provide food for the fungi, and the fungi provide a habitat for the algae. The close association of these two organisms provides two basic needs for the organisms—food and shelter.

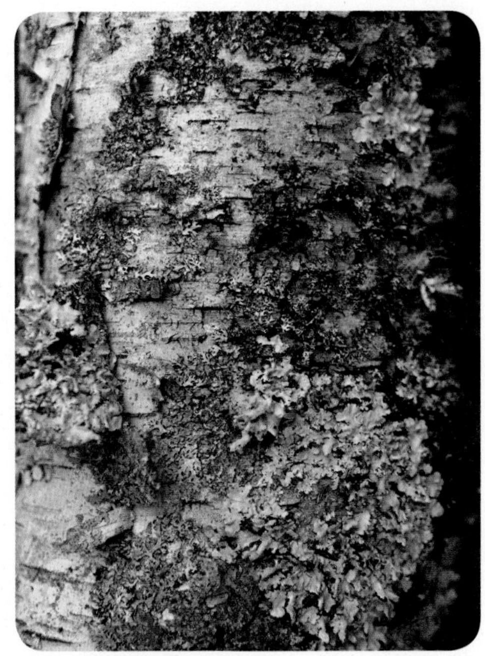

Figure 9 Algae and fungi form lichens through a mutualistic relationship.

Explain ***why lichens are an example of a mutualistic relationship.***

Data Analysis LAB 1

Based on Real Data*

Analyze the Data

Does temperature affect growth rates of protozoans? Researchers studied the effect of temperature on the growth rates of protozoans. They hypothesized that increasing temperature would increase the growth rate of the protozoans.

Data and Observations

The graph shows the effect of temperature on the growth rate of *Colpidium* and *Paramecium.*

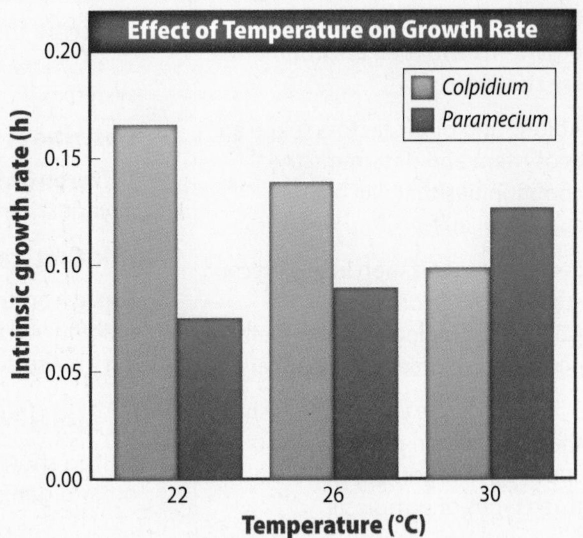

Think Critically

1. **Describe** the differences in population growth for the two species.
2. **Evaluate** what would be the next probable step in the researcher's investigation.

*Data obtained from: Jiang, L. and Kulczycki, A. 2004. Competition, predation, and species responses to environmental change. *Oikos* 106: 217–224.

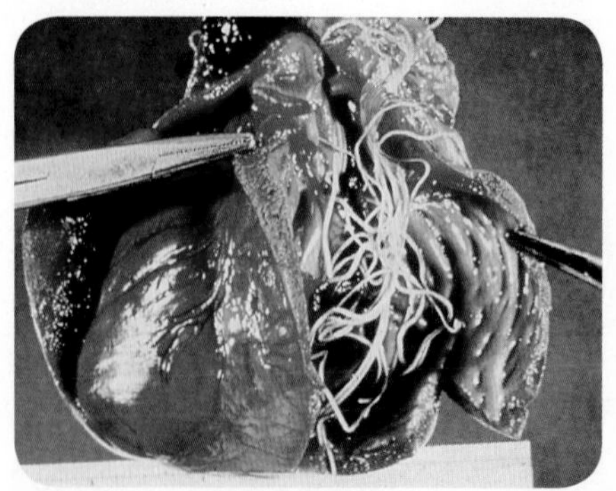

■ **Figure 10** This heart from a dog is infected with internal parasites called heartworms. Internal parasites depend on a host to supply their nutrients and habitat.

Commensalism Look back at **Figure 9.** This time, think about the relationship between the lichens and the tree. The lichens benefit from the relationship by gaining more exposure to sunlight, but they do not harm the tree. This type of relationship is commensalism. **Commensalism** (kuh MEN suh lih zum) is a relationship in which one organism benefits and the other organism is neither helped nor harmed.

The relationship between clownfish and sea anemones is another example of commensalism. Clownfish are small, tropical marine fish. Clownfish swim among the stinging tentacles of sea anemones without harm. The sea anemones protect the fish from predators while the clownfish eat bits of food missed by the sea anemones. This is likely a commensal relationship because the clownfish receives food and protection while the sea anemones are not harmed, nor helped.

Parasitism A symbiotic relationship in which one organism benefits at the expense of another organism is **parasitism** (PER us suh tih zum). Parasites can be external, such as ticks and fleas, or internal, such as bacteria, tapeworms, and roundworms. The heartworms in **Figure 10** show how destructive parasites can be. Pet dogs in many areas of the United States are treated to prevent heartworm infestation. Usually the heartworm (the parasite) does not kill the host, but it might harm or weaken it. In parasitism, if the host dies, the parasite also would die unless it quickly finds another host.

Another type of parasitism is brood parasitism. Brown-headed cowbirds demonstrate brood parasitism because they rely on other bird species to build their nests and incubate their eggs. A brown-headed cowbird lays its eggs in another bird's nest and abandons the eggs. The host bird incubates and feeds the young cowbirds. Often the baby cowbirds push the host's eggs or young from the nest, resulting in the survival of only the cowbirds. In some areas, the brown-headed cowbirds have significantly lowered the population of songbirds.

REVIEW IT! Organisms and Their Relationships

Section Summary

- Ecology is the branch of biology in which interrelationships between organisms and their environments are studied.
- Abiotic and biotic factors shape an ecosystem and determine the communities that will be successful in it.
- Levels of organization in ecological studies include organism, population, biological community, ecosystem, biome, and biosphere.
- Symbiosis is the close relationship that exists when two or more species live together. There are three types of symbiosis.

Self Check

Understand Main Ideas

1. MAINIDEA **Compare and contrast** biotic and abiotic factors.
2. **Describe** the levels of organization of an organism that lives in your biome. Then, relate those levels in your biome to each other and to the whole system.
3. **Describe** at least two populations that share your home.
4. **Differentiate** between the habitat and niche of an organism that is found in your community.

Think Critically

5. **Design** an experiment that determines the symbiotic relationship between a sloth, which is a slow-moving mammal, and a species of green algae that lives in the sloth's fur.

WRITING IN ▶ Biology

6. Write a short story that demonstrates the dependence of all organisms on other organisms.

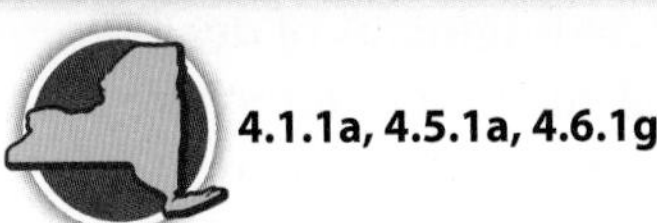

Science Notebook

2 Flow of Energy in an Ecosystem

4.1.1a, 4.5.1a, 4.6.1g

MAIN IDEA

Autotrophs capture energy, making it available for all members of a food web.

Essential Questions

- What are the producers and consumers in an ecosystem?
- How does energy flow through an ecosystem?
- What are food chains, food webs, and ecological pyramid models?

BIOLOGY 4U

When you eat a banana, you are supplying your body with energy. You might be surprised to learn that the Sun is the original source of energy for your body. How did the Sun's energy get into the banana?

Review Vocabulary

energy: the ability to cause change; energy cannot be created or destroyed, only transformed

New Vocabulary

autotroph
heterotroph
herbivore
carnivore
omnivore
detritivore
trophic level
food chain
food web
biomass

Multilingual eGlossary

Energy in an Ecosystem

One way to study the interactions of organisms within an ecosystem is to follow the energy that flows through an ecosystem. Organisms differ in how they obtain energy, and they are classified as autotrophs or heterotrophs based on how they obtain their energy in an ecosystem.

Autotrophs All of the green plants and other organisms that produce their own food in an ecosystem are primary producers called autotrophs. An **autotroph** (AW tuh trohf) is an organism that collects energy from sunlight or inorganic substances to produce food. Organisms that contain chlorophyll absorb energy during photosynthesis and use it to convert the inorganic substances carbon dioxide and water to organic molecules. In places where sunlight is unavailable, some bacteria use hydrogen sulfide and carbon dioxide to make organic molecules to use as food. Autotrophs are the foundation of all ecosystems because they make energy available for all other organisms in an ecosystem.

Heterotrophs A **heterotroph** (HE tuh roh trohf) is an organism that gets its energy requirements by consuming other organisms. Therefore, heterotrophs also are called consumers. A heterotroph that eats only plants is an **herbivore** (HUR buh vor) such as a cow, a rabbit, or grasshopper. Heterotrophs that prey on other heterotrophs, such as wolves, lions, and lynxes, shown in **Figure 11,** are called **carnivores** (KAR nuh vorz).

Frank Sommariva/Alamy

■ **Figure 11** This lynx is a heterotroph that is about to consume another heterotroph, a deer.
Identify ***an additional classification for each of these animals.***

■ **Figure 12** This fungus is obtaining food energy from the dead log. Fungi are decomposers that recycle materials found in dead organisms.

Explain ***why decomposers are important in an ecosystem.***

In addition to herbivores and carnivores, there are organisms that eat both plants and animals, called **omnivores** (AHM nih vorz). Bears, humans, and mockingbirds are examples of omnivores.

The **detritivores** (duh TRYD uh vorz), which eat fragments of dead matter in an ecosystem, return nutrients to the soil, air, and water where the nutrients can be reused by organisms. Detritivores include worms and many aquatic insects that live on stream bottoms. They feed on small pieces of dead plants and animals. Decomposers, similar to detritivores, break down dead organisms by releasing digestive enzymes. Fungi, such as those in **Figure 12,** and bacteria are decomposers.

All heterotrophs perform some decomposition when consuming another organism. Decomposers are the primary method and tool used to break down organic compounds and make nutrients available to producers for reuse. Without the presence and activities of detritivores and decomposers, organic material would not break down and the nutrients would no longer be available to other organisms.

GET IT? **Compare and contrast** the four different types of heterotrophs.

Models of Energy Flow

Ecologists use food chains and food webs to model the energy flow through an ecosystem. Like any model, food chains and food webs are simplified representations of the flow of energy. Each step in a food chain or food web is called a **trophic** (TROH fihk) **level.** Autotrophs make up the first trophic level in all ecosystems. Heterotrophs make up the remaining levels. With the exception of the first trophic level, organisms at each trophic level get their energy from the trophic level before it.

MiniLAB 1

Construct a Food Web

How is energy passed from organism to organism in an ecosystem? A food chain shows a single path for energy flow in an ecosystem. The overlapping relationships between food chains are shown in a food web.

Procedure

1. Read and complete the lab safety form.
2. Use the following information to construct a food web in a meadow ecosystem:
   - Red foxes feed on raccoons, crayfishes, grasshoppers, red clover, meadow voles, and gray squirrels.
   - Red clover is eaten by grasshoppers, muskrats, red foxes, and meadow voles.
   - Meadow voles, gray squirrels, and raccoons all eat parts of the white oak tree.
   - Crayfishes feed on green algae and detritus, and they are eaten by muskrats and red foxes.
   - Raccoons feed on muskrats, meadow voles, gray squirrels, and white oak trees.

Analysis

1. **Identify** all of the herbivores, carnivores, omnivores, and detritivores in the food web.
2. **Describe** how the muskrats would be affected if disease kills the white oak trees.

Food chains A **food chain** is a simple model that shows how energy flows through an ecosystem. **Figure 13** shows a typical grassland food chain. Arrows represent the one-way energy flow which typically starts with autotrophs and moves to heterotrophs. The flower uses energy from the Sun to make its own food. The grasshopper receives energy from eating the flower. The mouse obtains energy from eating the grasshopper. Finally, the snake gains energy from eating the mouse. Each organism uses a portion of the energy it obtains from the organism it eats for cellular processes to build new cells and tissues. The remaining energy is released into the surrounding environment and no longer is available to these organisms.

Food webs Feeding relationships usually are more complex than a single food chain because most organisms feed on more than one species. Birds, for instance, eat a variety of seeds, fruits, and insects. The model most often used to represent the feeding relationships in an ecosystem is a food web. A **food web** is a model representing the many interconnected food chains and pathways in which energy flows through a group of organisms. **Figure 14** shows a food web illustrating the feeding relationships in a desert community.

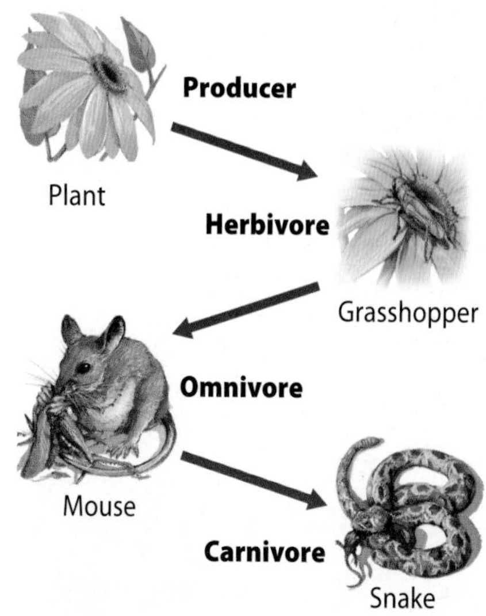

Figure 13 A food chain is a simplified model representing the transfer of energy from organism to organism.

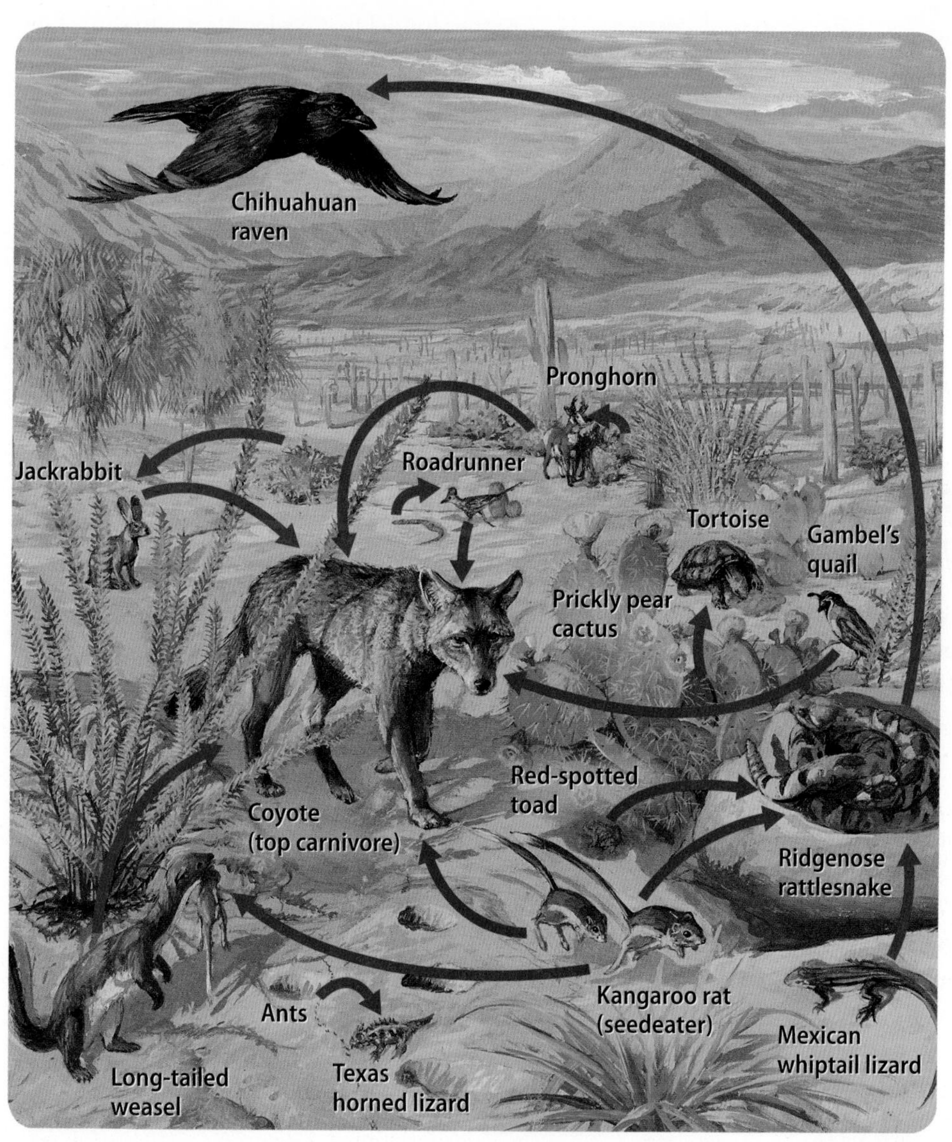

Figure 14 A food web is a model of the many ways in which energy flows through organisms.

Animation

Pyramid of Energy

In a pyramid of energy, each level represents the amount of energy that is available to that trophic level. With each step up, there is an energy loss of 90 percent.

Pyramid of Biomass

In a pyramid of biomass, each level represents the amount of biomass consumed by the level above it.

Pyramid of Numbers

In a pyramid of numbers, each level represents the number of individual organisms consumed by the level above it.

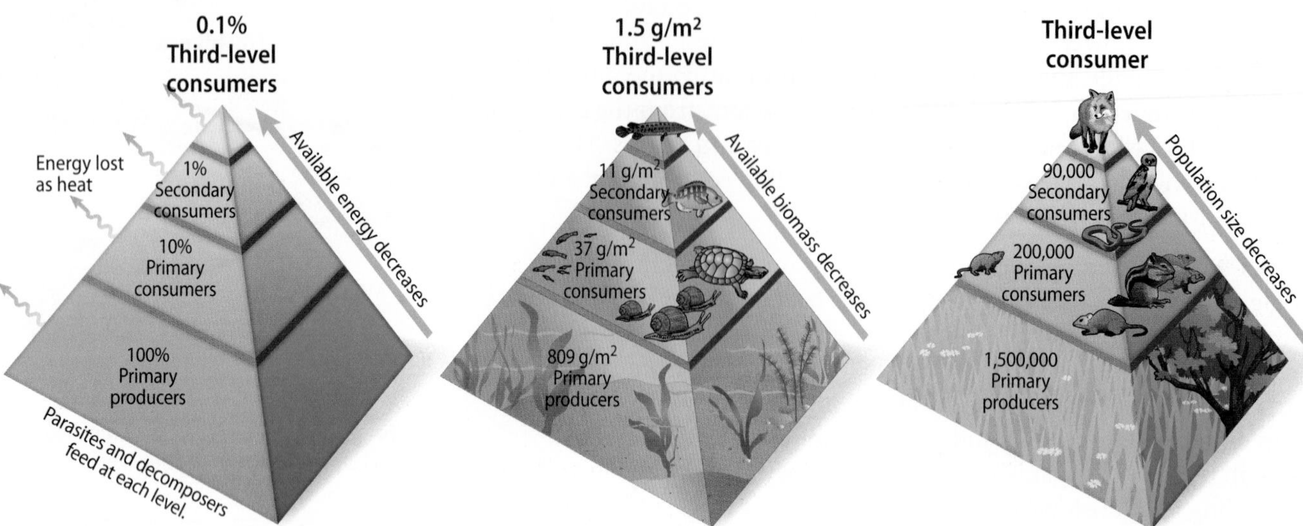

■ **Figure 15** Ecological pyramids are models used to represent trophic levels in ecosystems.

Ecological pyramids Another model that ecologists use to show how energy flows through ecosystems is the ecological pyramid. An ecological pyramid is a diagram that can show the relative amounts of energy, biomass, or numbers of organisms at each trophic level in an ecosystem.

Notice in **Figure 15** that in a pyramid of energy, only 10 percent of all energy is transferred to the level above it. This occurs because most of the energy contained in the organisms at each level is consumed by cellular processes or released to the environment as heat. Usually, the amount of **biomass**—the total mass of living matter at each trophic level—decreases at each trophic level. As shown in the pyramid of numbers, the relative number of organisms at each trophic level also decreases because there is less energy available to support organisms.

REVIEW IT! Flow of Energy in an Ecosystem

Section Summary

- Autotrophs capture energy from the Sun or use energy from certain chemical substances to make food.
- Heterotrophs include herbivores, carnivores, omnivores, and detritivores.
- A trophic level is a step in a food chain or food web.
- Food chains, food webs, and ecological pyramids are models used to show how energy moves through ecosystems.

Self Check

Understand Main Ideas

1. MAINIDEA **Compare and contrast** autotrophs and heterotrophs.
2. **Illustrate** the flow of energy through a simple food chain that ends with a lion as the final consumer.
3. **Classify** a pet dog as an autotroph or heterotroph and as an herbivore, carnivore, or omnivore. Explain.
4. **Evaluate** the impact on living organisms if the Sun began to produce less energy and then finally burned out.

Think Critically

5. **Create** a simple food web of organisms in your community.

MATH IN ▶ Biology

6. Draw an energy pyramid for a food chain made up of grass, a caterpillar, tiger beetle, lizard, snake, and a roadrunner. Assume that 100 percent of the energy is available for the grass. At each stage, show how much energy is lost and how much is available to the next trophic level.

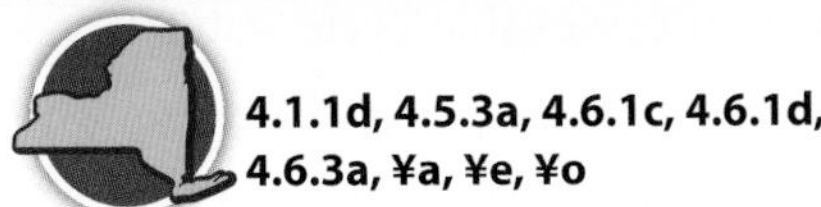

3 Cycling of Matter

4.1.1d, 4.5.3a, 4.6.1c, 4.6.1d, 4.6.3a, ¥a, ¥e, ¥o

MAIN IDEA
Essential nutrients are cycled through biogeochemical processes.

Essential Questions

- How do nutrients move through biotic and abiotic parts of an ecosystem?
- Why are nutrients important to living organisms?
- What are the biogeochemical cycles of nutrients and how are they alike?

BIOLOGY 4U

Do you recycle your empty soda cans? If so, then you know that materials such as glass, aluminum, and paper can be reused. Natural processes in the environment cycle nutrients to make them available for use by other organisms.

Review Vocabulary

cycle: a series of events that occur in a regular repeating pattern

New Vocabulary

matter
nutrient
biogeochemical cycle
nitrogen fixation
denitrification

Multilingual eGlossary

Cycles in the Biosphere

Energy is transformed into usable forms to support the functions of an ecosystem. A constant supply of usable energy is needed, but matter must be cycled through the biosphere.

The law of conservation of mass states that matter is not created or destroyed. Therefore, natural processes cycle matter through the biosphere. **Matter**—anything that takes up space and has mass—provides the nutrients needed for organisms to function. A **nutrient** is a chemical substance that an organism must obtain from its environment to sustain life and to undergo life processes. The bodies of all organisms are built from water and nutrients such as carbon, nitrogen, and phosphorus.

The cycling of nutrients in the biosphere involves both matter in living organisms and physical processes found in the environment such as weathering. Weathering breaks down large rocks into particles that become part of the soil used by plants and other organisms. The exchange of matter through the biosphere is called the **biogeochemical cycle.** As the name suggests, these cycles involve living organisms (*bio*), geological processes (*geo*), and chemical processes (*chemical*).

Connection to Chemistry In most ecosystems, plants obtain nutrients, in the form of elements and compounds, from the air, soil, or water. Plants convert some elements and compounds into organic molecules that they use. The nutrients flow through organisms in an ecosystem, such as the ecosystem shown in **Figure 16.** The green grass captures substances from the air, soil, and water, and then converts them into usable nutrients. The grass provides nutrients for the cow. If an organism eats the cow, the nutrients found in the cow are passed on to the next consumer. The nutrients are passed from producer—the green grass—to consumers. Decomposers return the nutrients to the cycle at every level.

GET IT? **Explain** why it is important to living organisms that nutrients are cycled.

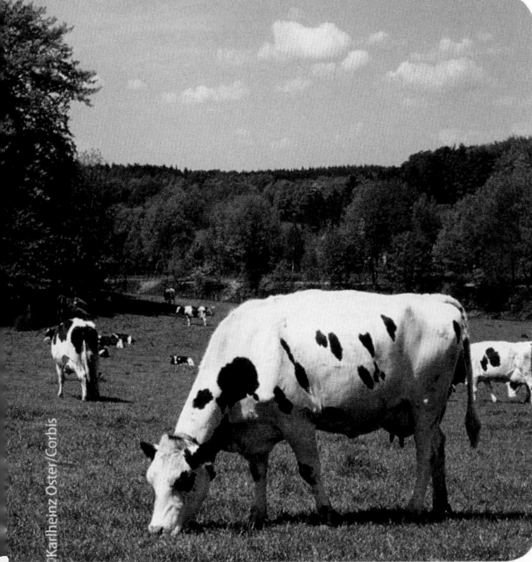

■ **Figure 16** Nutrients are cycled through the biosphere through organisms. In this example, the grasses are the producers and begin the cycle by capturing energy from the Sun.
Explain ***how nutrients continue to be cycled through the biosphere in this photo.***

CAREERS IN BIOLOGY

Hydrologist A hydrologist studies water processes, such as the distribution in nature, the water flow in a dam or river, or the water flow of a sewer or of a city drinking-water system.

The water cycle Organisms cannot live without water. Hydrologists study water found underground, in the atmosphere, and on Earth's surface in the form of lakes, streams, rivers, glaciers, ice caps, and oceans. Follow along with **Figure 17** to trace processes that cycle water through the biosphere.

Connection to Earth Science Water is constantly evaporating into the atmosphere from bodies of water, soil, and organisms. Water in the atmosphere is called water vapor. Water vapor rises and begins to cool in the atmosphere. Clouds form when the cooling water vapor condenses into droplets around dust particles in the atmosphere. Water falls from clouds as precipitation in the form of rain, sleet, snow, or hail, transferring water to Earth's surface. As shown in **Figure 17,** groundwater and runoff from land surfaces flow into streams, rivers, lakes, and oceans, where they evaporate into the atmosphere to continue through the water cycle. Approximately 90 percent of water vapor evaporates from oceans, lakes, and rivers; about 10 percent evaporates from the surfaces of plants through a process called transpiration.

Personal Tutor 

BrainPOP 

All living organisms rely on freshwater. Even ocean-dwelling organisms rely on freshwater flowing to oceans to prevent high saline content and to maintain ocean volume. Freshwater constitutes only about 3 percent of all water on Earth. Water available for living organisms is about 31 percent of all freshwater. The remaining 69 percent of all freshwater is frozen and found in ice caps and glaciers, which makes it unavailable for use by living organisms.

GET IT? **Identify** three processes in the water cycle.

Animation 

■ **Figure 17** The water cycle is the natural process by which water is continuously cycled through the biosphere.
Identify ***the largest reservoirs of water on Earth.***

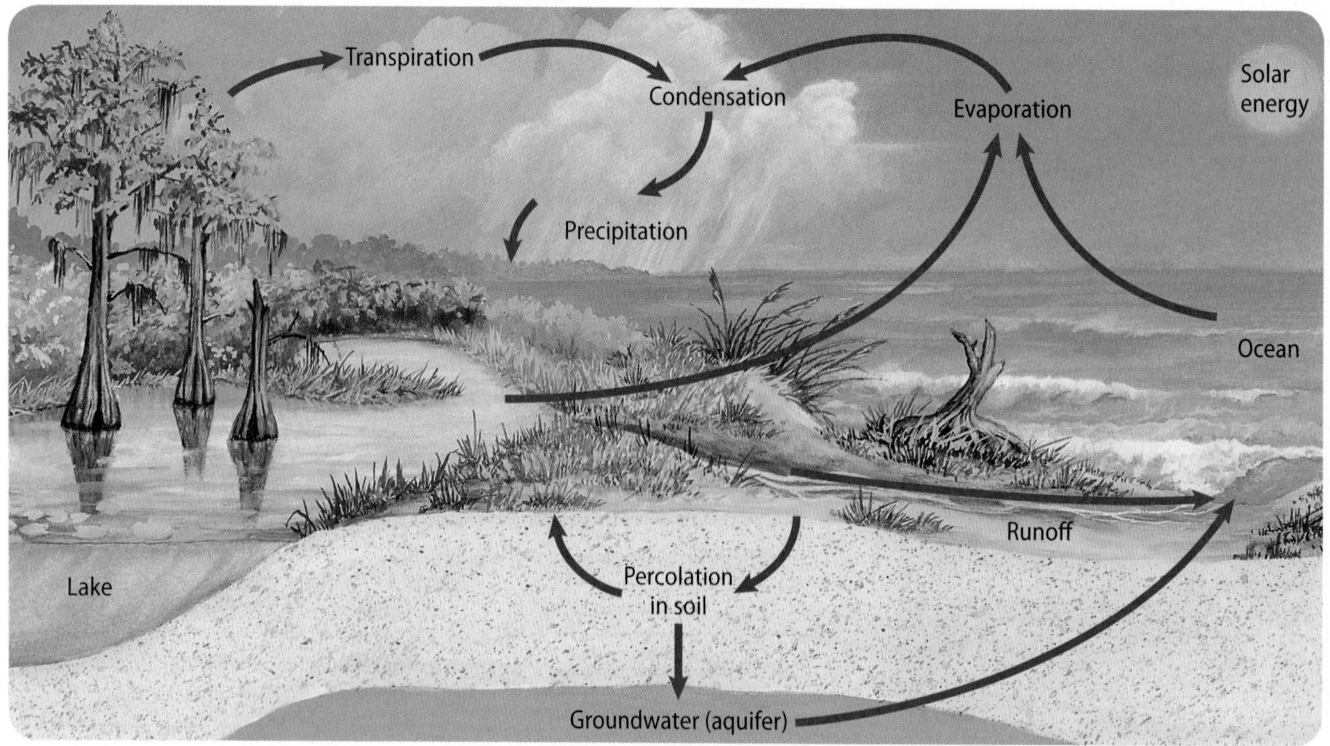

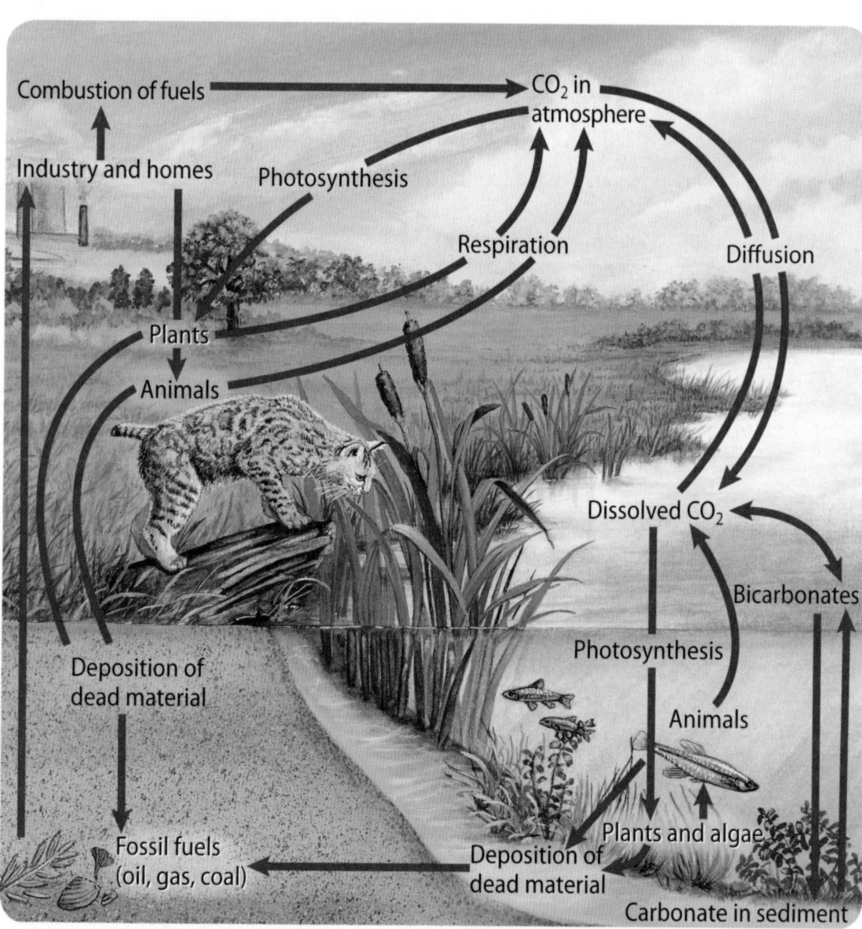

■ **Figure 18** The diagram shows how carbon and oxygen cycle through the environment.

Describe ***how carbon moves from the abiotic to the biotic parts of the ecosystem.***

Animation

The carbon and oxygen cycles All living things are composed of molecules that contain carbon. Atoms of carbon form the framework for important molecules such as proteins, carbohydrates, and fats. Oxygen is another element that is important to many life processes. Carbon and oxygen often make up molecules essential for life, including carbon dioxide and simple sugars.

Look at the cycles illustrated in **Figure 18.** During a process called photosynthesis, green plants and algae convert carbon dioxide and water into carbohydrates and release oxygen back into the air. These carbohydrates are used as a source of energy for all organisms in the food web. Carbon dioxide is recycled when autotrophs and heterotrophs release it back into the air during cellular respiration. Carbon and oxygen recycle relatively quickly through living organisms.

Carbon enters a long-term cycle when organic matter is buried underground and converted to peat, coal, oil, or gas deposits. The carbon might remain as fossil fuel for millions of years. Carbon is released from fossil fuels when they are burned, which adds carbon dioxide to the atmosphere.

In addition to combining to form fossil fuels, carbon and oxygen can combine with calcium and create calcium carbonate ($CaCO_3$). The white cliffs shown in **Figure 19** are made of calcium carbonate. Calcium carbonate is found in the shells of plankton and animals such as coral, clams, and oysters. These organisms fall to the ocean floor, creating vast deposits of limestone rock. Carbon and oxygen remain trapped in these deposits until the rocks are exposed to weathering and erosion and carbon and oxygen are released.

FOLDABLES®
Incorporate information from this section into your Foldable.

■ **Figure 19** The white cliffs in Dover, England, are composed almost entirely of calcium carbonate, or chalk. The carbon and oxygen found in these cliffs are in the long-term part of the cycle for carbon and oxygen.

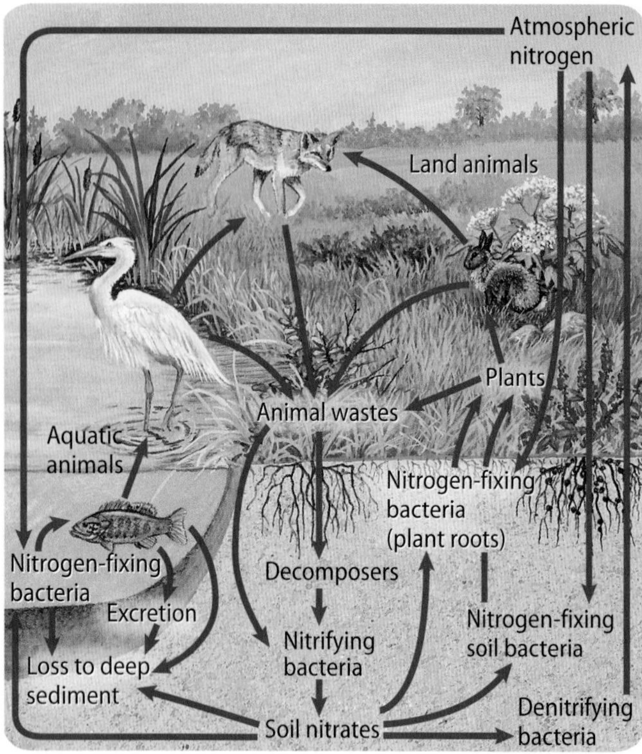

■ **Figure 20** Nitrogen is used and reused as it is cycled continuously through the biosphere.

 **Animation**

The nitrogen cycle Nitrogen is an element found in proteins. The largest concentration of nitrogen is found in the atmosphere. Plants and animals cannot use nitrogen directly from the atmosphere. Nitrogen gas is captured from the air by species of bacteria that live in water, the soil, or grow on the roots of some plants. The process of capture and conversion of nitrogen into a form that is usable by plants is called **nitrogen fixation.** Some nitrogen is also fixed during electrical storms when the energy from lightning bolts changes nitrogen gas to nitrates. Nitrogen is also added to soil when chemical fertilizers are applied to lawns, crops, or other areas.

Nitrogen enters the food web when plants absorb nitrogen compounds from the soil and convert them into proteins, as illustrated in **Figure 20.** Consumers get nitrogen by eating plants or animals that contain nitrogen. They reuse the nitrogen and make their own proteins. Because the supply of nitrogen in a food web depends on the amount of nitrogen that is fixed, nitrogen is often a factor that limits the growth of producers.

Nitrogen is returned to the soil in several ways, also shown in **Figure 20.** When an animal urinates, nitrogen returns to the water or soil and is reused by plants. When organisms die, decomposers transform the nitrogen in proteins and other compounds into ammonia. Organisms in the soil convert ammonia into nitrogen compounds that can be used by plants. Finally, in a process called **denitrification,** some soil bacteria convert fixed nitrogen compounds back into nitrogen gas, which returns it to the atmosphere.

MiniLAB 2

Test for Nitrates

How much nitrate is found in various water sources? One ion containing nitrogen found in water can be easily tested—nitrate. Nitrate is a common form of inorganic nitrogen that is used easily by plants.

Procedure 

1. Read and complete the lab safety form.
2. Prepare a data table to record your observations.
3. Obtain the **water samples** from different sources that are provided by your teacher.
4. Using a **nitrate test kit,** test the amount of nitrate in each water sample.
5. Dispose of your samples as directed by your teacher.

Analysis

1. **Determine** whether the samples contain differing amounts of nitrate. Explain.
2. **Identify** what types of human activities might increase the amount of nitrate in the water.
3. **Infer** what problems a high nitrate level could cause, considering that nitrates also increase the growth rate of algae in waterways.

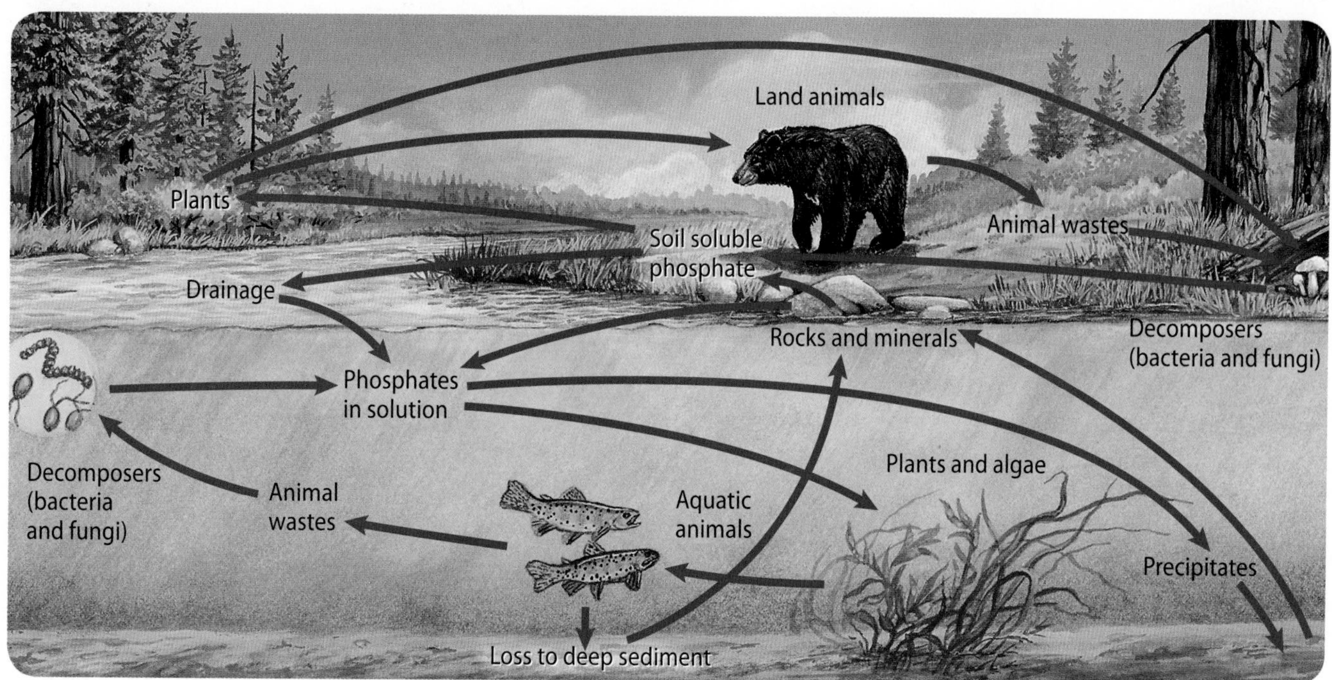

■ **Figure 21** The phosphorus cycle has a short-term cycle and a long-term cycle.

 **Animation**

The phosphorus cycle Phosphorus is an element that is essential for the growth and development of organisms. **Figure 21** illustrates the two cycles of phosphorus—a short-term and long-term cycle. In the short-term cycle, phosphorus in phosphates in solution, is cycled from the soil to producers and then from the producers to consumers. When organisms die or produce waste products, decomposers return the phosphorus to the soil where it can be used again. Phosphorus moves from the short-term cycle to the long-term cycle through precipitation and sedimentation to form rocks. In the long-term cycle, weathering or erosion of rocks that contain phosphorus slowly adds phosphorus to the cycle. Phosphorus, in the form of phosphates, might be present only in small amounts in soil and water. Therefore, phosphorus is a factor that limits the growth of producers.

REVIEW IT! Cycling of Matter

Section Summary

- Biogeochemical cycles include the exchange of important nutrients between the abiotic and biotic parts of an ecosystem.
- The carbon and oxygen cycles are closely intertwined.
- Nitrogen gas is limited in its ability to enter biotic portions of the environment.
- Phosphorus and carbon have short-term and long-term cycles.

 **Self Check**

Understand Main Ideas

1. **MAIN**IDEA **Name** four important biogeochemical processes that cycle nutrients.
2. **Compare and contrast** two of the cycles of matter.
3. **Explain** the importance of nutrients to an organism of your choice.
4. **Describe** how phosphorus moves through the biotic and abiotic parts of an ecosystem.

Think Critically

5. **Design** an experiment to test the amount of fertilizer to use on a lawn for the best results. Fertilizers usually contain nitrogen, phosphorus, and potassium. The numbers on the label represent the amount of each nutrient in the fertilizer. How would you experiment to determine the correct quantity of fertilizer?

BIOLOGY&society

1.1.3b, 4.3.1l, 4.7.3a, 4.7.3b

To Dam or Not to Dam

The Glen Canyon area is a popular location for whitewater rafting, fishing, hiking, and kayaking. The Glen Canyon area is also the location of a controversial dam, the Glen Canyon Dam. It was built between 1956 and 1963 in Arizona on the Colorado River. The dam holds and releases water from Lake Powell.

Economic benefits The Glen Canyon Dam provides electricity to many rural communities. It also provides water to California, New Mexico, Arizona, and Nevada. Lake Powell, which is one of the most visited tourist destinations of the southwest, provides jobs for many of the local residents. Millions of tourists visit Lake Powell each year for activities such as hiking, boating, fishing, and swimming.

■ The Glen Canyon Dam provides opportunities for recreation to millions of tourists every year. However, it also impacts the Colorado River ecosystem.

Impact on flora and fauna The construction of the dam has brought economic benefits to the area, but it also has negatively impacted the Colorado River ecosystem. The habitat of native fish has changed as a result of the dam. Three species of fish—the roundtail chub, the bonytail chub, and the Colorado squawfish—have become endangered.

The Lake Powell shoreline now is dominated by a nonnative, semidesert scrub known as saltcedar or tamarisk. The saltcedar outcompetes native vegetation such as the sandbar willow, Gooding's willow, and Fremont cottonwood. Saltcedar collects salt in its tissues over time. This salt eventually is released into the soil, making it unsuitable for many native plants.

Impact on temperature Before the dam was built, the water temperature of the Colorado River ranged from near freezing in the winter to a warm 29°C in the summer. Since the dam was built, the temperature of the water released downstream remains steady at 7–10°C. This temperature is fine for the nonnative trout that are bred for recreational activities; however, the native species do not fare as well.

The Bureau of Reclamation has proposed placing a temperature control device on the Glen Canyon Dam that would regulate the water temperature. Environmentalists suggest that this solution might not solve the problems for the native species because the native species need the fluctuating temperatures that were once part of the river system.

The Glen Canyon Dam has negatively impacted the ecosystem of the Colorado River area, but it has benefited the area economically. How do the costs weigh against the benefits? Biologists face real-world issues like these every day.

DEBATE IN ▶ Biology

Collaborate Form teams to debate whether the recreational and economic opportunities outweigh the costs of damming the Colorado River. Conduct additional research prior to the debate.

 **WebQuest**

BioLAB DESIGN YOUR OWN

1.2.1, 1.2.2a, 1.2.4, 1.3.3, 1.3.5b, 4.5.3a, 4.6.3a, ¥a, ¥b1, ¥e, ¥j, ¥n, ¥o

Field Investigation: Explore Habitat Size and Species Diversity

Background: Ecologists know that a major key to maintaining not only individual species but also a robust diversity of species is preserving the proper habitat for those species.

Question: *What effect does increasing the size of a habitat have on the species diversity within that habitat?*

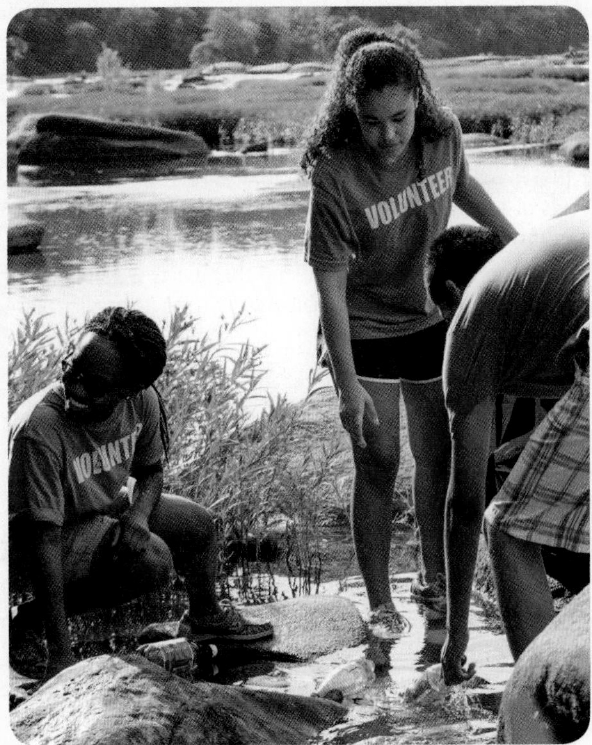

Materials

Choose materials that would be appropriate for the experiment you plan.

Safety Precautions

WARNING: ***Follow all safety rules regarding travel to and from the study site. Be alert on site and avoid contact with stinging or biting animals and poisonous plants.***

Plan and Perform the Experiment

1. Read and complete the lab safety form.
2. Form a hypothesis that you can test to answer the above question.
3. Record your procedure. List the materials you will use to test your hypothesis.
4. Make sure your experiment allows for the collection of quantitative data, which are data that can be expressed in units of measure.
5. Design and construct appropriate data tables.
6. Make sure your teacher approves your plan before you proceed.
7. Carry out the procedure at an appropriate field site.

Analyze and Conclude

1. **Graph Data** Prepare a graph of your data and the combined class data if they are available.
2. **Analyze** Do any patterns emerge as you analyze your group and class data and graphs? Explain.
3. **Conclude** Based on your data, was your initial hypothesis correct?
4. **Error Analysis** Compare your observations and conclusions with your classmates. Did your observations and conclusions match? If not, what could explain the differences? How could you verify your results?
5. **Determine** Did the populations and diversity change proportionally as the habitat was expanded? As the habitat expanded, did it become more or less suitable for supporting life?
6. **Hypothesize** Would you expect the same results if you performed this experiment in other habitats? Explain.
7. **Think Critically** Would you expect the same results 10 years from now? 20 years from now? Explain your answer.

APPLY YOUR SKILL

Presentation Diagram and explain at least one food chain that might exist in the habitat you explored in this lab.

CHAPTER 2 STUDY GUIDE

BIGIDEA **Energy is required to cycle materials through living and nonliving systems.**

SECTION 1 Organisms and Their Relationships

MAINIDEA Biotic and abiotic factors interact in complex ways in communities and ecosystems.

- Ecology is the branch of biology in which interrelationships between organisms and their environments are studied.
- Abiotic and biotic factors shape an ecosystem and determine the communities that will be successful in it.
- Levels of organization in ecological studies include organism, population, biological community, ecosystem, biome, and biosphere.
- Symbiosis is the close relationship that exists when two or more species live together. There are three types of symbiosis.

VOCABULARY
- **ecology**
- **biosphere**
- **biotic factor**
- **abiotic factor**
- **population**
- **biological community**
- **ecosystem**
- **biome**
- **habitat**
- **niche**
- **predation**
- **symbiosis**
- **mutualism**
- **commensalism**
- **parasitism**

SECTION 2 Flow of Energy in an Ecosystem

MAINIDEA Autotrophs capture energy, making it available for all members of a food web.

- Autotrophs capture energy from the Sun or use energy from certain chemical substances to make food.
- Heterotrophs include herbivores, carnivores, omnivores, and detritivores.
- A trophic level is a step in a food chain or food web.
- Food chains, food webs, and ecological pyramids are models used to show how energy moves through ecosystems.

VOCABULARY
- **autotroph**
- **heterotroph**
- **herbivore**
- **carnivore**
- **omnivore**
- **detritivore**
- **trophic level**
- **food chain**
- **food web**
- **biomass**

SECTION 3 Cycling of Matter

MAINIDEA Essential nutrients are cycled through biogeochemical processes.

- Biogeochemical cycles include the exchange of important nutrients between the abiotic and biotic parts of an ecosystem.
- The carbon and oxygen cycles are closely intertwined.
- Nitrogen gas is limited in its ability to enter biotic portions of the environment.
- Phosphorus and carbon have short-term and long-term cycles.

VOCABULARY
- **matter**
- **nutrient**
- **biogeochemical cycle**
- **nitrogen fixation**
- **denitrification**

ASSESSMENT

SECTION 1

Vocabulary Review

Replace each underlined word with the correct vocabulary term from the Study Guide page.

1. A niche is the place in which an organism lives.
2. The presence of interbreeding individuals in one place at a given time is called a biological community.
3. A group of biological communities that interact with the physical environment is the biosphere.

Understand Main Ideas

4. Which of these levels of organization includes all the other levels?
   A. community **C.** individual
   B. ecosystem **D.** population
5. Which would be an abiotic factor for a tree in the forest?
   A. a caterpillar eating its leaves
   B. wind blowing through its branches
   C. a bird nesting in its branches
   D. fungus growing on its roots

Use the photo below to answer questions 6 and 7.

6. The insect in the photo above is gathering pollen and nectar for food, but at the same time is aiding in the plant's reproduction. What does this relationship demonstrate?
   A. predation **C.** mutualism
   B. commensalism **D.** parasitism
7. What term best describes the bee's role of gathering pollen?
   A. niche **C.** parasite
   B. predator **D.** habitat

Use the illustration below to answer question 8.

8. Which type of heterotroph best describes this snake?
   A. herbivore **C.** omnivore
   B. carnivore **D.** detritivore

Constructed Response

9. **Short Answer** Explain the difference between a habitat and a niche.
10. **MAIN**IDEA Describe how abiotic factors affect biotic factors in your environment. Give specific examples.
11. **Relate** the levels of organization to each other and to the whole system.

Think Critically

12. **Identify** an example of a predator-prey relationship, a competitive relationship, and a symbiotic relationship in an ecosystem near where you live.
13. **Explain** why it is advantageous for organisms such as fungi and algae to form mutualistic relationships.

SECTION 2

Vocabulary Review

Explain how the terms in each set below are related.

14. heterotroph, omnivore, carnivore
15. food chain, food web, trophic level
16. decomposer, heterotroph, carnivore
17. autotroph, food chain, heterotroph

Understand Main Ideas

18. How does energy first enter a pond ecosystem?
    - **A.** through growth of algae
    - **B.** through light from the Sun
    - **C.** through decay of dead fish
    - **D.** through runoff from fields

19. Which statement is true about energy in an ecosystem?
    - **A.** Energy for most ecosystems originates from the Sun.
    - **B.** Energy most often is released as light from an ecosystem.
    - **C.** Energy flows from heterotrophs to autotrophs.
    - **D.** Energy levels increase toward the top of the food chain.

Use the illustration below to answer questions 20 and 21.

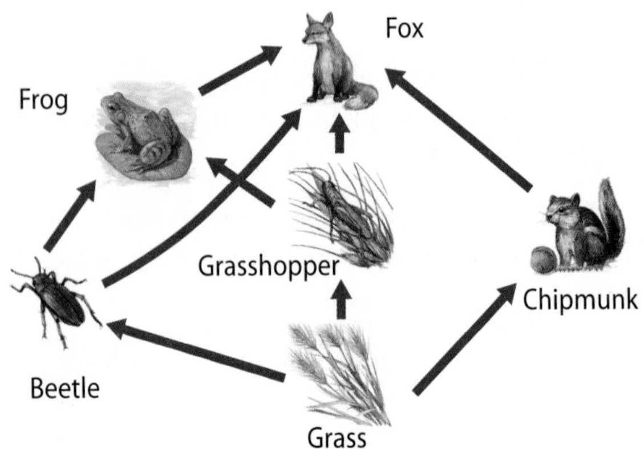

20. What does the illustration represent?
    - **A.** a food web
    - **B.** a food chain
    - **C.** an ecological pyramid
    - **D.** a pyramid of energy

21. Which organism in the illustration is an autotroph?
    - **A.** frog
    - **B.** grasshopper
    - **C.** fox
    - **D.** grass

22. Which is a detritivore?
    - **A.** cat
    - **B.** mouse
    - **C.** sunflower
    - **D.** crayfish

Constructed Response

23. **MAINIDEA** Create a food web that occurs in your community. Explain the importance of the autotrophs in the food web.

24. **THEME FOCUS** Describe why food webs usually are better models for explaining energy flow than food chains.

25. **Short Answer** Determine approximately how much total energy is lost from a three-step food chain if 1000 calories enter at the autotroph level.

Think Critically

26. **Apply Information** Create a poster of a food web that might exist in an ecosystem that differs from your community. Include as many organisms as possible in the food web.

SECTION 3

Vocabulary Review

Each of the following sentences is false. Make each sentence true by replacing the italicized word with a vocabulary term from the Study Guide page.

27. Because nitrogen is required for growth, it is considered an essential *nitrate.*

28. Converting nitrogen from a gas to a useable form by bacteria is *denitrification.*

29. The movement of chemicals on a global scale from abiotic through biotic parts of the environment is a *lithospheric process.*

Understand Main Ideas

30. What is the name of the process in which bacteria and lightning convert nitrogen into compounds that are useful to plants?
    - **A.** ammonification
    - **B.** denitrification
    - **C.** nitrate cycling
    - **D.** nitrogen fixation

Use the following diagram to answer question 31.

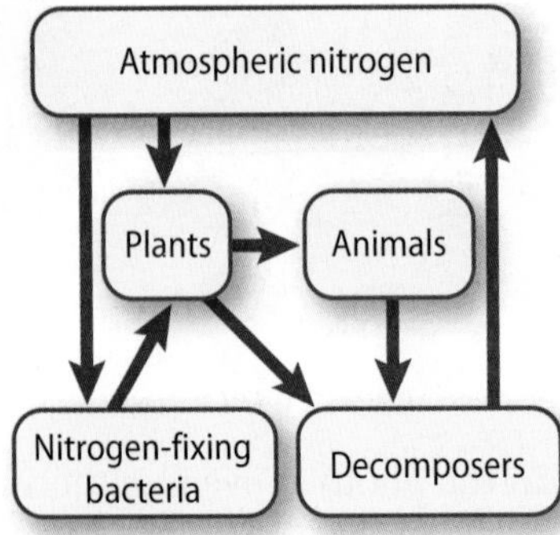

31. Where is the largest concentration of nitrogen found?
    - **A.** animals
    - **B.** atmosphere
    - **C.** bacteria
    - **D.** plants

32. What are the two major life processes that involve carbon and oxygen?
   A. coal formation and photosynthesis
   B. photosynthesis and respiration
   C. fuel combustion and open burning
   D. death and decay

33. Which process locks phosphorus in a long-term cycle?
   A. organic materials buried at the bottom of oceans
   B. phosphates released into the soil
   C. animals and plants eliminating wastes
   D. rain eroding mountains

Constructed Response

34. **Short Answer** Clarify what is meant by the following statement: Grass is just as important as mice in the diet of a carnivore such as a fox.

35. **Short Answer** The law of conservation of matter states that matter cannot be created or destroyed. How does this law relate to the cycling of carbon in an ecosystem?

36. **MAIN**IDEA Explain the role of decomposers in the nitrogen cycle.

Think Critically

Use the illustration below to answer question 37.

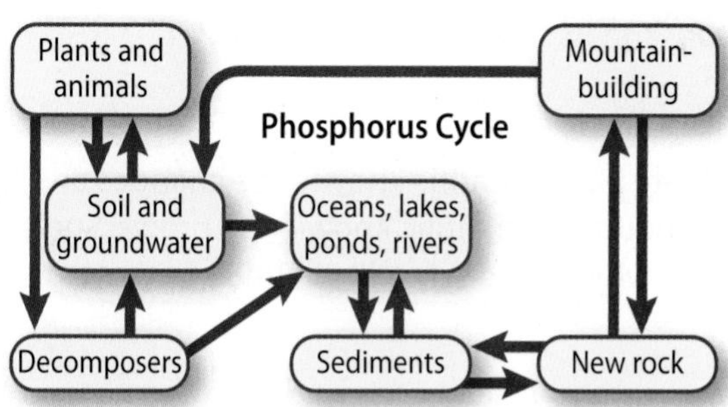

37. **Interpret Scientific Illustrations** Predict the effect of additional mountain building in the Rocky Mountains on the levels of phosphorus in the surrounding valleys.

38. **Explain** the consequences of disrupting the carbon and nitrogen cycles.

Summative Assessment

39. **BIG**IDEA Choose a specific organism from a food web in the chapter. Hypothesize how the energy from the Sun directly and indirectly affects its activities and life.

40. **WRITING**IN▶**Biology** Write a poem that includes vocabulary terms and concepts from the chapter.

41. **Summarize** What is the difference between a heterotroph and an autotroph?

DBQ Document-Based Questions

The following information pertains to an ancient sand dune in Florida that is now landlocked—Lake Wales Ridge. Read the passage and answer the following questions.

Data obtained from: Mohlenbrock, R. H. 2004–2005. Florida high. *Natural History* 113: 46–47.

The federally listed animals that live on the ridge are the blue-tailed mole skink, the Florida scrub jay, and the sand skink (which seems to "swim" through loose sand of the scrub). Other animals on the ridge are the eastern indigo snake (which can grow to more than eight feet long, making it the longest nonvenomous snake species in North America), the Florida black bear, the Florida gopher frog, the Florida mouse, the Florida pine snake, the Florida sandhill crane, the Florida scrub lizard, the gopher tortoise, Sherman's fox squirrel, and the short-tailed snake.

The gopher tortoise is particularly important because its burrows, sometimes as long as thirty feet, serve as homes for several of the rare species as well as many other more common organisms. The burrows also provide temporary havens when fires sweep through the area, or when temperatures reach high or low extremes.

42. Construct a simple food web using at least five of the organisms listed.

43. Explain how the burrows are used during fires and why they are effective.

CUMULATIVE

MULTIPLE CHOICE

Use the illustration below to answer questions 1 and 2.

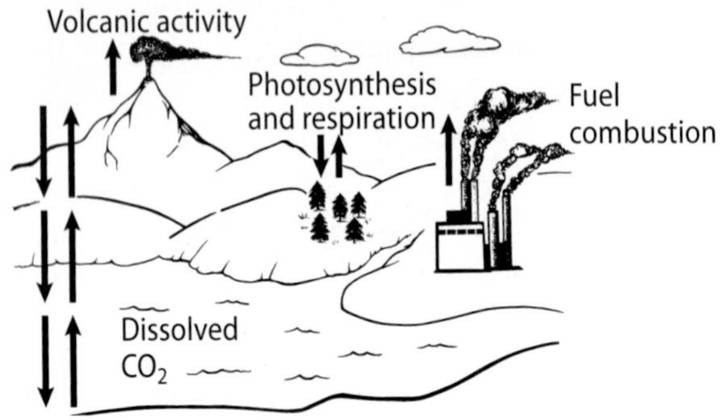

1 Which part of the diagram above relates to carbon leaving a long-term cycle?

A dissolved CO_2

B fuel combustion

C photosynthesis and respiration

D volcanic activity

2 Which part of the diagram above relates to carbon moving from an abiotic to a biotic part of the ecosystem?

A dissolved CO_2

B fuel combustion

C photosynthesis and respiration

D volcanic activity

3 Suppose two leaf-eating species of animals live in a habitat where there is a severe drought and many plants die as a result. Which term describes the kind of relationship the two species probably will have?

A commensalism

B competition

C mutualism

D predation

SHORT ANSWER

Use the illustration below to answer questions 4 and 5.

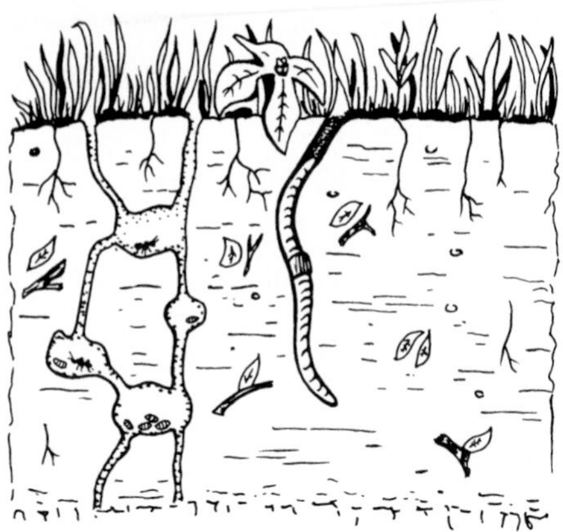

4 What are two biotic factors and two abiotic factors that affect a worm found in a situation similar to what is shown in the diagram?

5 Explain the portions of the following biogeochemical cycles that are related to the diagram above.

A nitrogen cycle

B oxygen cycle

C carbon cycle

6 Distinguish between the everyday use of the term *theory* and its true scientific meaning.

7 Evaluate how scientific knowledge changes and how the amount of scientific knowledge grows. Suggest a reason why it probably will continue to grow.

8 Describe how a forest ecosystem might be different without the presence of decomposers and detritivores.

9 Suppose that some unknown organisms are discovered in the deep underground of Earth. Give two examples of questions that biologists might try to answer by researching these organisms.

EXTENDED RESPONSE

Use this drawing to answer questions 10 and 11.

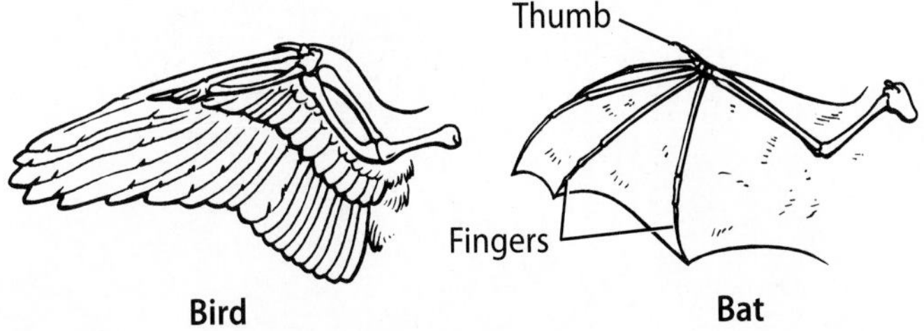

10 Someone tells you that bats and birds are closely related because they both have wings. Evaluate how this diagram could be used to critique the idea that bats and birds are not closely related.

11 Suppose you form a hypothesis that bats and birds are not closely related and you want to confirm this by comparing the way bats and birds fly. Design an experiment to test this hypothesis.

ESSAY QUESTION

Various substances or elements on Earth move through long-term and short-term biogeochemical cycles as they become part of different aspects of the biosphere. The amount of a substance that is involved in a long-term cycle has an effect on the availability of that substance for use by humans and other organisms on Earth.

Using the information in the paragraph above, answer the following question in essay format.

12 Choose a substance or element that you know is involved in both long-term and short-term biogeochemical cycles. In a well-organized essay, describe how it moves through both types of cycles, and how these cycles affect its availability to humans and other organisms.

TEST PRACTICE

Use the illustration below to answer questions 13 and 14.

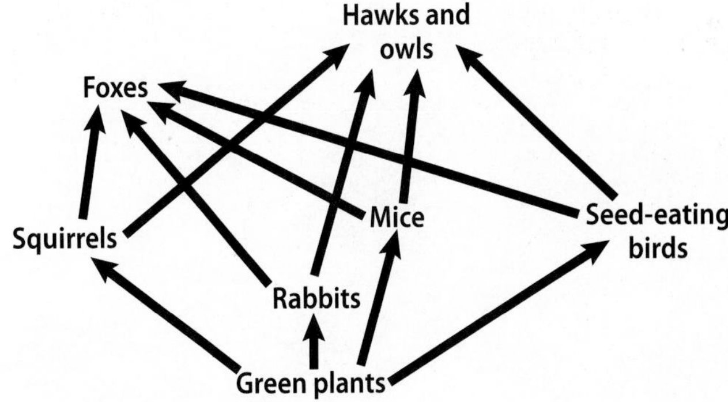

13 Which part of the food web above contains the greatest biomass?

A foxes

B green plants

C mice

D rabbits

14 What happens to the energy that the fox uses for maintaining its body temperature?

A It is taken up by decomposers that consume the fox.

B It moves into the surrounding environment.

C It stays in the fox through the metabolism of food.

D It travels to the next trophic level when the fox is eaten.

NEED EXTRA HELP?														
If You Missed Question . . .	1	2	3	4	5	6	7	8	9	10	11	12	13	14
Review Section . . .	2.3	2.3, 2.1	2.1	2.1	2.3	1.2	1.2	2.2	1.3	1.2	1.3	2.3	2.2	2.2

Coral reefs are among the most diverse ecosystems. Coral reefs are sensitive to changes in the environment. Ecologists monitor coral reefs to protect these delicate ecosystems.

LaunchLAB

What is my biological address?

Just as you have a postal address, you also have a biological "address." As a living organism, you are part of interwoven ecological units that vary in size from as large as the whole biosphere to the place you occupy right now.

CHAPTER 3

Communities, Biomes, and Ecosystems

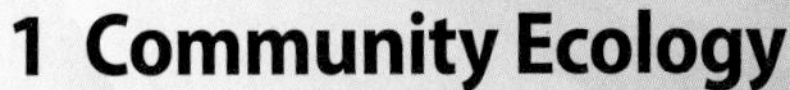

1 Community Ecology

4.1.1b, 4.1.1c, 4.1.1d, 4.5.3a, 4.6.1d, 4.6.1e, 4.6.1f, 4.6.3a, 4.6.3b

2 Terrestrial Biomes

4.1.1d, 4.5.3a, 4.6.1c, 4.6.3a, 4.6.3c, 4.7.1c, 4.7.2a, ¥a, ¥e, ¥n, ¥q

3 Aquatic Ecosystems

4.1.1e, 4.1.1f, 4.3.1l, 4.6.1g, 4.6.2a, 4.7.3b

THEMEFOCUS

Systems and system models Constantly changing communities of plants and animals drive succession.

BIGIDEA

Limiting factors and ranges of tolerance are factors that determine where terrestrial biomes and aquatic ecosystems exist.

Primary Succession

Make a shutter fold book using the labels shown. Use it to organize your notes on succession.

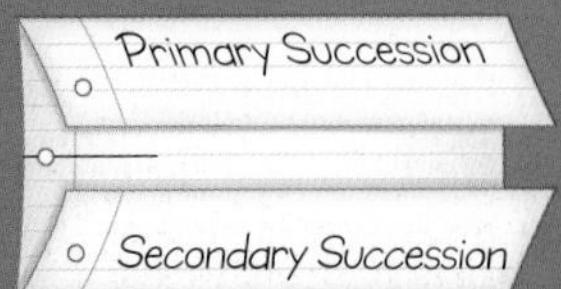

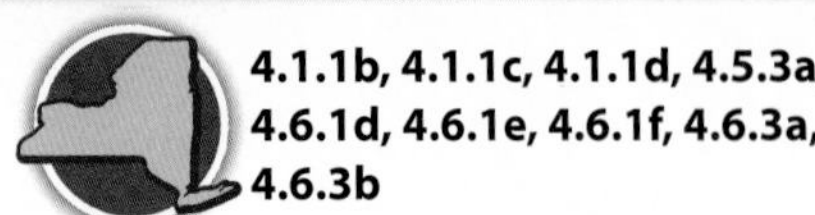

1 Community Ecology

4.1.1b, 4.1.1c, 4.1.1d, 4.5.3a, 4.6.1d, 4.6.1e, 4.6.1f, 4.6.3a, 4.6.3b

MAINIDEA
All living organisms are limited by factors in the environment.

Essential Questions

- How do unfavorable abiotic and biotic factors affect species?
- How do ranges of tolerance affect the distribution of organisms?
- What are the stages of primary and secondary succession?

BIOLOGY 4U

Wherever you live, you probably are used to the conditions of your environment. If it is cold outdoors, you might wear a coat, hat, and gloves. Bears have adaptations to the cold, such as their warm fur coats, so they do not need these types of clothes.

Review Vocabulary

abiotic factor: the nonliving part of an organism's environment

New Vocabulary

community
limiting factor
tolerance
ecological succession
primary succession
climax community
secondary succession

Multilingual eGlossary

Communities

When you describe your community, you probably include your family, the students in your school, and the people who live nearby. A biological **community** is a group of interacting populations that occupy the same area at the same time. Therefore, your community also includes plants, other animals, bacteria, and fungi. Not every community includes the same variety of organisms. An urban community is different from a rural community, and a desert community is different from a polar community.

You have learned that organisms depend on one another for survival. You also learned about abiotic factors and how they affect individual organisms. How might abiotic factors affect communities? Consider soil, which is an abiotic factor. If soil becomes too acidic, some species might die or become extinct. This might affect food sources for other organisms, resulting in a change in the community.

Organisms adapt to the conditions in which they live. For example, a wolf's heavy fur coat enables it to survive in harsh winter climates, and a cactus's ability to retain water enables it to tolerate the dry conditions of a desert. Depending on which factors are present and in what quantities, organisms can survive in some ecosystems but not in others. For example, the plants in the desert oasis shown in **Figure 1** decrease in number away from the water source.

Figure 1 Notice that populations of organisms live within a relatively small area surrounding the oasis.

Limiting factors Any abiotic factor or biotic factor that restricts the numbers, reproduction, or distribution of organisms is called a **limiting factor.** Abiotic limiting factors include sunlight, climate, temperature, water, nutrients, fire, soil chemistry, and space. Biotic limiting factors include living things, such as other plant and animal species. Factors that restrict the growth of one population might enable another to thrive. For example, in the oasis shown in **Figure 1,** water is a limiting factor for all of the organisms. Temperature also might be a limiting factor. Desert species must be able to withstand the heat of the Sun and the cold temperatures of desert nights.

Range of tolerance For any environmental factor, there is an upper limit and lower limit that define the conditions in which an organism can survive. For example, steelhead trout live in cool, clear coastal rivers and streams from California to Alaska. The ideal range of water temperature for steelhead trout is between 13°C and 21°C, as illustrated in **Figure 2.** However, steelhead trout can survive water temperatures from 9°C to 25°C. At these temperatures, steelhead trout experience physiological stress, such as inability to grow or reproduce. They will die if the water temperature goes beyond the upper and lower limits.

Have you ever had to tolerate a hot day or a boring activity? The ability of any organism to survive when subjected to abiotic factors or biotic factors is called **tolerance.** Consider **Figure 2** again. Steelhead trout tolerate a specific range of temperatures. That is, the range of tolerance of water temperature for steelhead is 9°C to 25°C. Notice that the greatest number of steelhead live in the optimum zone in which the temperature is best for survival. Between the optimum zone and the tolerance limits lies the zone of physiological stress. At these temperatures, there are fewer fish. Beyond the upper tolerance limit of 25°C and the lower tolerance limit of 9°C, there are no steelhead trout. Therefore, water temperature is a limiting factor for steelhead when water temperature is outside the range of tolerance.

GET IT? **Describe** the relationship between a limiting factor and a range of tolerance.

CAREERS IN BIOLOGY

Conservation Biologist Among other duties, a conservation biologist might tag and track animals in a community. Understanding the biotic and abiotic factors of the community can help explain changes in populations.

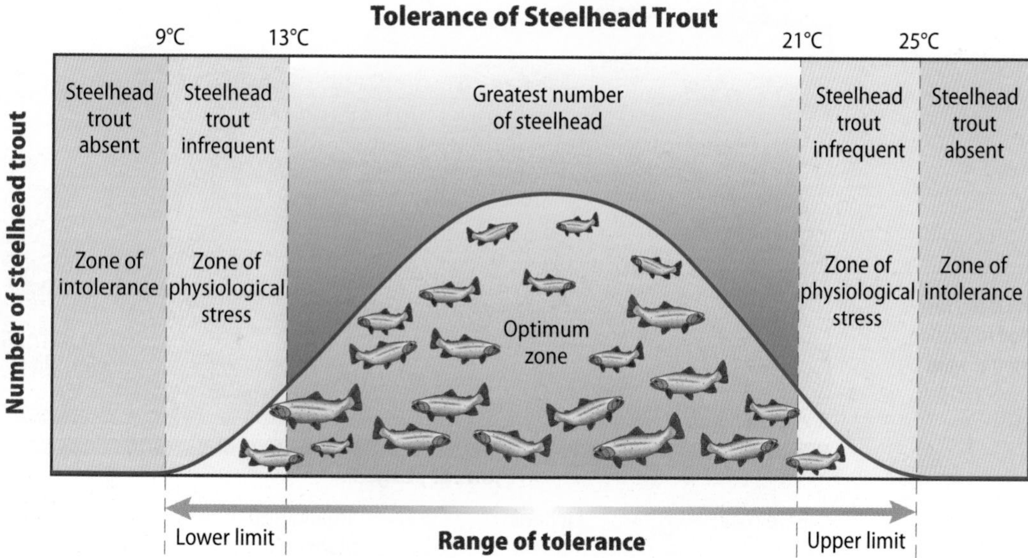

Figure 2 Steelhead trout are limited by the temperature of the water in which they live.
Infer ***which other abiotic factors might limit the survival of steelhead trout.***

FOLDABLES®

Incorporate information from this section into your Foldable.

Ecological Succession

Ecosystems are constantly changing. They might be modified in small ways, such as a tree falling in the forest, or in large ways, such as a forest fire. They also might alter the communities that exist in the ecosystem. Forest fires can be good and even necessary for the forest community. Forest fires return nutrients to the soil. Some plants, such as fireweed, have seeds that will not sprout until they are heated by fire. Some ecosystems depend on fires to get rid of debris. If fires are prevented, debris builds up to the point where the next fire might burn the shrubs and trees completely. A forest fire might change the habitat so drastically that some species no longer can survive, but other species might thrive in the new, charred conditions.

The change in an ecosystem that happens when one community replaces another as a result of changing abiotic and biotic factors is **ecological succession.** There are two types of ecological succession—primary succession and secondary succession.

VOCABULARY

SCIENCE USAGE V. COMMON USAGE

Primary

Science usage: first in rank, importance, value, or order

A doctor's primary concern should be the patient.

Common usage: the early years of formal education

Elementary grades, up to high school, are considered to comprise a student's primary education.

Primary succession On a solidified lava flow or exposed rocks on a cliff, no soil is present. If you took samples of each and looked at them under a microscope, the only biological organisms you would observe would be bacteria and perhaps fungal spores or pollen grains that drifted there on air currents. The establishment of a community in an area of exposed rock that does not have any topsoil is **primary succession,** which is illustrated in **Figure 3.** Primary succession usually occurs very slowly at first.

Almost all plants require soil for growth. But, how is soil formed? Usually lichens, a mutualistic combination of a fungus and algae, begin to grow on the rock. Because lichens, along with some mosses, are among the first organisms to appear, they are called pioneer species. Pioneer species help to create soil by secreting acids that help to break down rocks.

■ **Figure 3** The formation of soil is the first step in primary succession. Once soil formation starts, there is progressive succession toward a climax community.

 **Animation**

 **Video Lab**

As pioneer organisms die, their decaying organic materials, along with bits of sediment from the rocks, make up the first stage of soil development. At this point, small weedy plants, including ferns, and other organisms such as fungi and insects, become established. As these organisms die, additional soil is created. Seeds, transported by animals, water, or wind, begin to grow in the newly formed soil. Eventually, enough soil is present so that shrubs and trees can grow.

A mature community can eventually develop from bare rock, as illustrated in **Figure 3.** The stable, mature community that results when there is little change in the composition of species is a **climax community.** Scientists today realize that disturbances, such as climate change, are ongoing in communities; therefore, a true climax community is unlikely to occur.

Secondary succession Disturbances such as fire, flood, or a windstorm can disrupt a community. After a disturbance, new species of plants and animals might occupy the habitat. Over time, there is a natural tendency for the species belonging to the mature community to return. **Secondary succession** is the orderly and predictable change that takes place after a community of organisms has been removed but the soil has remained intact. Pioneer species—mainly plants that begin to grow in the disturbed area—are the first species to start secondary succession.

Data Analysis LAB 1

Based on Real Data*

Interpret the Data

How do soil invertebrates affect secondary succession in a grassland environment? An experiment was performed by adding soil invertebrates to controlled grassland communities. The growth of various plants was measured at four months, six months, and 12 months. Growth was measured by recording shoot biomass—the mass of the grass stems.

Data and Observations

The bars on the graph indicate the change in the biomass of the plants over time.

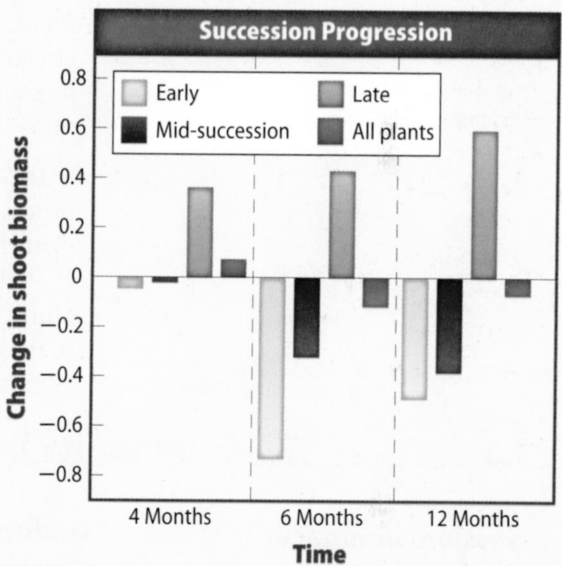

Think Critically

1. **Infer** what a negative value of change in shoot biomass indicates.
2. **Generalize** which communities were most positively affected and which were most negatively affected by the addition of soil invertebrates.

*Data obtained from: De Deyn, G.B. et al. 2003. Soil invertebrate fauna enhances grassland succession and diversity. *Nature* 422: 711–713.

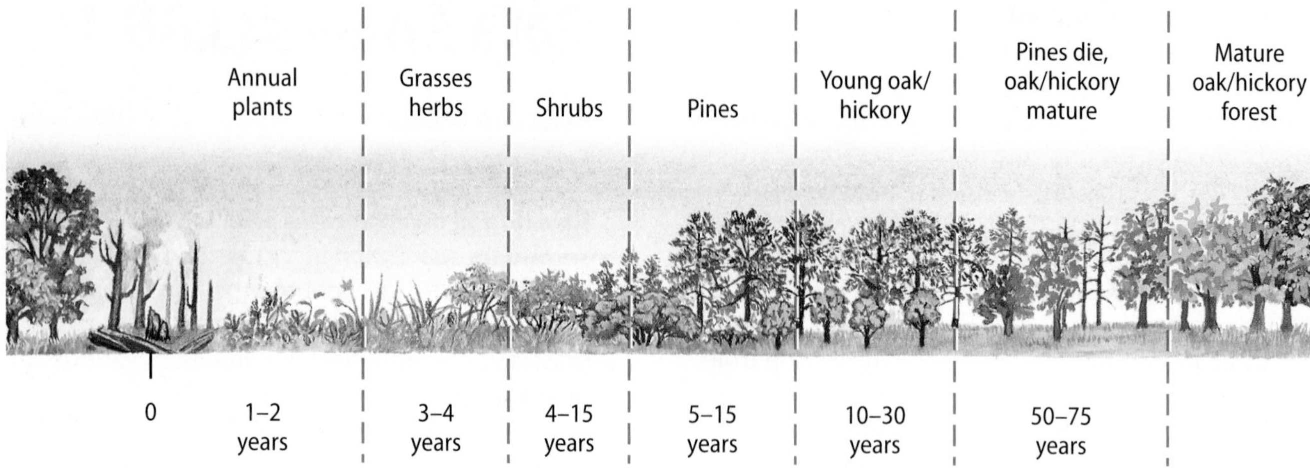

Figure 4 After a fire, a forest might appear devastated. However, a series of changes ultimately leads back to a mature community.

During secondary succession, as in primary succession, the community of organisms changes over a period of time. **Figure 4** shows how species composition changes after a forest fire. Secondary succession usually occurs faster than primary succession because soil already exists and some species still will be present (although there might be fewer of them). Also, undisturbed areas nearby can be sources of seeds and animals.

Succession's end point Ecological succession is a complex process that involves many factors. The end point of succession after a disturbance cannot be predicted. Natural communities are constantly changing at different rates, and the process of succession is very slow. Human activities also affect the species that might be present. Because of these factors, it is difficult to determine if succession has reached a climax community in many areas on Earth.

REVIEW IT! Community Ecology

Section Summary

- Abiotic and biotic limiting factors restrict the growth of a population within a community.
- Organisms have a range of tolerance for each limiting factor that they encounter.
- Primary succession occurs on areas of exposed rock or bare sand (no soil).
- Communities progress until there is little change in the composition of species.
- Secondary succession occurs as a result of a disturbance in a mature community.

Self Check

Understand Main Ideas

1. MAINIDEA **Identify** how temperature is a limiting factor for polar bears.
2. **Predict** how unfavorable abiotic and biotic factors affect an organism, population, and community.
3. **Describe** how ranges of tolerance affect the distribution of a species.
4. **Describe** how events and processes that occur in ecological succession can change populations or species diversity.

Think Critically

5. **Interpret Figure 2** and predict the general growth trend for steelhead trout in a stream that is 22°C.

MATH IN ▸ Biology

6. Graph the following data to determine the range of tolerance for catfish. The first number in each pair of data is temperature in degrees Celsius, and the second number is the number of catfish found in the stream: (0, 0); (5, 0); (10, 2); (15, 15); (20, 13); (25, 3); (30, 0); (35, 0).

2 Terrestrial Biomes

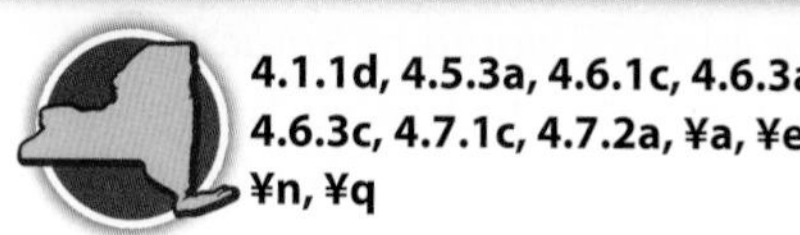
4.1.1d, 4.5.3a, 4.6.1c, 4.6.3a, 4.6.3c, 4.7.1c, 4.7.2a, ¥a, ¥e, ¥n, ¥q

MAIN IDEA

Ecosystems on land are grouped into biomes primarily based on the plant communities within them.

Essential Questions

- How is latitude related to the three major climate zones?
- What are the major abiotic factors that determine the location of a terrestrial biome?
- How are the terrestrial biomes distinguished based on climate and biotic factors?

BIOLOGY 4 U

If you live in the eastern part of the United States, you might live in an area surrounded by deciduous forests. If you live in the central part of the United States, there might be a grassy prairie nearby. Plant communities are specific to particular ecosystems.

Review Vocabulary

biome: a large group of ecosystems that share the same climate and have similar types of plant communities

New Vocabulary

weather
latitude
climate
tundra
boreal forest
temperate forest
woodland
grassland
desert
tropical savanna
tropical seasonal forest
tropical rain forest

Multilingual eGlossary 

Effects of Latitude and Climate

Regardless of where you live, you are affected by weather and climate. During a newscast, a meteorologist will make forecasts about the upcoming weather. **Weather** is the condition of the atmosphere at a specific place and time. What causes the variation in the weather patterns that you experience? What are the effects of these weather patterns on organisms that live in different areas on Earth? One of the keys to understanding communities is to be aware of latitude and climatic conditions.

Connection to Earth Science **Latitude** The distance of any point on the surface of Earth north or south from the equator is **latitude.** Latitudes range from 0° at the equator to 90° at the poles. Light from the Sun strikes Earth more directly at the equator than at the poles, as illustrated in **Figure 5.** As a result, Earth's surface is heated differently in different areas. Ecologists refer to these areas as polar, temperate, and tropical zones.

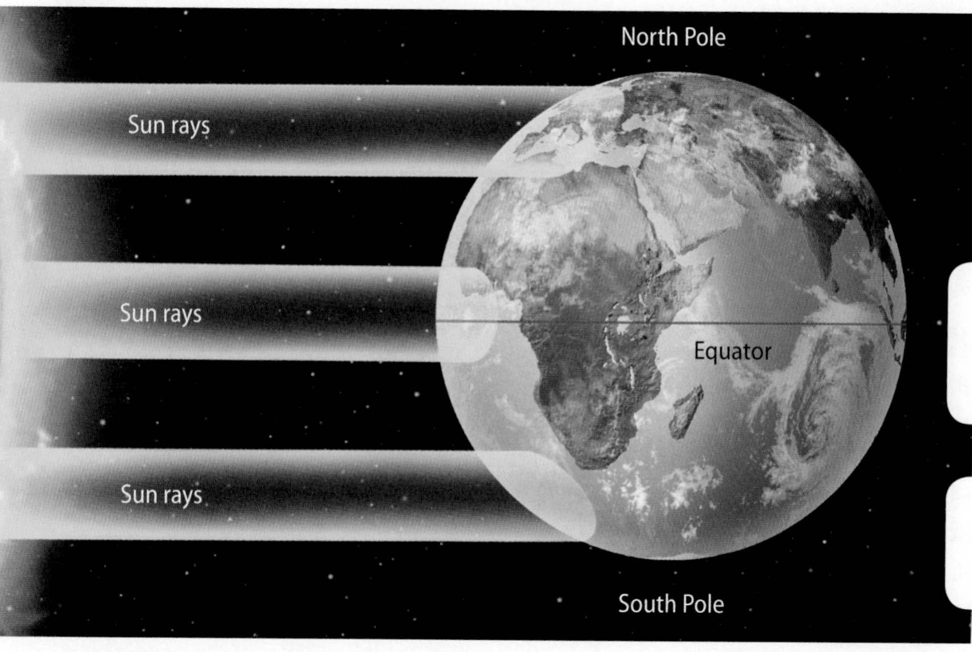
North Pole
Sun rays
Sun rays
Equator
Sun rays
South Pole
Near the poles, the Sun's energy strikes Earth at an angle, spreading out the energy received over a larger area than near the equator.
Each square meter of area at the equator receives more energy from the Sun than each square meter at the poles.

Figure 5 Because of Earth's curved surface, the Sun's rays strike the equator more directly than areas toward the north or south poles.

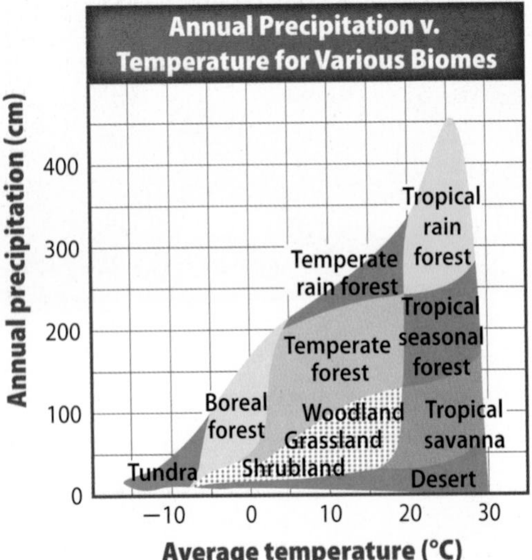

■ **Figure 6** Temperature and precipitation are two major factors that influence the kind of vegetation that can exist in an area.

***Analyze** which biome you would expect in an area that receives 200 cm of precipitation annually if the average annual temperature is 10°C.*

Personal Tutor 

BrainPOP 

Climate The average weather conditions in an area, including temperature and precipitation, describe the area's **climate.** An area's latitude has a large effect on its climate. If latitude were the only abiotic factor involved in climate, biomes would be spread in equal bands encircling Earth. However, other factors such as elevation, continental landmasses, and ocean currents also affect climate. The graph in **Figure 6** shows how temperature and precipitation influence the communities that develop in an area. You can investigate the relationship between temperature and latitude in **Minilab 1.**

A biome is a large group of ecosystems that share the same climate and have similar types of communities. It is a group of plant and animal communities that have adapted to a region's climate. A biome's ecosystems occur over a large area and have similar plant communities. Even a small difference in temperature or precipitation can affect the composition of a biome. Refer to **Figure 7** to learn how Earth's ocean currents and prevailing winds affect climate. Also illustrated in **Figure 7** are two ways humans might be affecting climate—through the hole in the ozone layer and through global warming. Global warming is in part a result of the greenhouse effect.

Major Land Biomes

Biomes are classified primarily according to the characteristics of their plants. Biomes also are characterized by temperature and precipitation. Animal species are an important characteristic of biomes as well. This section describes each of the major land biomes.

MiniLAB 1

Formulate a Climate Model

How are temperature and latitude related? At the equator the climate is very warm. However, as you change latitude and move north or south of the equator, temperatures also change. This results in different latitudinal climate belts around the world.

Procedure

1. Read and complete the lab safety form.
2. Position a **lamp** so that it shines directly on the equator of a **globe.**
3. Predict how the temperature readings will change as you move a **thermometer** north or south, away from the equator.
4. Prepare a data table to record your observations.
5. Use the thermometer to take temperature readings at different latitudes as instructed by your teacher. **WARNING: *The lamp and bulb will be very hot.***
6. Record temperature readings in your data table.

Analysis

1. **Model** climate belts by using your data to draw a diagram.
2. **Cause and Effect** Why do the temperature readings change as you move north or south of the equator?

VISUALIZING Global Effects on Climate

Figure 7 Some parts of Earth receive more heat from the Sun. Earth's winds and ocean currents contribute to climate and balance the heat on Earth. Many scientists think human impacts on the atmosphere upset this balance.

Winds on Earth

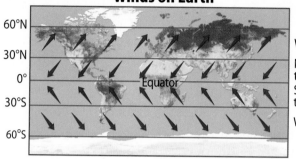

Winds are created from temperature imbalances. Distinct global wind systems transport cold air to warm areas and warm air to cold areas.

Earth's Ocean Currents

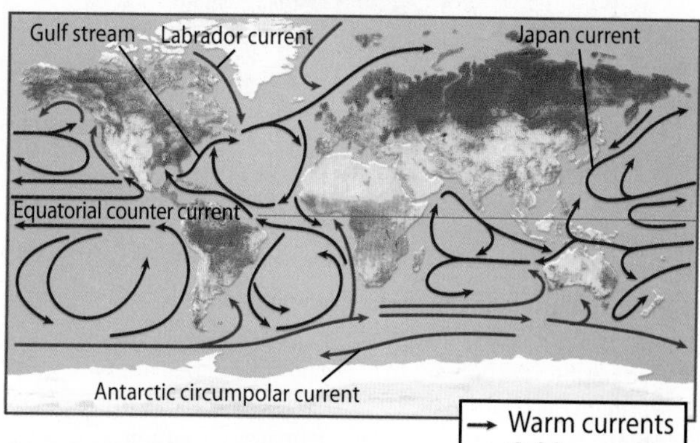

Ocean currents carry warm water toward the poles. As the water cools, it sinks toward the ocean floor and moves toward tropical regions.

Greenhouse Effect

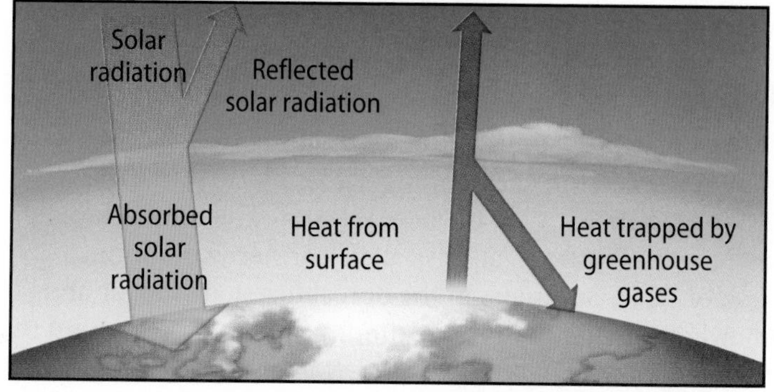

Earth's surface is warmed by the greenhouse effect. Certain gases in Earth's atmosphere, including naturally occurring water vapor, reduce the amount of energy Earth radiates into space. Other important greenhouse gases are carbon dioxide and methane.

Human Impact on the Atmosphere

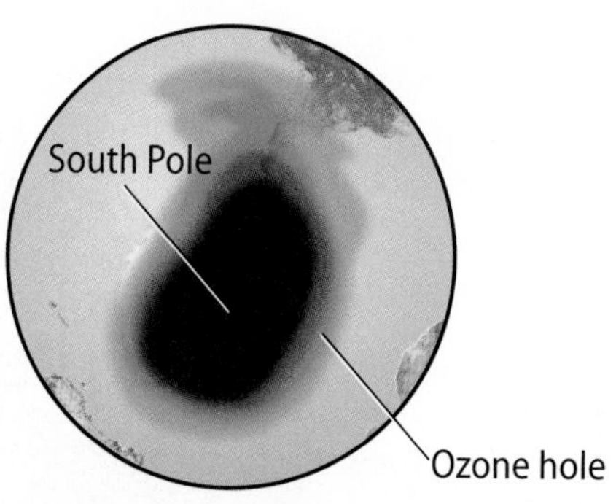

The ozone layer is a protective layer in the atmosphere that absorbs most of the harmful UV radiation from the Sun. Atmospheric studies have indicated that chlorofluorocarbons (CFCs) contribute to a seasonal reduction in ozone concentration over Antarctica, forming the Antarctic ozone hole.

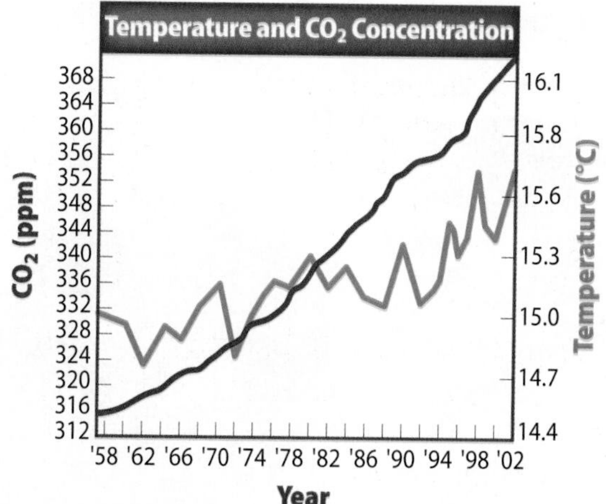

The measured increase of carbon dioxide (CO_2) in the atmosphere is mainly due to the burning of fossil fuels. As carbon dioxide levels have increased, the average global temperature has increased.

■ **Figure 8** Tundra
Average precipitation: 15–25 cm per year
Temperature range: −70°C–12°C
Plant species: short grasses, shrubs
Animal species: caribou, polar bears, birds, insects, wolves, arctic hares, musk ox
Geographic location: south of the polar ice caps in the Northern Hemisphere
Abiotic factors: soggy summers; permafrost; cold and dark much of the year

Tundra Extending in a band below the polar ice caps across northern Europe, North America, and Siberia in Asia is the tundra. The **tundra** is a treeless biome with a layer of permanently frozen soil below the surface called permafrost. Although the ground thaws to a depth of a few centimeters in the summer, its constant cycles of freezing and thawing do not allow tree roots to grow. Some animals and shallow-rooted plants that have adapted to tundra conditions are illustrated in **Figure 8.**

■ **Figure 9** Boreal forest
Average precipitation: 30–84 cm per year
Temperature range: −54°C–21°C
Plant species: spruce and fir trees, deciduous trees, small shrubs
Animal species: birds, moose, beavers, deer, wolverines, lynx
Geographic location: northern part of North America, Europe, and Asia
Abiotic factors: summers are short and moist; winters are long, cold, and dry

Boreal forest South of the tundra is a broad band of dense evergreen forest extending across North America, Europe, and Asia, called the boreal forest. The **boreal forest,** illustrated in **Figure 9,** also is called northern coniferous forest, or taiga. Summers in the boreal forest are longer and somewhat warmer than in the tundra, enabling the ground to remain warmer than in the tundra. Boreal forests, therefore, lack a permafrost layer.

■ **Figure 10** Temperate forest
Average precipitation: 75–150 cm per year
Temperature range: −30°C–30°C
Plant species: oak, beech, and maple trees, shrubs
Animal species: squirrels, rabbits, skunks, birds, deer, foxes, black bears, frogs, snakes
Geographic location: south of the boreal forests in eastern North America, eastern Asia, Australia, and Europe
Abiotic factors: well-defined seasons; summers are hot, and winters are cold

Temperate forest Temperate forests cover much of southeastern Canada, the eastern United States, most of Europe, and parts of Asia and Australia. As shown in **Figure 10,** the **temperate forest** is composed mostly of broad-leaved, deciduous (dih SIH juh wus) trees—trees that shed their leaves in autumn. The falling red, orange, and gold leaves return nutrients to the soil. All four seasons occur in temperate forests. In spring, warm temperatures and precipitation restart the growth cycles of plants and trees.

Temperate woodland and shrubland Open **woodlands** and mixed-shrub communities are found in areas with less annual rainfall than in temperate forests. The woodland biome occurs in areas surrounding the Mediterranean Sea, on the western coasts of North and South America, in South Africa, and Australia. Areas that are dominated by shrubs, such as in California, are called the chaparral. **Figure 11** illustrates woodland and shrub communities.

■ **Figure 11** Temperate woodland and shrubland
Average precipitation: 38–100 cm per year
Temperature range: 10°C–40°C
Plant species: evergreen shrubs, corn oak
Animal species: foxes, jackrabbits, birds, bobcats, coyotes, lizards, snakes, butterflies
Geographic location: surrounds the Mediterranean Sea, western coasts of North and South America, South Africa, and Australia
Abiotic factors: summers are very hot and dry; winters are cool and wet

■ **Figure 12** Temperate grassland
Average precipitation: 50–89 cm per year
Temperature range: −40°C–38°C
Plant species: grasses, herbs, flowers
Animal species: gazelles, bison, horses, lions, deer, mice, coyotes, foxes, wolves, birds, snakes, grasshoppers, spiders
Geographic location: North America, South America, Asia, Africa, and Australia
Abiotic factors: summers are hot, winters are cold, moderate rainfall, fires possible

Temperate grassland A biome that is characterized by fertile soils that are able to support a thick cover of grasses is called **grassland,** illustrated in **Figure 12.** Drought, grazing animals, and fires keep grasslands from becoming forests. Due to their underground stems and buds, perennial grasses and herbs are not eliminated by the fires that destroy most shrubs and trees. Temperate grasslands are found in the middle latitudes of North America, South America, Asia, Africa, and Australia. Grasslands are called steppes in Asia; prairies in North America; pampas and llanos in South America; savannas in Africa; and rangelands in Australia.

Desert Deserts exist on every continent except Europe. A **desert** is any area in which the annual rate of evaporation exceeds the rate of precipitation. You might imagine a desert as a desolate place full of sand dunes, but many deserts do not match that description. As shown in **Figure 13,** deserts can be home to a wide variety of plants and animals.

■ **Figure 13** Desert
Average precipitation: 2–26 cm per year
Temperature range: high: 20°C–49°C, low: −18°C–10°C
Plant species: cacti, Joshua trees, succulents
Animal species: lizards, bobcats, birds, tortoises, rats, antelope, desert toads
Geographic location: every continent except Europe
Abiotic factors: varying temperatures, low rainfall

■ **Figure 14** Tropical savanna
Average precipitation: 50–130 cm per year
Temperature range: 20°C–30°C
Plant species: grasses and scattered trees
Animal species: lions, hyenas, cheetahs, elephants, giraffes, zebras, birds, insects
Geographic location: Africa, South America, and Australia
Abiotic factors: summers are hot and rainy, winters are cool and dry

Tropical savanna A **tropical savanna** is characterized by grasses and scattered trees in climates that receive less precipitation than some other tropical areas. Tropical savanna biomes occur in Africa, South America, and Australia. The plants and animals shown in **Figure 14** are common to tropical savannas.

Tropical seasonal forest **Figure 15** illustrates a tropical seasonal forest. **Tropical seasonal forests,** also called tropical dry forests, grow in areas of Africa, Asia, Australia, and South and Central America. In one way, the tropical seasonal forest resembles the temperate deciduous forest because during the dry season, almost all of the trees drop their leaves to conserve water.

GET IT? **Compare and contrast** tropical savannas and tropical seasonal forests.

■ **Figure 15** Tropical seasonal forest
Average precipitation: >200 cm per year
Temperature range: 20°C–25°C
Plant species: deciduous and evergreen trees, orchids, mosses
Animal species: elephants, tigers, monkeys, koalas, rabbits, frogs, spiders
Geographic location: Africa, Asia, Australia, and South and Central America
Abiotic factors: rainfall is seasonal

Figure 16 Tropical rain forest
Average precipitation: 200–1000 cm per year
Temperature range: 24°C–27°C
Plant species: broadleaf evergreens, bamboo, ferns, orchids
Animal species: chimpanzees, Bengal tigers, elephants, orangutans, bats, toucans, sloths, cobra snakes
Geographic location: Central and South America, southern Asia, west central Africa, and northeastern Australia
Abiotic factors: humid all year, hot and wet

Tropical rain forest Warm temperatures and large amounts of rainfall throughout the year characterize the **tropical rain forest** biome illustrated in **Figure 16.** Tropical rain forests are found in much of Central and South America, southern Asia, west central Africa, and northeastern Australia. The tropical rain forest is the most diverse of all land biomes. Tall, broad-leaved trees with branches heavy with mosses, ferns, and orchids make up the canopy of the tropical rain forest. Shorter trees, shrubs, and plants, such as ferns and creeping plants, make up another layer, or understory, of tropical rain forests.

Other Terrestrial Areas

You might have noticed that the list of terrestrial biomes does not include some important areas. Many ecologists omit mountains from the list. Mountains are found throughout the world and do not fit the definition of a biome because their climate characteristics and plant and animal life vary depending on elevation. Polar regions also are not considered true biomes because they are ice masses and not true land areas with soil.

Virtual Lab 

STUDY TIP

SUMMARIES Review the terrestrial biomes featured in this section. Choose one or two biomes and write two sentences that summarize the information.

Mountains If you go up a mountain, you might notice that abiotic conditions, such as temperature and precipitation, change with increasing elevation. These variations allow many communities to exist on a mountain. As **Figure 17** illustrates, biotic communities also change with increasing altitude, and the tops of tall mountains may support communities that resemble those of the tundra.

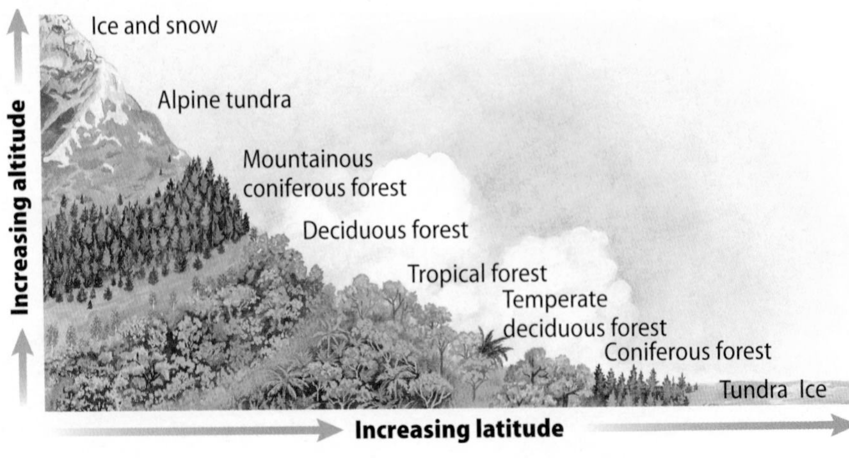

Figure 17 As you climb a mountain or increase in latitude, the temperature drops and the climate changes.
***Describe** the relationship between altitude and latitude.*

■ **Figure 18** A surprising number of species inhabit the polar regions, including these penguins in Antarctica.

Polar regions Polar regions border the tundra at high latitudes, and these regions are cold all year. The coldest temperature ever recorded, −89°C, was in Antarctica, the continent that lies in the southern polar region. In the northern polar region lies the ice-covered Arctic Ocean and Greenland. Covered by a thick layer of ice, the polar regions might seem incapable of sustaining life. However, as shown in **Figure 18,** colonies of penguins live in Antarctica. Additionally, whales and seals patrol the coasts, preying on penguins, fish, or shrimplike invertebrates called krill. The arctic polar region supports even more species, including polar bears and arctic foxes. Human societies have also inhabited this region throughout history. Although the average winter temperature is about −30°C, the arctic summer in some areas is warm enough for vegetables to be grown.

CAREERS IN BIOLOGY

Climatologist Unlike meteorologists, who study current weather conditions, climatologists study long-term climate patterns and determine how climate changes affect ecosystems.

REVIEW IT! Terrestrial Biomes

Section Summary

- Latitude affects terrestrial biomes according to the angle at which sunlight strikes Earth.
- Latitude, elevation, ocean currents, and other abiotic factors determine climate.
- Two major abiotic factors define terrestrial biomes.
- There are nine major terrestrial biomes. There are two additional terrestrial regions that do not fit into these categories.

Self Check

Understand Main Ideas

1. MAINIDEA **Describe** the nine major terrestrial biomes.
2. **Describe** the abiotic factors that determine a terrestrial biome.
3. **Summarize** variations in climate among three major zones as you travel south from the equator toward the South Pole.
4. **Indicate** the differences between temperate grasslands and tropical savannas.
5. **Compare and contrast** the climate and biotic factors of tropical seasonal forests and temperate forests.

Think Critically

6. **Hypothesize** why the tropical rain forests have the greatest diversity of living things.

WRITING IN ▶ Biology

7. Tropical forests are being felled at a rate of 17 million hectares per year, which represents almost two percent of the forest area. Use this information to write a pamphlet describing how much rain forest area exists and when it might be gone.

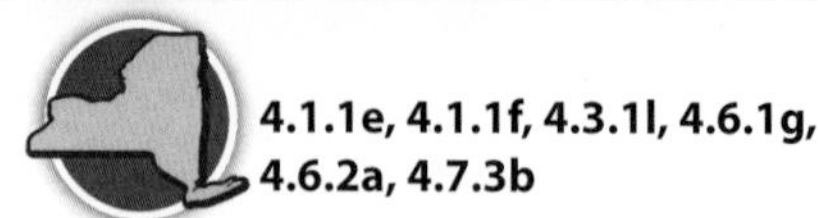

3 Aquatic Ecosystems

4.1.1e, 4.1.1f, 4.3.1l, 4.6.1g, 4.6.2a, 4.7.3b

MAINIDEA

Aquatic ecosystems are grouped based on abiotic factors such as water flow, depth, distance from shore, salinity, and latitude.

Essential Questions

- What are the major abiotic factors that determine the aquatic ecosystems?
- What are transitional aquatic ecosystems and why are they important?
- What are the zones of marine ecosystems?

BIOLOGY 4 U

Think about the body of water that is closest to where you live. What are its characteristics? How deep is it? Is it freshwater or salt water? For centuries, bodies of water have been central to cultures around the world.

Review Vocabulary

salinity: a measure of the amount of salt in a body of water

New Vocabulary

sediment
littoral zone
limnetic zone
plankton
profundal zone
wetlands
estuary
intertidal zone
photic zone
aphotic zone
benthic zone
abyssal zone

Multilingual eGlossary

The Water on Earth

When you think about water on Earth, you might recall a vacation at the ocean or a geography lesson in which you located Earth's oceans and seas. You probably have heard about other large bodies of water, such as the Amazon river and the Great Salt Lake. A globe of Earth is mainly blue in color because the planet is largely covered with water. Ecologists recognize the importance of water because of the biological communities that water supports. In this section, you will read about freshwater, transitional, and marine aquatic ecosystems. You also will read about the abiotic factors that affect these ecosystems.

Freshwater Ecosystems

The major freshwater ecosystems include ponds, lakes, streams, rivers, and wetlands. Plants and animals in these ecosystems are adapted to the low salt content in freshwater and are unable to survive in areas of high salt concentration. Only about 2.5 percent of the water on Earth is freshwater, as illustrated by the circle graph on the left in **Figure 19.** The graph on the right in **Figure 19** shows that of that 2.5 percent, 68.9 percent is contained in glaciers, 30.8 percent is groundwater, and only 0.3 percent is found in lakes, ponds, rivers, streams, and wetlands. Interestingly, almost all of the freshwater species live in this 0.3 percent.

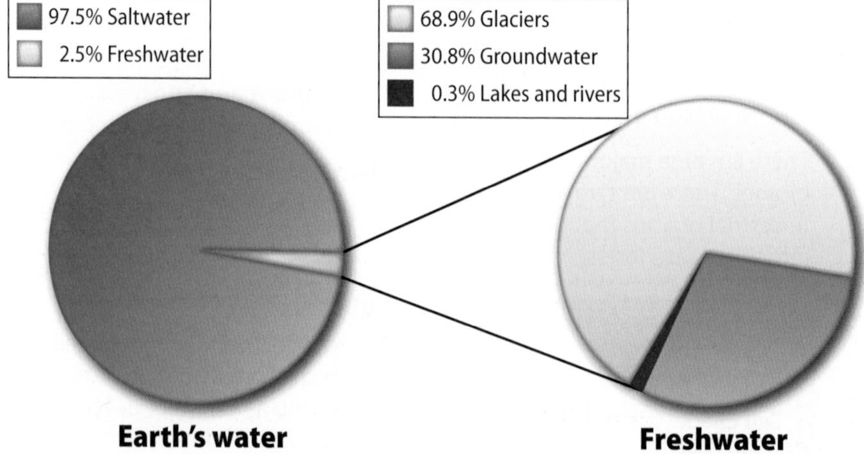

Figure 19 The vast majority of Earth's water is salt water. Most of the freshwater supply is locked in glaciers.

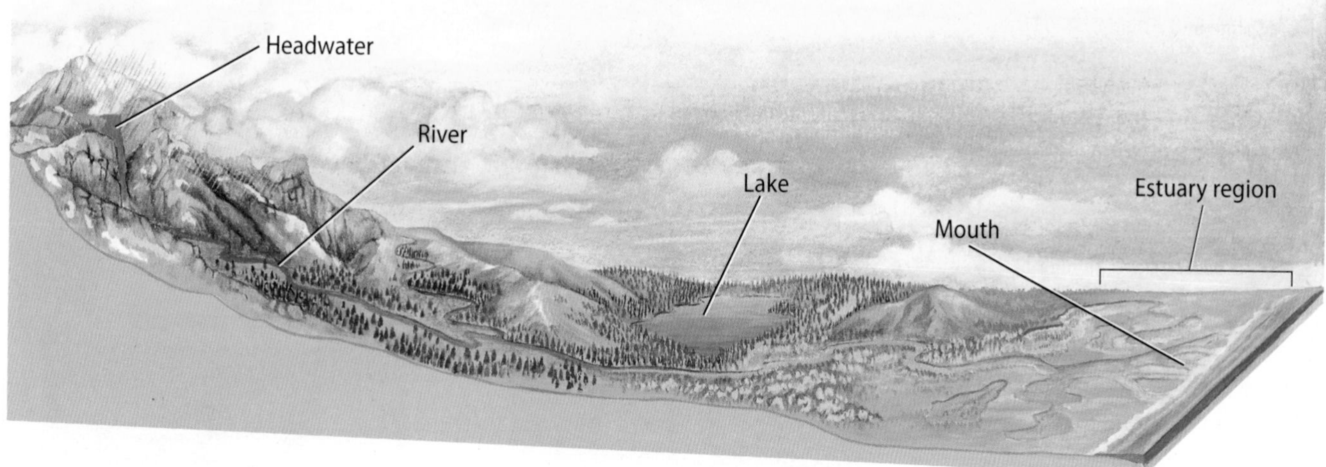

■ **Figure 20** Mountain streams have clear, cold water that is highly oxygenated and supports the larvae of many insects and the coldwater fish that feed on them. Rivers become increasingly wider, deeper, and slower. At the mouth, many rivers divide into many channels where wetlands or estuaries form.

Rivers and streams The water in rivers and streams flows in one direction, beginning at a source called a headwater and traveling to the mouth, where the flowing water empties into a larger body of water, as illustrated in **Figure 20.** Rivers and streams also might start from underground springs or from snowmelt. The slope of the landscape determines the direction and speed of the water flow. When the slope is steep, water flows quickly, causing a lot of sediment to be picked up and carried by the water. **Sediment** is material that is deposited by water, wind, or glaciers. As the slope levels, the speed of the water flow decreases and sediments are deposited in the form of silt, mud, and sand.

The characteristics of rivers and streams change during the journey from the source to the mouth. Interactions between wind and the water stir up the water's surface, which adds a significant amount of oxygen to the water. Interactions between land and water result in erosion, in nutrient availability, and in changing the path of the river or stream.

The currents and turbulence of fast-moving rivers and streams prevent much accumulation of organic materials and sediment. For this reason, there are usually fewer species living in rapid waters similar to that in **Figure 21.** An important characteristic of life in rivers and streams is the ability to withstand the constant water current. Plants that root themselves into the streambed are common in areas where water is slowed by rocks or sandbars. Young fish hide in these plants and feed on the drifting microscopic organisms and aquatic insects.

In slow-moving water, insect larvae are the primary food source for many fish, including American eel, brown bullhead catfish, and trout. Other organisms, such as crabs and worms, are sometimes present in calm water. Animals that live in slow-moving water include newts, tadpoles, and frogs.

GET IT? **Describe** key abiotic factors that define rivers and streams.

■ **Figure 21** The turbulent churning action of fast-moving rivers and streams does not allow for many plants to take root or for other species to inhabit these waters.

Creatas/PunchStock

■ **Figure 22** The temperature of lakes and ponds varies depending on the season. During spring and autumn, deep water receives oxygen from the surface water and surface water receives inorganic nutrients from the deep water.

***Compare** the type of life that might live in a shallow lake in the tropics to one in the mid-latitudes.*

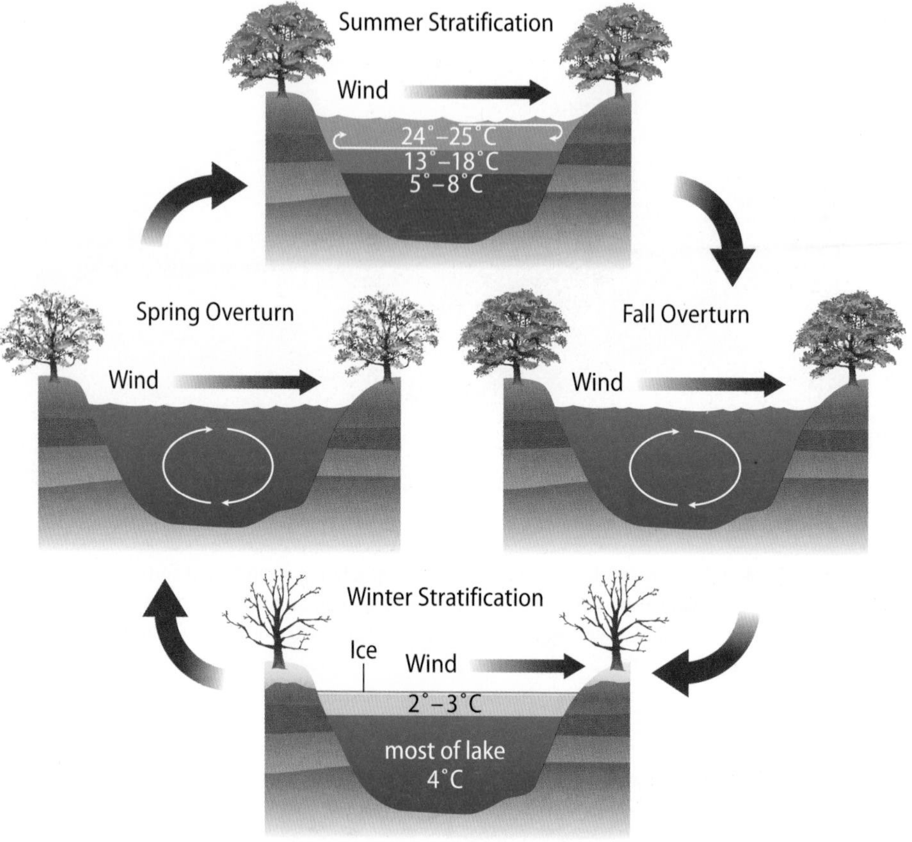

Lakes and ponds An inland body of standing water is called a lake or a pond. It can be as small as a few square meters or as large as thousands of square meters. Some ponds might be filled with water for only a few weeks or months each year, whereas some lakes have existed for thousands of years. **Figure 22** illustrates how in temperate regions the temperature of lakes and ponds varies depending on the season.

During the winter, most of the water in a lake or pond is the same temperature. In the summer, the warmer water on top is less dense than the colder water at the bottom. During the spring and fall, as the water warms or cools, turnover occurs. The top and bottom layers of water mix, often due to winds, and this results in a uniform water temperature. This mixing circulates oxygen and brings nutrients from the bottom to the surface.

Nutrient-poor lakes, called oligotrophic (uh lih goh TROH fihk) lakes, often are found high in the mountains. Few plant and animal species are present as a result of small amounts of organic matter and nutrients. Nutrient-rich lakes, called eutrophic (yoo TROH fihk) lakes, usually are found at lower altitudes. Many plant and animal species are present as a result of organic matter and plentiful nutrients, some of which come from agricultural and urban activities.

VOCABULARY

WORD ORIGIN

Eutrophic/oligotrophic

eu– prefix; from Greek, meaning *well*

oligo– prefix; from Greek, meaning *few*

–***trophic***; from Greek, meaning *nourish*

Lakes and ponds are divided into three zones based on the amount of sunlight that penetrates the water. The area closest to the shore is the **littoral** *(LIH tuh rul)* **zone.** The water in this zone is shallow, which allows sunlight to reach the bottom. Many producers, such as aquatic plants and algae, live in these shallow waters. The abundance of light and producers make the littoral zone an area of high photosynthesis. Many consumers also inhabit this zone, including frogs, turtles, worms, crustaceans, insect larvae, and fish.

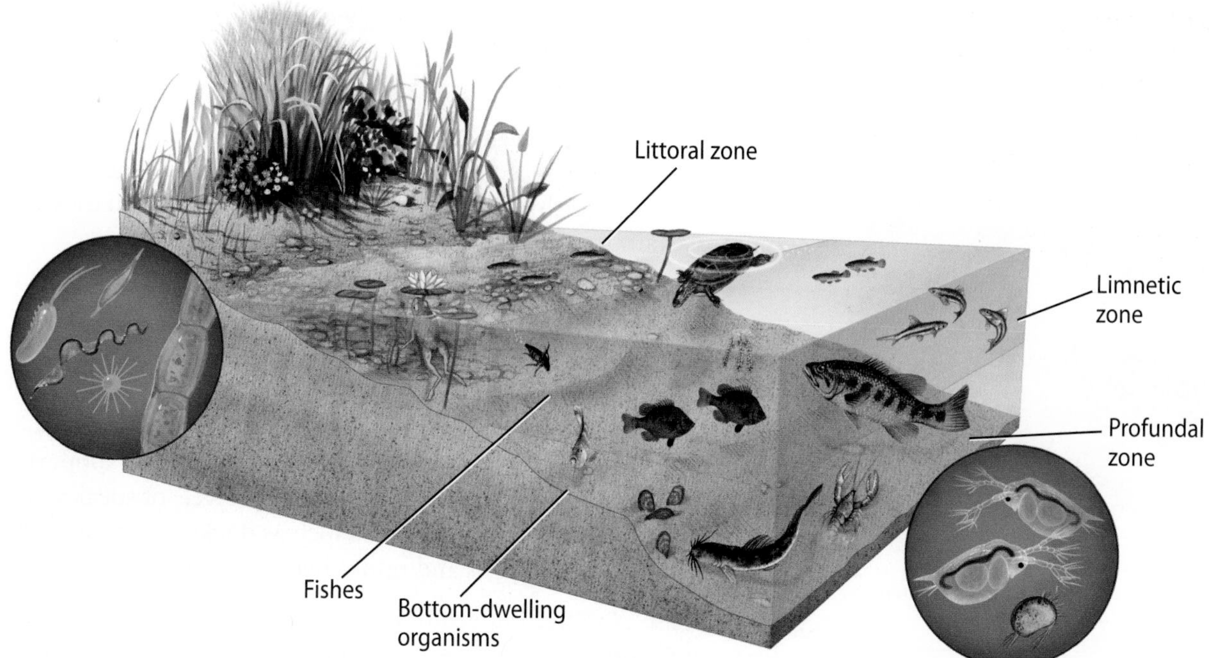

Figure 23 Most of a lake's biodiversity is found in the littoral and limnetic zones. However, many species of bottom dwellers depend on nutrients and materials that drift down from above.

The **limnetic** (lihm NEH tihk) **zone** is the open water area that is well lit and is dominated by plankton. **Plankton** are free-floating photosynthetic autotrophs that live in freshwater or marine ecosystems. Many species of freshwater fish live in the limnetic zone because food, such as plankton, is readily available.

Minimal light is able to penetrate through the limnetic zone into the deepest areas of a large lake, which is called the **profundal** (pruh FUN dul) **zone.** The profundal zone is therefore much colder and lower in oxygen than the other two zones. A limited number of species live in this harsh environment. **Figure 23** identifies the zones and biodiversity of lakes and ponds.

MiniLAB 2

Prepare a Scientific Argument

Should an environment be disturbed? One of the greatest challenges that we face as a species is balancing the needs of an ever-growing human global population with the needs of wildlife and the quality of the global environment. Imagine this scenario: The county commissioners are considering a proposal to build a road through the local pond and wetlands. This road will provide much-needed access to areas of work, and will help boost the economy of a struggling town. This will mean that the pond and surrounding wetlands must be drained and filled. Many people support the proposal, while many people oppose it. How will a compromise be reached?

Procedure

1. Prepare a comparison table in which you can list pros and cons.
2. Identify the pros and cons for draining the pond and building the road, for keeping the pond and not building the road, or for building the road elsewhere.

Analysis

1. **Design** a plan to support one course of action. What steps could you take to achieve your goal? Be prepared to share and defend your plan to the rest of the class.
2. **Think critically** about why decisions involving the environment are difficult to make.

■ **Figure 24** Bogs are a type of wetland characterized by moist, decaying plant material and dominated by mosses.

Transitional Aquatic Ecosystems

In many areas, aquatic ecosystems do not look like a stream or a pond or even an ocean. In fact, many aquatic environments are a combination of two or more different environments. These areas, which ecologists call transitional aquatic ecosystems, can be areas where land and water or salt water and freshwater intermingle. Wetlands and estuaries are common examples of transitional aquatic ecosystems.

Wetlands Areas of land such as marshes, swamps, and bogs that are saturated with water and that support aquatic plants are called **wetlands.** Plant species that grow in the moist, humid conditions of wetlands include duckweed, pond lilies, cattails, sedges, mangroves, cypress, and willows. Bogs, like the cedar bog shown in **Figure 24,** are wet and spongy areas of decomposing vegetation that also support many species of organisms. Wetlands have high levels of species diversity. Many amphibians, reptiles, birds (such as ducks and herons), and mammals (such as raccoons and mink) live in wetlands.

Estuaries Another important transitional ecosystem is an estuary, shown in **Figure 25.** Estuaries are among the most diverse ecosystems, rivaled only by tropical rain forests and coral reefs. An **estuary** (ES chuh wer ee) is an ecosystem that is formed where freshwater from a river or stream merges with salt water from the ocean. Estuaries are places of transition, from freshwater to saltwater and from land to sea, that are inhabited by a wide variety of species. Algae, seaweeds, and marsh grasses are the dominant producers. However, many animals, including a variety of worms, oysters, and crabs, depend on detritus for food. Detritus (dih TRY tus) is comprised of tiny pieces of organic material.

VOCABULARY

ACADEMIC VOCABULARY

Comprise
to be made up of
Your community is comprised of your family, your classmates, and people who live nearby.

Mangrove trees also can be found in tropical estuaries, such as the Everglades National Park in Florida, where they sometimes form swamps. Many species of marine fishes and invertebrates, such as shrimp, use estuaries as nurseries for their young. Waterfowl, such as ducks and geese, depend on estuary ecosystems for nesting, feeding, and migration rest areas.

■ **Figure 25** Salt-tolerant plants above the low-tide line dominate estuaries formed in temperate areas.
***Infer** how an estuary would differ in a tropical area.*

Salt marshes are transitional ecosystems similar to estuaries. Salt-tolerant grasses dominate above the low-tide line, and seagrasses grow in submerged areas of salt marshes. Salt marshes support different species of animals, such as shrimp and shellfish.

Marine Ecosystems

Virtual Lab

Connection to Earth Science Earth is sometimes called "the water planet." As such, marine ecosystems have a significant impact on the planet. For example, through photosynthesis, marine algae consume carbon dioxide from the atmosphere and produce over 50 percent of the atmosphere's oxygen. Additionally, the evaporation of water from oceans eventually provides the majority of precipitation—rain and snow. Like ponds and lakes, oceans are separated into distinct zones.

Intertidal zone The **intertidal** (ihn tur TY dul) **zone** is a narrow band where the ocean meets land. Organisms that live in this zone must be adapted to the constant changes that occur as daily tides and waves alternately submerge and expose the shore. The intertidal zone is further divided into vertical zones, as illustrated in **Figure 26.** The area of the spray zone is dry most of the time. It is only during high tides that this part of the shoreline is sprayed with salt water, and few plants and animals are able to live in this environment. The high-tide zone is under water only during high tides. However, this area receives more water than the spray zone, so more plants and animals are able to live there. The mid-tide zone undergoes severe disruption twice a day as the tides cover and uncover the shoreline with water. Organisms in this area must be adapted to long periods of air and water. The low-tide zone is covered with water unless the tide is unusually low and is the most populated area of the intertidal zone.

GET IT? **Describe** environmental variation in intertidal zones.

■ **Figure 26** The intertidal zone is further divided into zones where different communities exist.

Compare and contrast ***the zones illustrated in Figures 23 and 26.***

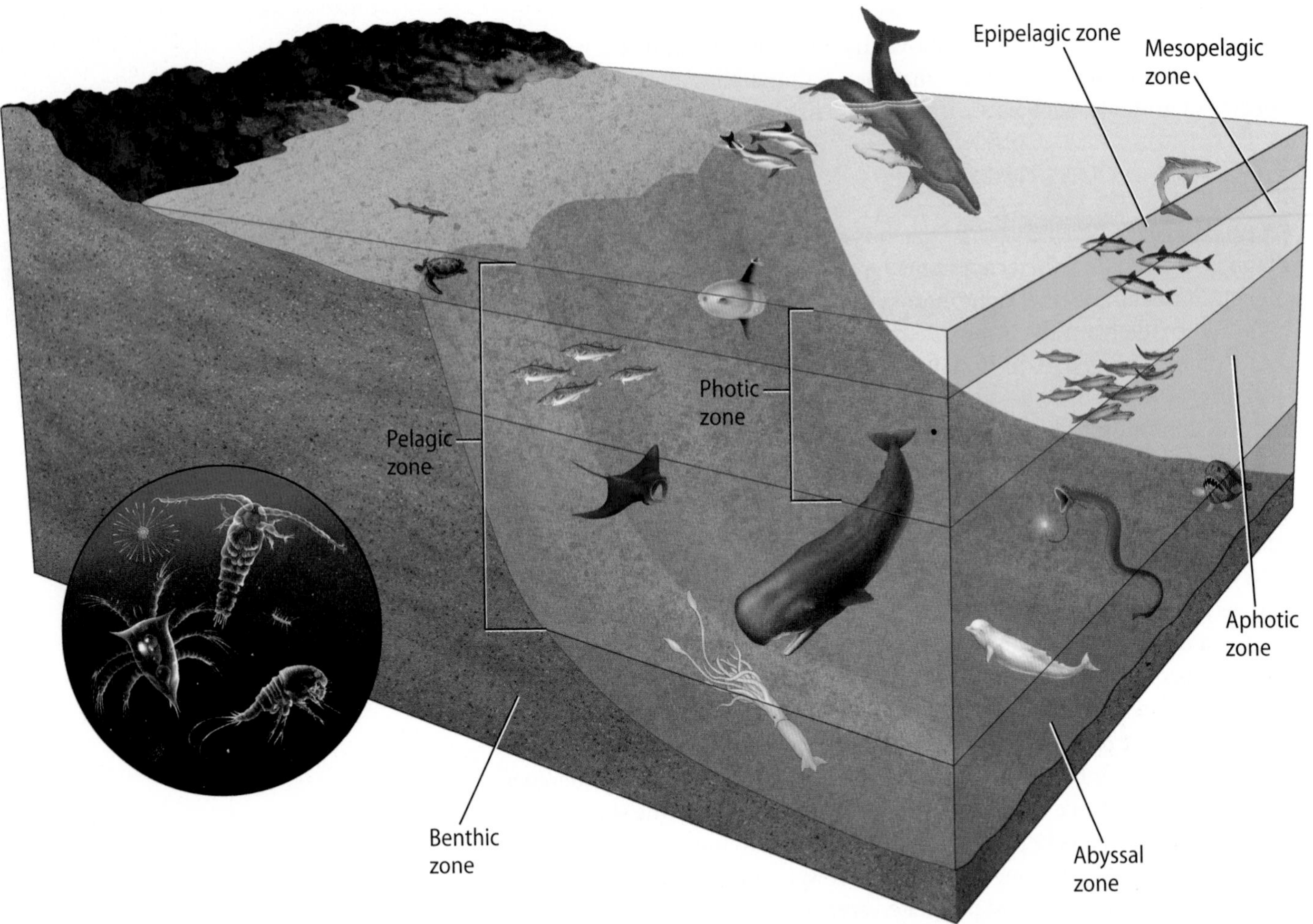

■ **Figure 27** Producers are found in the photic zone. Consumers live in the pelagic, abyssal, and benthic zones.

Open ocean ecosystems As illustrated in **Figure 27,** the zones in the open ocean include the pelagic (puh LAY jihk) zone, abyssal (uh BIH sul) zone, and benthic zone. The area to a depth of about 200 m of the pelagic zone is the **photic zone,** also called the euphotic zone. The photic zone is shallow enough that sunlight is able to penetrate. As depth increases, light decreases. Autotrophic organisms in the photic zone include surface seaweeds and plankton. Animals in the photic zone include many species of fish, sea turtles, jellyfish, whales, and dolphins. Many of these animals feed on plankton, but others feed on larger species. The photic zone is subdivided into the epipelagic zone and the mesopelagic zone, as shown in **Figure 27.**

Below the photic zone lies the **aphotic zone,** an area where sunlight is unable to penetrate. This region of the pelagic zone remains in constant darkness and generally is cold, but there is thermal layering with a mixing of warm and cold ocean currents. Organisms that depend on light energy to survive cannot live in the aphotic zone.

The **benthic zone** is the area along the ocean floor that consists of sand, silt, and dead organisms. In shallow benthic zones, sunlight can penetrate to the bottom of the ocean floor. As depth increases, light and temperature decrease. Species diversity tends to decrease with depth, except in areas with hydrothermal vents, where shrimp, crabs, and many species of tubeworms are found. Many species of fishes, octopuses, and squids live in the benthic zone.

VOCABULARY

WORD ORIGIN

Photic
comes from the Greek word *photos*, meaning *light*.

The deepest region of the ocean is called the **abyssal zone.** Water in this area is very cold. Most organisms in this zone rely on food materials that drift down from the zones above. However, on the seafloor along the boundaries of Earth's plates, hydrothermal vents spew large amounts of hot water, hydrogen sulfide, and other minerals. Scientists have found bacterial communities existing in these locations that can use the sulfide molecules for energy. These organisms are at the bottom of a food chain that includes invertebrates, such as clams and crabs, and vertebrates, such as fishes.

■ **Figure 28** Coral reefs off the southern tip of Florida are among the world's largest and most diverse reefs.

Coastal ocean and coral reefs One of the world's largest coral reefs is off the southern coast of Florida. Coral reefs are among the most diverse ecosystems. They are widely distributed in warm shallow marine waters. Coral reefs form natural barriers along continents that protect shorelines from erosion. The dominant organisms in coral reefs are corals. When you think of coral, you might picture a hard, stony structure, but this is only the framework secreted by tiny animal polyps. Corals are soft-bodied invertebrates that live in the stonelike structures.

Most coral polyps have a symbiotic relationship with algae called zooxanthellae (zoo uh zan THEL uh). These algae provide corals with food, and in turn, the coral provides protection and access to light for the algae. Corals also feed by extending tentacles to obtain plankton from the water. Other coral reef animals include species of microorganisms, sea slugs, octopuses, sea urchins, sea stars, and fishes. **Figure 28** shows only a small portion of the diversity of Florida's coral reef.

Like all ecosystems, coral reefs are sensitive to changes in the environment. Changes that are the result of naturally occurring events, such as increased sediment from a tsunami, can cause the death of a reef. Human activities, such as land development and harvesting for calcium carbonate, also can damage or kill a coral reef. Today, ecologists monitor reefs and reef environments to help protect these delicate ecosystems.

REVIEW IT! Aquatic Ecosystems

Section Summary

- Freshwater ecosystems include ponds, lakes, streams, rivers, and wetlands.
- Wetlands and estuaries are transitional aquatic ecosystems.
- Marine ecosystems are divided into zones that are classified according to abiotic factors.
- Estuaries and coral reefs are among the most diverse of all ecosystems.

Self Check

Understand Main Ideas

1. MAINIDEA **List** the abiotic factors that are used to classify aquatic ecosystems.
2. **Apply** what you know about ponds. Do you think the same organisms that would live in a seasonal pond would live in a pond that existed year-round? Explain.
3. **Describe** an ecological function of an estuary.
4. **Describe** the zones of the open ocean.

Think Critically

5. **Infer** how autotrophs in the abyssal zone of the ocean are different from those of the photic zone.

MATH IN ▶ Biology

6. In November 2004, the floodgates of Glen Canyon Dam opened in an attempt to improve the Colorado River habitat. The release topped 1161 m^3/s—four times the usual daytime flow. Based on this information, about how much water normally flows through the dam on a daily basis?

IN THE FIELD

1.1.1b, 1.1.1c, 4.5.3a, 4.6.3a

A Change of Heart: The Story of the Austin Bats

Today, the bats under the Congress Avenue Bridge are a symbol of Austin. With a minor league hockey team, a statue, and a festival all in honor of the bats, Austin truly is the nation's "bat capital." Thousands of people gather each summer night to view the emergence of the bats. But the bats have not always been so highly regarded in the Texas capital city.

The Bats Arrive The story of the bats began in the late 1970's when the Congress Avenue Bridge in downtown Austin was reconstructed. A civil engineer named Mark Bloschock worked on the project. Soon after the reconstruction, bats began roosting in the crevices in the bridge—the reconstruction inadvertently created the perfect bat roost! Austin residents reacted with fear and attempted to eradicate the bats.

Then in the mid-1980's, a biologist named Merlin Tuttle came to Austin. His organization, Bat Conservation International, educated the residents about the benefits that the bats can provide and ensured them that they have nothing to fear. Eventually, Tuttle convinced officials to assess the situation before eradicating the bats.

An Important Study Several years later, Mark Bloschock invited Merlin Tuttle to speak at a bridge design conference that he was planning. Following the conference, Bloschock was able to convince the director of the Texas Department of Transportation (TxDOT) to fund a study of bats in Texas bridges. For the study, the TxDOT partnered with Bat Conservation International. The study focused on how the bats use the bridges and on the effects of the bats on the structure of the bridges, health of the public, and quality of the water beneath the bridge. Meanwhile, Mark Bloschock attended a bat conservation and management workshop where the designs for incorporating bat roosts into new highway culverts were developed.

This bat statue in Austin, named "Nightwing," was constructed in 1998 in honor of the 1.5 million Mexican free-tailed bats that live under the Congress Avenue Bridge each summer.

The results of the study had a beneficial impact on the public's perception of the bats. The study received a large amount of media attention. So much, in fact, that a national Bats and Bridges Project was started in 1998. Today, many new bridges across the nation are designed to be good bat habitats and existing bridges are often retrofitted to make them suitable to house bats. As a result of the collaboration between engineers and biologists across the nation, bridges have become important bat habitat and continue to have an important role in their conservation.

Investigate

Communicate and Apply Today, engineers intentionally design bridges to encourage roosting. Use appropriate Internet sites to find out how the New York Department of Transportation engineers incorporate bat roosting spaces into new and existing bridges. What methods could you use to create bat roosts near your school? Make a plan to provide artificial habitat for bats in your area.

WebQuest

BioLAB DESIGN YOUR OWN 1.2.1, 1.2.4, 1.3.5b, ¥a, ¥o

FIELD INVESTIGATION: A POND IN A JAR

Background: Ecologists study parts of the biosphere. Each part is a unit containing many complex interactions between living things, such as food chains and food webs and the physical environment, the water cycle, and the mineral cycle. Smaller parts of the biosphere, such as communities and ecosystems, are the most practical for ecologists to explore and investigate.

Question: *What can we learn from studying a miniaturized biological ecosystem?*

Materials

glass or clear plastic gallon jars
pond water
pond mud
appropriate cultures and select living organisms
Choose any other materials that would be appropriate to this lab.

Safety Precautions

WARNING: *Use care when handling jars of pond water.*

Plan and Perform the Experiment

1. Read and complete the lab safety form.
2. Prepare an observation table as instructed.
3. Brainstorm and plan the step-by-step miniaturization of a pond community. Make sure your teacher has approved your plan before you proceed.
4. Decide on a particular aspect of your miniature community to evaluate and design an appropriate experiment. For example, you might test the effect of sunlight on your ecosystem.
5. Carry out your experiment.

Analyze and Conclude

1. **Explain** why you conducted your experiment slowly in a step-by-step manner. What might have happened if you poured everything into the jar all at once?
2. **Identify** the independent variable and the dependent variable.
3. **Design an experiment** Did your experiment have a control? Explain.
4. **Analyze and conclude** how your community differs from a pond community found in nature.
5. **Error analysis** How effective was your design? Explain possible sources of errors.

Matt Meadows

WRITING IN ▶ Biology

Communicate Write a short story in which you describe what it would be like to be a microscopic animal living in your pond-in-a-jar.

CHAPTER 3 STUDY GUIDE

BIGIDEA **Limiting factors and ranges of tolerance are factors that determine where terrestrial biomes and aquatic ecosystems exist.**

SECTION 1 Community Ecology

MAINIDEA All living organisms are limited by factors in the environment.

- Abiotic and biotic limiting factors restrict the growth of a population within a community.
- Organisms have a range of tolerance for each limiting factor that they encounter.
- Primary succession occurs on areas of exposed rock or bare sand (no soil).
- Communities progress until there is little change in the composition of species.
- Secondary succession occurs as a result of a disturbance in a mature community.

VOCABULARY

- **community**
- **limiting factor**
- **tolerance**
- **ecological succession**
- **primary succession**
- **climax community**
- **secondary succession**

SECTION 2 Terrestrial Biomes

MAINIDEA Ecosystems on land are grouped into biomes primarily based on the plant communities within them.

- Latitude affects terrestrial biomes according to the angle at which sunlight strikes Earth.
- Latitude, elevation, ocean currents, and other abiotic factors determine climate.
- Two major abiotic factors define terrestrial biomes.
- There are nine major terrestrial biomes. There are two additional terrestrial regions that do not fit into these major categories.

VOCABULARY

- **weather**
- **latitude**
- **climate**
- **tundra**
- **boreal forest**
- **temperate forest**
- **woodland**
- **grassland**
- **desert**
- **tropical savanna**
- **tropical seasonal forest**
- **tropical rain forest**

SECTION 3 Aquatic Ecosystems

MAINIDEA Aquatic ecosystems are grouped based on abiotic factors such as water flow, depth, distance from shore, salinity, and latitude.

- Freshwater ecosystems include ponds, lakes, streams, rivers, and wetlands.
- Wetlands and estuaries are transitional aquatic ecosystems.
- Marine ecosystems are divided into zones that are classified according to abiotic factors.
- Estuaries and coral reefs are among the most diverse of all ecosystems.

VOCABULARY

- **sediment**
- **littoral zone**
- **limnetic zone**
- **plankton**
- **profundal zone**
- **wetlands**
- **estuary**
- **intertidal zone**
- **photic zone**
- **aphotic zone**
- **benthic zone**
- **abyssal zone**

SECTION 1

Vocabulary Review

Choose the correct italicized term to complete each sentence.

1. An area of forest that experiences very little change in species composition is a *climax community/ primary succession.*
2. The amount of oxygen in a fish tank is a *tolerance zone/limiting factor* that affects the number of fish that can live in the tank.
3. *Ecological succession/Secondary succession* describes the events that take place on a hillside that has experienced a destructive mudslide.

Understand Main Ideas

4. Lack of iron in the photic zone of the open ocean restricts the size of plankton populations. Iron is what kind of factor for marine plankton?
   A. distribution
   B. tolerance
   C. limiting
   D. biotic

For questions 5–7, use the generalized graph below that describes an organism's tolerance to a particular factor.

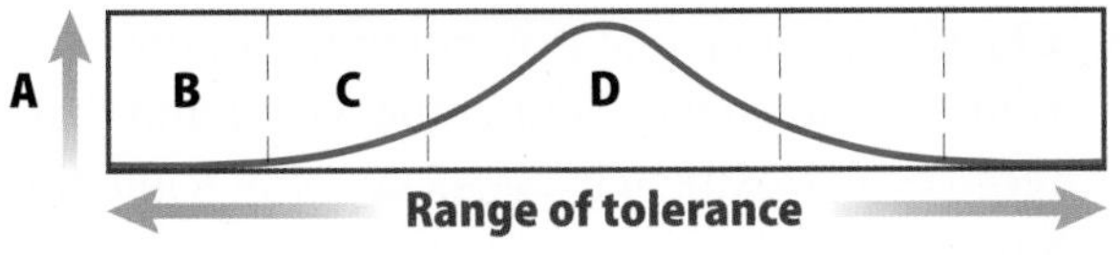

5. According to the graph, which letter represents the zone of intolerance for the factor in question?
   A. A **C.** C
   B. B **D.** D
6. What does the letter "D" represent in the graph?
   A. zone of intolerance
   B. zone of physiological stress
   C. optimum range
   D. upper limit
7. Which letter in the graph represents the zone of physiological stress?
   A. A **C.** C
   B. B **D.** D
8. Which place would you most likely find pioneer species growing?
   A. climax forest **C.** disturbed grassland
   B. coral reef **D.** newly formed volcano

Constructed Response

9. **CAREERS IN ▶ Biology** A state park and wildlife department stocks several bodies of water, including rivers and lakes, with rainbow trout. The trout survive but do not reproduce. In terms of tolerance, discuss what might be happening.

Use the image below to answer question 10.

10. **Short Answer** Describe how the successional stages would differ from primary succession.
11. **MAIN IDEA** Explain why the concepts of limiting factors and tolerance are important in ecology.

Think Critically

12. **THEME FOCUS** Infer whether species diversity increases or decreases after a fire on a grassland. Explain your response.
13. **Generalize** the difference between a successional stage and a climax community.

SECTION 2

Vocabulary Review

Choose the vocabulary term from the Study Guide page that best fits each definition below.

14. the condition of the atmosphere
15. the average conditions in an area
16. a biome characterized by evaporation exceeding precipitation

Understand Main Ideas

17. Which best describes the distribution of communities on a tall mountain?
    - **A.** Evergreen forests exist up to the tree line and no vegetation is found above the tree line.
    - **B.** Several communities might be stratified according to altitude and might end in an ice field at the top of the highest mountains.
    - **C.** As altitude increases, tall trees are replaced by shorter trees, and ultimately are replaced by grasses.
    - **D.** Tundra-like communities exist at the top of the highest mountains, and deserts are found at the lower elevations.

Use the diagram below to answer question 18.

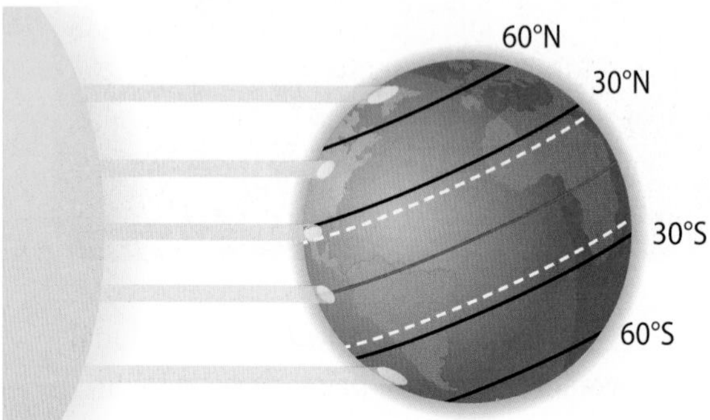

18. Which area receives the least amount of solar energy per unit of surface area?
    - **A.** north of 60°N and south of 60°S
    - **B.** south of 30°N and north of 30°N
    - **C.** between the Tropic of Cancer and the Tropic of Capricorn
    - **D.** north and south temperate zones

19. What is the name for large geographic areas with similar climax communities?
    - **A.** assemblages
    - **B.** communities
    - **C.** successions
    - **D.** biomes

20. Which biome occurs in the United States and once contained huge herds of grazing herbivores?
    - **A.** boreal forest
    - **B.** temperate forest
    - **C.** grassland
    - **D.** savanna

21. Which land biome contains the greatest species diversity?
    - **A.** tundra
    - **B.** grassland
    - **C.** desert
    - **D.** tropical rain forest

Constructed Response

Use the image below to answer question 22.

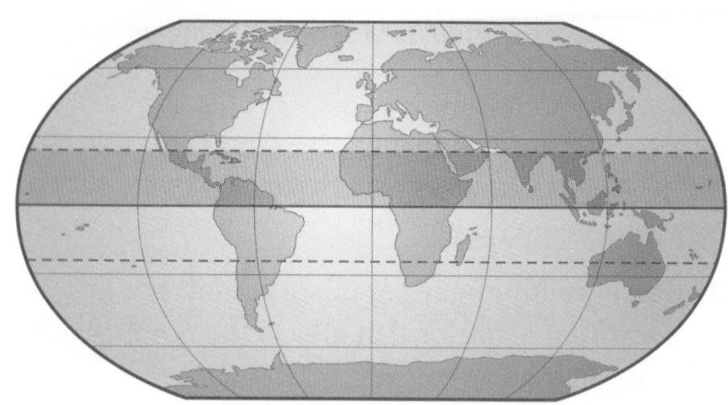

22. **Open Ended** Describe a biome that might be found in the shaded area shown above.

23. **Open Ended** In December 2004, a huge iceberg caused a large number of penguin chicks to die of starvation. Ice shelves broke apart in areas where the air temperature increased. The parents of the penguins were cut off from their food source. How is this an example of temperature as a limiting factor?

Think Critically

24. **MAIN**IDEA Suggest why land biomes are classified according to their plant characteristics rather than according to the animals that inhabit them.

25. **Classify** a biome that is warm to hot in the summer and cool or cold in the winter and that receives approximately 50–89 cm of precipitation annually.

SECTION 3

Vocabulary Review

Replace the underlined words with the correct terms from the Study Guide page.

26. A(n) <u>area where freshwater and salt water meet</u> provides habitat for a diversity of organisms.

27. The <u>well-lit portion of the ocean</u> is the area where all of the photosynthetic organisms live.

28. The <u>shoreline of the ocean</u> contains communities that are layered depending on how long they are submerged by tides.

Understand Main Ideas

29. Where is the largest percentage of water located?
    - **A.** groundwater
    - **B.** rivers
    - **C.** oceans
    - **D.** glaciers

Use the diagram below to answer question 30.

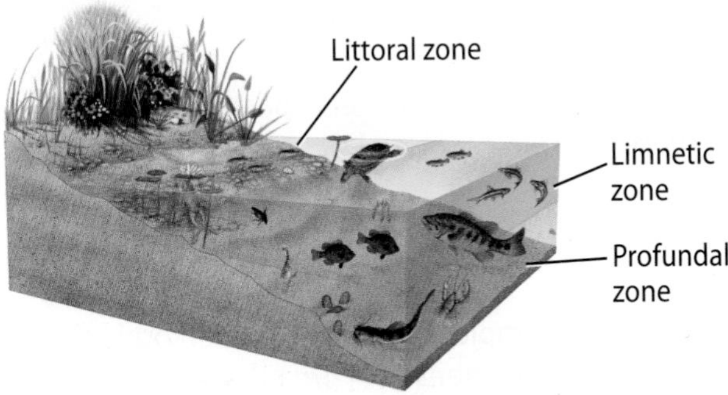

30. In which area of the lake is there likely to be the greatest diversity of plankton?
    - **A.** littoral zone
    - **B.** limnetic zone
    - **C.** profundal zone
    - **D.** aphotic zone

31. Which best describes the intertidal zone on a rocky shore?
    - **A.** The dominant low-energy community is likely to be an estuary.
    - **B.** The communities are adapted to shifting sands due to incoming waves.
    - **C.** The communities are stratified from the high-tide line to the low-tide line.
    - **D.** The organisms in the community constantly require dissolved oxygen.

Constructed Response

32. **Short Answer** How is light a limiting factor in oceans?

33. **Short Answer** Describe characteristics of an estuary.

34. **Open Ended** Describe adaptations of an organism living in the abyssal zone of the ocean.

Think Critically

35. **Analyze** the consequences a drought would have on a river such as the Mississippi River.

36. **MAINIDEA** Compare the intertidal zone with the photic zone in terms of tidal effect.

Summative Assessment

37. **BIGIDEA** Explain the importance of limiting factors and ranges of tolerance for a specific biome or ecosystem.

38. **WRITINGIN▶Biology** Choose a biome other than the one in which you live. Write an essay explaining what you think you would like and what you think you would dislike about living in your chosen biome.

DBQ Document–Based Questions

"Leaf mass per area (LMA) measures the leaf dry-mass investment per unit of light-intercepting leaf area deployed. Species with high LMA have a thicker leaf blade or denser tissue, or both."

"Plant ecologists have emphasized broad relationships between leaf traits and climate for at least a century. In particular, a general tendency for species inhabiting arid and semi-arid regions to have leathery, high-LMA leaves has been reported. Building high-LMA leaves needs more investment per unit leaf area. Construction cost per unit leaf mass varies relatively little between species: leaves with high protein content (typically low-LMA leaves) tend to have low concentrations of other expensive compounds such as lipids or lignin, and high concentrations of cheap constituents such as minerals. Leaf traits associated with high LMA (for example, thick leaf blade; small, thick-walled cells) have been interpreted as adaptations that allow continued leaf function (or at least postpone leaf death) under very dry conditions, at least in evergreen species."

Data obtained from: Wright, I.J. et al. The worldwide leaf economics spectrum. *Nature* 428:821–828.

39. From the information presented, would you expect leaves on trees in the tropical rain forest to contain large quantities of lipids? Explain your answer in terms of energy investment.

40. Hypothesize how high-LMA leaves are adapted for dry conditions.

CUMULATIVE

MULTIPLE CHOICE

1 If science can be characterized as discovery, then technology can be characterized as which?

A application

B information

C manufacturing

D reasoning

2 Which process is associated with long-term cycling of matter through the biosphere?

A breakdown of organic material by decomposers

B formation and weathering of minerals in rocks

C formation of compounds used for food by living organisms

D movement of fresh water from the land into bodies of water through run-off

3 Which of these organisms is a decomposer?

A a bacterium that makes food from inorganic compounds

B a clam that takes in water and filters food

C a fungus that gets nutrients from dead logs

D a plant that makes food using sunlight

4 Which distinguishes scientific ideas from popular opinions?

A Popular opinions are always rational and logical.

B Popular opinions depend on research and evidence.

C Scientific ideas are always testable and repeatable.

D Scientific ideas depend on anecdotes and hearsay.

SHORT ANSWER

5 How is a tundra similar to and different from a boreal forest? Use a Venn diagram to organize information about the similarities and differences of these biomes.

6 What is the role of a pioneer species in primary succession?

7 Give two examples of how the human body shows the living characteristic of organization.

8 Suppose a certain insect species lives only in a specific species of tree. It feeds off the sap of the tree and produces a chemical that protects the tree from certain fungi. What kind of relationship is this?

9 Why would you expect to find different animals in the photic and aphotic zones of the ocean?

10 Suppose a gardener learns that the soil in a garden has low nitrogen content. Describe two ways to increase the nitrogen available for plants in the garden.

11 Explain how the establishment of a climax community through primary succession differs from the establishment of a climax community that occurs through secondary succession.

12 Why is the ability to adapt an important characteristic of living things?

EXTENDED RESPONSE

Use the illustration below to answer question 13.

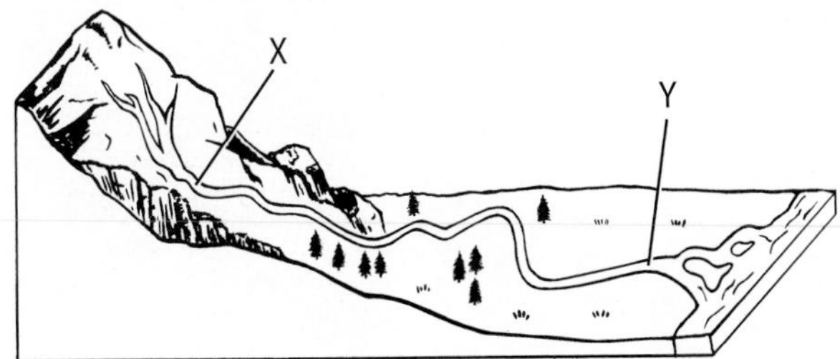

13 Based on the information in the illustration above, what can you infer about the major differences between the freshwater ecosystems at Point X and Point Y?

14 Suppose a nonnative species is introduced into an ecosystem. What is one kind of community interaction you might expect from the other organisms in that ecosystem?

ESSAY QUESTION

Suppose there is a dense temperate forest where people do not live. After a few hot, dry months, forest fires have started to spread through the forest area. There is no threat of the fires reaching areas inhabited by humans. Some people are trying to get the government to intervene to control the fires, while others say the fires should be allowed to run their natural course.

Using the information in the paragraph above, answer the following question in essay format.

15 Explain which side of this debate you would support. Provide evidence based on what you know about change in ecosystems.

TEST PRACTICE

Use the illustration below to answer questions 16 and 17.

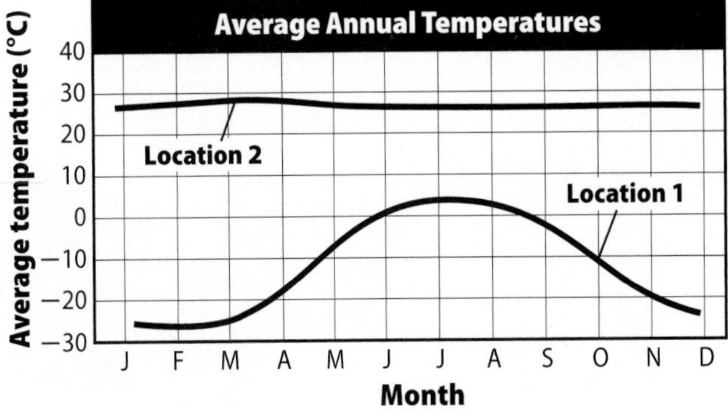

16 Based on the graph above, which term describes Location 2?

A oceanic

B polar

C temperate

D tropical

17 Suppose that in Location 2 there is very little rainfall during the year. What would be the name of that biome in this region?

A desert

B tundra

C temperate forest

D tropical rain forest

NEED EXTRA HELP?																	
If You Missed Question . . .	1	2	3	4	5	6	7	8	9	10	11	12	13	14	15	16	17
Review Section . . .	3.2	2.3	2.2	1.3	3.2	3.1	1.1	2.1	3.3	2.3	3.1	1.1	3.3	3.3	3.1, 3.2	3.2	3.2

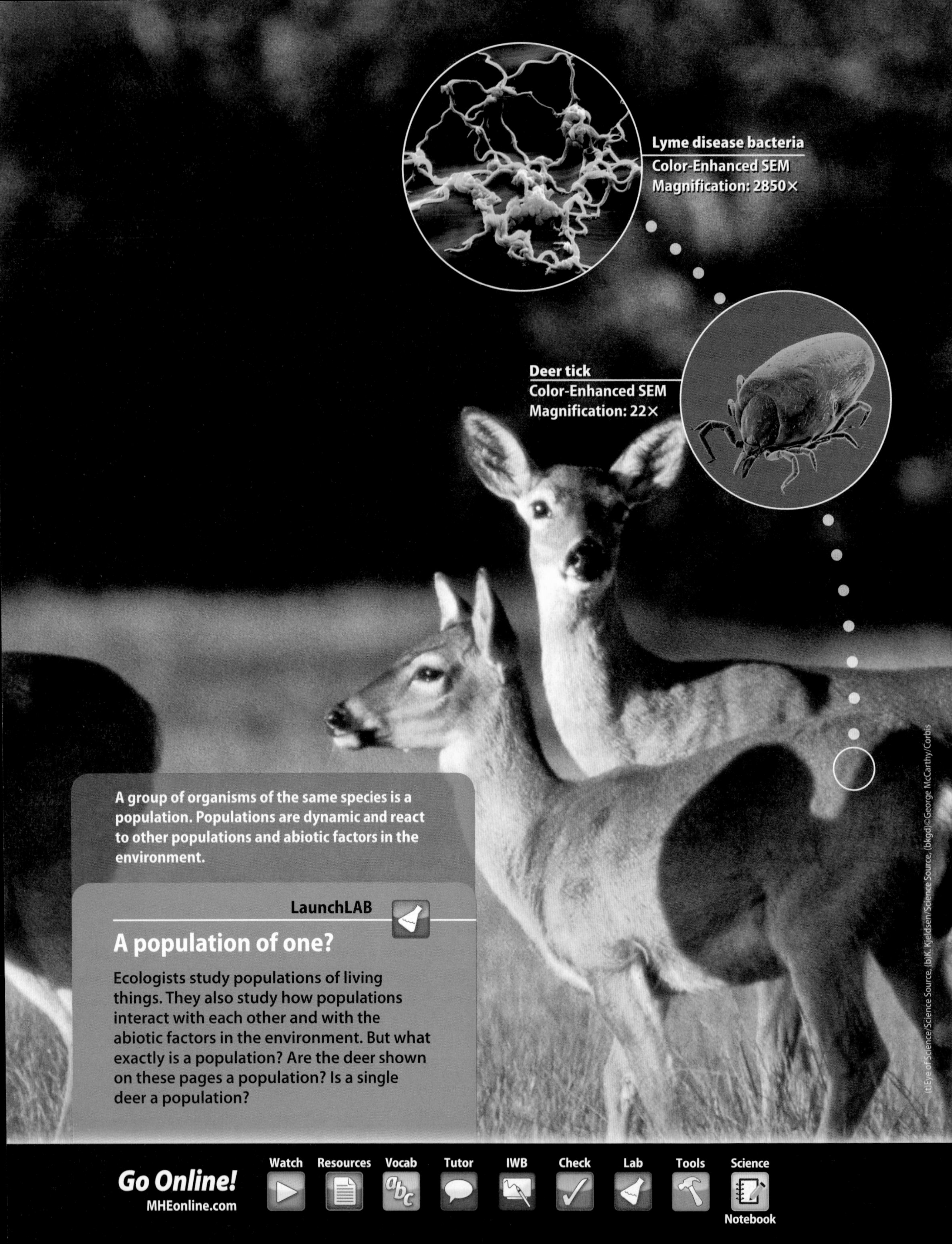

A group of organisms of the same species is a population. Populations are dynamic and react to other populations and abiotic factors in the environment.

LaunchLAB

A population of one?

Ecologists study populations of living things. They also study how populations interact with each other and with the abiotic factors in the environment. But what exactly is a population? Are the deer shown on these pages a population? Is a single deer a population?

CHAPTER 4

Population Ecology

1 Population Dynamics

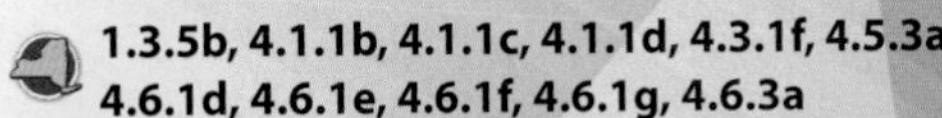

1.3.5b, 4.1.1b, 4.1.1c, 4.1.1d, 4.3.1f, 4.5.3a, 4.6.1d, 4.6.1e, 4.6.1f, 4.6.1g, 4.6.3a

2 Human Population

1.1.1b, 4.1.1b, 4.1.1c, 4.5.2f, 4.5.3a, 4.6.1e, 4.6.1f, 4.6.3a, 4.7.3b

THEMEFOCUS

Stability and change Many factors influence homeostasis within a population.

BIGIDEA

Population growth is a critical factor in a species' ability to maintain homeostasis within its environment.

FOLDABLES® Study Organizer

Population Characteristics

Make a three-tab book using the labels shown. Use it to organize your notes on populations.

Population Characteristics

Population Density | Spatial Distribution | Growth Rate

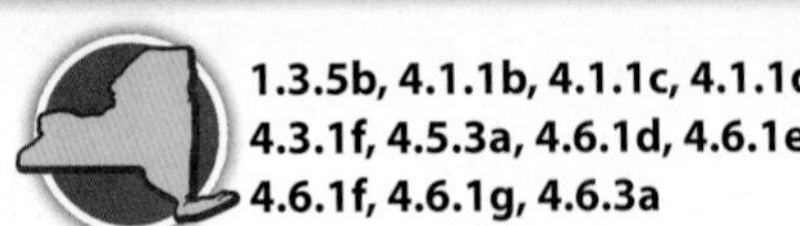

Science Notebook

1 Population Dynamics

1.3.5b, 4.1.1b, 4.1.1c, 4.1.1d, 4.3.1f, 4.5.3a, 4.6.1d, 4.6.1e, 4.6.1f, 4.6.1g, 4.6.3a

MAINIDEA

Populations of species are described by density, spatial distribution, and growth rate.

Essential Questions

- What are the characteristics of populations and how they are distributed?
- What are the differences between density-independent and density-dependent limiting factors?
- What are the similarities between the different models used to quantify the growth of a population?
- How does carrying capacity affect reproductive rates?

BIOLOGY 4U

Have you ever observed a beehive or an ant farm? The population had certain characteristics that could be used to describe it. Ecologists study population characteristics that are used to describe all populations of organisms.

REVIEW VOCABULARY

population: the members of a single species that share the same geographic location at the same time

NEW VOCABULARY

population density
dispersion
density-independent factor
density-dependent factor
population growth rate
emigration
immigration
carrying capacity

Multilingual eGlossary

Population Characteristics

All species occur in groups called populations. There are certain characteristics that all populations have, such as population density, spatial distribution, and growth rate. These characteristics are used to classify all populations of organisms, including bacteria, animals, and plants.

Population density One characteristic of a population is its **population density,** which is the number of organisms per unit area. For example, the population density of cattle egrets, shown with the Cape buffalo in **Figure 1,** is greater near the buffalo than farther away. Near the Cape buffalo, there might be three birds per square meter. Fifty meters from the Cape buffalo, the density of birds might be zero.

Spatial distribution Another characteristic of a population is called **dispersion**—the pattern of spacing of a population within an area. **Figure 2** shows the three main types of dispersion—uniform, clumped groups, and random. Black bears are typically dispersed in a uniform arrangement. American bison are dispersed in clumped groups or herds. White-tailed deer are dispersed randomly with unpredictable spacing. One of the primary factors in the pattern of dispersion for all organisms is the availability of resources such as food.

Beverly Joubert/National Geographic/Getty Images

■ **Figure 1** The population density of the cattle egrets is greater near the Cape buffalo.

***Suggest** the type of dispersion you would expect these birds to have.*

VISUALIZING
VISUALIZING

VISUALIZING Population Characteristics

Figure 2 Population density describes how many individual organisms live in a given area. Dispersion describes how the individuals are spaced within that area. Population range describes a species' distribution.

Black Bear

Dispersion: American black bear males usually are dispersed uniformly within territories as large as several hundred square kilometers. Females have smaller territories that overlap those of males.

Density: one bear per several hundred square kilometers

Black Bear Distribution (in purple)

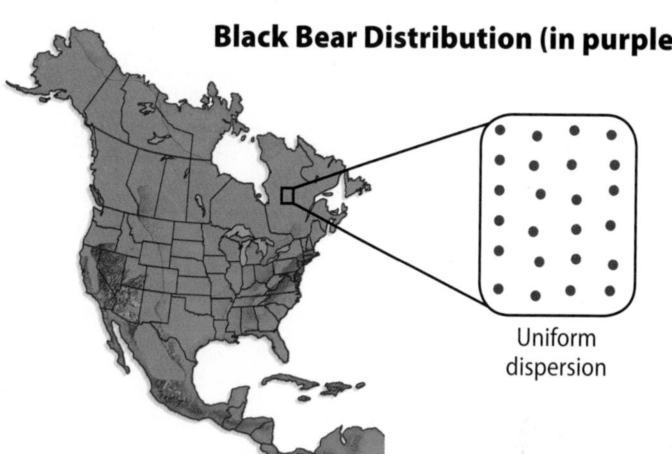

American Bison

Dispersion: American bison are found in clumped groups called herds.

Density: four bison/km^2 in Northern Yellowstone in 2000

Bison Distribution (historic range prior to 1865 in orange)

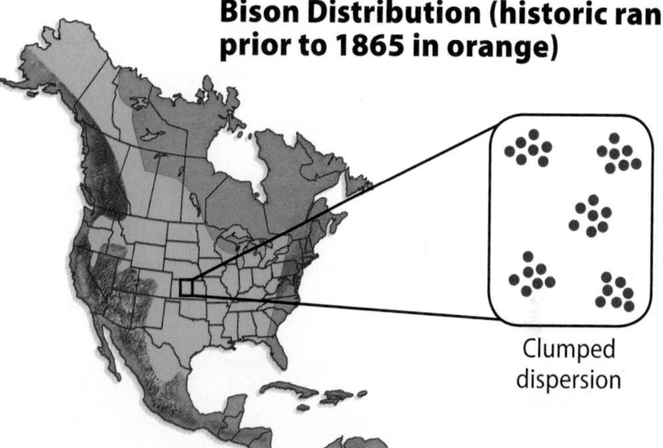

White-tailed Deer

Dispersion: White-tailed deer are dispersed randomly throughout appropriate habitats.

Density: 10 deer/km^2 in some areas of the northeastern United States

White-tailed Deer Distribution (in blue)

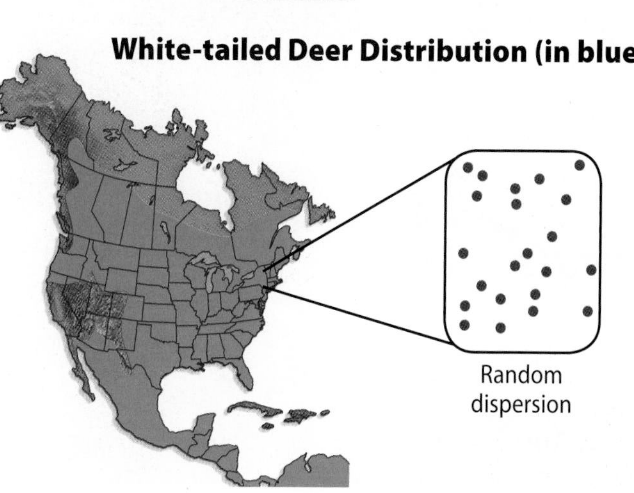

VOCABULARY

SCIENCE USAGE V. COMMON USAGE

Distribution

Science usage: the area where something is located or where a species lives and reproduces
The white-tailed deer has a wide distribution that covers much of the United States.

Common usage: the handing out or delivery of items to a number of people
The distribution of report cards to students occurred today.

Population ranges No population, not even the human population, occupies all habitats in the biosphere. Some species, such as the Hawaiian honeycreeper shown in **Figure 3,** have a very limited population range, or distribution. This songbird is found only on some of the islands of Hawaii. Other species, such as the peregrine falcon shown in **Figure 3,** have a vast distribution. Peregrine falcons are found on all continents except Antarctica. Note the distribution of the animals in **Figure 2.**

You might have learned that organisms adapt to the biotic and abiotic factors in their environment. A species might not be able to expand its population range because it cannot survive the abiotic conditions found in the expanded region. A change in temperature range, humidity level, annual rainfall, or sunlight might make a new geographic area uninhabitable for the species. In addition, biotic factors, such as predators, competitors, and parasites, present threats that might make the new location difficult for survival.

GET IT? **Describe** two reasons why a species might not be able to expand its range.

Population-Limiting Factors

Limiting factors are biotic or abiotic factors that keep a population from continuing to increase indefinitely. Decreasing a limiting factor, such as the available food supply, often changes the number of individuals that are able to survive in a given area. In other words, if the food supply increases a larger population might result, and if the food supply decreases a smaller population might result.

Density-independent factors There are two categories of limiting factors—density-independent factors and density-dependent factors. Any factor in the environment that does not depend on the number of members in a population per unit area is a **density-independent factor.** These factors usually are abiotic and include natural phenomena such as weather events. Weather events that limit populations include drought or flooding, extreme heat or cold, tornadoes, and hurricanes.

■ **Figure 3** The Hawaiian honeycreeper lives only on some of the Hawaii islands. The peregrine falcon is found worldwide.

Hawaiian honeycreeper

Peregrine falcon

(l)Michael Ord/Science Source, (r)Arco Images GmbH/Alamy

Crown fire damage

Managed ground fire damage

■ **Figure 4** A crown fire is a density-independent factor that can limit population growth. However, small ground fires can promote growth of pines in a pine forest community.

Explain ***why these two situations involving fire have different results on the pine tree populations.***

Figure 4 shows an example of the effects that fire can have on a population. Fire has damaged this ponderosa pine forest community. Sometimes the extreme heat from a crown fire, which is a fire that advances to the tops of the trees, can destroy many mature ponderosa pine trees—a dominant species in forests of the western United States. In this example, the fire limits the population of ponderosa trees by killing many of the trees. However, smaller but more frequent ground fires have the opposite effect on the population. By thinning lower growing plants that use up nutrients, a healthier population of mature ponderosa pines is produced.

Populations can be limited by the unintended results of human alterations of the landscape. For example, over the last 100 years, human activities on the Colorado River, such as building dams, water diversions, and water barriers, have significantly reduced the amount of water flow and changed the water temperature of the river. In addition, the introduction of nonnative fish species altered the biotic factors in the river. Because of the changes in the river, the number of small fish called humpback chub was reduced. During the 1960s, the number of humpback chub dropped so low that they were in danger of disappearing from the Colorado River altogether.

Air, land, and water pollution are the result of human activities that also can limit populations. Pollution reduces the available resources by making some of the resources toxic.

Density-dependent factors Any factor in the environment that depends on the number of members in a population per unit area is a **density-dependent factor.** Density-dependent factors are often biotic factors such as predation, disease, parasites, and competition. A study of density-dependent factors was done on the wolf–moose populations in northern Michigan on Isle Royale, located in Lake Superior.

CAREERS IN **BIOLOGY**

Population Biologist A population biologist studies the characteristics of populations, such as growth, size, distribution, or genetics. They use their findings to predict the future of populations and determine what can be done to lessen the negative impacts.

■ **Figure 5** The long-term study of the wolf and moose populations on Isle Royale shows the relationship between the number of predators and prey over time.

Infer ***what might have caused the increase in the number of moose in 1995.***

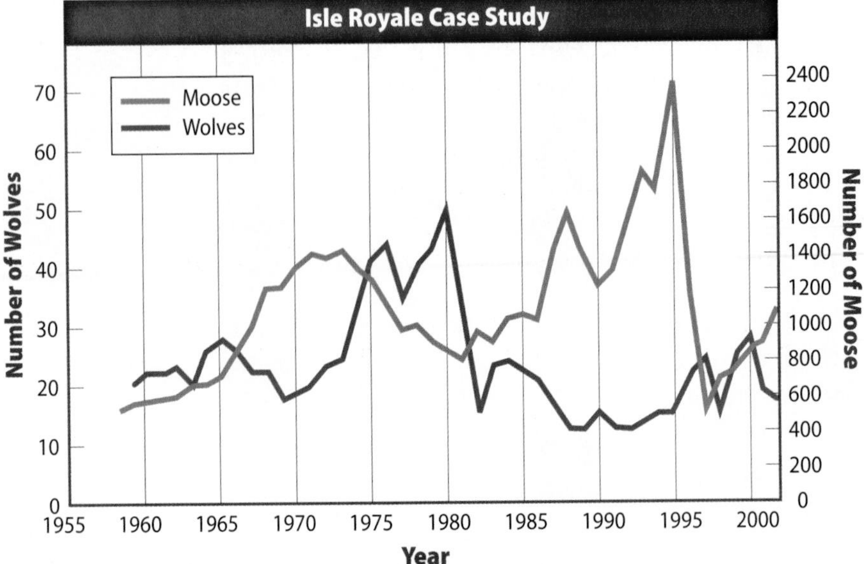

FOLDABLES®
Incorporate information from this section into your Foldable.

Prior to the winter of 1947–48, apparently there were no wolves on Isle Royale. During that winter, a single pair of wolves crossed the ice on Lake Superior, reaching the island. During the next ten years, the population of wolves reached about twenty individuals. **Figure 5** shows some of the results from the long-term study conducted by population biologists. Notice that the rise and fall of the numbers of each group was dependent on the other group. For example, follow the wolves' line on the graph. As the number of wolves decreased, the number of moose increased.

Virtual Lab 

Disease Another density-dependent factor is disease. Outbreaks of disease tend to occur when population size has increased and population density is high. When population density is high, disease is transmitted easily from one individual to another because contact between individuals is more frequent. Therefore, the disease spreads easily and quickly through a population. This is just as true for human populations as it is for populations of protists, plants, and other species of animals.

■ **Figure 6** Lemmings are mammals that produce offspring in large numbers when food is plentiful. When the food supply diminishes, lemmings starve and many die.

Competition Competition between organisms also increases when density increases. When the population increases to a size so that resources such as food or space become limited, individuals in the population must compete for the available resources. Competition can occur within a species or between two different species that use the same resources. Competition for insufficient resources might result in a decrease in population density in an area due to starvation or to individuals leaving the area in search of additional resources. As the population size decreases, competition becomes less severe.

The lemmings shown in **Figure 6** are an example of a population that often undergoes competition for resources. Lemmings are small mammals that live in the tundra biome. When food is plentiful, their population increases exponentially. As food becomes limited, many lemmings begin to starve and their population size decreases significantly.

Parasites Populations also can be limited by parasites, in a way similar to disease, as population density increases. The presence of parasites is a density-dependent factor that can negatively affect population growth at higher densities.

Population growth rate An important characteristic of any population is its growth rate. The **population growth rate** (PGR) explains how fast a given population grows. One of the characteristics of the population ecologists must know, or at least estimate, is natality. The natality of a population is the birthrate, or the number of individuals born in a given time period. Ecologists also must know the mortality—the number of deaths that occur in the population during a given time period.

The number of individuals emigrating or immigrating also is important. **Emigration** (em uh GRAY shun) is the term ecologists use to describe the number of individuals moving away from a population. **Immigration** (ih muh GRAY shun) is the term ecologists use to describe the number of individuals moving into a population. In most instances, emigration is about equal to immigration. Therefore, natality and mortality usually are most important in determining the population growth rate.

Some populations tend to remain approximately the same size from year to year. Other populations vary in size depending on conditions within their habitats. To better understand why populations grow in different ways, you should understand two mathematical models for population growth—the exponential growth model and the logistic growth model.

Exponential growth model Look at **Figure 7** to see how a population of mice would grow if there were no limits placed on it by the environment. Assume that two adult mice breed and produce a litter of young, two of which are able to reproduce in one month. If all of the offspring survive to breed, the population grows slowly at first. This slow growth period is defined as the lag phase. The rate of population growth soon begins to increase rapidly because the total number of organisms that are able to reproduce has increased. After only two years, the experimental mouse population would reach more than three million.

Connection to Math Notice in **Figure 7** that once the mice begin to reproduce rapidly, the graph becomes J-shaped. A J-shaped growth curve illustrates exponential growth. Exponential growth, also called geometric growth, occurs when the growth rate is proportional to the size of the population. All populations grow exponentially until some limiting factor slows the population's growth. It is important to recognize that even in the lag phase, the use of available resources is exponential. Because of this, the resources soon become limited and population growth slows.

Logistic growth model Many populations grow like the model shown in **Figure 8** rather than the model shown in **Figure 7.** Notice that the graphs look exactly the same through some of the time period. However, the second graph curves into an S-shape. An S-shaped curve is typical of logistic growth. Logistic growth occurs when the population's growth slows or stops following exponential growth, at the population's carrying capacity. A population stops increasing when the number of births is less than the number of deaths or when emigration exceeds immigration.

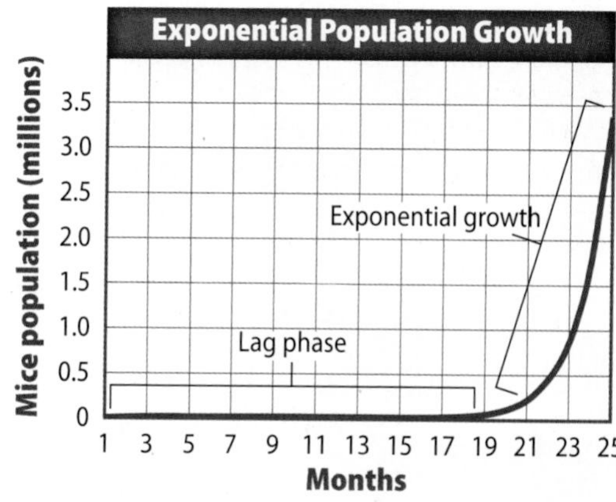

■ **Figure 7** If two mice were allowed to reproduce unhindered, the population would grow slowly at first but would accelerate quickly.

Infer ***why mice or other populations do not continue to grow exponentially.***

Animation

■ **Figure 8** When a population exhibits growth that results in an S-shaped graph, it exhibits logistic growth. The population levels off at a limit called the carrying capacity.

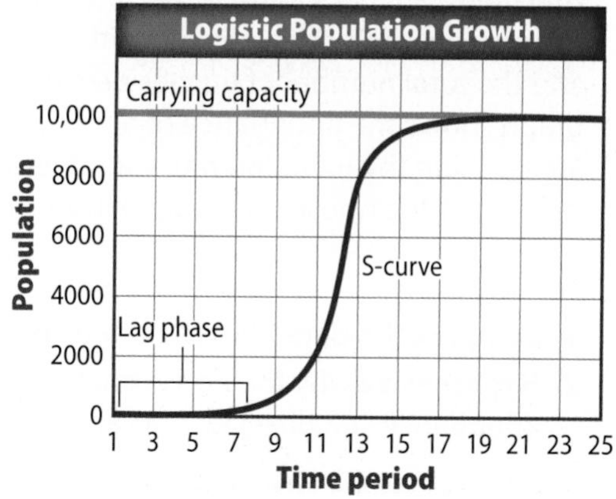

■ **Figure 9** Locusts, which are an example of *r*-strategists, produce many offspring in their short lifetimes.

Infer ***what specific factors might fluctuate in a locust's environment.***

Carrying capacity In **Figure 8** on the previous page, notice that logistic growth levels off at the line on the graph identified as the carrying capacity. The maximum number of individuals in a species that an environment can support for the long term is the **carrying capacity.** Carrying capacity is limited by the energy, water, oxygen, and nutrients available. When populations develop in an environment with plentiful resources, there are more births than deaths. The population soon reaches or passes the carrying capacity. As a population nears the carrying capacity, resources become limited. If a population exceeds the carrying capacity, deaths outnumber births because adequate resources are not available to support all of the individuals. The population then falls below the carrying capacity as individuals die. The concept of carrying capacity is used to explain why many populations tend to stabilize.

Reproductive patterns The graph in **Figure 8** shows the number of individuals increasing until the carrying capacity is reached. However, there are several additional factors that must be considered for real populations. Species of organisms vary in the number of births per reproduction cycle, in the age that reproduction begins, and in the life span of the organism. Both plants and animals are placed into groups based on their reproductive factors.

Members of one of the groups are called the *r*-strategists. The rate strategy, or *r*-strategy, is an adaptation for living in an environment where fluctuation in biotic or abiotic factors occur. Fluctuating factors might be availability of food or changing temperatures. An *r*-strategist is generally a small organism such as a fruit fly, a mouse, or the locusts shown in **Figure 9.** *R*-strategists usually have short life spans and produce many offspring.

Data Analysis LAB 1

Based on Real Data*

Recognize Cause and Effect

Do parasites affect the size of a host population? In 1994, the first signs of a serious eye disease caused by the bacterium *Mycoplasma gallisepticum* were observed in house finches that were eating in backyard bird feeders. Volunteers collected data beginning three different years on the number of finches infected with the parasite and the total number of finches present. The graph shows the abundance of house finches in areas where the infection rate was at least 20 percent of the house finch population.

Data and Observations

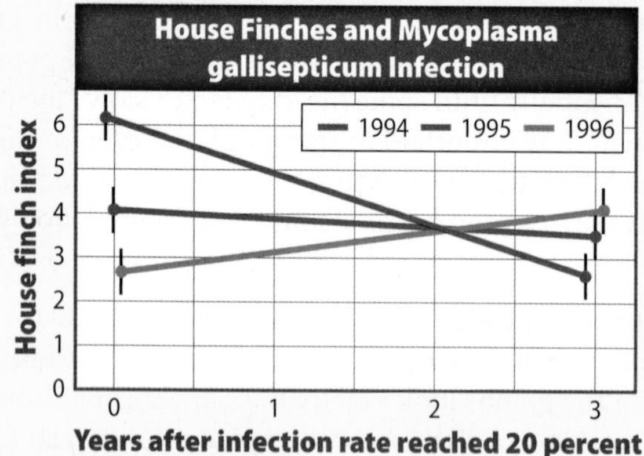

Think Critically

1. **Compare** the data from the three areas.
2. **Hypothesize** why the house finch abundance stabilized in 1995 and 1996.
3. **Infer** whether the parasite, *Mycoplasma gallisepticum,* is effective in limiting the size of house finch populations. Explain.

*Data obtained from: Gregory, R., et al. 2000. Parasites take control. *Nature* 406: 33–34.

■ **Figure 10** Elephants are *k*-strategists that produce few offspring, but they invest a lot of care in the raising of their offspring.

The reproductive strategy of an *r*-strategist is to produce as many offspring as possible in a short time period in order to take advantage of some environmental factor. They typically expend little or no energy in raising their young to adulthood. Populations of *r*-strategists usually are controlled by density-independent factors, and they usually do not maintain a population near the carrying capacity.

Just as some environments fluctuate, others are fairly predictable. The elephants in **Figure 10** experience a carrying capacity that changes little from year to year. The carrying-capacity strategy, or *k*-strategy, is an adaptation for living in these environments. A *k*-strategist generally is a larger organism that has a long life span and produces few offspring, and its population reaches equilibrium at the carrying capacity. The reproductive strategy of a *k*-strategist is to produce only a few offspring that have a better chance of living to reproductive age because of the energy, resources, and time invested in the care for the young. Populations of *k*-strategists usually are controlled by density-dependent factors.

VOCABULARY

ACADEMIC VOCABULARY

Fluctuate
to vary or change measured levels or from one thing to another in an unpredictable way
The speed of a car fluctuates when you are driving on narrow, winding roads.

REVIEW IT! Population Dynamics

Section Summary

- There are population characteristics that are common to all populations of organisms, including plants, animals, and bacteria.
- Populations tend to be distributed randomly, uniformly, or in clumps.
- Population limiting factors are either density-independent or density-dependent.
- Populations tend to stabilize near the carrying capacity of their environment.

 Self Check

Understand Main Ideas

1. MAINIDEA **Compare and contrast** spatial distribution, population density, and population growth rate.
2. **Summarize** the concepts of carrying capacity and limiting factors and their effects on reproductive patterns.
3. **Sketch** diagrams showing population dispersion patterns.
4. **Analyze** the impact a nonnative species might have on a native species in terms of population dynamics.

Think Critically

5. **Design** an experiment that you could perform to determine which population growth model applies to fruit fly populations.

WRITING IN ▶ Biology

6. Write a newspaper article describing how a weather event, such as drought, has affected a population of animals in your community.

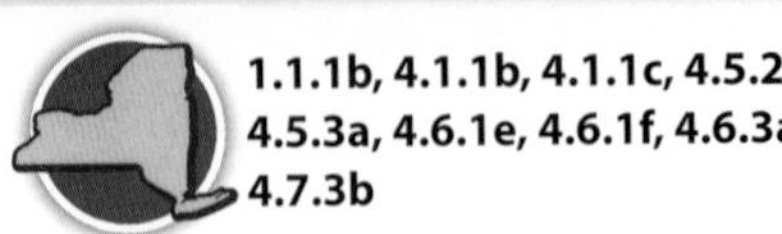

2 Human Population

1.1.1b, 4.1.1b, 4.1.1c, 4.5.2f, 4.5.3a, 4.6.1e, 4.6.1f, 4.6.3a, 4.7.3b

MAINIDEA

Human population growth changes over time.

Essential Questions

- What aspects affect human population growth?
- What are the trends in human population growth?
- What are the age structures of representative nongrowing, slowly growing, and rapidly growing countries?
- What might be the consequences of continued population growth?

BIOLOGY 4U

Has someone you know recently had a baby? The odds of babies surviving to adulthood are greater than ever before in most countries today.

Review Vocabulary

carrying capacity: the maximum number of individuals in a species that an environment can support for the long term

New Vocabulary

demography
demographic transition
zero population growth (ZPG)
age structure

Multilingual eGlossary

Human Population Growth

The study of human population size, density, distribution, movement, and birth and death rates is **demography** (de MAH gra fee). The graph in **Figure 11** shows demographers' estimated human population on Earth for several thousand years.

Notice that the graph in **Figure 11** shows a relatively stable number of individuals over thousands of years—until recently. Notice also the recovery of the human population after the outbreak of the bubonic plague in the 1300s when an estimated one-third of the population of Europe died. Perhaps the most significant feature in this graph is the increase in human population in recent times. In 1804, the population of Earth was an estimated one billion people. Earth reached a milestone in 1999, when our planet's population was recorded at six billion people. With the current growth rate at just over 80 million people per year we are expected to reach a population of seven billion by 2012, and nine billion by 2050.

Figure 11 The human population on Earth was relatively constant until recent times, when the human population began to grow at an exponential rate.

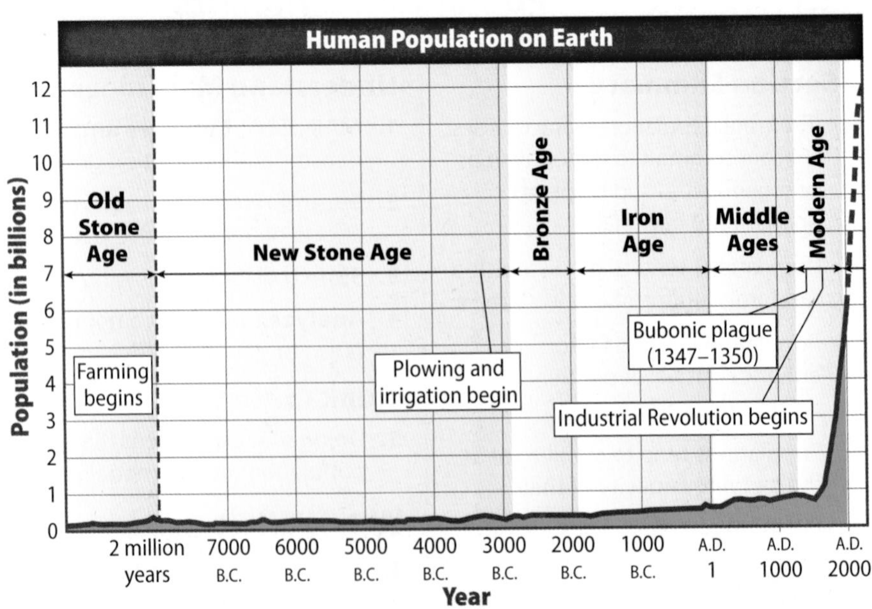

Technological advances For thousands of years, environmental conditions kept the size of the human population at a relatively constant number below the environment's carrying capacity. Humans have learned to alter the environment in ways that appear to have changed its carrying capacity. Agriculture and domestication of animals have increased the human food supply. Technological advances and medicine have improved the chances of human survival by reducing the number of deaths from parasites and disease. In addition, improvements in shelter have made humans less vulnerable to climatic impact.

GET IT? **Explain** why an improvement in shelter increased the survival rate of the human population.

Human population growth rate Although the human population is still growing, the rate of its growth has slowed. **Figure 12** shows the percent increase in human population from the late 1940s through 2009. The graph also includes the projected population increase through 2050. Notice the sharp dip in human population growth in the 1960s. This was due primarily to a famine in China in which about 60 million people died. The graph also shows that human population growth reached its peak at over 2.2 percent in 1963. By 2009, the percent increase in human population growth had dropped to less than 1.2 percent. Population models predict the overall population growth rate to be below 0.6 percent by 2050. The decline in human population growth is due primarily to diseases such as AIDS and voluntary population control.

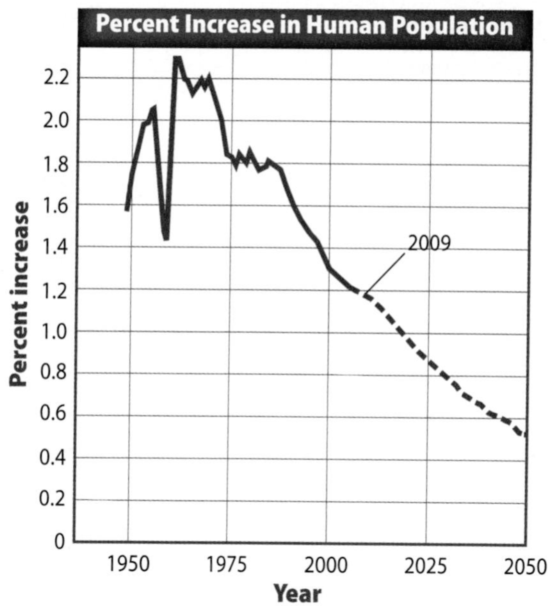

Figure 12 This graph shows the percent increase in the global human population using data from the late 1940s through 2009 and the projected percent increase to 2050.

Determine ***the approximate population increase in the year 2025.***

MiniLAB 1

Evaluate Factors

What factors affect the growth of a human population? Technological advances have resulted in a rapid growth in human population. However, human population growth is not equal in all countries.

Procedure

1. The graph shows one factor affecting human population growth. Use the data to predict how this factor will affect the population in each country between now and the year 2050.
2. Brainstorm a list of factors, events, or conditions that affect the growth of human populations in these countries. Predict the effect of each factor on the population growth rate.

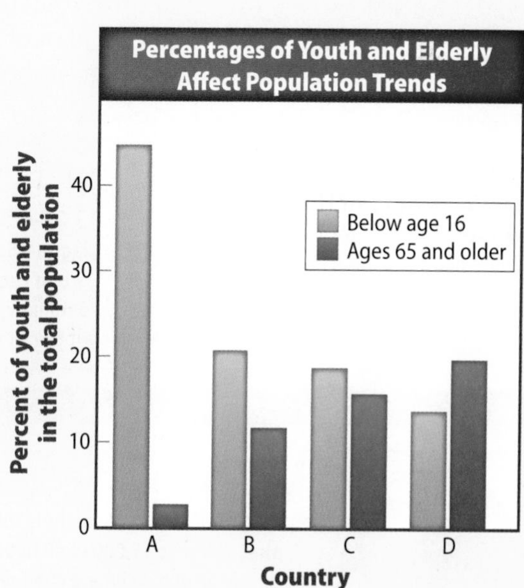

Analysis

Think Critically In your opinion, what factors or groups of factors have the greatest impact on population growth? Justify your answer.

VOCABULARY

WORD ORIGIN

Demography
demo– from the Greek word demos; meaning *people*
–ography from the French word *graphie;* meaning *writing*

Trends in Human Population Growth

The graph in **Figure 12** is somewhat deceptive. Population trends can be altered by events such as disease and war. **Figure 13** shows a few historical events that have changed population trends. **Figure 12** could also easily be misinterpreted because human population growth is not the same in all countries. However, population growth trends are often similar in countries that have similar economies.

For example, one trend that has developed during the previous century is a change in the population growth rate in industrially developed countries such as the United States. An industrially developed country is advanced in industrial and technological capabilities and has a population with a high standard of living. In its early history, the United States had a high birthrate and a high death rate. It was not uncommon for people to have large families and for individuals to die by their early forties. Many children also died before reaching adulthood. Presently, the birthrate in the United States has decreased dramatically and the life expectancy is greater than seventy years. This change in a population from high birth and death rates to low birth and death rates is called a **demographic transition.**

Launch Lab

Review Based on what you've read about populations, how would you now answer the analysis questions?

Connection to Math How do population growth rates (PGR) compare in industrially developed countries and developing countries? As an example, we will compare the 2008 populations for the United States and Honduras, a small country in Central America. The calculation for PGR is

$$\frac{\text{birthrate} - \text{deathrate} + \text{migration rate}}{10} = \text{PGR (\%)}$$

In our example, we'll have to divide the final answer by 10 to get a percentage because the rates are calculated per 1000.

The United States has birthrate 14.1 (per 1000), death rate 8.3 (per 1000), and migration rate 2.9 (per 1000). This gives a PGR of 0.87 percent for the United States. Honduras has birthrate 26.9 (per 1000), death rate 5.4 (per 1000), and migration rate −1.3 (per 1000). This gives a PGR of 2.02 percent for Honduras.

Figure 13 History of Human Population Trends Many factors have affected human population growth throughout history.

1347–1351 The bubonic plague kills one-third of Europe's population and 75 million people throughout the world.

1800 The Industrial Revolution leads to a dramatic population explosion.

0 · 1350 · 1800

69,000 B.C. Researchers think that as few as 15,000 to 40,000 people survived global climate changes that resulted from the eruption of the Toba supervolcano.

1798 The first essay on human population is written by Thomas Malthus, who predicted exponential population growth leading to famine, poverty, and war.

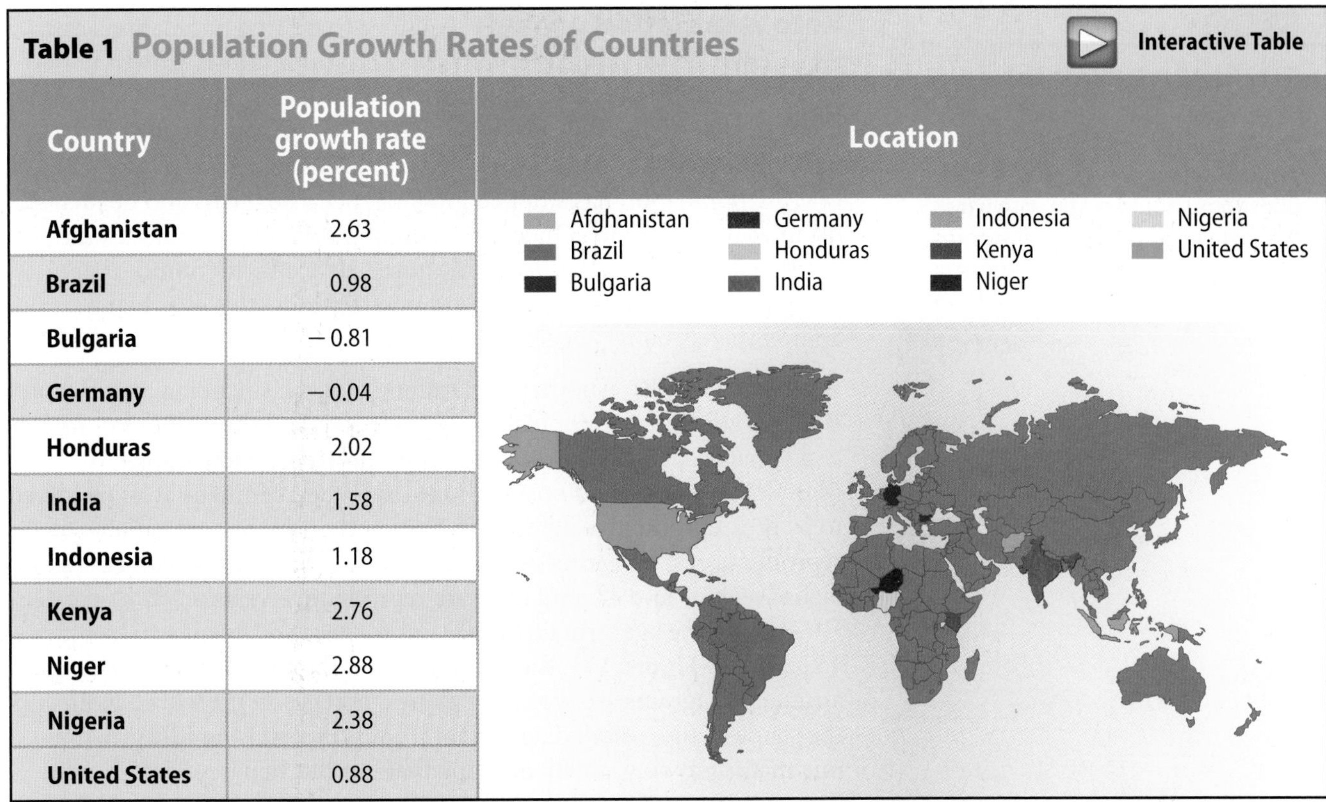

Table 1 Population Growth Rates of Countries

Interactive Table

Country	Population growth rate (percent)	Location
Afghanistan	2.63	
Brazil	0.98	
Bulgaria	– 0.81	
Germany	– 0.04	
Honduras	2.02	
India	1.58	
Indonesia	1.18	
Kenya	2.76	
Niger	2.88	
Nigeria	2.38	
United States	0.88	

Afghanistan
Brazil
Bulgaria
Germany
Honduras
India
Indonesia
Kenya
Niger
Nigeria
United States

Developing countries will add more people to the world population as compared to the amount of people added in the industrially developed countries. For example, between now and 2050, the developing country Niger—shown in **Table 1**—will be one of the fastest growing countries. Its population is expected to expand from 13 to 53 million people. The industrially developed country Bulgaria is expected to have a population decline from seven to five million people in the same time period.

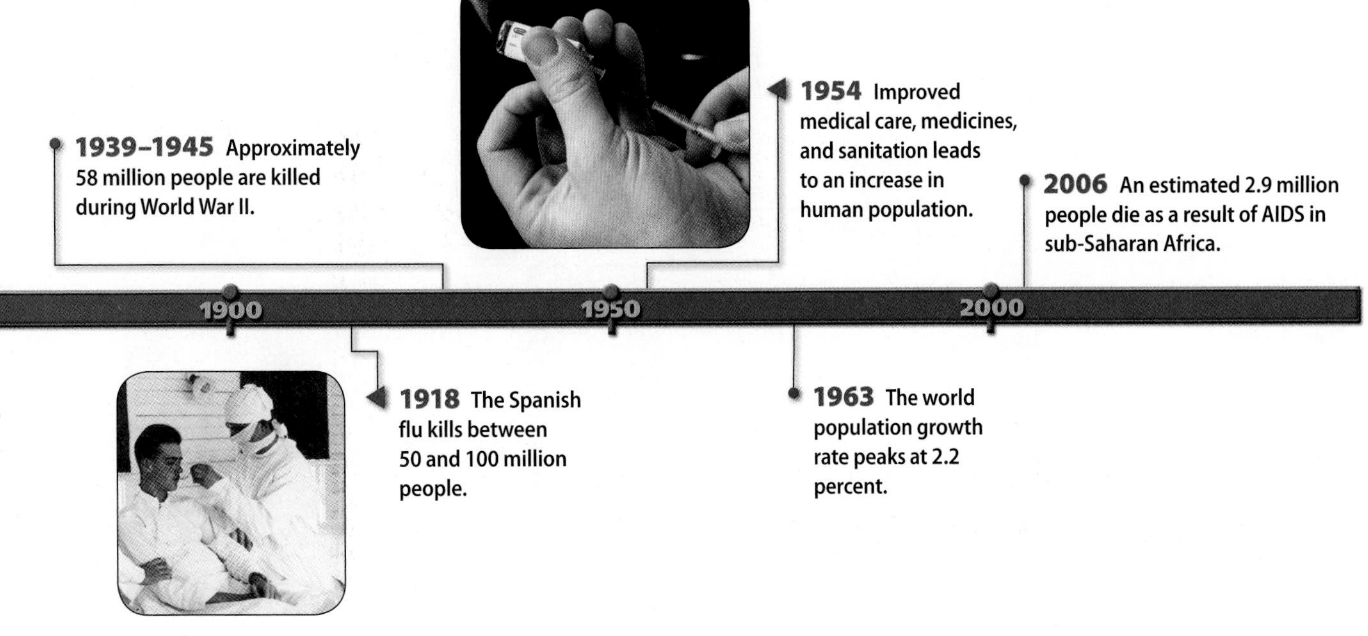
1939–1945 Approximately 58 million people are killed during World War II.
1954 Improved medical care, medicines, and sanitation leads to an increase in human population.
2006 An estimated 2.9 million people die as a result of AIDS in sub-Saharan Africa.
1900
1950
2000
1918 The Spanish flu kills between 50 and 100 million people.
1963 The world population growth rate peaks at 2.2 percent.

(l)MPI/Archive Photos/Getty Images, (r)John Griffin/The Image Works

STUDY TIP

INTERACTIVE READING As you read, write three questions on sticky notes about human population dynamics. The questions should begin with *why, how, where,* or *when.* Use the notes to ask a partner questions about the content in the chapter.

Zero population growth Another trend that populations can experience is zero population growth. **Zero population growth** (ZPG) occurs when births plus immigration equals deaths plus emigration. One estimate is that the world will reach ZPG between 2020 with 6.64 billion people and 2029 with 6.90 billion people. This will mean that the population has stopped growing, because births and deaths occur at the same rate. Once the world population reaches ZPG, the age structure eventually should be more balanced with numbers at pre-reproductive, reproductive, and post-reproductive ages being approximately equal.

Age structure Another important characteristic of any population is its age structure. A population's **age structure** is the number of males and females in each of three age groups: pre-reproductive stage, reproductive stage, and post-reproductive stage. Humans are considered to be pre-reproductive before age 20 even though they are capable of reproduction at an earlier age. The reproductive years are considered to be between 20 and 44, and the post-reproductive years are after age 44.

BrainPOP 

Analyze the age structure diagrams for three different representative countries in **Figure 14**—their locations are shown in **Table 1.** The age structure diagrams are typical of many countries in the world. Notice the shape of the overall diagram for a country that is rapidly growing, one that is growing slowly, and one that has reached negative growth. The age structure for the world's human population looks more like that of a rapidly growing country.

GET IT? **Compare and contrast** the age structures of the countries shown in **Figure 14.**

■ **Figure 14** The relative numbers of individuals in pre-reproductive, reproductive, and post-reproductive years are shown for three representative countries.

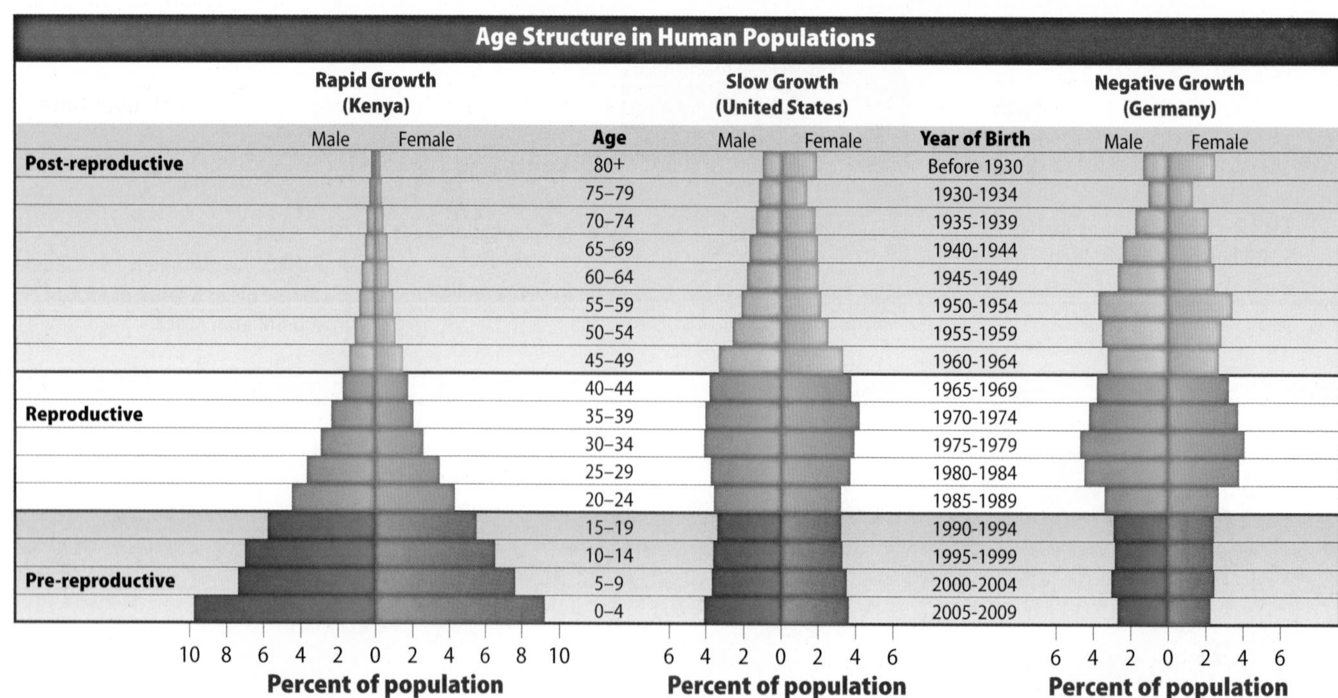

Human carrying capacity Calculating population growth rates is not just a mathematical exercise. Scientists are concerned about the human population reaching or exceeding the carrying capacity. As you learned in Section 1, all populations have carrying capacities, and the human population is no exception. Many scientists suggest that human population growth needs to be reduced. In many countries, voluntary population control is occurring through family planning. Unfortunately, if the human population continues to grow—as most populations do—and areas become overcrowded, disease and starvation will occur. However, technology has allowed humans to increase Earth's carrying capacity, at least temporarily. It might be possible for technology and planning to keep the human population at or below its carrying capacity.

Another important factor in keeping the human population at or below the carrying capacity is the amount of resources from the biosphere that are used by each person. Currently, individuals in industrially developed countries use far more resources than those individuals in developing countries, as shown in **Figure 15.** This graph shows the estimated amount of land required to support a person through his or her life, including land used for production of food, forest products and housing, and the additional forest land required to absorb the carbon dioxide produced by the burning of fossil fuels. Countries such as India are becoming more industrialized, and they have a high growth rate. These countries are adding more people and are increasing their use of resources. At some point, the land needed to sustain each person on Earth might exceed the amount of land that is available.

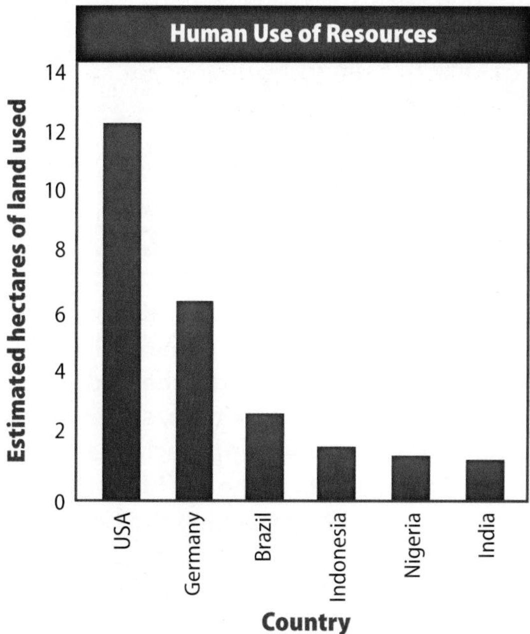

Figure 15 The amount of resources used per person varies around the world. Refer to **Table 1** for the locations of these countries.

REVIEW IT! Human Population

Section Summary

- Human population growth rates vary in industrially developing countries and industrialized countries.
- Zero population growth occurs when the birthrate and immigration rate of a population equals the death rate and the emigration rate.
- The age structure of the human population is a contributing factor to population growth in some countries.
- Earth has an undefined carrying capacity for the human population.

Self Check

Understand Main Ideas

1. MAINIDEA **Describe** the change in human population growth over time.
2. **Describe** the differences between the age structure graphs of nongrowing, slowly growing, and rapidly growing countries.
3. **Assess** the consequences of exponential population growth of any population.
4. **Summarize** why the human population began to grow exponentially in the Modern Age.

Think Critically

5. **Predict** the short-term and long-term effects of a newly emerging disease on industrially developing and developed countries.

MATH IN Biology

6. Construct an age-structure diagram using the following percentages: 0–19 years: 44.7; 20–44 years: 52.9; 45 years and over: 2.4. Which type of growth is this country experiencing?

cutting-edge BIOLOGY

1.1.3b, 4.5.3a, 4.6.3a, 4.6.3c, 4.7.1c, 4.7.2a, 4.7.3b

Polar Bear Ecology

In late 2006, the U.S. Fish and Wildlife Service proposed that the polar bear be listed as a threatened species under the Endangered Species Act of 1973. Since then, scientists have undertaken a novel approach to studying the ecological needs of the world's largest terrestrial predator—not by tracking the bears themselves but by tracking the receding ice habitat in which the bears reside, which is vital to their survival.

Scott Bergen, an ecologist with the Wildlife Conservation Society, will work with other scientists utilizing satellites and meteorological data to predict where sea ice will remain in the near future. Conservation efforts will focus on these locations.

Bear necessities Polar bears only live in the circumpolar north, which includes the countries of the United States (Alaska), Canada, Russia, Denmark (Greenland), and Norway. The sea ice that forms each winter creates passages in which the bears travel, as well as creating an optimal environment for hunting. Polar bears rely on seasonal sea ice to stalk their favorite prey—ringed and bearded seals. As the sea ice dwindles, so does the polar bears' ability to effectively hunt these fast-swimming marine mammals.

The cold, hard facts Scientists plan to combine daily satellite and meteorological data from the past 30 years, including global climate change projections, to extrapolate where conservation efforts to save the species would be most successful. The data will also be used to create a Geographical Information Systems (GIS) map.

Approximately 60 percent of the polar bear population reside in Canada.

Using the GIS map, scientists think they will be able to determine short-term seasonal effects as well as large-scale phenomena (like the Arctic and North Atlantic oscillations) and their effect on the Arctic's megafauna. A scientist with the project contends, "The survival of some polar bear populations depends on the decisions we make within the next year."

WRITING IN ▶ Biology

Persuasive Letter Research what criteria must be met to have a species added to the Endangered Species list. Then choose a species and write a persuasive letter to emphasize the importance that the species be added to the list.

WebQuest

Joanna McCarthy/Getty Images

BioLAB

1.1.1c, 1.2.2a, 1.3.3, 4.5.3a, 4.6.1g, 4.6.3a, ¥a, ¥b1, ¥b2, ¥b3, ¥b4, ¥b5, ¥e, ¥i, ¥j, ¥m, ¥n, ¥o, ¥p

Do plants of the same species compete with one another?

Background: Ecologists often study plant competition by comparing the biomass of individual plants in plant populations. In this lab, you will study intraspecific competition—competition among plants of the same species. As with most ecological studies, you will need to collect data for several weeks.

Question: *Do plant populations of various densities grow differently due to competition?*

Materials

marigold seeds or radish seeds
9-cm plastic pots (6)
clean potting soil
rulers
shallow tray for pots
small garden trowels
masking tape
permanent markers
balance (accurate to 0.1 g)
watering can

Safety Precautions

Procedure

1. Read and complete the lab safety form.
2. Plant seeds in several pots as instructed by your teacher. Your goal should be to have pots with the following densities of plants: 2, 4, 8, 16, 32, and 64.
3. Place the pots in a shallow tray near a sunny window or under a grow light. Continue to keep the soil moist—not drenched—throughout the course of the experiment.
4. After the seeds have sprouted, weed out any extra plants so that you have the correct density.
5. Write a hypothesis about the effect plant density will have on the average biomass of each pot's population.
6. Construct a data table. Observe the plants once each week for a 5–6 week period. Record your observations.
7. At the end of the experiment, with precision and accuracy, measure the biomass of the plants in each pot by cutting each plant at soil level and quickly weighing all the plants from the same pot together. Record your measurements. Calculate the average per-plant biomass of each pot.
8. **Cleanup and Disposal** Wash and return all reusable materials. Wash your hands after watering or working with the plants. Dispose of the plants at the end of the lab as instructed by your teacher.

Analyze and Conclude

1. **Graph Data** Prepare a graph showing the relationship between the average plant biomass and the density of plants. Draw a best-fit line for your data points. What was the effect of plant density on the average biomass of each pot's population? Does this graph support your hypothesis?
2. **Infer** Draw a second graph that compares the total biomass for each population to the number of plants in each population.
3. **Think Critically** Based on your results, infer how human population growth is affected by population density.
4. **Error Analysis** What sources of error might have affected your results?

SHARE YOUR DATA

Poster Session Create a poster using the graphs you produced as a result of your experiment. If a digital camera is available, take photos of each pot of plants to include on your poster. Add headings and legends for each graph and photograph that explain and summarize your findings. Display your poster in the classroom or a hallway of your school.

CHAPTER 4 STUDY GUIDE

BIGIDEA **Population growth is a critical factor in a species' ability to maintain homeostasis within its environment.**

SECTION 1 Population Dynamics

MAINIDEA Populations of species are described by density, spatial distribution, and growth rate.

- There are population characteristics that are common to all populations of organisms, including plants, animals, and bacteria.
- Populations tend to be distributed randomly, uniformly, or in clumps.
- Population limiting factors are either density-independent or density-dependent.
- Populations tend to stabilize near the carrying capacity of their environment.

VOCABULARY
- **population density**
- **dispersion**
- **density-independent factor**
- **density-dependent factor**
- **population growth rate**
- **emigration**
- **immigration**
- **carrying capacity**

SECTION 2 Human Population

MAINIDEA Human population growth changes over time.

- Human population growth rates vary in industrially developing countries and industrialized countries.
- Zero population growth occurs when the birthrate and immigration rate of a population equals the death rate and the emigration rate.
- The age structure of the human population is a contributing factor to population growth in some countries.
- Earth has an undefined carrying capacity for the human population.

VOCABULARY
- **demography**
- **demographic transition**
- **zero population growth (ZPG)**
- **age structure**

ASSESSMENT

SECTION 1

Vocabulary Review

Replace the underlined words with the correct vocabulary term from the Study Guide page.

1. The number added to a population by movement can considerably increase a population's size.
2. Drought is a density-dependent factor.
3. Were it not for the long-term limit, a population would continue to grow exponentially.

Understand Main Ideas

Use the illustration to answer questions 4–6.

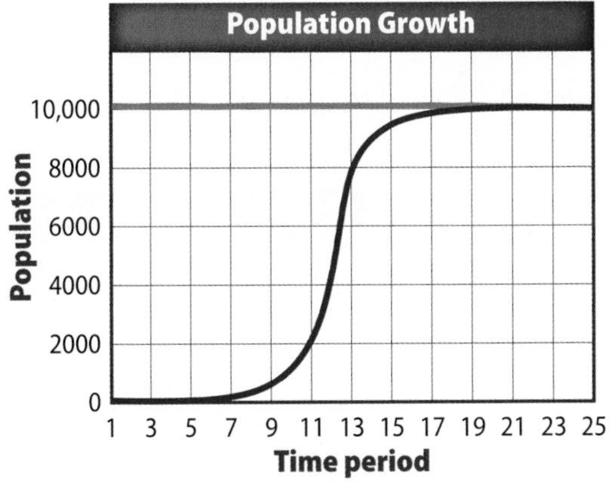

4. Which population growth model does this graph illustrate?
   A. exponential growth
   B. lag phase
   C. logistic growth
   D. straight-line growth
5. What is the horizontal line on this graph called?
   A. carrying capacity **C.** geometric growth
   B. exponential growth **D.** straight-line growth
6. What do the time periods 1–7 represent?
   A. acceleration phase **C.** exponential growth
   B. carrying capacity **D.** lag phase
7. If angelfish produce hundreds of young several times a year, which statement below is true?
   A. Angelfish have a *k*-strategy reproductive pattern.
   B. Angelfish have an *r*-strategy reproductive pattern.
   C. Angelfish probably have a low mortality rate.
   D. Angelfish provide a lot of care for their young.

8. If an aquarium holds 80 L of water and contains 170 guppies, what is the approximate density of the guppy population?
   A. 1 guppy/L **C.** 3 guppies/L
   B. 2 guppies/L **D.** 4 guppies/L
9. Which is a density-independent factor?
   A. a severe drought
   B. an intestinal parasite
   C. a fatal virus
   D. severe overcrowding

Use the photo below to answer questions 10 and 11.

10. Why is the life span of this finch with an eye disease most likely reduced?
    A. The bird cannot mate.
    B. The bird cannot find food or water.
    C. The bird spreads the disease to others.
    D. The bird cannot survive a temperature change.
11. Which is a possible reason for the relatively quick spread of the shown disease?
    A. an abiotic factor
    B. a decreased food supply
    C. increased population density
    D. increased immunity
12. What is the dispersion pattern of herding animals, birds that flock together, and fish that form schools?
    A. clumped **C.** uniform
    B. random **D.** unpredictable

Constructed Response

13. **Short Answer** Female Atlantic right whales can reproduce at ten years of age and live more than fifty years. They can produce a calf every three to five years. Assuming that a right whale begins to reproduce at age ten, produces a calf every four years, and gives birth to its last calf at age fifty, how many whales will this female produce in her lifetime?

14. **Short Answer** What is the population density of Canada and the United States if they have a combined area of approximately 12.4 million square kilometers and a combined population of approximately 524 million?

15. **Short Answer** How does the carrying capacity affect *k*-strategists?

16. **Open Ended** Give two examples of how two different density-independent factors can limit a specific population.

17. **Open Ended** Give two examples of how two different density-dependent factors can limit a specific population.

18. **Short Answer** Explain how competition limits a population's growth.

Think Critically

19. **Predict** the shape of a population growth curve for a game park in which a male and a female rhinoceros are released.

Use the photo below to answer question 20.

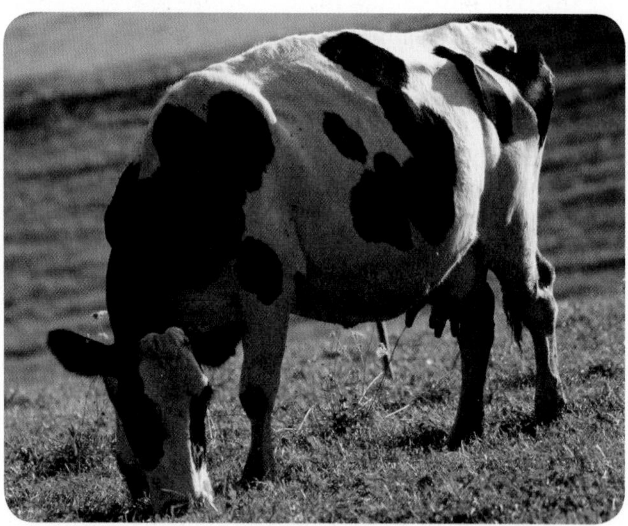

20. **Infer** the reproductive strategy of the animal in the photo. Explain your answer.

21. MAINIDEA Opossums are solitary animals that usually meet in nature only to mate. What is their probable dispersion pattern?

22. Select from the following list the species that are *r*-strategists: minnow, giraffe, human, beetle, bacteria, eagle, and cougar.

SECTION 2

Vocabulary Review

Using the list of vocabulary words from the Study Guide, identify the term described by the scenario.

23. A population has an equal number of births and deaths.

24. Twenty percent of a population is in pre-reproductive years, 50 percent is in the reproductive years, and 30 percent is in the post-reproductive years.

25. The size, density, birth rates, and death rates of a human population are studied.

Understand Main Ideas

Use the graph below of the growth of the human population through history to answer questions 26 and 27.

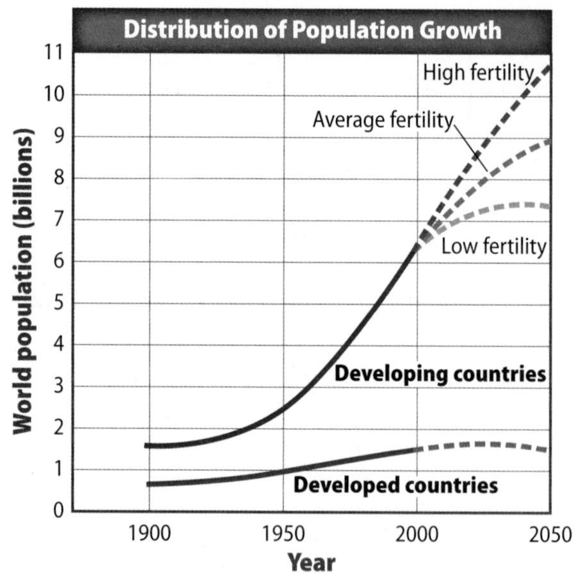

26. What is the projected population of developed countries by 2050?
    - **A.** 1.5 billion
    - **B.** 7.3 billion
    - **C.** 9 billion
    - **D.** 10.5 billion

27. What is the approximate population difference between developing countries that have low fertility rates and developing countries that have high fertility rates in 2050?
    - **A.** 1.5 billion
    - **B.** 1.7 billion
    - **C.** 3.2 billion
    - **D.** 9 billion

28. When did the human population begin to increase exponentially? Use **Figure 11** as a reference.
   A. 2 million years ago
   B. 6500 B.C.
   C. 1800 B.C.
   D. 1500 A.D.

29. Japan had a birthrate of eight and a death rate of nine in 2008. What was the PGR?
   A. 0.01 percent
   B. 1 percent
   C. −1 percent
   D. −10 percent

30. Georgia, a country in western Asia, had a birthrate of 11 and a death rate of 10 in 2008. What was the PGR of Georgia in that year?
   A. 1 percent
   B. 0.11 percent
   C. 1.1 percent
   D. 11 percent

Constructed Response

31. **Open Ended** Do you think the birthrate or the death rate is more important to human populations? Explain your answer.

32. **THEME FOCUS** Why might a population continue to grow when the number of births equals deaths?

33. **MAINIDEA** Study **Figure 11** and identify which phase of growth occurred between the Old Stone Age and the Middle Ages.

Think Critically

34. **Hypothesize** the shape of the age diagram for Switzerland, a developed country in Europe.

Use the graph below to answer question 35.

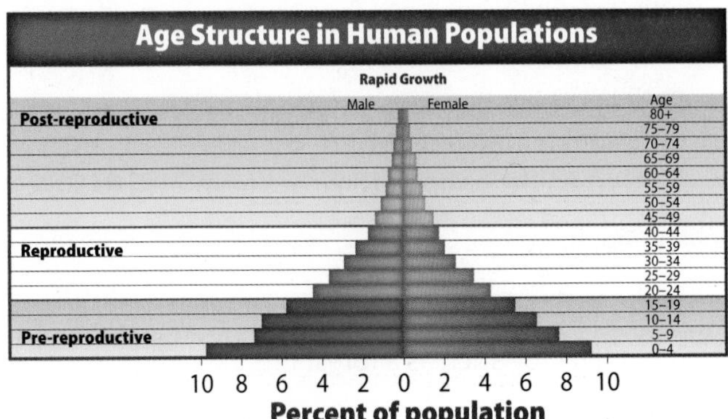

35. **Describe** the advantages and disadvantages of a population that has this type of age structure.

Summative Assessment

36. **BIGIDEA** Create an imaginary community in which a particular population has been growing exponentially fast. What factors can you adjust to create a thriving, but steady, community?

37. **WRITING IN ▶ Biology** Write a letter to the editor of your student newspaper expressing your views on the effect of human activities on a population of animals in your area.

DBQ Document-Based Questions

Northern right whales were once abundant in the northwestern Atlantic Ocean. By 1900, their numbers were almost depleted. Today, there are an estimated 300 individuals remaining.

Use the graph below to answer the following questions.

Data obtained from: Fujiwara, M., et al. 2001. Demography of the endangered North Atlantic right whale. *Nature* 414: 537–540.

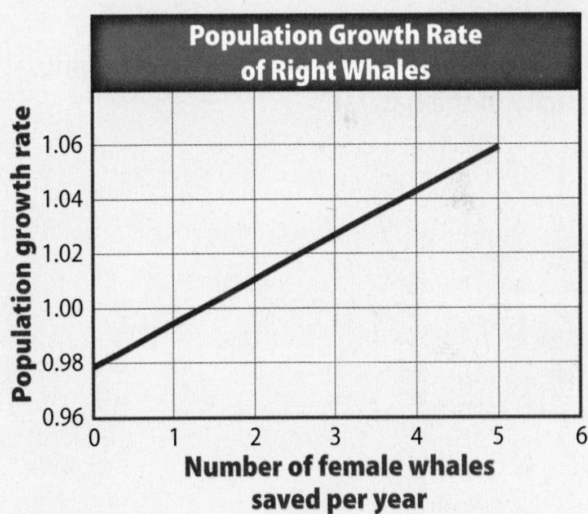

38. Predict the population growth rate if six female North Atlantic right whales were saved each year.

39. Saving females isn't the only factor to take into consideration when trying to restore the whale population. Write a hypothetical plan of action that takes into account two other factors that you think might help.

CUMULATIVE

MULTIPLE CHOICE

1 Which is the main benefit of scientific debate for scientists?

A challenging accepted theories

B creating controversy

C gaining research funding

D publishing results

Use the graph below to answer question 2.

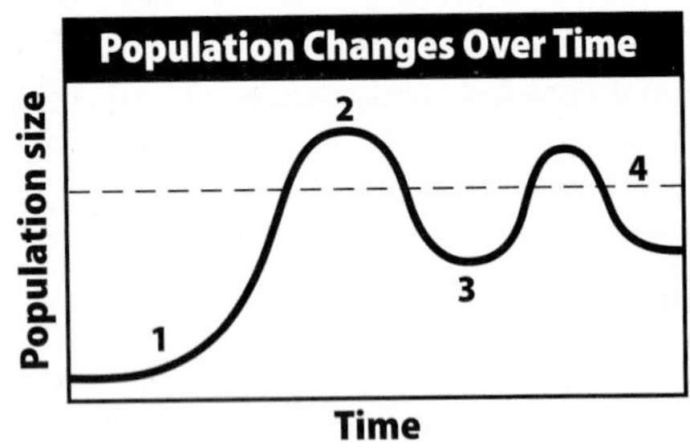

2 Which part of the graph indicates the carrying capacity of the habitat?

A 1

B 2

C 3

D 4

3 Which statement describes the first changes in a forest that would follow a forest fire?

A A climax community is established.

B New plants grow from seeds that the wind carries to the area.

C New soil forms.

D Pioneer species are established.

SHORT ANSWER

Use this graph to answer questions 4 and 5.

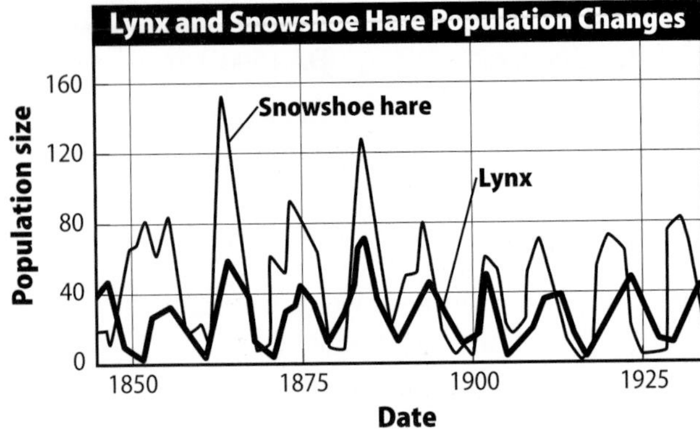

4 Assess what happened to the hare population after a sharp rise in the lynx population.

5 Lynxes hunt hares for food. Predict what would happen to the lynx population if a disease killed all of the hares.

6 Using your knowledge of current events or history, give an example of when ignorance about biology had a harmful effect on people.

7 Compare and contrast how density-dependent and density-independent factors regulate the growth of populations.

8 Describe what happens to organisms whose optimum temperature zone is between 21°C and 32°C when the temperature rises from 21°C to 50°C.

9 Give some examples of the ways that an environmental factor, such as a forest fire, can affect a population.

10 Explain how a population relates to an ecosystem.

EXTENDED RESPONSE

Use these graphs to answer question 11.

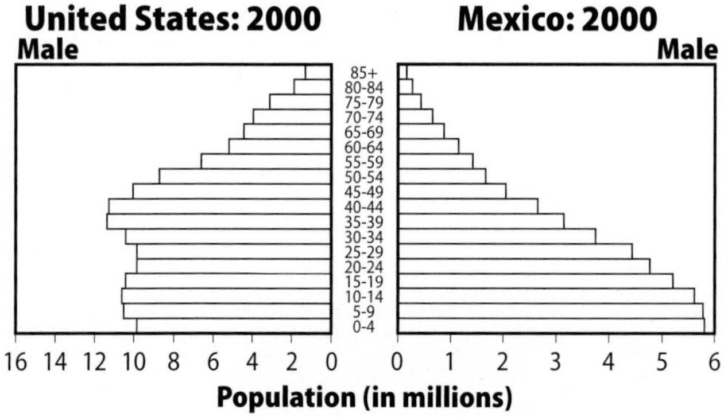

11 State what you think is the most significant area of difference between the two populations and justify your reasoning.

12 Many vertebrates that live in temperate forests hibernate in the winter. How do you think this adaptation helps with survival in this biome?

ESSAY QUESTION

Author Carrie P. Snow once said, "Technology… is a queer thing. It brings you great gifts with one hand, and it stabs you in the back with the other."
C. P. Snow, New York Times, 15 March 1971

Using the information contained in the quotation above, answer the following question in essay format.

13 You are in charge of organizing a debate about whether technology is good or bad. Using your prior knowledge, choose a position and write a summary of the key points you would debate.

TEST PRACTICE

Use this graph to answer question 14.

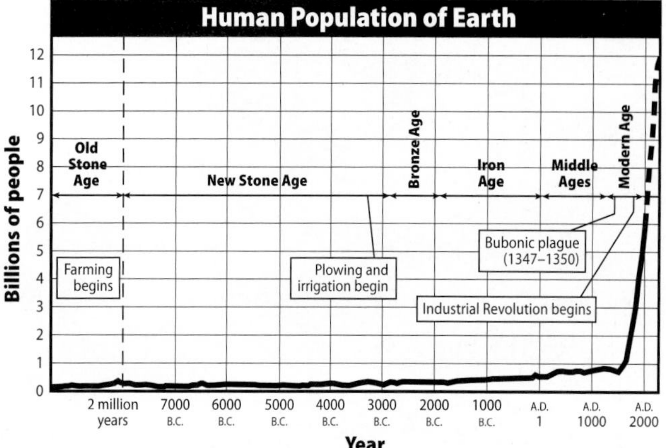

14 Which event appears to coincide with a gradual increase in human population?

A bubonic plague

B farming

C Industrial Revolution

D plowing and irrigation

15 Suppose an organism is host to a parasitic tapeworm. Which would be beneficial to the tapeworm?

A death of the host from disease caused by the tapeworm

B absorbing enough nutrients to sustain the tapeworm without harming the host

C treatment of the host with antitapeworm drugs

D weakening of the host by the tapeworm

NEED EXTRA HELP?															
If You Missed Question . . .	1	2	3	4	5	6	7	8	9	10	11	12	13	14	15
Review Section . . .	1.2	4.1	3.1	4.4	4.1	1.1	4.1	3.2	4.1	2.1	4.2	3.2	1.2	4.2	2.1

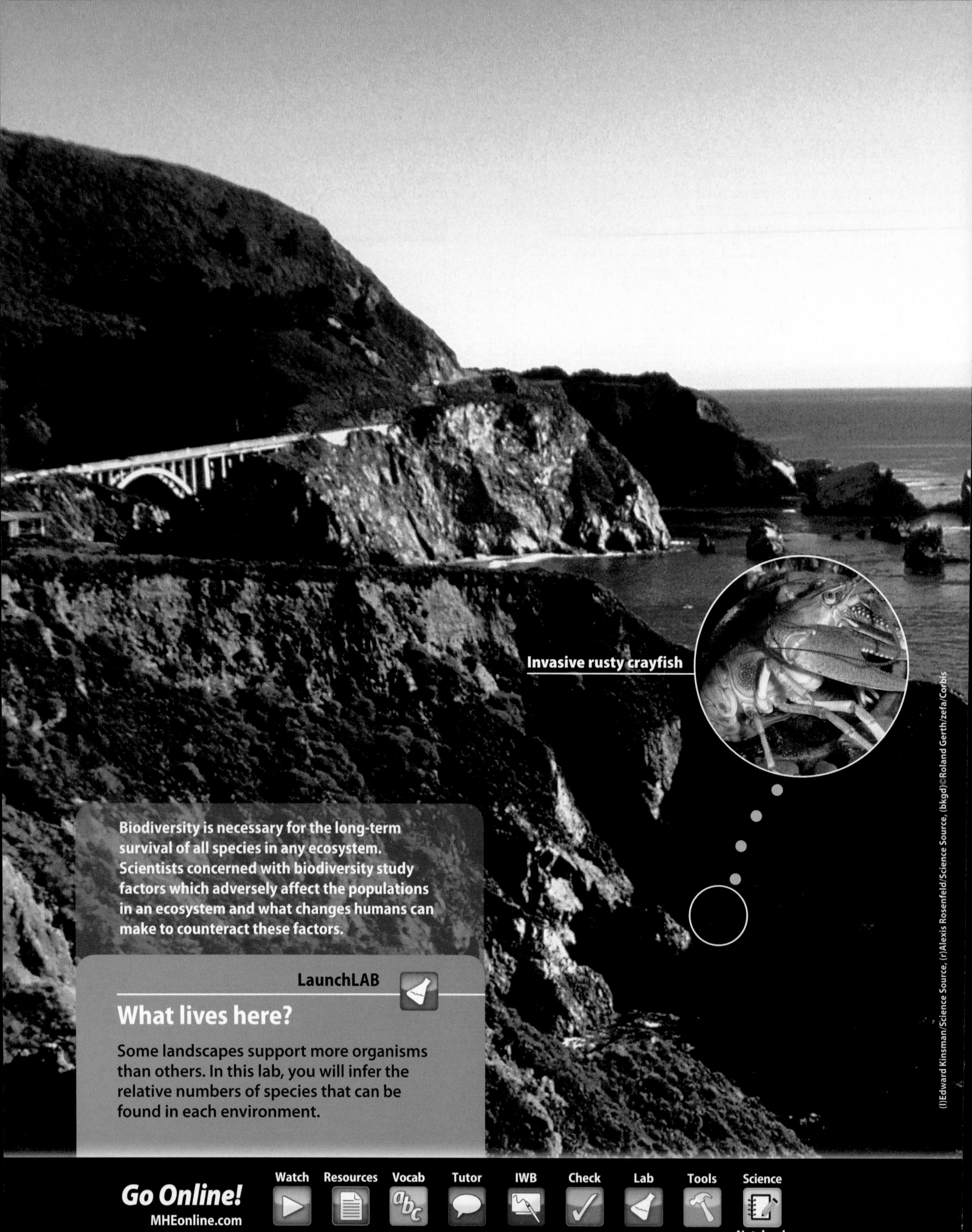

Biodiversity is necessary for the long-term survival of all species in any ecosystem. Scientists concerned with biodiversity study factors which adversely affect the populations in an ecosystem and what changes humans can make to counteract these factors.

LaunchLAB

What lives here?

Some landscapes support more organisms than others. In this lab, you will infer the relative numbers of species that can be found in each environment.

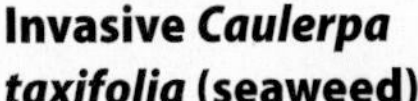

Invasive *Caulerpa taxifolia* (seaweed)

CHAPTER 5

Biodiversity and Conservation

1 Biodiversity

1.1.3b, 1.3.5b, 4.3.1g, 4.3.1h, 4.6.2b, 4.7.3b

2 Threats to Biodiversity

1.3.5b, 4.1.1a, 4.1.1b, 4.1.1c, 4.1.1d, 4.1.1e, 4.1.1f, 4.3.1l, 4.5.3a, 4.6.1d, 4.6.1e, 4.6.2a, 4.6.1f, 4.6.3a, 4.6.3c, 4.7.1c, 4.7.2a, 4.7.2b, 4.7.3b, ¥a, ¥e, ¥o

3 Conserving Biodiversity

1.1.1c, 4.1.1b, 4.1.1c, 4.1.1d, 4.1.1e, 4.1.1f, 4.3.1l, 4.5.3a, 4.6.1d, 4.6.1e, 4.6.1f, 4.6.2a, 4.6.3a, 4.6.3c, 4.7.1a, 4.7.1b, 4.7.1c, 4.7.2a, 4.7.2b, 4.7.2c, 4.7.3b

THEMEFOCUS

Cause and effect Sudden change in an ecosystem, such as a forest fire, can decrease biodiversity.

BIGIDEA

Community and ecosystem homeostasis depend on a complex set of interactions among biologically diverse individuals.

Biodiversity

Make a three-tab foldable using the labels shown. Use it to organize your notes about biodiversity.

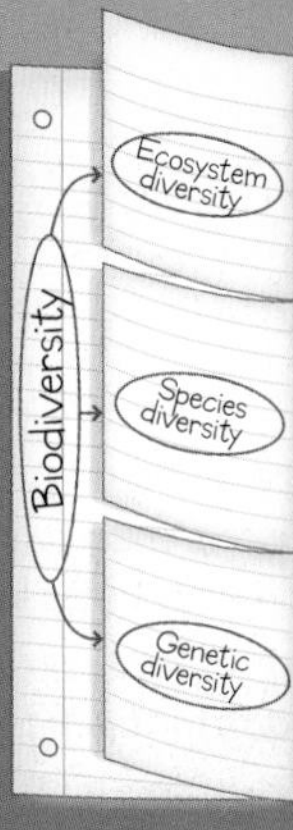

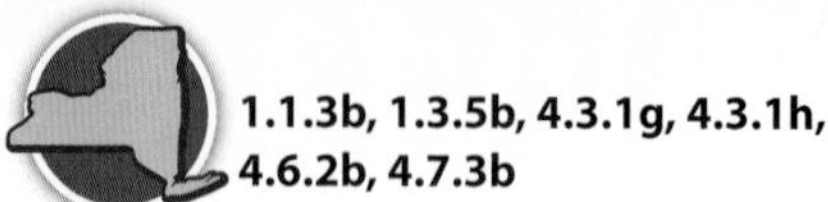

1 Biodiversity

1.1.3b, 1.3.5b, 4.3.1g, 4.3.1h, 4.6.2b, 4.7.3b

MAINIDEA

Biodiversity maintains a healthy biosphere and provides direct and indirect value to humans.

Essential Questions

- What are three types of biodiversity?
- Why is biodiversity important?
- What are the direct and indirect values of biodiversity?

BIOLOGY 4U

Stop for a moment and consider the effect of all the jackrabbits in a food web dying suddenly. What would happen to the other members of the food web? Is the disappearance of one species from Earth important? Will another species fill its niche?

Review Vocabulary

gene: functional unit that controls the expression of inherited traits and is passed from generation to generation

New Vocabulary

extinction
biodiversity
genetic diversity
species diversity
ecosystem diversity

Multilingual eGlossary

What is biodiversity?

The loss of an entire species in a food web is not an imaginary situation. Entire species permanently disappear from the biosphere when the last member of the species dies in a process called **extinction.** As species become extinct, the variety of species in the biosphere decreases, which decreases the health of the biosphere. **Biodiversity** is the variety of life in an area that is determined by the number of different species in that area. Biodiversity increases the stability of an ecosystem and contributes to the health of the biosphere. There are three types of biodiversity to consider: genetic diversity, species diversity, and ecosystem diversity.

Genetic diversity The variety of genes or inheritable characteristics that are present in a population comprises its **genetic diversity. Figure 1** shows characteristics that are shared by Asian ladybird beetles, such as general body structure. The variety of colors demonstrates a form of genetic diversity. The beetles have other characteristics that differ, but they are not as apparent as their color. These characteristics might include resistance to a particular disease, the ability to recover from a disease, or the ability to obtain nutrients from a new food source should the old food source disappear. The beetles with these characteristics are more likely to survive and reproduce than beetles without these characteristics.

Genetic diversity within interbreeding populations increases the chances that some individuals will survive during changing environmental conditions or during an outbreak of disease.

PSU Entomology/Science Source

Figure 1 These Asian ladybird beetles, *Harmonia axyridis*, demonstrate some visible genetic diversity because of their different colors.
***Suggest** some other characteristics that might vary among the beetles.*

■ **Figure 2** Many species gather at this watering hole, making it a habitat rich in species diversity.

Species diversity The number of different species and the relative abundance of each species in a biological community is called **species diversity.** As you look at **Figure 2,** notice how many different species of organisms are in this one area. This habitat represents an area with a high level of species diversity because there are so many species present in one location. Species diversity, however, is not evenly distributed over the biosphere. As you move geographically from the polar regions to the equator, species diversity increases. For example, **Figure 3** shows the number of bird species from Alaska to Central America. Use the color key to see how diversity changes as you move toward the equator.

FOLDABLES®
Incorporate information from this section into your Foldable.

GET IT? **Compare and contrast** genetic and species diversity.

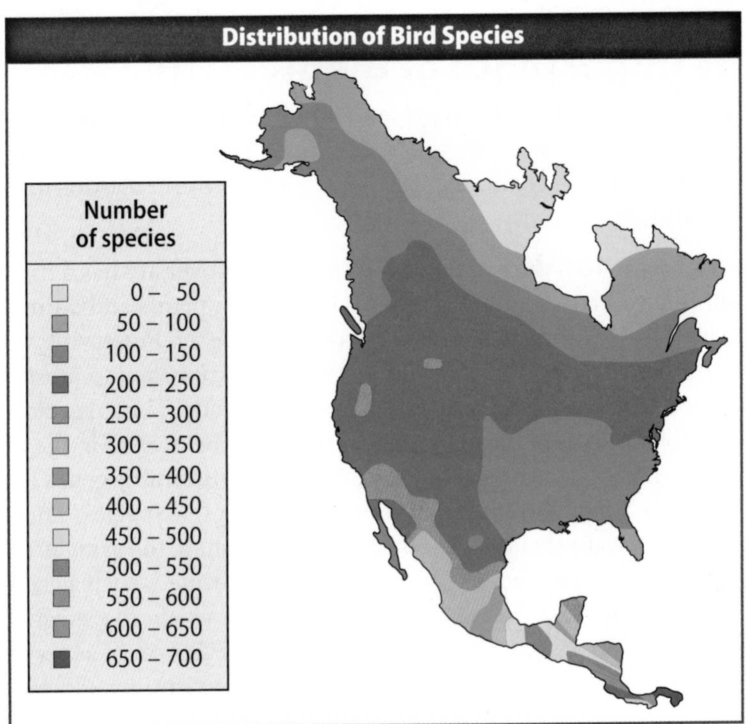

■ **Figure 3** This map shows the distribution of bird species in North and Central America. As you move toward the tropics, biodiversity increases.
Estimate ***the number of bird species where you live.***

Dall Sheep, *Ovis dalli*, in Alaska

Tropical birds in Peru

■ **Figure 4** The biosphere contains many ecosystems with diverse abiotic factors that support a variety of organisms.

Ecosystem diversity The variety of ecosystems that are present in the biosphere is called **ecosystem diversity.** An ecosystem is made up of interacting populations and the abiotic factors that support them. The interactions of organisms affect the development of stable ecosystems. Different locations around the world have different abiotic factors that support different types of life. For example, an ecosystem in Alaska has a set of abiotic factors that supports Dall sheep, which are shown in **Figure 4.** An ecosystem in South America has a different set of abiotic factors that supports tropical birds, also shown in **Figure 4.** Like these ecosystems, most of the ecosystems on Earth support a diverse collection of organisms.

VOCABULARY

ACADEMIC VOCABULARY

Diverse

made of different qualities

The colors and shapes of flowers are very diverse.

GET IT? **Explain** why ecosystem diversity results in species diversity in a healthy biosphere.

The Importance of Biodiversity

There are several reasons to preserve biodiversity. Many humans work to preserve and protect the species on Earth for future generations. In addition, there are economic, aesthetic, and scientific reasons for preserving biodiversity.

Direct economic value Maintaining biodiversity has a direct economic value to humans. Humans depend on plants and animals to provide food, clothing, energy, medicine, and shelter. Preserving species that are used directly is important, but it also is important to preserve the genetic diversity in species that are not used directly. Those species serve as possible sources of desirable genes that might be needed in the future.

The reason there might be a future need for desirable genes is that most of the world's food crops come from just a few species. These plants have relatively little genetic diversity and share the same problems that all species share when genetic diversity is limited, such as lacking resistance to disease. In many cases, close relatives of crop species still grow wild in their native habitat. These wild species serve as reservoirs of desirable genetic traits that might be needed to improve domestic crop species.

Teosinte plant

Commercial corn plant

■ **Figure 5** The teosinte plant contains genes that are resistant to several viral diseases that affect commercial corn plants. These genes have been used to produce virus-resistant commercial corn varieties.

The distant relative of corn, teosinte, shown in **Figure 5,** is resistant to the viral diseases that damage commercial corn crops. Using this wild species, plant pathologists developed disease-resistant corn varieties. If this wild species had not been available, this genetic diversity would have been lost, and the ability to develop disease-resistant corn varieties would also have been lost.

In addition, biologists are beginning to learn how to transfer genes that control inherited characteristics from one species to the other. This process is sometimes referred to as genetic engineering. Crops have been produced that are resistant to some insects, that have increased nutritional value, and that are more resistant to spoilage. Most wild species of plants and animals have not been evaluated for useful genetic traits. The opportunity to benefit from these genes is lost forever if wild species of plants and animals become extinct. This increases the importance of species that currently have no perceived economic value because their economic value might increase in the future.

GET IT? **Explain** why preserving biodiversity is important for the human food supply.

Connection to Health Many of the medicines that are used today are derived from plants or other organisms. You probably know that penicillin, a powerful antibiotic discovered in 1928 by Alexander Fleming, is derived from bread mold. Ancient Greeks, Native Americans, and others extracted salicin, a painkiller, from the willow tree. Today, a version of this drug is synthesized in laboratories and is known as aspirin. **Figure 6** shows a Madagascar periwinkle flower, which recently was found to yield an extract that is useful in treating some forms of leukemia. This extract has been used to develop drugs that have increased the survival rate for some leukemia patients from 20 percent to more than 95 percent.

Scientists continue to find new extracts from plants and other organisms that help in the treatment of human diseases. However, many species of organisms are yet to be identified, especially in remote regions of Earth, so their ability to provide extracts or useful genes is unknown.

■ **Figure 6** Medicines developed from an extract from Madagascar periwinkle, *Catharanthus roseus*, are used to treat forms of leukemia.

Summarize ***Why is it important to maintain biodiversity for medical reasons?***

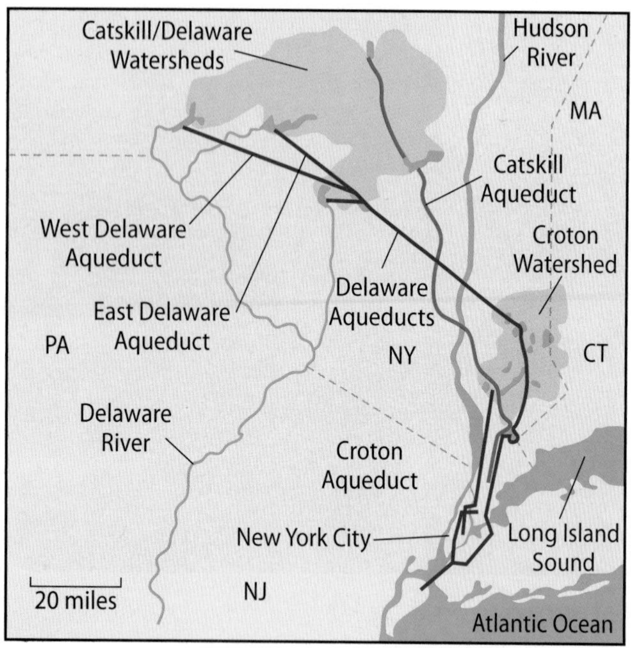

■ **Figure 7** New York City's drinking water is supplied by the Catskill and Delaware watersheds.

Infer ***What types of human activities could affect a watershed and decrease its water quality?***

Indirect economic value A healthy biosphere provides many services to humans and other organisms that live on Earth. For example, green plants provide oxygen to the atmosphere and remove carbon dioxide. Natural processes provide drinking water that is safe for human use. Substances are cycled through living organisms and nonliving processes, providing nutrients for all living organisms. As you will soon learn, healthy ecosystems provide protection against floods and drought, generate and preserve fertile soils, detoxify and decompose wastes, and regulate local climates.

It is difficult to attach an economic value to the services that a healthy biosphere provides. However, some scientists and economists have attempted to do just that. In the 1990s, New York City was faced with the decision of how to improve the quality of its drinking water. A large percentage of New York City's drinking water was supplied by watersheds, as shown in **Figure 7.** Watersheds are land areas where the water on them or the water underneath them drains to the same place. The Catskill and Delaware watersheds did not meet clean water standards and no longer could supply quality drinking water to the city.

The city was faced with two choices: build a new water filtration system for more than $6 billion or preserve and clean up the watersheds for approximately 1.5 billion dollars. The economic decision was clear in this case. A healthy ecosystem was less expensive to maintain than using technology to perform the same services.

MiniLAB 1

Investigate Threats to Biodiversity

What are the threats to natural habitats in your local area? Investigate these threats and brainstorm possible remedies with which you can educate others.

Procedure

1. Read and complete the lab safety form.
2. With your lab group, choose one factor that is threatening the biodiversity in your community and study how it has affected the climax community.
3. Brainstorm ways that this threat could be reversed.
4. Organize this information about threats and possible solutions with your classmates.

Analysis

1. **Evaluate** What are the most important pieces of information that the public needs to know about this threat?
2. **Infer** Imagine you have implemented one plan to reverse a threat you studied. Now it is 100 years later. What does the ecosystem look like? What changes have occurred? What species are there now?

■ **Figure 8** Emerald Bay in Lake Tahoe is an environment with many aesthetic qualities. Lake Tahoe was once pristine, but urbanization, increased runoff, and other forms of pollution have harmed the environment's health. Many groups are working together to keep Lake Tahoe healthy and beautiful.

This example shows that nature can provide services, such as water that is safe for human consumption, at less expense than using technology to provide the same service. Some scientists think the natural way should be the first choice for providing these services. Research indicates that when healthy ecosystems are preserved, the services the ecosystems provide will continue to be less expensive than performing the same services with technology.

Aesthetic and scientific values Two additional considerations for maintaining biodiversity and healthy ecosystems are the aesthetic and scientific values that they provide. It is difficult to attach a value to something that is beautiful, such as the ecosystem shown in **Figure 8,** or something that is interesting to study. However, scientists are finding ways to show the value in protecting and studying the environment.

REVIEW IT! Biodiversity

Section Summary

- Biodiversity is important to the health of the biosphere.
- There are three types of biodiversity: genetic, species, and ecosystem.
- Biodiversity has aesthetic and scientific values, and direct and indirect economic value.
- It is important to maintain biodiversity to preserve the reservoir of genes that might be needed in the future.
- Healthy ecosystems can provide some services at a lesser expense than the use of technology.

Self Check

Understand Main Ideas

1. MAINIDEA **Explain** why biodiversity is important to the biosphere.
2. **Summarize** the three types of biodiversity.
3. **Generalize** why maintaining biodiversity has a direct economic value to humans.
4. **Differentiate** between the direct and indirect economic value of biodiversity.
5. **Evaluate and discuss** the importance of maintaining biodiversity for future medical needs.

Think Critically

6. **Design a course of action** for the development of a building project in your community, such as a shopping mall, housing development, city park, or highway, that provides for the maintenance of biodiversity in the plan.

WRITING IN ▶ Biology

7. Write a short report explaining the desirability of maintaining genetic diversity in domesticated animals, such as dogs, cats, pigs, cattle, and chickens. Include the advantages and disadvantages in your report.

Adam Jones/Science Source

2 Threats to Biodiversity

1.3.5b, 4.1.1a, 4.1.1b, 4.1.1c, 4.1.1d, 4.1.1e, 4.1.1f, 4.3.1l, 4.5.3a, 4.6.1d, 4.6.1e, 4.6.2a, 4.6.1f, 4.6.3a, 4.6.3c, 4.7.1c, 4.7.2a, 4.7.2b, 4.7.3b, ¥a, ¥e, ¥o

MAINIDEA

Some human activities reduce biodiversity in ecosystems, and current evidence suggests that reduced biodiversity might have serious long-term effects on the biosphere.

Essential Questions

- What are the threats to biodiversity?
- How is the current extinction rate different from the background extinction rate?
- How can the decline of a single species affect an entire ecosystem?

BIOLOGY 4U

Have you ever built a structure with blocks and then tried to remove individual blocks without causing the entire structure to collapse? Similarly, if you remove one species from a food web, the food web can collapse.

Review Vocabulary

food web: a model representing the many interconnected food chains and pathways in which energy and matter flow through a group of organisms

New Vocabulary

background extinction
mass extinction
natural resource
overexploitation
habitat fragmentation
edge effect
biological magnification
eutrophication
introduced species

Multilingual eGlossary

Extinction Rates

Many species have become extinct, and paleontologists study fossils of those extinct species. The gradual process of species becoming extinct is known as **background extinction.** Stable ecosystems can be changed by the activity of other organisms, climate changes, or natural disasters. This natural process of extinction is not what concerns scientists. Instead, many worry about a recent increase in the rate of extinction. Some scientists predict that between one-third and two-thirds of all plant and animal species will become extinct during the second half of this century. Most of these extinctions will occur near the equator.

Some scientists estimate that the current rate of extinction is about 1000 times the normal background extinction rate. These scientists think that we are witnessing a period of mass extinction. **Mass extinction** is an event in which a large percentage of all living species become extinct in a relatively short period of time. The last mass extinction occurred about 65 million years ago, as illustrated in **Table 1,** when the last of the surviving dinosaurs became extinct.

Table 1 Five Most Recent Mass Extinctions — Interactive Table

	Ordovician Period	Devonian Period	Permian Period	Triassic Period	Cretaceous Period
Time	about 444 million years ago	about 360 million years ago	about 251 million years ago	about 200 million years ago	about 65 million years ago
Example	Graptolites	*Dinichthys*	Trilobite	*Cynognathus*	Ammonite

Table 2 Estimated Number of Extinctions Since 1600

Interactive Table

Group	Mainland	Island	Ocean	Total	Approximate Number of Known Species	Percent of Group Extinct
Mammals	30	51	4	85	4000	2.1
Birds	21	92	0	113	9000	1.3
Reptiles	1	20	0	21	6300	0.3
Amphibians*	2	0	0	2	4200	0.05
Fish	22	1	0	23	19,100	0.1
Invertebrates	49	48	1	98	1,000,000+	0.01
Flowering plants	245	139	0	384	250,000	0.2

*An alarming decrease of amphibian populations has occurred since the mid-1970s, and many species might be on the verge of extinction.

Connection to History The accelerated loss of species began several centuries ago. **Table 2** shows the estimated number of extinctions that have occurred by group since 1600. Many of the species' extinctions in the past have occurred on islands. For example, 60 percent of the mammals that have become extinct in the past 500 years lived on islands, and 81 percent of bird extinctions occurred on islands.

Species on islands are particularly vulnerable to extinction because of several factors. Many of these species evolved without the presence of natural predators. As a result, when a predator, such as a dog, cat, rat, or human, is introduced to the population, the native animals do not have the ability or skills to escape. When a nonnative species is introduced to a new population, it can be a carrier of a disease to which the native population has no resistance. The native population often dies off as a result. In addition, islands typically have relatively small population sizes and individual animals rarely travel between islands, both of which increases the vulnerability of island species to extinction.

Vocabulary

Word origin

Native

from the Latin word *nativus,* meaning to be born

GET IT? **Explain** why organisms found on islands are more vulnerable to extinction than other organisms.

Factors That Threaten Biodiversity

Scientists point out that today's high rate of extinction differs from past mass extinctions. The current high rate of extinction is a result of the activities of a single species—*Homo sapiens.* After a mass extinction in the past, new species evolved and biodiversity recovered after several million years. This time, the recovery might be different. Humans are changing conditions on Earth faster than new traits can evolve in some species to cope with the new conditions. Evolving species might not have the natural resources they need. **Natural resources** are all materials and organisms found in the biosphere, including minerals, fossil fuels, nuclear fuels, plants, animals, soil, clean water, clean air, and solar energy.

■ **Figure 9** The ocelot and all species of rhinos, including the white rhinoceros, are in danger of becoming extinct, due in part to overexploitation.

Ocelot

White rhinoceros

Overexploitation One of the factors that is increasing the current rate of extinction is the **overexploitation,** or excessive use, of species that have economic value. For example, the great herds of bison that once roamed the central plains of North America were hunted to the brink of extinction because their meat and hides could be sold commercially and because they were hunted for sport. At one time, it is estimated that there were 50 million bison. By 1889, there were less than 1000 bison left.

Passenger pigeons are another example of a species that has been overexploited. At one time, there were huge flocks of these birds that would darken the skies of North America during their migration. Unfortunately, they were overhunted and forced from their habitats. By the early 1900s, they had become extinct.

The ocelot, shown in **Figure 9,** is in danger of becoming extinct. The increasing loss of their habitat and the commercial value of their fur are reasons for their declining numbers. The white rhinoceros, also shown in **Figure 9,** is one of five species of rhinos, all of which are in danger of becoming extinct. They are hunted and killed for their horns, which are then sold for medicinal purposes. Historically, overexploitation was the primary cause of species extinction. However, the number one cause of species extinction today is the loss or destruction of habitat.

GET IT? **Explain** the term overexploitation as it relates to species extinction.

■ **Figure 10** Cleared land often is used for agricultural crops or as grazing land for livestock. Planting large expanses of crops reduces the biodiversity of the area.

Natural tropical rain forest

Cleared tropical rain forest

Habitat loss There are several ways that species can lose their habitats. If a habitat is destroyed or disrupted, the native species might have to relocate or they will die. For example, humans are clearing areas of tropical rain forests and are replacing the native plants with agricultural crops or grazing land.

Destruction of habitat The clearing of tropical rain forests, like what is shown in **Figure 10,** has a direct impact on global biodiversity. As mentioned earlier, the tropical latitudes contain much of the world's biodiversity in their native populations. In fact, estimates show that more than half of all species on Earth live in the tropical rain forests. The removal of so much of the natural forest will cause many species on Earth to become extinct as a result of habitat loss.

■ **Figure 11** A declining population of one species can affect an entire ecosystem. When the number of harbor seals and sea lions declined, killer whales ate more sea otters. The decline in sea otter population led to an increase in sea urchins, which eat kelp. This led to the ultimate decline in kelp forests.

Disruption of habitat Some habitats might not be destroyed, but they can be disrupted. For example, off the coast of Alaska, a chain of events occurred in the 1970s that demonstrates how the declining numbers of one member of a food web can affect the other members. As you can see from the chain of events shown in **Figure 11,** the decline of one species can affect an entire ecosystem. When one species plays such a large role in an ecosystem, that species is called a keystone species. A decline in various fish populations, possibly due to overfishing, has led to a decline in sea lion and harbor seal populations. Some scientists hypothesize that global warming also played a role in the decline. This started a chain reaction within the marine ecosystem that affected many species.

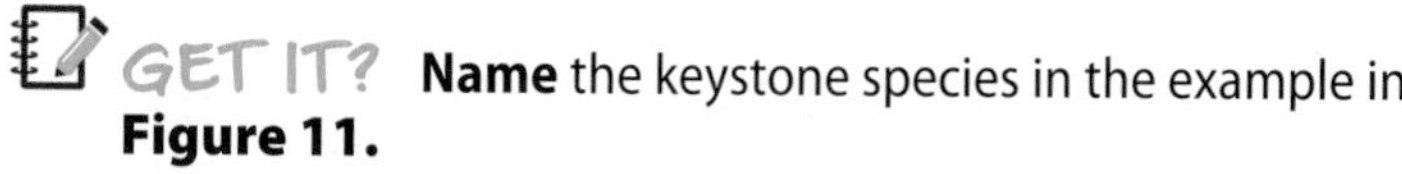
GET IT? **Name** the keystone species in the example in **Figure 11.**

Fragmentation of habitat The separation of an ecosystem into small pieces of land is called **habitat fragmentation.** Populations often stay within the confines of the small parcel because they are unable or unwilling to cross the human-made barriers. This causes several problems for the survival of various species.

First, the smaller the parcel of land, the fewer species it can support. Second, fragmentation reduces the opportunities for individuals in one area to reproduce with individuals from another area. For this reason, genetic diversity often decreases over time in habitat fragments. Smaller, separated, and less genetically diverse populations are less able to resist disease or respond to changing environmental conditions.

■ **Figure 12** The smaller the habitat size, the greater percentage of the habitat that is subject to edge effects.

Personal Tutor

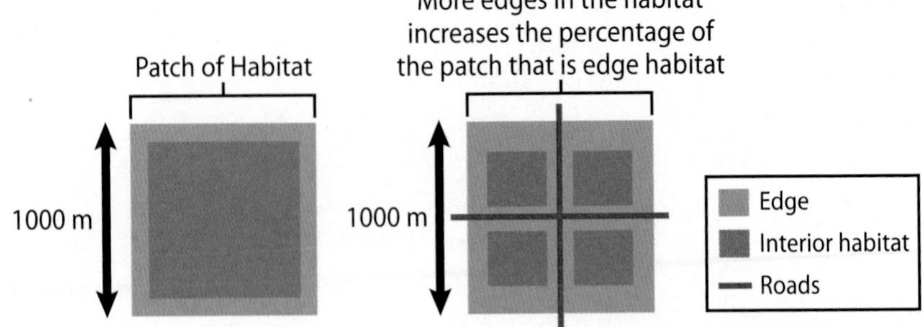

Third, carving the large ecosystem into small parcels increases the number of edges, creating edge effects, as illustrated in **Figure 12.** **Edge effects** are different environmental conditions that occur along the boundaries of an ecosystem. For example, edges of a forest near a road have different abiotic factors, such as temperature, wind, and humidity, than does the interior of a forest. Typically, the temperature and wind will be higher and the humidity lower on the edges in a tropical forest. Species that thrive deep in the dense forest might perish on the edges of the ecosystem. Predators and parasites also thrive on the boundaries of ecosystems, which makes the species in these areas more vulnerable to attack. Edge effects do not always create a disadvantage for all species. Some species find these conditions favorable, and they thrive.

GET IT? **Explain** how a larger percentage of land is affected by edge effects when the piece of land is fragmented.

■ **Figure 13** The concentration of toxic substances increases as the trophic level in a food chain increases.

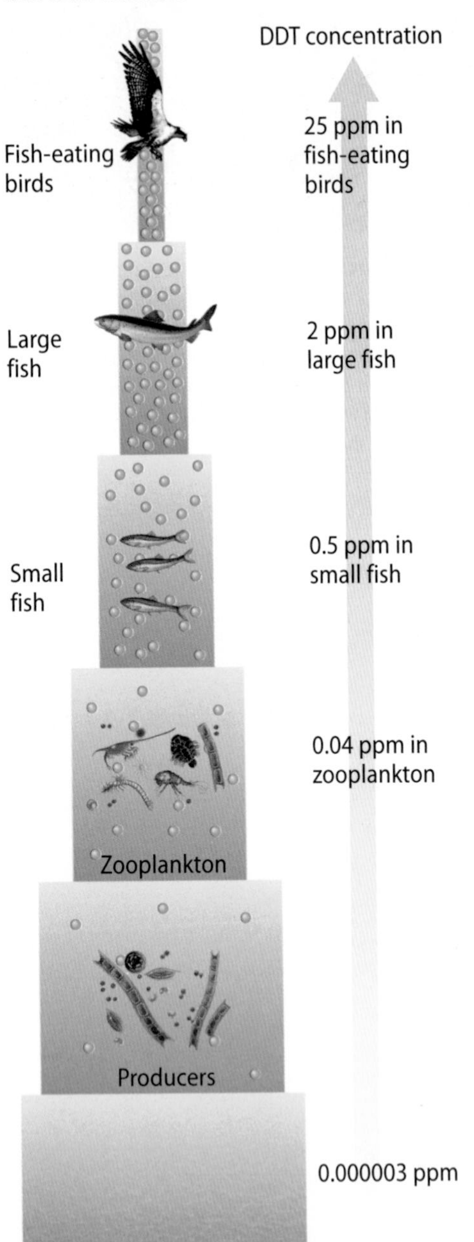

Pollution Pollution and atmospheric changes threaten biodiversity and global stability. Pollution changes the composition of air, soil, and water. There are many types of pollution. Substances—including many human-made chemicals that are not found in nature—are released into the environment. Pesticides, such as DDT (dichloro-diphenyl-trichloroethane), and industrial chemicals, such as PCBs (polychlorinated biphenyls), are examples of substances that are found in food webs. These substances are ingested by organisms when they drink water or eat other organisms that contain the toxic substances. Some substances are metabolized by an organism and excreted with other waste products. However, other substances, such as DDT and PCBs, accumulate in the tissues of organisms.

Carnivores at the higher trophic levels seem to be most affected by the accumulation of toxic substances because of a process called biological magnification. **Biological magnification** is the increasing concentration of toxic substances in organisms as trophic levels increase in a food chain or food web, as shown in **Figure 13.** The concentration of a toxic substance is relatively low when it enters the food web. The concentration of a toxic substance in individual organisms increases as it spreads to higher trophic levels.

Current research implies that these substances might disrupt normal processes in some organisms. For example, DDT might have played a role in the near extinction of the American bald eagle and the peregrine falcon. DDT is a pesticide that was used from the 1940s to the 1970s to control crop-eating and disease-carrying insects. DDT proved to be a highly effective pesticide, but evidence suggested that it caused the eggshells of fish-eating birds to be fragile and thin, which led to the death of the developing birds. Once these toxic effects were discovered, the use of DDT was banned in some parts of the world.

Acid precipitation Another pollutant that affects biodiversity is acid precipitation. When fossil fuels are burned, sulfur dioxide is released into the atmosphere. In addition, the burning of fossil fuels in automobile engines releases nitrogen oxides into the atmosphere. These compounds react with water and other substances in the air to form sulfuric acid and nitric acid. These acids eventually fall to the surface of Earth in rain, sleet, snow, or fog. Acid precipitation removes calcium, potassium, and other nutrients from the soil, depriving plants of these nutrients. It damages plant tissues and slows their growth, as shown in **Figure 14.** Sometimes, the acid concentration is so high in lakes, rivers, and streams that fish and other organisms die, also as shown in **Figure 14.**

Eutrophication Another form of water pollution, called eutrophication, destroys underwater habitats for fish and other species. **Eutrophication** (yoo troh fih KAY shun) occurs when fertilizers, animal waste, sewage, or other substances rich in nitrogen and phosphorus flow into waterways, causing extensive algae growth. The algae use up the oxygen supply during their rapid growth and after their deaths during the decaying process. Other organisms in the water suffocate. In some cases, algae also give off toxins that poison the water supply for other organisms. Eutrophication is a natural process, but human activities often accelerate the rate at which it occurs.

Forest damage

Fish kill

■ **Figure 14** Acid precipitation damages plant tissues and can kill fish if the acid concentration is high.

Infer ***Which areas of the United States would most likely have acid precipitation problems?***

 **Virtual Lab**

MiniLAB 2

Survey Leaf Litter Samples

How do you calculate biodiversity? Scientists calculate the biodiversity in a sample area and use that data to estimate the biodiversity in similar areas.

Procedure

1. Read and complete the lab safety form.
2. In the **leaf-litter sample** that your teacher has provided, count and record the species in a section that is visible to the eye. Look up any unknown species in a **field guide.**
3. Record your observations in a data table.
4. Calculate the index of diversity (IOD), using the following equation (unique species is different species observed; total individuals is the total of every individual observed):

$$\text{IOD} = \frac{\text{\# of unique species} \times \text{\# of samples}}{\text{\# of total individuals}}$$

Analysis

1. **Classify** which observed species are native and nonnative to your area.
2. **Infer** from your survey the effects, if any, that the nonnative species have on the native species. Are these nonnative species invasive? How do you know this?
3. **Hypothesize** whether the IOD has changed in your area over the last 200 years. Explain.

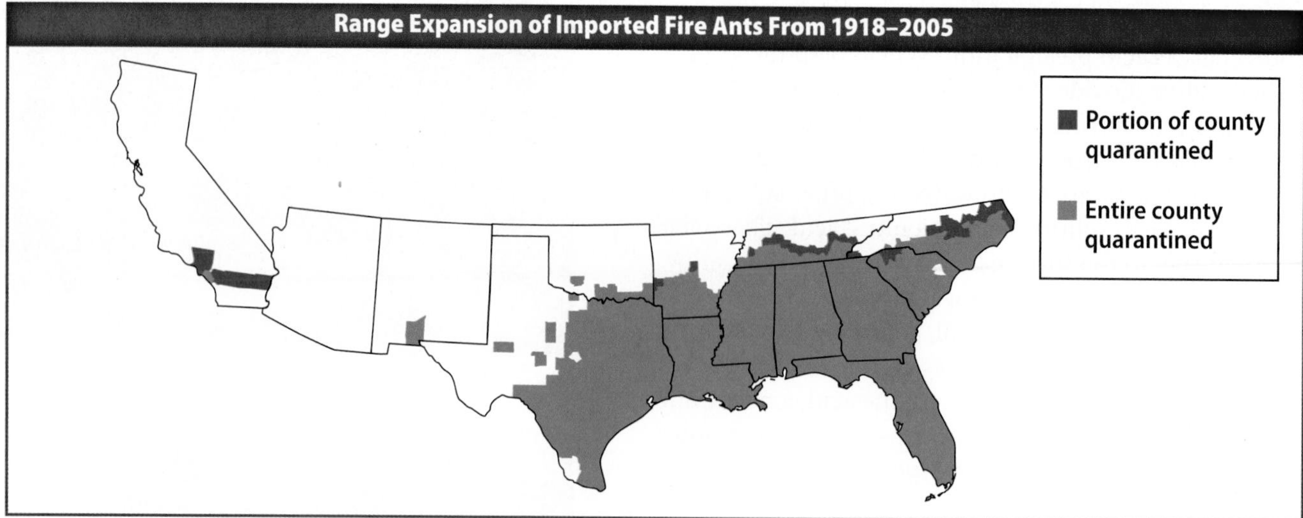

Figure 15 Fire ants were transported accidentally by ship to the port of Mobile in Alabama. The ants spread throughout the southern and southwestern United States.

Launch Lab

Review Based on what you've read about biodiversity, how would you now answer the analysis question?

Introduced species Nonnative species that are either intentionally or unintentionally transported to a new habitat are known as **introduced species.** These species are not a threat to biodiversity in their native habitats. Predators, parasites, and competition between species keep the native ecosystem in balance. However, when these species are introduced into a new area, these controlling factors are not in place. Introduced species often reproduce in large numbers because of a lack of predators and become invasive species in their new habitat.

The imported fire ant is a species that was accidentally introduced to the United States through the port of Mobile, Alabama, in the 1920s by ships from South America. The fire ants spread throughout the southern and southwestern United States, as illustrated in **Figure 15.** Fire ants attack and feed on some wildlife, such as newborn deer and hatching or newly hatched ground-nesting birds.

Introduced species are a worldwide environmental problem. An estimated 40 percent of the extinctions that have occurred since 1750 are a result of introduced species, and billions of dollars are spent every year in an effort to clean up or control the damage caused by introduced species.

REVIEW IT! Threats to Biodiversity

Section Summary

- Some scientists estimate that the current rate of species extinction is abnormally high.
- Species on islands are particularly vulnerable to extinction.
- Historically, overexploitation by humans has led to the extinction of some species.
- Human activities can result in a decrease in biodiversity.

Self Check

Understand Main Ideas

1. MAINIDEA **Explain** three ways that humans threaten biodiversity.
2. **Summarize** what has caused a recent increase in the rate of extinction.
3. **Choose** one of the factors that threatens biodiversity and suggest one way in which biodiversity can be preserved in a real-life scenario.
4. **Summarize** how the overharvesting of a single species, such as baleen whales, can affect an entire ecosystem.

Think Critically

5. **Design** a planned community that preserves biodiversity and accommodates the human population. Work in small groups to accomplish this task.
6. **Survey** your community to identify at least five threats to biodiversity and suggest ways in which biodiversity can be preserved.

USE IT! Science Notebook

3 Conserving Biodiversity

1.1.1c, 4.1.1b, 4.1.1c, 4.1.1d, 4.1.1e, 4.1.1f, 4.3.1l, 4.5.3a, 4.6.1d, 4.6.1e, 4.6.1f, 4.6.2a, 4.6.3a, 4.6.3c, 4.7.1a, 4.7.1b, 4.7.1c, 4.7.2a, 4.7.2b, 4.7.2c, 4.7.3b

MAIN IDEA

People are using many approaches to slow the rate of extinctions and to preserve biodiversity.

Essential Questions

- What are the two classes of natural resources?
- What are the methods used to conserve biodiversity?
- What are two techniques used to restore biodiversity?

BIOLOGY 4 U

Have you ever broken a decorative item and repaired it? You probably carefully searched for all of the pieces and then carefully glued them together again. Repairing a damaged ecosystem is a similar process. Scientists carefully search for all of the pieces of the ecosystem, repair the damages, and secure the location to protect the ecosystem from future damage.

Review Vocabulary

natural resources: materials and organisms found in the biosphere

New Vocabulary

renewable resource
nonrenewable resource
sustainable use
endemic
bioremediation
biological augmentation

Multilingual eGlossary

Natural Resources

The biosphere currently supplies the basic needs for more than six billion humans in the form of natural resources. The human population continues to grow, and the growth is not evenly distributed throughout the world. An increase in human population growth increases the need for natural resources to supply the basic needs of the population.

The consumption rate of natural resources is also not evenly distributed. **Figure 16** shows the consumption of natural resources per person for selected countries. The natural resource consumption rate is much higher for people living in developed countries than for people living in developing countries. As developing countries become more industrialized and the standard of living increases, the rate of natural resource consumption also increases. Because of the rising human population growth and an increased rate of consumption of natural resources, a long-term plan for the use and conservation of natural resources is important.

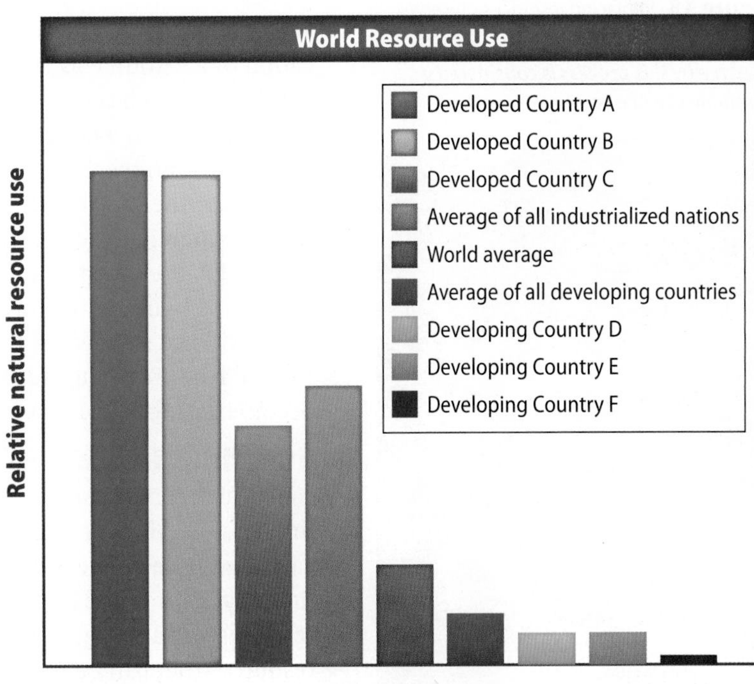

■ **Figure 16** This graph shows the consumption of natural resources per person for selected countries based on the equivalent kilograms of oil.
***Explain** why the use of natural resources is high for Developed Country A and for Developed Country B, but is low for Developing Country E and for Developing Country F.*

■ **Figure 17** This cleared forest is considered a nonrenewable resource because there is not enough of the forest intact to provide a habitat for the organisms that live there.

Renewable resources Plans for long-term use of natural resources must take into consideration the difference between the two groups of natural resources—renewable and nonrenewable resources. Those resources that are replaced by natural processes faster than they are consumed are called **renewable resources.** Solar energy is considered a renewable resource because the supply appears to be endless. Agricultural plants, animals, clean water, and clean air are considered renewable because they are normally replaced faster than they are consumed. However, the supply of these resources is not unlimited. If the demand exceeds the supply of any resource, the resource might become depleted.

Nonrenewable resources Resources that are found on Earth in limited amounts or that are replaced by natural processes over extremely long periods of time are called **nonrenewable resources.** Fossil fuels and mineral deposits, such as radioactive uranium, are considered nonrenewable resources. Species are considered renewable resources until the last of a species dies. When extinction occurs, a species is nonrenewable because it is lost forever.

Renewable versus nonrenewable resources The classification of a resource as renewable or nonrenewable depends on the context in which the resource is being discussed. A single tree or a small group of trees in a large forest ecosystem is renewable because replacement trees can be planted or can regrow from seeds present in the soil. Enough of the forest is still intact to serve as a habitat for the organisms that live there. However, when the entire forest is cleared, as shown in **Figure 17,** the forest is not considered a renewable resource. The organisms living in the forest have lost their habitat, and they most likely will not survive. In this example, it is possible that more than one natural resource is nonrenewable: the forest and any species that might become extinct.

■ **Figure 18** Replacing resources preserves the health of the biosphere.
Explain ***why this process is considered a sustainable use of a resource.***

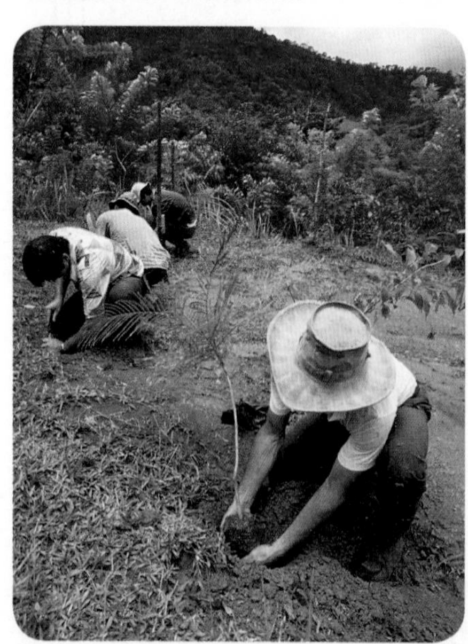

Sustainable use One approach to using natural resources, called sustainable use, is demonstrated in **Figure 18.** Just as the name implies, **sustainable use** means using resources at a rate at which they can be replaced or recycled while preserving the long-term environmental health of the biosphere. Conservation of resources includes reducing the amount of resources that are consumed, recycling resources that can be recycled, and preserving ecosystems, as well as using them in a responsible manner.

Protecting Biodiversity

In Section 2, you learned how human activities have affected many ecosystems. Many efforts are underway worldwide to slow the loss of biodiversity and to work toward sustainable use of natural resources.

Protected areas in the United States Conservation biologists recognize the importance of establishing protected areas where biodiversity can flourish. The United States established its first national park, Yellowstone National Park, in 1872 to protect the area's geological features. Many additional national parks and nature reserves have been established since 1872.

International protected areas The United States is not the only country to establish national parks and nature reserves. Currently, about seven percent of the world's land is set aside as some type of reserve. Historically, these protected areas have been small islands of habitat surrounded by areas that contain human activity. Because the reserves are small, they are impacted heavily by human activity. The United Nations supports a system of Biosphere Reserves and World Heritage sites. Costa Rica has established megareserves. These reserves contain one or more zones that are protected from human activity by buffer zones, areas in which sustainable use of natural resources is permitted. This approach creates large managed areas for preserving biodiversity while providing natural resources to local populations.

GET IT? **Explain** the advantages of megareserves.

Data Analysis LAB 1

Based on Real Data*

Use Maps

How is the biodiversity of perching birds distributed in the Americas? The distribution of birds, like that of other species, is not even. Perching birds appear to be more concentrated in some areas of the Americas than others.

Data and Observations

Use the map to answer the following questions about the biodiversity of perching birds.

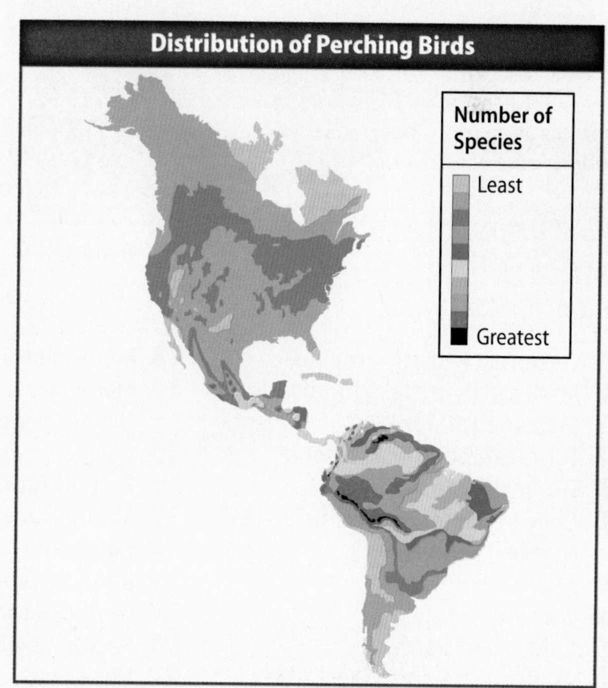

Think Critically

1. **Determine** the location of the highest concentration of perching birds.
2. **Generalize** the trend in the number of perching birds as you move from Canada to South America.
3. **Infer** Why does the number of perching birds change as you move toward the southern tip of South America?

*Data obtained from: Pimm, S.L. and Brown J.H. 2004. Domains of diversity. *Science* 304: 831–833.

VISUALIZING Biodiversity Hot Spots

Figure 19 Biodiversity hot spots, highlighted in red on the map, are ecosystems where endemic species are threatened. If these species become extinct, biodiversity will decrease.

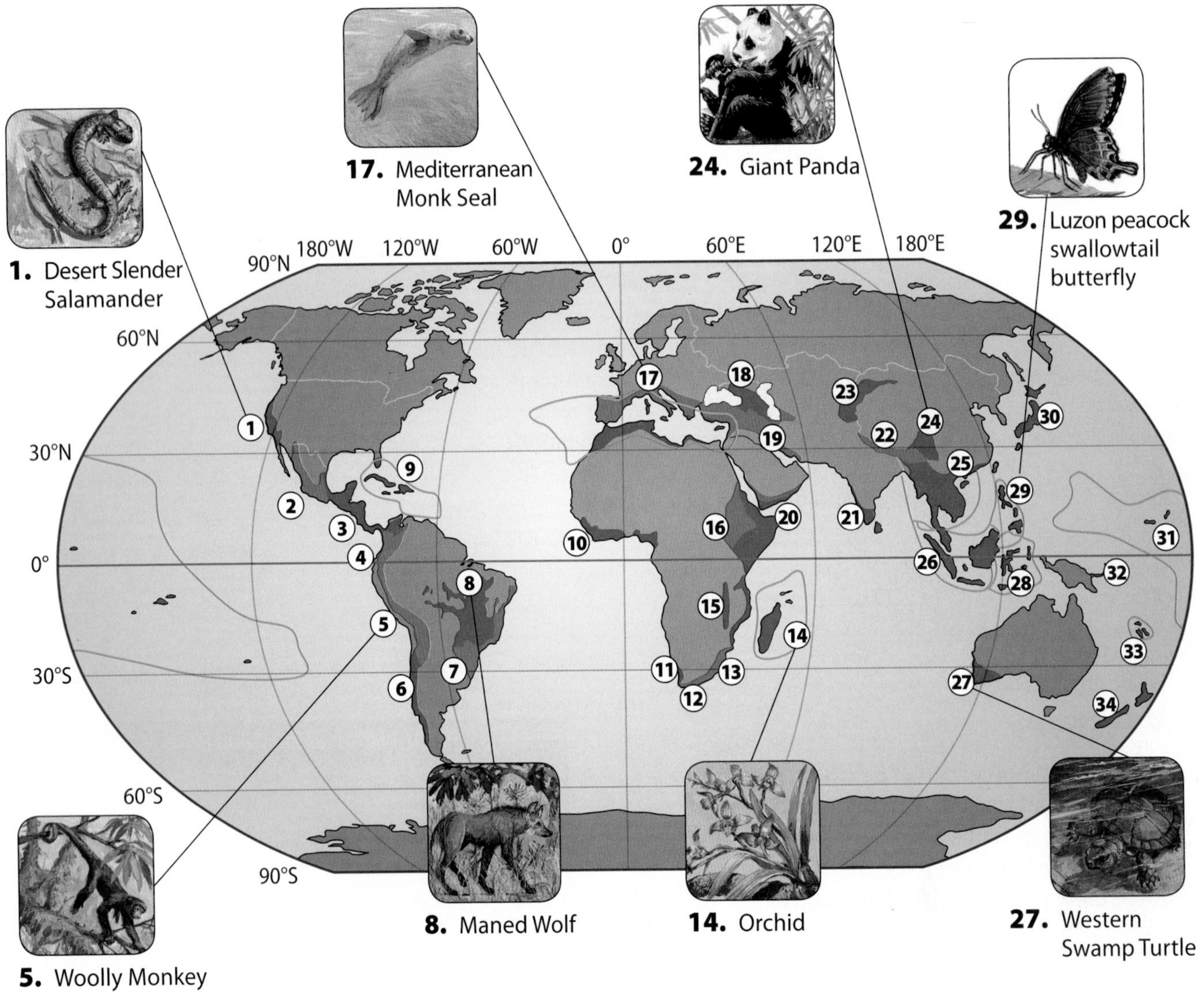

1. Desert Slender Salamander

17. Mediterranean Monk Seal

24. Giant Panda

29. Luzon peacock swallowtail butterfly

90°N 180°W 120°W 60°W 0° 60°E 120°E 180°E

60°N

30°N

0°

30°S

60°S

90°S

5. Woolly Monkey

8. Maned Wolf

14. Orchid

27. Western Swamp Turtle

1 California Floristic Province
2 Madrean Pine-Oak Woodlands
3 Mesomerica
4 Tumbes-Chocó-Magdalena
5 Tropical Andes
6 Chilean Winter Rainfall-Valdivian Forests
7 Atlantic Forest
8 Cerrado
9 Caribbean Islands
10 Guinean Forests of West Africa
11 Succulent Karoo
12 Cape Floristic Region
13 Maputaland-Pondoland-Albany
14 Madagascar and the Indian Ocean Islands
15 Coastal Forests of Eastern Africa
16 Eastern Aforomontane
17 Mediterranean Basin
18 Caucasus
19 Irano-Anatolian
20 Horn of Africa
21 Western Ghats and Sri Lanka
22 Himalayas
23 Mountains of Central Asia
24 Mountains of Southwest China
25 Indo-Burma
26 Sundaland
27 Southwest Australia
28 Wallacea
29 Philippines
30 Japan
31 Polynesia-Micronesia
32 East Melanesian Islands
33 New Caledonia
34 New Zealand

Biodiversity hot spots Conservation biologists have identified locations around the world that are characterized by exceptional levels of **endemic** species—species that are only found in that specific geographic area—and critical levels of habitat loss. To be called a hot spot, a region must meet two criteria. First, there must be at least 1500 species of vascular plants that are endemic, and the region must have lost at least 70 percent of its original habitat. The 34 internationally recognized hot spots are shown in **Figure 19.**

Approximately half of all plant and animal species are found in hot spots. These hot spots originally covered 17 percent of Earth's surface; however, only about a tenth of that habitat remains.

Biologists in favor of recovery efforts in these areas argue that focusing on a limited area would save the greatest number of species. Other biologists argue that concentrating funding on saving species in these hot spots does not address the serious problems that are occurring elsewhere. For example, saving a wetland area might save fewer species, but the wetland provides greater services by filtering water, regulating floods, and providing a nursery for fish. These biologists think that funding should be spent in areas around the world rather than focused on the biodiversity hot spots.

Corridors between habitat fragments Conservation ecologists also are focusing on improving the survival of biodiversity by providing corridors, or passageways, between habitat fragments. Corridors, such as those shown in **Figure 20,** are used to connect smaller parcels of land. These corridors allow organisms from one area to move safely to the other area. This creates a larger piece of land that can sustain a wider variety of species and a wider variety of genetic variation. However, corridors do not completely solve the problem of habitat destruction. Diseases easily pass from one area to the next as infected animals move from one location to another. This approach also increases edge effect. One large habitat would have fewer edges, but often a large habitat is hard to preserve.

VOCABULARY

SCIENCE USAGE V. COMMON USAGE

Corridor

Science usage: a passageway between two habitat fragments

The deer uses the corridor to safely travel between the two habitat fragments.

Common usage: a passageway, as in a hotel, into which rooms open

The ice machine is in the hotel corridor by the elevators.

Alan Sirulnikoff/Science Source

■ **Figure 20** Corridors between habitat fragments allow safe passage for animals.

Describe ***What are the advantages and disadvantages of corridors?***

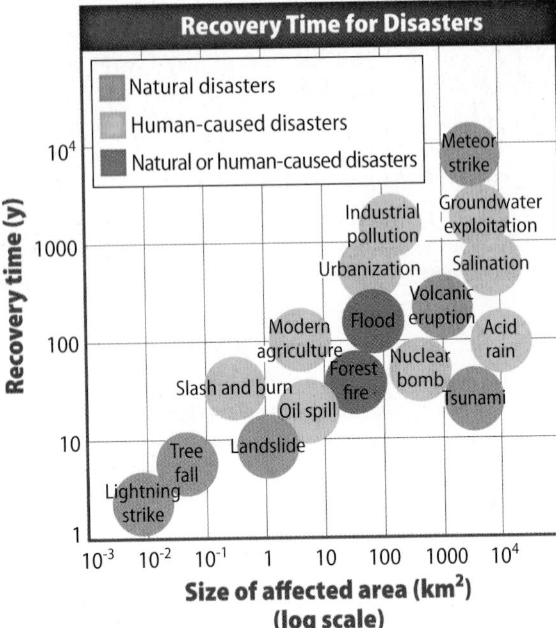

■ **Figure 21** The recovery time for disasters is dependent upon the size of the area affected and on the type of disturbance.

Determine ***the approximate recovery time for a landslide.***

Restoring Ecosystems

Sometimes, biodiversity is destroyed in an area such that it no longer provides the abiotic and biotic factors needed for a healthy ecosystem. For example, the soil from cleared tropical rain forests becomes unproductive for farming after a few years. After mining activities are completed, land might be abandoned in a condition that does not support biodiversity. Accidental oil spills and toxic chemical spills might pollute an area to such a degree that the native species cannot live there.

Given time, biological communities can recover from natural and human-made disasters, as illustrated in **Figure 21.** The size of the area affected and the type of disturbance are determining factors for recovery time. The length of time for recovery is not related directly to whether the disaster is natural or human-made. In general, the larger the affected area, the longer it takes for the biological community to recover. Ecologists use two methods to speed the recovery process of these damaged ecosystems: bioremediation and biological augmentation.

Bioremediation The use of living organisms, such as prokaryotes, fungi, or plants, to detoxify a polluted area is called **bioremediation.** In 1975, a leak from a fuel-storage facility in South Carolina released about 80,000 gallons of kerosene-based jet fuel. The fuel soaked into the sandy soil and contaminated the underground water table. Microorganisms that naturally are found in the soil break down these carbon-based fuels into carbon dioxide. Scientists found that by adding additional nutrients to the soil, the rate at which the microorganisms decontaminated the area increased. In a few years, the contamination in the area was greatly reduced. These microorganisms can be used in other ecosystems to remove toxins from soils that are contaminated by accidental oil or fuel spills.

Some species of plants are being used to remove toxic substances, such as zinc, lead, nickel, and organic chemicals, from damaged soils, as shown in **Figure 22.** These plants are planted in contaminated soils, where they store the toxic metals in their tissues. The plants then are harvested, and the toxic metals are removed from the ecosystem. Bioremediation is relatively new, but there appears to be great promise in using organisms to detoxify some ecosystems that have been damaged.

Robert Brook/Science Source

■ **Figure 22** Chemical waste from an industrial complex is being treated using reed beds. Bacteria and fungi in the reed beds transform a wide range of pollutants into harmless substances.

Biological augmentation Adding natural predators to a degraded ecosystem is called **biological augmentation.** For example, aphids—very small insects—eat vegetables and other plants, which can result in the destruction of farm crops. Aphids also can transmit plant diseases. Some farmers rely on ladybugs to control pests that eat their crops. Certain species of ladybugs eat aphids, as shown in **Figure 23,** and can be used to control aphid infestation. The ladybugs do not harm the crops, and the fields are kept free of aphids.

■ **Figure 23** Ladybugs can be introduced into an ecosystem to control aphid populations.

Legally Protecting Biodiversity

During the 1970s, a great deal of attention was focused on destruction of the environment and maintaining biodiversity. Laws were enacted in countries around the world, and many treaties between countries were signed in an effort to preserve the environment. In the United States, the Endangered Species Act was enacted in 1973. It was designed to legally protect the species that were becoming extinct or in danger of becoming extinct. An international treaty, the Convention on International Trade in Endangered Species of Wild Fauna and Flora (CITES), was signed in 1975. It outlawed the trade of endangered species and animal parts, such as ivory elephant tusks and rhinoceros horns. Since the 1970s, many more laws and treaties have been enacted and signed with the purpose of preserving biodiversity for future generations.

REVIEW IT! Conserving Biodiversity

Section Summary

- One approach to using natural resources is sustainable use.
- There are many approaches used to conserve biodiversity in the world.
- Biodiversity hot spots contain a large number of endemic species that are threatened with extinction.
- Two techniques used to restore an ecosystem are bioremediation and biological augmentation.
- Since the 1970s, many forms of legislation have been passed to protect the environment.

Self Check

Understand Main Ideas

1. MAINIDEA **Describe** three approaches used to slow down the rate of extinction or to preserve biodiversity.
2. **Define** the two classes of natural resources.
3. **Choose** a human-caused disaster from **Figure 21.** Discuss the methods that could be used to restore biodiversity.
4. **Examine** how long-term survival of species is dependent on resources that are ever-changing and limited.

Think Critically

5. **Create** a script of dialogue that could occur between a conservationist and a person who lives in a biodiversity hot spot. The local person wants to use the natural resources to provide a living for his or her family. The dialogue should include a compromise in which both sides are satisfied with the use of resources.

MATH IN ▶ Biology

6. If Earth has 150,100,000 km^2 of land area, how much land area is included in the biodiversity hot spots?

IN THE FIELD

1.1.1b, 1.1.1c, 4.7.3b

Career: Conservationist

Wangari Maathai: Planting Seeds of Change

Living and working in her homeland of Kenya, Wangari Maathai was disturbed by the plight of women in rural areas of the country. Limited firewood, scarce water resources, and poor soil made it difficult for rural women to meet their families' needs. Maathai's solution? Plant trees, and teach other women to do the same.

What began with planting trees in 1977 evolved into the Green Belt Movement, with Maathai as its energetic leader. This grassroots, non-governmental organization involves Kenyans in reducing the environmental and social effects of deforestation. While tree planting is the focal activity, the movement also promotes environmental consciousness, volunteerism, conservation of local biodiversity, community development, and self-empowerment, particularly for Kenyan women and girls. Maathai was awarded the Nobel Peace Prize in 2004 for her contribution to sustainable development, democracy, and peace.

Positive change in Kenya As a leader for environmental change in Kenya, Maathai's work has helped Kenyans achieve a deeper understanding of their role in environmental conservation. Today, there are more than 600 community networks throughout Kenya that oversee about 6000 tree nurseries. These nurseries are staffed primarily by Kenyan women, and provide an income source for their families and for rural communities. Individuals working within community networks have planted more than 30 million trees throughout the country. Degraded forested areas are experiencing regrowth, resulting in areas that can support plant and animal biodiversity.

Wangari Maathai

Soil erosion has slowed, and both soil fertility and water-holding capacity in planted areas has increased. By promoting the planting of fruit trees and other food plants, hunger has been reduced and nutrition has improved in rural households.

The impact of the Green Belt Movement, now more than 30 years old, has been phenomenal. Expanding beyond Kenya, Green Belt methods have been adopted in other African countries, including Tanzania, Uganda, Malawi, Lesotho, Ethiopia, and Zimbabwe.

COMMUNITY SERVICE

Action Plan How can you get involved with tree planting in your community? Develop an action plan that includes contacting local groups for information, designing the project, obtaining resources, and implementing the activity.

WebQuest

BioLAB 1.2.2a, 4.5.3a, 4.6.3a, ¥a, ¥e, ¥o

FIELD INVESTIGATION: How can surveying a plot of land around your school help you understand the health of your ecosystem?

Background One of the jobs of a conservation biologist is to survey land and provide an analysis of the health of the ecosystem. Then, if problems are discovered, he or she would propose possible solutions, decide on a course of action, and implement the plan.

Question: *How can an ecosystem be restored to its natural state?*

Materials

wire coat hangers or 1-m stakes (61)
field notebook
field guide of area species (plant, animal, and fungus)
colored plastic ribbon(50 m)
string (600 m)
pencil

Safety Precautions

WARNING: ***Use care in observing wildlife; do not disturb the species.***

Procedure

1. Read and complete the lab safety form.
2. Determine a site to be studied. Make sure the site owner has given permission to conduct a survey on that site.
3. With four stakes, mark off a 15 m × 15 m area within that site.
4. Further divide the area into 1 m × 1 m squares with 57 remaining stakes and string. These will be your sampling areas.
5. Using the method you used in **MiniLab 2,** survey your site and calculate the index of diversity.
6. Research the history of your area. How has it changed since it was first settled?
7. Research and recommend appropriate methods to care for the plot of land you surveyed in an environmentally responsible manner, perhaps by restoring it to its original state.
8. Make a plan to implement your methods. What limitations might you encounter?
9. If possible, implement part of your plan.

Analyze and Conclude

1. **Predict** how your methods of care would impact your plot of land. Why is this important?
2. **Determine** Is there a key species you expect to be affected by your plan?
3. **Analyze** What are some possible negative consequences of your plan?
4. **Defend** Is there another possible conservation biology technique that could be used? Explain.
5. **Calculate** What might the index of diversity be if you made the changes you recommended?
6. **Interpret** Was an increase in biodiversity your goal? Why or why not?

SHARE YOUR DATA

Present As a class, create a presentation of your plan to give to school administration. The presentation should use multimedia to show the data you collected, the time, money, and resources needed to implement your plan, and a strong argument for implementing your plan.

CHAPTER 5 STUDY GUIDE

BIGIDEA **Community and ecosystem homeostasis depends on a complex set of interactions among biologically diverse individuals.**

SECTION 1 Biodiversity

MAINIDEA Biodiversity maintains a healthy biosphere and provides direct and indirect value to humans.

- Biodiversity is important to the health of the biosphere.
- There are three types of biodiversity: genetic, species, and ecosystem.
- Biodiversity has aesthetic and scientific values, and direct and indirect economic value.
- It is important to maintain biodiversity to preserve the reservoir of genes that might be needed in the future.
- Healthy ecosystems can provide some services at a lesser expense than the use of technology.

VOCABULARY

- **extinction**
- **biodiversity**
- **genetic diversity**
- **species diversity**
- **ecosystem diversity**

SECTION 2 Threats to Biodiversity

MAINIDEA Some human activities reduce biodiversity in ecosystems, and current evidence suggests that reduced biodiversity might have serious long-term effects on the biosphere.

- Some scientists estimate that the current rate of species extinction is abnormally high.
- Species on islands are particularly vulnerable to extinction.
- Historically, overexploitation of some species by humans has led to their extinction.
- Human activities can result in a decrease in biodiversity.

VOCABULARY

- **background extinction**
- **mass extinction**
- **natural resource**
- **overexploitation**
- **habitat fragmentation**
- **edge effect**
- **biological magnification**
- **eutrophication**
- **introduced species**

SECTION 3 Conserving Biodiversity

MAINIDEA People are using many approaches to slow the rate of extinctions and to preserve biodiversity.

- One approach to using natural resources is sustainable use.
- There are many approaches used to conserve biodiversity in the world.
- Biodiversity hot spots contain a large number of endemic species that are threatened with extinction.
- Two techniques used to restore an ecosystem are bioremediation and biological augmentation.
- Since the 1970s, many forms of legislation have been passed to protect the environment.

VOCABULARY

- **renewable resource**
- **nonrenewable resource**
- **sustainable use**
- **endemic**
- **bioremediation**
- **biological augmentation**

SECTION 1

Vocabulary Review

Each of the following sentences is false. Make each sentence true by replacing the italicized word with a vocabulary term from the Study Guide page.

1. *Biodiversity* of a species occurs when the last member of the species dies.
2. *Genetic diversity* refers to the variety of ecosystems that are present in the biosphere.
3. *Ecosystem diversity* is the number of different species and the relative abundance of each species in a biological community.

Understand Main Ideas

4. In which location would you expect to find the greatest species diversity?
   A. Canada
   B. Costa Rica
   C. Mexico
   D. United States

Use the photo below to answer questions 5 and 12.

5. Which term best describes what the rabbits in the photo demonstrate?
   A. ecosystem diversity
   B. genetic diversity
   C. species richness
   D. species diversity
6. Refer to **Figure 3.** What is the species diversity in southern Florida?
   A. 0–50 species
   B. 50–100 species
   C. 100–150 species
   D. 150–200 species
7. Which represents an indirect economic value of biodiversity?
   A. food
   B. clothing
   C. flood protection
   D. medicines
8. Which term best describes this collection of locations: a forest, a freshwater lake, an estuary, and a prairie?
   A. ecosystem diversity
   B. extinction
   C. genetic diversity
   D. species diversity

Constructed Response

9. **Open Ended** Infer why there is more species diversity in southern Florida than there is in northern Alaska.
10. **THEME FOCUS** Explain why increased ecosystem diversity contributes to increased biodiversity in the biosphere.
11. **MAIN IDEA** Describe three values that the biosphere provides.
12. **Short Answer** Explain how a trait such as the one demonstrated in the photo on the left helps the species survive.

Think Critically

13. **Explain** why it is difficult to attach a value to the aesthetic qualities of biodiversity.
14. **Describe** a service that an ecosystem provides in your community that should be protected to ensure that the quality of the service continues.

SECTION 2

Vocabulary Review

Explain the difference between each pair of terms below. Then explain how the terms are related.

15. background extinction, mass extinction
16. habitat fragmentation, edge effect
17. overexploitation, introduced species

Understand Main Ideas

18. Which group of organisms listed in **Table 2** has the greatest number of extinctions overall?
A. birds
B. flowering plants
C. invertebrates
D. mammals

19. Which group listed in **Table 2** has the greatest percentage of extinctions?
A. birds
B. fish
C. mammals
D. reptiles

Use the figure below to answer questions 20 and 21.

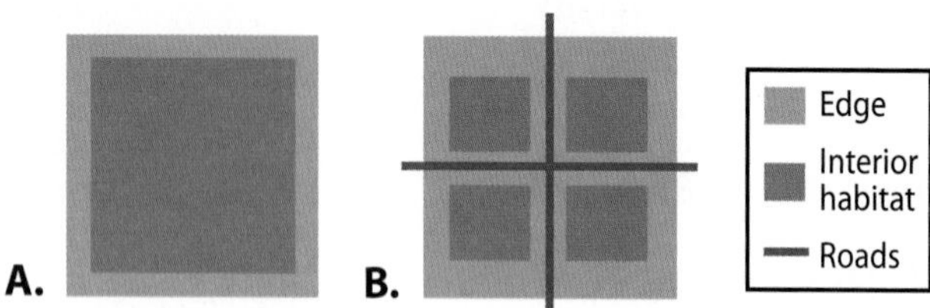

20. Which habitat has the greatest impact resulting from edge effects?
A. A
B. B
C. A and B equally
D. neither A nor B

21. Which habitat naturally supports the greater amount of biodiversity?
A. A
B. B
C. A and B equally
D. neither A nor B

22. Which is not a way in which species lose their habitats?
A. background extinction
B. destruction
C. disruption
D. pollution

23. Approximately how much greater is the current background extinction compared to the normal rate?
A. 1 time
B. 10 times
C. 1000 times
D. 10,000 times

24. Which condition triggered the chain of events off the coast of Alaska that caused the kelp forests to begin to disappear?
A. a decrease in the amount of plankton
B. an increase in the number of sea otters
C. overharvesting of plankton-eating whales
D. pollution caused by pesticides

Constructed Response

25. **MAIN**IDEA Explain why rhinos are in danger of becoming extinct.

Think Critically

26. **Recommend** ways in which eutrophication can be reduced in waterways.

27. **Explain** why it is not a good idea to release exotic pets into a local ecosystem.

SECTION 3

Vocabulary Review

Answer each question with a vocabulary term from the Study Guide page.

28. What are resources called that are replaced by natural processes faster than they are consumed?

29. What are species called that are found in only one geographic location?

30. What is the name of the process of using living organisms to detoxify a location?

31. What are resources called that are found in limited amounts or are replaced by natural processes over extremely long periods of time?

Understand Main Ideas

32. Which term is a method that is used to restore biodiversity to a polluted or damaged area?
A. biological augmentation
B. biological corridor
C. renewable resource
D. sustainable use

Use the figure below to answer question 33.

33. Which is an advantage of the habitat corridor shown above?
A. Corridors increase the edge effect in the area.
B. Diseases are passed easily from one area to another.
C. Parasites are passed easily from one area to another.
D. Members of species can move safely from one area to another.

Alan Sirulnikoff/Science Source

Use the graph below to answer questions 34 and 35.

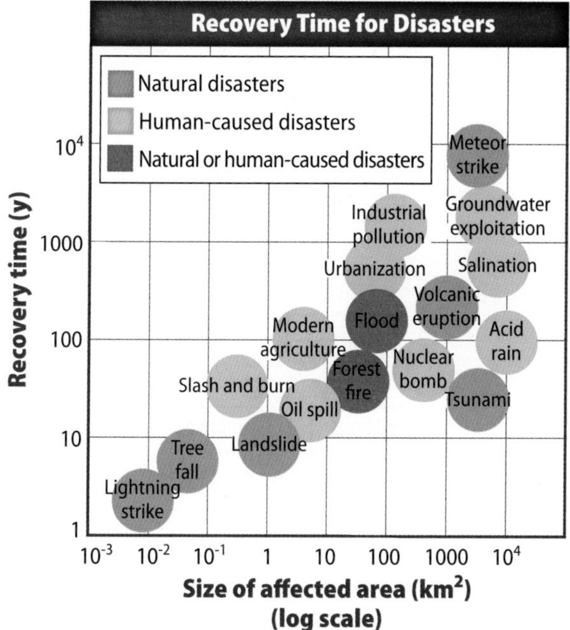

34. Which human-caused disaster requires the greatest recovery time?
A. groundwater exploitation
B. industrial pollution
C. nuclear bomb
D. oil spill

35. Which natural disaster requires the least amount of recovery time?
A. lightning strike
B. meteor strike
C. tsunami
D. volcanic eruption

Constructed Response

36. MAINIDEA Explain why reserves protect biodiversity.

37. **CAREERS IN ▶ Biology** Explain how an environmental microbiologist might use bioremediation to detoxify polluted areas.

Think Critically

38. **Evaluate** why it is important to develop a sustainable-use plan for the use of natural resources.

39. **Evaluate** how a sustainable-use plan for natural resources will change as the world population continues to grow and people living in developing countries increase their standards of living.

Summative Assessment

40. **BIGIDEA** Consider how community and ecosystem homeostasis can be disrupted as a result of a decrease in biodiversity. Write your answer in an essay format.

41. **WRITING IN ▶ Biology** Write a short essay about the importance of preserving biodiversity.

42. **WRITING IN ▶ Biology** Choose an organism that is in danger of becoming extinct, and write a song or poem detailing the organism's situation.

43. Select an endangered plant or animal and investigate what factors are contributing to its near extinction. Evaluate the organism's chances for survival, taking into consideration genetic diversity, species diversity, and ecosystem diversity.

DBQ Document-Based Questions

Data obtained from: Wilson, E.O. 1980. Resolutions for the 80s. *Harvard Magazine* (January–February): 20.

The quote below was obtained from one of Pulitzer Prize winner Edward O. Wilson's journal articles.

"The worst that can happen—will happen—is not energy depletion, economic collapse, limited nuclear war, or conquest by a totalitarian government. As terrible as these catastrophes would be for us, they can be repaired within a few generations. The one process ongoing in the 1980s that will take millions of years to correct is the loss of genetic and species diversity by the destruction of natural habitats. This is the folly our descendants are least likely to forgive us."

44. How do you think biodiversity has changed since the 1980s?

45. Why do you think Wilson compares the loss of biodiversity with energy depletion, economic collapse, nuclear war, and conquest?

46. What does Wilson mean when he says, "This is the folly our descendants are least likely to forgive us"?

CUMULATIVE

MULTIPLE CHOICE

Use the graph below to answer questions 1 and 2.

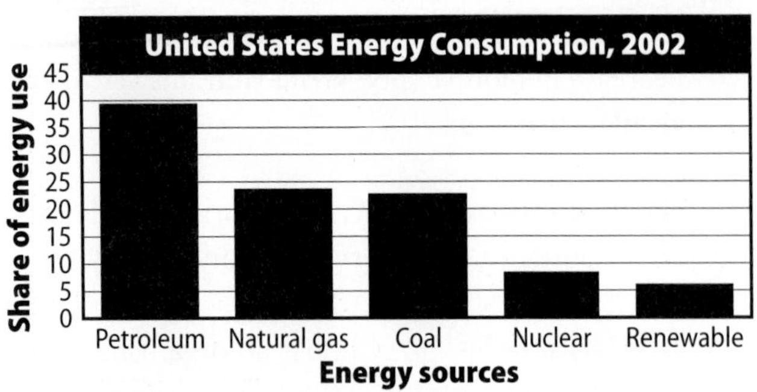

1 What percentage of the United States energy consumption in 2002 was fossil fuels?

A 23

B 24

C 39

D 86

2 What percentage of the United States energy consumption in 2002 was nonrenewable resources?

A 8

B 23

C 39

D 94

3 Which situation is an abiotic limiting factor for the habitat of coral organisms?

A annual rainfall

B soil chemistry

C temperature throughout the year

D zooanthellae in the reef

SHORT ANSWER

Use the diagram below to answer questions 4 and 5.

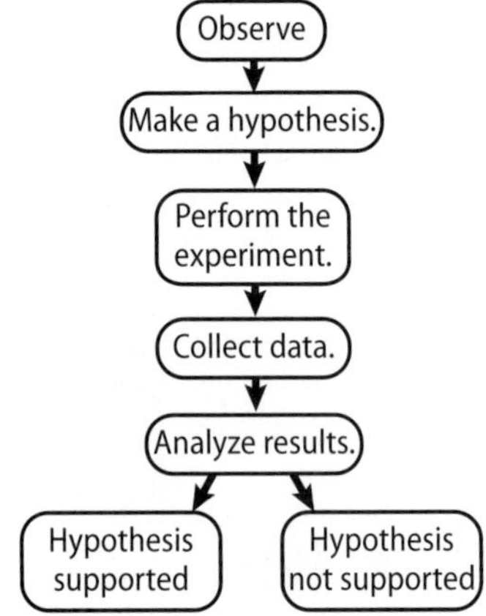

4 Explain what a scientist should do if the experimental data do not support his or her hypothesis.

5 Scientists do not always follow the same scientific method step-by-step. Name one step in the scientific method shown above that often is omitted. Justify your answer.

6 If a population is experiencing a decrease in size, how do the birth and death rates compare?

7 List an example of a renewable resource and a nonrenewable resource, and analyze why they are classified as such.

8 Explain the type of information that is displayed on an age-structure graph.

9 The ginger plant is considered an invasive species in Hawaii. Justify why park officials in Hawaii have to kill ginger plants.

EXTENDED RESPONSE

Use the illustration below to answer question 10.

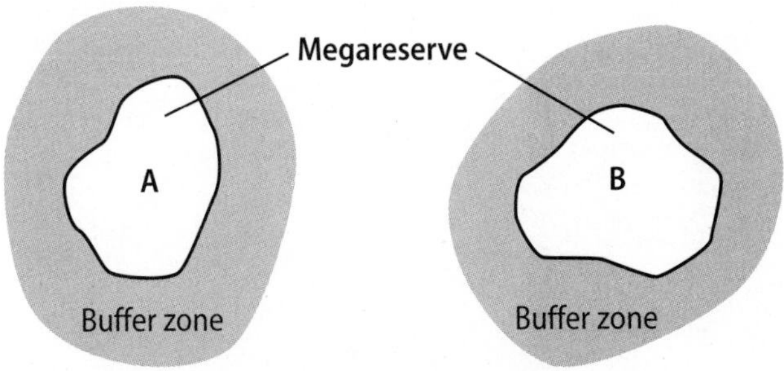

10 The map above shows two megareserves surrounded by buffer zones. Appraise a positive and negative point about these protected zones for a bird species living in Area A.

11 Explain why two species involved in a symbiotic relationship probably evolved around the same time.

ESSAY QUESTION

The U.S. government takes a census of the population every ten years. The first census took place in 1790 and recorded 3.9 million people. In the 2000 census, the U.S. population was nearly a quarter of a billion people. The census also shows population trends, such as people moving from rural areas to cities.

Using the information in the paragraph above, answer the following question in an essay format.

12 The census provides a snapshot of the U.S. population every ten years. Many things can happen between census dates that affect the population. Describe some of the factors that could contribute to a radical change in the U.S. population between each census.

TEST PRACTICE

Use the graph below to answer questions 13 and 14.

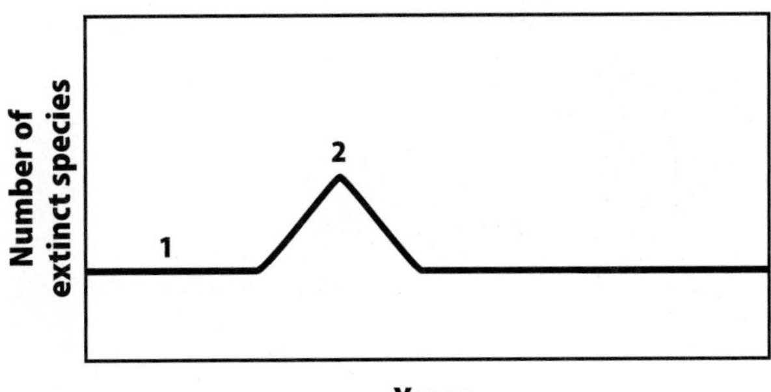

13 Which term best describes the section of the graph labeled *1*?

A background extinction

B habitat destruction

C mass extinction

D species overexploitation

14 The peak labeled *2* on the graph would not be caused by which event?

A destruction of a native animal's habitat as humans populate an island

B increasing industrialization and human influence over time

C introduction of a nonnative animal into an island ecosystem

D a fatal disease affecting a single population

NEED EXTRA HELP?														
If You Missed Question . . .	1	2	3	4	5	6	7	8	9	10	11	12	13	14
Review Section . . .	5.3	5.3	3.2	1.3	1.3	4.2	5.3	4.2	5.2	5.3	2.1	4.2	5.2	5.2

UNIT 2

(bkgd)Balint Porneczi/Bloomberg/Getty Images, (inset)Balint Porneczi/Bloomberg/Getty Images

CAREERS USING BIOLOGY

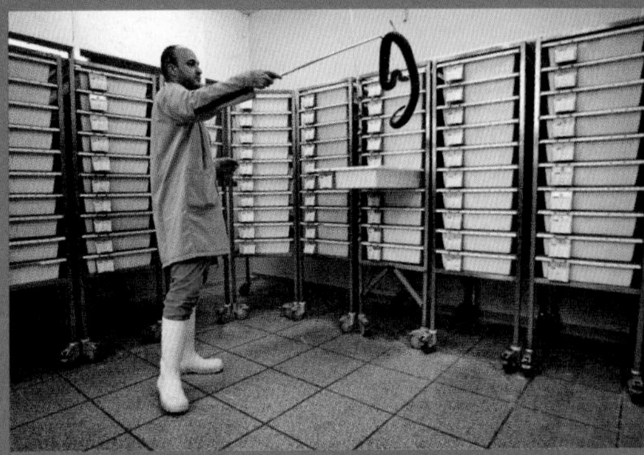

Career in Action Animal technicians that specialize in snake handling are specially trained to safely and humanely handle snakes.

BIOdiscoveries

See **page 208** for more information about the importance of snake venom in medical research.

ANIMAL TECHNICIAN

Animal technicians can work with any species of animal that is used for research. The job duties can vary greatly depending on the species of animal and the nature of the research. Generally, animal technicians must clean cages, feed and water animals, and monitor their health. Animal technicians at the NNTRC care for about 500 venomous snakes. They are also responsible for "milking" the snakes to extract their venom.

Related Careers

herpetologist
biomedical scientist
molecular biologist
oncologist
lab technician
pharmaceutical chemist

 **Career Resources**

WHAT'S THAT? Animal technicians collect snake venom that will be used in life-saving medical research. For example, at the National Natural Toxins Research Center (NNTRC) at Texas A&M University in Kingsville, researchers are working to uncover the medical importance of snake venom toxins. They are researching the ability of snake venom to treat strokes, heart attacks, and even cancer.

Investigate

Research What venomous snakes are found in New York? What type of toxins are found in their venom? What effects do these toxins have on the human body? Are any of the toxins used for medical treatment or research? If so, which ones?

Everything is made of atoms, elements, and compounds. Living things are made of carbon compounds called proteins, fats, and lipids. Collagen fibers, the main components of connective tissue, are made from proteins.

LaunchLAB

How does the nutrient content of foods compare?

Your body's structures and functions depend on chemical elements including those found in proteins, carbohydrates, fats, vitamins, minerals, and water. In this lab, you will investigate nutrients that provide those elements.

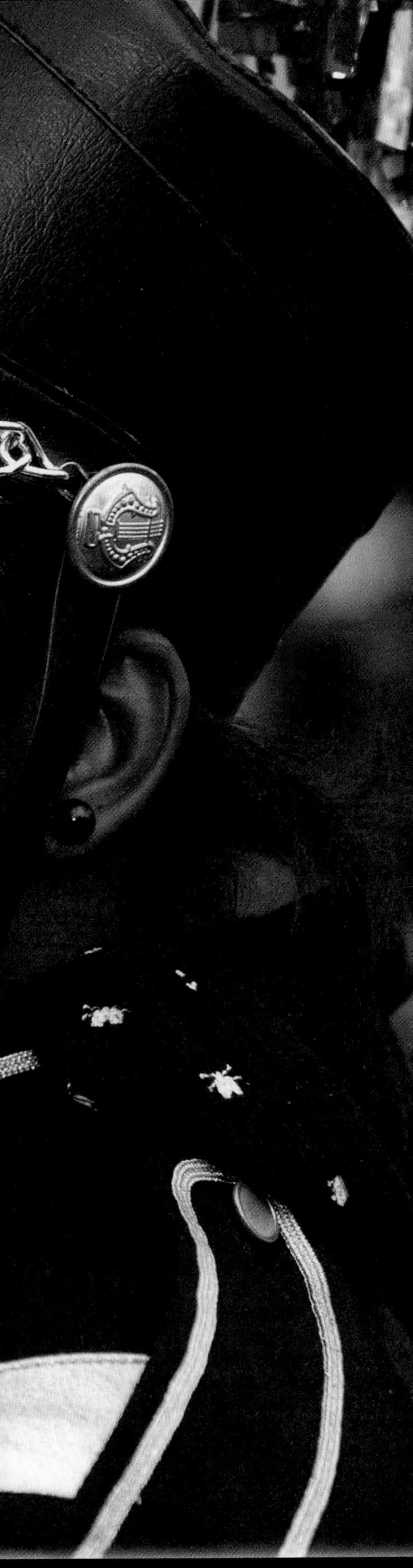

CHAPTER 6

Chemistry in Biology

1 Atoms, Elements, and Compounds

¥a, ¥b1, ¥b2, ¥b3, ¥b4, ¥b5, ¥e, ¥g, ¥m, ¥n

2 Chemical Reactions

1.2.2a, 4.5.1c, 1.3.5b, 4.1.2h, 4.5.1f, 4.6.1b, ¥a, ¥e, ¥i, ¥m, ¥o

3 Water and Solutions

4.5.1c

4 The Building Blocks of Life

4.1.2h, 4.2.1f, 4.2.1g, 4.2.1i, 4.5.1c, 4.5.1g, 4.6.1c

THEMEFOCUS

Energy and matter In every chemical reaction, there is a change in energy.

BIGIDEA

Atoms are the foundation of biological chemistry and the building blocks of all living organisms.

Enzyme Activity

Make a four-door book using the labels shown. Use it to organize your notes on enzyme activity.

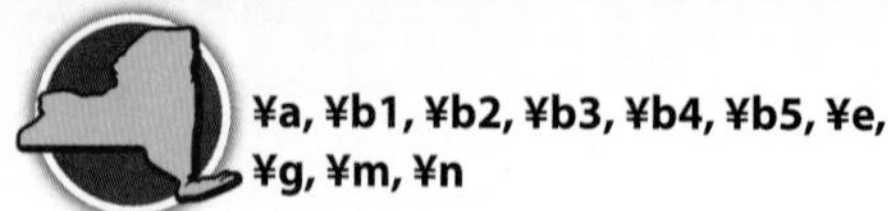

1 Atoms, Elements, and Compounds

¥a, ¥b1, ¥b2, ¥b3, ¥b4, ¥b5, ¥e, ¥g, ¥m, ¥n

BIOLOGY 4 U

Many scientists think that the universe began with a sudden, rapid expansion billions of years ago. They think that the building blocks that make up the amazing diversity of life we see today are a result of that expansion. The study of those building blocks is the science of chemistry.

Review Vocabulary

substance: a form of matter that has a uniform and unchanging composition

New Vocabulary

atom
nucleus
proton
neutron
electron
element
isotope
compound
covalent bond
molecule
ion
ionic bond
van der Waals force

Multilingual eGlossary

BrainPOP

MAIN IDEA

Matter is composed of tiny particles called atoms.

Essential Questions

- What are atoms?
- How are the particles that make up atoms diagrammed?
- What are the similarities between covalent and ionic bonds?
- How are van der Waals forces described?

Atoms

Chemistry is the study of matter, its composition, and properties. Matter is anything that has mass and takes up space. All of the organisms that you study in biology are made up of matter. **Atoms** are the building blocks of matter.

Connection to History In the fifth century B.C., Greek philosophers Leucippus and Democritus first proposed the idea that all matter is made up of tiny, indivisible particles. It wasn't until the 1800s that scientists began to collect experimental evidence to support the existence of atoms. As technology improved over the next two centuries, scientists proved not only that atoms exist but also that they are made up of even smaller particles.

The structure of an atom An atom is so small that billions of them could fit on the head of a pin. Yet, atoms are made up of even smaller particles called neutrons, protons, and electrons, as illustrated in **Figure 1.** Neutrons and protons are located at the center of the atom, which is called the **nucleus. Protons** are positively charged particles (p^+), and **neutrons** are particles that have no charge (n^0). **Electrons** are negatively charged particles (e^-) that are located outside the nucleus. Electrons constantly move around an atom's nucleus in energy levels. The basic structure of an atom is the result of the attraction between protons and electrons. Atoms contain an equal number of protons and electrons, so the overall charge of an atom is zero.

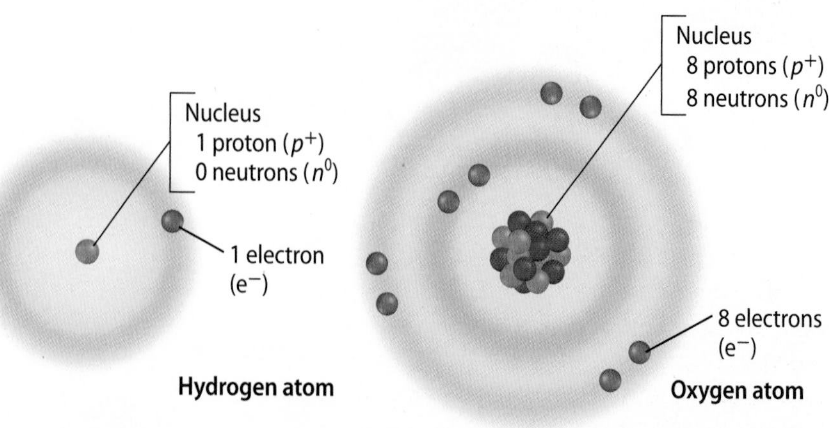

Figure 1 Hydrogen has only one proton and one electron. Oxygen has eight protons, eight neutrons, and eight electrons. The electrons move around the nucleus in two energy levels (shown as the darker shaded rings).

Infer ***the charge of an atom if it contained more electrons than protons.***

PERIODIC TABLE OF THE ELEMENTS

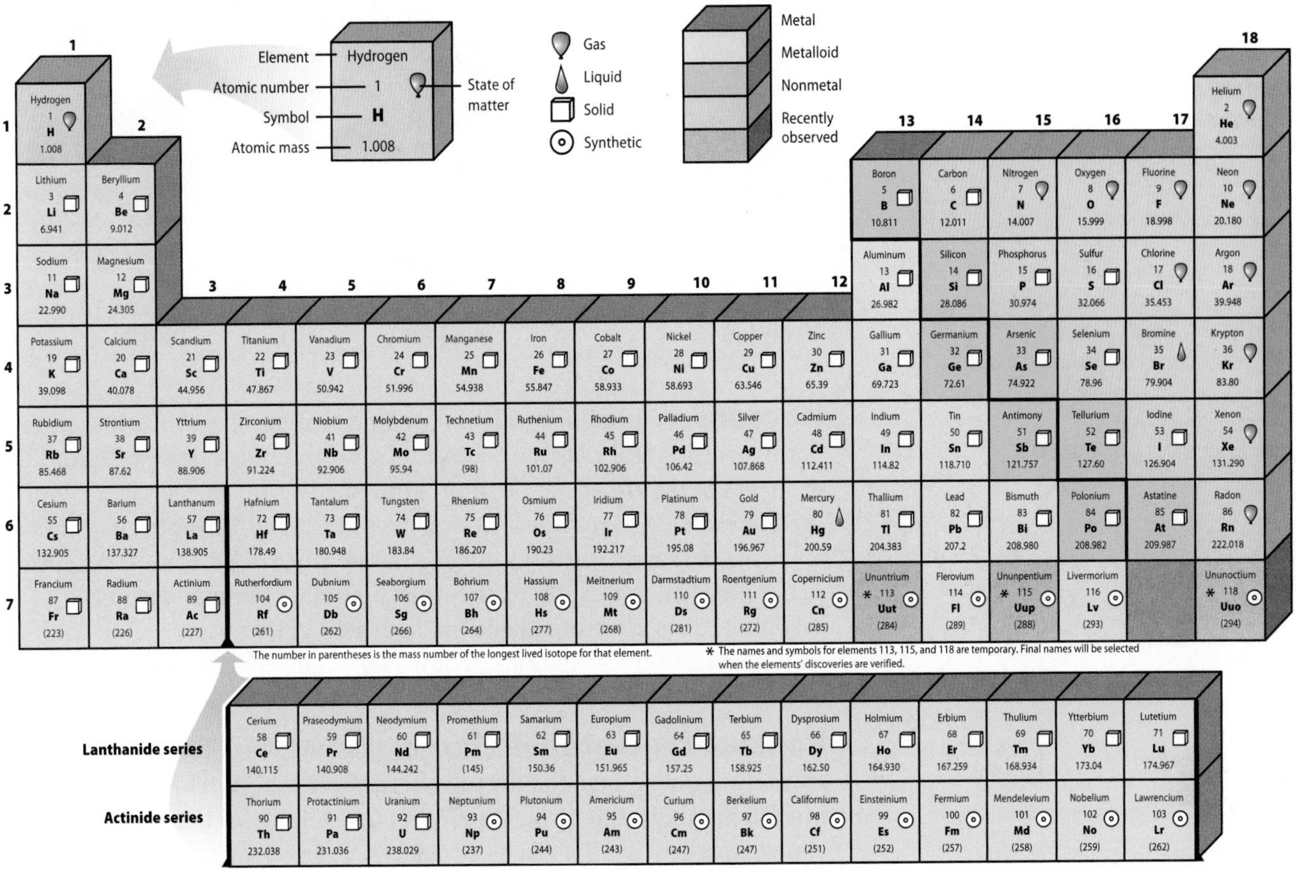

Element — Hydrogen
Atomic number — 1
Symbol — H
Atomic mass — 1.008
State of matter

Gas
Liquid
Solid
Synthetic

Metal
Metalloid
Nonmetal
Recently observed

	1	2	3	4	5	6	7	8	9	10	11	12	13	14	15	16	17	18
1	Hydrogen 1 H 1.008																	Helium 2 He 4.003
2	Lithium 3 Li 6.941	Beryllium 4 Be 9.012											Boron 5 B 10.811	Carbon 6 C 12.011	Nitrogen 7 N 14.007	Oxygen 8 O 15.999	Fluorine 9 F 18.998	Neon 10 Ne 20.180
3	Sodium 11 Na 22.990	Magnesium 12 Mg 24.305											Aluminum 13 Al 26.982	Silicon 14 Si 28.086	Phosphorus 15 P 30.974	Sulfur 16 S 32.066	Chlorine 17 Cl 35.453	Argon 18 Ar 39.948
4	Potassium 19 K 39.098	Calcium 20 Ca 40.078	Scandium 21 Sc 44.956	Titanium 22 Ti 47.867	Vanadium 23 V 50.942	Chromium 24 Cr 51.996	Manganese 25 Mn 54.938	Iron 26 Fe 55.847	Cobalt 27 Co 58.933	Nickel 28 Ni 58.693	Copper 29 Cu 63.546	Zinc 30 Zn 65.39	Gallium 31 Ga 69.723	Germanium 32 Ge 72.61	Arsenic 33 As 74.922	Selenium 34 Se 78.96	Bromine 35 Br 79.904	Krypton 36 Kr 83.80
5	Rubidium 37 Rb 85.468	Strontium 38 Sr 87.62	Yttrium 39 Y 88.906	Zirconium 40 Zr 91.224	Niobium 41 Nb 92.906	Molybdenum 42 Mo 95.94	Technetium 43 Tc (98)	Ruthenium 44 Ru 101.07	Rhodium 45 Rh 102.906	Palladium 46 Pd 106.42	Silver 47 Ag 107.868	Cadmium 48 Cd 112.411	Indium 49 In 114.82	Tin 50 Sn 118.710	Antimony 51 Sb 121.757	Tellurium 52 Te 127.60	Iodine 53 I 126.904	Xenon 54 Xe 131.290
6	Cesium 55 Cs 132.905	Barium 56 Ba 137.327	Lanthanum 57 La 138.905	Hafnium 72 Hf 178.49	Tantalum 73 Ta 180.948	Tungsten 74 W 183.84	Rhenium 75 Re 186.207	Osmium 76 Os 190.23	Iridium 77 Ir 192.217	Platinum 78 Pt 195.08	Gold 79 Au 196.967	Mercury 80 Hg 200.59	Thallium 81 Tl 204.383	Lead 82 Pb 207.2	Bismuth 83 Bi 208.980	Polonium 84 Po 208.982	Astatine 85 At 209.987	Radon 86 Rn 222.018
7	Francium 87 Fr (223)	Radium 88 Ra (226)	Actinium 89 Ac (227)	Rutherfordium 104 Rf (261)	Dubnium 105 Db (262)	Seaborgium 106 Sg (266)	Bohrium 107 Bh (264)	Hassium 108 Hs (277)	Meitnerium 109 Mt (268)	Darmstadtium 110 Ds (281)	Roentgenium 111 Rg (272)	Copernicium 112 Cn (285)	Ununtrium * 113 Uut (284)	Flerovium 114 Fl (289)	Ununpentium * 115 Uup (288)	Livermorium 116 Lv (293)		Ununoctium * 118 Uuo (294)

The number in parentheses is the mass number of the longest lived isotope for that element.

* The names and symbols for elements 113, 115, and 118 are temporary. Final names will be selected when the elements' discoveries are verified.

Lanthanide series	Cerium 58 Ce 140.115	Praseodymium 59 Pr 140.908	Neodymium 60 Nd 144.242	Promethium 61 Pm (145)	Samarium 62 Sm 150.36	Europium 63 Eu 151.965	Gadolinium 64 Gd 157.25	Terbium 65 Tb 158.925	Dysprosium 66 Dy 162.50	Holmium 67 Ho 164.930	Erbium 68 Er 167.259	Thulium 69 Tm 168.934	Ytterbium 70 Yb 173.04	Lutetium 71 Lu 174.967
Actinide series	Thorium 90 Th 232.038	Protactinium 91 Pa 231.036	Uranium 92 U 238.029	Neptunium 93 Np (237)	Plutonium 94 Pu (244)	Americium 95 Am (243)	Curium 96 Cm (247)	Berkelium 97 Bk (247)	Californium 98 Cf (251)	Einsteinium 99 Es (252)	Fermium 100 Fm (257)	Mendelevium 101 Md (258)	Nobelium 102 No (259)	Lawrencium 103 Lr (262)

■ **Figure 2** The periodic table of the elements organizes all of the known elements. Examine the biologists' guide to the periodic table on the back cover of this book.

Elements

An **element** is a pure substance that cannot be broken down into other substances by physical or chemical means. Elements are made of only one type of atom. There are over 100 known elements, 92 of which occur naturally. Scientists have collected a large amount of information about the elements, such as the number of protons and electrons each element has and the atomic mass of each element. Also, each element has a unique name and symbol. All of these data, and more, are collected in an organized table called the periodic table of the elements.

The periodic table of the elements As shown in **Figure 2,** the periodic table is organized into horizontal rows, called periods, and vertical columns, called groups. Each individual block in the grid represents an element. The table is called periodic because elements in the same group have similar chemical and physical properties. This organization even allows scientists to predict elements that have not yet been discovered or isolated. As shown in **Figure 3,** elements found in living organisms also are found in Earth's crust.

■ **Figure 3** The elements in Earth's crust and living organisms vary in their abundance. Living things are composed primarily of three elements: carbon, hydrogen, and oxygen.

Interpret ***what the most abundant element is that exists in living things.***

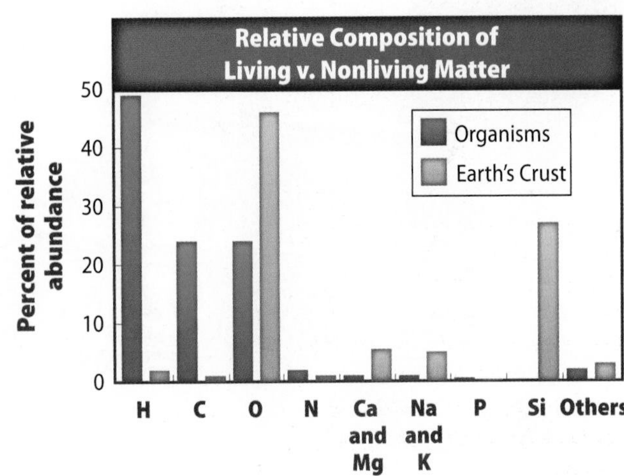

■ **Figure 4** Carbon-12 and carbon-13 occur naturally in living and nonliving things. All living things also contain a small amount of carbon-14.

Compare ***the similarities and differences of isotopes.***

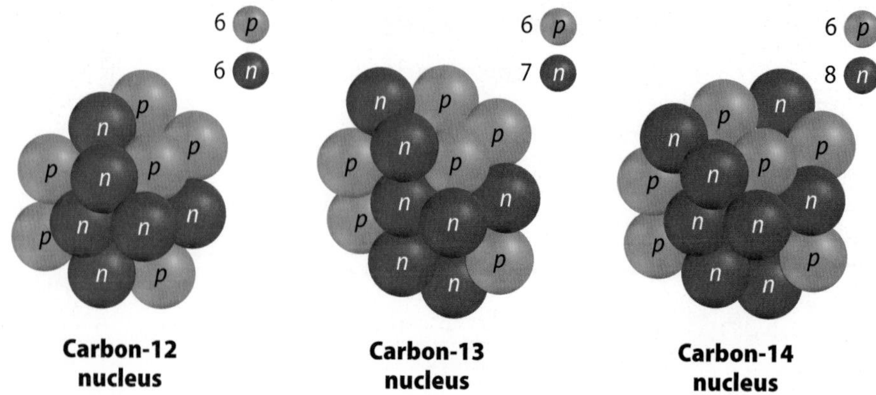

Isotopes Although atoms of the same element have the same number of protons and electrons, atoms of an element can have different numbers of neutrons, as shown in **Figure 4.** Atoms of the same element that have different numbers of neutrons are called **isotopes.** Isotopes of an element are identified by adding the number of protons and neutrons in the nucleus. For example, the most abundant form of carbon, carbon-12, has six protons and six neutrons in its nucleus. One carbon isotope—carbon-14—has six protons and eight neutrons. Isotopes of elements have the same chemical characteristics.

Radioactive isotopes Changing the number of neutrons in an atom does not change the overall charge of the atom. However, changing the number of neutrons can affect the stability of the nucleus, in some cases causing the nucleus to decay, or break apart. When a nucleus breaks apart, it gives off radiation that can be detected. Isotopes that give off radiation are called radioactive isotopes.

Carbon-14 is a radioactive isotope that is found in all living things. Scientists know the half-life, or the amount of time it takes for half of carbon-14 to decay, so they can calculate the age of an object by finding how much carbon-14 remains in the sample. Other radioactive isotopes have medical uses, as shown in **Figure 5.**

GET IT? **State** the difference between an isotope and a radioactive isotope.

■ **Figure 5** Radioactive isotopes are used to help doctors diagnose disease, and locate and treat certain types of cancer.

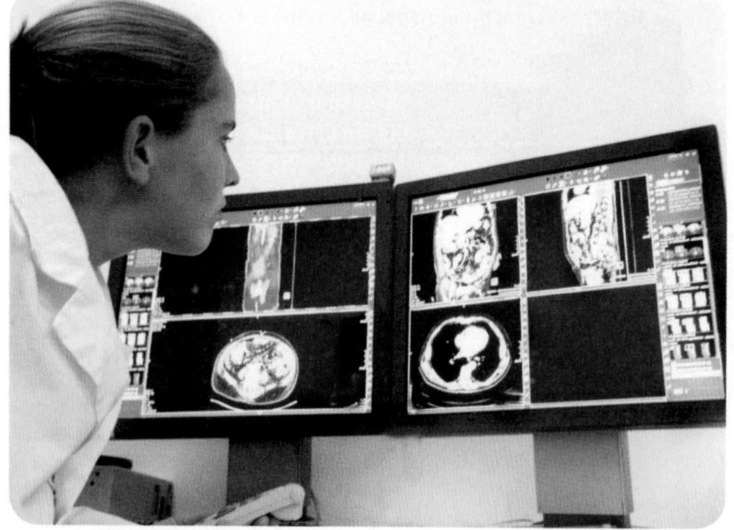

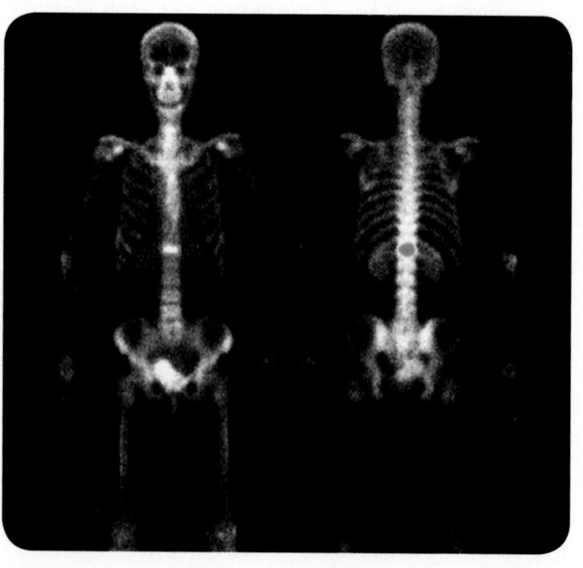

(l)Sigrid Gombert/Getty Images, (r)Neil Borden/Science Source

Brilliant fireworks displays depend on compounds such as the metal strontium.

Table salt is the compound NaCl.

Wetlands are sources of living things made of complex compounds and the simple compound methane (CH_4).

■ **Figure 6** You and your world are made of compounds.

Compounds

Elements can combine to form more complex substances. A **compound** is a pure substance formed when two or more different elements combine. There are millions of known compounds and thousands more discovered each year. **Figure 6** shows a few of them. Each compound has a chemical formula made up of the chemical symbols from the periodic table. You might know that water is the compound H_2O. Sodium chloride (NaCl) is the compound commonly called table salt. The fuel people use in cars is a mixture of hydrocarbon compounds. Hydrocarbons have only hydrogen and carbon atoms. Methane (CH_4) is the simplest hydrocarbon. Bacteria in areas such as the wetlands shown in **Figure 6** release 76 percent of global methane from natural sources by decomposing plants and other organisms. They are made of compounds, too.

Compounds have several unique characteristics. First, compounds are always formed from a specific combination of elements in a fixed ratio. Water always is formed in a ratio of two hydrogen atoms and one oxygen atom, and each water molecule has the same structure. Second, compounds are chemically and physically different from the elements that comprise them. For example, water has different properties than hydrogen and oxygen.

Another characteristic of compounds is that they cannot be broken down into simpler compounds or elements by physical means, such as tearing or crushing. Compounds, however, can be broken down by chemical means into simpler compounds or into their original elements. Consider again the example of water. You cannot pass water through a filter and separate the hydrogen from the oxygen, but a process called electrolysis, illustrated in **Figure 7,** can break water down into hydrogen gas and oxygen gas.

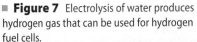

■ **Figure 7** Electrolysis of water produces hydrogen gas that can be used for hydrogen fuel cells.

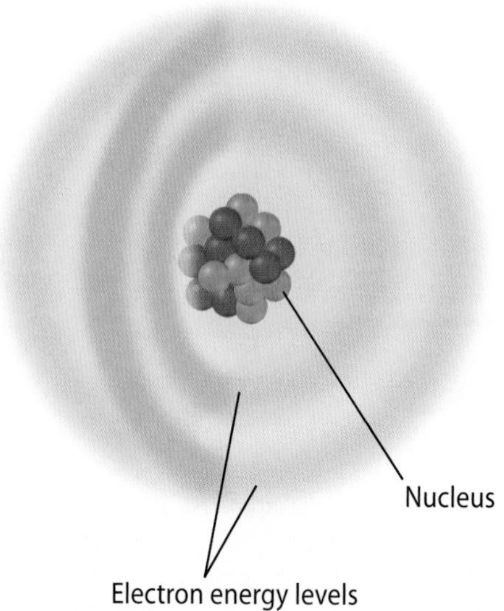

■ **Figure 8** Electrons are moving constantly within the energy levels surrounding the nucleus.

Chemical Bonds

Compounds such as water, salt, and methane are formed when two or more substances combine. The force that holds the substances together is called a chemical bond. Think back to the protons, neutrons, and electrons that make up an atom. The nucleus determines the chemical identity of an atom, and the electrons are involved directly in forming chemical bonds. Electrons travel around the nucleus of an atom in areas called energy levels, as illustrated in **Figure 8.** Each energy level has a specific number of electrons that it can hold at any time. The first energy level, which is the level closest to the nucleus, can hold up to two electrons. The second can hold up to eight electrons.

A partially filled energy level is not as stable as an energy level that is empty or completely filled. Atoms become more stable by losing electrons or attracting electrons from other atoms. This results in the formation of chemical bonds between atoms. It is the forming of chemical bonds that stores energy and the breaking of chemical bonds that provides energy for processes of growth, development, adaptation, and reproduction in living things. There are two main types of chemical bonds—covalent bonds and ionic bonds.

Covalent bonds When you were younger, you probably learned to share. If you had a book that your friend wanted to read as well, you could enjoy the story together. In this way, you both benefited from the book. Similarly, one type of chemical bond forms when atoms share electrons in their outer energy levels.

The chemical bond that forms when electrons are shared is called a **covalent bond. Figure 9** illustrates the covalent bonds between oxygen and hydrogen that form water. Each hydrogen (H) atom has one electron in its outermost energy level, and oxygen (O) has six. Because the outermost energy level of oxygen is the second level, which can hold up to eight electrons, oxygen has a strong tendency to fill the energy level by sharing the electrons from the two nearby hydrogen atoms. Hydrogen does not completely give up the electrons; it also has a strong tendency to share electrons with oxygen to fill its outermost energy level. Two covalent bonds form, which creates water.

Most compounds in living organisms have covalent bonds holding them together. Water and other substances with covalent bonds are called molecules. A **molecule** is a compound in which the atoms are held together by covalent bonds. Depending on the number of pairs of electrons that are shared, covalent bonds can be single, double, or triple, as shown in **Figure 10.**

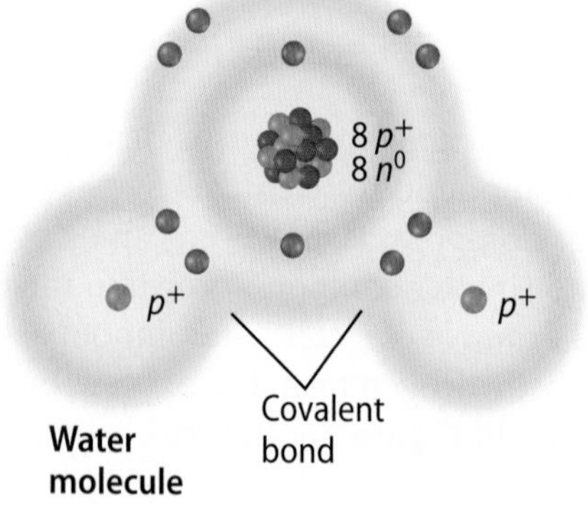

■ **Figure 9** In water (H_2O), two hydrogen atoms each share one electron with one oxygen atom. Because the oxygen atom needs two electrons to fill its outer energy level, it forms two covalent bonds, one with each hydrogen atom.

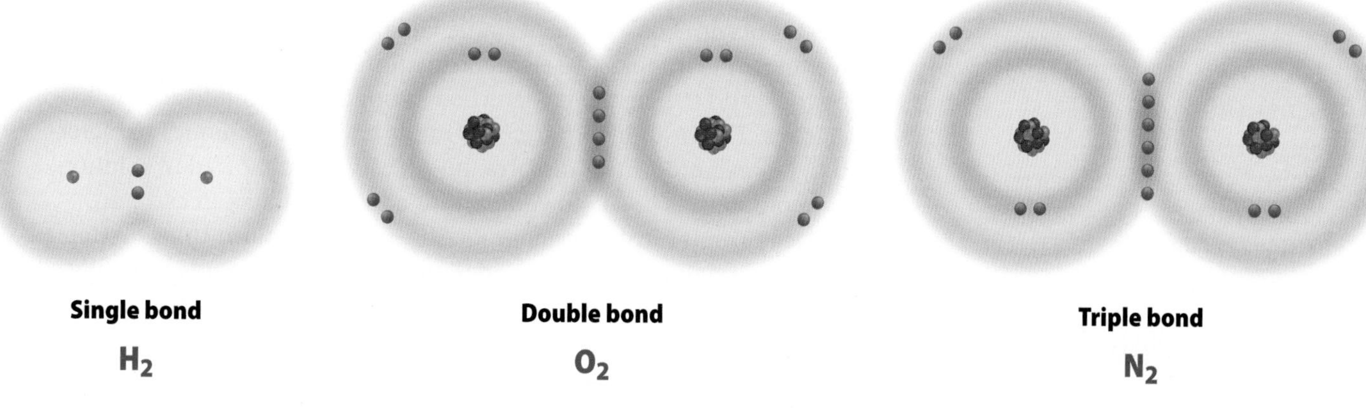

Figure 10 A single bond has one pair of shared electrons, a double bond has two pairs, and a triple bond has three pairs.

Ionic bonds Recall that atoms are neutral; they do not have an electric charge. Also recall that for an atom to be most stable, the outermost energy level should be either empty or completely filled. Some atoms tend to give up (donate) or obtain (accept) electrons to empty or fill the outer energy level to be stable. An atom that has lost or gained one or more electrons becomes an **ion** and carries an electric charge. For example, sodium has one electron in its outermost energy level. Sodium can become more stable if it gives up this one electron, leaving its outer energy level empty. When it gives away this one negative charge, the neutral sodium atom becomes a positively charged sodium ion (Na^+). Similarly, chlorine has seven electrons in its outer energy level and needs just one electron to fill it. When chlorine accepts an electron from a donor atom, such as sodium, chlorine becomes a negatively charged ion (Cl^-).

An **ionic bond** is an electrical attraction between two oppositely charged atoms or groups of atoms called ions. **Figure 11** shows how an ionic bond forms as a result of the electrical attraction between Na^+ and Cl^- to produce NaCl (sodium chloride). Substances formed by ionic bonds are called ionic compounds.

Ions in living things include sodium, potassium, calcium, chloride, and carbonate ions. They help maintain homeostasis as they travel in and out of cells. In addition, ions help transmit signals among cells that allow you to see, taste, hear, feel, and smell.

Figure 11 To form ions, sodium donates an electron and chlorine gains an electron. An ionic bond forms when the oppositely charged ions come close together.

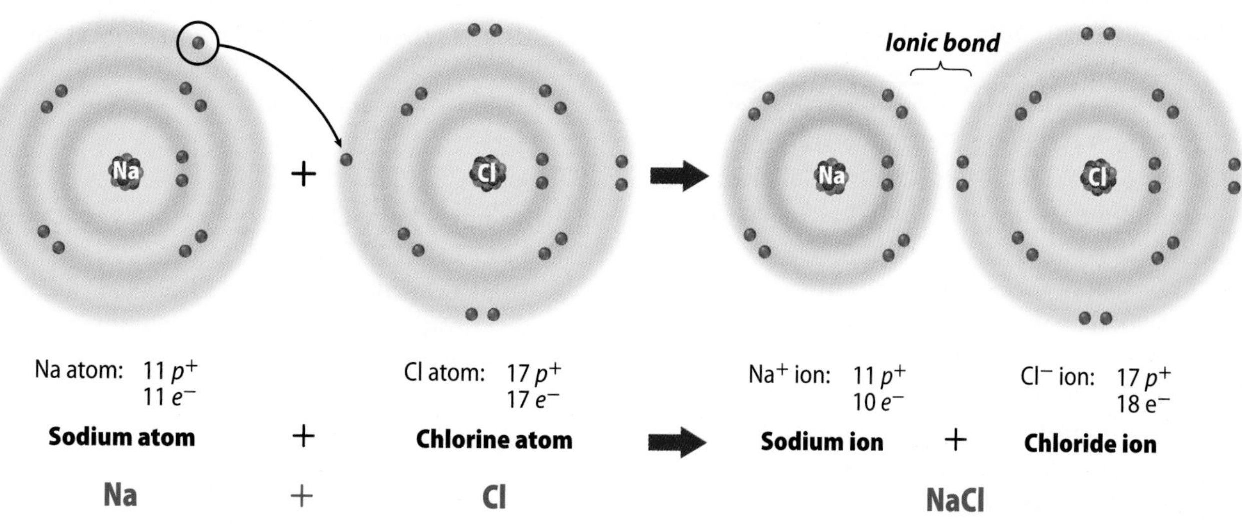

VOCABULARY

WORD ORIGIN

Atom
comes from the Greek word *atomos,* meaning *not divisible*

Some atoms tend to donate or accept electrons more easily than other atoms do. Look at the periodic table of elements inside the back cover of this textbook. The elements identified as metals tend to donate electrons, and the elements identified as nonmetals tend to accept electrons. The resulting ionic compounds have some unique characteristics. For example, most dissolve in water. When dissolved in solution, ionic compounds break down into ions and these ions can carry an electric current. Most ionic compounds, such as sodium chloride (table salt), are crystalline at room temperature. Ionic compounds generally have higher melting points than do molecular compounds formed by covalent bonds.

Although most ionic compounds are solid at room temperature, other ionic compounds are liquid at room temperature. Like their solid counterparts, ionic liquids are made up of positively and negatively charged ions. Ionic liquids have important potential in real-world applications as safe and environmentally friendly solvents that can possibly replace other harmful solvents. The key characteristic of ionic liquid solvents is that they typically do not evaporate and release chemicals into the atmosphere. Most ionic liquids are safe to handle and store, and they can be recycled after use. For these reasons, ionic liquids are attractive to industries that are dedicated to environmental responsibility.

GET IT? **Compare** ionic solids and liquids.

MiniLAB 1

Test for Simple Sugars

What common foods contain glucose? Glucose is a simple sugar that provides energy for cells. In this lab, you will use a reagent called Benedict's solution, which indicates the presence of –CHO (carbon, hydrogen, oxygen) groups. A color change determines the presence of glucose and other simple sugars in common foods.

Procedure 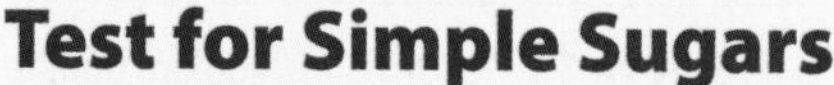

1. Read and complete the lab safety form.
2. Create a data table with columns labeled *Food Substance, Sugar Prediction, Observations,* and *Results.*
3. Choose four **food substances** from those provided by your teacher. Read the food labels and predict the presence of simple sugar in each food. Record your prediction.
4. Prepare a **hot water bath** with a temperature between 40°–50°C using a **hot plate** and **1000-mL beaker.**
5. Label four **test tubes.** Obtain a **graduated cylinder.** Add 10 mL of a different food substance to each test tube. Then add 10 mL of **distilled water.** Swirl gently to mix.
6. Add 5 mL of **Benedict's solution** to each tube. Use a clean **stirring rod** to mix the contents.
7. Using **test-tube holders,** warm the test tubes in the hot water bath for 2–3 min. Record your observations and results.

Analysis

1. **Interpret Data** Did any of the foods contain simple sugars? Explain.
2. **Think Critically** Could a food labeled "sugar-free" test positive using Benedict's solution as an indicator? Explain.

van der Waals Forces

You have learned that positive ions and negative ions form based on the ability of an atom to attract electrons. If the nucleus of the atom has a weak attraction for the electron, it will donate the electron to an atom with a stronger attraction. Similarly, elements in a covalent bond do not always attract electrons equally. Recall also that the electrons in a molecule are in random motion around the nuclei. This movement of electrons can cause an unequal distribution of the electron cloud around the molecule, creating temporary areas of slightly positive and negative charges.

When molecules come close together, the attractive forces between these positive and negative regions pull on the molecules and hold them together. These attractions between the molecules are called **van der Waals forces,** named for Dutch physicist Johannes van der Waals, who first described the phenomenon. The strength of the attraction depends on the size of the molecule, its shape, and its ability to attract electrons. Although van der Waals forces are not as strong as covalent and ionic bonds, they play a key role in biological processes.

Scientists have determined that geckos can climb smooth surfaces because of van der Waals forces between the atoms in the hairlike structures on their toes, shown in **Figure 12,** and the atoms on the surface they are climbing.

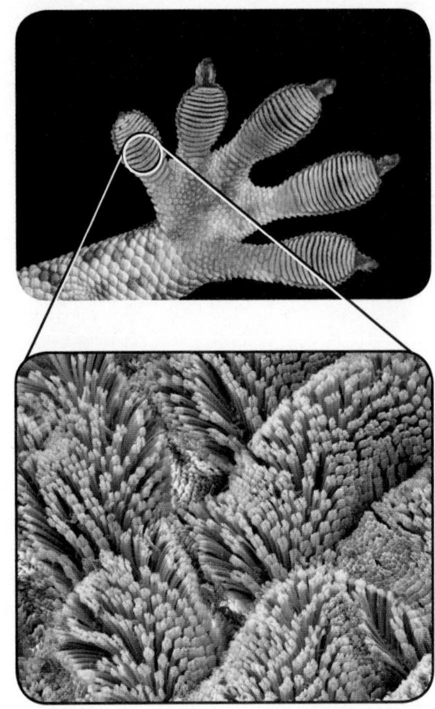

SEM Magnification: 240 ×

■ **Figure12** Geckos have millions of microscopic hairs on the bottoms of their feet that are about as long as two widths of a human hair. Each spreads into 1000 smaller pads.

van der Waals forces in water Consider how van der Waals forces work in a common substance—water. The areas of slight positive and negative charges around the water molecule are attracted to the opposite charge of other nearby water molecules. These forces hold the water molecules together. Without van der Waals forces, water molecules would not form droplets, and droplets would not form a surface of water. It is important to understand that van der Waals forces are the attractive forces between the water molecules, not the forces between the atoms that make up water.

REVIEW IT! Atoms, Elements, and Compounds

Section Summary

- Elements are pure substances made up of only one kind of atom.
- Isotopes are forms of the same element that have a different number of neutrons.
- Compounds are substances with unique properties that are formed when elements combine.
- Elements can form covalent and ionic bonds.

Self Check

Understand Main Ideas

1. MAINIDEA **Diagram** Sodium has 11 protons and 11 neutrons in its nucleus. Draw a sodium atom. Be sure to label the particles.
2. **Explain** why carbon monoxide (CO) is or is not an atom.
3. **Explain** Are all compounds molecules? Why or why not?
4. **Compare** van der Waals forces, ionic bonds, and covalent bonds.

Think Critically

5. **Explain** how the number of electrons in an energy level affects bond formation.

MATH IN ▶ Biology

6. Beryllium has four protons in its nucleus. How many neutrons are in beryllium-9? Explain how you calculated your answer.

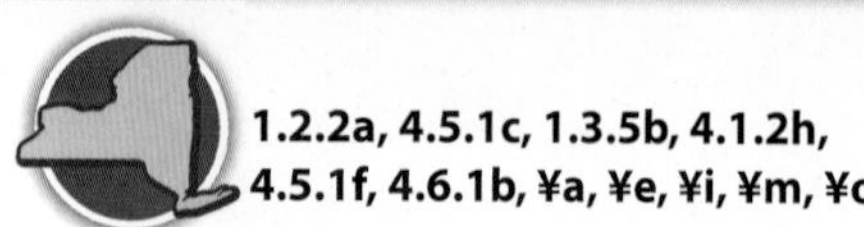

2 Chemical Reactions

1.2.2a, 4.5.1c, 1.3.5b, 4.1.2h, 4.5.1f, 4.6.1b, ¥a, ¥e, ¥i, ¥m, ¥o

MAIN IDEA

Chemical reactions allow living things to grow, develop, reproduce, and adapt.

Essential Questions

- What are the parts of a chemical reaction?
- How can energy changes be related to chemical reactions?
- What is the importance of enzymes in living organisms?

BIOLOGY 4U

When you lie down for the night, you might think that your body is completely at rest. In fact, you are still digesting the food that you ate that day, the scrape on your elbow is healing, and your muscles and bones are growing and developing. All the things that happen inside your body are the result of chemical reactions.

REVIEW VOCABULARY

process: a series of steps or actions that produce an end product

NEW VOCABULARY

chemical reaction
reactant
product
activation energy
catalyst
enzyme
substrate
active site

Multilingual eGlossary 

Reactants and Products

A new car with shining chrome and a clean appearance is appealing to many drivers. Over time, however, the car might get rusty and lose some of its appeal. Rust is a result of a chemical change called a chemical reaction. A **chemical reaction** is the process by which atoms or groups of atoms in substances are reorganized into different substances. Chemical bonds are broken and formed during chemical reactions. The rust on the chain in **Figure 13** is a compound called iron oxide (Fe_2O_3), and it was formed when oxygen (O_2) in the air reacted with iron (Fe).

It is important to know that substances can undergo changes that do not involve chemical reactions. For example, consider the water in **Figure 13.** The water is undergoing a physical change. A physical change alters a substance's appearance but not its composition. The water is water before and after the change.

How do you know when a chemical reaction has taken place? Although you might not be aware of all the reactions taking place inside your body, you know that the surface of the chain in **Figure 13** has changed. What was once silver and shiny is now dull and orange-brown. Other clues that a chemical reaction has taken place include the production of heat or light, and the formation of a new gas, liquid, or solid.

Figure 13 After a chemical change, such as rusting, a new substance is formed. During a physical change, such as ice melting or water boiling, the chemical makeup of the water is not altered.

Chemical change

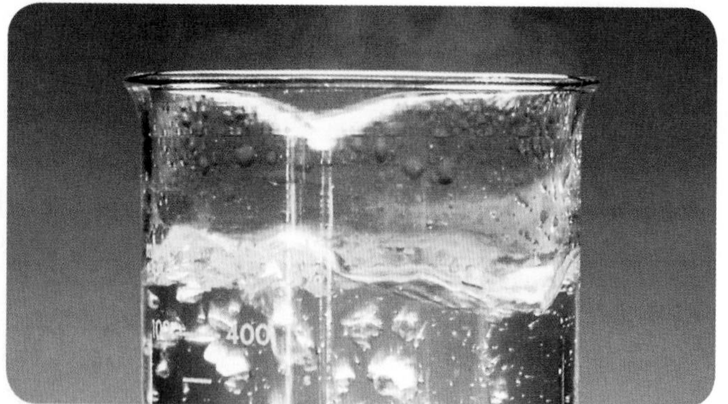

Physical change

Chemical equations When scientists write chemical reactions, they express each component of the reaction in a chemical equation. In written chemical equations, chemical formulas describe the substances in the reaction with arrows indicating the process of change.

Reactants and products A chemical equation shows the **reactants,** the starting substances, on the left side of the arrow. The **products,** the substances formed during the reaction, are on the right side of the arrow. The arrow can be read as "yields" or "react to form."

$$\text{Reactants} \longrightarrow \text{Products}$$

The following chemical equation can be written to describe the reaction that provides energy to the volleyball players in **Figure 14.**

$$C_6H_{12}O_6 + O_2 \longrightarrow CO_2 + H_2O$$

Glucose and oxygen react to form carbon dioxide and water.

Figure 14 The process that provides your body with energy involves the reaction of glucose with oxygen to form carbon dioxide and water.

Balanced equations In chemical reactions, matter cannot be created or destroyed. This principle is called the law of conservation of mass. Accordingly, all chemical equations must show this balance of mass. This means that the number of atoms of each element on the reactant side must equal the number of atoms of the same element on the product side. Coefficients are used to make the number of atoms on each side of the arrow equal.

$$C_6H_{12}O_6 + 6O_2 \longrightarrow 6CO_2 + 6H_2O$$

Multiply the coefficient by the subscript for each element. You can see in this example that there are six carbon atoms, twelve hydrogen atoms, and eighteen oxygen atoms on each side of the arrow. The equation confirms that the number of atoms on each side is equal, and therefore the equation is balanced.

GET IT? **Explain** why chemical equations must be balanced.

VOCABULARY

ACADEMIC VOCABULARY

Coefficient

in a chemical equation, the number written in front of a reactant or a product

The number 6 in $6Fe_2O_3$ is a coefficient.

Energy of Reactions

Connection to Physics A sugar cookie is made with flour, sugar, and other ingredients mixed together, but it is not a cookie until it is baked. Something must start the change from dough to cookie. The key to starting a chemical reaction is energy. For the chemical reactions that transform the dough to a cookie, energy in the form of heat is needed. Similarly, most compounds in living things cannot undergo chemical reactions without energy.

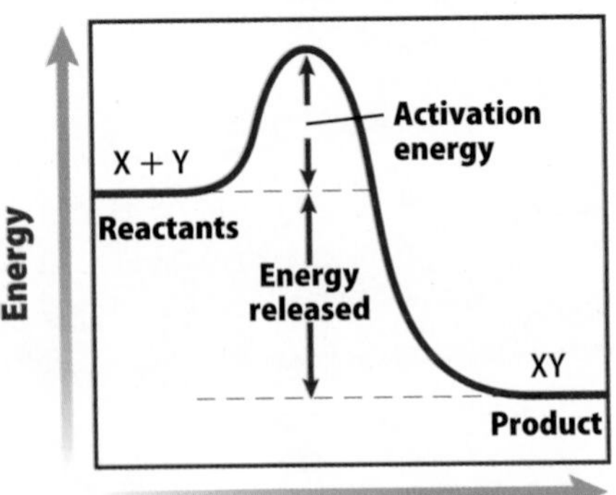

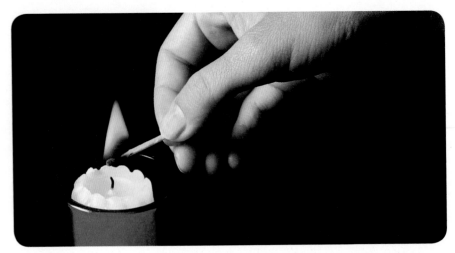

■ **Figure 15** The flame of the match provides activation energy—the amount of energy needed to begin a reaction. The reaction gives off energy in the form of heat and light.

Activation energy The minimum amount of energy needed for reactants to form products in a chemical reaction is called the **activation energy.** For example, you know that a candle will not burn until you light its wick. The flame provides the activation energy for the reaction of the substances in the candle wick with oxygen. In this case, once the reaction begins, no further input of energy is needed and the candle continues to burn on its own. **Figure 15** shows that for the reactants X and Y to form product XY, energy is required to start the reaction. The peak in the graph represents the amount of energy that must be added to the system to make the reaction occur. Some reactions rarely happen because they have a very high activation energy.

Virtual Lab 

Video Lab 

Energy change in chemical reactions Compare how energy changes during the reaction in **Figure 15** to how energy changes during the reaction in **Figure 16.** Both reactions require activation energy to get started. However, the reaction in **Figure 15** has lower energy in the product than in the reactants. This reaction is exothermic—it released energy in the form of heat. The reaction in **Figure 16** is endothermic—it absorbed heat energy. The energy of the products is higher than the energy of the reactants. In every chemical reaction, there is a change in energy caused by the making and breaking of chemical bonds as reactants form products. Exothermic reactions keep your internal body temperature at about 37°C.

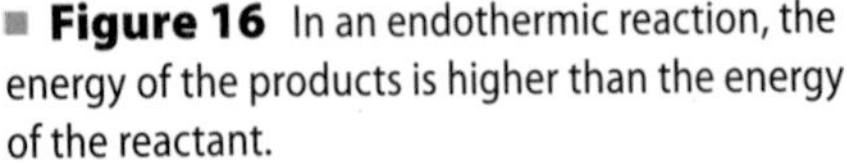
■ **Figure 16** In an endothermic reaction, the energy of the products is higher than the energy of the reactant.

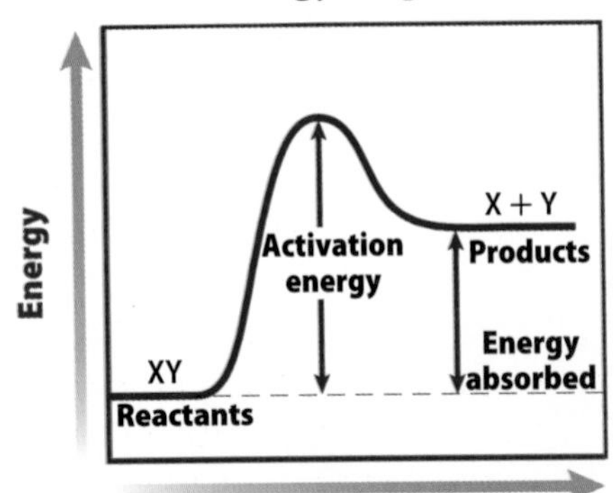

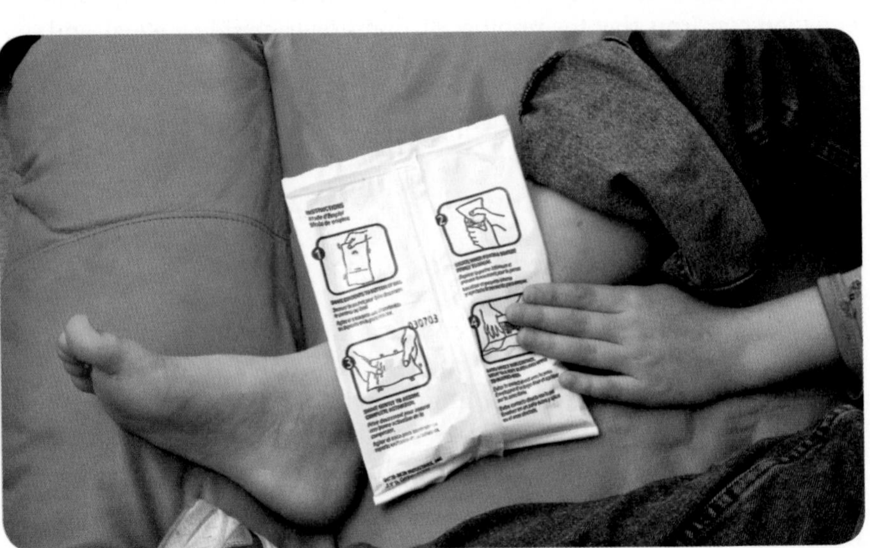

Enzymes

All living things are chemical factories driven by chemical reactions. However, these chemical reactions proceed very slowly when carried out in the laboratory because the activation energy is high. To be useful to living organisms, additional substances must be present where the chemical reactions occur to reduce the activation energy and allow the reaction to proceed quickly.

A **catalyst** is a substance that lowers the activation energy needed to start a chemical reaction. Although a catalyst is important in speeding up a chemical reaction, it does not increase how much product is made and it does not get used up in the reaction. Scientists use many types of catalysts to make reactions occur thousands of times faster than the reaction would be able to occur without the catalyst.

Special proteins called **enzymes** are the biological catalysts that speed up the rate of chemical reactions in biological processes. Enzymes are essential to life. Compare the progress of the reaction described in **Figure 17** to see the effect of an enzyme on a chemical reaction. Like all catalysts, the enzyme is not used up by the chemical reaction. Once it has participated in a chemical reaction, it can be used again.

An enzyme's name describes what it does. For example, amylase is an important enzyme found in saliva. Digestion of food begins in the mouth when amylase speeds the breakdown of amylose, one of the components of starch. Like amylase, most enzymes are specific to one reaction.

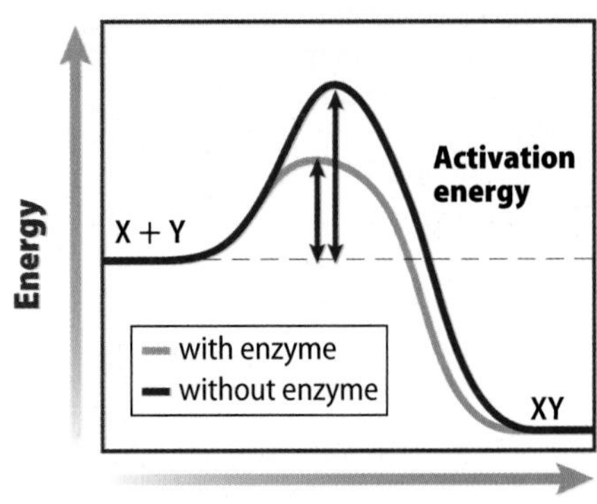

Figure 17 When an enzyme acts as a biological catalyst, the reaction occurs at a rate that is useful to cells.

Compare ***the activation energy of the reaction without an enzyme to the activation energy of the reaction with an enzyme.***

MiniLAB 2

Investigate Enzymatic Browning

What factors affect enzymatic browning? When sliced, an apple's soft tissue is exposed to oxygen, causing a chemical reaction called oxidation. Enzymes in the apple speed this reaction, producing darkened, discolored fruit. In this lab, you will investigate methods used to slow enzymatic browning.

Procedure

1. Read and complete the lab safety form.
2. Predict the relative amount of discoloration that each of the following apple wedges will show when exposed to air. Justify your predictions.
   Sample 1: Untreated apple wedge
   Sample 2: Apple wedge submerged in boiling water
   Sample 3: Apple wedge submerged in lemon juice
   Sample 4: Apple wedge submerged in sugar solution
3. Prepare 75 mL of each of the following: **boiling water, lemon juice,** and **sugar solution** in three **250-mL beakers.**
4. Slice an **apple** into four wedges. Immediately use **tongs** to submerge each wedge in a different liquid. Put one wedge aside.
5. Submerge the wedges for three minutes, then place them on a **paper towel,** skin-side down. Observe for 10 min, and then record the relative amount of discoloration of each apple wedge.

Analysis

1. **Analyze** how each treatment affected the chemical reaction that occurred on the fruit's soft tissue. Why were some of the treatments successful?
2. **Think critically** about what factors a restaurant owner who wants to serve fresh-cut fruit might consider when choosing a recipe and preparation method.

Figure 18 Substrates interact with enzymes at specific places called active sites. Only substrates with a specific shape can bind to the active site of an enzyme.

Animation

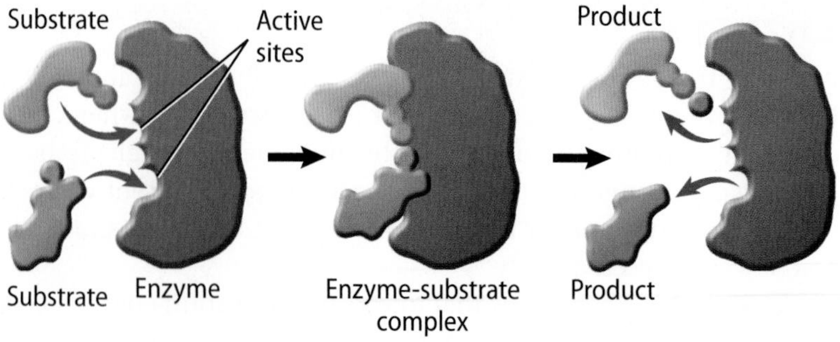

FOLDABLES®
Incorporate information from this section into your Foldable.

Follow **Figure 18** to learn how an enzyme works. The reactants that bind to the enzyme are called **substrates.** The specific location where a substrate binds on an enzyme is called the **active site.** The active site and the substrate have complementary shapes. This enables them to interact in a precise manner, similar to the way in which puzzle pieces fit together. As shown in **Figure 18,** only substrates with the same size and shape as the active site will bind to the enzyme.

Once the substrates bind to the active site, the active site changes shape and forms the enzyme-substrate complex. The enzyme-substrate complex helps chemical bonds in the reactants to be broken and new bonds to form—the substrates react to form products. The enzyme then releases the products.

Factors such as pH, temperature, and other substances affect enzyme activity. For example, most enzymes in human cells are most active at an optimal temperature close to 37°C. However, enzymes in other organisms, such as bacteria, can be active at other temperatures.

Enzymes affect many biological processes. When a person is bitten by a venomous snake, enzymes in the venom break down the membranes of that person's red blood cells. Hard green apples ripen because of the action of enzymes. Photosynthesis and cellular respiration provide energy for the cell with the help of enzymes. Just as worker bees are important for the survival of a beehive, enzymes are the chemical workers in cells.

REVIEW IT! Chemical Reactions

Section Summary

- Balanced chemical equations must show an equal number of atoms for each element on both sides.
- Activation energy is the energy required to begin a reaction.
- Catalysts are substances that alter chemical reactions.
- Enzymes are biological catalysts.

Self Check

Understand Main Ideas

1. MAINIDEA **Identify** the parts of this chemical reaction: $A + B \rightarrow AB$.
2. **Diagram** the energy changes that can take place in a chemical reaction.
3. **Explain** why the number of atoms of reactants must equal the number of atoms of products formed.
4. **Identify and investigate** the role of enzymes to living organisms.

Think Critically

MATH IN ▶ Biology

5. For the following chemical reaction, label the reactants and products, and then balance the chemical equation. ____$H_2O_2 \rightarrow$ ____$H_2O +$ ____O_2

WRITING IN ▶ Biology

6. Draw a diagram of a roller coaster and write a paragraph relating the ride to activation energy and a chemical reaction.

3 Water and Solutions

MAIN IDEA
The properties of water make it well suited to help maintain homeostasis in an organism.

Essential Questions

- How does the structure of water make it a good solvent?
- What are the similarities and differences between solutions and suspensions?
- What are the differences between acids and bases?

BIOLOGY 4 U

You probably know that the main color on a globe is blue. That's because water covers about 70 percent of Earth's surface, giving it the blue color you see from a distance. Now imagine zooming in to a single cell of an organism on Earth. Water accounts for approximately 70 percent of that cell's mass. It is one of the most important molecules for life.

Review Vocabulary

physical property: characteristic of matter, such as color or melting point, that can be observed or measured without changing the composition of the substance

New Vocabulary

polar molecule	solute
hydrogen bond	acid
mixture	base
solution	pH
solvent	buffer

Water's Polarity

Earlier in this chapter, you discovered that water molecules are formed by covalent bonds that link two hydrogen (H) atoms to one oxygen (O) atom. Because electrons are more strongly attracted to the oxygen atom's nucleus, the electrons in the covalent bond with hydrogen are not shared equally. In water, the electrons spend more time near the oxygen atom's nucleus than they do near the hydrogen atoms' nuclei. **Figure 19** shows that there is an unequal distribution of electrons in a water molecule. This, along with the bent shape of water molecules, results in the oxygen end of the molecule having a slightly negative charge and the hydrogen ends of the molecule having a slightly positive charge. Molecules that have an unequal distribution of charges are called **polar molecules,** meaning that they have oppositely charged regions.

Polarity is the property of having two opposite poles, or ends. A magnet has polarity—there is a north pole and a south pole. When the two ends are brought close to each other, they attract each other. Similarly, when a charged region of a polar molecule comes close to the oppositely charged region of another polar molecule, a weak electrostatic attraction results. In water, the electrostatic attraction is called a hydrogen bond. A **hydrogen bond** is a weak interaction involving a hydrogen atom and a fluorine, oxygen, or nitrogen atom. Hydrogen bonding is a strong type of van der Waals force. **Figure 20** describes polarity and the other unique properties of water that make it important to living things.

Figure 19 Because water molecules have a bent shape and electrons are not shared equally between hydrogen and oxygen, hydrogen bonds form among the molecules. Due to the attraction among the atoms that make up water, the surface of water supports a water strider.

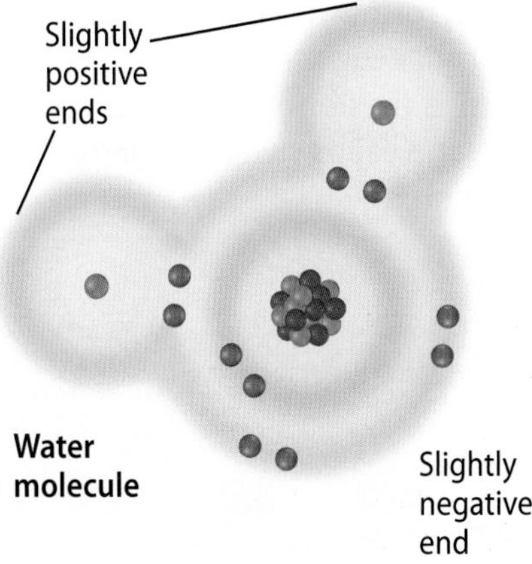

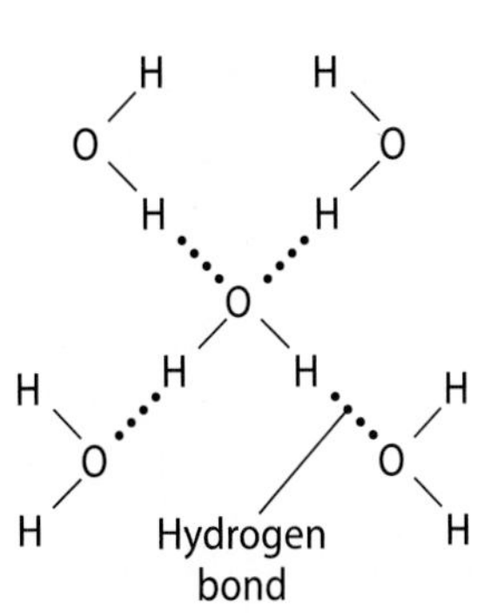

Water strider

NPS Photo by Rosalie LaRue

VISUALIZING Properties of Water

Figure 20 Water is vital to life on Earth. Its properties allow it to provide environments suitable for life and to help organisms maintain homeostasis. Humans can survive many days without food but only a few days without water.

Water Molecule

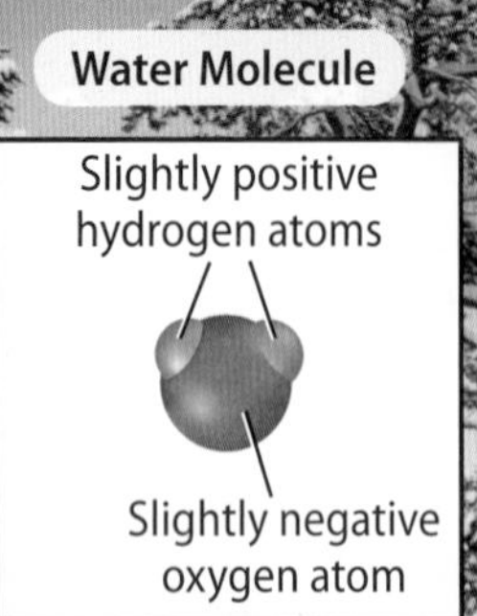

A water molecule is made up of one oxygen atom and two hydrogen atoms.
A water molecule is polar. Its bent shape results in a slightly positive charge on the hydrogen atoms and a slightly negative charge on the oxygen atom. As a result, it forms hydrogen bonds.
Water is called the universal solvent because many substances dissolve in it.

Hydrogen Bonding

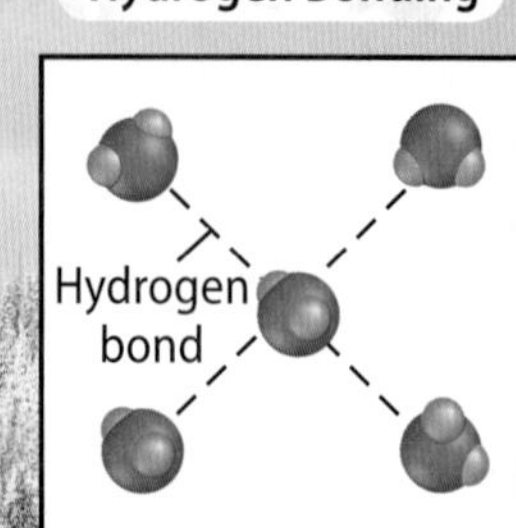

Solid

Liquid water becomes more dense as it cools to 4°C. Yet, ice is less dense than liquid water. As a result, nutrients in bodies of water mix because of changes in water density during spring and fall. Also, fish can survive in winter because ice floats—they continue to live and function in the water beneath the ice.

Liquid

Water is adhesive—it forms hydrogen bonds with molecules on other surfaces. Capillary action is the result of adhesion. Water travels up the stem of a plant, and seeds swell and germinate by capillary action.

Water is cohesive—the molecules are attracted to each other because of hydrogen bonds. This attraction creates surface tension, which causes water to form droplets and allows insects and leaves to rest on the surface of a body of water.

Mixtures with Water

You are probably familiar with powdered drink products that dissolve in water to form a flavored beverage. When you add a powdered substance to water, it does not react with water to form a new product. You create a mixture. A **mixture** is a combination of two or more substances in which each substance retains its individual characteristics and properties.

Homogeneous mixtures When a mixture has a uniform composition throughout, it is called a homogeneous (hoh muh JEE nee us) mixture. A **solution** is another name for a homogeneous mixture. For example, in the powdered drink mix solution shown in **Figure 21,** the drink mix is on top, in the middle, and at the bottom of the container. The water retains its properties and the drink mix retains its properties.

In a solution, there are two components: a solvent and a solute. A **solvent** is a substance in which another substance is dissolved. A **solute** is the substance that is dissolved in the solvent. In the case of the drink mix, water is the solvent and the powdered substance is the solute. A mixture of salt and water is another example of a solution because the solute (salt) dissolves completely in the solvent (water). Saliva moistens your mouth and begins the digestion of some of your food. Saliva is a solution that contains water, proteins, and salts. In addition, the air you breathe is a solution of gases.

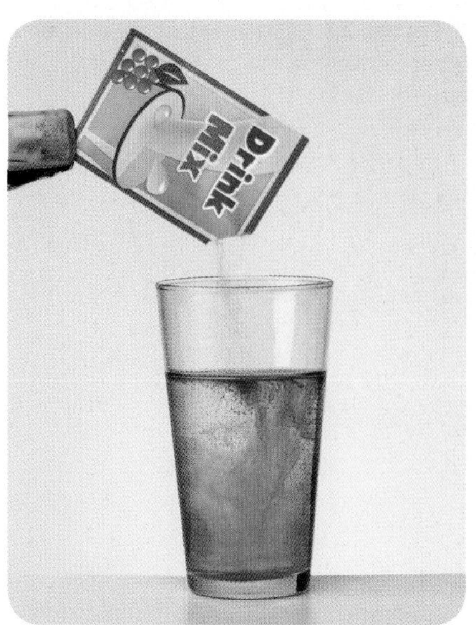

■ **Figure 21** The drink mix forms a homogeneous mixture in water. The particles of the solute (drink mix) are dissolved and spread throughout the solvent (water).

Heterogeneous mixtures Think about the last time you ate a salad. Perhaps it contained lettuce and other vegetables, croutons, and salad dressing. Your salad was a heterogeneous mixture. In a heterogeneous mixture, the components remain distinct, that is, you can tell what they are individually. Compare the mixture of sand and water to the solution of salt and water next to it in **Figure 22.** Sand and water form a type of heterogeneous mixture called a suspension. Over time, the particles in a suspension settle to the bottom.

A colloid is a heterogeneous mixture in which the particles do not settle out like the sand settled from the water. You are probably familiar with many colloids, including fog, smoke, butter, mayonnaise, milk, paint, and ink. Blood is a colloid made up of plasma, cells, and other substances.

VOCABULARY

ACADEMIC VOCABULARY

Suspend
to keep from falling or sinking
A slender thread suspended the spider from the web.

GET IT? **Distinguish** between solutions and suspensions.

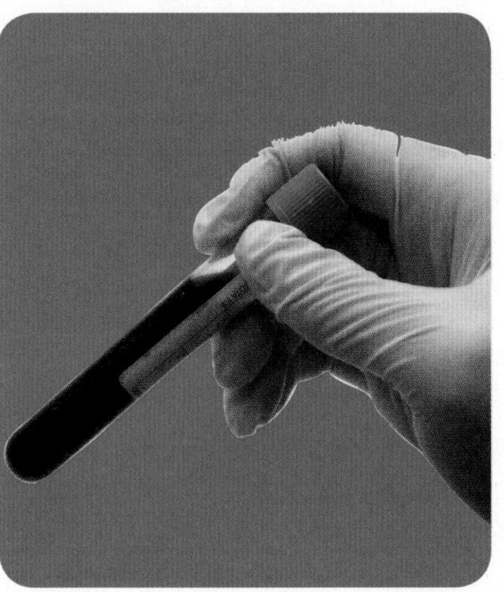

■ **Figure 22**
Left: Sand and water form a heterogeneous mixture; you can see both the liquid and the solid. The homogeneous mixture of salt and water is a liquid; you cannot see the salt.
Right: Blood is a heterogeneous mixture called a colloid.

■ **Figure 23** Substances that release H^+ in water are acids. Substances that release OH^- in water are bases.

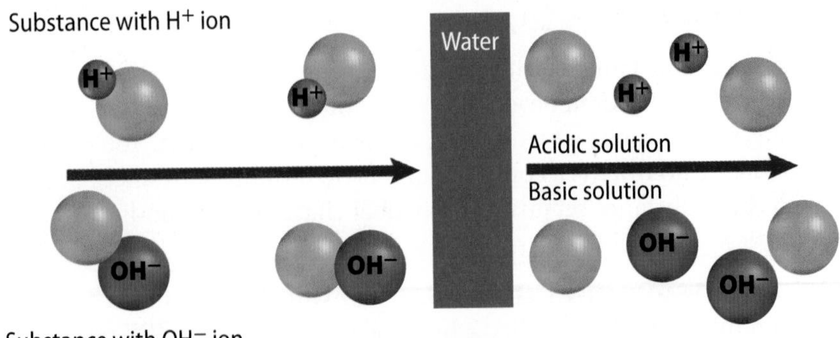

Acids and bases Many solutes readily dissolve in water because of water's polarity. This means that an organism, which might be as much as 70 percent water, can be a container for a variety of solutions. When a substance that contains hydrogen is dissolved in water, the substance might release a hydrogen ion (H^+) because it is attracted to the negatively charged oxygen atoms in water, as shown in **Figure 23.** Substances that release hydrogen ions when they are dissolved in water are called **acids.** The more hydrogen ions a substance releases, the more acidic the solution becomes.

Similarly, substances that release hydroxide ions (OH^-) when they are dissolved in water are called **bases.** Sodium hydroxide (NaOH) is a common base that breaks apart in water to release sodium ions (Na^+) and hydroxide ions (OH^-). The more hydroxide ions a substance releases, the more basic the solution becomes.

Acids and bases are key substances in biology. Many of the foods and beverages that we eat and drink are acidic, and the substances in the stomach that break down the food, called gastric juices, are highly acidic.

Data Analysis LAB 1

Based on Real Data*

Recognize Cause and Effect

How do pH and temperature affect protease activity? Proteases are enzymes that break down protein. Bacterial proteases often are used in detergents to help remove stains such as egg, grass, blood, and sweat from clothes.

Data and Observations

A protease from a newly isolated strain of bacteria was studied over a range of pH values and temperatures.

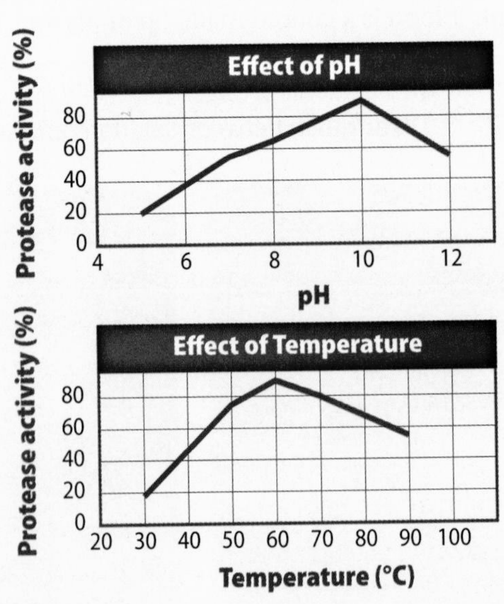

Think Critically

1. **Identify** the range of pH values and temperatures used in the experiment.
2. **Summarize** the results of the two graphs.
3. **Infer** If a laundry detergent is basic and requires hot water to be most effective, would this protease be useful? Explain.

*Data obtained from: Adinarayana, et al. 2003. Purification and partial characterization of thermostable serine alkaline protease from a newly isolated *Bacillus subtilis* PE-11. *AAPS PharmSciTech 4: article 56.*

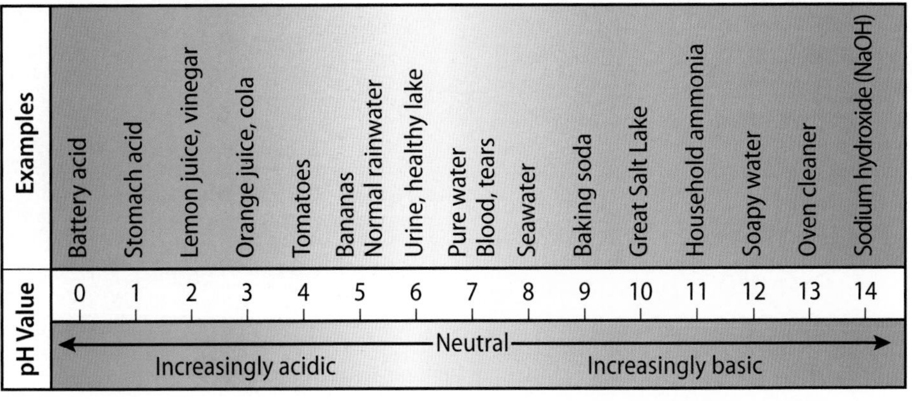

Figure 24 The pH scale is used to indicate the relative strength of acids and bases—in other words, the amount of hydrogen ions (H^+) in a solution.

pH and buffers The amount of hydrogen ions or hydroxide ions in a solution determines the strength of an acid or base. Scientists have devised a convenient way to measure how acidic or basic a solution is. The measure of concentration of H^+ in a solution is called **pH.** As shown in **Figure 24,** pure water is neutral and has a pH value of 7.0. Acidic solutions have an abundance of H^+ and have pH values lower than 7. Basic solutions have more OH^- than H^+ and have pH values higher than 7.

Connection to Health The majority of biological processes carried out by cells occur between pH 6.5 and 7.5. In order to maintain homeostasis, it is important to control H^+ levels. If you've ever had an upset stomach, you might have taken an antacid to feel better. The antacid tablet is a buffer to help neutralize the stomach acid. **Buffers** are mixtures that can react with acids or bases to keep the pH within a particular range. In cells, buffers keep the pH in a cell within the 6.5 to 7.5 pH range. Your blood, for example, contains buffers that keep the pH about 7.4.

CAREERS IN BIOLOGY

Pool Technician Every recreational body of water, such as a recreational swimming pool, training spa, or medical therapy pool, must meet strict requirements for water quality. Pool technicians make sure these requirements are met by monitoring water pH, bacteria and algae levels, and water clarity.

REVIEW IT! Water and Solutions

Section Summary

- Water is a polar molecule.
- Solutions are homogeneous mixtures formed when a solute is dissolved in a solvent.
- Acids are substances that release hydrogen ions into solutions. Bases are substances that release hydroxide ions into solutions.
- pH is a measure of the concentration of hydrogen ions in a solution.

Self Check

Understand Main Ideas

1. MAINIDEA **Describe** one way in which water helps maintain homeostasis in an organism.
2. **Relate** the structure of water to its ability to act as a solvent.
3. **Draw** a pH scale and label water (H_2O), hydrochloric acid (HCl), and sodium hydroxide (NaOH) in their general areas on the scale.
4. **Compare and contrast** solutions and suspensions. Give examples of each.

Think Critically

5. **Explain** how baking soda ($NaHCO_3$) is basic. Describe the effect of baking soda on the H^+ ion concentration of stomach contents with pH 4.
6. **Predict** If you add hydrochloric acid (HCl) to water, what effect would this have on the H^+ ion concentration? On the pH?

4 The Building Blocks of Life

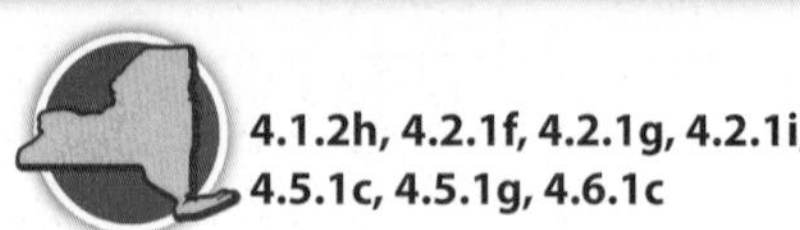

MAINIDEA

Organisms are made up of carbon-based molecules.

Essential Questions

- What is the role of carbon in living organisms?
- What are the four major families of biological macromolecules?
- What are the functions of each group of biological macromolecules?

BIOLOGY 4 U

Children enjoy toy trains because they can link long lines of cars together and make patterns by joining cars of similar color or function. Similarly, in biology, there are large molecules made of many smaller units joined together.

Review Vocabulary

organic compound: a carbon-based substance that is the basis of living matter

New Vocabulary

macromolecule
polymer
carbohydrate
lipid
protein
amino acid
nucleic acid
nucleotide

Multilingual eGlossary 

Organic Chemistry

The element carbon is a component of almost all biological molecules. For this reason, life on Earth often is considered carbon-based. Because carbon is an essential element, scientists have devoted an entire branch of chemistry, called organic chemistry, to the study of organic compounds, which are those compounds containing carbon.

As shown in **Figure 25,** carbon has four electrons in its outermost energy level. Recall that the second energy level can hold eight electrons, so one carbon atom can form four covalent bonds with other atoms. These covalent bonds enable the carbon atoms to bond to each other, which results in a variety of important organic compounds. These compounds can be in the shape of straight chains, branched chains, and rings, such as those illustrated in **Figure 25.** Together, carbon compounds lead to the diversity of life on Earth.

■ **Figure 25** The amazing diversity of life is based on the variety of carbon compounds. The half-filled outer energy level of carbon allows for the formation of straight chain, branched, and ring molecules.

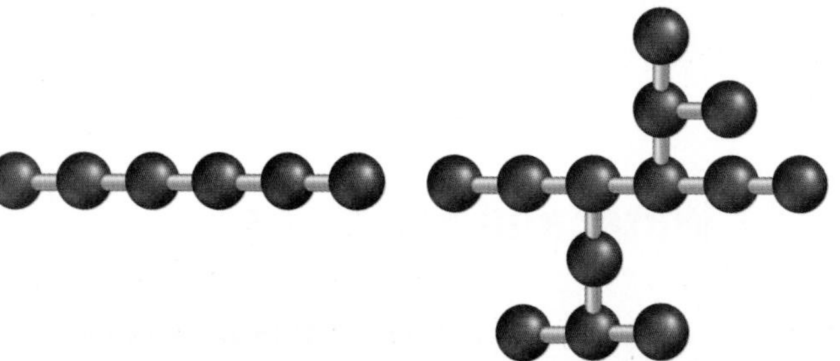

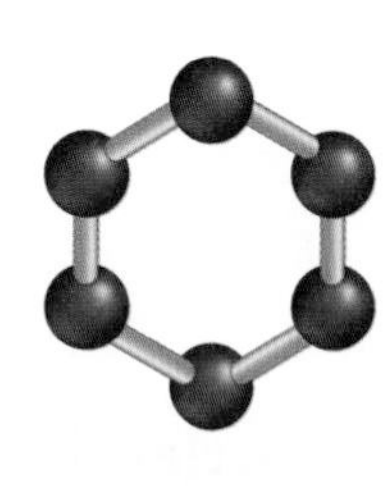

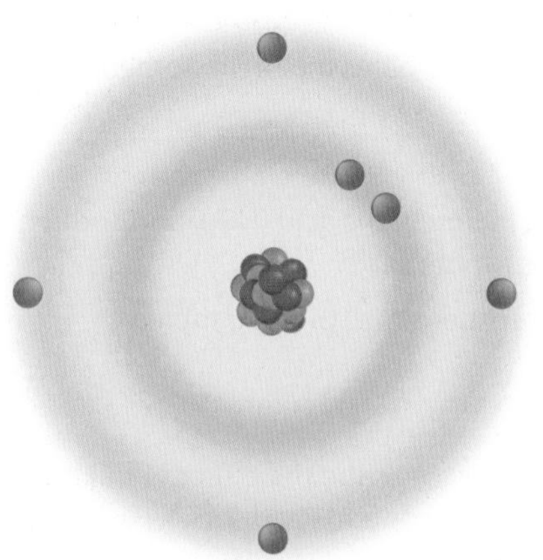

Seth Lazar/Alamy

Macromolecules

Carbon atoms can be joined to form carbon molecules. Similarly, most cells store small carbon compounds that serve as building blocks for large molecules. **Macromolecules** are large molecules that are formed by joining smaller organic molecules together. These large molecules are also called polymers. **Polymers** are molecules made from repeating units of identical or nearly identical compounds called monomers that are linked together by a series of covalent bonds. As shown in **Table 1,** biological macromolecules are organized into four major categories: carbohydrates, lipids, proteins, and nucleic acids.

GET IT? **Use an analogy** to describe macromolecules.

VOCABULARY

WORD ORIGIN

Polymer

poly- prefix; from Greek, meaning *many*

-meros from Greek, meaning *part*

Table 1 Biological Macromolecules — Interactive Table

Group	Example	Function
Carbohydrates	**Bread and grains**	• Store energy • Provide structural support
Lipids	**Bees' wax**	• Store energy • Provide barriers
Proteins	**Hemoglobin**	• Transport substances • Speed reactions • Provide structural support • Make hormones
Nucleic acids	**DNA**	• Store and communicate genetic information

STUDY TIP

DOUBLE-ENTRY NOTES Fold a piece of paper in half lengthwise and write the boldfaced subheadings that appear under the *Biological Macromolecules* heading on the left side. As you read the text, make a bulleted list of notes about the important ideas and terms.

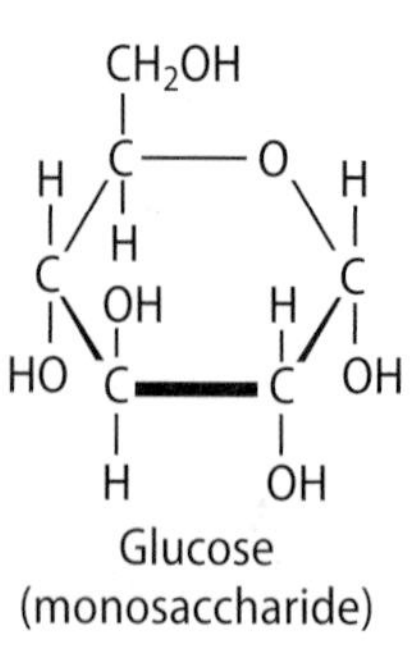

Sucrose
(disaccharide)

Glycogen
(polysaccharide)

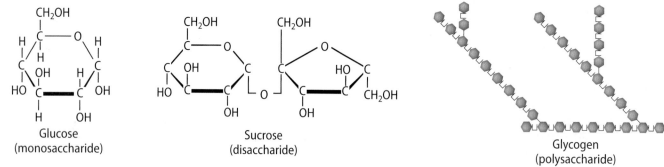

■ **Figure 26** Glucose is a monosaccharide. Sucrose is a disaccharide composed of glucose and fructose monosaccharides. Glycogen is a branched polysaccharide made from glucose monomers.

Carbohydrates Compounds composed of carbon, hydrogen, and oxygen in a ratio of one oxygen and two hydrogen atoms for each carbon atom are called **carbohydrates.** A general formula for carbohydrates is written as $(CH_2O)_n$. Here the subscript n indicates the number of CH_2O units in a chain. Biologically important carbohydrates that have values of n ranging from three to seven are called simple sugars, or monosaccharides (mah nuh SA kuh ridz). The monosaccharide glucose, shown in **Figure 26,** plays a central role as an energy source for organisms.

Personal Tutor

Monosaccharides can be linked to form larger molecules. Two monosaccharides joined together form a disaccharide (di SA kuh rid). Like glucose, disaccharides serve as energy sources. Sucrose, also shown in **Figure 26,** which is table sugar, and lactose, which is a component of milk, are both disaccharides. Longer carbohydrate molecules are called polysaccharides. One important polysaccharide is glycogen, which is shown in **Figure 26.** Glycogen is an energy storage form of glucose that is found in the liver and skeletal muscle. When the body needs energy between meals or during physical activity, glycogen is broken down into glucose.

In addition to their roles as energy sources, carbohydrates have other important functions in biology. In plants, a carbohydrate called cellulose provides structural support in cell walls. As shown in **Figure 27,** cellulose is made of chains of glucose linked together into tough fibers that are well suited for their structural role. Chitin (KI tun) is a nitrogen-containing polysaccharide that is the main component in the hard outer shells of shrimp, lobsters, and some insects, as well as the cell walls of some fungi.

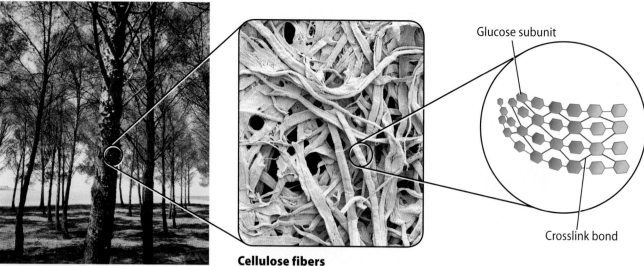

■ **Figure 27** The cellulose in plant cells provides the structural support for trees to stand in a forest.

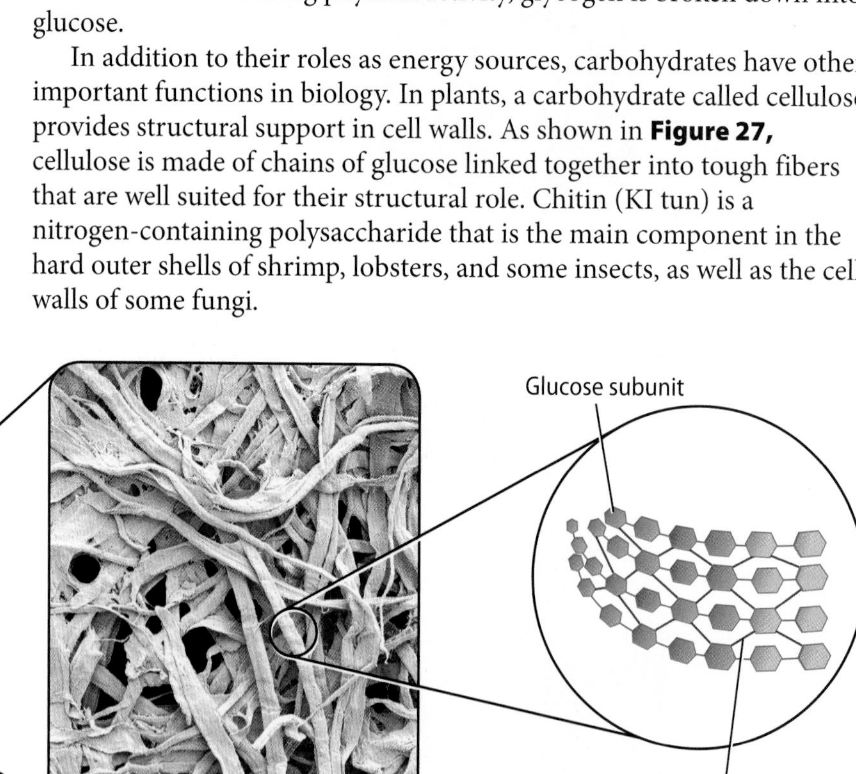

Lipids Another important group of biological macromolecules is the lipid group. **Lipids** are molecules made mostly of carbon and hydrogen that make up the fats, oils, and waxes. Lipids are composed of fatty acids, glycerol, and other components. The primary function of lipids is to store energy. A lipid called a triglyceride (tri GLIH suh rid) is a fat if it is solid at room temperature and an oil if it is liquid at room temperature. In addition, triglycerides are stored in the fat cells of the body. Plant leaves are coated with lipids called waxes to prevent water loss, and the honeycomb in a beehive is made of beeswax.

Saturated and unsaturated fats Organisms need lipids to function properly. The basic structure of a lipid includes fatty acid tails, as shown in **Figure 28.** Each tail is a chain of carbon atoms bonded to hydrogen and other carbon atoms by single or double bonds. Lipids that have tail chains with only single bonds between the carbon atoms are called saturated fats because no more hydrogens can bond to the tail. Lipids that have at least one double bond between carbon atoms in the tail chain can accommodate at least one more hydrogen and are called unsaturated fats. Fats with more than one double bond in the tail are called polyunsaturated fats.

Phospholipids A special lipid shown in **Figure 28,** called a phospholipid, is responsible for the structure and function of the cell membrane. Lipids are hydrophobic, which means they do not dissolve in water. This characteristic is important because it allows lipids to serve as barriers in biological membranes.

Steroids Another important category of lipids is the steroid group. Steroids include substances such as cholesterol and hormones. Despite its reputation as a "bad" lipid, cholesterol provides the starting point for other necessary lipids such as vitamin D and the hormones estrogen and testosterone.

Data Analysis LAB 2

Based on Real Data*

Interpret the Data

Does soluble fiber affect cholesterol levels? High amounts of a steroid called cholesterol in the blood are associated with the development of heart disease. Researchers study the effects of soluble fiber in the diet on cholesterol.

Data and Observations

This experiment evaluated the effects of three soluble fibers on cholesterol levels in the blood: pectin (PE), guar gum (GG), and psyllium (PSY). Cellulose was the control (CNT).

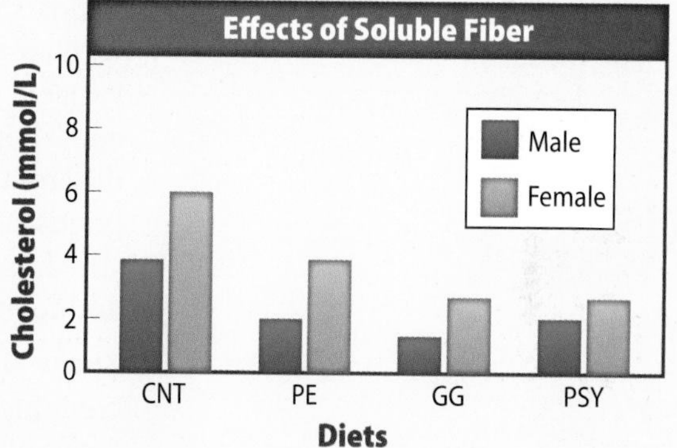

Think Critically

1. **Calculate** the percentage of change in cholesterol levels as compared to the control.
2. **Describe** the effects that soluble fiber appears to have on cholesterol levels in the blood.

*Data obtained from: Shen, et al. 1998. Dietary soluble fiber lowers plasma LDL cholesterol concentrations by altering lipoprotein metabolism in female Guinea pigs. *Journal of Nutrition* 128: 1434–1441.

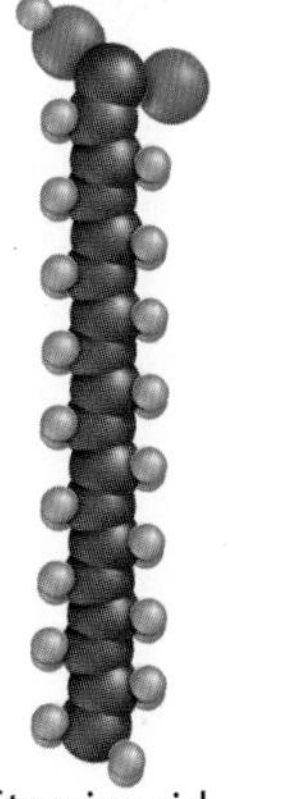
Stearic acid

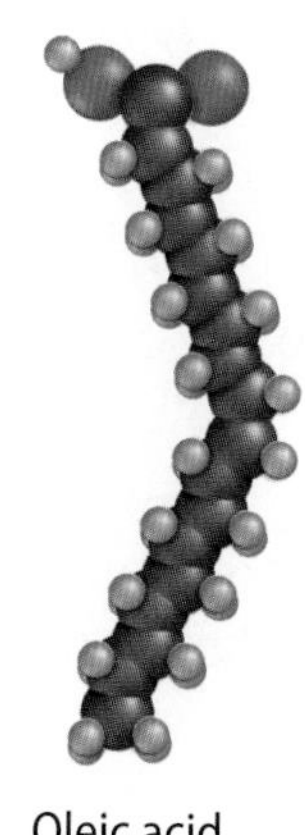
Oleic acid

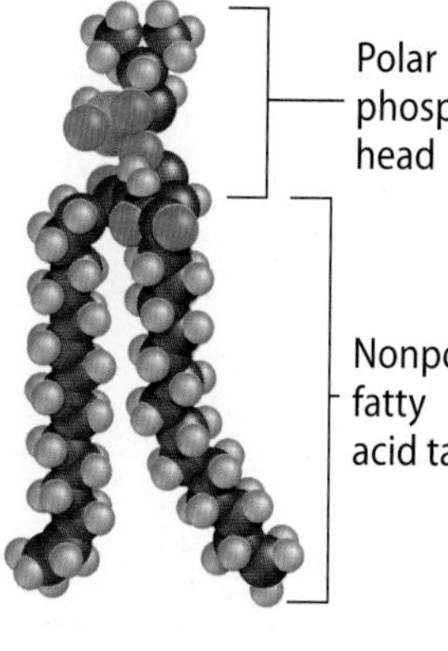

Phospholipid

■ **Figure 28** Stearic acid has no double bonds between carbon atoms; oleic acid has one double bond. Phospholipids have a polar head and two nonpolar tails.

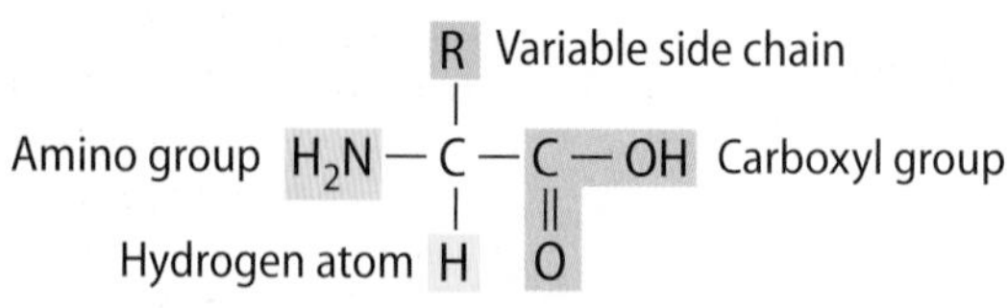

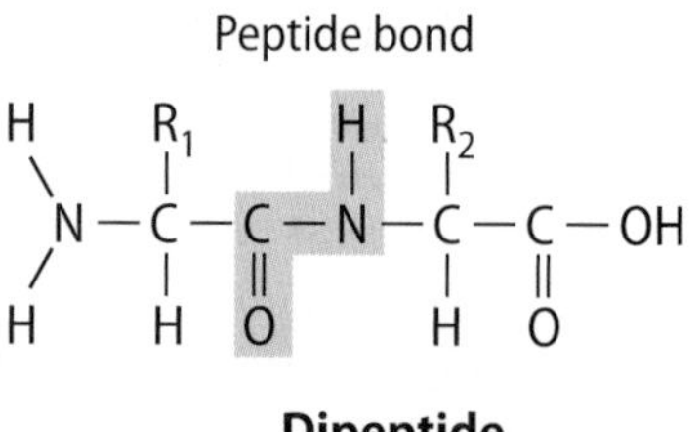

■ **Figure 29**
Left: The general structure of an amino acid has four groups around a central carbon.
Right: The peptide bond in a protein happens as a result of a chemical reaction.
***Interpret** which other molecule is a product when a peptide bond forms.*

Animation

Proteins Another primary building block of living things is protein. A **protein** is a compound made of small carbon compounds called amino acids. **Amino acids** are small compounds that are made of carbon, nitrogen, oxygen, hydrogen, and sometimes sulfur. All amino acids share the same general structure.

Amino acid structure Amino acids have a central carbon atom like the one shown in **Figure 29.** Recall that carbon can form four covalent bonds. One of those bonds is with hydrogen. The other three bonds are with an amino group ($-NH_2$), a carboxyl group ($-COOH$), and a variable group ($-R$). The variable group makes each amino acid different. There are 20 different variable groups, and proteins are made of different combinations of all 20 different amino acids. Several covalent bonds called peptide bonds join amino acids together to form proteins, which is also shown in **Figure 29.** A peptide bond forms between the amino group of one amino acid and the carboxyl group of another.

Three-dimensional protein structure Based on the variable groups contained in the different amino acids, proteins can have up to four levels of structure. The number of amino acids in a chain and the order in which the amino acids are joined define the protein's primary structure. After an amino acid chain is formed, it folds into a unique three-dimensional shape, which is the protein's secondary structure. **Figure 30** shows two basic secondary structures: the helix and the pleat. A protein might contain many helices, pleats, and folds. The tertiary structure of many proteins is globular, such as the hemoglobin protein shown in **Table 1,** but some proteins form long fibers. Some proteins form a fourth level of structure by combining with other proteins.

Protein function Proteins make up about 15 percent of your total body mass and are involved in nearly every function of your body. For example, your muscles, skin, and hair are made of proteins. Your cells contain about 10,000 different proteins that provide structural support, transport substances inside the cell and between cells, communicate signals within a cell and between cells, speed up chemical reactions, and control cell growth.

■ **Figure 30** The shape of a protein depends on the interactions among the amino acids. Hydrogen bonds help the protein hold its shape.

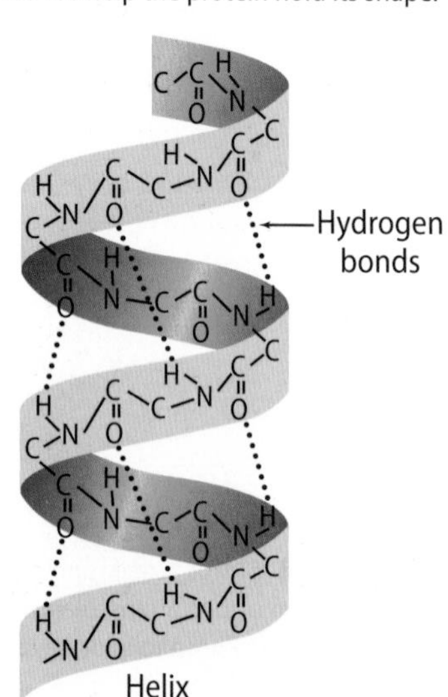

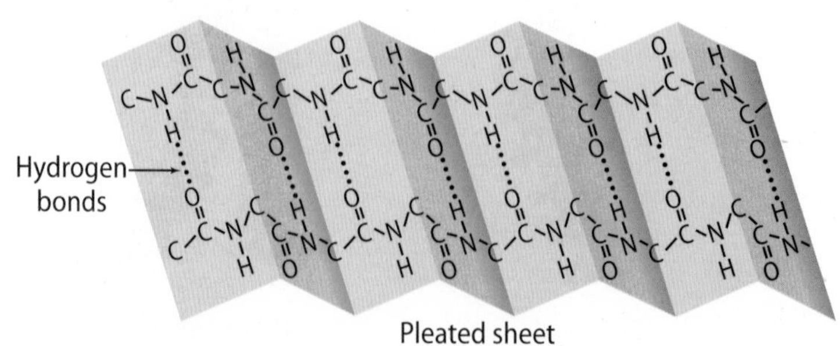

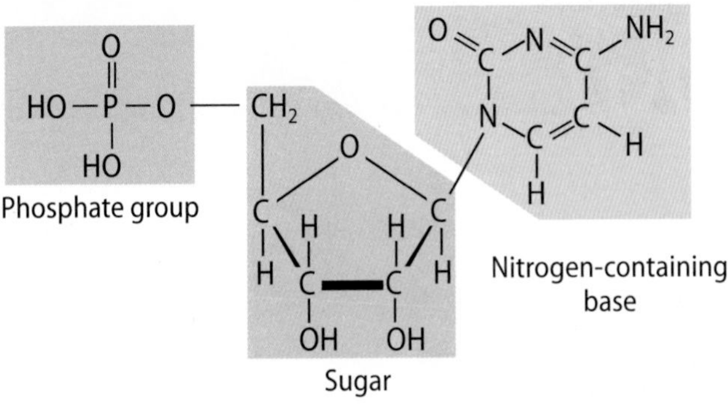

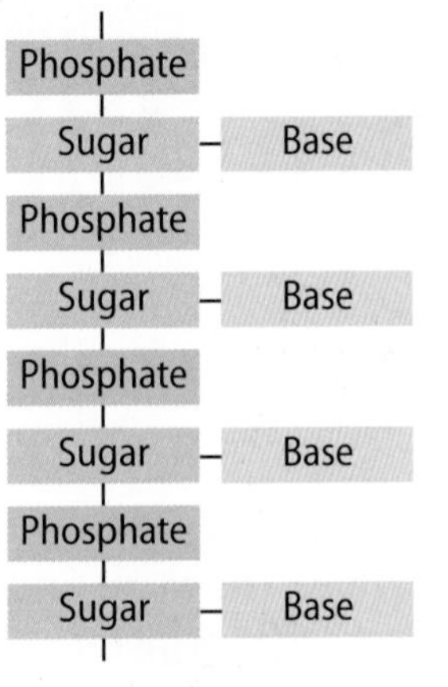

Figure 31
Left: DNA nucleotides contain the sugar deoxyribose. RNA nucleotides contain the sugar ribose.
Right: Nucleotides are joined together by bonds between their sugar group and phosphate group.

Nucleic acids The fourth group of biological macromolecules are nucleic acids. **Nucleic acids** are complex macromolecules that store and transmit genetic information. Nucleic acids are made of smaller repeating subunits composed of carbon, nitrogen, oxygen, phosphorus, and hydrogen atoms, called **nucleotides. Figure 31** shows the basic structure of a nucleotide and nucleic acid. There are six major nucleotides, all of which have three units—a phosphate, a nitrogenous base, and a ribose sugar.

There are two types of nucleic acids found in living organisms: deoxyribonucleic (dee AHK sih rib oh noo klay ihk) acid (DNA) and ribonucleic (rib oh noo KLAY ihk) acid (RNA). In nucleic acids such as DNA and RNA, the sugar of one nucleotide bonds to the phosphate of another nucleotide. The nitrogenous base that sticks out from the chain is available for hydrogen bonding with other bases in other nucleic acids.

A nucleotide with three phosphate groups is adenosine triphosphate (ATP). ATP is a storehouse of chemical energy that can be used by cells in a variety of reactions. It releases energy when the bond between the second and third phosphate group is broken. Less energy is released when the bond between the first and second phosphate group is broken.

REVIEW IT! The Building Blocks of Life

Section Summary

- Carbon compounds are the basic building blocks of living organisms.
- Biological macromolecules are formed by joining small carbon compounds into polymers.
- There are four types of biological macromolecules.
- Peptide bonds join amino acids in proteins.
- Chains of nucleotides form nucleic acids.

Self Check

Understand Main Ideas

1. MAINIDEA **Explain** If an unknown substance found on a meteorite is determined to contain no trace of carbon, can scientists conclude that there is life at the meteorite's origin?
2. **Compare** the structure and function of each type of biological macromolecule.
3. **Determine** the components of carbohydrates and proteins.
4. **Discuss** the importance of amino acid order to a protein's function.

Think Critically

5. **Summarize** Given the large number of proteins in the body, explain why the shape of an enzyme is important to its function.
6. **Draw** two structures (one straight chain and one ring) of a carbohydrate with the chemical formula $(CH_2O)_6$.

cutting-edgeBIOLOGY

4.6.1c

Sweeter Than Sugar

The reason why people love desserts is right on the tips of their tongues—literally. The taste buds in that location are the receptors that register sweetness most strongly. Many of the small bumps, called papillae, that you see on your tongue contain taste buds.

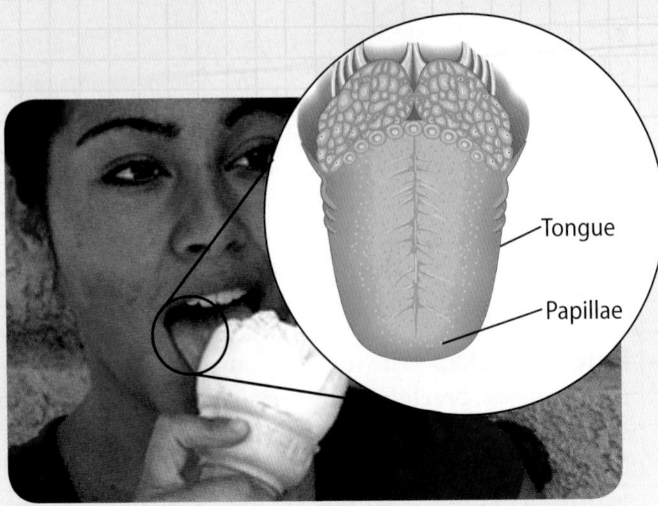

Taste buds on your tongue send impulses to your brain so that your brain can interpret how the food or drink tastes.

Registering Sweetness When you eat, the molecules from food temporarily bind themselves to protein molecules in the receptor cells of your tongue. As a result, the receptors send electrical impulses through your nerves to your brain. Your brain interprets the impulses as taste. Sometimes the taste is what you think of as sweet.

Natural vs. Artificial Sweeteners are substances added to foods to make them taste sweet. There are many natural sweeteners, such as table sugar and honey. An artificial sweetener is a man-made substance that has the same effect on taste buds as sugar does. Artificial sweeteners, such as saccharin, cyclamate, and aspartame, are hundreds of times sweeter than any naturally occurring sugar.

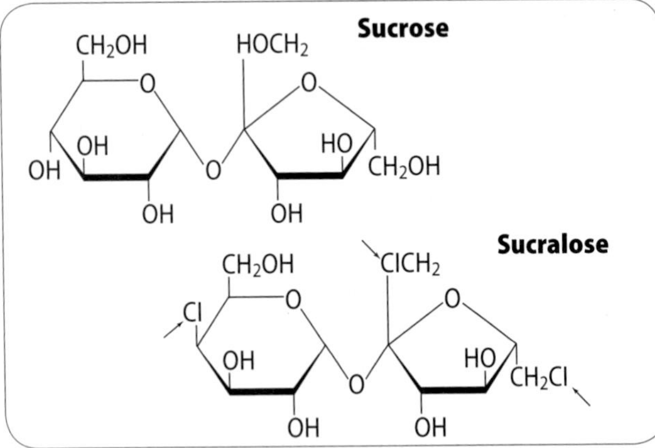

The difference between sucrose and sucralose is the substitution of three chlorine (Cl) atoms for three hydroxyl (OH) groups.

The molecules of these artificial sweeteners mimic the geometry and composition of natural sweeteners and are able to bind to the receptor cells in human taste buds.

One recently developed artificial sweetener, sucralose, has a chemical structure that is nearly identical to sucrose, or table sugar. The only difference is three hydroxyl (OH) groups in sucrose are replaced by chlorine atoms (Cl) in sucralose. This keeps the human body from metabolizing sucralose and makes it calorie-free.

Artificial sweeteners are used in many products, from diet sodas to children's medications. They provide the sweetness that people crave without the calories that natural sweeteners contain. Scientists continue to search for new sweeteners that are economical and healthful to customers.

WRITING IN ▶ Biology

Marketing Campaign Research an artificial sweetener that has been approved by the FDA. Use promotional materials from artificial sweeteners to build your campaign. Your marketing campaign might include a press release, television or radio commercials, Web ads, social networking sites, or other methods of spreading information.

WebQuest

Tony Freeman/PhotoEdit

BioLAB DESIGN YOUR OWN

1.2.2a, 1.3.3, 1.3.5b, 4.5.1f, ¥a, ¥b1, ¥b2, ¥b3, ¥b4, ¥b5, ¥e, ¥i, ¥j, ¥m, ¥n, ¥o

What factors affect an enzyme reaction?

Background: The compound hydrogen peroxide, H_2O_2, is produced when organisms metabolize food, but hydrogen peroxide damages cell parts. Organisms combat the buildup of H_2O_2 by producing the enzyme peroxidase. Peroxidase speeds up the breakdown of hydrogen peroxide into water and oxygen.

Question: *What factors affect peroxidase activity?*

Possible Materials

400-mL beaker
kitchen knife
hot plate
test-tube rack
ice
beef liver
dropper
distilled water
18-mm × 150-mm test tubes
buffer solutions (pH 5, pH 6, pH 7, pH 8)
50-mL graduated cylinder
10-mL graduated cylinder
tongs or large forceps
square or rectangular pan
stopwatch or timer
nonmercury thermometer
3% hydrogen peroxide
potato slices

Safety Precautions

CAUTION: *Use only GFCI-protected circuits for electrical devices.*

Plan and Perform the Experiment

1. Read and complete the lab safety form.
2. Develop questions that you can answer while performing the lab.
3. Choose a factor to test. Possible factors include temperature, pH, and substrate (H_2O_2) concentration.
4. Form a hypothesis about how the factor will affect the reaction rate of peroxidase.
5. Design an experiment to test your hypothesis. Create a procedure and identify the controls and variables.
6. Create a data table for recording your observations and measurements.
7. Make sure your teacher approves your plan before you proceed.
8. Conduct your approved experiment.
9. **Cleanup and Disposal** Clean up all equipment as instructed by your teacher and return everything to its proper place. Wash your hands thoroughly with soap and water.

Analyze and Conclude

1. **Describe** how the factor you tested affected the enzyme activity of peroxidase.
2. **Graph** your data, and then analyze and interpret your graph.
3. **Discuss** whether or not your data supported your hypothesis.
4. **Infer** why hydrogen peroxide is not the best choice for cleaning an open wound.
5. **Error Analysis** Identify any experimental errors or other errors in your data that might have affected the accuracy of your results.

SHARE YOUR DATA

Compare your data with the data collected by other groups in the class that tested the same factor. Infer reasons why your group's data might differ from the data collected by other groups.

CHAPTER 6 STUDY GUIDE

BIGIDEA **Atoms are the foundation of biological chemistry and the building blocks of all living things.**

SECTION 1 Atoms, Elements, and Compounds

MAINIDEA Matter is composed of tiny particles called atoms.

- Atoms consist of protons, neutrons, and electrons.
- Elements are pure substances made up of only one kind of atom.
- Isotopes are forms of the same element that have a different number of neutrons.
- Compounds are substances with unique properties that are formed when elements combine.
- Elements can form covalent and ionic bonds.

VOCABULARY

- **atom**
- **nucleus**
- **proton**
- **neutron**
- **electron**
- **element**
- **isotope**
- **compound**
- **covalent bond**
- **molecule**
- **ion**
- **ionic bond**
- **van der Waals force**

SECTION 2 Chemical Reactions

MAINIDEA Chemical reactions allow living things to grow, develop, reproduce, and adapt.

- Balanced chemical equations must show an equal number of atoms for each element on both sides.
- Activation energy is the energy required to begin a reaction.
- Catalysts are substances that alter chemical reactions.
- Enzymes are biological catalysts.

VOCABULARY

- **chemical reaction**
- **reactant**
- **product**
- **activation energy**
- **catalyst**
- **enzyme**
- **substrate**
- **active site**

SECTION 3 Water and Solutions

MAINIDEA The properties of water make it well suited to help maintain homeostasis in an organism.

- Water is a polar molecule.
- Solutions are homogeneous mixtures formed when a solute is dissolved in a solvent.
- Acids are substances that release hydrogen ions into solutions. Bases are substances that release hydroxide ions into solutions.
- pH is a measure of the concentration of hydrogen ions in a solution.

VOCABULARY

- **polar molecule**
- **hydrogen bond**
- **mixture**
- **solution**
- **solvent**
- **solute**
- **acid**
- **base**
- **pH**
- **buffer**

SECTION 4 The Building Blocks of Life

MAINIDEA Organisms are made up of carbon-based molecules.

- Carbon compounds are the basic building blocks of living organisms.
- Biological macromolecules are formed by joining small carbon compounds into polymers.
- There are four types of biological macromolecules.
- Peptide bonds join amino acids in proteins.
- Chains of nucleotides form nucleic acids.

VOCABULARY

- **macromolecule**
- **polymer**
- **carbohydrate**
- **lipid**
- **protein**
- **amino acid**
- **nucleic acid**
- **nucleotide**

SECTION 1

Vocabulary Review

Describe the difference between the terms in each pair.

1. electron, proton
2. ionic bond, covalent bond
3. isotope, element
4. atom, ion

Understand Main Ideas

Use the photo below to answer question 5.

5. What does the image above show?
   - **A.** a covalent bond
   - **B.** a physical property
   - **C.** a chemical reaction
   - **D.** van der Waals forces

6. Which process changes a chlorine atom into a chloride ion?
   - **A.** electron gain
   - **B.** electron loss
   - **C.** proton gain
   - **D.** proton loss

7. **MAINIDEA** Which of these is a pure substance that cannot be broken down by a chemical reaction?
   - **A.** a compound
   - **B.** a mixture
   - **C.** an element
   - **D.** a neutron

8. How do the isotopes of hydrogen differ?
   - **A.** in the number of protons
   - **B.** in the number of electrons
   - **C.** in the number of energy levels
   - **D.** in the number of neutrons

Constructed Response

9. **Short Answer** What is a radioactive isotope? List uses of radioactive isotopes.

10. **Short Answer** What factor determines that an oxygen atom can form two covalent bonds while a carbon atom can form four?

11. **Open Ended** Why is it important for living organisms to have both strong bonds (covalent and ionic) and weak bonds (hydrogen and van der Waals forces)?

Think Critically

Use the graph below to answer question 12.

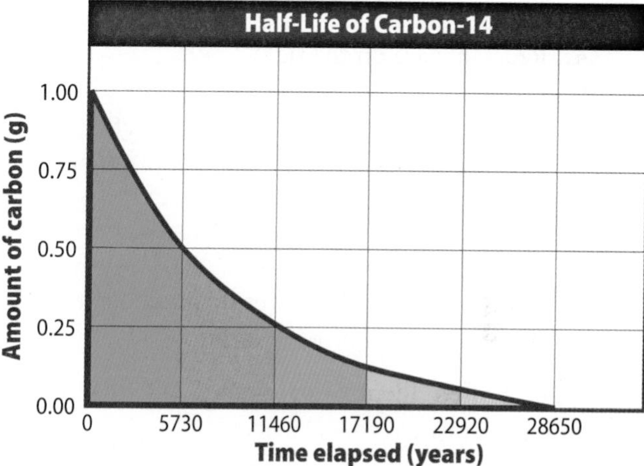

12. **Analyze** According to the data, what is the half-life of carbon-14? How can this information be used by scientists?

13. **Explain** The gecko is a reptile that climbs on smooth surfaces such as glass using van der Waals forces to adhere to the surfaces. How is this method of adhesion more advantageous than covalent interactions?

SECTION 2

Vocabulary Review

Match the term on the left with the correct definition on the right.

14. activation energy	**A.** a protein that speeds up a reaction
15. substrate	**B.** a substance formed by a chemical reaction
16. enzyme	**C.** the energy required to start a reaction
17. product	**D.** a substance that binds to an enzyme

Understand Main Ideas

18. **THEME FOCUS** Which of the following is a substance that lowers the activation energy?
    A. an ion
    B. a reactant
    C. a catalyst
    D. a substrate

19. In which of the following are bonds broken and new bonds formed?
    A. chemical reactions
    B. elements
    C. isotopes
    D. polar molecules

20. Which statement is true of chemical equations?
    A. Reactants are on the right.
    B. Products are on the right.
    C. Products have fewer atoms than reactants.
    D. Reactants have fewer atoms than products.

Constructed Response

21. **Short Answer** What features do all reactions involving enzymes have in common?

22. **Open Ended** Identify and describe factors that can influence enzyme activity.

Think Critically

Use the graph to answer questions 23 and 24.

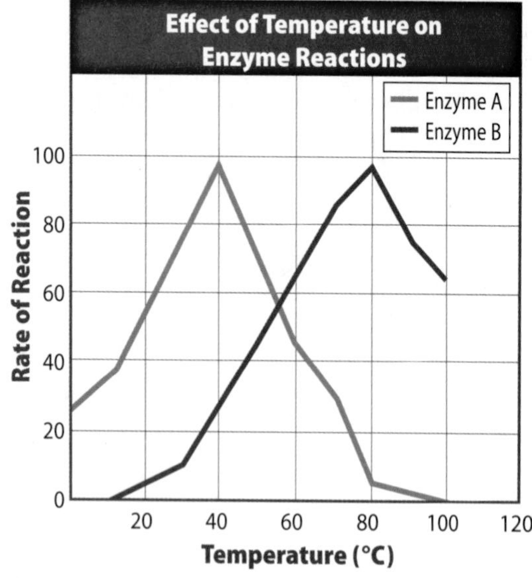

23. **Describe** the effect that temperature has on the rate of the reactions using the graph above.

24. MAINIDEA Which enzyme is more active in a human cell? Why?

SECTION 3

Vocabulary Review

State the relationship between the terms in each pair.

25. solution, mixture

26. pH, buffer

27. acid, base

28. solvent, solute

29. polar molecule, hydrogen bond

Understand Main Ideas

Use the figure below to answer question 30.

30. What does the image above show?
    A. a heterogeneous mixture
    B. a homogeneous mixture
    C. a solution
    D. a suspension

31. Which statement is not true about pure water?
    A. It has a pH of 7.0.
    B. It is composed of polar molecules.
    C. It is composed of ionic bonds.
    D. It is a good solvent.

32. Which is a substance that produces OH^- ions when it is dissolved in water?
    A. a base
    B. an acid
    C. a buffer
    D. salt

Constructed Response

33. MAINIDEA Why are hydrogen bonds so important for living organisms?

34. **Short Answer** Hydrochloric acid (HCl) is a strong acid. What ions are formed when HCl dissolves in water? What is the effect of HCl on the pH of water?

35. **Open Ended** Explain the importance of buffers to living organisms.

Ryouchin/Getty Images

Think Critically

36. **Predict** two places in the body where buffers are used to limit sharp changes in pH.

37. **Draw** a diagram of table salt (NaCl) dissolved in water.

SECTION 4

Vocabulary Review

Complete the following sentences with vocabulary terms from the Study Guide page.

38. Carbohydrates, lipids, proteins, and nucleic acids are ________.

39. Proteins are made from ________ that are joined by ________.

40. ________ make up fats, oils, and waxes.

41. DNA and RNA are examples of ________.

Understand Main Ideas

42. Which two elements are always found in amino acids?
    A. nitrogen and sulfur
    B. carbon and oxygen
    C. hydrogen and phosphorus
    D. sulfur and oxygen

43. Which joins amino acids together?
    A. peptide bonds
    B. hydrogen bonds
    C. van der Waals forces
    D. ionic bonds

44. Which substance is not part of a nucleotide?
    A. a phosphate
    B. a base
    C. a sugar
    D. water

Constructed Response

45. **Open Ended** Why do cells contain both macromolecules and small carbon compounds?

46. **Open Ended** Why can't humans digest all carbohydrates?

Think Critically

47. **MAINIDEA** **Create** a table for the four main biological macromolecules that lists their structures and functions.

Summative Assessment

48. **BIGIDEA** Diagram the basic unit of matter, describe the parts, and relate them to each other.

49. **WRITINGIN▶Biology** Research and write a job description for a biochemist. Include the types of tasks that biochemists perform and materials that are used in their research.

DBQ Document–Based Questions

Starch is the major carbon storehouse in plants. Experiments were performed to determine if trehalose might regulate starch production in plants. Leaf disks were incubated for three hours in sorbitol (the control), sucrose, and trelahose solutions. Then, levels of starch and sucrose in the leaves were measured. Use the data to answer the questions below.

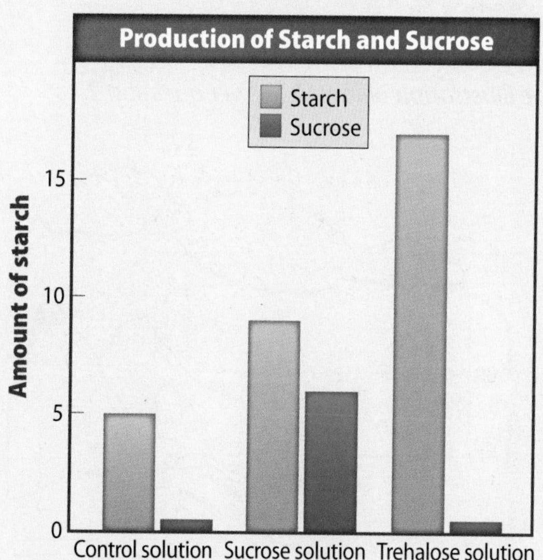

Data obtained from: Kolbe, et al. Trehalose 6-phosphate regulates starch synthesis via post translational redox activation of ADP-glucose pyrophophorylase. *Proceedings of the National Academy of Sciences of the USA* 102(31): 11118–11123.

50. Summarize the production of starch and sucrose in the three solutions.

51. What conclusion might the researchers have reached based on these data?

CUMULATIVE
MULTIPLE CHOICE

1 If a population of parrots has greater genetic diversity than a hummingbird population in the same region, which outcome could result?

A The parrot population could have a greater resistance to disease than the hummingbird population.

B Other parrot populations in different regions could become genetically similar to this one.

C The parrot population could have a greater variety of abiotic factors with which to interact.

D The parrot population could interact with a greater variety of other populations.

Use the illustration below to answer question 2.

2 The figure above is a model of the water cycle. Which term describes the part of the cycle labeled A?

A condensation

B evaporation

C runoff

D precipitation

SHORT ANSWER

3 Assess what might happen if there were no buffers in human cells.

4 Choose an example of an element and a compound and then contrast them.

5 Explain which property of populations might be described as random, clumped, or uniform. Give an example of each.

Use the chart below to answer question 6.

Factors Affecting Coral Survival	
Factor	**Optimal Range**
Water temperature	23°C to 25°C
Salinity	30 to 40 parts per million
Sedimentation	little or no sedimentation
Depth	up to 48 m

6 Using the data in the chart, describe which region of the world would be optimal for coral growth.

7 Form a hypothesis to explain the increase in species diversity as you move from the polar regions to the tropics. How would you test your hypothesis?

8 In a country with a very slow growth rate, predict which age groups are the largest in the population.

9 Why is it important that enzymes can bind only to specific substrates?

EXTENDED RESPONSE

10 Draw a graphical representation of exponential growth. Explain the regions of your curve in terms of population growth.

11 Suddenly, after very heavy rains, many fish in a local lake begin to die, yet algae in the water seem to be doing very well. You know that the lake receives runoff from local fields and roads. Form a hypothesis about why the fish are dying, and suggest how to stop the deaths.

12 When scientists first discovered atoms, they thought they were the smallest parts into which matter could be divided. Relate how later discoveries led scientists to revise this definition.

13 Identify and describe three types of symbiotic relationships and provide an example of each.

ESSAY QUESTION

Many kinds of molecules found in living organisms are made of smaller monomers that are put together in different sequences, or in different patterns. For example, organisms use a small number of nucleotides to make nucleic acids. Thousands of different sequences of nucleotides in nucleic acids provide the basic coding for all the genetic information in living things.

Using the information in the paragraph above, answer the following question in essay format.

14 Describe how it is beneficial for organisms to use monomers to create complex macromolecules.

TEST PRACTICE

Use the diagram below to answer questions 15 and 16.

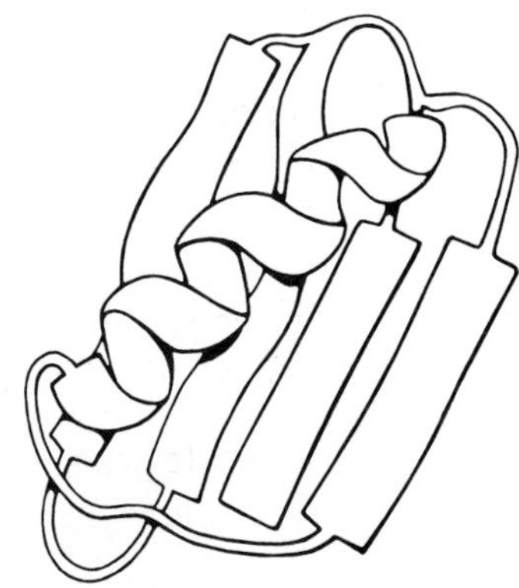

15 Which type of macromolecule can have a structure like the one shown?

A a carbohydrate

B a lipid

C a nucleotide

D a protein

16 Which molecular activity requires a folded structure?

A behavior as a nonpolar compound

B function of an active site

C movement through cell membranes

D role as energy storage for the cell

NEED EXTRA HELP?																
If You Missed Question . . .	1	2	3	4	5	6	7	8	9	10	11	12	13	14	15	16
Review Section . . .	5.1	4.1	6.3	5.3	5.1	3.1, 3.3	5.1	4.2	6.2	4.1	5.2	6.1	2.1	6.4	6.4	6.4

Humans have around 1.6 trillion skin cells. Every hour, between 30,000 and 40,000 skin cells fall off. So in the course of one day, a person can lose nearly one million skin cells.

LaunchLAB

What is a cell?

All things are made of atoms and molecules, but only in living things are the atoms and molecules organized into cells. In this lab, you will use a compound microscope to view slides of living things and nonliving things.

CHAPTER 7

Cellular Structure and Function

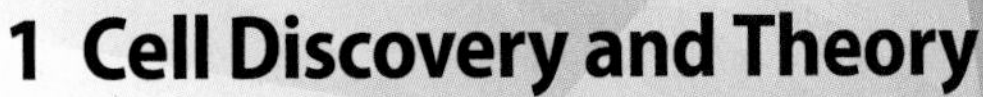

1 Cell Discovery and Theory

1.1.1a, 1.1.1b, 1.1.4a, 1.3.5b, 4.1.2f, 4.1.3a, ¥a, ¥c1, ¥c2, ¥c3, ¥c4, ¥e, ¥m, ¥n

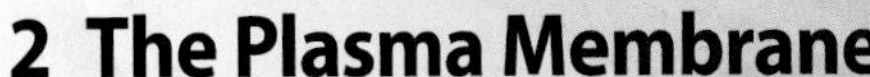

2 The Plasma Membrane

4.1.2g, 4.1.2i, 4.5.1c

3 Structures and Organelles

1.3.5b, 4.1.2f, 4.1.2h, 4.1.2i, 4.5.1c

4 Cellular Transport

1.3.5b, 4.5.1c, ¥a, ¥m, ¥o

THEMEFOCUS

Structure and function Diversity exists within a cell due to the presence of various macromolecules, structures, functions, and processes.

BIGIDEA

Cells are the structural and functional units of all living organisms.

Cellular Transport

Make a layered-look book using the titles shown. Use it to organize your notes on cellular transport.

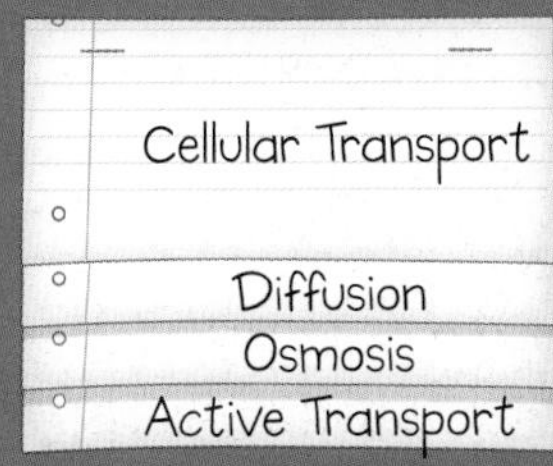

USE IT! **Science Notebook**

1 Cell Discovery and Theory

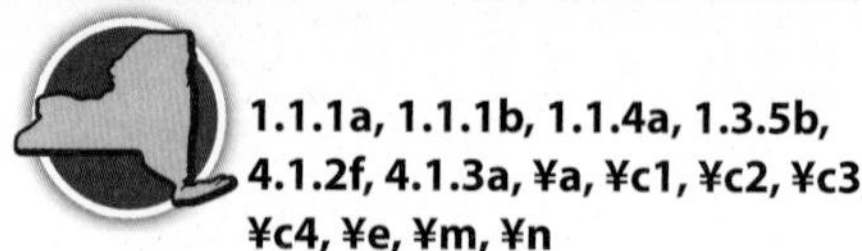

1.1.1a, 1.1.1b, 1.1.4a, 1.3.5b, 4.1.2f, 4.1.3a, ¥a, ¥c1, ¥c2, ¥c3, ¥c4, ¥e, ¥m, ¥n

MAINIDEA

The invention of the microscope led to the discovery of cells.

Essential Questions

- How are the advances in microscope technology related to discoveries about cells?
- What are the similarities and differences between compound light microscopes and electron microscopes?
- What are the principles of the cell theory?
- What are the differences between a prokaryotic cell and a eukaryotic cell?

BIOLOGY 4U

The different parts of your body might seem to have nothing in common. Your heart, for example, pumps blood throughout your body, while your skin protects and helps cool you. What do body parts such as the heart and skin have in common? And how do cells allow parts of the body to function together?

Review Vocabulary

organization: the orderly structure shown by living things

New Vocabulary

cell
cell theory
plasma membrane
organelle
eukaryotic cell
nucleus
prokaryotic cell

Multilingual eGlossary

History of the Cell Theory

For centuries, scientists had no idea that the human body consists of trillions of cells. Cells are so small that their existence was unknown before the invention of the microscope. In 1665, as indicated in **Figure 1,** an English scientist named Robert Hooke made a simple microscope and looked at a piece of cork, the dead cells of oak bark. Hooke observed small, box-shaped structures, such as those shown in **Figure 2.** He called them cellulae (the Latin word meaning *small rooms*) because the boxlike cells of cork reminded him of the cells in which monks live at a monastery. It is from Hooke's work that we have the term *cell.* A **cell** is the basic structural and functional unit of all living organisms.

During the late 1600s, Dutch scientist Anton van Leeuwenhoek (LAY vun hook) designed his own microscope after he was inspired by a book written by Hooke. To his surprise, he saw living organisms in pond water, milk, and various other substances. The work of these scientists and others led to new branches of science and many new and exciting discoveries.

■ **Figure 1 Microscopes in Focus**
The invention of microscopes, improvements to the instruments, and new microscope techniques have led to the development of the cell theory and a better understanding of cells.

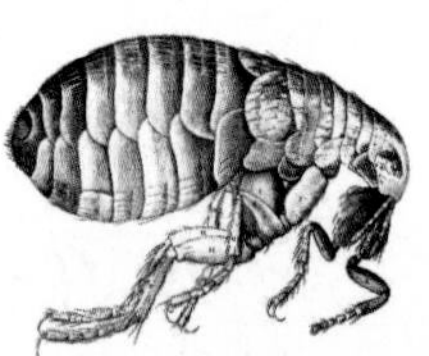

1500 — 1600 — 1700 — 1800

1590 Dutch lens grinders Hans and Zacharias Janssen invent the first compound microscope by placing two lenses in a tube.

1665 Robert Hooke observes cork and names the tiny chambers that he sees ***cells.*** He publishes drawings of cells, fleas, and other minute bodies in his book ***Micrographia.***

1683 Dutch biologist Anton van Leeuwenhoek discovers single-celled, animal-like organisms, now called protozoans.

1830–1855 Scientists discover the cell nucleus (1833) and propose that both plants and animals are composed of cells (1839).

The cell theory Scientists continued observing the living microscopic world using glass lenses. In 1838, German scientist Matthias Schleiden carefully studied plant tissues and concluded that all plants are composed of cells. A year later, another German scientist, Theodor Schwann, reported that animal tissues also consisted of individual cells. Prussian physician Rudolph Virchow proposed in 1855 that all cells are produced from the division of existing cells. The observations and conclusions of these scientists and others are summarized as the cell theory. The **cell theory** is one of the fundamental ideas of modern biology and includes the following three principles:

1. All living organisms are composed of one or more cells.
2. Cells are the basic unit of structure and organization of all living organisms.
3. Cells arise only from previously existing cells, with cells passing copies of their genetic material on to their daughter cells.

GET IT? **Explain** Can cells appear spontaneously without genetic material from previous cells?

LM Magnification: 100×

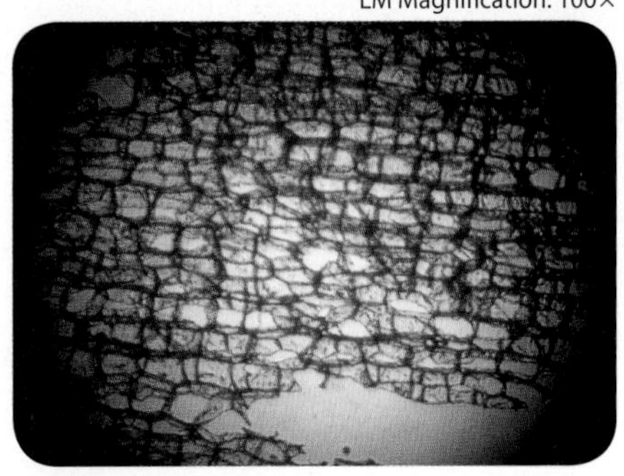

■ **Figure 2** Robert Hooke used a basic light microscope to see what looked like empty chambers in a cork sample.

Infer ***what you think Hooke would have seen if these were living cells.***

Launch Lab

Inquiry Based on what you've read about cells, how would you now answer the analysis questions?

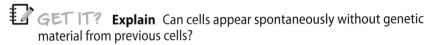

Microscope Technology

The discovery of cells and the development of the cell theory would not have been possible without microscopes. Improvements made to microscopes have enabled scientists to study cells in detail, as described in **Figure 1.**

Turn back to the opening pages of this chapter and compare the illustrations of the skin shown there. Note that the detail increases as the magnification and resolution—the ability of the microscope to make individual components visible—increase. Hooke and van Leewenhoek would not have been able to see the individual structures within human skin cells with their microscopes. Developments in microscope technology have given scientists the ability to study cells in greater detail than early scientists ever thought possible.

1880–1890 Louis Pasteur and Robert Koch, using compound microscopes, pioneered the study of bacteria.

1900

1939 Ernest Everett Just writes the textbook ***Biology of the Cell Surface*** after years of studying the structure and function of cells.

1970 Lynn Margulis, a microbiologist, proposes the idea that some organelles found in eukaryotes were once free-living prokaryotes.

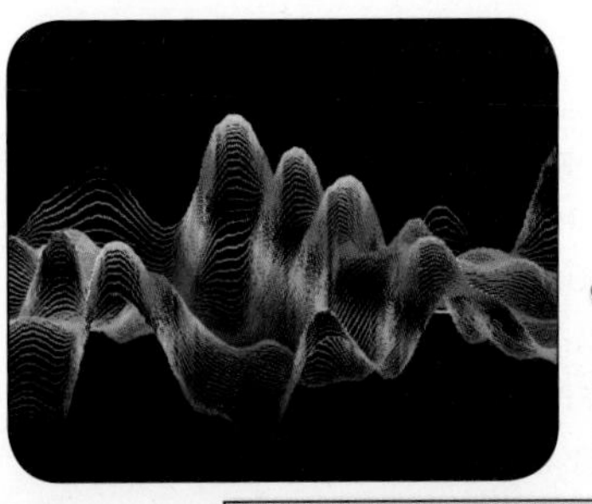

1981 The scanning tunneling microscope (STM) allows scientists to see individual atoms.

2000

2008 3-dimensional structured illumination microscopy (3D-SIM) combines a 3-D view, high resolution, and multiple colors.

Compound light microscopes The modern compound light microscope consists of a series of glass lenses and uses visible light to produce a magnified image. Each lens in the series magnifies the image of the previous lens. For example, when two lenses each individually magnify 10 times, the total magnification is 100 times (10×10). Scientists often stain cells with dyes to see them better when using a light microscope because cells are so tiny, thin, and translucent. Over the years, scientists have developed various techniques and modifications for light microscopes, but the properties of visible light will always limit resolution with these microscopes. Objects cause light to scatter, which blurs images. The maximum magnification without blurring is around 1000×.

CAREERS IN BIOLOGY

Technology Representative Companies that manufacture scientific equipment employ representatives to demonstrate and explain their products to the scientific community. A technology representative is an expert in these new technology products and brings this expertise to scientists who might use the products in the laboratory.

Electron microscopes As they began to study cells, scientists needed greater magnification to see the details of tiny parts of cells. During the second World War, in the 1940s, they developed the electron microscope. Instead of lenses, the electron microscope uses magnets to aim a beam of electrons at thin slices of cells. This type of electron microscope is called a transmission electron microscope (TEM) because electrons are passed, or transmitted, through a specimen to a fluorescent screen. Thick parts of the specimen absorb more electrons than thin parts, forming a black-and-white shaded image of the specimen. Transmission electron microscopes can magnify up to 500,000×, but the specimen must be dead, sliced very thin, and stained with heavy metals.

Over the past 65 years, many modifications have been made to the original electron microscopes. For example, the scanning electron microscope (SEM) is one modification that directs electrons over the surface of the specimen, producing a three-dimensional image. One disadvantage of using a TEM and an SEM is that only nonliving cells and tissues can be observed. Photomicrographs made with electron microscopes can be found online.

MiniLAB 1

Discover Cells

How can you describe a new discovery? Imagine that you are a scientist looking through the eyepiece of some newfangled instrument called a microscope and you see a field of similarly shaped objects. You might recognize that the shapes that you see are not merely coincidence and random objects. Your whole idea of the nature of matter is changing as you view these objects.

Procedure

1. Read and complete the lab safety form.
2. Prepare a data table in which you will record observations and drawings for three slides.
3. View the **slide images** that your teacher projects for the class.
4. Describe and draw what you see. Be sure to include enough detail in your drawings to convey the information to other scientists who have not observed cells.

Analysis

1. **Describe** what analogies or terms could explain the images in your drawings.
2. **Determine** the limitations Hooke had in the 1600s.
3. **Explain** how you could show Hooke, with twenty-first-century technology, that his findings were valid.

Another type of microscope, the scanning tunneling electron microscope (STM), involves bringing the charged tip of a probe extremely close to the specimen so that the electrons "tunnel" through the small gap between the specimen and the tip. This instrument has enabled scientists to create three-dimensional computer images of objects as small as atoms. Unlike TEM and SEM, STM can be used with live specimens. **Figure 3** shows DNA, the cell's genetic material, magnified with a scanning tunneling electron microscope.

The atomic force microscope (AFM) measures various forces between the tip of a probe and the cell surface. The AFM creates a visual image of a cell using a microscopic sensor that scans the cell.

False-Color STM Magnification: 2,000,000×

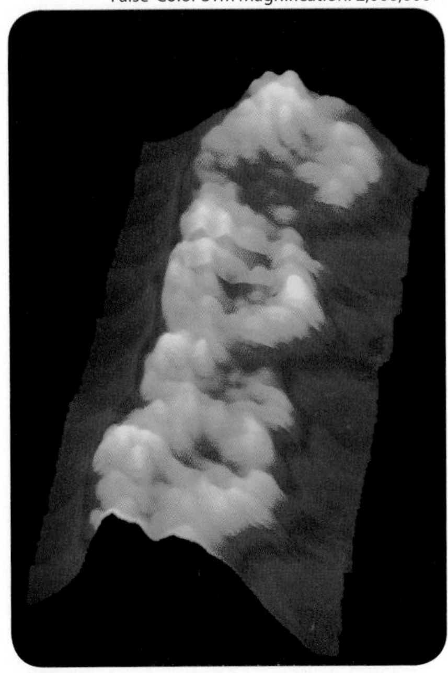

DNA

■ **Figure 3** The scanning tunneling microscope (STM) provides images, such as this DNA molecule, in which cracks and depressions appear darker and raised areas appear lighter.
Name ***an application for which an STM might be used.***

Basic Cell Types

You have learned, according to the cell theory, that cells are the basic units of all living organisms. By observing your own body and the living things around you, you might infer that cells must exist in various shapes and sizes. You also might infer that cells differ based on the functions they perform for an organism. However, all cells have at least one physical trait in common: they all have a structure called a plasma membrane. A **plasma membrane,** labeled in **Figure 4,** is a special boundary that helps control what enters and leaves the cell. Each of your skin cells has a plasma membrane, as do the cells of a rattlesnake. This critical structure is described in detail in the next section.

Cells generally have a number of functions in common. For example, most cells have genetic material in some form that provides instructions for making substances that the cell needs. Cells also break down molecules to generate energy. Scientists have grouped cells into two broad categories. These categories are prokaryotic (pro kar ee AW tik) cells and eukaryotic (yew kar ee AW tik) cells. **Figure 4** shows TEM photomicrographs of these two cell types. The images of the prokaryotic cell and eukaryotic cell have been enlarged so that you can compare the cell structures. Eukaryotic cells generally are one to one hundred times larger than prokaryotic cells.

Video Lab

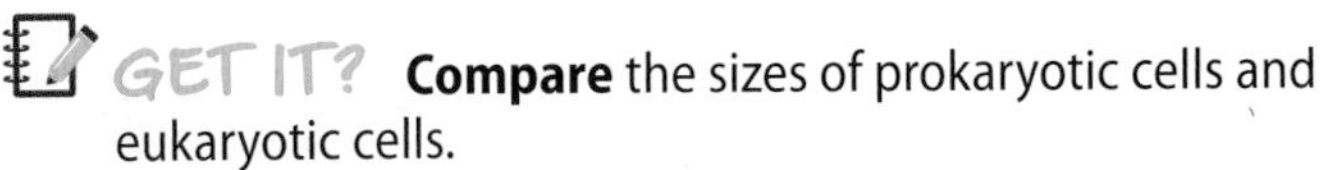

Compare the sizes of prokaryotic cells and eukaryotic cells.

■ **Figure 4** The prokaryotic cell on the left is smaller and appears less complex than the eukaryotic cell on the right. The prokaryotic cell has been enlarged for the purpose of comparing each cell's internal structures.

Color-Enhanced TEM Magnification: 15,000×

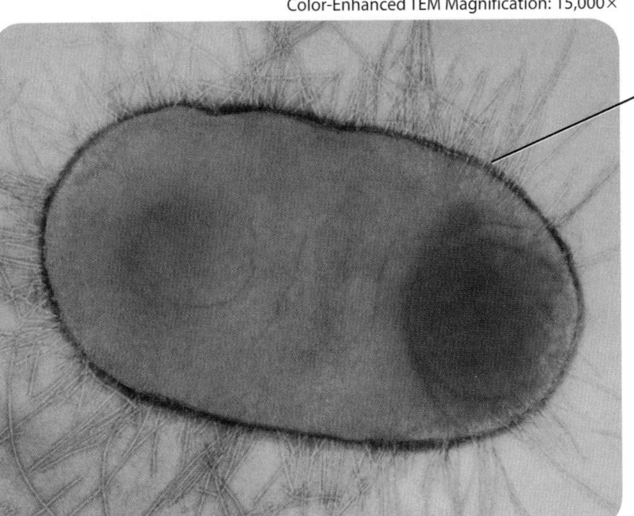

Prokaryotic cell

Plasma membrane

Color-Enhanced Magnification: unavailable

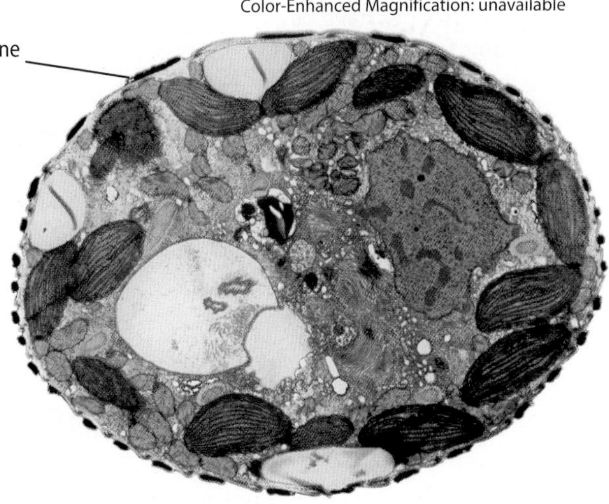

Eukaryotic cell

(t)Driscoll, Youngquist & Baldeschwieler, California Institute of Technology/Science Source, (bl)©Lester V. Bergman/Corbis; (br)Biophoto Associates/Science Source

BrainPOP 

Refer again to **Figure 4** and compare the types of cells to see why scientists place them into two broad categories that are based on internal structures. Both have a plasma membrane, but one cell contains many distinct internal structures called **organelles**—specialized structures that carry out specific cell functions.

Eukaryotic cells contain a nucleus and other organelles that are bound by membranes, also referred to as membrane-bound organelles. The **nucleus** is a distinct central organelle that contains the cell's genetic material in the form of DNA. Organelles enable cell functions to take place in different parts of the cell at the same time. Most organisms are made up of eukaryotic cells and are called eukaryotes. However, some unicellular organisms, such as some algae and yeast, also are eukaryotes.

VOCABULARY

WORD ORIGIN

Eukaryote
Prokaryote

eu– prefix; from Greek, meaning *true*
pro– prefix; from Greek, meaning *before*
–***kary*** from Greek, meaning *nucleus*

Prokaryotic cells are defined as cells without a nucleus or other membrane-bound organelles. As you can see in **Figure 4,** prokaryotic cells are simpler than eukaryotic cells. Most unicellular organisms, such as bacteria, are prokaryotic cells. Thus, they are called prokaryotes. Many scientists think that prokaryotes are similar to the first organisms that lived on Earth.

Origin of cell diversity Scientists continue to investigate why there are two basic types of cells. The answer might be that eukaryotic cells evolved from prokaryotic cells millions of years ago. According to the endosymbiont theory, a symbiotic relationship involves one prokaryotic cell living inside of another and both cells benefiting from the relationship.

Imagine how organisms would be different if the eukaryotic form had not evolved. Because eukaryotic cells are larger and have distinct organelles, these cells have developed specific functions. Having specific functions has led to cell diversity, and thus more diverse organisms that can adapt better to their environments. Life-forms more complex than bacteria might not have evolved without eukaryotic cells.

REVIEW IT! Cell Discovery and Theory

Section Summary

- Microscopes have been used as tools for scientific study since the late 1500s.
- Scientists use different types of microscopes to study cells.
- The cell theory summarizes three principles.
- There are two broad groups of cell types: prokaryotic cells and eukaryotic cells.

 Self Check

Understand Main Ideas

1. MAINIDEA **Explain** how the development and improvement of microscopes changed the study of living organisms and potentially changed theories.
2. **Compare and contrast** a compound light microscope and an electron microscope.
3. **Summarize** the cell theory.
4. **Differentiate** the plasma membrane and the organelles.

Think Critically

5. **Describe** how you would determine whether the cells of a newly discovered organism were prokaryotic or eukaryotic.

MATH IN ▶ Biology

6. If the overall magnification of a series of two lenses is 30×, and one lens magnifies 5×, what is the magnification of the other lens? Calculate the total magnification if the 5× lens is replaced by a 7× lens.

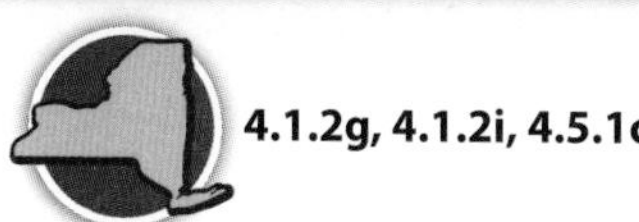

USE IT! Science Notebook

2 The Plasma Membrane

4.1.2g, 4.1.2i, 4.5.1c

MAINIDEA

The plasma membrane helps to maintain a cell's homeostasis.

Essential Questions

- How does a cell's plasma membrane function?
- What are the roles of proteins, carbohydrates, and cholesterol in the plasma membrane?

BIOLOGY 4 U

When you approach your school, you might pass through a gate in a fence that surrounds the school grounds. The fence prevents people who should not be there from entering, and the gate allows students, staff, and parents to enter. Similarly, prokaryotic cells and eukaryotic cells have structures that maintain control of their internal environments.

Review Vocabulary

ion: an atom or group of atoms with a positive or negative electric charge

New Vocabulary

selective permeability
phospholipid bilayer
transport protein
fluid mosaic model

Multilingual eGlossary

Function of the Plasma Membrane

Recall that the process of maintaining balance in an organism's internal environment is called homeostasis. Homeostasis is essential to the survival of a cell. One of the structures that is primarily responsible for homeostasis is the plasma membrane. The plasma membrane is a thin, flexible boundary between a cell and its environment that allows nutrients into the cell and allows waste and other products to leave the cell. All prokaryotic cells and eukaryotic cells have a plasma membrane to separate them from the watery environments in which they exist.

A key property of the plasma membrane is **selective permeability** (pur mee uh BIH luh tee), by which a membrane allows some substances to pass through while keeping others out. Consider a fish net as an analogy of selective permeability. The net shown in **Figure 5** has holes that allow water and other substances in the water to pass through, but not the fish. Depending on the size of the holes in the net, some kinds of fish might pass through, while others are caught. The diagram in **Figure 5** illustrates selective permeability of the plasma membrane. The arrows show that substances enter and leave the cell through the plasma membrane. Control of how, when, and how much of these substances enter and leave a cell relies on the structure of the plasma membrane.

GET IT? **Define** the term *selective permeability.*

■ **Figure 5**
Left: The fish net selectively captures fish while allowing water and other debris to pass through.
Right: Similarly, the plasma membrane selects substances entering and leaving the cell.

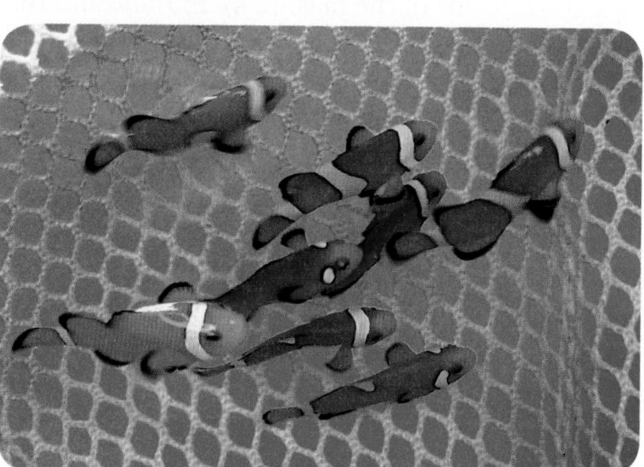

Jill Barton/AP Images

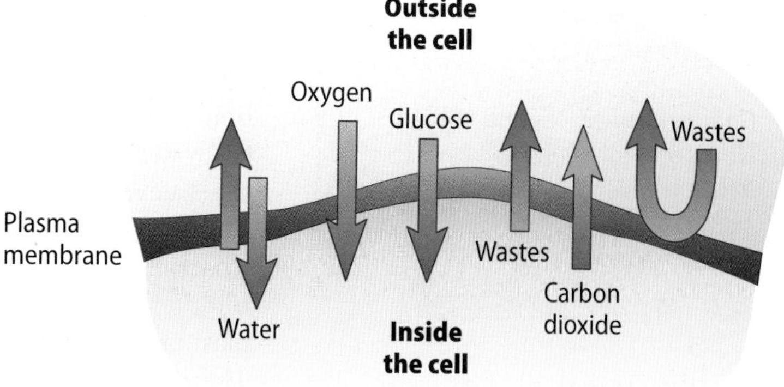

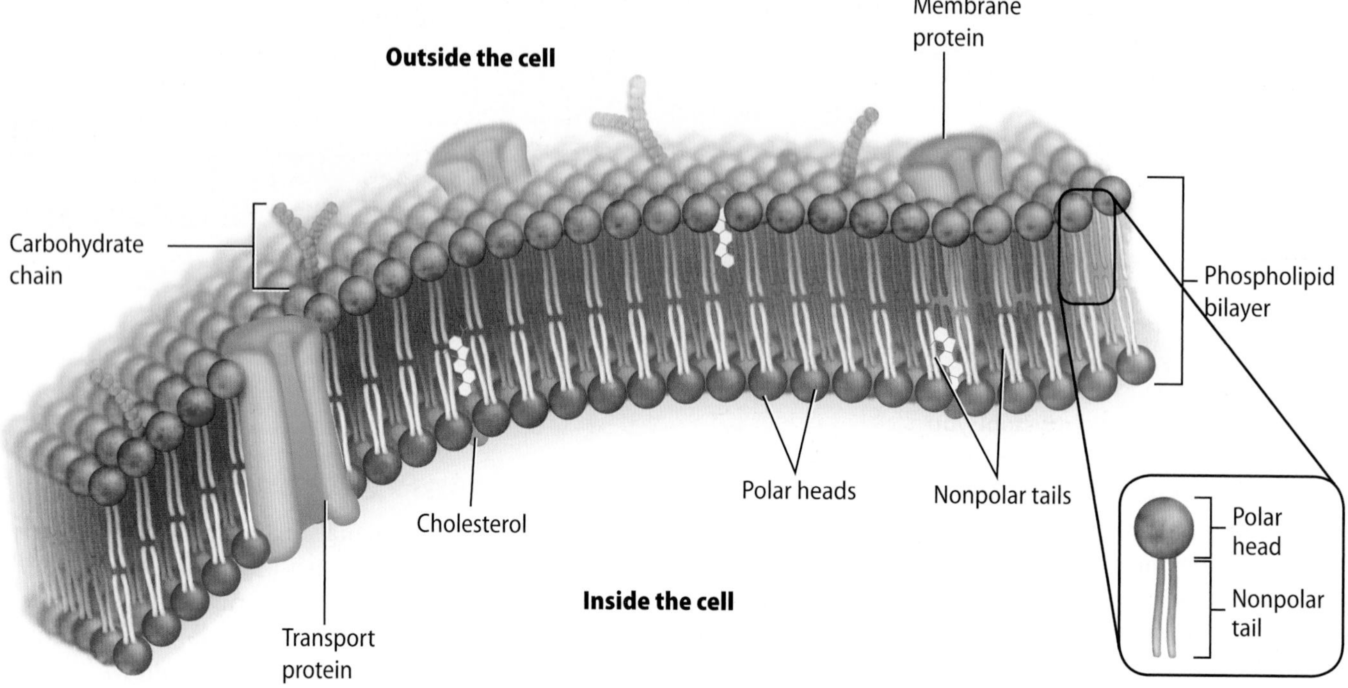

■ **Figure 6** The phospholipid bilayer looks like a sandwich, with the polar heads facing the outside and the nonpolar tails facing the inside.

***Infer** how hydrophobic substances cross a plasma membrane.*

Structure of the Plasma Membrane

Connection to Chemistry Most of the molecules in the plasma membrane are lipids. Lipids are large molecules that are composed of glycerol and three fatty acids. If a phosphate group replaces a fatty acid, a phospholipid forms. A phospholipid (fahs foh LIH pid) is a molecule that has a glycerol backbone, two fatty acid chains, and a phosphate-containing group. The plasma membrane is composed of a **phospholipid bilayer,** in which two layers of phospholipids are arranged tail-to-tail, as shown in **Figure 6.** In the plasma membrane, phospholipids arrange themselves in a way that allows the plasma membrane to exist in the watery environment.

VOCABULARY

SCIENCE USAGE V. COMMON USAGE

Polar

Science usage: completely opposite
Water and phospholipids are polar molecules because they have positively-charged ends and negatively-charged ends.

Common usage: relating to Earth's North or South Pole
Polar bears live in the region near the North Pole.

The phospholipid bilayer

Notice in **Figure 6** that each phospholipid is diagrammed as a head with two tails. The phosphate group in each phospholipid makes the head polar. The polar head is attracted to water because water also is polar. The two fatty acid tails are nonpolar and are repelled by water.

The two layers of phospholipid molecules resemble a sandwich, with the fatty acid tails forming the interior of the plasma membrane and the phospholipid heads facing the watery environments found inside and outside the cell, as shown in **Figure 6.** This bilayer structure is critical for the formation and function of the plasma membrane. The phospholipids are arranged in such a way that the polar heads can be closest to the water molecules and the nonpolar tails can be farthest away from the water molecules.

When many phospholipid molecules come together in this manner, a barrier is created that is polar at its surfaces and nonpolar in the middle. Water-soluble substances will not move easily through the plasma membrane because they are stopped by the nonpolar middle. Therefore, the plasma membrane can separate the environment inside the cell from the environment outside the cell.

Other components of the plasma membrane Moving with and among the phospholipids in the plasma membrane are cholesterol, proteins, and carbohydrates. When found on the outer surface of the plasma membrane, proteins called receptors transmit signals to the inside of the cell. Proteins at the inner surface anchor the plasma membrane to the cell's internal support structure, giving the cell its shape. Other proteins span the entire membrane and create tunnels through which certain substances enter and leave the cell. These **transport proteins** move needed substances or waste materials through the plasma membrane and therefore contribute to the selective permeability of the plasma membrane.

STUDY TIP

QUESTION SESSION Work with a partner and ask each other questions about the plasma membrane. Summarize your partner's answers out loud to make sure you understand them. Ask as many questions as you think of while taking turns.

GET IT? **Describe** the benefit of the bilayer structure of the plasma membrane.

Locate the cholesterol molecules in **Figure 6.** Nonpolar cholesterol is repelled by water and is positioned among the phospholipids. Cholesterol helps to prevent the fatty-acid tails of the phospholipid bilayer from sticking together, which contributes to the fluidity of the plasma membrane. Although avoiding a high-cholesterol diet is recommended, cholesterol plays a critical role in plasma membrane structure and it is an important substance for maintaining homeostasis in a cell.

Other substances in the membrane, such as carbohydrates attached to proteins, stick out from the plasma membrane to define the cell's characteristics and help cells identify chemical signals. For example, carbohydrates in the membrane might help disease-fighting cells recognize and attack a potentially harmful cell.

Data Analysis LAB 1

Based on Real Data*

Interpret the Diagram

How are protein channels involved in the death of nerve cells after a stroke? A stroke occurs when a blood clot blocks the flow of oxygen-containing blood in a portion of the brain. Nerve cells in the brain that release glutamate are sensitive to the lack of oxygen and release a flood of glutamate when oxygen is low. During the glutamate flood, the calcium pump is destroyed. This affects the movement of calcium ions into and out of nerve cells. When cells contain excess calcium, homeostasis is disrupted.

Think Critically

1. **Interpret** how the glutamate flood destroys the calcium pump.
2. **Predict** what would happen if Ca^{2+} levels were lowered in the nerve cell during a stroke.

Data and Observations

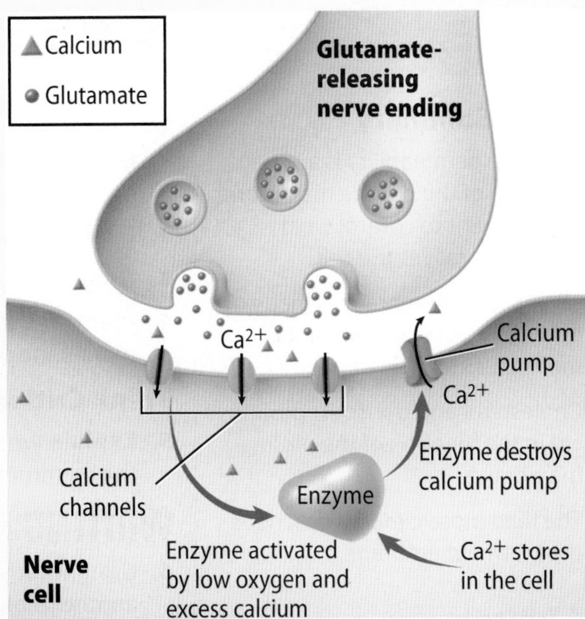

* Data obtained from: Choi, D.W. 2005. Neurodegeneration: cellular defences destroyed. *Nature* 433: 696–698.

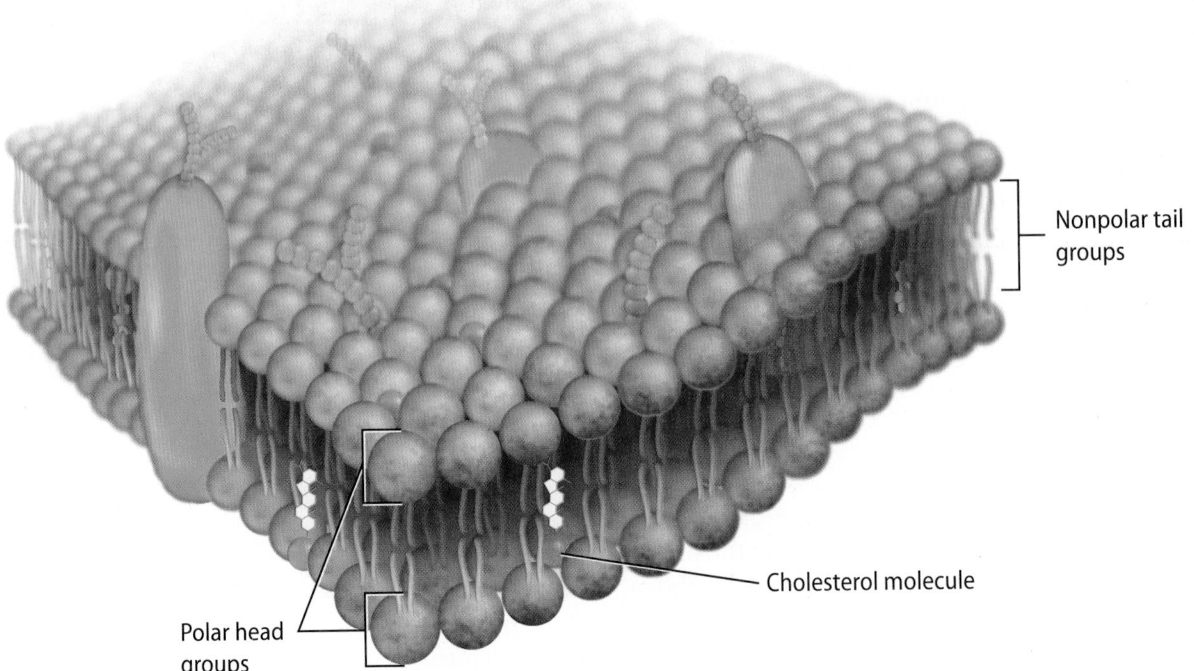

■ **Figure 7** The fluid mosaic model refers to a plasma membrane with substances that can move around within the membrane.

Animation

Together, the phospholipids in the bilayer create a "sea" in which other molecules can float, like apples floating in a barrel of water. This "sea" concept is the basis for the **fluid mosaic model** of the plasma membrane. The phospholipids can move sideways within the membrane, just as apples move around in water. At the same time, other components in the membrane, such as proteins, also move among the phospholipids. Because there are different substances in the plasma membrane, a pattern, or mosaic, is created on the surface. You can see this pattern in **Figure 7.** The components of the plasma membrane are in constant motion, sliding past one another.

REVIEW IT! The Plasma Membrane

Section Summary

- Selective permeability is a property of the plasma membrane that allows it to control what enters and leaves the cell.
- The plasma membrane is made up of two layers of phospholipid molecules.
- Cholesterol and transport proteins aid in the function of the plasma membrane.
- The fluid mosaic model describes the plasma membrane.

Self Check

Understand Main Ideas

1. MAINIDEA **Describe** how the plasma membrane helps maintain homeostasis in a cell.
2. **Explain** how the inside of a cell remains separate from its environment.
3. **Diagram** the plasma membrane and label each component.
4. **Identify** the molecules in the plasma membrane that provide basic membrane structure, cell identity, and membrane fluidity.

Think Critically

5. **Explain** what effect more cholesterol in the plasma membrane will have on the membrane.

WRITING IN ▶ Biology

6. Using what you know about the term *mosaic,* write a paragraph describing another biological mosaic.

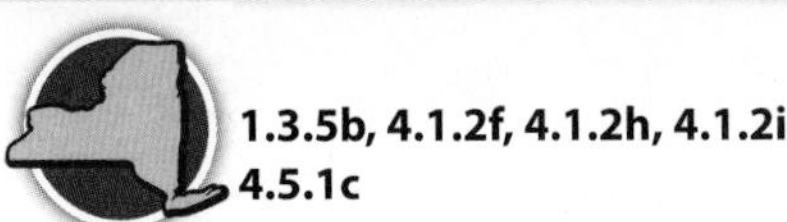

3 Structures and Organelles

1.3.5b, 4.1.2f, 4.1.2h, 4.1.2i, 4.5.1c

MAINIDEA

Eukaryotic cells contain organelles that allow the specialization and the separation of functions within the cell.

Essential Questions

- What are the structures of a typical eukaryotic cell, and what are their functions?
- What are the similarities and differences between plant and animal cells?

BIOLOGY 4U

A company that manufactures hiking boots could make each boot individually by one person, but it's more efficient to use an assembly line. Similarly, eukaryotic cells have specialized structures that perform specific tasks, much like a factory.

Review Vocabulary

enzyme: a protein that speeds up the rate of a chemical reaction

New Vocabulary

cytoplasm
cytoskeleton
ribosome
nucleolus
endoplasmic reticulum
Golgi apparatus
vacuole
lysosome
centriole
mitochondrion
chloroplast
cell wall
cilium
flagellum

Multilingual eGlossary

Cytoplasm and Cytoskeleton

You just have investigated the part of a cell that functions as the boundary between the inside and outside environments. The environment inside the plasma membrane is a semifluid material called **cytoplasm.** In a prokaryotic cell, all of the chemical processes of the cell, such as breaking down sugar to generate the energy used for other functions, take place directly in the cytoplasm. Eukaryotic cells perform these processes within organelles in their cytoplasm. At one time, scientists thought that cell organelles floated in a sea of cytoplasm.

More recently, cell biologists have discovered that organelles do not float freely in a cell, but are supported by a structure within the cytoplasm similar to the structure shown in **Figure 8.** The **cytoskeleton** is a supporting network of long, thin protein fibers that form a framework for the cell and provide an anchor for the organelles inside the cells. The cytoskeleton also has a function in cell movement and other cellular activities.

The cytoskeleton is made of substructures called microtubules and microfilaments. Microtubules are long, hollow protein cylinders that form a rigid skeleton for the cell and assist in moving substances within the cell. Microfilaments are thin protein threads that help give the cell shape and enable the entire cell or parts of the cell to move. Microtubules and microfilaments rapidly assemble and disassemble and slide past one another. This allows cells and organelles to move.

■ **Figure 8** Microtubules and microfilaments make up the cytoskeleton.

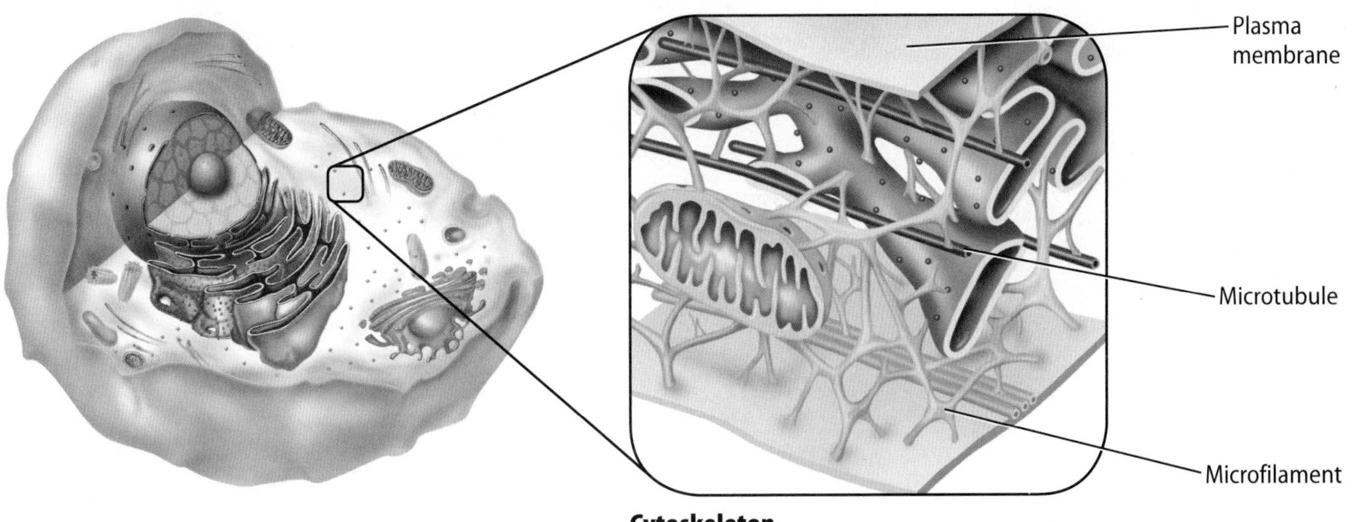

VISUALIZING Cells

Figure 9 Compare the illustrations of a plant cell, animal cell, and prokaryotic cell. Some organelles are found only in plant cells; others are found only in animal cells. Prokaryotic cells do not have membrane-bound organelles.

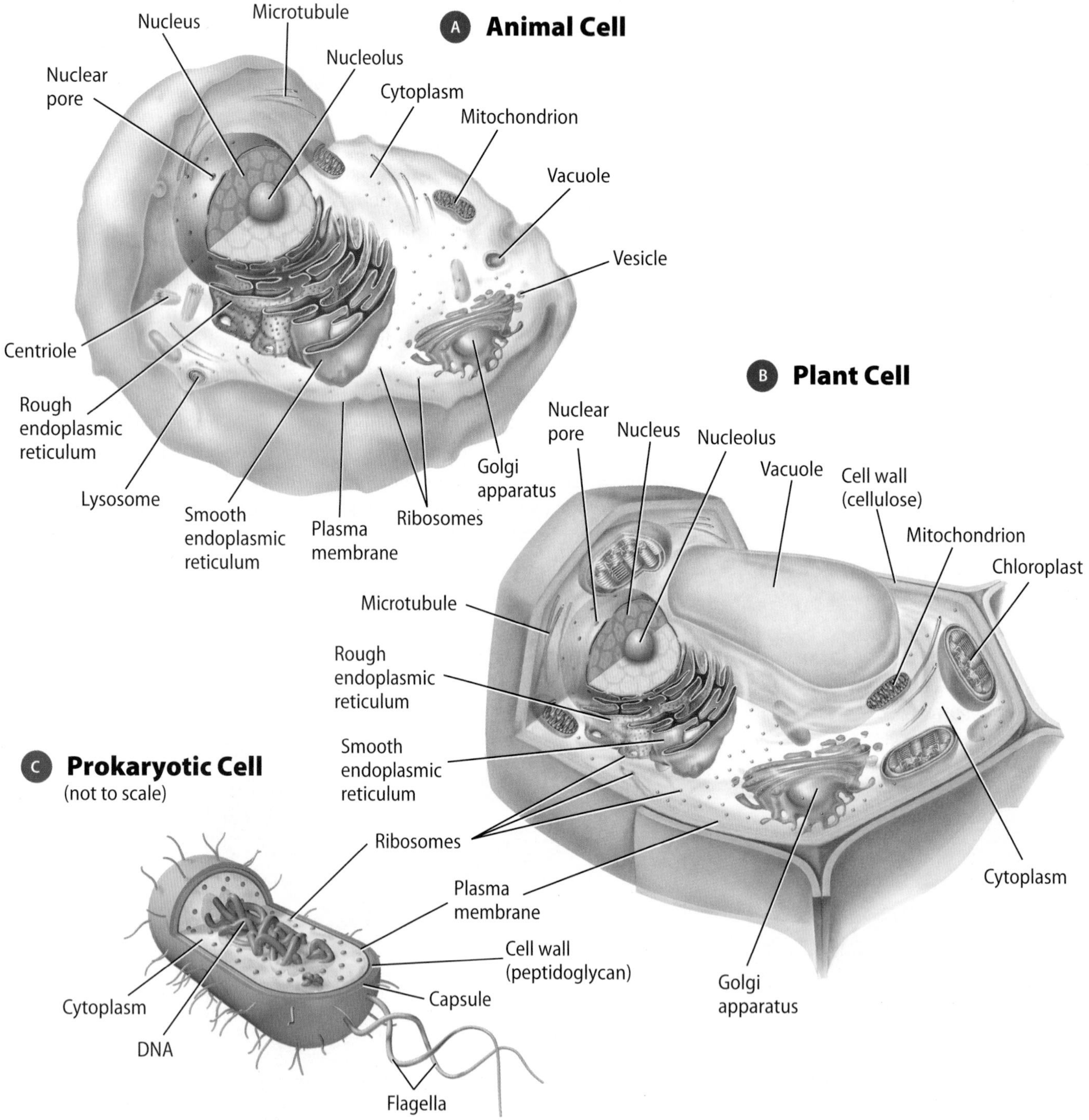

A Animal Cell

Nucleus
Microtubule
Nucleolus
Nuclear pore
Cytoplasm
Mitochondrion
Vacuole
Vesicle
Centriole
Rough endoplasmic reticulum
Lysosome
Smooth endoplasmic reticulum
Plasma membrane
Ribosomes
Golgi apparatus

B Plant Cell

Nuclear pore
Nucleus
Nucleolus
Vacuole
Cell wall (cellulose)
Mitochondrion
Chloroplast
Microtubule
Rough endoplasmic reticulum
Smooth endoplasmic reticulum
Ribosomes
Plasma membrane
Cytoplasm
Golgi apparatus

C Prokaryotic Cell
(not to scale)

Ribosomes
Plasma membrane
Cell wall (peptidoglycan)
Capsule
Cytoplasm
DNA
Flagella

Cell Structures

In a factory, there are separate areas set up for performing different tasks. Eukaryotic cells also have separate areas for tasks. Membrane-bound organelles make it possible for different chemical processes to take place at the same time in different parts of the cytoplasm. Organelles carry out essential cell processes, such as protein synthesis, energy transformation, digestion of food, excretion of wastes, and cell division. Each organelle has a unique structure and function. You can compare organelles to a factory's offices, assembly lines, and other important areas that keep the factory running. As you read about the different organelles, refer to the diagrams of plant and animal cells in **Figure 9** to see the organelles of each type.

VOCABULARY

WORD ORIGIN

Cytoplasm
Cytoskeleton

cyte– prefix; from Greek, meaning *cell*

The nucleus Just as a factory needs a manager, a cell needs an organelle to direct the cell processes. The nucleus, shown in **Figure 10,** is the cell's managing structure. It contains most of the cell's DNA, which stores information used to make proteins for cell growth, function, and reproduction.

BrainPOP

The nucleus is surrounded by a double membrane called the nuclear envelope. The nuclear envelope is similar to the plasma membrane, except the nuclear membrane has nuclear pores that allow larger-sized substances to move in and out of the nucleus. Chromatin, which is a complex DNA attached to protein, is spread throughout the nucleus.

GET IT? **Describe** the role of the nucleus.

Ribosomes One of the functions of a cell is to produce proteins. The organelles that help manufacture proteins are called **ribosomes.** Ribosomes are made of two components—RNA and protein—and are not bound by a membrane like other organelles are. Within the nucleus is the site of ribosome production called the **nucleolus,** shown in **Figure 10.**

Cells have many ribosomes that produce a variety of proteins that are used by the cell or are moved out and used by other cells. Some ribosomes float freely in the cytoplasm, while others are bound to another organelle called the endoplasmic reticulum. Free-floating ribosomes produce proteins for use within the cytoplasm of the cell. Bound ribosomes produce proteins that will be bound within membranes or used by other cells.

■ **Figure 10** The nucleus of a cell is a three-dimensional shape. The photomicrograph shows a cross section of a nucleus.

Infer ***why all of the cross sections of a nucleus are not identical.***

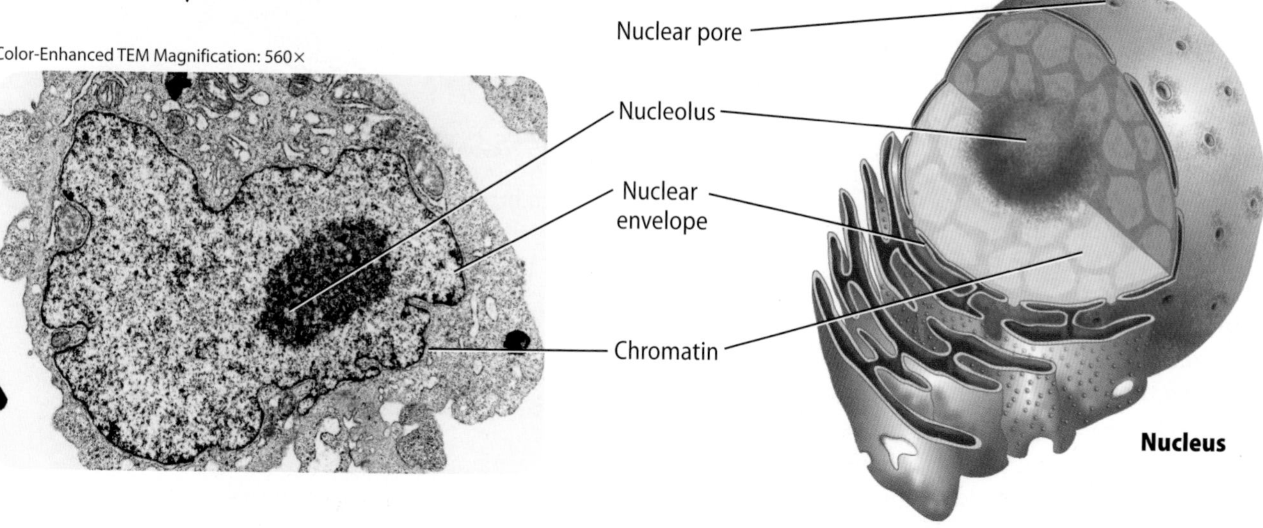

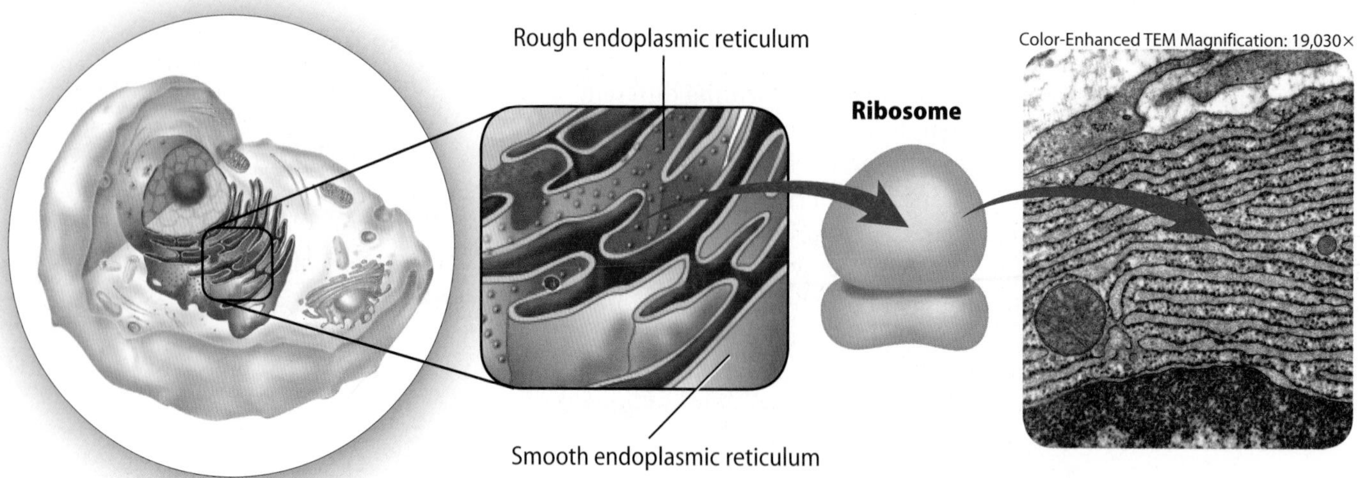

■ **Figure 11** Ribosomes are simple structures made of RNA and protein that may be attached to the surface of the rough endoplasmic reticulum. They look like bumps on the endoplasmic reticulum.

Endoplasmic reticulum The **endoplasmic reticulum** (en duh PLAZ mihk • rih TIHK yuh lum), also called ER, is a membrane system of folded sacs and interconnected channels that serves as the site for protein and lipid synthesis. The pleats and folds of the ER provide a large amount of surface area where cellular functions can take place. The area of ER where ribosomes are attached is called rough endoplasmic reticulum. Notice in **Figure 11** that the rough ER appears to have bumps on it. These bumps are the attached ribosomes that will produce proteins for export to other cells.

Figure 11 also shows that there are areas of the ER that do not have ribosomes attached. The area of ER where no ribosomes are attached is called smooth endoplasmic reticulum. Although the smooth ER has no ribosomes, it does perform important functions for the cell. For example, the smooth ER provides a membrane surface where a variety of complex carbohydrates and lipids, including phospholipids, are synthesized. Smooth ER in the liver detoxifies harmful substances.

Virtual Lab 

Data Analysis LAB 2

Based on Real Lab Data*

Interpret the Data

How is vesicle traffic from the ER to the Golgi apparatus regulated? Some proteins are synthesized by ribosomes on the endoplasmic reticulum (ER). The proteins are processed in the ER, and vesicles containing these proteins pinch off and migrate to the Golgi apparatus. Scientists currently are studying the molecules that are involved in fusing these vesicles to the Golgi apparatus.

Data and Observations

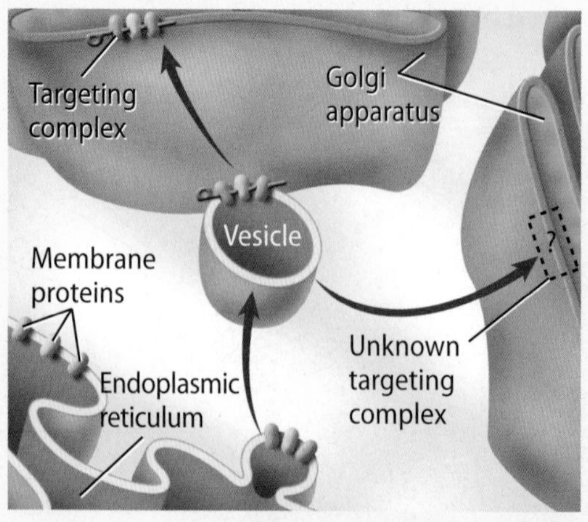

Think Critically

1. **Interpret the diagram** by naming two complexes on the Golgi apparatus that might be involved in vesicle fusion.
2. **Hypothesize** an explanation for vesicle transport based on what you have read about cytoplasm and the cytoskeleton.

* Data obtained from: Brittle, E. E., and Waters, M. G. 2000. ER-to-golgi traffic—this bud's for you. *Science* 289: 403–404.

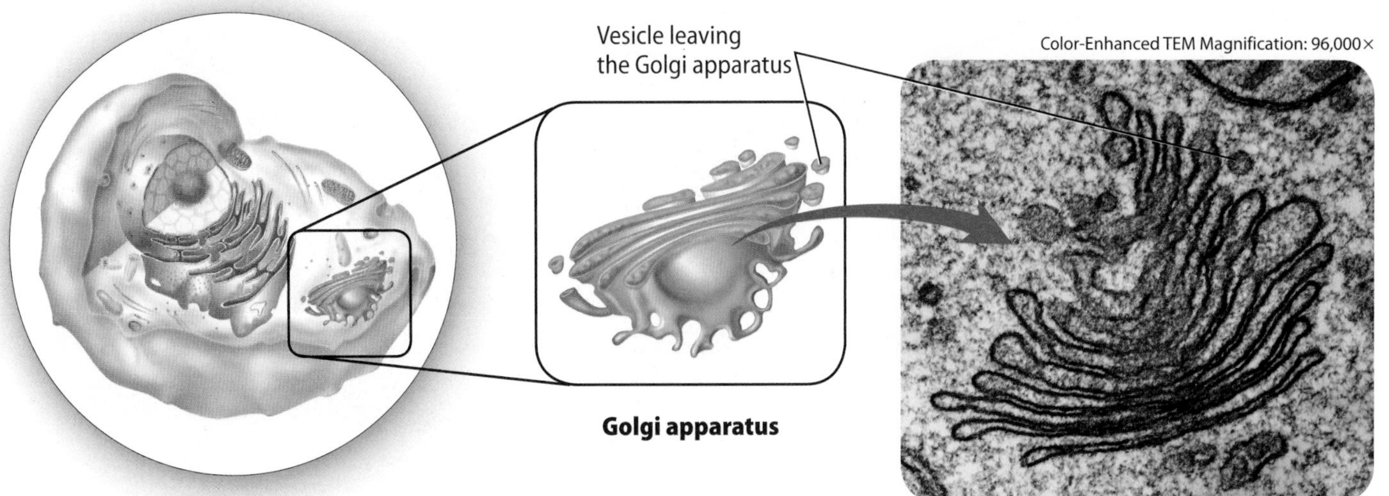

■ **Figure 12** Flattened stacks of membranes make up the Golgi apparatus.

Golgi apparatus After hiking boots are made in a factory, they must be organized into pairs, boxed, and shipped. Similarly, after proteins are made in the endoplasmic reticulum, some might be transferred to the Golgi (GAWL jee) apparatus, illustrated in **Figure 12.** The **Golgi apparatus** is a flattened stack of membranes that modifies, sorts, and packages proteins into sacs called vesicles. Vesicles then can fuse with the cell's plasma membrane to release proteins to the environment outside the cell. Observe the vesicle in **Figure 12.**

Vacuoles A factory needs a place to store materials and waste products. Similarly, cells have membrane-bound vesicles called vacuoles for temporary storage of materials within the cytoplasm. A **vacuole,** such as the plant vacuole shown in **Figure 13,** is a sac used to store food, enzymes, and other materials needed by a cell. Some vacuoles store waste products. Interestingly, animal cells usually do not contain vacuoles. If animal cells do have vacuoles, they are much smaller than those in plant cells.

■ **Figure 13** Plant cells have large membrane-bound storage compartments called vacuoles.

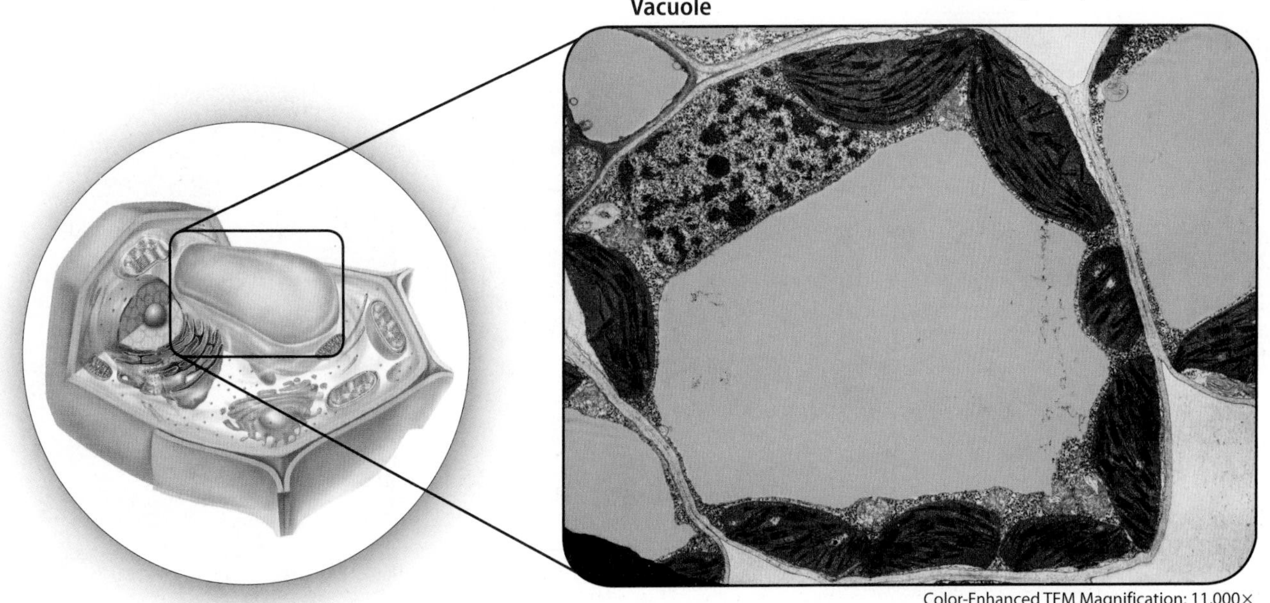

(t & b)Biophoto Associates/Science Source

Color-Enhanced LM Magnification: 11,000×

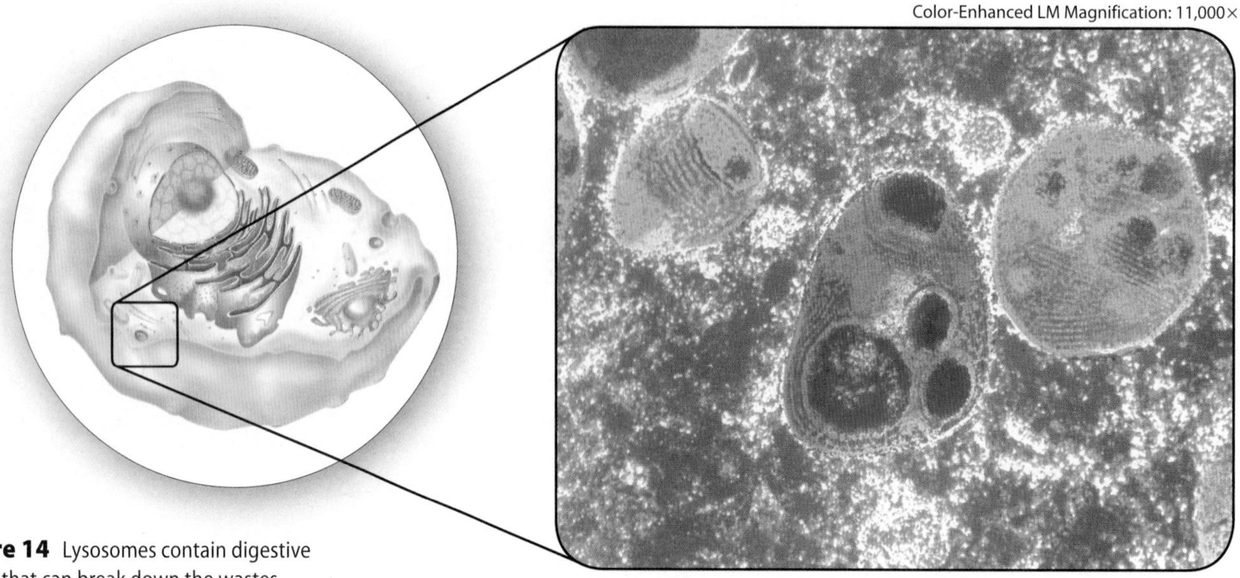

Lysosome

■ **Figure 14** Lysosomes contain digestive enzymes that can break down the wastes contained in vacuoles.

Lysosomes Factories and cells also need cleanup crews. In a cell, there are **lysosomes,** shown in **Figure 14,** which are vesicles that contain substances that digest excess or worn-out organelles and food particles. Lysosomes also digest bacteria and viruses that have entered the cell. The membrane surrounding a lysosome prevents the digestive enzymes inside from destroying the cell. Lysosomes can fuse with vacuoles and dispense their enzymes into the vacuoles. These enzymes digest the wastes inside.

Centrioles Previously in this section, you read about microtubules and the cytoskeleton. Groups of microtubules form another structure called a centriole (SEN tree ol). **Centrioles,** shown in **Figure 15,** are organelles made of microtubules that function during cell division. Centrioles are located in the cytoplasm of animal cells and most protists and usually are near the nucleus.

■ **Figure 15** Centrioles are made of microtubules and play a role in cell division.

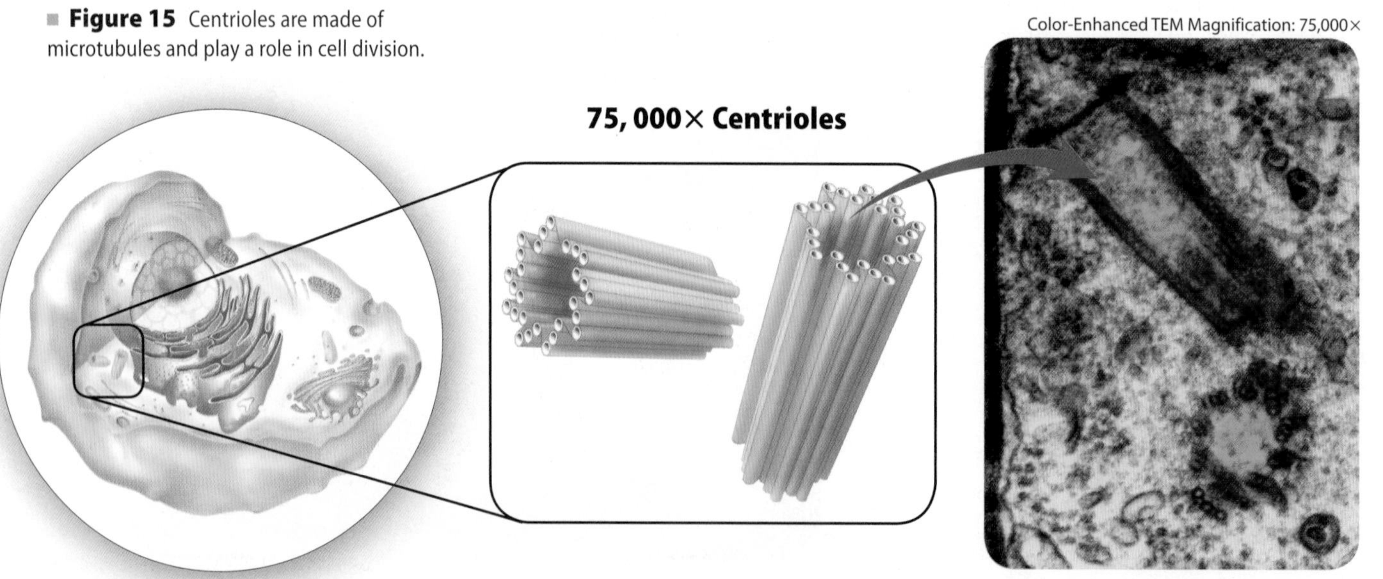

(t)EM Research Services, Newcastle University; (b)Biophoto Associates/Science Source

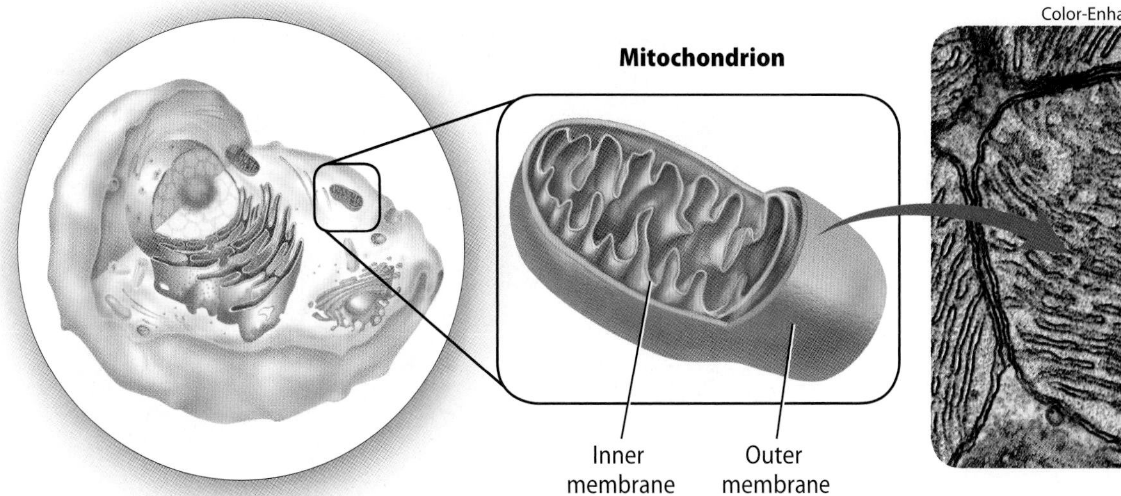

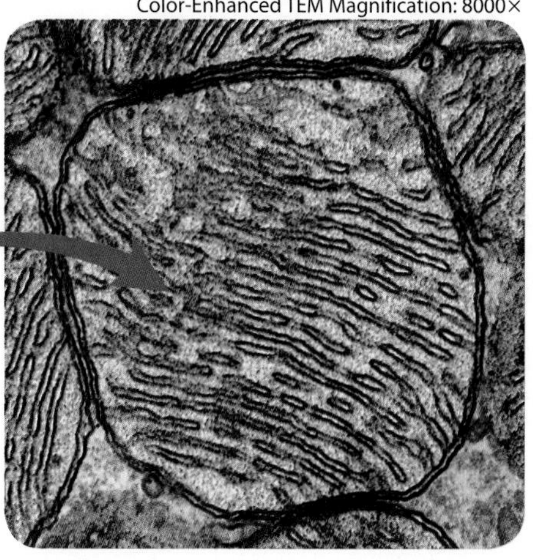

■ **Figure 16** Mitochondria make energy available to the cell.

Describe ***the membrane structure of a mitochondrion.***

Mitochondria Imagine now that a boot factory has its own generator that produces the electricity it needs. Cells also have energy generators called **mitochondria** (mi tuh KAHN dree uh; singular, mitochondrion), which convert fuel particles (mainly sugars) into usable energy. **Figure 16** shows that a mitochondrion has an outer membrane and a highly folded inner membrane that provides a large surface area for breaking the bonds in sugar molecules. The energy produced from that breakage is stored in the bonds of other molecules and later used by the cell. For this reason, mitochondria often are referred to as the "powerhouses" of cells.

Chloroplasts Factory machines need electricity that is generated by burning fossil fuels or by collecting energy from alternative sources, such as the Sun. Plant cells have their own way of using solar energy. In addition to mitochondria, plants and some other eukaryotic cells contain **chloroplasts,** which are organelles that capture light energy and convert it to chemical energy through a process called photosynthesis. Examine **Figure 17** and notice that inside the inner membrane are many small, disk-shaped compartments called thylakoids. It is there that the energy from sunlight is trapped by a pigment called chlorophyll. Chlorophyll gives leaves and stems their green color.

Chloroplasts belong to a group of plant organelles called plastids, some of which are used for storage. Some plastids store starches or lipids. Others, such as chromoplasts, contain red, orange, or yellow pigments that trap light energy and give color to plant structures such as flowers and leaves.

■ **Figure 17** In plants, chloroplasts capture and convert light energy to chemical energy.

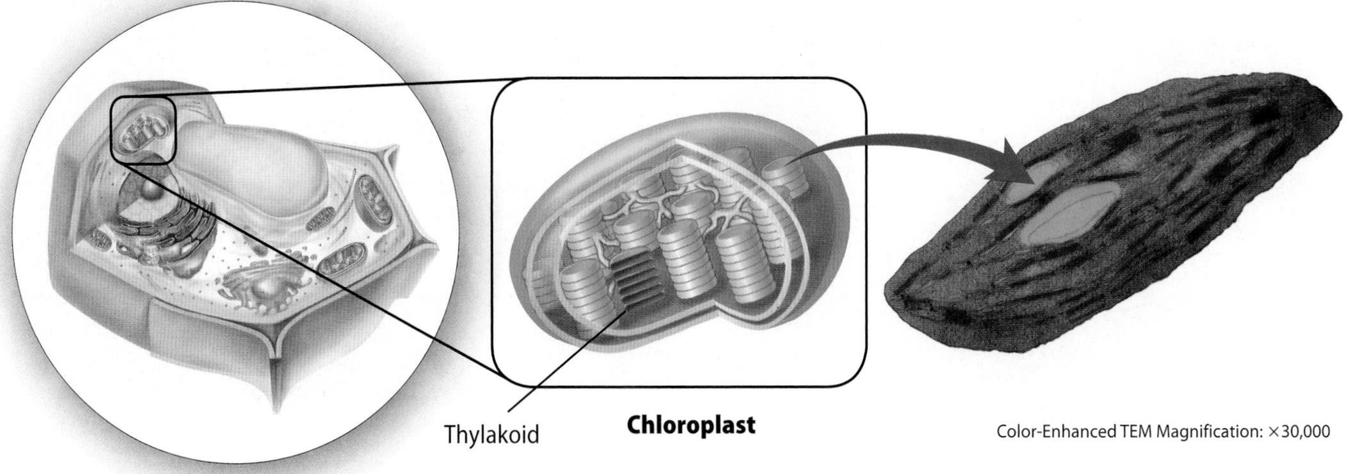

(t)Thomas Deerinck, NCMIR/Science Source; (b)Biophoto Associates/Science Source

Color-Enhanced TEM Magnification: 38,000×

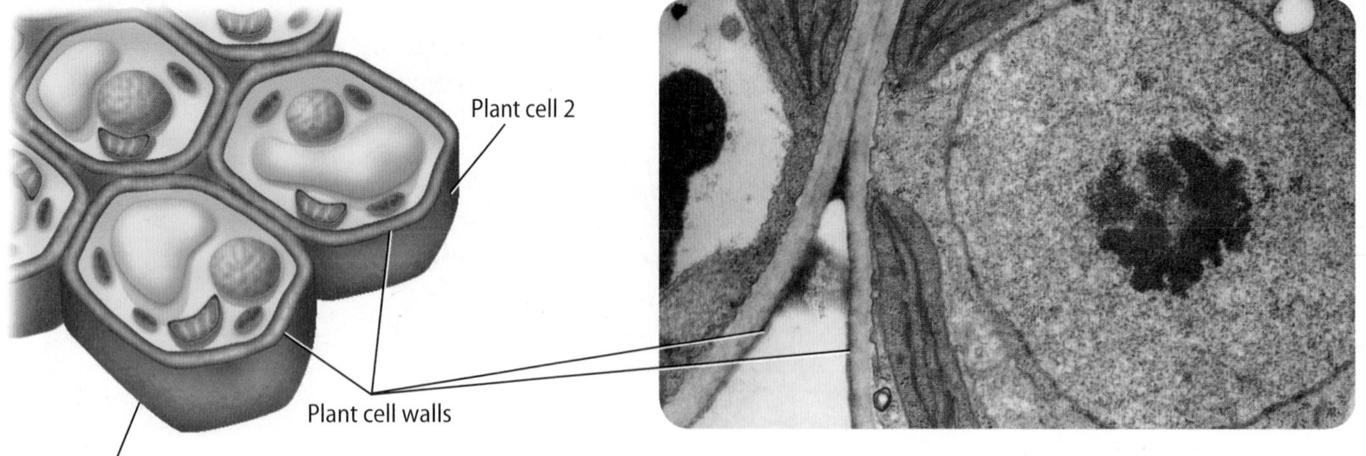

■ **Figure 18** The illustration shows plant cells and their cell walls. Compare this to the transmission electron micrograph showing the cell walls of adjacent plant cells.

Cell wall Another structure associated with plant cells is the cell wall, shown in **Figure 18.** The **cell wall** is a thick, rigid, mesh of fibers that surrounds the outside of the plasma membrane, protects the cell, and gives it support. Rigid cell walls allow plants to stand at various heights—from blades of grass to California redwood trees. Plant cell walls are made of a carbohydrate called cellulose, which gives the cell walls their inflexible characteristics. **Table 1** summarizes cell walls and various other cell structures.

Cilia and flagella Some eukaryotic cell surfaces have structures called cilia and flagella that project outside the plasma membrane. As shown in **Figure 19, cilia** (singular, cilium) are short, numerous projections that look like hairs. The motion of cilia is similar to the motion of oars in a rowboat. **Flagella** (singular, flagellum) are longer and less numerous than cilia. These projections move with a whiplike motion. Cilia and flagella are composed of microtubules arranged in a 9 + 2 configuration, in which nine pairs of microtubules surround two single microtubules. Typically, a cell has one or two flagella.

Prokaryotic cilia and flagella contain cytoplasm and are enclosed by the plasma membrane. These structures are made of complex proteins. While both structures are used for cell movement, cilia are also found on stationary cells.

■ **Figure 19** The hairlike structures in the photomicrograph are cilia, and the tail-like structures are flagella. Both structures function in cell movement.

Infer ***where in the body of an animal you would predict cilia might be found.***

Color-Enhanced SEM Magnification: 12000×

Cilia on the surface of a *Paramecium*

Color-Enhanced TEM Magnification: unavailable

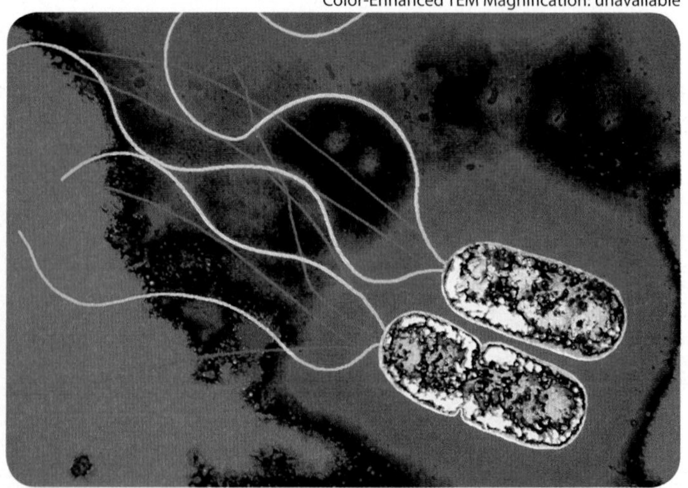

Bacteria with flagella

Table 1 Summary of Cell Structures

Interactive Table

Cell Structure	Example	Function	Cell Type
Cell wall		An inflexible barrier that provides support and protects the plant cell	Plant cells, fungi cells, and some prokaryotes
Centrioles		Organelles that occur in pairs and are important for cell division	Animal cells and most protist cells
Chloroplast		A double-membrane organelle with thylakoids containing chlorophyll; where photosynthesis takes place	Plant cells and some protist cells
Cilia		Projections from cell surfaces that aid in locomotion and feeding; also used to sweep substances along surfaces	Some animal cells, protist cells, and prokaryotes
Cytoskeleton		A framework for the cell within the cytoplasm	All eukaryotic cells
Endoplasmic reticulum		A highly folded membrane that is the site of protein synthesis	All eukaryotic cells
Flagella		Projections that aid in locomotion and feeding	Some animal cells, prokaryotes, and some plant cells
Golgi apparatus		A flattened stack of tubular membranes that modifies proteins and packages them for distribution outside the cell	All eukaryotic cells
Lysosome		A vesicle that contains digestive enzymes for the breakdown of excess or worn-out cellular substances	Animal cells and rare in plant cells
Mitochondrion		A membrane-bound organelle that makes energy available to the rest of the cell	All eukaryotic cells
Nucleus		The control center of the cell that contains coded directions for the production of proteins and cell division	All eukaryotic cells
Plasma membrane		A flexible boundary that controls the movement of substances into and out of the cell	All cells
Ribosome		Organelle that is the site of protein synthesis	All cells
Vacuole		A membrane-bound vesicle for the temporary storage of materials	Plant cells–one large; rarely animal cells–a few small

CAREERS IN BIOLOGY

Science Communications Specialist Many publishers of scientific material hire communications specialists to write about research and its importance to the general public. This often is accomplished through press releases, ads, pamphlets, and targeted mailings.

Comparing Cells

Table 1 summarizes the structures of eukaryotic plant cells and animal cells. Notice that plant cells contain chlorophyll; they can capture and transform energy from the Sun into a usable form of chemical energy. This is one of the main characteristics that distinguishes plants from animals. In addition, recall that animal cells usually do not contain vacuoles. If they do, vacuoles in animal cells are much smaller than vacuoles in plant cells. Also, animal cells do not have cell walls. Cell walls give plant cells protection and support.

Organelles at Work

With a basic understanding of the structures found within a cell, it becomes easier to envision how those structures work together to perform cell functions. Take, for example, the synthesis of proteins.

Protein synthesis begins in the nucleus with the information contained in the DNA. Genetic information is copied and transferred to another genetic molecule called RNA. Then RNA and ribosomes, which have been manufactured in the nucleolus, leave the nucleus through the pores of the nuclear membrane. Together, RNA and ribosomes manufacture proteins. Each protein made on the rough ER has a particular function; it might become a protein that forms a part of the plasma membrane, a protein that is released from the cell, or a protein transported to other organelles. Other ribosomes will float freely in the cytoplasm and also make proteins.

Most of the proteins made on the surface of the ER are sent to the Golgi apparatus. The Golgi apparatus packages the proteins in vesicles and transports them to other organelles or out of the cell. Other organelles use the proteins to carry out cell processes. For example, lysosomes use proteins, enzymes in particular, to digest food and waste. Mitochondria use enzymes to produce a usable form of energy for the cell.

After reading about the organelles in a cell, it becomes clear why people equate the cell to a factory. Each organelle has its job to do, and the health of the cell depends on all of the components working together.

REVIEW IT! Structures and Organelles

Section Summary

- Eukaryotic cells contain membrane-bound organelles in the cytoplasm that perform cell functions.
- Ribosomes are the sites of protein synthesis.
- Mitochondria are the powerhouses of cells.
- Plant and animal cells contain many of the same organelles, while other organelles are unique to either plant cells or animal cells.

Self Check

Understand Main Ideas

1. MAINIDEA **Identify** the role of the nucleus in a eukaryotic cell.
2. **Summarize** the role of the endoplasmic reticulum.
3. **Create** a flowchart comparing the parts of a cell to an automobile production line.
4. **Compare and contrast** structures of plant and animal cells.

Think Critically

5. **Hypothesize** how lysosomes would be involved in changing a caterpillar into a butterfly.

WRITING IN ▶ Biology

6. Categorize the structures and organelles in **Table 1** into lists based on cell type and then draw a concept map illustrating your organization.

USE IT! Science Notebook

4 Cellular Transport

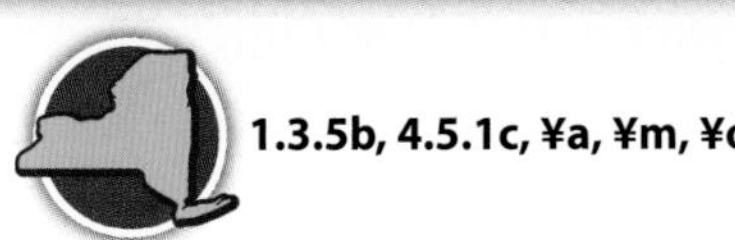

1.3.5b, 4.5.1c, ¥a, ¥m, ¥o

MAINIDEA

Cellular transport moves substances within the cell and moves substances into and out of the cell.

Essential Questions

- What are the processes of diffusion, facilitated diffusion, and active transport?
- What is the effect of a hypotonic, hypertonic, or isotonic solution on a cell?
- How do large particles enter and exit cells?

BIOLOGY 4U

Imagine studying in your room while cookies are baking in the kitchen. As the cookies baked, the movement of the aroma from the kitchen to your room happened through a process called diffusion.

Review Vocabulary

homeostasis: the regulation of the internal environment of a cell or organism to maintain conditions suitable for life

New Vocabulary

diffusion
dynamic equilibrium
facilitated diffusion
osmosis
isotonic solution
hypotonic solution
hypertonic solution
active transport
endocytosis
exocytosis

Multilingual eGlossary

Diffusion

Connection to Chemistry As the aroma of baking cookies makes its way to you, the particles are moving and colliding with each other in the air. This happens because the particles in gases, liquids, and solids are in random motion. Similarly, substances dissolved in water move constantly in random motion called Brownian motion. This random motion causes **diffusion,** which is the net movement of particles from an area where there are many particles of the substance to an area where there are fewer particles of the substance. The amount of a substance in a particular area is called concentration. Therefore, substances diffuse from areas of high concentration to low concentration. **Figure 20** illustrates the process of diffusion. Additional energy input is not required for diffusion because the particles already are in motion.

For example, if you drop red and blue ink into a container of water at opposite ends of the container, which is similar to the watery environment of a cell, the process of diffusion begins, as shown in **Figure 20(A).** In a short period of time, the ink particles have mixed as a result of diffusion to the point where a purple-colored blended area is visible. **Figure 20(B)** shows the initial result of this diffusion.

Figure 20 Diffusion causes the inks to move from high-ink concentration to low-ink concentration until the colors become evenly blended in the water.

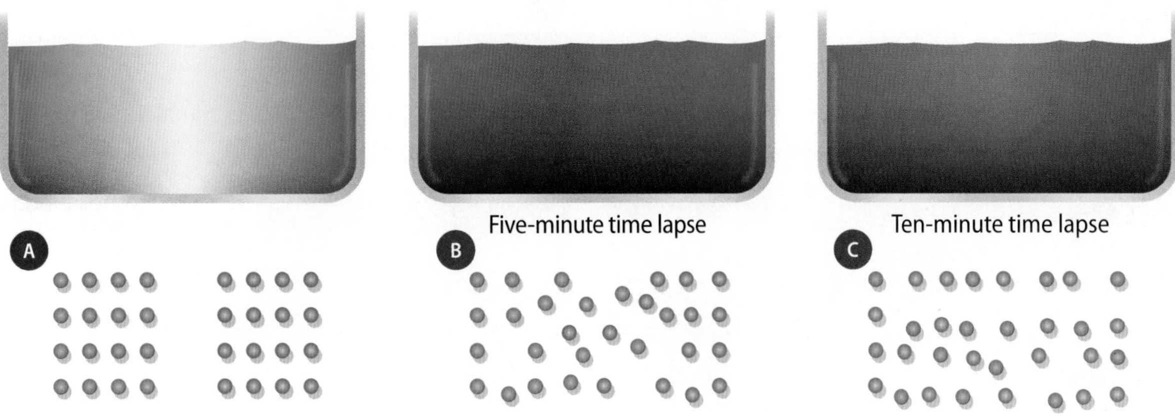

Given more time, the ink particles continue to mix and, in this case, continue to form the uniform purple mixture shown in **Figure 20(C).** Mixing continues until the concentrations of red ink and blue ink are the same in all areas. The final result is the purple solution. After this point, the particles continue to move randomly, but no further change in concentration will occur. This condition, in which there is continuous movement but no overall change, is called **dynamic equilibrium.**

VOCABULARY

ACADEMIC VOCABULARY

Concentration
the amount of a component in a given area or volume
The concentration of salt in the aquarium was too high, causing the fishes to die.

One of the key characteristics of diffusion is the rate at which diffusion takes place. Three main factors affect the rate of diffusion: concentration, temperature, and pressure. When concentration is high, diffusion occurs more quickly because there are more particles that collide. Similarly, when temperature or pressure increases, the number of collisions increases, thus increasing the rate of diffusion. Recall that at higher temperatures particles move faster, and at higher pressure the particles are closer together. In both cases, more collisions occur and diffusion is faster. The size and charge of a substance also affects the rate of diffusion.

FOLDABLES®
Incorporate information from this section into your Foldable.

Diffusion across the plasma membrane In addition to water, cells need certain ions and small molecules, such as chloride ions and sugars, to perform cellular functions. Water can diffuse across the plasma membrane, as shown in **Figure 21(A),** but most other substances cannot. Another form of transport, called **facilitated diffusion,** uses transport proteins to move other ions and small molecules across the plasma membrane. By this method, substances move into the cell through a water-filled transport protein, called a channel protein, that opens and closes to allow the substance to diffuse through the plasma membrane, as shown in **Figure 21(B).** Another type of transport protein, called a carrier protein, also can help substances diffuse across the plasma membrane. Carrier proteins change shape as the diffusion process continues to help move the particle through the membrane, as illustrated in **Figure 21(C).**

Diffusion of water and facilitated diffusion of other substances require no additional input of energy because the particles are moving from an area of high concentration to an area of lower concentration. This is also known as passive transport. You will learn later in this section about a form of cellular transport that does require energy input.

GET IT? **Describe** how sodium (Na^+) ions get into cells.

■ **Figure 21** Although water moves freely through the plasma membrane, other substances cannot pass through the phospholipid bilayer on their own. Such substances enter the cell by facilitated transport.

Animation

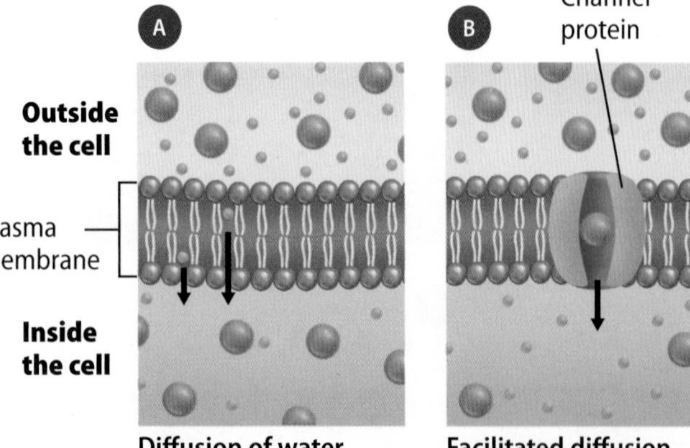

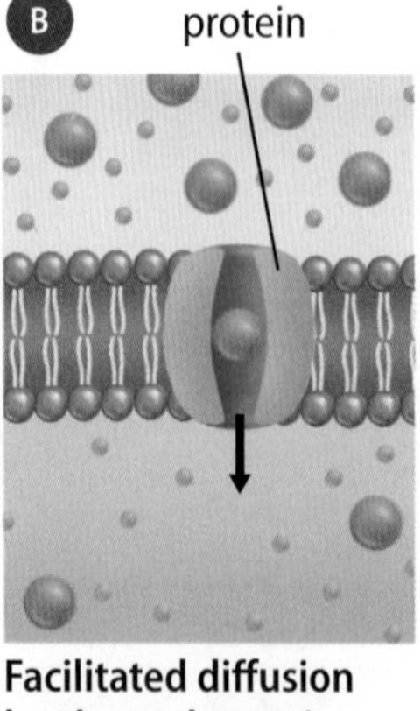

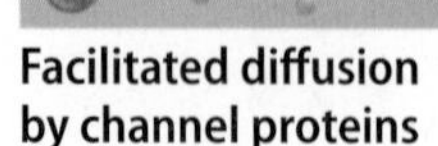

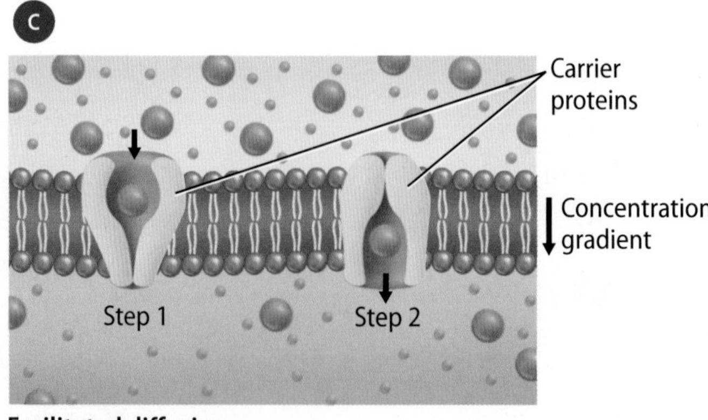

Osmosis: Diffusion of Water

Water is a substance that passes freely into and out of a cell through the plasma membrane. The diffusion of water across a selectively permeable membrane is called **osmosis** (ahs MOH sus). Regulating the movement of water across the plasma membrane is an important factor in maintaining homeostasis within the cell.

How osmosis works Recall that in a solution, a substance called the solute is dissolved in a solvent. Water is the solvent in a cell and its environment. Concentration is a measure of the amount of solute dissolved in a solvent. The concentration of a solution decreases when the amount of solvent increases.

Examine **Figure 22,** showing a U-shaped tube containing solutions with different sugar concentrations separated by a selectively permeable membrane. What will happen if the solvent (water) can pass through the membrane but the solute (sugar) cannot?

Water molecules diffuse toward the side with the greater sugar concentration—the right side. As water moves to the right, the concentration of the sugar solution decreases. The water continues to diffuse until dynamic equilibrium occurs—the concentration of the solutions is the same on both sides. Notice in **Figure 22** that the result is an increase in solution level on the right side. During dynamic equilibrium, water molecules continue to diffuse back and forth across the membrane. But, the concentrations on each side no longer change.

GET IT? **Compare and contrast** diffusion and osmosis.

MiniLAB 2

Investigate Osmosis

What will happen to cells placed in a strong salt solution? Regulating the flow and amount of water into and out of a cell is critical to the survival of that cell. Osmosis is one method used to regulate a cell's water content.

Procedure

1. Read and complete the lab safety form.
2. Prepare a control **slide** using **onion epidermis, water,** and **iodine stain** as directed by your teacher.
3. Prepare a test slide using onion epidermis, **salt water,** and iodine stain as directed by your teacher.
4. Predict the effect, if any, that the salt solution will have on the onion cells in the test slide.
5. View the control slide using a **compound microscope** under low power and sketch several onion cells.
6. View the test slide under the same magnification and sketch your observations.

Analysis

1. **Analyze and conclude** whether your prediction was correct or incorrect. Explain.
2. **Explain** Use the process of osmosis to explain what you observe.

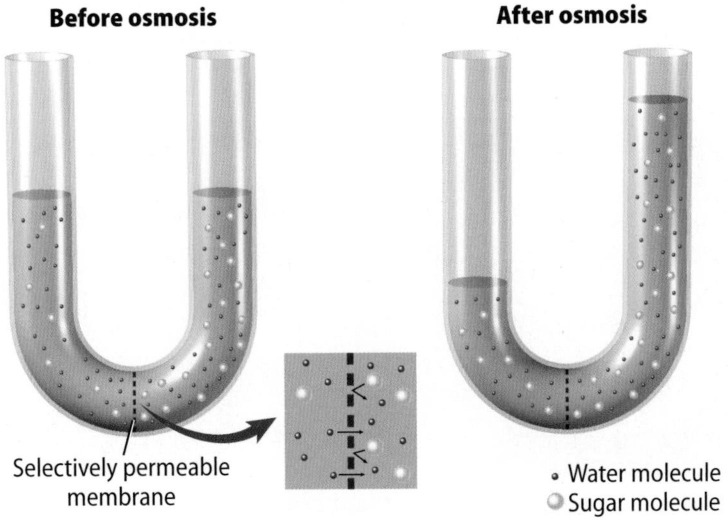

Figure 22 Before osmosis, the sugar concentration is greater on the right side. After osmosis, the concentrations are the same on both sides.

Name ***the term for this phenomenon.***

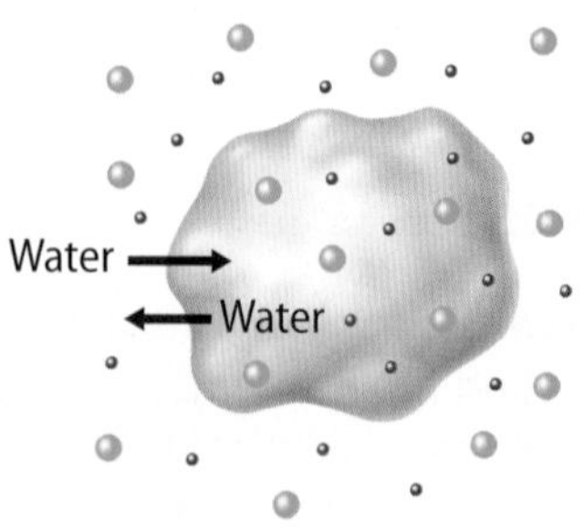

Color-Enhanced SEM. Magnification: 15,000×

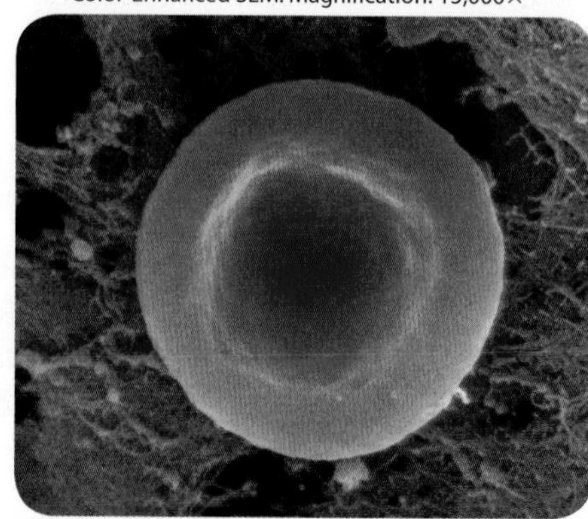
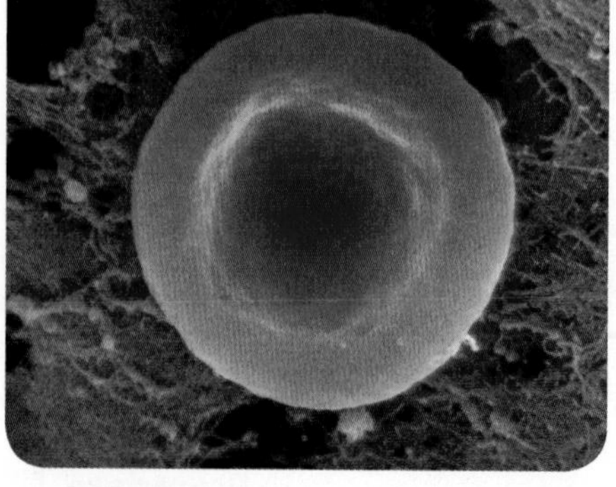

Animal cells

LM Magnification: 250×

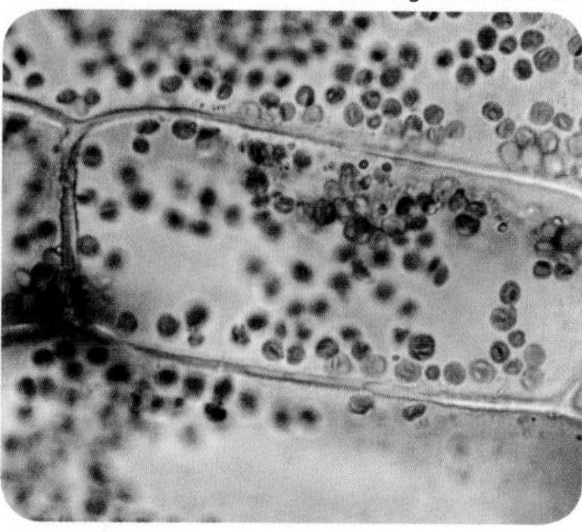

Plant cells

■ **Figure 23** In an isotonic solution, water molecules move into and out of the cell at the same rate, and cells retain their normal shape. The animal cell and the plant cell have their normal shapes in an isotonic solution.

Animation

Cells in an isotonic solution When a cell is in a solution that has the same concentration of water and solutes—ions, sugars, proteins, and other substances—as its cytoplasm, the cell is said to be in an **isotonic solution.** *Iso-* comes from the Greek word meaning *equal.* Water still moves through the plasma membrane, but water enters and leaves the cell at the same rate. The cell is at equilibrium with the solution, and there is no net movement of water. The cells retain their normal shape, as shown in **Figure 23.** Most cells in organisms are in isotonic solutions, such as blood.

Cells in a hypotonic solution If a cell is in a solution that has a lower concentration of solute, the cell is said to be in a **hypotonic solution.** *Hypo-* comes from the Greek word meaning *under.* There is more water outside of the cell than inside. As a result of osmosis, the net movement of water through the plasma membrane is into the cell, as illustrated in **Figure 24.** Pressure generated as water flows through the plasma membrane is called osmotic pressure. In an animal cell, as water moves into the cell, the pressure increases and the plasma membrane swells. If the solution is extremely hypotonic, the plasma membrane might be unable to withstand this pressure and the cell might burst.

Because they have a rigid cell wall that supports them, plant cells do not burst when in a hypotonic solution. As the pressure inside a cell increases, the plant's central vacuole fills with water, pushing the plasma membrane against the cell wall, shown in the plant cells in **Figure 24.** Instead of bursting, the plant cell becomes firmer. Grocers use this process to keep produce looking fresh by misting fruits and vegetables with water.

■ **Figure 24** In a hypotonic solution, water enters a cell by osmosis, causing the cell to swell. Animal cells may continue to swell until they burst. Plant cells swell beyond their normal size as internal pressure increases.

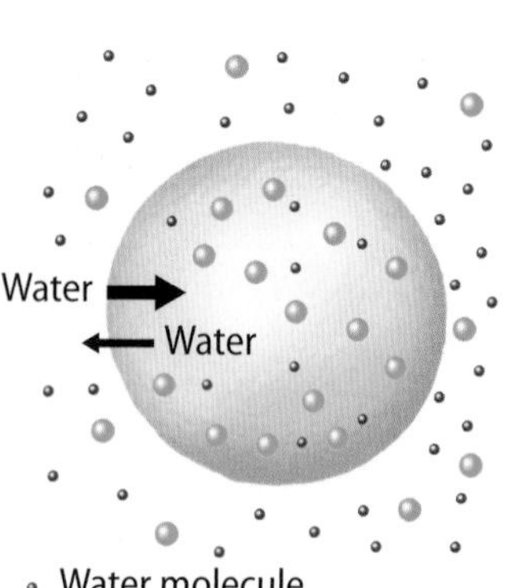

Red blood cell in hypotonic solution. Magnification: 15,000×

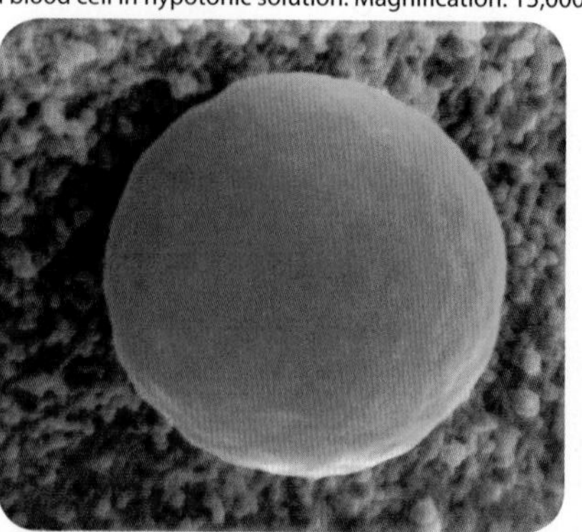

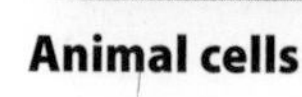

Animal cells

LM Magnification: 250×

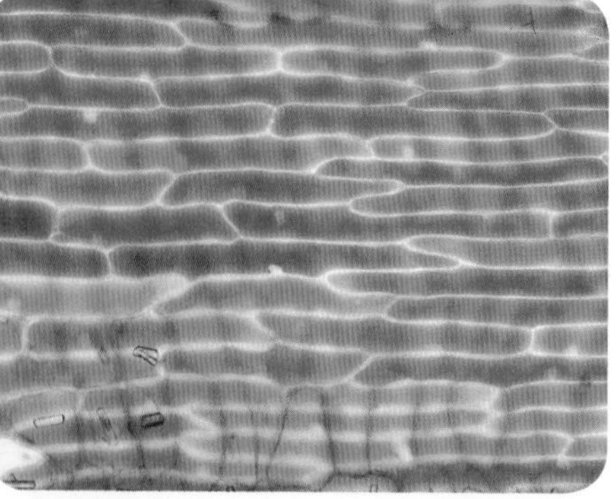

Plant cells

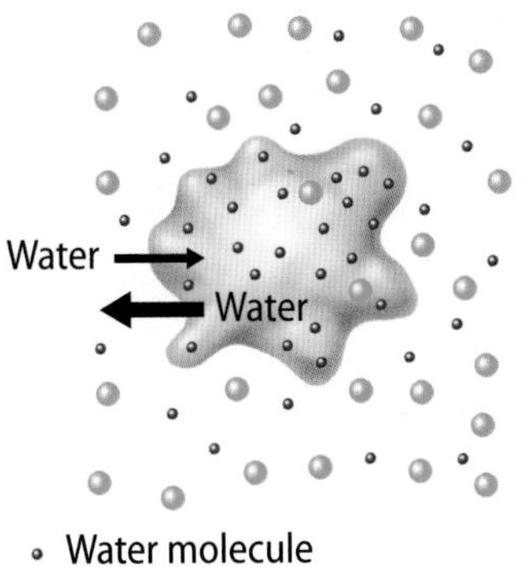

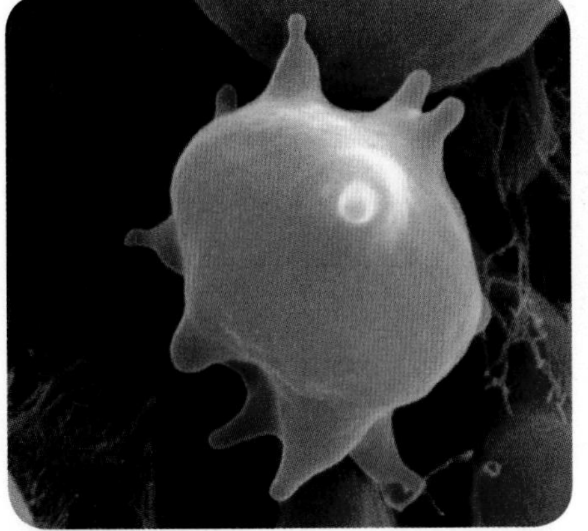

Animal cells

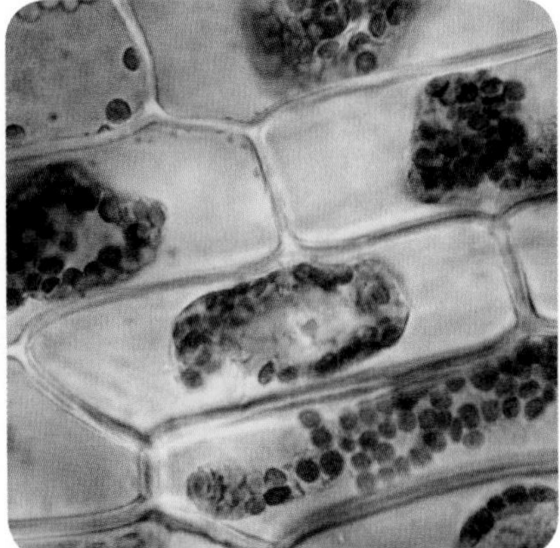

Plant cells

■ **Figure 25** In a hypertonic solution, water leaves a cell by osmosis, causing the cell to shrink. Animal cells shrivel up as they lose water. As plant cells lose internal pressure, the plasma membrane shrinks away from the cell wall.

Cells in a hypertonic solution When a cell is placed in a **hypertonic solution,** the concentration of the solute outside of the cell is higher than it is inside. *Hyper-* comes from the Greek word meaning *above.* During osmosis, the net movement of water is out of the cell, as illustrated in **Figure 25.** Animal cells in a hypertonic solution shrivel because of decreased pressure in the cells. Plant cells in a hypertonic solution lose water, mainly from the central vacuole. The plasma membrane shrinks away from the cell wall. Loss of water in a plant cell causes wilting.

GET IT? **Compare and contrast** the three types of solutions.

Active Transport

Sometimes substances must move from a region of lower concentration to a region of higher concentration against the passive movement from higher to lower concentration. This movement of substances across the plasma membrane against a concentration gradient requires energy; therefore, it is called **active transport. Figure 26** illustrates how active transport occurs with the aid of carrier proteins, commonly called pumps. Some pumps move one type of substance in only one direction, while others move two substances either across the membrane in the same direction or in opposite directions. Because of active transport, the cell maintains the proper balance of substances it needs. Active transport helps maintain homeostasis.

■ **Figure 26** Carrier proteins pick up and move substances across the plasma membrane against the concentration gradient and into the cell.

Explain ***why active transport requires energy.***

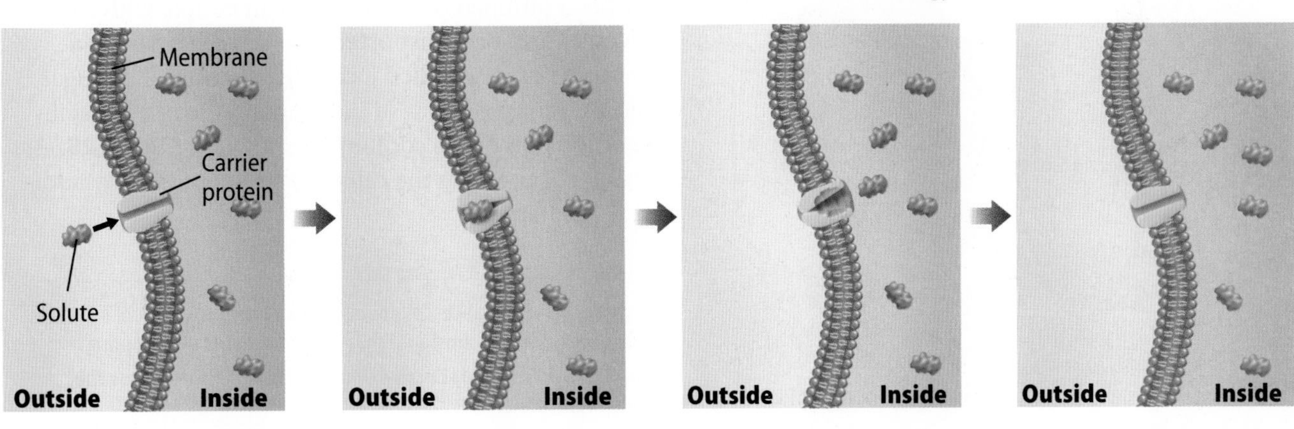

(l)David M. Phillips/Science Source, (r)Ed Reschke/Photolibrary/Getty Images

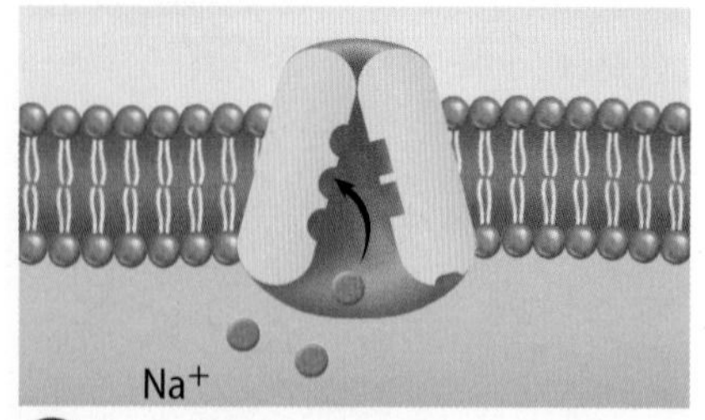

A Protein in the membrane binds intracellular sodium ions.

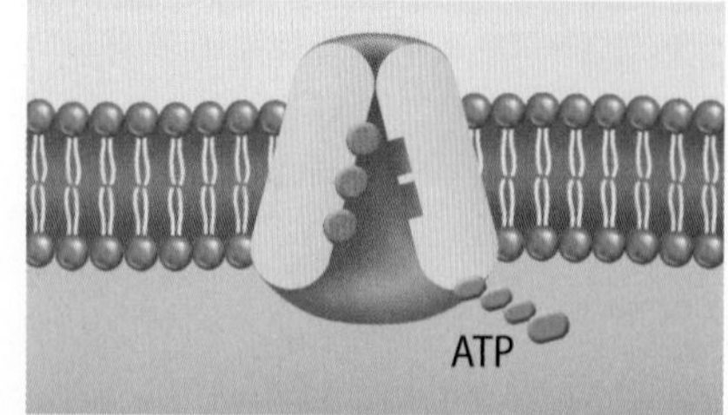

B ATP attaches to protein with bound sodium ions.

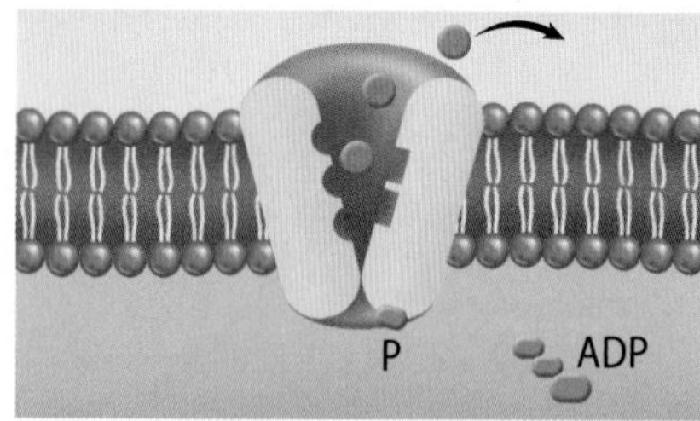

C The breakdown of ATP causes shape change in protein, allowing sodium ions to leave.

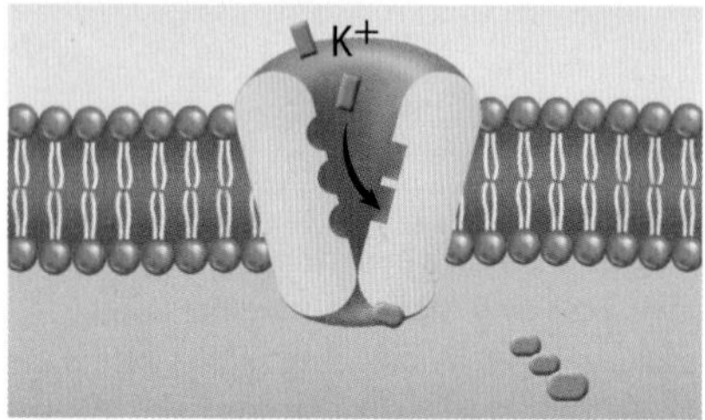

D Extracellular potassium ions bind to exposed sites.

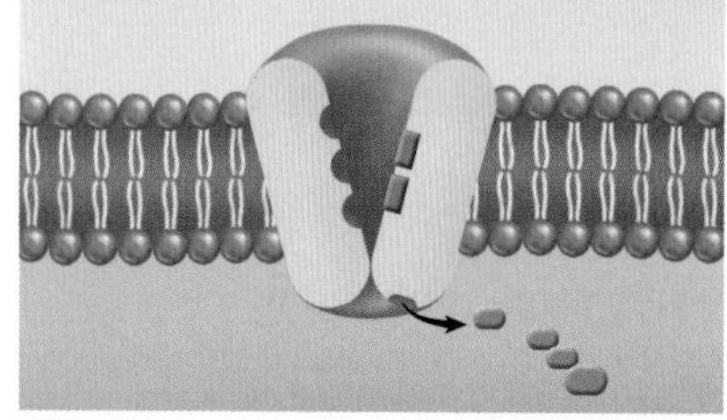

E Binding of potassium causes release of phosphate from protein.

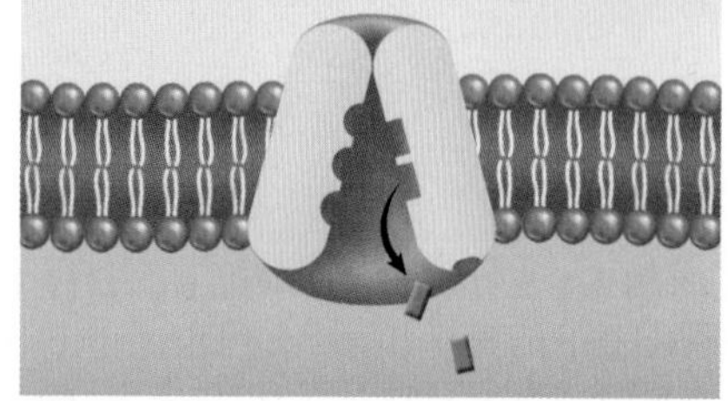

F Phosphate release changes protein back to its original shape, and potassium ions move into the cell.

■ **Figure 27** Some cells use elaborate pumping systems, such as the Na^+/K^+ ATPase pump shown here, to help move substances through the plasma membrane.

Animation

Personal Tutor

Na^+/K^+ ATPase pump One common active transport pump is called the sodium-potassium ATPase pump. This pump is found in the plasma membrane of animal cells. The pump maintains the level of sodium ions (Na^+) and potassium ions (K^+) inside and outside the cell. This protein pump is an enzyme that catalyzes the breakdown of an energy-storing molecule. The pump uses the energy to transport three sodium ions out of the cell while moving two potassium ions into the cell. The high level of sodium on the outside of the cell creates a concentration gradient. Follow the steps in **Figure 27** to see the action of the Na^+/K^+ ATPase pump.

The activity of the Na^+/K^+ ATPase pump can result in yet another form of cellular transport. Substances, such as sugar molecules, must come into the cell from the outside, where the concentration of the substance is lower than it is inside. This requires energy. Recall, however, that the Na^+/K^+ ATPase pump moves Na^+ out of the cell, which creates a low concentration of Na^+ inside the cell. In a process called coupled transport, the Na^+ ions that have been pumped out of the cell can couple with sugar molecules and be transported into the cell through a membrane protein called a coupled channel. The sugar molecule, coupled to a Na^+ ion, enters the cell by facilitated diffusion of the sodium, as shown in **Figure 28.** As a result, sugar enters the cell without spending any additional cellular energy.

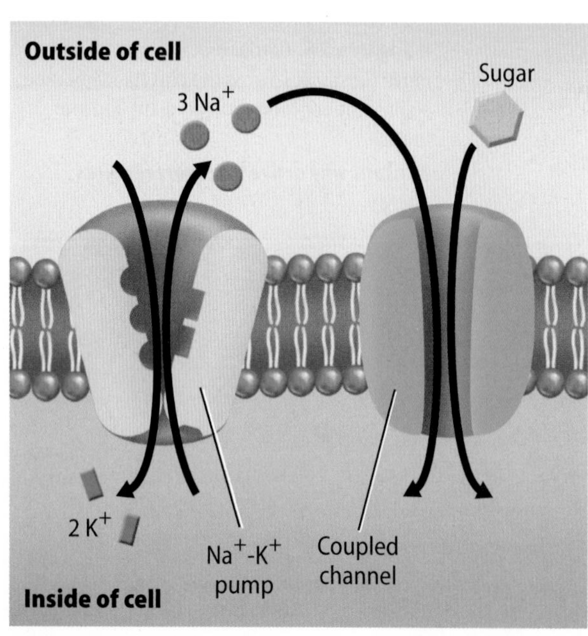

■ **Figure 28** Substances "piggy-back" their way into or out of a cell by coupling with another substance that uses an active transport pump.
Compare and contrast ***active and passive transport across the plasma membrane.***

Endocytosis

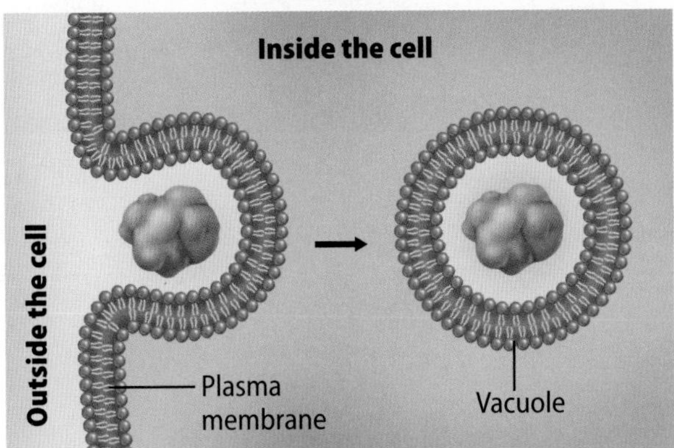

Exocytosis

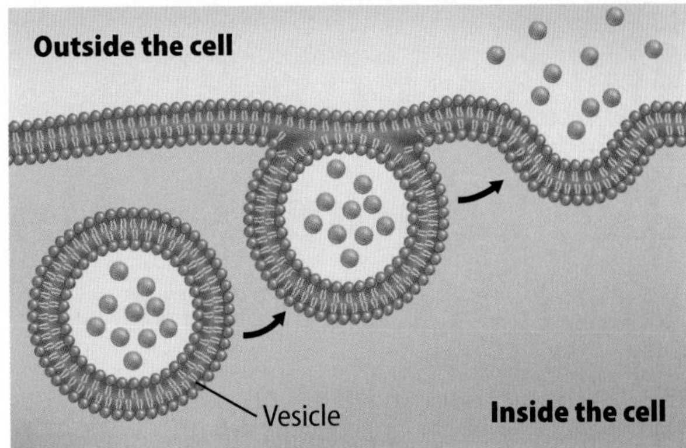

■ **Figure 29**
Left: Large substances can enter a cell by endocytosis.
Right: Substances can be deposited outside the cell by exocytosis.

Transport of Large Particles

Some substances are too large to move through the plasma membrane by diffusion or transport proteins and must get inside the cell by a different process. **Endocytosis** is the process by which a cell surrounds a substance in the outside environment, enclosing the substance in a portion of the plasma membrane. The membrane then pinches off and leaves the substance inside the cell. The substance shown on the left in **Figure 29** is engulfed and enclosed by a portion of the cell's plasma membrane. The membrane then pinches off inside of the cell, and the resulting vacuole, with its contents, moves to the inside of the cell.

Exocytosis is the secretion of materials at the plasma membrane. The illustration on the right in **Figure 29** shows that exocytosis is the reverse of endocytosis. Cells use exocytosis to expel wastes and to secrete substances, such as hormones, produced by the cell. Both endocytosis and exocytosis require the input of energy. Cells maintain homeostasis by moving substances into and out of the cell. Some transport processes require additional energy input, while others do not. Together, the different types of transport allow a cell to interact with its environment while maintaining homeostasis.

REVIEW IT! Cellular Transport

Section Summary

- Cells maintain homeostasis using passive and active transport.
- Concentration, temperature, and pressure affect the rate of diffusion.
- Cells must maintain homeostasis in all types of solutions, including isotonic, hypotonic, and hypertonic.
- Some large molecules are moved into and out of the cell using endocytosis and exocytosis.

Self Check

Understand Main Ideas

1. MAINIDEA **List and describe** the types of cellular transport.
2. **Describe** how the plasma membrane controls what goes into and comes out of a cell.
3. **Sketch** a before and an after diagram of an animal cell placed in a hypotonic solution.
4. **Contrast** how facilitated diffusion is different from active transport.

Think Critically

5. **Describe** Some organisms that normally live in pond water contain water pumps. These pumps continually pump water out of the cell. Describe a scenario that might reverse the action of the pump.
6. **Summarize** the role of the phospholipid bilayer in cellular transport in living cells.

BIOdiscoveries

1.1.3b

Snake Venom: An Unlikely Cancer Treatment

How can something that can kill you also have the potential to save your life? Snakes use their venom to alter specific functions in the body. Some types of venom disrupt the nervous system, others disrupt the circulatory system, and still others cause paralysis. Because the action of different venom toxins is so specific, researchers believe that they can be medically valuable. Scientists at university research centers are investigating snake venom toxins as a treatment for cancer.

It may seem crazy, but the idea isn't new. The Chinese have been using toad venom as a natural cancer treatment for about 1,000 years.

Endless Possibilities Venoms are very complex. Each snake species has a different venom and there are even variations within a species. There is an enormous supply of snake venom proteins that can be used in drug discovery. Specific proteins from the venom can be isolated and purified for use in medical research. Because the venom toxins are purified, they are not as dangerous as the venom that is injected into your body when bitten by a snake.

The proteins in snake venom that are of interest to cancer researchers are called disintegrins. Disintegrins interrupt cell receptors called integrins. Certain disintegrins could help stop cancer cells from spreading by preventing them from latching on to other cells and by preventing new blood vessels, which feed cancer growth, from forming. Cancer cells need to be able to develop new blood vessels to grow and spread. The disintegrins have the ability to prevent the spread of cancer cells and cut off its blood supply—all without damaging healthy cells!

Treatments using disintegrins from venom toxins are preferred over chemotherapy because they have such a specific function and target only certain types of cells. They do not attack the entire body and cause the unwanted side effects associated with chemotherapy.

Venom is collected from snakes like this western diamondback rattlesnake. It is dried and purified and used in medical research around the world.

Success Stories Though snake venom therapies are still in early stages of testing, it has been shown to be effective in the treatment of prostate cancer and has had success in shrinking breast, ovarian, and brain tumors. Most of the early studies have been on lab animals; however, they have been so successful that some clinical trials using humans have begun.

Investigate

Pamphlet Describe the activities of the researchers at the National Natural Toxins Research Center. How do they identify molecules from snake venom that might be of medical importance? Communicate your findings with an illustrated pamphlet that highlights the activities of the researchers.

WebQuest

BioLAB 1.1.1c, 1.3.5b, 4.5.1c, ¥a, ¥b1, ¥b2, ¥b3, ¥b4, ¥b5, ¥e, ¥i, ¥m, ¥n, ¥o

Which substances will pass through a selectively permeable membrane?

Background: All membranes in cells are selectively permeable. In this lab, you will examine the movement of some biologically important molecules through a dialysis membrane that is analogous to the plasma membrane. Because a dialysis membrane has tiny pores, it is permeable only for tiny molecules.

Question: *Which substances pass through a dialysis membrane?*

Materials

- cellulose dialysis tubing (2)
- 400-mL beakers (2)
- string
- scissors
- distilled water
- small plastic dishpan
- starch solution
- albumin solution
- glucose solution
- NaCl solution
- iodine solution (tests starch)
- anhydrous Benedict's reagent (tests glucose)
- silver nitrate solution (tests NaCl)
- biuret reagent (tests albumin)
- 10-mL graduated cylinder
- test tubes (2)
- test-tube rack
- funnel
- wax pencil
- eye droppers

Safety Precautions

Procedure

1. Read and complete the lab safety form.
2. Construct a data table as instructed by your teacher. Predict which substances will pass through the dialysis membrane.
3. Collect two lengths of dialysis tubing, two 400-mL beakers, and the two solutions that you have been assigned to test.
4. Label the beakers with the type of solution that you place in the dialysis tubing.
5. With a partner, prepare and fill one length of dialysis tubing with one solution. Rinse the outside of the bag thoroughly. Place the filled tubing bag into a beaker that contains distilled water.
6. Repeat Step 5 using the second solution.
7. After 45 minutes, transfer some of the water from each beaker into separate test tubes.
8. Add a few drops of the appropriate test reagent to the water.
9. Record your results and determine whether your prediction was correct. Compare your results with those of other groups in your class and record the results for the two solutions that you did not test.
10. **Cleanup and Disposal** Wash and return all reusable materials. Dispose of test solutions and used dialysis tubing as directed by your teacher. Wash your hands thoroughly after using any chemical reagent.

Analyze and Conclude

1. **Evaluate** Did your test molecules pass through the dialysis tubing? Explain.
2. **Think Critically** What characteristics of a plasma membrane give it more control over the movement of molecules than the dialysis membrane has?
3. **Error Analysis** How could failing to rinse the dialysis tube bags with distilled water prior to placing them in the beaker cause a false positive test for the presence of a dissolved molecule? What other sources of error might lead to inaccurate results?

POSTER SESSION

Communicate A disease called cystic fibrosis occurs when plasma membranes lack a molecule that helps transport chloride ions. Research this disease and present your finding to your class using a poster.

CHAPTER 7 STUDY GUIDE

BIGIDEA **Cells are the structural and functional units of all living things.**

SECTION 1 Cell Discovery and Theory

MAINIDEA The invention of the microscope led to the discovery of cells.

- Microscopes have been used as tools for scientific study since the late 1500s.
- Scientists use different types of microscopes to study cells.
- The cell theory summarizes three principles.
- There are two broad groups of cell types: prokaryotic cells and eukaryotic cells.
- Eukaryotic cells each contain a nucleus and organelles.

VOCABULARY
- **cell**
- **cell theory**
- **plasma membrane**
- **eukaryotic cell**
- **nucleus**
- **organelle**
- **prokaryotic cell**

SECTION 2 Plasma Membrane

MAINIDEA The plasma membrane helps to maintain a cell's homeostasis.

- Selective permeability is the property of the plasma membrane that allows it to control what enters and leaves the cell.
- The plasma membrane is made up of two layers of phospholipid molecules.
- Cholesterol and transport proteins aid in the function of the plasma membrane.
- The fluid mosaic model describes the plasma membrane.

VOCABULARY
- **selective permeability**
- **phospholipid bilayer**
- **transport protein**
- **fluid mosaic model**

SECTION 3 Structures and Organelles

MAINIDEA Eukaryotic cells contain organelles that allow the specialization and the separation of functions within the cell.

- Eukaryotic cells contain membrane-bound organelles in the cytoplasm that perform cell functions.
- Ribosomes are the sites of protein synthesis.
- Mitochondria are the powerhouses of cells.
- Plant and animal cells contain many of the same organelles, while other organelles are unique to either plant cells or animal cells.

VOCABULARY
- **cytoplasm**
- **cytoskeleton**
- **nucleolus**
- **ribosome**
- **endoplasmic reticulum**
- **Golgi apparatus**
- **vacuole**
- **centriole**
- **lysosome**
- **chloroplast**
- **mitochondrion**
- **cell wall**
- **cilium**
- **flagellum**

SECTION 4 Cellular Transport

MAINIDEA Cellular transport moves substances within the cell and moves substances into and out of the cell.

- Cells maintain homeostasis using passive and active transport.
- Concentration, temperature, and pressure affect the rate of diffusion.
- Cells must maintain homeostasis in all types of solutions, including isotonic, hypotonic, and hypertonic.
- Some large molecules are moved into and out of the cell using endocytosis and exocytosis.

VOCABULARY
- **diffusion**
- **dynamic equilibrium**
- **facilitated diffusion**
- **osmosis**
- **hypotonic solution**
- **isotonic solution**
- **active transport**
- **hypertonic solution**
- **endocytosis**
- **exocytosis**

CHAPTER 7 ASSESSMENT

SECTION 1

Vocabulary Review

Each of the following sentences is false. Make each sentence true by replacing the italicized word with a vocabulary term from the Study Guide page.

1. The *nucleus* is a structure that surrounds a cell and helps control what enters and exits the cell.
2. A(n) *prokaryote* has membrane-bound organelles.
3. *Organelles* are basic units of all organisms.

Understand Main Ideas

4. If a microscope has a series of three lenses that magnify individually 5×, 5×, and 7×, what is the total magnification of the microscope?
   A. 25× **C.** 17×
   B. 35× **D.** 175×

5. Which is not part of the cell theory?
   A. The basic unit of life is the cell.
   B. Cells came from preexisting cells.
   C. All living organisms are composed of cells.
   D. Cells contain membrane-bound organelles.

Use the photo to answer question 6.

Color-Enhanced TEM Magnification: 15,000×

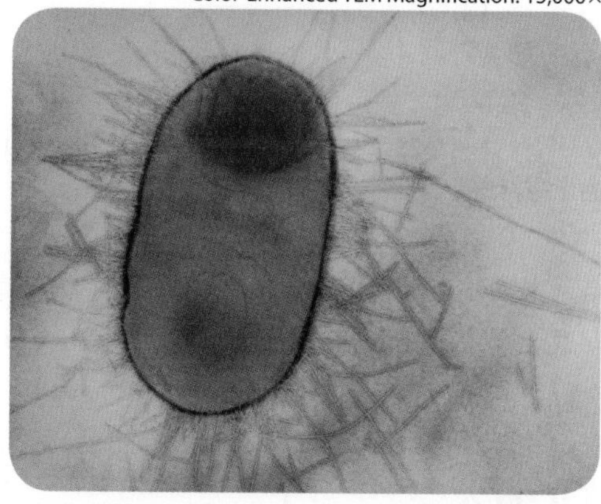

6. The photomicrograph shows which kind of cell?
   A. prokaryotic cell **C.** animal cell
   B. eukaryotic cell **D.** plant cell

Constructed Response

7. **MAIN**IDEA Explain how the development of the microscope changed how scientists studied living organisms.

8. **Short Answer** Compare and contrast prokaryotic cells and eukaryotic cells.

Think Critically

9. **THEME FOCUS** Why might a microscopist, who specializes in the use of microscopes to examine specimens, use a light microscope instead of an electron microscope?

10. **Analyze** A material is found in an asteroid that might be a cell. What criteria must the material meet to be considered a cell?

SECTION 2

Vocabulary Review

Complete the sentences below using vocabulary terms from the Study Guide page.

11. A __________ is the basic structure that makes up the plasma membrane.
12. __________ proteins move needed substances or waste materials through the plasma membrane.
13. __________ is the property that allows only some substances in and out of a cell.

Understand Main Ideas

14. Which of the following orientations of phospholipids best represents the phospholipid bilayer of the plasma membrane?

A. 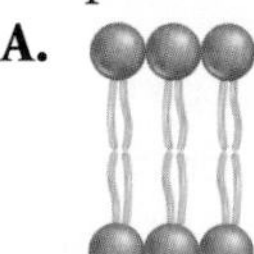 **C.** 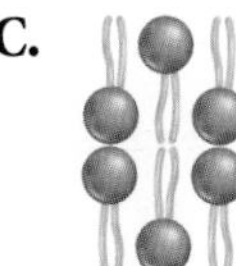

B. **D.** 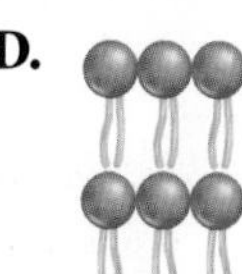

15. Which situation would increase the fluidity of a phospholipid bilayer?
   A. decreasing the temperature
   B. increasing the number of proteins
   C. increasing the number of cholesterol molecules
   D. increasing the number of unsaturated fatty acids

Constructed Response

16. **MAIN IDEA** Explain how the plasma membrane maintains homeostasis within a cell.

17. **Open Ended** Explain what a mosaic is and then explain why the term *fluid mosaic model* is used to describe the plasma membrane.

18. **Short Answer** How does the orientation of the phospholipids in the bilayer allow a cell to interact with its internal and external environments?

Think Critically

19. **Hypothesize** how a cell would be affected if it lost the ability to be selectively permeable.

20. **Predict** What might happen to a cell if it no longer could produce cholesterol?

SECTION 3

Vocabulary Review

Fill in each blank with the vocabulary term from the Study Guide page that matches the function definition.

21. __________ stores wastes

22. __________ produces ribosomes

23. __________ generates energy for a cell

24. __________ sorts proteins into vesicles

Understand Main Ideas

Use the diagram below to answer questions 25 and 26.

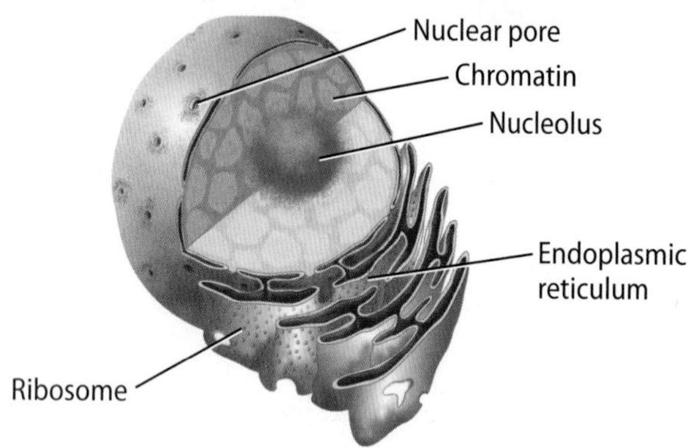

25. Which structure synthesizes proteins that will be used by the cell?
    A. chromatin
    B. nucleolus
    C. ribosome
    D. endoplasmic reticulum

26. Which is the site of protein synthesis?
    A. nuclear pore
    B. endoplasmic reticulum
    C. chromatin
    D. nucleolus

27. In which structure would you expect to find a cell wall?
    A. human skin cell
    B. cell from an oak tree
    C. blood cell from a cat
    D. liver cell from a mouse

Constructed Response

28. **Short Answer** Describe why the cytoskeleton within the cytoplasm was a recent discovery.

29. **Short Answer** Compare the structures and functions of the mitochondrion and chloroplast below.

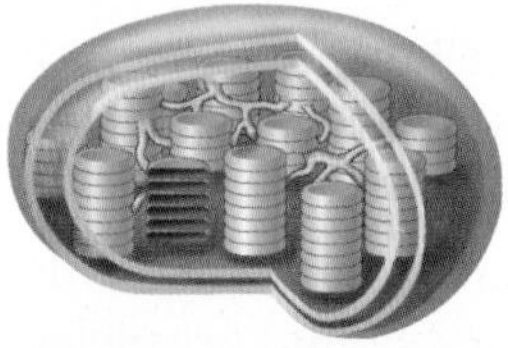

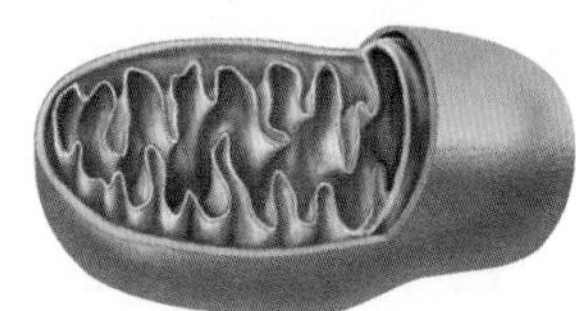

30. **MAIN IDEA** Suggest a reason why packets of proteins collected in a vacuole might merge with lysosomes.

Think Critically

31. **Identify** a specific example in which the cell wall structure has aided the survival of a plant in its natural habitat.

32. **Infer** why plant cells that transport water against the force of gravity contain many more mitochondria than other plant cells do.

SECTION 4

Vocabulary Review

Explain the difference in the terms in each pair below. Then explain how the terms are related.

33. active transport, facilitated diffusion

34. endocytosis, exocytosis

35. hypertonic solution, hypotonic solution

Understand Main Ideas

36. Which is not a factor that affects the rate of diffusion?
    A. conductivity
    B. concentration
    C. pressure
    D. temperature

37. Which type of transport requires energy input from the cell?
    A. active transport
    B. facilitated diffusion
    C. osmosis
    D. simple diffusion

Constructed Response

38. **Short Answer** Why is active transport an energy-utilizing process?

39. **Short Answer** Some protists that live in a hypotonic pond environment have cell membrane adaptations that slow water uptake. What adaptations might this protist living in the hypertonic Great Salt Lake have?

LM Magnification: 75×

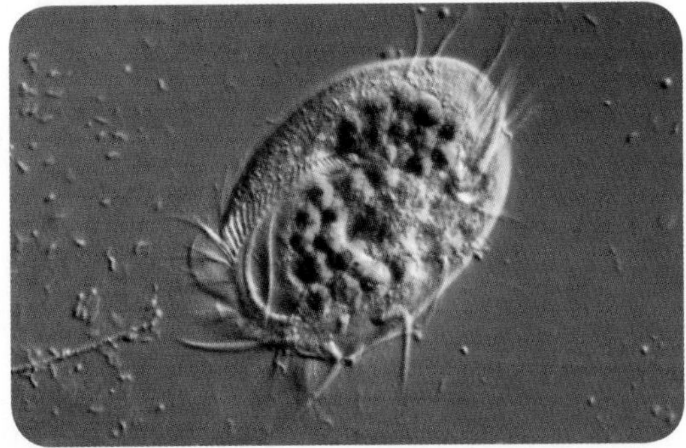

40. **MAINIDEA** Summarize how cellular transport helps maintain homeostasis within a cell.

Think Critically

41. **Hypothesize** how oxygen crosses the plasma membrane if the concentration of oxygen is lower inside the cell than it is outside the cell.

42. **Analyze** Farming and watering that are done in very dry regions of the world leave salts that accumulate in the soil as water evaporates. Based on what you know about concentration gradients, why does increasing soil salinity have adverse effects on plant cells?

M. I. Walker/Science Source

Summative Assessment

43. **BIGIDEA** Cells are the structural and functional units of living things. Create an analogy where "smaller parts" provide structure and function for a "whole." Relate it to cells and living things by giving specific examples.

44. Use what you have learned about osmosis and cellular transport to design an apparatus that would enable a freshwater fish to survive in a saltwater habitat.

45. **WRITING IN ▶ Biology** Create a poem that describes the functions of at least five cell organelles.

DBQ Document-Based Questions

The graph below describes the relationship between the amount of glucose entering a cell and the rate at which the glucose enters the cell with the help of carrier proteins. Use this graph to answer questions 46 and 47.

Data obtained from: Raven, P.H., and Johnson, G.B. 2002. *Biology,* 6th ed.: 99.

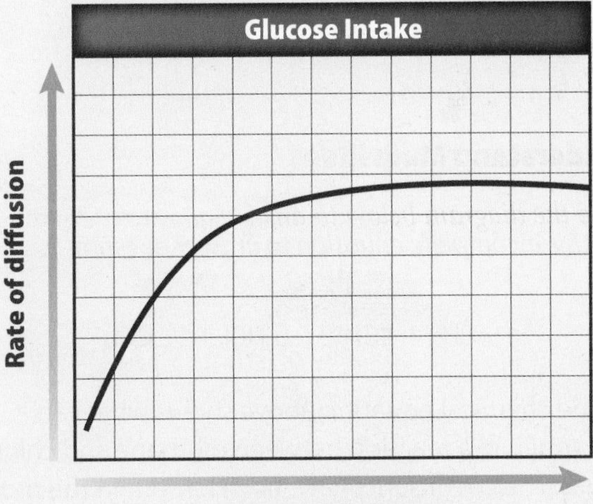

46. Summarize the relationship between the amount of glucose and the rate of diffusion.

47. Infer why the rate of diffusion tapers off with higher amounts of glucose. Make an illustration to explain your answer.

CUMULATIVE

MULTIPLE CHOICE

1 Compare and contrast plant and animal cells. In which type of cell would you find a chloroplast?

A prokaryote

B animal only

C plant only

D all eukaryotic cells

2 Compare and contrast plant and animal cells. In which type of cell would you find mitochondria?

A prokaryote

B animal only

C plant only

D all eukaryotic cells

Use this incomplete equation to answer question 3.

$$CH_4 + 4Cl_2 \rightarrow \_\_HCl + \_\_CCl_4$$

3 The chemical equation above shows what can happen in a reaction between methane and chlorine gas. The coefficients have been left out in the product side of the equation. Which is the correct coefficient for HCl?

A 1

B 2

C 4

D 8

SHORT ANSWER

4 Use a flowchart to organize information about cell organelles and protein synthesis. For each step, analyze the role of the organelle in protein synthesis.

5 Compare and contrast the structures and functions of the macromolecules carbohydrates, lipids, proteins, and nucleic acids.

6 Relate why the polarity of water molecules makes water a good solvent to water's role in cellular transport.

Use the figure below to answer question 7.

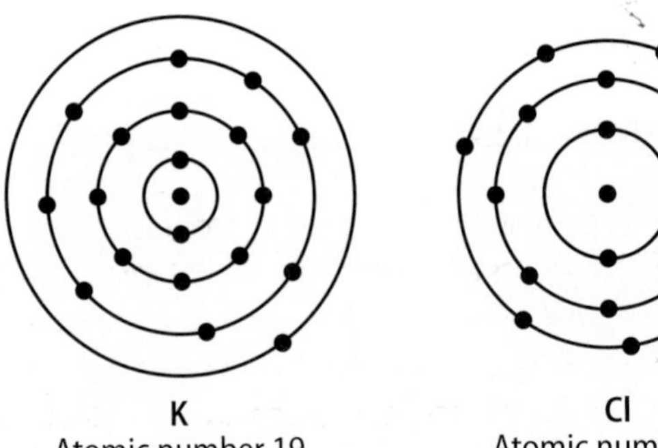

7 Use the figure to describe how the ionic compound potassium chloride (KCl) is formed.

8 What might happen if cell membranes were not selectively permeable?

9 Choose a specific natural resource and develop a plan for the sustainable use of that resource.

10 What can you infer about the evolution of bacterial cells from studying their structures?

EXTENDED RESPONSE

The illustration below shows a single animal cell in an isotonic solution. Use the illustration to answer question 11.

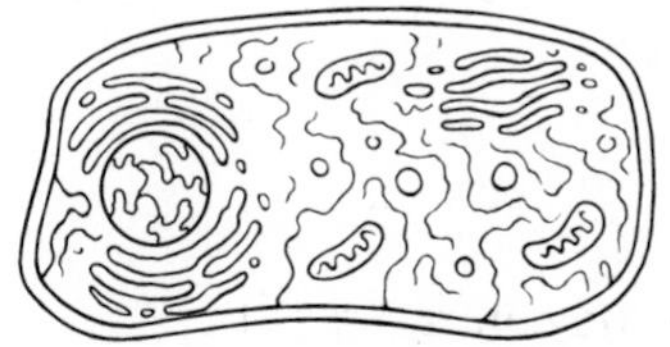

11 Describe what would happen to this cell in a hypertonic solution and in a hypotonic solution.

12 Explain why direct economic value is not the only important consideration of biodiversity.

13 Analyze why an electron microscope can produce higher magnification than a light microscope can.

14 Assess why transport proteins are needed to move certain substances across a cell membrane.

ESSAY QUESTION

Recently, some international trade agreements have allowed scientists and companies to patent the discoveries they make about organisms and their genetic material. For instance, it is possible to patent seeds that have genes for disease resistance and plants that can be used in medicine or industry. Owners of patents now have greater control over the use of these organisms.

Using the information in the paragraph above, answer the following question in essay format.

15 Based on what you know about biodiversity, identify some pros and cons of a patent system. Write an essay exploring the pros and cons of patenting discoveries about organisms.

TEST PRACTICE

Use the illustration below to answer questions 16 and 17.

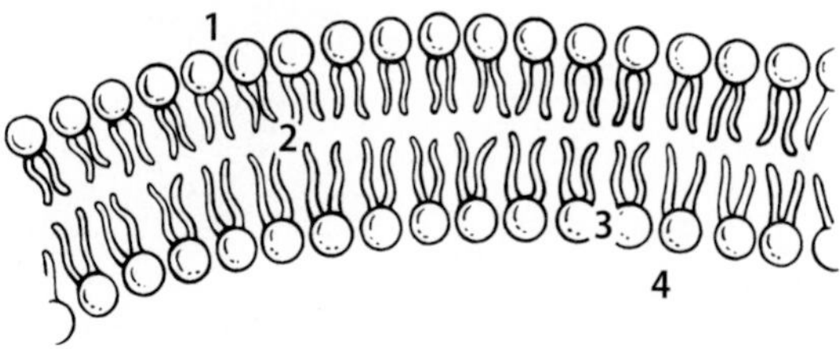

16 Which number in the model represents the location where you would expect to find water-insoluble substances?

A 1

B 2

C 3

D 4

17 Which is the effect of having the polar and nonpolar ends of phospholipid molecules oriented as they are in the model?

A It allows transport proteins to move easily through the membrane.

B It controls the movement of substances across the membrane.

C It helps the cell to maintain its characteristic shape.

D It makes more room inside the phospholipid bilayer.

NEED EXTRA HELP?																	
If You Missed Question . . .	1	2	3	4	5	6	7	8	9	10	11	12	13	14	15	16	17
Review Section . . .	7.3	7.3	6.2	7.3	6.4	6.3	6.1	7.2	5.3	7.1	7.4	5.1	7.1	7.4	5.2	7.2	7.2

Directly or indirectly, nearly all the energy for life comes from the Sun. The grass directly derives its energy from the sun, and the sheep indirectly derives its energy.

4.5.1c LaunchLAB

How is energy transformed?

The flow of energy in living systems is driven by a variety of chemical reactions and chemical processes. Energy is transformed from the Sun's radiant energy to chemical energy to other forms of energy along the way. In this lab, you will observe two processes in which energy is transformed.

CHAPTER 8

Cellular Energy

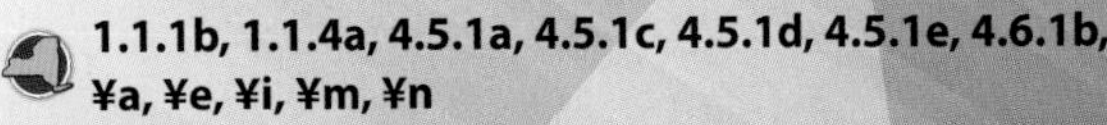

THEMEFOCUS

Energy and matter The Sun is the source of nearly all of the energy on Earth.

BIGIDEA

Photosynthesis converts the Sun's energy into chemical energy, while cellular respiration uses chemical energy to carry out life functions.

FOLDABLES® Study Organizer

Cellular Respiration

Make a pocket book using the titles shown. Use it to organize your notes on stages of cellular respiration.

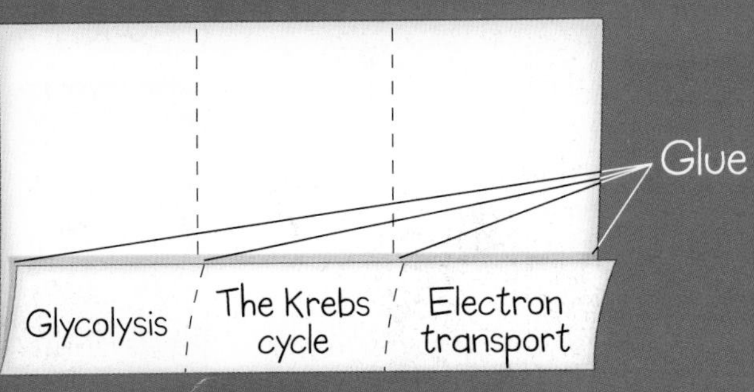

1 How Organisms Obtain Energy

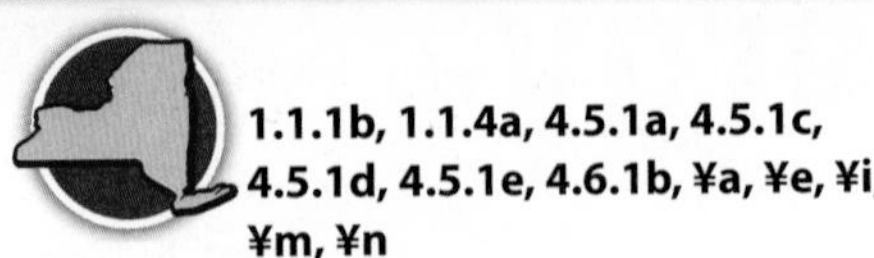

MAIN IDEA
All living organisms use energy to carry out all biological processes.

Essential Questions
- What are the two laws of thermodynamics?
- What is the difference between an anabolic pathway and a catabolic pathway?
- How does ATP work in a cell?

BIOLOGY 4 U

New York City is sometimes called "the city that never sleeps." Much like the nonstop movement of a big city, living cells are sites of constant activity.

Review Vocabulary

trophic level: each step in a food chain or a food web

New Vocabulary

energy
thermodynamics
metabolism
photosynthesis
cellular respiration
adenosine triphosphate (ATP)

Multilingual eGlossary

Transformation of Energy

Many chemical reactions and processes in your cells are ongoing, even when you might not think that you are using any energy. Macromolecules are assembled and broken down, substances are transported across cell membranes, and genetic instructions are transmitted. All of these cellular activities require **energy**—the ability to do work. **Figure 1** shows some of the major advancements in the study of cellular energy. **Thermodynamics** is the study of the flow and transformation of energy in the universe.

Laws of thermodynamics The first law of thermodynamics is the law of conservation of energy, which states that energy can be converted from one form to another, but it cannot be created nor destroyed. For example, the stored energy in food is converted to chemical energy when you eat and to mechanical energy when you run or kick a ball.

■ **Figure 1 Understand Cellular Energy**
Scientific discoveries have led to a greater understanding of photosynthesis and cellular respiration.

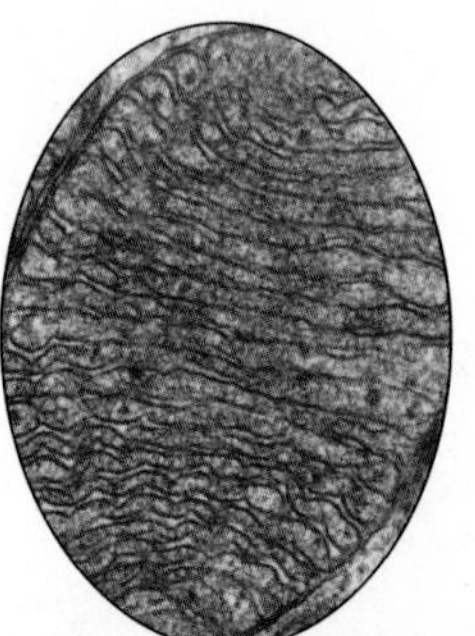

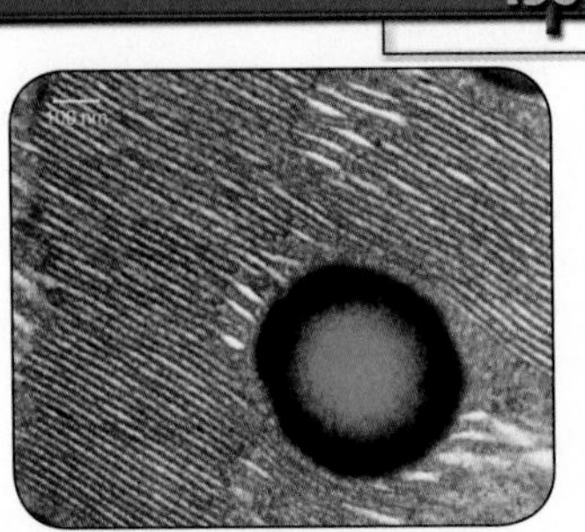

1800 — 1900 — 1940

1772 Joseph Priestley determines that plants take in carbon dioxide and emit oxygen.

1844 Hugo von Mohl first observes chloroplasts in plant cells.

1881–82 Chloroplasts are shown to be the organelles responsible for photosynthesis.

1948 Eugene Kennedy and Albert Lehninger discover that mitochondria are responsible for cellular respiration.

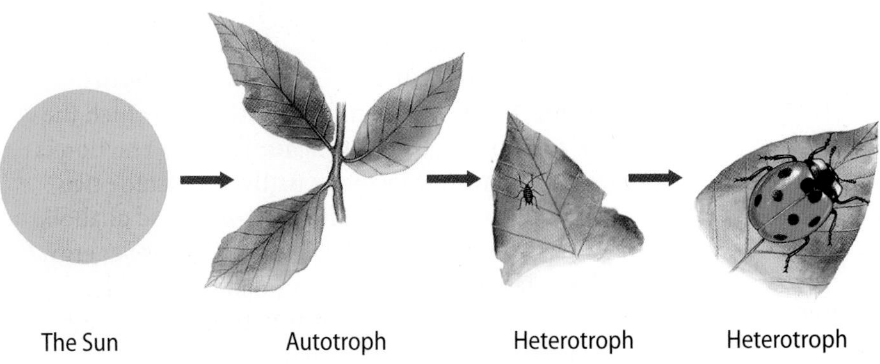

Figure 2 Almost all the energy in living organisms originates from the Sun, and energy flows from autotrophs to heterotrophs.
Relate ***the laws of thermodynamics to the organisms in the figure.***

The second law of thermodynamics states that energy cannot be converted without the loss of usable energy. The energy that is "lost" is generally converted to thermal energy. Entropy (EN truh pee) is the measure of disorder, or unusable energy, in a system. Therefore, the second law of thermodynamics can also be stated as "entropy increases." One example of the second law of thermodynamics is evident in food chains. Recall that in a food chain, the amount of usable energy that is available to the next trophic level decreases.

Vocabulary
Word origin
Autotroph
comes from the Greek word *autotrophos,* meaning *supplying one's own food*

Autotrophs and heterotrophs All organisms need energy to live. Directly or indirectly, nearly all the energy for life comes from the Sun. Some organisms make their own food, while others must obtain it from other organisms. Autotrophs are organisms that make their own food. Some autotrophs, called chemoautotrophs, use inorganic substances such as hydrogen sulfide as a source of energy. Other autotrophs, such as the plant in **Figure 2,** convert light energy from the Sun into chemical energy. Autotrophs that convert energy from the Sun are called photoautotrophs. Heterotrophs, such as the aphid and the ladybug in **Figure 2,** are organisms that need to ingest food to obtain energy.

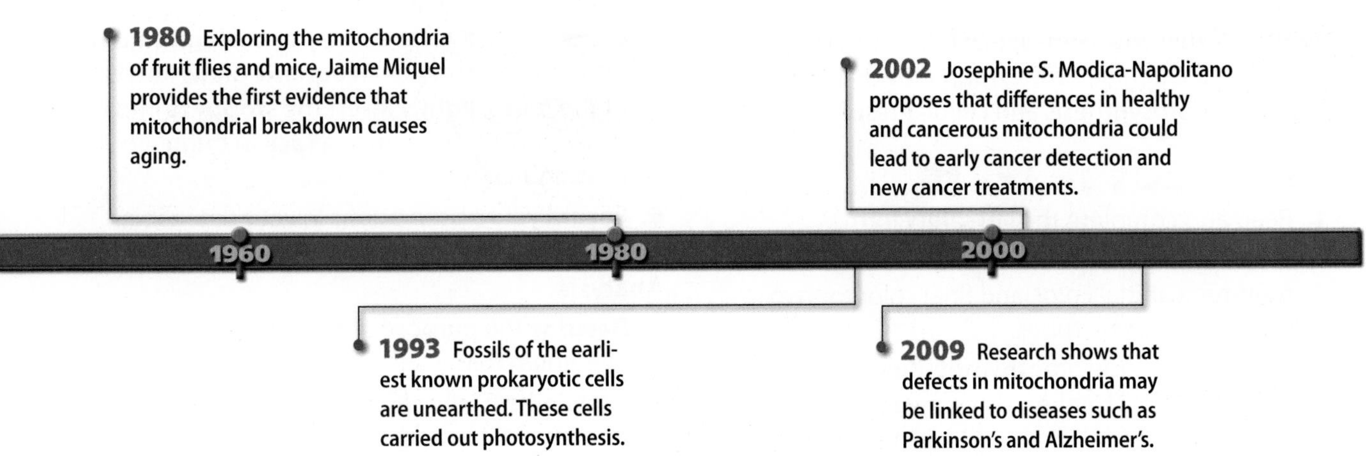

1980 Exploring the mitochondria of fruit flies and mice, Jaime Miquel provides the first evidence that mitochondrial breakdown causes aging.
2002 Josephine S. Modica-Napolitano proposes that differences in healthy and cancerous mitochondria could lead to early cancer detection and new cancer treatments.
1960
1980
2000
1993 Fossils of the earliest known prokaryotic cells are unearthed. These cells carried out photosynthesis.
2009 Research shows that defects in mitochondria may be linked to diseases such as Parkinson's and Alzheimer's.

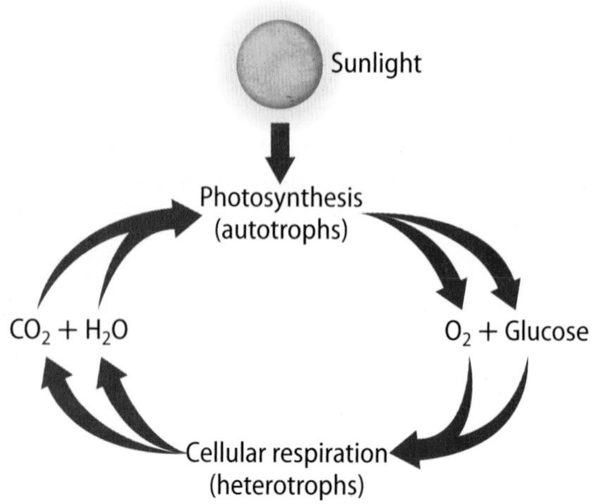

Figure 3 In an ecosystem, photosynthesis and cellular respiration form a cycle.

Identify ***the anabolic and catabolic pathways in the figure.***

 **Launch Lab**

Review Based on what you have read about energy transformations, how would you now answer the analysis questions?

Metabolism

All of the chemical reactions in a cell are referred to as the cell's **metabolism.** A series of chemical reactions in which the product of one reaction is the substrate for the next reaction is called a metabolic pathway. Metabolic pathways include two broad types: catabolic (ka tuh BAH lik) pathways and anabolic (a nuh BAH lik) pathways. Catabolic pathways release energy by breaking down larger molecules into smaller molecules. Anabolic pathways use the energy released by catabolic pathways to build larger molecules from smaller molecules. The relationship of anabolic and catabolic pathways results in the continual flow of energy within an organism.

Energy continually flows between the metabolic reactions of organisms in an ecosystem. **Photosynthesis** is the anabolic pathway in which light energy from the Sun is converted to chemical energy for use by the cell. In this reaction, autotrophs use light energy, carbon dioxide, and water to form glucose and oxygen. The energy stored in the glucose produced by photosynthesis can be transferred to other organisms when the molecules are consumed as food.

Cellular respiration is the catabolic pathway in which organic molecules are broken down to release energy for use by a cell. In cellular respiration, oxygen is used to break down organic molecules, resulting in the production of carbon dioxide and water. Notice the cyclical nature of these processes in **Figure 3,** where the products of one reaction are the reactants for the other reaction.

MiniLAB 1

Relate Photosynthesis to Cellular Respiration

How do photosynthesis and cellular respiration work together in an ecosystem? Use a chemical indicator to examine how carbon dioxide is transferred in photosynthesis and cellular respiration.

Procedure

1. Read and complete the lab safety form.
2. Prepare a data table to record the contents, treatment, initial color, and final color for two experimental test tubes.
3. Pour 100 mL of **bromothymol blue (BTB) solution** into a **beaker.** Using a **straw,** exhale gently into the solution until it just turns yellow. **WARNING:** ***Do not exhale so much that the solution bubbles over or that you get a headache. Do not suck on the straw.***
4. Fill two large **test tubes** three-quarters full with the yellow BTB solution.
5. Cover one test tube entirely with **aluminum foil.** Place a 6-cm sprig of an **aquatic plant** into both of the tubes, tightly insert the **stoppers** into the tubes, and place them in a **rack** in bright light overnight.
6. Record your observations in your data table.

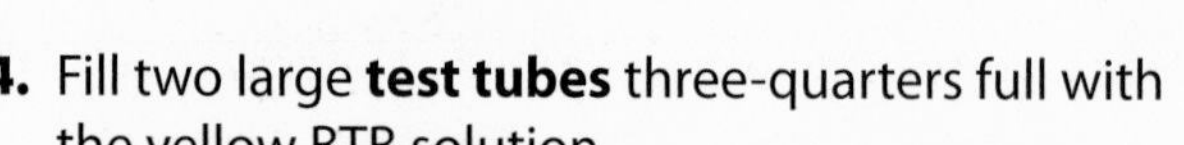

Analysis

1. **Describe** the purpose of the tube covered with aluminum foil.
2. **Explain** how your results demonstrate that photosynthesis and cellular respiration depend on one another.
3. **Describe** the energy conversions that took place during this investigation.

ATP: The Unit of Cellular Energy

Connection to Chemistry Energy exists in many forms, including light energy, mechanical energy, thermal energy, and chemical energy. In living organisms, chemical energy is stored in biological molecules and can be converted to other forms of energy when needed. For example, the chemical energy in biological molecules is converted to mechanical energy when muscles contract. **Adenosine triphosphate** (uh DEN uh seen • tri FAHS fayt)—ATP—is the most important biological molecule that provides chemical energy.

ATP structure ATP is a multipurpose storehouse of chemical energy that can be used by cells in a variety of reactions. Although other carrier molecules transport energy within cells, ATP is the most abundant energy-carrier molecule in cells and is found in all types of organisms. As shown in **Figure 4,** ATP is a nucleotide made of an adenine base, a ribose sugar, and three phosphate groups.

ATP function ATP releases energy when the bond between the second and third phosphate groups is broken, forming a molecule called adenosine diphosphate (ADP) and a free phosphate group, as shown in **Figure 4.** Energy is stored in the phosphate bond formed when ADP receives a phosphate group and becomes ATP. As shown in **Figure 4,** ATP and ADP can be interchanged by the addition or removal of a phosphate group. Sometimes ADP becomes adenosine monophosphate (AMP) by losing an additional phosphate group. There is less energy released in this reaction, so most of the energy reactions in the cell involve ATP and ADP.

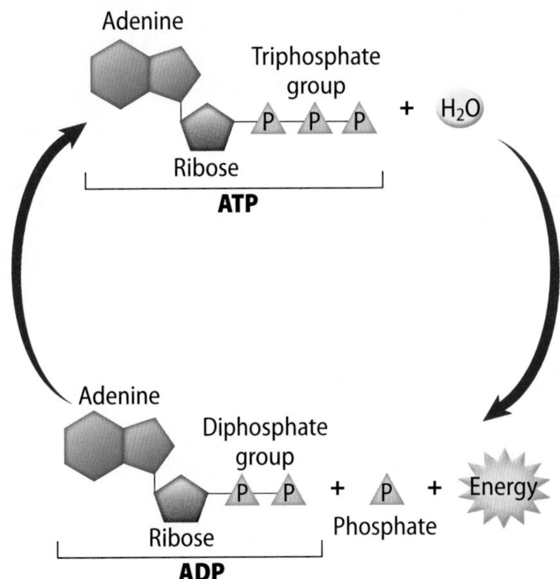

Figure 4 The breakdown of ATP releases energy for powering cellular activities in organisms.

Animation

REVIEW IT! How Organisms Obtain Energy

Section Summary

- The laws of thermodynamics control the flow and transformation of energy in organisms.
- Some organisms produce their own food, whereas others obtain energy from the food they ingest.
- Cells store and release energy through coupled anabolic and catabolic reactions.
- The energy released from the breakdown of ATP drives cellular activities.

Understand Main Ideas

1. MAINIDEA **Identify** the major source of energy for living organisms.
2. **Describe** an example of the first law of thermodynamics.
3. **Compare and contrast** anabolic and catabolic pathways.
4. **Analyze and evaluate** the formation of ATP.

Think Critically

WRITING IN ▶ Biology

5. Write an essay describing the laws of thermodynamics. Use examples related to biology to support your ideas.
6. **Create** an analogy to describe the relationship between photosynthesis and cellular respiration.

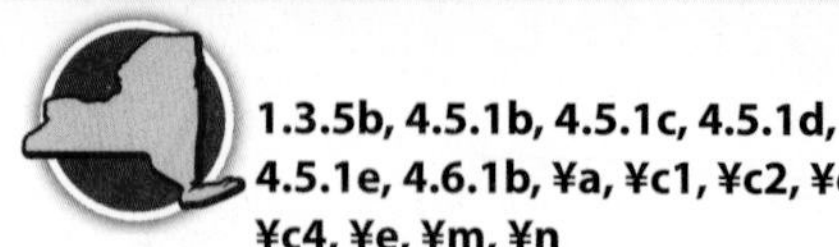

USE IT! Science Notebook

2 Photosynthesis

1.3.5b, 4.5.1b, 4.5.1c, 4.5.1d, 4.5.1e, 4.6.1b, ¥a, ¥c1, ¥c2, ¥c3, ¥c4, ¥e, ¥m, ¥n

MAINIDEA

Light energy is trapped and converted into chemical energy during photosynthesis.

Essential Questions

- What are the two phases of photosynthesis?
- What is the function of a chloroplast during the light reactions?
- How can electron transport be described and diagramed?

BIOLOGY 4U

Energy is transformed all around us every day. Batteries convert chemical energy into electric energy, and radios convert electric energy into the energy carried by sound waves. Similarly, some autotrophs convert light energy into chemical energy through photosynthesis.

Review Vocabulary

carbohydrate: an organic compound containing only carbon, hydrogen, and oxygen, usually in a 1:2:1 ratio

New Vocabulary

thylakoid
granum
stroma
pigment
$NADP^+$
Calvin cycle
rubisco

Multilingual eGlossary

Overview of Photosynthesis

Most autotrophs, including plants, make organic compounds, such as sugars, by a process called photosynthesis. Recall that photosynthesis is a process in which light energy is converted into chemical energy. The overall chemical equation for photosynthesis is shown below.

$$6CO_2 + 6H_2O \xrightarrow{\text{light}} C_6H_{12}O_6 + 6O_2$$

Photosynthesis occurs in two phases. The locations of these phases are shown in **Figure 5.** In phase one, the light-dependent reactions, light energy is absorbed and then converted into chemical energy in the form of ATP and NADPH. In phase two, the light-independent reactions, the ATP and NADPH that were formed in phase one are used to make glucose. Once glucose is produced, it can be joined to other simple sugars to form larger molecules. These larger molecules are complex carbohydrates, such as starch. Recall that carbohydrates are composed of repeating units of small organic molecules. The end products of photosynthesis also can be used to make other organic molecules, such as proteins, lipids, and nucleic acids.

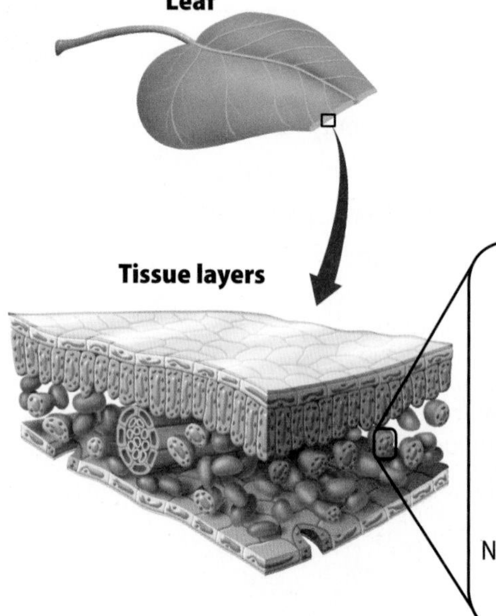

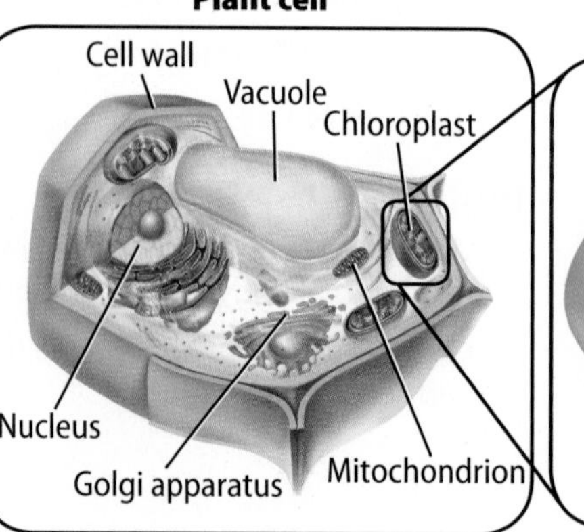

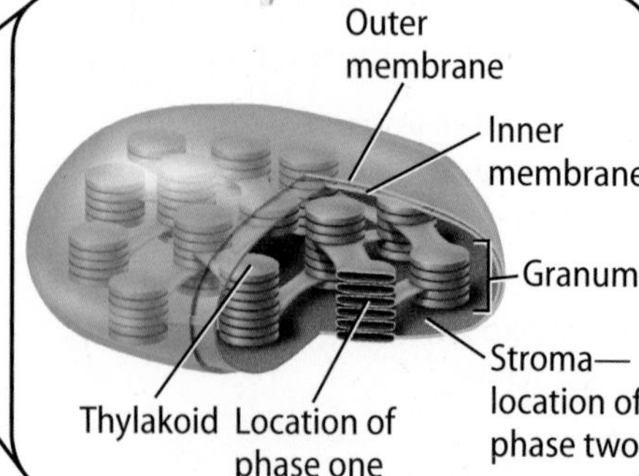

Figure 5 Photosynthesis occurs inside pigmented organelles called chloroplasts.

Phase One: Light Reactions

The absorption of light is the first step in photosynthesis. Plants have special organelles to capture light energy. Once the energy is captured, two energy storage molecules, NADPH and ATP, are produced to be used in the light-independent reactions.

Chloroplasts Large organelles, called chloroplasts, capture light energy in photosynthetic organisms. In plants, chloroplasts are found mainly in the cells of leaves. As shown in **Figure 5,** chloroplasts are disk-shaped organelles that contain two main compartments essential to photosynthesis. The first compartment is called the thylakoid (THI la koyd). **Thylakoids** are flattened, saclike membranes that are arranged in stacks. These stacks are called **grana** (singular, granum). Light-dependent reactions take place within the thylakoids. The second important compartment is called the **stroma,** the fluid-filled space that is outside the grana. This is the location of the light-independent reactions in phase two of photosynthesis.

Pigments Light-absorbing colored molecules called **pigments** are found in the thylakoid membranes of chloroplasts. Different pigments absorb specific wavelengths of light, as illustrated in **Figure 6.**

The major light-absorbing pigments in plants are chlorophylls. There are several types of chlorophylls, but the most common two are chlorophyll *a* and chlorophyll *b*. The structure of chlorophyll can differ from one molecule to another, enabling distinct chlorophyll molecules to absorb light at unique areas of the visible spectrum. In general, chlorophylls absorb most strongly in the violet-blue region of the visible light spectrum and reflect light in the green region of the spectrum. This is why plant parts that contain chlorophyll appear green to the human eye.

Distinguish between thylakoids and stroma.

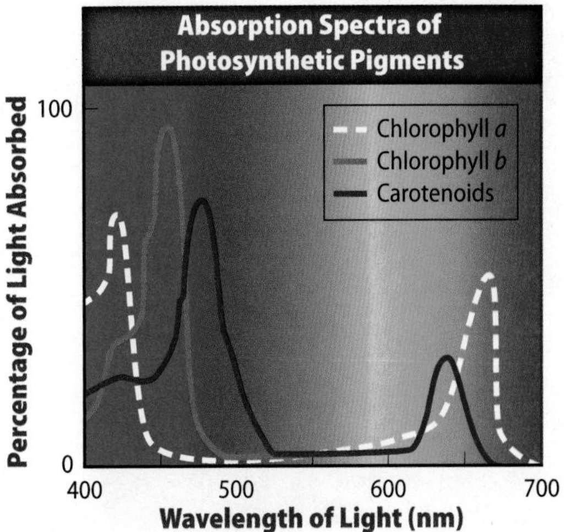

Figure 6 Colorful pigments found in the leaves of trees differ in their ability to absorb specific wavelengths of light.

Hypothesize ***the effect on light absorption if a plant did not have chlorophyll*** **b.**

MiniLAB 2

Observe Chloroplasts

What do chloroplasts look like? Most ecosystems and organisms in the world depend on tiny organelles called chloroplasts. Discover what chloroplasts look like in this investigation.

Procedure

1. Read and complete the lab safety form.
2. Observe the **slides of plant and algae cells** with a **microscope.**
3. Identify the chloroplasts in the cells that you observe.
4. Make a data table to record your observations, and sketch the chloroplasts in the cells.

Analysis

1. **Compare and contrast** the physical features of the chloroplasts that you observed in the different cells.
2. **Hypothesize** why plant leaves vary in color.

■ **Figure 7** When chlorophyll breaks down in the leaves of some trees, the other pigments become visible.

In addition to chlorophylls, most photosynthetic organisms contain accessory pigments that allow plants to trap additional light energy from other areas of the visible spectrum. One such group of accessory pigments is the carotenoids (kuh ROH tuh noydz). Carotenoids, such as ß-carotene (beta-carotene), absorb light mainly in the blue and green regions of the spectrum, while reflecting most light in the yellow, orange, and red regions. Carotenoids produce the colors of carrots.

Chlorophylls are more abundant than other pigments in leaves, and thus hide the colors of the other pigments. However, autumn in certain parts of the United States can bring out shades of yellow, red, and orange as the leaves turn colors, as shown in **Figure 7.** As trees prepare to lose their leaves before winter, the chlorophyll molecules break down, revealing the colors of the other pigments.

Electron transport The structure of the thylakoid membrane is the key to efficient energy transfer during electron transport. Thylakoid membranes have a large surface area, which provides the space needed to hold large numbers of electron-transporting molecules and two types of protein complexes called photosystems. Photosystem I and photosystem II contain light-absorbing pigments and proteins that play important roles in the light reactions. Follow along in **Figure 8** as you continue to read about electron transport.

- First, the light energy excites electrons in photosystem II. The light energy also causes a water molecule to split, releasing an electron into the electron transport system, a hydrogen ion (H^+)—also called a proton—into the thylakoid space, and oxygen (O_2) as a waste product. This breakdown of water is essential for photosynthesis to occur.
- The excited electrons move from photosystem II to an electron-acceptor molecule in the thylakoid membrane.
- Next, the electron-acceptor molecule transfers the electrons along a series of electron-carriers to photosystem I.
- In the presence of light, photosystem I transfers the electrons to a protein called ferrodoxin. The electrons lost by photosystem I are replaced by electrons shuttled from photosystem II.
- Finally, ferrodoxin transfers the electrons to the electron carrier **$NADP^+$,** forming the energy-storage molecule NADPH.

VOCABULARY

ACADEMIC VOCABULARY

Transport
to carry something from one place to another
$NADP^+$ molecules transport electrons during photosynthesis.

Chemiosmosis ATP is produced in conjunction with electron transport by the process of chemiosmosis—the mechanism by which ATP is produced as a result of the flow of electrons down a concentration gradient. The breakdown of water is essential not only for providing the electrons that initiate the electron transport chain, but also for providing the protons (H^+) necessary to drive ATP synthesis during chemiosmosis. The H^+ released during electron transport accumulate in the interior of the thylakoid. As a result of a high concentration of H^+ in the thylakoid interior and a low concentration of H^+ in the stroma, H^+ protons diffuse down their concentration gradient out of the thylakoid interior into the stroma through ion channels spanning the membrane, as shown in **Figure 8.** These channels are enzymes called ATP synthases. As H^+ moves through ATP synthases, ATP is formed in the stroma.

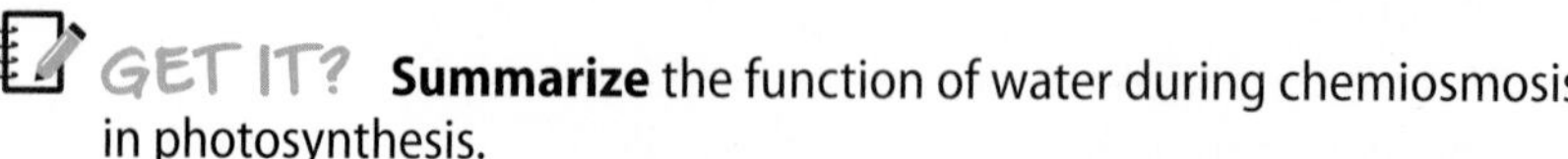

GET IT? **Summarize** the function of water during chemiosmosis in photosynthesis.

VISUALIZING Electron Transport

Figure 8 Activated electrons are passed from one molecule to another along the thylakoid membrane in a chloroplast. The energy from electrons is used to form a proton gradient. As protons move down the gradient, a phosphate is added to ADP, forming ATP.

Stroma

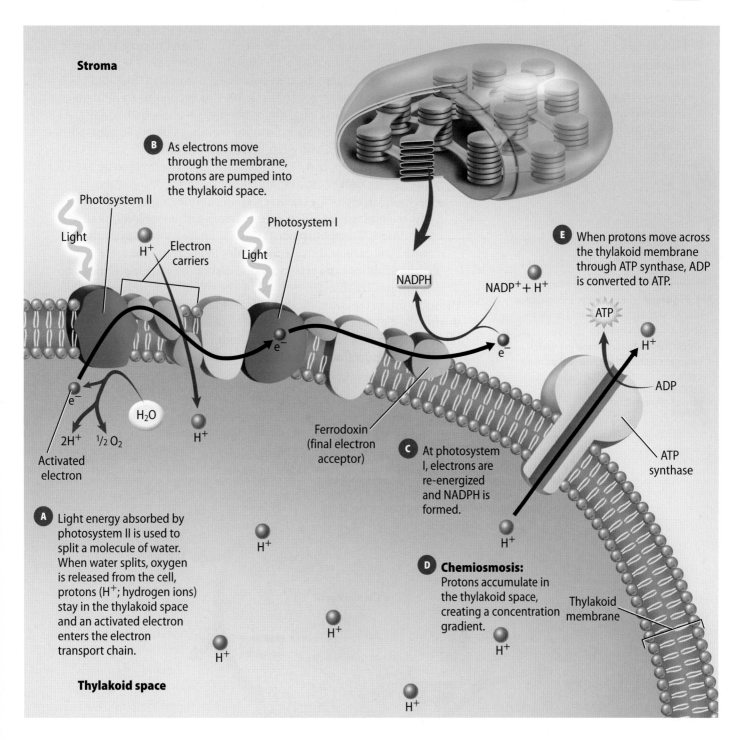

B As electrons move through the membrane, protons are pumped into the thylakoid space.

Photosystem II

Light

H^+

Electron carriers

Light

Photosystem I

NADPH

$NADP^+ + H^+$

E When protons move across the thylakoid membrane through ATP synthase, ADP is converted to ATP.

ATP

H^+

e^-

e^-

ADP

e^-

H_2O

$2H^+$ $\frac{1}{2} O_2$

H^+

Ferrodoxin (final electron acceptor)

C At photosystem I, electrons are re-energized and NADPH is formed.

ATP synthase

Activated electron

A Light energy absorbed by photosystem II is used to split a molecule of water. When water splits, oxygen is released from the cell, protons (H^+; hydrogen ions) stay in the thylakoid space and an activated electron enters the electron transport chain.

H^+

H^+

D **Chemiosmosis:** Protons accumulate in the thylakoid space, creating a concentration gradient.

Thylakoid membrane

H^+

H^+

H^+

Thylakoid space

H^+

Phase Two: The Calvin Cycle

Although NADPH and ATP provide cells with large amounts of energy, these molecules are not stable enough to store chemical energy for long periods of time. Thus, there is a second phase of photosynthesis called the **Calvin cycle,** in which energy is stored in organic molecules such as glucose. The reactions of the Calvin cycle are also referred to as the light-independent reactions. Follow along in **Figure 9** as you learn the steps of the Calvin cycle.

- In the first step of the Calvin cycle, called carbon fixation, six carbon dioxide (CO_2) molecules combine with six 5-carbon compounds to form twelve 3-carbon molecules called 3-phosphoglycerate (fahs foh GLI suh rayt) (3-PGA). The joining of carbon dioxide with other organic molecules is called carbon fixation.
- In the second step, the chemical energy stored in ATP and NADPH is transferred to the 3-PGA molecules to form high-energy molecules called glyceraldehyde 3-phosphates (G3P). ATP supplies the phosphate groups for forming G3P molecules, while NADPH supplies hydrogen ions and electrons.
- In the third step, two G3P molecules leave the cycle to be used for the production of glucose and other organic compounds.
- In the final step of the Calvin cycle, an enzyme called **rubisco** converts the remaining ten G3P molecules into 5-carbon molecules called ribulose 1, 5-bisphosphates (RuBP). These molecules combine with new carbon dioxide molecules to continue the cycle.

Because rubisco converts inorganic carbon dioxide molecules into organic molecules that can be used by the cell, it is considered one of the most important biological enzymes. Plants use the sugars formed during the Calvin cycle both as a source of energy and as building blocks for complex carbohydrates, including cellulose, which provides structural support for plants.

CAREERS IN BIOLOGY

Phytochemist A biologist who studies the chemical products of plants is a phytochemist. Phytochemists might work in medical research to find new treatments for diseases.

■ **Figure 9** The Calvin cycle joins carbon dioxide with organic molecules inside the stroma of the chloroplast.

Determine ***the compound in which energy is stored at the end of the Calvin cycle.***

 **Animation**

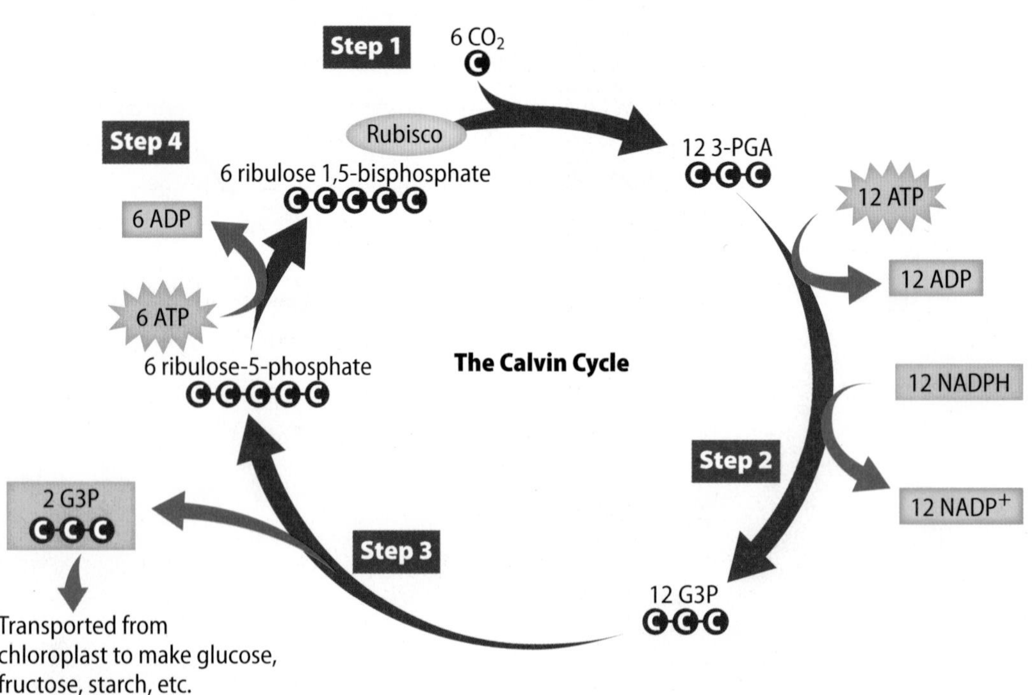

Alternative Pathways

The environment in which an organism lives can impact the organism's ability to carry out photosynthesis. Environments in which the amount of water or carbon dioxide available is insufficient can decrease the ability of a photosynthetic organism to convert light energy into chemical energy. For example, plants in hot, dry environments are subject to excessive water loss that can lead to decreased photosynthesis. Many plants in extreme climates have alternative photosynthesis pathways to maximize energy conversion.

Figure 10 This pineapple plant is an example of a CAM plant.

C_4 plants One adaptive pathway that helps plants maintain photosynthesis while minimizing water loss is called the C_4 pathway. The C_4 pathway occurs in plants such as sugarcane and corn. These plants are called C_4 plants because they fix carbon dioxide into four-carbon compounds instead of three-carbon molecules during the Calvin cycle. C_4 plants also have significant structural modifications in the arrangement of cells in the leaves. In general, C_4 plants keep their stomata (plant cell pores) closed during hot days, while the four carbon compounds are transferred to special cells where CO_2 enters the Calvin cycle. This allows for sufficient carbon dioxide uptake, while simultaneously minimizing water loss.

CAM plants Another adaptive pathway used by some plants to maximize photosynthetic activity is called crassulacean (KRAH soo lay shun) acid metabolism (CAM photosynthesis). The CAM pathway occurs in water-conserving plants that live in deserts, salt marshes, and other environments where access to water is limited. CAM plants, such as cacti, orchids, and the pineapple in **Figure 10,** allow carbon dioxide to enter the leaves only at night, when the atmosphere is cooler and more humid. At night, these plants fix carbon dioxide into organic compounds. During the day, carbon dioxide is released from these compounds and enters the Calvin cycle. This pathway also allows for sufficient carbon dioxide uptake while minimizing water loss.

REVIEW IT! Photosynthesis

Section Summary

- Plants contain chloroplasts with light-absorbing pigments that convert light energy into chemical energy.
- Photosynthesis is a two-phase process that consists of light reactions and the Calvin cycle.
- In the light reactions, autotrophs trap and convert light energy into chemical energy in the form of NADPH and ATP.
- In the Calvin cycle, chemical energy in ATP and NADPH is used to synthesize carbohydrates such as glucose.

Self Check

Understand Main Ideas

1. MAINIDEA **Explain** how chemical energy is formed from the conversion of light energy during photosynthesis.
2. **Relate** the structure of a chloroplast to the phases of photosynthesis.
3. **Analyze and evaluate** the formation of organic carbon molecules in C_4 plants.
4. **Summarize** the steps in the Calvin cycle.
5. **Diagram** and explain electron transport.

Think Critically

6. **Write** the equation for photosynthesis and compare the reactants and products.

WRITING IN ▶ Biology

7. Research the effects of global warming on photosynthesis. Write an article summarizing your findings.

3 Cellular Respiration

1.3.5b, 4.5.1c, 4.5.1d, 4.5.1e, ¥o

MAIN IDEA

Living organisms obtain energy by breaking down organic molecules during cellular respiration.

Essential Questions

- What are the stages of cellular respiration?
- What is the role of electron carriers in each stage of cellular respiration?
- What are the similarities between alcoholic fermentation and lactic acid fermentation?

BIOLOGY 4 U

Monarch butterflies must constantly feed on nectar from flowers to provide energy to sustain themselves during their winter migration to parts of Mexico and California each year. Similarly, humans and other living organisms need reliable food sources to supply energy to survive and grow.

Review Vocabulary

cyanobacterium: a type of bacterium that is a photosynthetic autotroph

New Vocabulary

anaerobic process
aerobic respiration
aerobic process
glycolysis
Krebs cycle
fermentation

Multilingual eGlossary

Overview of Cellular Respiration

Recall that organisms obtain energy in a process called cellular respiration. The function of cellular respiration is to harvest electrons from carbon compounds, such as glucose, and use that energy to make ATP. ATP is used to provide energy for cells to do work. The overall chemical equation for cellular respiration is shown below. Notice the equation for cellular respiration is the opposite of the equation for photosynthesis.

$$C_6H_{12}O_6 + 6O_2 \rightarrow 6CO_2 + 6H_2O + \text{Energy}$$

Cellular respiration occurs in two main parts: glycolysis and aerobic respiration. The first stage, glycolysis, is an anaerobic process. **Anaerobic processes** do not require oxygen. **Aerobic respiration** includes the Krebs cycle and electron transport and is an aerobic process. **Aerobic processes** require oxygen. Cellular respiration with aerobic respiration is summarized in **Figure 11.**

Figure 11 Cellular respiration occurs in the mitochondria, the energy powerhouse organelles of a cell.

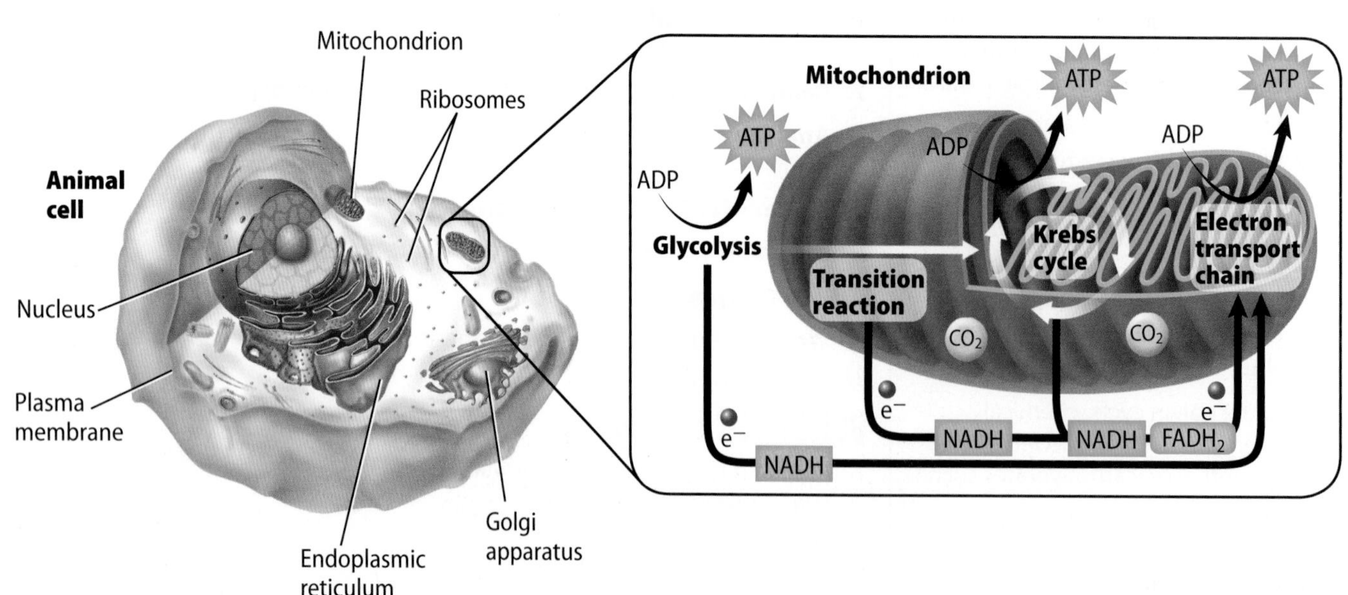

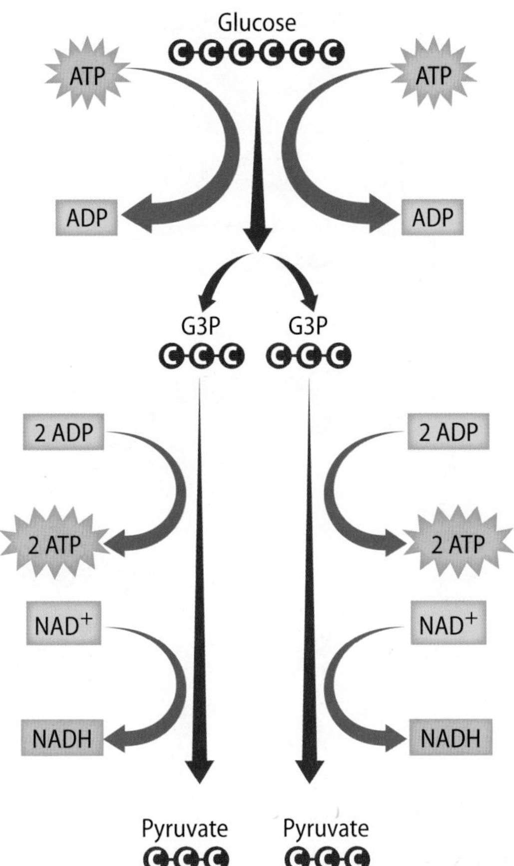

■ **Figure 12** Glucose is broken down during glycolysis inside the cytoplasm of cells.

Summarize ***the reactants and products of glycolysis.***

Personal Tutor

Glycolysis

Glucose is broken down in the cytoplasm through the process of **glycolysis.** Two molecules of ATP and two molecules of NADH are formed for each molecule of glucose that is broken down. Follow along with **Figure 12** as you read about the steps of glycolysis.

First, two phosphate groups, derived from two molecules of ATP, are joined to glucose. Notice that some energy, two ATP, is required to start the reactions that will produce energy for the cell. The 6-carbon molecule is then broken down into two 3-carbon compounds. Next, two phosphates are added and electrons and hydrogen ions (H^+) combine with two NAD^+ molecules to form two NADH molecules. NAD^+ is similar to NADP, an electron carrier used during photosynthesis. Last, the two 3-carbon compounds are converted into two molecules of pyruvate. At the same time, four molecules of ATP are produced.

VOCABULARY

WORD ORIGIN

Glycolysis
comes from the Greek words *glykys*, meaning *sweet*
and *lysis*, meaning *to rupture or break*

FOLDABLES®
Incorporate information from this section into your Foldable.

GET IT? **Explain** why there is a net yield of two, not four, ATP molecules in glycolysis.

Krebs Cycle

Glycolysis has a net result of two ATP and two pyruvate molecules. Most of the energy from the glucose is still contained in the pyruvate. In the presence of oxygen, pyruvate is transported into the mitochondrial matrix, where it is eventually converted to carbon dioxide. The series of reactions in which pyruvate is broken down into carbon dioxide is called the **Krebs cycle,** or the tricarboxylic acid (TCA) cycle. This cycle also is referred to as the citric acid cycle.

Figure 13 Pyruvate is broken down into carbon dioxide during the Krebs cycle inside the mitochondria of cells.

Trace ***Follow the path of carbon molecules that enter and leave the Krebs cycle.***

Animation

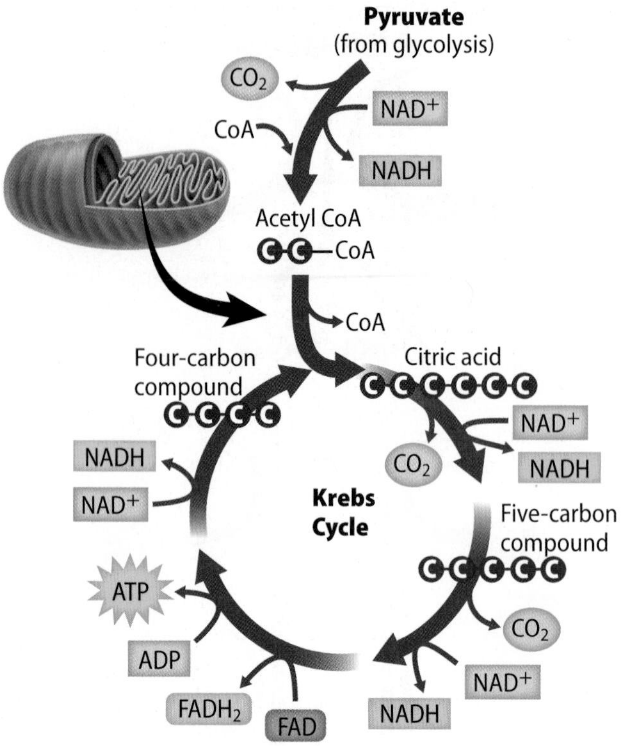

Steps of the Krebs cycle Prior to the Krebs cycle, pyruvate first reacts with coenzyme A (CoA) to form a 2-carbon intermediate called acetyl CoA. At the same time, carbon dioxide is released and NAD^+ is converted to NADH. Acetyl CoA then moves to the mitochondrial matrix. The reaction results in the production of two carbon dioxide molecules and two NADH molecules. Follow along in **Figure 13** as you continue reading about the steps of the Krebs cycle.

- The Krebs cycle begins with acetyl CoA combining with a 4-carbon compound to form a 6-carbon compound known as citric acid.
- Citric acid is then broken down in the next series of steps, releasing two molecules of carbon dioxide and generating one ATP, three NADH, and one $FADH_2$. FAD is another electron carrier similar to NAD^+ and $NADP^+$.
- Finally, acetyl CoA and citric acid are generated and the cycle continues.

Recall that two molecules of pyruvate are formed during glycolysis, resulting in two "turns" of the Krebs cycle for each glucose molecule. The net yield from the Krebs cycle is six carbon dioxide molecules, two ATP, eight NADH, and two $FADH_2$. Ten NADH and two $FADH_2$ move on to play a significant role in the next stage of aerobic respiration.

STUDY TIP

CLARIFYING STATEMENT Work with a partner to read the text and discuss unfamiliar words and difficult concepts. Write a clarifying statement to summarize the Krebs cycle.

Electron Transport

In aerobic respiration, electron transport is the final step in the breakdown of glucose. It also is the point at which most of the ATP is produced. High-energy electrons and hydrogen ions from NADH and $FADH_2$ produced in the Krebs cycle are used to convert ADP to ATP.

CAREERS IN BIOLOGY

Bioenergeticist A researcher who studies energy transfers in cells is a bioenergeticist. Some bioenergeticists study mitochondria and their relationship to aging and disease.

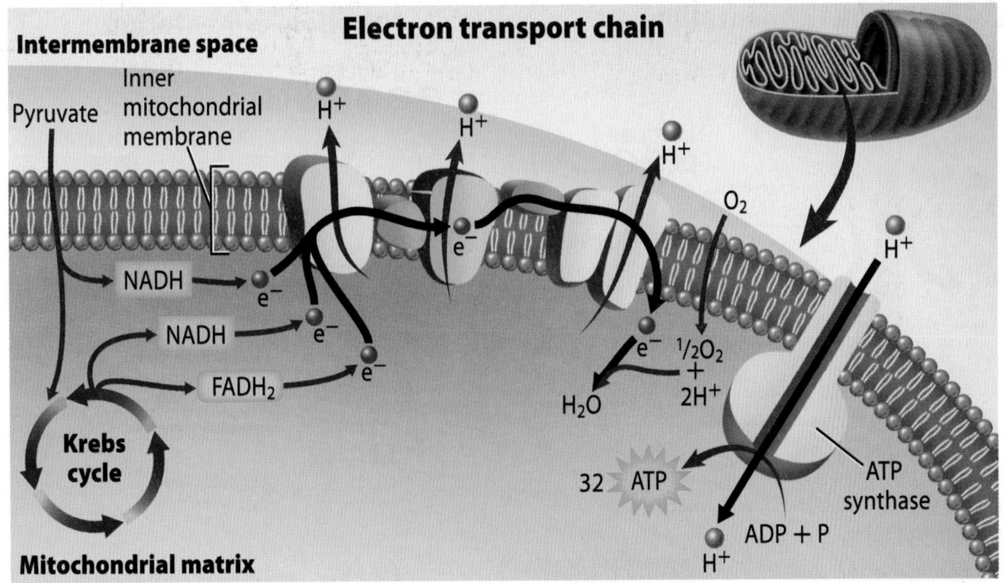

■ **Figure 14** Electron transport occurs along the mitochondrial membrane.
Compare and contrast ***electron transport in cellular respiration and photosynthesis.***

As shown in **Figure 14,** electrons move along the mitochondrial membrane from one protein to another. As NADH and $FADH_2$ release electrons, the energy carriers are converted to NAD^+ and FAD, and H^+ ions are released into the mitochondrial matrix. The H^+ ions are pumped out of the mitochondrial matrix across the inner mitochondrial membrane. H^+ ions then diffuse down their concentration gradient back across the membrane and into the matrix through ATP synthase molecules in chemiosmosis. Electron transport and chemiosmosis in cellular respiration are similar to these processes in photosynthesis. Oxygen is the final electron acceptor in the electron transport system in cellular respiration. Protons and electrons are transferred to oxygen to form water.

Overall, electron transport produces 32 ATP. Each NADH molecule produces three ATP and each group of three $FADH_2$ produces two ATP. In eukaryotes, one molecule of glucose yields 36 ATP molecules at the end of cellular respiration under ideal conditions.

Prokaryotic cellular respiration Some prokaryotes also undergo aerobic respiration. Because prokaryotes do not have mitochondria, there are differences in the process. The main difference involves the use of the prokaryotic cellular membrane as the location of electron transport. In eukaryotic cells, pyruvate is transported to the mitochondria. In prokaryotes, this movement is unnecessary, saving the prokaryotic cell two ATP, and increasing the net total of ATP produced to 38.

VOCABULARY
SCIENCE USAGE V. COMMON USAGE
Concentration
Science usage: the relative amount of a substance dissolved in another substance
The concentration of hydrogen ions is greater on one side of the membrane than on the other.

Common usage: the directing of close, undivided attention
The student's concentration was focused on the exam.

Anaerobic Respiration

Some cells can function for a short time when oxygen levels are low. Some prokaryotes are anaerobic organisms—they grow and reproduce without oxygen. In some cases these cells continue to produce ATP through glycolysis. However, there are problems with solely relying on glycolysis for energy. Glycolysis provides only two net ATP for each molecule of glucose, and a cell has a limited amount of NAD^+. Glycolysis will stop when all the NAD^+ is used up if there is not a process to replenish NAD^+. The anaerobic pathway that follows glycolysis is anaerobic respiration, or fermentation. **Fermentation** occurs in the cytoplasm and regenerates the cell's supply of NAD^+ while producing a small amount of ATP. The two main types of fermentation are lactic acid fermentation and alcohol fermentation.

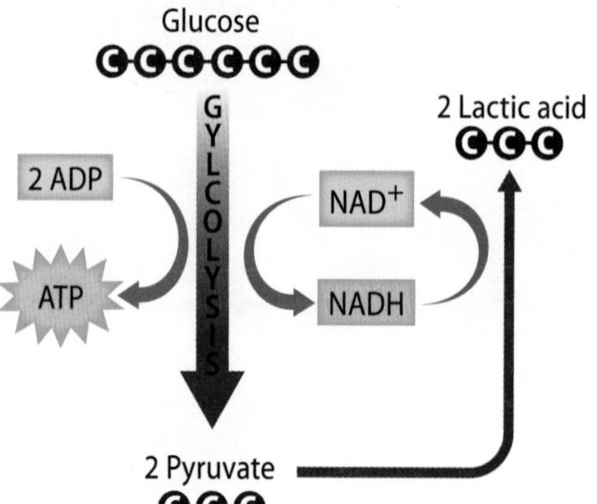

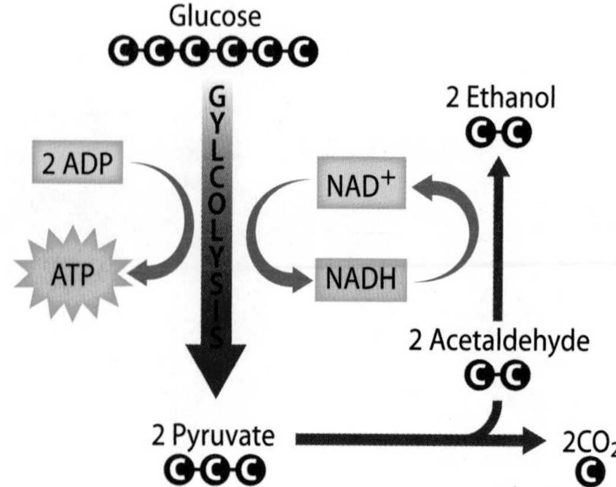

■ **Figure 15** When oxygen is absent or in limited supply, fermentation can occur.

Compare and contrast ***lactic acid fermentation and alcohol fermentation.***

Virtual Lab 

Connection to Health **Lactic acid fermentation** In lactic acid fermentation, enzymes convert the pyruvate made during glycolysis to lactic acid, as shown in **Figure 15.** This involves the transfer of high-energy electrons and protons from NADH. Skeletal muscles produce lactic acid when the body cannot supply enough oxygen, such as during periods of strenuous exercise. When lactic acid builds up in muscle cells, muscles become fatigued and might feel sore. Lactic acid also is produced by several microorganisms that often are used to produce many foods, including cheese, yogurt, and sour cream.

Alcohol fermentation Alcohol fermentation occurs in yeast and some bacteria. **Figure 15** shows the chemical reaction that occurs during alcohol fermentation when pyruvate is converted to ethyl alcohol and carbon dioxide. Similar to lactic acid fermentation, NADH donates electrons during this reaction and NAD^+ is regenerated.

Data Analysis LAB 1

Based on Real Data*

Interpret the Data

How does viral infection affect cellular respiration? Infection by viruses can significantly affect cellular respiration and the ability of cells to produce ATP. To test the effect of viral infection on the stages of cellular respiration, cells were infected with a virus, and the amount of lactic acid and ATP produced were measured.

Think Critically

1. **Analyze** how the virus affected lactic acid production in the cells.
2. **Calculate** After 8 hours, by what percentage was the lactic acid higher in the virus group than in the control group? By what percentage was ATP production decreased?

Data and Observations

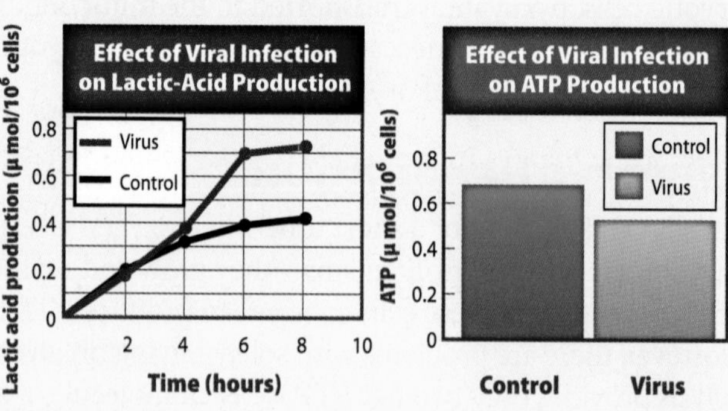

3. **Infer** why having a virus such as the flu might make a person feel tired.

*Data obtained from: El-Bacha, T., et al. 2004. Mayaro virus infection alters glucose metabolism in cultured cells through activation of the enzyme 6-phosphofructo 1-kinase. *Molecular and Cellular Biochemistry* 266: 191–198.

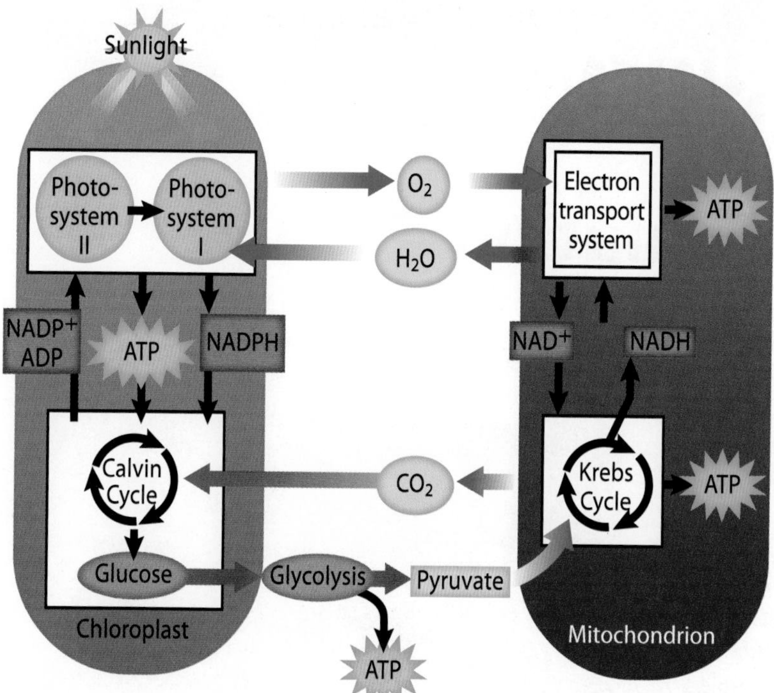

Figure 16 Photosynthesis and cellular respiration form a cycle in which the products of one metabolic pathway form the reactants of the other metabolic pathway.

Photosynthesis and Cellular Respiration

As you have learned, photosynthesis and cellular respiration are two important processes that cells use to obtain energy. They are metabolic pathways that produce and break down simple carbohydrates. **Figure 16** shows how these two processes are related. Recall that the products of photosynthesis are oxygen and glucose, the reactants needed for cellular respiration. The products of cellular respiration, which are carbon dioxide and water, are the reactants for photosynthesis.

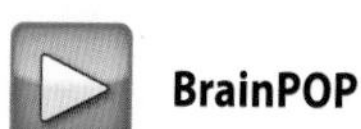

BrainPOP

REVIEW IT! Cellular Respiration

Section Summary

- Many living organisms use cellular respiration to break down glucose.
- NADH and $FADH_2$ are important electron carriers for cellular respiration.
- In the absence of oxygen, cells can sustain glycolysis by fermentation.

Self Check

Understand Main Ideas

1. MAINIDEA **Summarize** the stages of cellular respiration.
2. **Identify** how many carbons from one glucose molecule enter one round of the Krebs cycle.
3. **Explain** how high-energy electrons are used in electron transport.
4. **Describe** the role of fermentation in maintaining ATP and NAD^+ levels.

Think Critically

MATH IN ▶ Biology

5. How many ATP, NADH, and $FADH_2$ are produced in each step of cellular respiration? How is the number of ATP produced different from the net ATP available?
6. **Compare** the reactants and products of cellular respiration.

1.1.2a, 1.1.2b, 1.3.5b

Tracking Human Evolution

DNA evidence has been used to solve mysteries that were decades, or even centuries old—but imagine trying to unravel a mystery that is millions of years old. This is exactly what scientists are doing when they use DNA analysis to track human evolution.

Mitochondrial DNA You might wonder what mitochondria have to do with DNA analysis and human evolution. Mitochondria often are called the powerhouses of the cell. They are the organelles in which cells release the energy stored in food. Mitochondria have their own DNA, which is much smaller than nuclear DNA and more abundant due to its presence outside the nucleus and the number of mitochondria in most cells. Mitochondrial DNA (mtDNA) is easier to detect and extract than nuclear DNA, making it a useful tool for unlocking some of science's toughest mysteries.

One particular characteristic of mtDNA makes it especially useful for tracking human evolution. Mitochondria are inherited through maternal lineage. When a sperm and egg combine at fertilization, the nuclear DNA of the two gametes combine, but the mitochondria in the offspring are supplied solely by the egg. Therefore, mtDNA can be used as a marker to trace motherhood from generation to generation.

Tracing evolution Scientists use DNA analysis to trace the path of prehuman creatures, called hominids, as they spread around the world. The genomic DNA that is found in the nuclei of cells often is degraded or present in miniscule amounts in these ancient samples. However, scientists discovered that mtDNA is found abundantly and can be used for their analysis.

EM Magnification: 150,000×

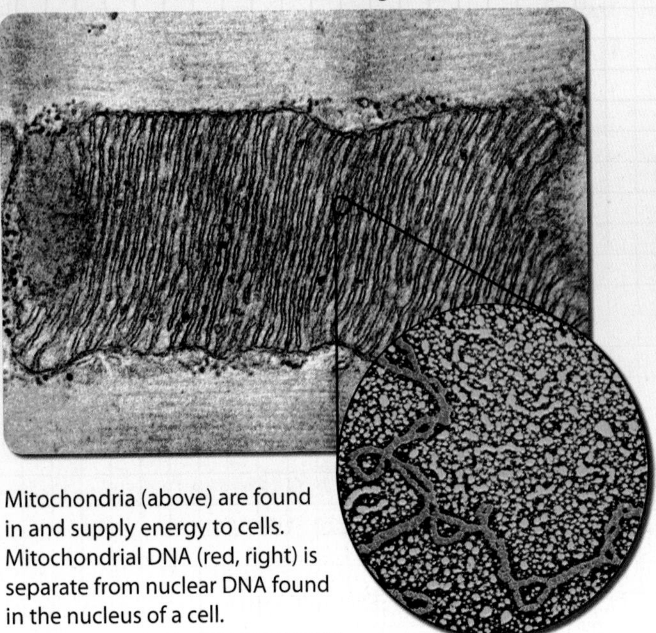

Mitochondria (above) are found in and supply energy to cells. Mitochondrial DNA (red, right) is separate from nuclear DNA found in the nucleus of a cell.

Mutations in mtDNA occur in relatively predictable patterns, and those patterns are studied and compared by scientists. By comparing mutations in mtDNA, scientists can trace mtDNA inheritance. Based on these studies of mtDNA, scientists have determined that the most recent maternal common ancestor of people living on Earth today is "Mitochondrial Eve." Mitochondrial Eve is thought to be a woman who lived in Africa approximately 200,000 years ago.

Based on the theory of Mitochondrial Eve, an international study is being conducted to trace the migration and ancestry of early humans. The project uses mtDNA sequences in females, but uses sequences from the Y chromosome to trace ancestry in males.

WRITING IN ▶ Biology

Research Paper Research mtDNA. Choose one aspect of the current research with mtDNA and write a research paper about it.

WebQuest

BioLAB DESIGN YOUR OWN

1.1.1c, 1.2.1, 1.2.2a, 1.2.4, 1.3.3, 1.3.5b, ¥a, ¥b1, ¥b2, ¥b3, ¥b4, ¥b5, ¥e, ¥i, ¥j, ¥m, ¥n, ¥o, ¥p

Do different wavelengths of light affect the rate of photosynthesis?

Background: Photosynthesizing organisms need light to complete photosynthesis. White light is composed of the different colors of light found in the visible light spectrum, and each color of light has a specific wavelength. During this lab, you will design an experiment to test the effect of different light wavelengths on the rate of photosynthesis.

Question: *How do different wavelengths of light affect photosynthesis rates?*

Possible Materials

Choose materials that would be appropriate for this lab.

aquatic plant material
Erlenmeyer flasks
test tubes (15 mL)
graduated cylinder (10 mL)
metric ruler
colored cellophane (assorted colors)
aluminum foil
lamp with reflector and 150 W bulb
baking soda solution (0.25%)
watch with a second hand

Safety Precautions

Plan and Perform the Experiment

1. Read and complete the lab safety form.
2. Hypothesize how different wavelengths of light will affect the rate of photosynthesis in your plant.
3. Design an experiment to test your prediction. Write a list of steps that you will follow, and identify the controls and variables that you will use.
4. Explain how you will generate light with different wavelengths, supply the plant with carbon dioxide, and measure the oxygen production of the plant with precision and accuracy.
5. Create a data table for recording your observations and measurements.
6. Make sure your teacher approves your plan before you begin.
7. Conduct your experiment as approved.
8. **Cleanup and Disposal** Clean up all equipment as instructed by your teacher, and return everything to its proper place. Dispose of plant material as instructed by your teacher. Wash your hands thoroughly with soap and water.

Analyze and Conclude

1. **Identify** the controls and variables in your experiment.
2. **Explain** how you measured the rate of photosynthesis.
3. **Graph** your data.
4. **Describe** how the rate of photosynthesis is affected by different wavelengths of light based on your data.
5. **Discuss** whether or not your data supported your prediction.
6. **Error Analysis** Identify possible sources of error in your experimental design, procedure, and data collection.
7. **Suggest** how you would reduce these sources of error if you repeated the experiment.

COMMUNICATE

Peer Review Post your data and graph at the front of the room. Review data posted by other students. Discuss and use comments from other students to improve your own methods.

CHAPTER 8 STUDY GUIDE

BIGIDEA **Photosynthesis converts the Sun's energy into chemical energy, while cellular respiration uses chemical energy to carry out life functions.**

SECTION 1 How Organisms Obtain Energy

MAINIDEA All living organisms use energy to carry out all biological processes.

- The laws of thermodynamics control the flow and transformation of energy in organisms.
- Some organisms produce their own food, whereas others obtain energy from the food they ingest.
- Cells store and release energy through coupled anabolic and catabolic reactions.
- The energy released from the breakdown of ATP drives cellular activities.

VOCABULARY

- **energy**
- **thermodynamics**
- **metabolism**
- **photosynthesis**
- **cellular respiration**
- **adenosine triphosphate (ATP)**

SECTION 2 Photosynthesis

MAINIDEA Light energy is trapped and converted into chemical energy during photosynthesis.

- Plants contain chloroplasts with light-absorbing pigments that convert light energy into chemical energy.
- Photosynthesis is a two-phase process that consists of light reactions and the Calvin cycle.
- In the light reactions, autotrophs trap and convert light energy into chemical energy in the form of NADPH and ATP.
- In the Calvin cycle, chemical energy in ATP and NADPH is used to synthesize carbohydrates such as glucose.

VOCABULARY

- **thylakoid**
- **granum**
- **stroma**
- **pigment**
- **$NADP^+$**
- **Calvin cycle**
- **rubisco**

SECTION 3 Cellular Respiration

MAINIDEA Living organisms obtain energy by breaking down organic molecules during cellular respiration.

- Many living organisms use cellular respiration to break down glucose.
- The stages of cellular respiration are glycolysis, the Krebs cycle, and electron transport.
- NADH and $FADH_2$ are important electron carriers for cellular respiration.
- In the absence of oxygen, cells can sustain glycolysis by fermentation.

VOCABULARY

- **anaerobic process**
- **aerobic respiration**
- **aerobic process**
- **glycolysis**
- **Krebs cycle**
- **fermentation**

SECTION 1

Vocabulary Review

Each of the following sentences is false. Make each sentence true by replacing the italicized word with a vocabulary term from the Study Guide page.

1. *Metabolism* is the energy currency of the cell.
2. The study of the flow and transformation of energy is called *energy.*
3. *Bioenergetics* can exist in many forms.
4. Chemical reactions that convert energy within a cell are referred to as *autotrophs.*
5. Light energy is converted into chemical energy during the process of *sunlight.*

Understand Main Ideas

6. Which is not a characteristic of energy?
   - **A.** cannot be created nor destroyed
   - **B.** is the capacity to do work
   - **C.** exists in forms such as chemical, light, and mechanical
   - **D.** changes spontaneously from disorder to order
7. Which organism depends on an external source of organic compounds?
   - **A.** autotroph
   - **B.** heterotroph
   - **C.** chemoautotroph
   - **D.** photoautotroph

Use the figure below to answer question 8.

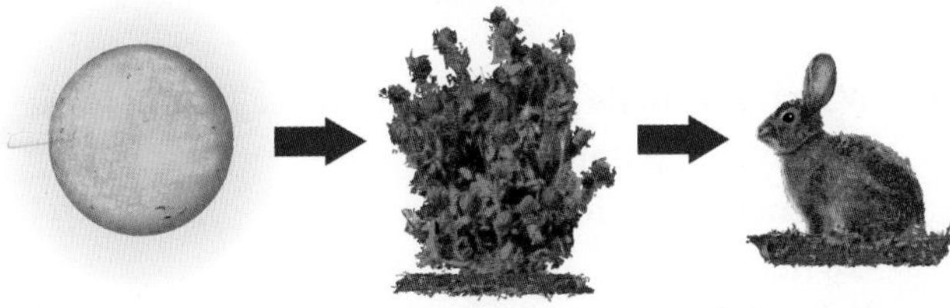

8. **THEME FOCUS** Which part of this food chain provides energy to just one other part?
   - **A.** the chemoautotroph
   - **B.** the heterotroph
   - **C.** the Sun
   - **D.** the photoautotroph
9. What do cells store and release as the main source of chemical energy?
   - **A.** ATP
   - **B.** ADP
   - **C.** $NADP^+$
   - **D.** NADPH

Constructed Response

10. **MAIN IDEA** How do autotrophs and heterotrophs differ in the way in which they obtain energy?
11. **Open Ended** Use an analogy to describe the role of ATP in living organisms.

Think Critically

12. **Explain** how energy is released from ATP.
13. **Relate** anabolic and catabolic reactions. Create an analogy for the relationship between photosynthesis and cellular respiration.

SECTION 2

Vocabulary Review

Write the vocabulary term from the Study Guide page for each definition.

14. the location of the light reactions
15. a stack of thylakoids
16. a colored molecule that absorbs light
17. a process in which energy is stored in organic molecules

Understand Main Ideas

Use the equation below to answer question 18.

$$6CO_2 + 6H_2O \xrightarrow{\text{energy}} C_6H_{12}O_6 + ?$$

18. What waste product of photosynthesis is released to the environment?
    - **A.** carbon dioxide
    - **B.** water
    - **C.** oxygen
    - **D.** ammonia

19. Which is the internal membrane of the chloroplast that is organized into flattened membranous sacs?
   A. thylakoids
   B. mitochondria
   C. theca
   D. stroma

Use the figure below to answer question 20.

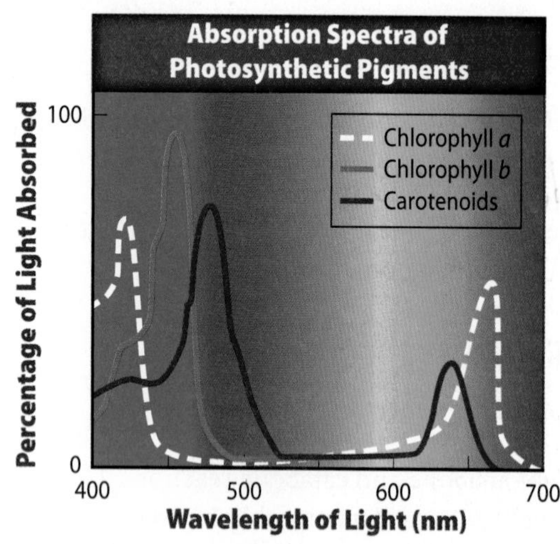

20. Of which wavelength of light do carotenoids absorb the greatest percentage?
   A. 400
   B. 500
   C. 600
   D. 700

21. Which supplies energy used to synthesize carbohydrates during the Calvin cycle?
   A. CO_2 and ATP
   B. ATP and NADPH
   C. NADPH and H_2O
   D. H_2O and O_2

Constructed Response

22. **MAIN IDEA** Summarize the phases of photosynthesis. Describe where each phase occurs in the chloroplast.

23. **Short Answer** Why is hydrogen ion generation essential for ATP production during photosynthesis?

24. **Short Answer** Explain why the Calvin cycle depends on light reactions.

Think Critically

25. **Explain** the following statement: The oxygen generated by photosynthesis is simply a by-product formed during the production of ATP and carbohydrates.

26. **Predict** the effect of the loss of forests on cellular respiration in other organisms.

27. **Describe** two alternative photosynthesis pathways found in plants. Suggest how these adaptations might help plants.

SECTION 3

Vocabulary Review

Define each vocabulary term in a complete sentence.

28. Krebs cycle

29. anaerobic process

30. fermentation

31. aerobic

32. glycolysis

Understand Main Ideas

Use the figure below to answer questions 33 and 34.

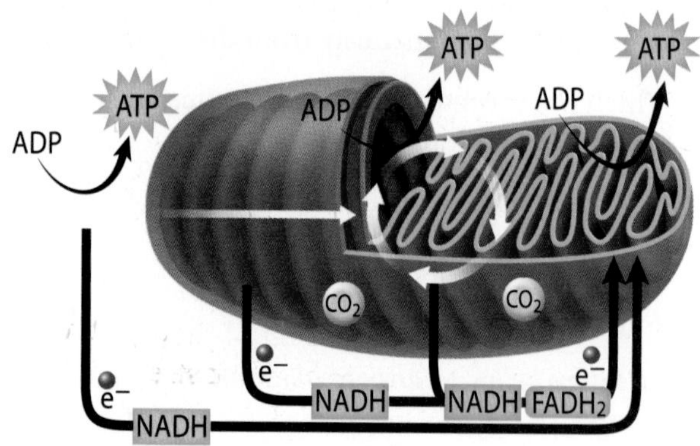

33. Which organelle is illustrated in the figure?
   A. Golgi apparatus
   B. mitochondrion
   C. nucleus
   D. endoplasmic reticulum

34. Which process does not occur in the organelle illustrated above?
   A. glycolysis
   B. Krebs cycle
   C. conversion of pyruvate to acetyl CoA
   D. electron transport

35. Which is not a stage of cellular respiration?
    A. glycolysis
    B. Krebs cycle
    C. electron transport chain
    D. lactic acid fermentation

36. What is produced when the electrons leave the electron transport chain in cellular respiration and bind to the final electron acceptor for the chain?
    A. H_2O
    B. O_2
    C. CO_2
    D. CO

37. In which molecule is most of the energy of glucose stored at the end of glycolysis?
    A. pyruvate
    B. acetyl CoA
    C. ATP
    D. NADH

Constructed Response

38. **Short Answer** Discuss the roles of NADH and $FADH_2$ in cellular respiration.

39. **Short Answer** In cellular respiration, where do the electrons in the electron transport chain originate? What is the final destination of the electrons?

40. **Short Answer** Why do your muscles hurt for some time after a large amount of strenuous exercise? How has homeostasis been disrupted?

Think Critically

41. **Explain** The end products of cellular respiration are CO_2 and H_2O. Where do the oxygen atoms in the CO_2 originate? Where does the oxygen atom in H_2O originate?

42. MAINIDEA What is the advantage of aerobic metabolism over anaerobic metabolism in energy production in living organisms?

43. **Compare and contrast** electron transport in photosynthesis and cellular respiration.

Summative Assessment

44. **BIGIDEA** What are the chemical equations for photosynthesis and cellular respiration? Analyze the relationship between photosynthesis and cellular respiration using the equations for both processes.

45. **WRITINGIN▶Biology** Write an article using what you know about the relationship between photosynthesis and cellular respiration to explain the importance of plants in an ecosystem.

DBQ Document–Based Questions

Cadmium is a heavy metal that is toxic to humans, plants, and animals. It is often found as a contaminant in soil. Use the data below to answer questions about the effect of cadmium on photosynthesis in tomato plants.

Data obtained from: Chaffei, C., et al. 2004. Cadmium toxicity induced changes in nitrogen management in *Lycopersicon esculentum* leading to a metabolic safeguard through an amino acid storage strategy. *Plant and Cell Physiology* 45(11): 1681–1693.

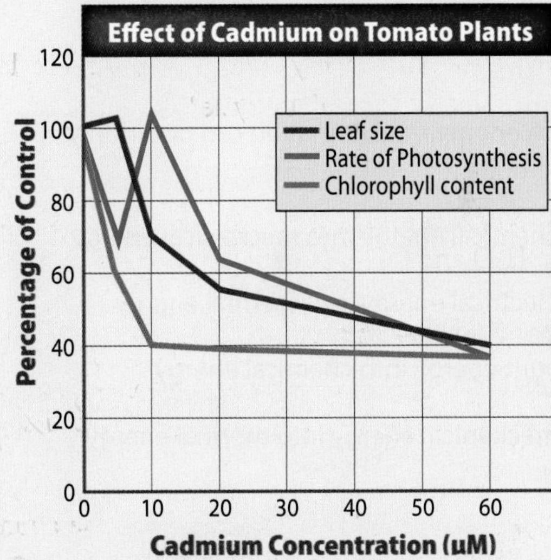

46. What was the effect of cadmium on leaf size, chlorophyll content, and photosynthesis rate?

47. At what concentration of cadmium was the largest effect on leaf size observed? On chlorophyll content? On photosynthesis rate?

48. Predict the effects on cellular respiration if an animal eats contaminated tomatoes.

CUMULATIVE

MULTIPLE CHOICE

1 Which type of transport does NOT require the input of additional energy?

A active transport

B diffusion

C endocytosis

D exocytosis

2 Which step occurs during the Calvin cycle?

A formation of ATP

B formation of six-carbon sugars

C release of oxygen gas

D transport of electrons by $NADP^+$

3 Which energy transformation can occur only in autotrophs?

A chemical energy into mechanical energy

B electrical energy into thermal energy

C light energy into chemical energy

D mechanical energy into thermal energy

4 Which statement does the cell theory support?

A Cells can form from proteins in the environment.

B Cells contain membrane-bound organelles.

C Life-forms are made of one or more cells.

D Organelles are the smallest form of life.

SHORT ANSWER

Use the illustration below to answer question 5.

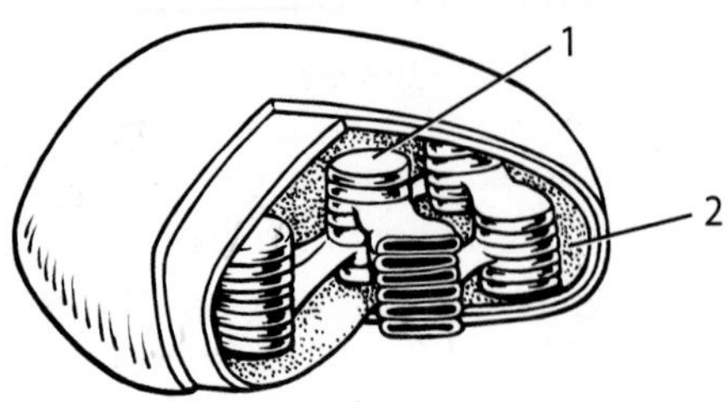

5 The diagram above shows a chloroplast. Name the two parts shown in the diagram and state which phase of photosynthesis occurs in each part.

6 Compare and contrast the structure of a cell wall and the structure of a cell membrane.

7 Relate the bonds between phosphate groups in ATP to the release of energy when a molecule of ATP is changed to ADP.

8 Name three components of a cell's plasma membrane and explain why each component is important for the function of the cell.

9 What kind of mixture is formed by stirring a small amount of table salt into water until the salt all dissolves? Identify the components of this mixture.

10 In which parts of a plant would you expect to find cells with the most chloroplasts? Explain your answer.

11 Long-distance runners often talk about training to raise their anaerobic threshold. The anaerobic threshold is the point at which certain muscles do not have enough oxygen to perform aerobic respiration and begin to perform anaerobic respiration. Hypothesize why you think it is important for competitive runners to raise their anaerobic threshold.

EXTENDED RESPONSE

Use the graph below to answer question 12.

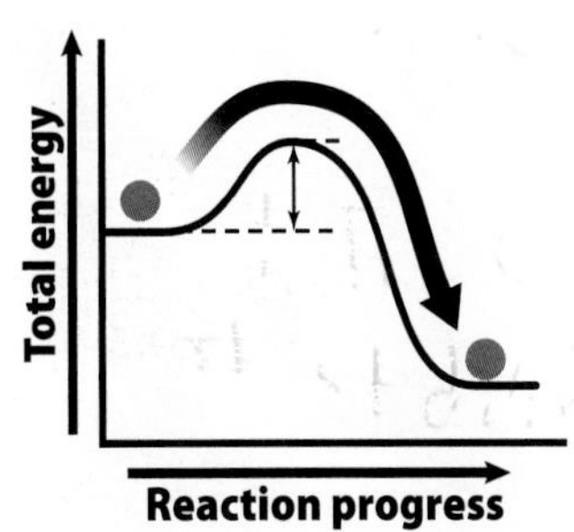

12 The graph shows the effect of an enzyme involved in the breakdown of proteins in the digestive system. Hypothesize how protein digestion would be different in a person who does not have this enzyme.

13 Which organelle would you expect to find in large numbers in cells that pump stomach acid out against a concentration gradient? Give a reason for your answer.

ESSAY QUESTION

The human body constantly interacts with the environment, taking in some substances and releasing others. Many substances taken in by humans have a specific role in maintaining basic cellular processes such as respiration, ion transport, and synthesis of various macromolecules. Likewise, many of the substances released by the body are waste products of cellular processes.

Using the information in the paragraph above, answer the following question in essay format.

14 Write an essay that explains how humans take in substances that are important for cellular respiration, and how they release the waste products from this process.

TEST PRACTICE

15

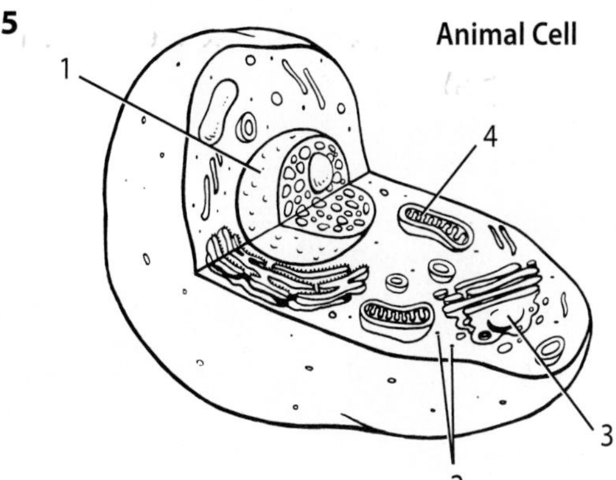

Identify the organelle in which cellular respiration occurs.

A 1

B 2

C 3

D 4

16 Identify the process of aerobic respiration.

A glycolysis → electron transport → Krebs cycle

B glycolysis → Krebs cycle → electron transport

C Krebs cycle → glycolysis → electron transport

D Krebs cycle → electron transport → glycolysis

17 Students in a class planned and implemented a scientific investigation. They swapped procedures and data for evaluation. Which part of a scientific method are they doing?

A forming a hypothesis

B publishing results

C making an observation

D peer review

NEED EXTRA HELP?

If You Missed Question . . .	1	2	3	4	5	6	7	8	9	10	11	12	13	14	15	16	17
Review Section . . .	7.4	8.2	8.1	7.1	8.2	7.3	8.1	7.2	6.3	7.3	8.3	6.2	7.2, 7.4	8.3	8.3	8.3	1.3

The cells in an organism grow and divide constantly. This division allows the organism to grow larger. In other cases, the constant growing and dividing replaces dying cells the organism needs to survive.

LaunchLAB

From where do healthy cells come?

All living things are composed of cells. The only way an organism can grow or heal itself is by cellular reproduction. Healthy cells perform vital life functions and they reproduce to form more cells. In this lab you will investigate the appearance of different cell types.

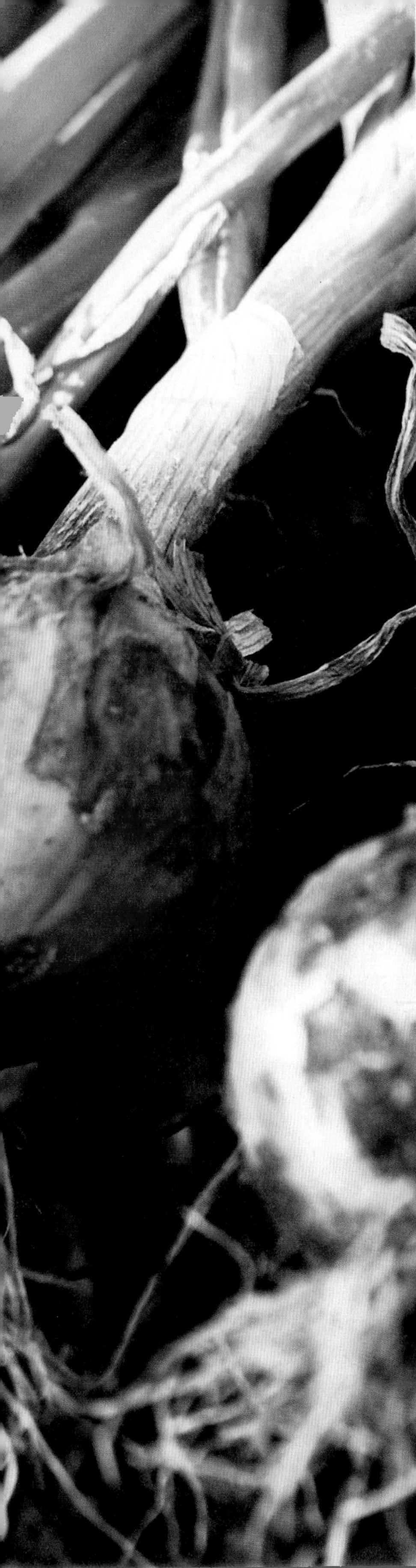

CHAPTER 9

Cellular Reproduction

THEMEFOCUS

Stability and change **Cells go through several changes as they grow and reproduce.**

BIGIDEA

Cells go through a life cycle that includes interphase, mitosis, and cytokinesis.

Mitosis Phases and Cytokinesis

Make a layered-look book using the titles shown. Use it to organize your notes on phases of mitosis.

Mitosis Phases and Cytokinesis

- Prophase
- Metaphase
- Anaphase
- Telophase
- Cytokinesis

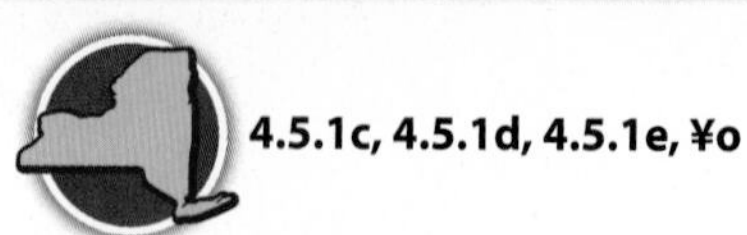

1 Cellular Growth

4.5.1c, 4.5.1d, 4.5.1e, ¥o

MAINIDEA

Cells grow until they reach their size limit, then they either stop growing or divide.

Essential Questions

- Why are cells relatively small?
- What are the primary stages of the cell cycle?
- What are the stages of interphase?

BIOLOGY 4U

If you've ever played a doubles match in tennis, you probably felt that you and your partner could effectively cover your half of the court. However, if the court were much larger, perhaps you could no longer reach your shots. For the best game, the tennis court must be kept at regulation size. Cell size also must be limited to ensure that the needs of the cell are met.

Review Vocabulary

selective permeability: process in which a membrane allows some substances to pass through while keeping others out

New Vocabulary

cell cycle
interphase
mitosis
cytokinesis
chromosome
chromatin

Multilingual eGlossary

Cell Size Limitations

Most cells are less than 100 µm (100×10^{-6} m) in diameter, which is smaller than the period at the end of this sentence. Why are most cells so small? This section investigates several factors that influence cell size.

Ratio of surface area to volume The key factor that limits the size of a cell is the ratio of its surface area to its volume. The surface area of the cell refers to the area covered by the plasma membrane. The plasma membrane is the structure through which all nutrients and waste products must pass. The volume refers to the space taken up by the inner contents of the cell, including the organelles in the cytoplasm and the nucleus.

Connection to Math To illustrate the ratio of surface area to volume, consider the small cube in **Figure 1,** which has sides of one micrometer (µm) in length. This is approximately the size of a bacterial cell. To calculate the surface area of the cube, multiply length times width times the number of sides (1 µm × 1 µm × 6 sides), which equals 6 µm^2. To calculate the volume of the cell, multiply length times width times height (1 µm × 1 µm × 1 µm), which equals 1 µm^3. The ratio of surface area to volume is 6:1.

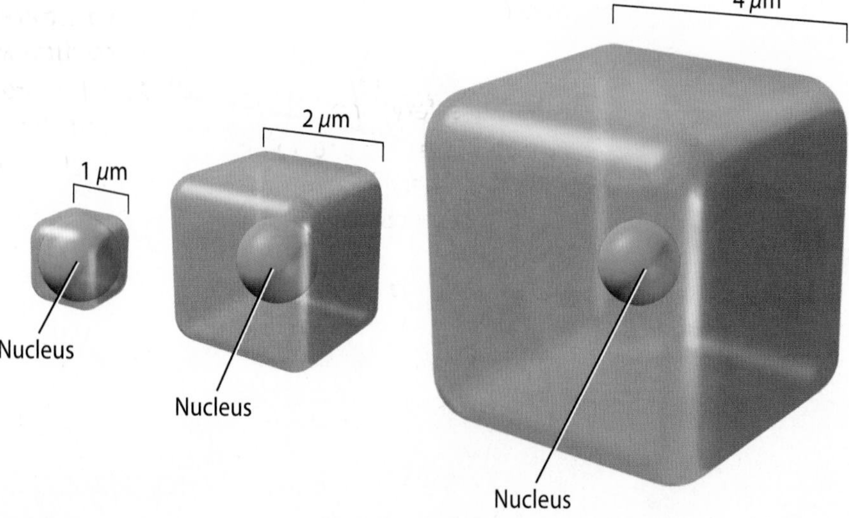

■ **Figure 1** The ratio of surface area to volume decreases as a cell gets bigger. The smallest cube shown has a ratio of 6 (1 µm × 1 µm × 6 sides) to 1 (1 µm × 1 µm × 1 µm), while the largest cube has a ratio of 96 (4 µm × 4 µm × 6 sides) to 64 (4 µm × 4 µm × 4 µm), or 3:2.

If the cubic cell grows to 2 μm per side, as represented in **Figure 1,** the surface area becomes 24 μm^2 and the volume is 8 μm^3. The ratio of surface area to volume is now 3:1, which is less than it was when the cell was smaller. If the cell continues to grow, the ratio of surface area to volume will continue to decrease, as shown by the third cube in **Figure 1.** As the cell grows, its volume increases much more rapidly than the surface area. This means that the cell might have difficulty supplying nutrients and expelling enough waste products. By remaining small, cells have a higher ratio of surface area to volume and can sustain themselves more easily.

GET IT? **Explain** why a high ratio of surface area to volume benefits a cell.

Transport of substances Another task that can be managed more easily in a small cell than in a large cell is the movement of substances. Recall that the plasma membrane controls cellular transport because it is selectively permeable. Once inside the cell, substances move by diffusion or by motor proteins pulling them along the cytoskeleton. Diffusion over large distances is slow and inefficient because it relies on random movement of molecules and ions. Similarly, the cytoskeleton transportation network, shown in **Figure 2,** becomes less efficient for a cell if the distance to travel becomes too large. Small cell size maximizes the ability of diffusion and motor proteins to transport nutrients and waste products. Small cells maintain more efficient transport systems.

LM Magnification: ×670

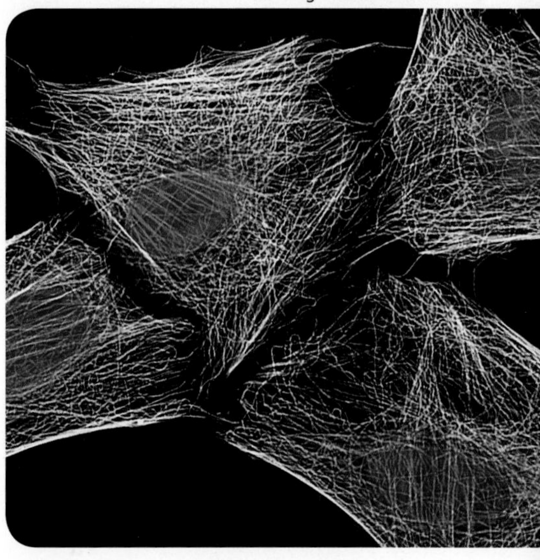

Figure 2 In order for the cytoskeleton to be an efficient transportation railway, the distances that substances have to travel within a cell must be limited.

MiniLAB 1

Investigate Cell Size

Could a cell grow large enough to engulf your school? What would happen if the size of an elephant were doubled? At the organism level, an elephant cannot grow significantly larger, because its legs would not support the increase in mass. Do the same principles and limitations apply at the cellular level? Do the math!

Procedure

1. Read and complete the lab safety form.
2. Prepare a data table for surface area and volume data calculated for five hypothetical cells. Assume the cell is a cube. (Dimensions given are for one face of a cube.)
   Cell 1: 0.00002 m (the average diameter of most eukaryotic cells)
   Cell 2: 0.001 m (the diameter of a squid's giant nerve cell)
   Cell 3: 2.5 cm
   Cell 4: 30 cm
   Cell 5: 15 m
3. Calculate the surface area for each cell using the formula: length × width × number of sides (6).
4. Calculate the volume for each cell using the formula: length × width × height.

Analysis

1. **Cause and Effect** Based on your calculations, confirm why cells do not become very large.
2. **Infer** Are large organisms, such as redwood trees and elephants, large because they contain extra large cells or just more standard-sized cells? Explain.

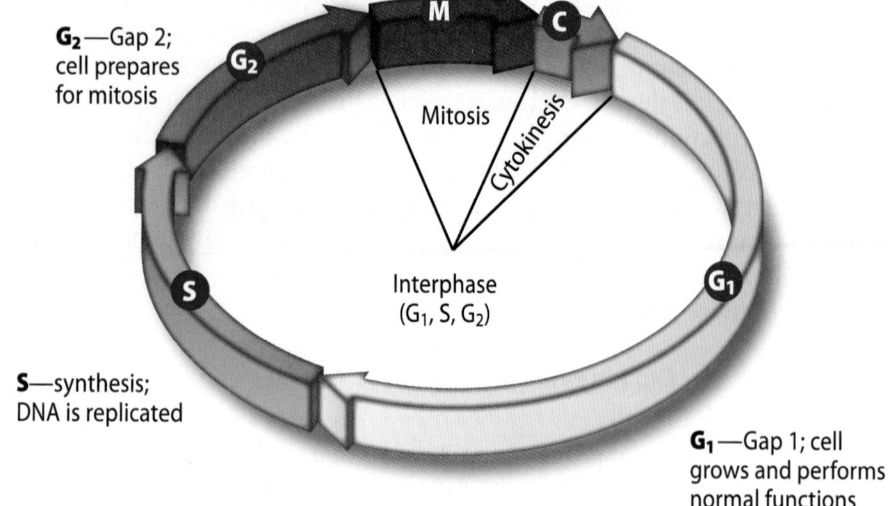

Figure 3 The cell cycle involves three stages—interphase, mitosis, and cytokinesis. Interphase is divided into three substages.
Hypothesize ***why cytokinesis represents the smallest amount of time that a cell spends in the cell cycle.***

Cellular communications The need for signaling proteins to move throughout the cell also limits cell size. In other words, cell size affects the ability of the cell to communicate instructions for cellular functions. If the cell becomes too large, it becomes almost impossible for cellular communications, many of which involve movement of substances and signals to various organelles, to take place efficiently. For example, the signals that trigger protein synthesis might not reach the ribosome fast enough for protein synthesis to occur to sustain the cell.

BrainPOP 

The Cell Cycle

Once a cell reaches its size limit, something must happen—either it will stop growing or it will divide. Most cells will eventually divide. Cell division not only prevents the cell from becoming too large, but it is also the way the cell reproduces. Cellular reproduction allows you to grow and heal certain injuries. Cells reproduce by a cycle of growing and dividing called the **cell cycle.** Each time a cell goes through one complete cycle, it becomes two cells. When the cell cycle is repeated continuously, the result is a continuous production of new cells. A general overview of the cell cycle is presented in **Figure 3.**

There are three main stages of the cell cycle. **Interphase** is the stage during which the cell grows, carries out cellular functions, and replicates, or makes copies of its DNA in preparation for the next stage of the cycle. Interphase is divided into three substages, as indicated by the segment arrows in **Figure 3.** **Mitosis** (mi TOH sus) is the stage of the cell cycle during which the cell's nucleus and nuclear material divide. Mitosis is divided into four substages. Near the end of mitosis, a process called cytokinesis begins. **Cytokinesis** (si toh kih NEE sis) is the method by which a cell's cytoplasm divides, creating a new cell. You will read more about mitosis and cytokinesis in Section 2.

The duration of the cell cycle varies, depending on the cell that is dividing. Some eukaryotic cells might complete the cycle in as few as eight minutes, while other cells might take up to one year. For most normal, actively dividing animal cells, the cell cycle takes approximately 12–24 hours. When you consider all that takes place during the cell cycle, you might find it amazing that most of your cells complete the cell cycle in about a day.

VOCABULARY
WORD ORIGIN
Cytokinesis
cyto– prefix; from the Greek word *kytos,* meaning *hollow vessel*
–kinesis from the Greek word *kinetikos,* meaning putting *in motion*

The stages of interphase During interphase, the cell grows, develops into a mature, functioning cell, duplicates its DNA, and prepares for division. Interphase is divided into three stages, as shown in **Figure 3:** G_1, S, and G_2, also called Gap 1, synthesis, and Gap 2.

The first stage of interphase, G_1, is the period immediately after a cell divides. During G_1, a cell is growing, carrying out normal cell functions, and preparing to replicate DNA. Some cells, such as muscle and nerve cells, exit the cell cycle at this point and do not divide again.

The second stage of interphase, S, is the period when a cell copies its DNA in preparation for cell division. **Chromosomes** (KROH muh sohmz) are the structures that contain the genetic material that is passed from generation to generation of cells. **Chromatin** (KROH muh tun) is the relaxed form of DNA in the cell's nucleus. As shown in **Figure 4,** when a specific dye is applied to a cell in interphase, the nucleus stains with a speckled appearance. This speckled appearance is due to individual strands of chromatin that are not visible under a light microscope without the dye.

The G_2 stage follows the S stage and is the period when the cell prepares for the division of its nucleus. A protein that makes microtubules for cell division is synthesized at this time. During G_2, the cell also takes inventory and makes sure it is ready to continue with mitosis. When these activities are completed, the cell begins the next stage of the cell cycle—mitosis.

Stained LM Magnification: 400×

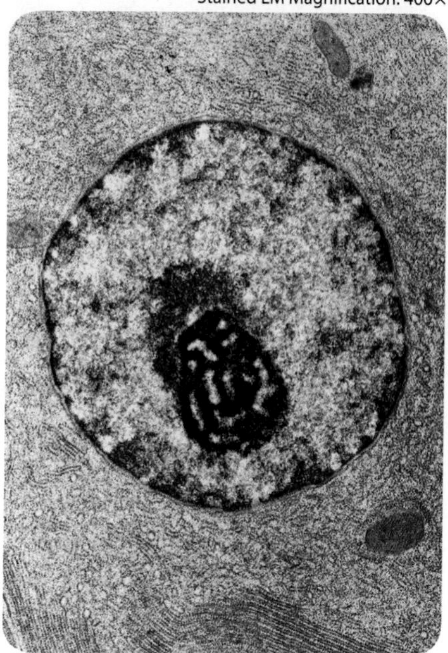

Figure 4 The grainy appearance of this nucleus from a rat liver cell is due to chromatin, the relaxed material that condenses to form chromosomes.

Mitosis and cytokinesis The stages of mitosis and cytokinesis follow interphase. In mitosis, the cell's nuclear material divides and separates into opposite ends of the cell. In cytokinesis, the cell divides into two daughter cells with identical nuclei. These important stages of the cell cycle are described in Section 2.

Prokaryotic cell division The cell cycle is the method by which eukaryotic cells reproduce themselves. Prokaryotic cells, which you have learned are simpler cells, reproduce by a method called binary fission.

REVIEW IT! Cellular Growth

Section Summary

- The ratio of surface area to volume describes the size of the plasma membrane relative to the volume of the cell.
- Cells are limited in size, with most cells having a diameter of less than 100 μm.
- The cell cycle is the process of cellular reproduction.
- A cell spends the majority of its lifetime in interphase.

Self Check

Understand Main Ideas

1. MAINIDEA **Relate** cell size to cell functions, and explain why cell size is limited.
2. **Summarize** the primary stages of the cell cycle.
3. **Describe** what happens to DNA during the S stage of interphase.
4. **Create** a diagram of the stages of the cell cycle and describe what happens in each.

Think Critically

5. **Hypothesize** what the result would be if a large cell managed to divide, despite the fact that it had grown beyond an optimum size.

MATH IN ▶ Biology

6. If a cube representing a cell is 100 μm on a side, calculate the surface area-to-volume ratio, and explain why this is or is not a good size for a cell.

USE IT! Science Notebook

2 Mitosis and Cytokinesis

4.5.1c

MAINIDEA

Eukaryotic cells reproduce by mitosis, the process of nuclear division, and cytokinesis, the process of cytoplasm division.

Essential Questions

- What are the events of each stage of mitosis?
- What is the process of cytokinesis?

BIOLOGY 4U

Many familiar events are cyclic in nature. The course of a day or the changing of seasons year after year are some examples of cyclic events. Cells also have a cycle of growth and reproduction.

Review Vocabulary

life cycle: the sequence of growth and development stages that an organism goes through during its life

New Vocabulary

prophase
sister chromatid
centromere
spindle apparatus
metaphase
anaphase
telophase

Multilingual eGlossary 

Mitosis

You learned in the last section that cells cycle through interphase, mitosis, and cytokinesis. During mitosis, the cell's replicated genetic material separates and the cell prepares to split into two cells. The key activity of mitosis is the accurate separation of the cell's replicated DNA. This enables the cell's genetic information to pass into the new cells intact, resulting in two daughter cells that are genetically identical. In multicellular organisms, the process of mitosis increases the number of cells as a young organism grows to its adult size. Organisms also use mitosis to replace damaged cells. Recall the last time you were accidentally cut. The body's process of healing the cut involves generating new skin cells. These new cells are produced by your existing skin cells. Under the scab, the existing skin cells divided by mitosis and cytokinesis to create new skin cells that filled the gap in the skin caused by the injury.

The Stages of Mitosis

Like interphase, mitosis is divided into stages: prophase, metaphase, anaphase, and telophase.

Prophase The first stage and longest phase of mitosis is called **prophase.** In this stage, the cell's chromatin tightens, or condenses, into chromosomes. In prophase, the chromosomes are shaped like an X, as shown in **Figure 5.** At this point, each chromosome is a single structure that contains the genetic material that was replicated in interphase. Each half of this X is called a sister chromatid. **Sister chromatids** are structures that contain identical copies of DNA. The structure at the center of the chromosome where the sister chromatids are attached is called the **centromere.** This structure is important because it ensures that a complete copy of the replicated DNA will become part of the daughter cells at the end of the cell cycle. Locate prophase in the cell cycle illustrated in **Figure 6,** and note the position of the sister chromatids. As you continue to read about the stages of mitosis, refer back to **Figure 6** to follow the chromatids through the cell cycle.

■ **Figure 5** Chromosomes in prophase are actually sister chromatids that are attached at the centromere.

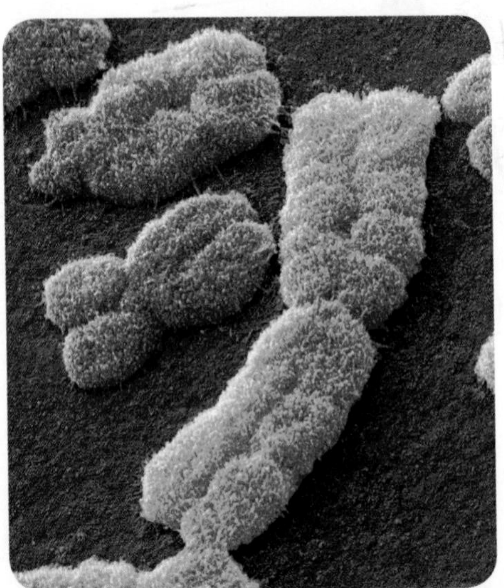

Color-Enhanced SEM magnification: 6875×

Andrew Syred/Science Source

GET IT? **Compare** the key activity of interphase with the key activity of mitosis.

VISUALIZING the Cell Cycle

Figure 6 The cell cycle begins with interphase. Mitosis follows, occurring in four stages—prophase, metaphase, anaphase, and telophase. Mitosis is followed by cytokinesis, then the cell cycle repeats with each new cell.

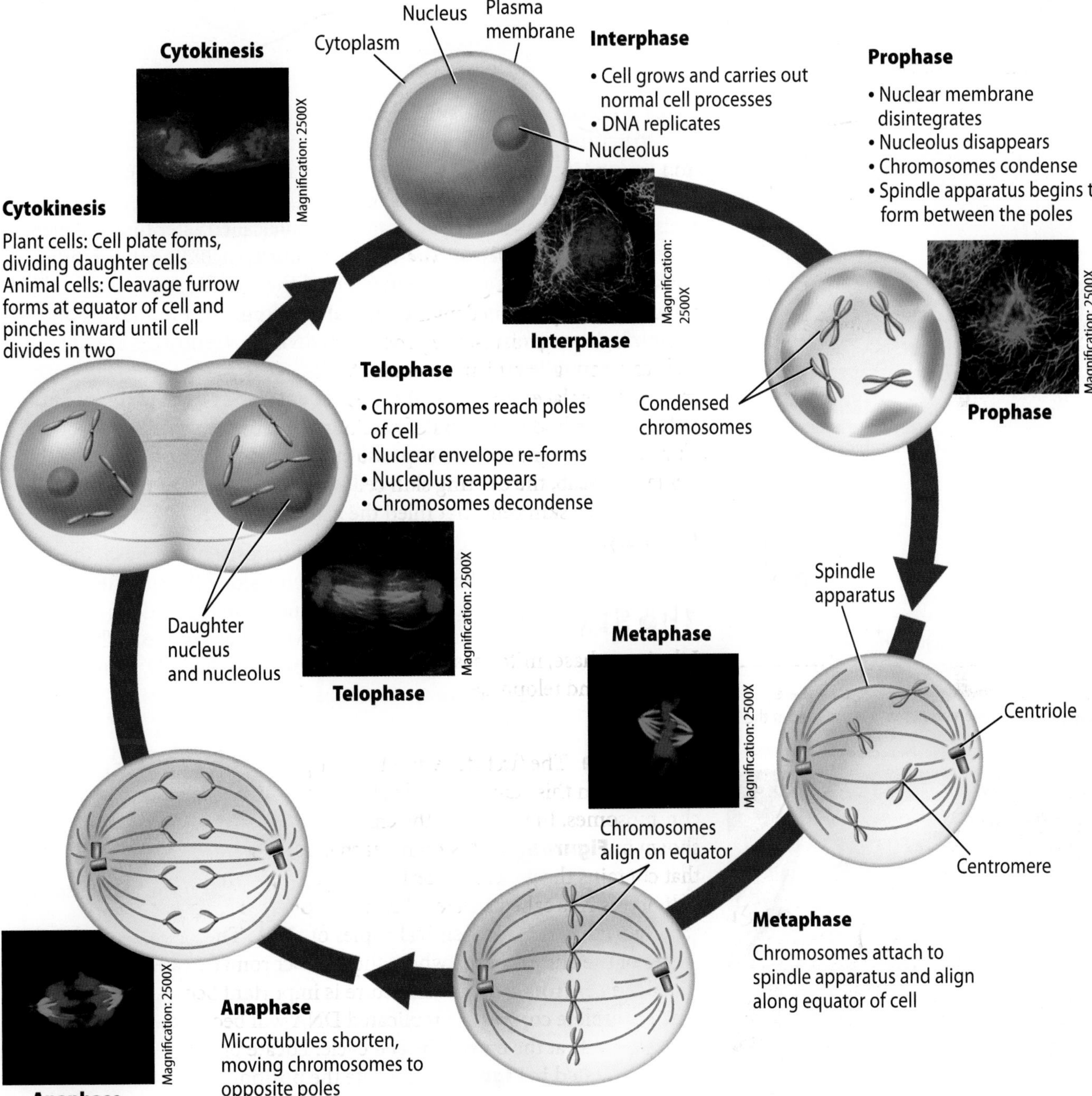

Cytokinesis
Magnification: 2500X
Cytokinesis
Plant cells: Cell plate forms, dividing daughter cells
Animal cells: Cleavage furrow forms at equator of cell and pinches inward until cell divides in two
Nucleus
Plasma membrane
Cytoplasm
Interphase
• Cell grows and carries out normal cell processes
• DNA replicates
Nucleolus
Magnification: 2500X
Interphase
Prophase
• Nuclear membrane disintegrates
• Nucleolus disappears
• Chromosomes condense
• Spindle apparatus begins to form between the poles
Magnification: 2500X
Prophase
Condensed chromosomes
Telophase
• Chromosomes reach poles of cell
• Nuclear envelope re-forms
• Nucleolus reappears
• Chromosomes decondense
Magnification: 2500X
Telophase
Daughter nucleus and nucleolus
Spindle apparatus
Metaphase
Magnification: 2500X
Centriole
Centromere
Chromosomes align on equator
Metaphase
Chromosomes attach to spindle apparatus and align along equator of cell
Magnification: 2500X
Anaphase
Anaphase
Microtubules shorten, moving chromosomes to opposite poles

LM Magnification: 100×

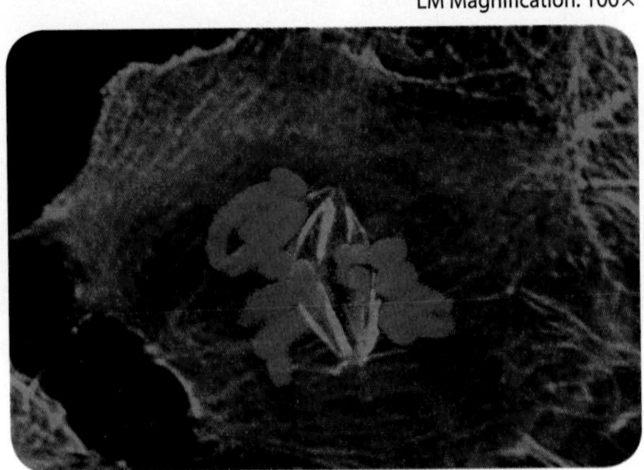

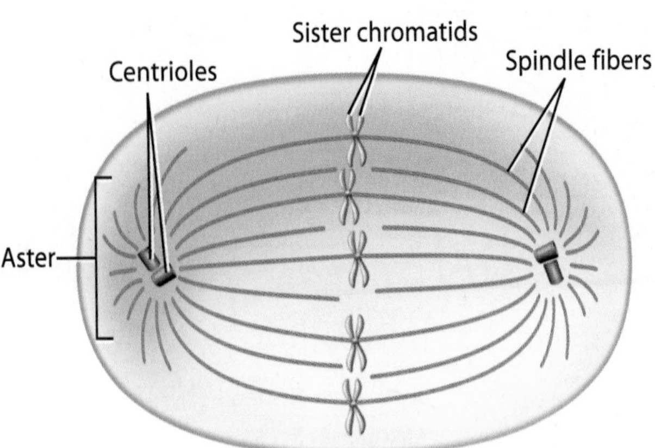

■ **Figure 7** In animal cells, the spindle apparatus is made of spindle fibers, centrioles, and aster fibers.

As prophase continues, the nucleolus seems to disappear. Microtubule structures called spindle fibers form in the cytoplasm. In animal cells and most protist cells, another pair of microtubule structures called centrioles migrates to the ends, or poles, of the cell. Coming out of the centrioles are yet another type of microtubule called aster fibers, which have a starlike appearance. The whole structure, including the spindle fibers, centrioles, and aster fibers, is called the **spindle apparatus** and is shown in **Figure 7.** The spindle apparatus is important in moving and organizing the chromosomes before cell division. Centrioles are not part of the spindle apparatus in plant cells.

Incorporate information from this section into your Foldable.

Near the end of prophase, the nuclear envelope seems to disappear. The spindle fibers attach to the sister chromatids of each chromosome on both sides of the centromere and then attach to opposite poles of the cell. This arrangement ensures that each new cell receives one complete copy of the DNA.

Metaphase During the second stage of mitosis, **metaphase,** the sister chromatids are pulled by motor proteins along the spindle apparatus toward the center of the cell and they line up in the middle, or equator, of the cell, as shown in **Figure 8.** Metaphase is one of the shortest stages of mitosis, but when completed successfully, it ensures that the new cells have accurate copies of the chromosomes.

■ **Figure 8** In metaphase, the chromosomes align along the equator of the cell.
Infer ***why the chromosomes align along the equator.***

Photomicrograph Magnification: 450×

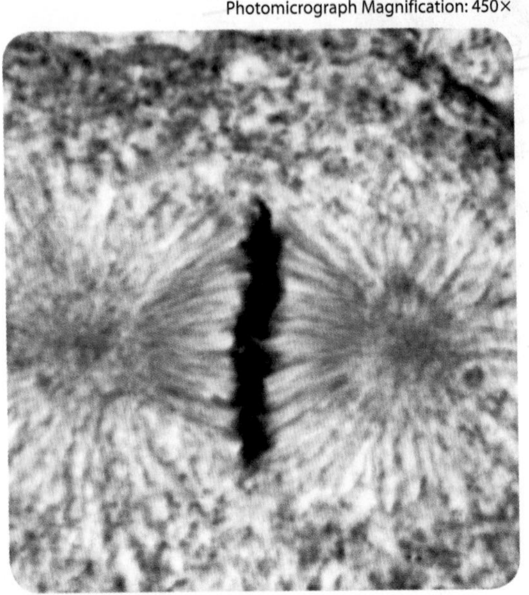

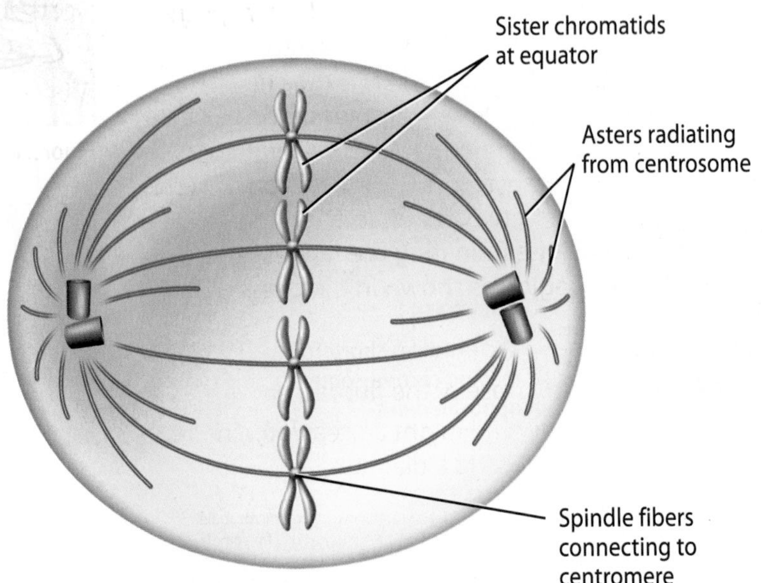

LM Magnification: 450×

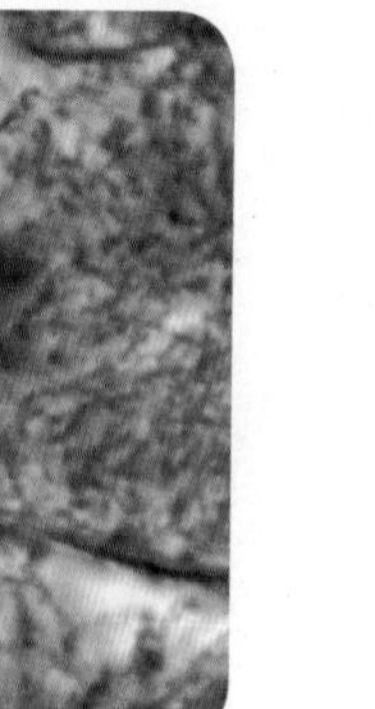

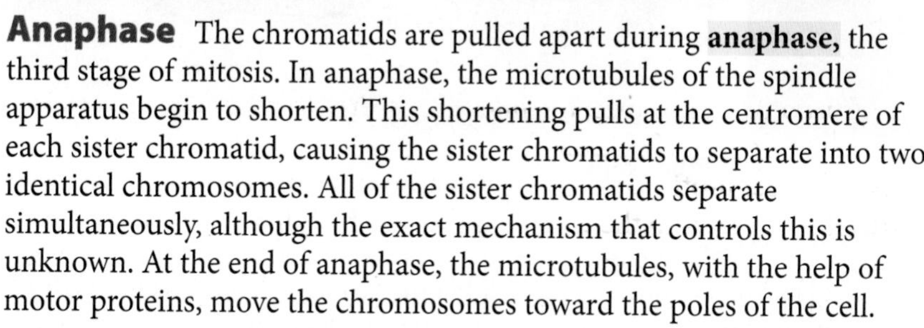

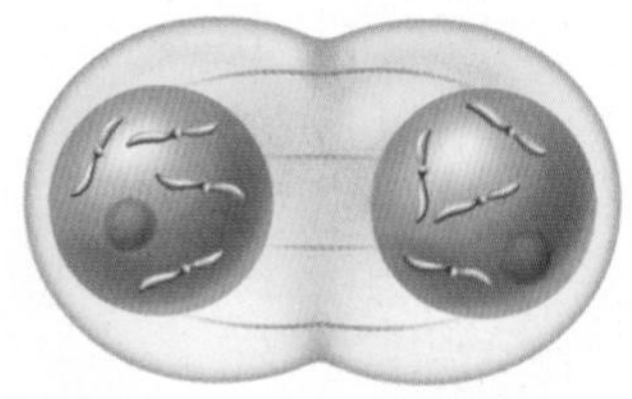

■ **Figure 9** By the end of telophase, the cell has completed the work of duplicating the genetic material and dividing it into two "packages," but the cell has not completely divided.

Anaphase The chromatids are pulled apart during **anaphase,** the third stage of mitosis. In anaphase, the microtubules of the spindle apparatus begin to shorten. This shortening pulls at the centromere of each sister chromatid, causing the sister chromatids to separate into two identical chromosomes. All of the sister chromatids separate simultaneously, although the exact mechanism that controls this is unknown. At the end of anaphase, the microtubules, with the help of motor proteins, move the chromosomes toward the poles of the cell.

Telophase The last stage of mitosis is called telophase. **Telophase** is the stage of mitosis during which the chromosomes arrive at the poles of the cell and begin to relax, or decondense. As shown in **Figure 9,** two new nuclear membranes begin to form and the nucleoli reappear. The spindle apparatus disassembles and some of the microtubules are recycled by the cell to build various parts of the cytoskeleton. Although the four stages of mitosis are now complete and the nuclear material is divided, the process of cell division is not yet complete.

Data Analysis LAB 1

Based on Real Data*

Predict the Results

What happens to the microtubules? Scientists performed experiments tracking chromosomes along microtubules during mitosis. They hypothesized that the microtubules are broken down, releasing microtubule subunits as the chromosomes are moved toward the poles of the cell. The microtubules were labeled with a yellow fluorescent dye, and using a laser, the microtubules were marked midway between the poles and the chromosomes by eliminating the fluorescence in the targeting region as shown in the diagram.

Data and Observations

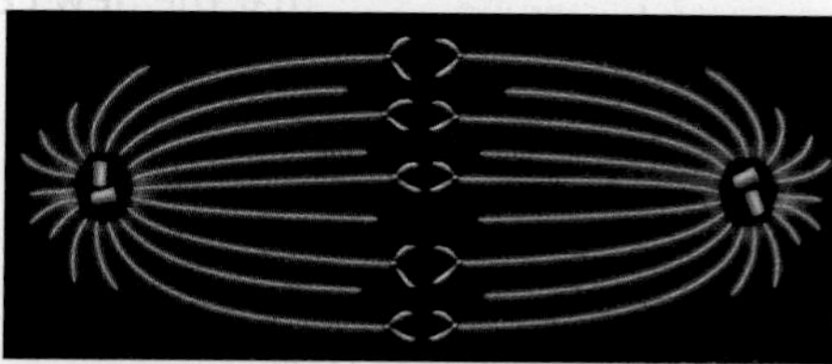

Fluorescent-labeled microtubules

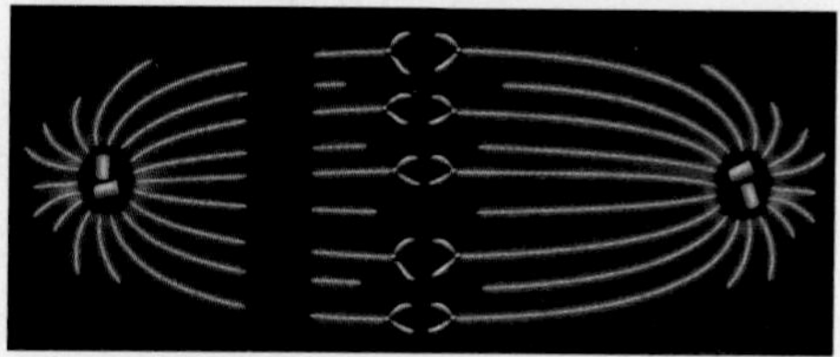

Laser-marked microtubules

Think Critically

1. **Explain** the purpose of the fluorescent dye.
2. **Predict** how the cell might appear later in anaphase by drawing a diagram.

*Data obtained from: Maddox, P., et al. 2003. Direct observation of microtubule dynamics at kinetochores in *Xenopus* extract spindles: implications for spindle mechanics. *The Journal of Cell Biology* 162: 377–382. Maddox, et al. 2004. Controlled ablations of microtubules using picosecond laser. *Biophysics Journal* 87: 4203–4212.

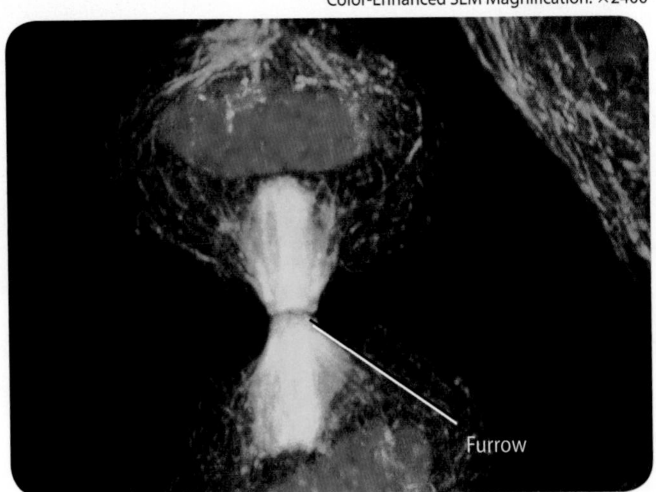

Animal cell

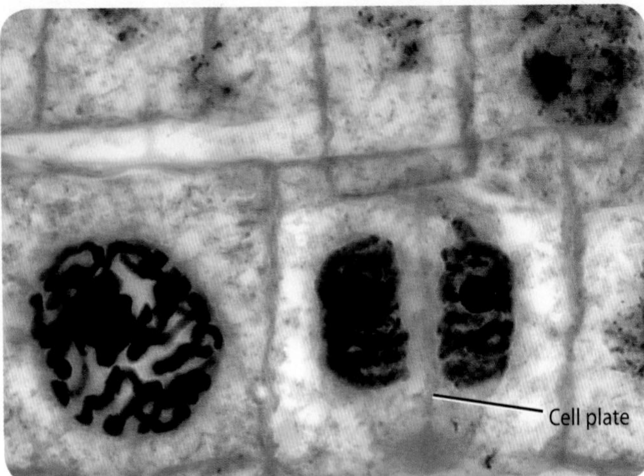

Plant cells

■ **Figure 10**
Left: In animal cells, cytokinesis begins with a furrow that pinches the cell and eventually splits the two cells apart.
Right: Plant cells build a cell plate that divides the cell into the two daughter cells.

Cytokinesis

Toward the end of mitosis, the cell begins another process called cytokinesis that will divide the cytoplasm. This results in two cells, each with identical nuclei. In animal cells, cytokinesis is accomplished by using microfilaments to constrict, or pinch, the cytoplasm, as shown in **Figure 10.** The area where constriction occurs is called the furrow.

Recall that plant cells have a rigid cell wall covering their plasma membrane. Instead of pinching in half, a new structure called a cell plate forms between the two daughter nuclei, as illustrated in **Figure 10.** Cell walls then form on either side of the cell plate. Once this new wall is complete, there are two genetically identical cells.

Prokaryotic cells, which divide by binary fission, finish cell division in a different way. When prokaryotic DNA is duplicated, both copies attach to the plasma membrane. As the plasma membrane grows, the attached DNA molecules are pulled apart. The cell completes fission, producing two new prokaryotic cells.

REVIEW IT! Mitosis and Cytokinesis

Section Summary

- Mitosis is the process by which the duplicated DNA is divided.
- The stages of mitosis include prophase, metaphase, anaphase, and telophase.
- Cytokinesis is the process of cytoplasm division that results in genetically identical daughter cells.

Self Check

Understand Main Ideas

1. MAINIDEA **Explain** why mitosis alone does not produce daughter cells.
2. **Describe** the events of each stage of mitosis.
3. **Diagram** and label a chromosome in prophase. Explain your diagram to a classmate.
4. **Identify** the stage of mitosis in which a cell spends the most time.
5. **Contrast** cytokinesis in a plant cell and an animal cell.

Think Critically

6. **Hypothesize** what might happen if a drug that stopped microtubule movement but did not affect cytokinesis was applied to a cell.

MATH IN ▶ Biology

7. If a plant cell completes the cell cycle in 24 hours, how many cells will be produced in a week?

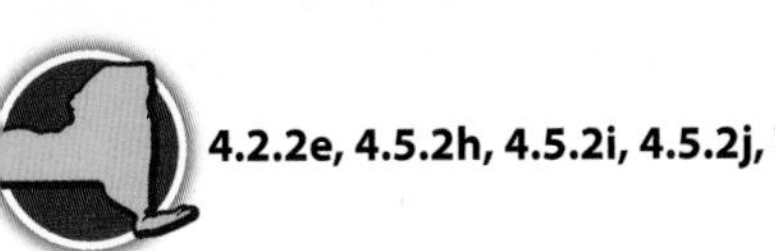

USE IT! Science Notebook

3 Cell Cycle Regulation

4.2.2e, 4.5.2h, 4.5.2i, 4.5.2j, ¥a

MAINIDEA

The normal cell cycle is regulated by cyclin proteins.

Essential Questions

- What is the role of cyclin proteins in controlling the cell cycle?
- How does cancer relate to the cell cycle?
- What is the role of apoptosis?
- What are the two types of stem cells and what are their potential uses?

BIOLOGY 4 U

No matter how many new homes a builder builds, even if building the same design, the crew always relies on blueprint instructions. Similarly, cells have specific instructions for completing the cell cycle.

Review Vocabulary

nucleotide: subunit that makes up DNA and RNA molecules

New Vocabulary

cyclin
cyclin-dependent kinase
cancer
carcinogen
apoptosis
stem cell

Multilingual eGlossary

Normal Cell Cycle

The timing and rate of cell division are important to the health of an organism. The rate of cell division varies depending on the type of cell. A mechanism involving proteins and enzymes controls the cell cycle.

The role of cyclins To start most cars, it takes a key turning in the ignition to signal the engine to start. Similarly, the cell cycle in eukaryotic cells is driven by a combination of two substances that signal the cellular reproduction processes. Proteins called **cyclins** bind to enzymes called **cyclin-dependent kinases** (CDKs) in the stages of interphase and mitosis to start the various activities that take place in the cell cycle. Different cyclin/CDK combinations control different activities at different stages in the cell cycle. **Figure 11** illustrates where some of the important combinations are active.

In the G_1 stage of interphase, the combination of cyclin with CDK signals the start of the cell cycle. Different cyclin/CDK combinations signal other activities, including DNA replication, protein synthesis, and nuclear division throughout the cell cycle. The same cyclin/CDK combination also signals the end of the cell cycle.

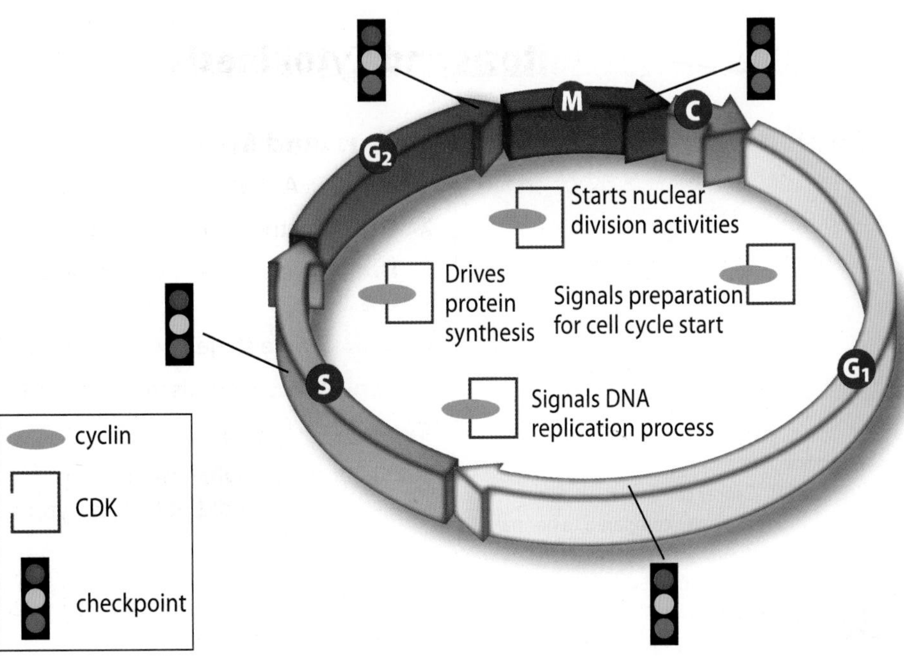

■ **Figure 11** Signaling molecules made of a cyclin bound to a CDK kick off the cell cycle and drive it through mitosis. Checkpoints monitor the cell cycle for errors and can stop the cycle if an error occurs.

Personal Tutor

CAREERS IN
BIOLOGY

Pharmaceutical QC Technician
Just as the cell cycle has built-in quality control checkpoints, so do biological product manufacturing processes. A QC (quality control) technician in a pharmaceutical manufacturing company uses various science and math skills to monitor processes and ensure product quality.

Quality control checkpoints Recall the process of starting a car. Many manufacturers use a unique microchip in the key to ensure that only a specific key will start each car. This is a checkpoint against theft. The cell cycle also has built-in checkpoints that monitor the cycle and can stop it if something goes wrong. For example, a checkpoint near the end of the G_1 stage monitors for DNA damage and can stop the cycle before entering the S stage of interphase. There are other quality control checkpoints during the S stage and after DNA replication in the G_2 stage. Spindle checkpoints also have been identified in mitosis. If a failure of the spindle fibers is detected, the cycle can be stopped before cytokinesis. **Figure 11** shows the location of key checkpoints in the cell cycle.

Abnormal Cell Cycle: Cancer

Connection to Health Although the cell cycle has a system of quality control checkpoints, it is a complex process that sometimes fails. When cells do not respond to the normal cell cycle control mechanisms, a condition called cancer can result. **Cancer** is the uncontrolled growth and division of cells—a failure in the regulation of the cell cycle. When unchecked, cancer cells can kill an organism by crowding out normal cells, resulting in the loss of tissue function. Cancer cells spend less time in interphase than do normal cells, which means cancer cells grow and divide unrestrained as long as they are supplied with essential nutrients. **Figure 12** shows how cancer cells can intrude on normal cells.

Video 

Virtual Lab 

Causes of cancer Cancer does not just occur in a weak organism. In fact, cancer occurs in many healthy, active, and young organisms. The changes that occur in the regulation of cell growth and division of cancer cells are due to mutations or changes in the segments of DNA that control the production of proteins, including proteins that regulate the cell cycle. Often, the genetic change or damage that occurs is repaired by various repair systems. But if the repair systems fail, cancer can result. Various environmental factors can affect the occurrence of cancer cells. Substances and agents that are known to cause cancer are called **carcinogens** (kar SIH nuh junz).

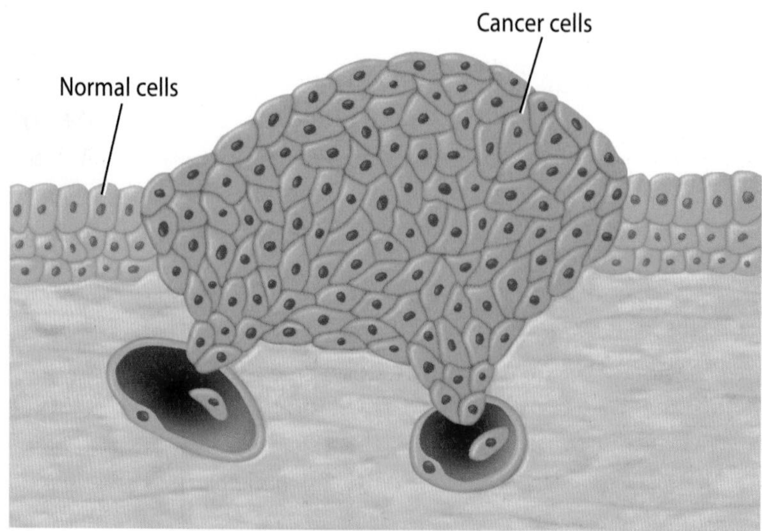

■ **Figure 12** Cancer cells often have an abnormal, irregular shape compared to normal cells. In this image some cancer cells are entering vessels, which might carry them to another part of the body. This is one way cancer can spread from one body part to another.

Although not all cancers can be prevented, avoiding known carcinogens can help reduce the risk of cancer. A governmental agency called the Food and Drug Administration (FDA) works to make sure that the things you eat and drink are safe. The FDA requires labels and warnings for products that might be carcinogens. Industrial laws help protect people from exposure to cancer-causing chemicals in the workplace. Avoiding tobacco of all kinds, even secondhand smoke and smokeless tobacco, can reduce the risk of cancer.

Some radiation, such as ultraviolet radiation from the Sun, is impossible to avoid completely. There is a connection between the amount of ultraviolet radiation to which a person is exposed and the risk of developing skin cancer. Therefore, sunscreen is recommended for everyone who is exposed to the Sun. Other forms of radiation, such as X-rays, are used for medical purposes, such as to view a broken bone or to check for cavities in teeth. To protect against exposure, you might have worn a heavy lead apron when an X-ray was taken.

GET IT? **Identify** carcinogens to which you are regularly exposed.

Cancer genetics More than one change in DNA is required to change an abnormal cell into a cancer cell. Over time, there might be many changes in DNA. This might explain why the risk of cancer increases with age. An individual who inherits one or more changes from a parent is at a higher risk for developing cancer than someone who does not inherit these changes.

Review Based on what you've read about the abnormal cell cycle and its results, how would you now answer the analysis questions?

VOCABULARY

SCIENCE USAGE V. COMMON USAGE

Inheritance

Science usage: the passing of genetic traits from parent to offspring via DNA
A person's body structure and facial appearance are the result of genetic inheritance.

Common usage: assets acquired from a deceased person that can be given to surviving family members
The house was Jim's inheritance from his uncle.

MiniLAB 2

Compare Sunscreens

Do sunscreens really block sunlight? Sunscreens contain a variety of different compounds that absorb UVB from sunlight. UVB is linked to mutations in DNA that can lead to skin cancer. Find out how effective at blocking sunlight various sunscreens are.

Procedure

1. Read and complete the lab safety form.
2. Choose one of the **sunscreen products** provided by your teacher. Record the active ingredients and the Sun protection factor (SPF) on a data sheet.
3. Obtain **two sheets of plastic wrap.** On one sheet use a **permanent marker** to draw two widely spaced circles. Place a drop of sunscreen in the middle of one circle and a drop of **zinc oxide** in the middle of the other.
4. Lay the second sheet on top of both circles. Spread the drops by pressing with a **book.**
5. Take a covered piece of **Sun-sensitive paper** and your two pieces of plastic wrap to a sunny area. Quickly uncover the paper, lay the two pieces of plastic wrap on top, and place in the sunlight.
6. After the paper is fully exposed (1–5 minutes), remove it from the sunlight and develop according to instructions.

Analysis

1. **Think Critically** Why did you compare the sunscreens to zinc oxide?
2. **Draw Conclusions** After examining the developed Sun-sensitive papers from your class, which sunscreens do you think would be most likely to prevent DNA mutations?
3. **Research** promotional materials for products and services related to tanning. Compare the health-related aspects of tanning to the promotional materials you research.

Apoptosis

Not every cell is destined to survive. Some cells go through a process called **apoptosis** (a pup TOH sus), or programmed cell death. Cells going through apoptosis actually shrink and shrivel in a controlled process. All animal cells appear to have a "death program" that can be activated.

One example of apoptosis occurs during the development of the human hand and foot. When the hands and feet begin to develop, cells occupy the spaces between the fingers and toes. Normally, this tissue undergoes apoptosis, with the cells shriveling and dying at the appropriate time so that the webbing is not present in the mature organism. An example of apoptosis in plants is the localized death of cells that results in leaves falling from trees during autumn. Apoptosis also occurs in cells that are damaged beyond repair, including cells with DNA damage that could lead to cancer. Apoptosis can help to protect organisms from developing cancerous growths.

VOCABULARY

ACADEMIC VOCABULARY

Mature
to have reached full natural growth or development
After mitosis, the two new cells must mature before they divide.

Stem Cells

The majority of cells in a multicellular organism are designed for a specialized function. For instance, during development some cells are signaled to become skin cells. The type of cell that can be directed to become a specialized cell is called a **stem cell,** illustrated in **Figure 13.** There are two basic types of stem cells: embryonic stem cells and adult stem cells.

Embryonic stem cells After a sperm fertilizes an egg, the resulting mass of cells divides repeatedly until there are about 100–150 cells. These cells have not become specialized and are called embryonic stem cells. As development continues, the DNA in specific embryonic stem cells receive signals to produce RNA which commits those cells to become specialized cells. As the embryo continues to divide, the cells specialize into various tissues, organs, and organ systems. If separated, each embryonic stem cell has all of the DNA needed to develop into a wide variety of specialized cells. Embryonic stem cell research is controversial because of ethical concerns about the source of the cells.

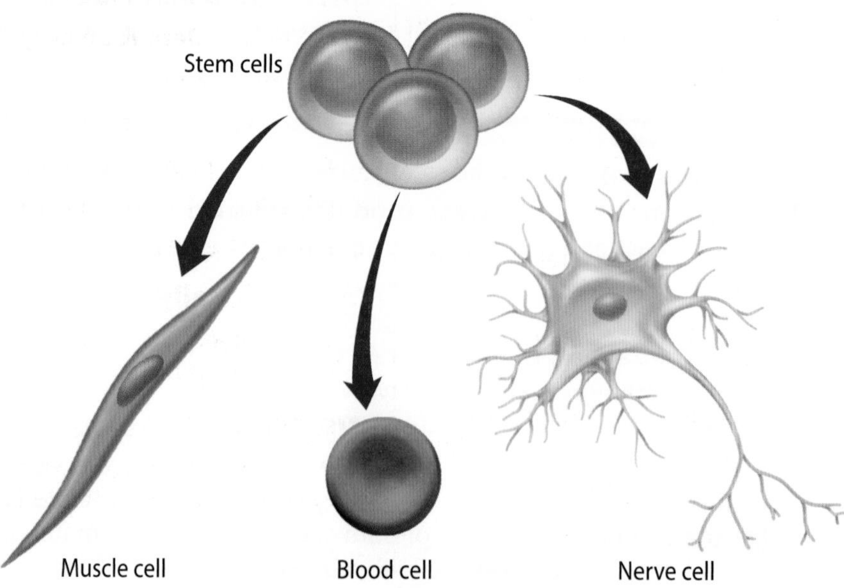

■ **Figure 13** Because stem cells are not locked into becoming one particular type of cell, they might be the key to curing many medical conditions and genetic defects.
Explain ***how stem cells could be used to cure nerve damage.***

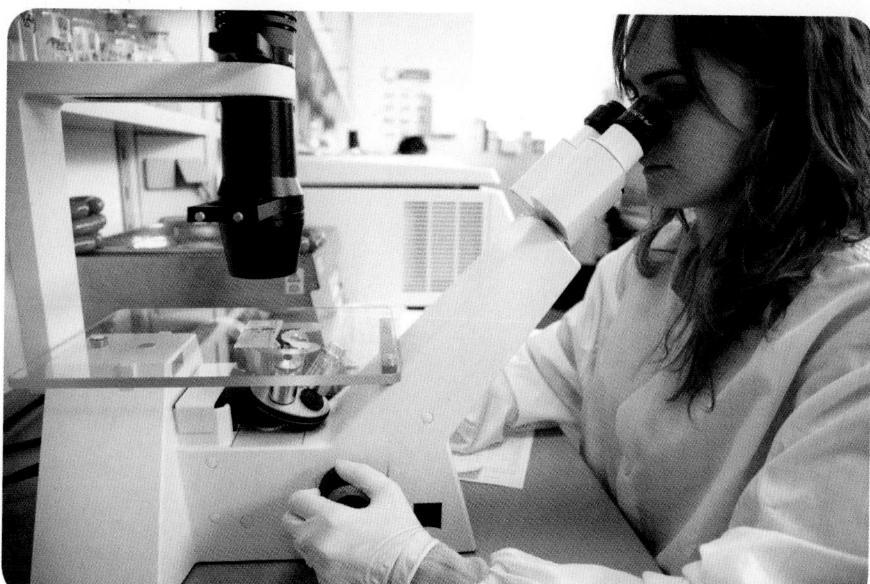

■ **Figure 14** Research with adult stem cells has led to advances in treatments for numerous injuries and diseases.

Adult stem cells The second type of stem cells—adult stem cells—is found in various tissues in the body and might be used to maintain and repair the same kind of tissue in which they are found. The term "adult stem cells" might be somewhat misleading because even a newborn has adult stem cells. Like embryonic stem cells, certain kinds of adult stem cells also might be able to develop into different kinds of cells, providing new treatments for many diseases and conditions. In 1999, researchers at Harvard Medical School used nervous system stem cells to restore lost brain tissue in mice. In 2008, researchers used adult stem cells along with an enzyme called PKA to create new bone tissue for repair in mice. Research with adult stem cells, like that shown in **Figure 14,** is much less controversial because the adult stem cells can be obtained with the consent of their donors.

REVIEW IT! Cell Cycle Regulation

Section Summary

- The cell cycle of eukaryotic cells is regulated by cyclins.
- Checkpoints occur during most of the stages of the cell cycle to ensure that the cell divides accurately.
- Cancer is the uncontrolled growth and division of cells.
- Apoptosis is a programmed cell death.
- Stem cells are unspecialized cells that can develop into specialized cells with the proper signals.

Pixtal/age fotostock

Self Check

Understand Main Ideas

1. MAINIDEA **Describe** how cyclins control the cell cycle.
2. **Explain** how the cancer cell cycle is different from a normal cell cycle.
3. **Describe** why the cell cycle is important to the growth of organisms.
4. **Contrast** apoptosis and cancer.
5. **Describe** a possible application for stem cells.
6. **Explain** the difference between embryonic stem cells and adult stem cells.

Think Critically

7. **Hypothesize** what might happen if apoptosis did not occur in cells that have significant DNA damage.

WRITING IN ▶ Biology

8. Write a public service announcement about carcinogens. Choose a specific type of cancer, and write about the carcinogens linked to it.

BIOLOGY&society

1.1.3b

Stem Cells: Paralysis Cured?

A race car driver is paralyzed in a crash. A teen is paralyzed after diving into shallow water. Until recently, these individuals would have little hope of regaining the full use of their bodies, but new research on adult stem cells shows promise for reversing paralysis.

How can stem cells be used? Scientists are trying to find ways to grow stem cells in cell cultures and manipulate them to generate specific cell types. When adult stem cells are given the correct chemical signals, genes are turned on—DNA is transcribed into RNA, and RNA is translated into protein. This gene expression guides cells to finish specializing. For example, heart stem cells might be used to repair cardiac tissue after a heart attack, or nerve stem cells might be used to repair spinal cells to reverse paralysis. Stem cell research in Ecuador involves bone marrow stem cells being used to grow blood vessels.

Stem cells and paralysis In Portugal, Dr. Carlos Lima and his team of researchers found that tissue taken from the nasal cavity is a rich source of adult stem cells. These stem cells become nerve cells when transplanted into the site of a spinal cord injury. The new nerve cells replace the cells that were damaged.

More than forty patients with paralysis due to accidents have undergone the Portuguese procedure. All patients have regained some sensation in paralyzed body areas. Most have regained some motor control. With intensive physical therapy, about ten percent of the patients now can walk with the aid of supportive devices, such as walkers and braces. This is promising news to the many individuals facing illnesses or injuries that have robbed them of the full use of their bodies.

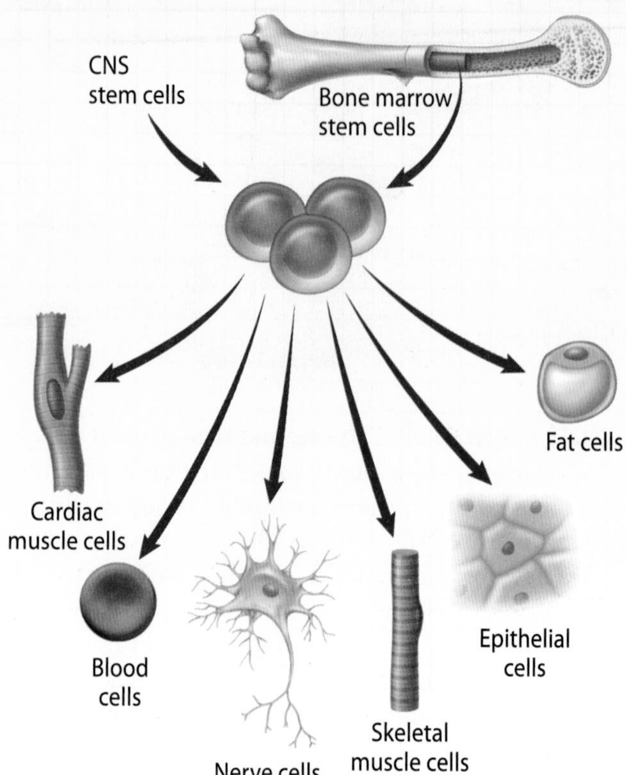

Stem cells from bone marrow or the central nervous system can be manipulated to generate many cell types that can be transplanted to treat illness or repair damage.

Stem cells and the future Scientists are eager to do the research necessary to make adult stem cell treatments a regular part of health care. Paralysis might not have to be permanent; stem cells could provide the cure.

WRITING IN ▶ Biology

Pamphlet Create an illustrated pamphlet depicting the benefits of adult stem cell research. Research adult stem cells in order to include the research methodology, treatment, examples, cell physiology, and history of adult stem cell research.

WebQuest

BioLAB

1.2.2a, 1.3.5b, 4.2.2e, ¥a, ¥m, ¥n, ¥o

Does sunlight affect mitosis in yeast?

Background: Ultraviolet (UV) radiation is a component of sunlight that can damage DNA and interrupt the cell cycle.

Question: *Can sunscreens prevent damage to UV-sensitive yeast?*

Materials

sterile pipettes (10)
aluminum foil
test-tube rack
sterile spreaders or sterile cotton swabs (10)
dilution of UV-sensitive yeast
yeast extract dextrose (YED) agar plates (10)
sunscreens with various amounts of SPF

Safety Precautions

Procedure

1. Read and complete the lab safety form.
2. Obtain a test tube containing a diluted broth culture of the UV-sensitive yeast.
3. Formulate a hypothesis, then choose a sunscreen and predict how it will affect the yeast when exposed to sunlight.
4. Label ten YED agar plates with your group name. Label two plates as control. The control plates will not be placed in the sunlight. Label four of the experimental plates as "no sunscreen" and four as "sunscreen."
5. Spread a 0.1 mL sample of the yeast dilution on all ten YED agar plates. Wrap the control plates in foil and give them to your teacher for incubation.
6. With direction from your teacher, decide how long to expose each of the experimental plates and label each plate accordingly. Prepare a table in which to collect your data.
7. Wrap the "no sunscreen" plates in foil. Apply sunscreen to the lids of the four sunscreen plates and wrap them in foil.
8. Remove only enough aluminum foil from each of the experimental plates to expose the dish lids. Expose the plates for the planned times. Re-cover the plates after exposure and give them to your teacher for incubation.
9. After incubation, count and record the number of yeast colonies on each plate.
10. **Cleanup and Disposal** Wash and return all reusable materials. Dispose of the YED plates as instructed by your teacher. Disinfect your work area. Wash your hands thoroughly with soap and water.

Analyze and Conclude

1. **Estimate** Assume that each yeast colony on a YED plate grew from one yeast cell in the dilution. Use the number of yeast colonies on your control plate to determine the percent of yeast that survived on each exposed plate.
2. **Graph Data** Draw a graph with the percent survival on the *y*-axis and the exposure time on the *x*-axis. Use a different color to graph the data from the plates with and without sunscreen.
3. **Evaluate** Was your hypothesis supported by your data? Explain.
4. **Error Analysis** Describe several possible sources of error.

APPLY YOUR SKILL

Brainstorm Work with classmates to research and locate information and ideas about how UV-sensitive yeast could be used as a biological monitor to detect increases in the amounts of UV light reaching Earth's surface.

CHAPTER 9 **STUDY GUIDE**

BIGIDEA **Cells go through a life cycle that includes interphase, mitosis, and cytokinesis.**

SECTION 1 Cellular Growth

MAINIDEA Cells grow until they reach their size limit, then they either stop growing or divide.

- The ratio of surface area to volume describes the size of the plasma membrane relative to the volume of the cell.
- Cells are limited in size, with most cells having a diameter of less than 100 μm.
- The cell cycle is the process of cellular reproduction.
- A cell spends the majority of its lifetime in interphase.

VOCABULARY

- **cell cycle**
- **interphase**
- **mitosis**
- **cytokinesis**
- **chromosome**
- **chromatin**

SECTION 2 Mitosis and Cytokinesis

MAINIDEA Eukaryotic cells reproduce by mitosis, the process of nuclear division, and cytokinesis, the process of cytoplasm division.

- Mitosis is the process by which the duplicated DNA is divided.
- The stages of mitosis include prophase, metaphase, anaphase, and telophase.
- Cytokinesis is the process of cytoplasm division that results in genetically identical daughter cells.

VOCABULARY

- **prophase**
- **sister chromatid**
- **centromere**
- **spindle apparatus**
- **metaphase**
- **anaphase**
- **telophase**

SECTION 3 Cell Cycle Regulation

MAINIDEA The normal cell cycle is regulated by cyclin proteins.

- The cell cycle of eukaryotic cells is regulated by cyclins.
- Checkpoints occur during most of the stages of the cell cycle to ensure that the cell divides accurately.
- Cancer is the uncontrolled growth and division of cells.
- Apoptosis is a programmed cell death.
- Stem cells are unspecialized cells that can develop into specialized cells with the proper signals.

VOCABULARY

- **cyclin**
- **cyclin-dependent kinase**
- **cancer**
- **carcinogen**
- **apoptosis**
- **stem cell**

ASSESSMENT

SECTION 1

Vocabulary Review

Match the correct vocabulary term from the Study Guide page to the following definitions.

1. the period in which the cell is not dividing
2. the process of nuclear division
3. the sequence of events in the life of a eukaryotic cell

Understand Main Ideas

4. Which is a reason why cells remain small?
   A. Large cells have difficulty diffusing nutrients rapidly enough.
   B. As cells grow, their ratio of surface area to volume increases.
   C. Transportation of wastes becomes a problem for large cells.
   D. All of the above.

Use the hypothetical cell shown below to answer question 5.

5. What is the ratio of surface area to volume?
   A. 2:1 **C.** 4:1
   B. 3:1 **D.** 6:1
6. Of the surface area-to-volume ratio, what does the surface area represent in a cell?
   A. nucleus
   B. plasma membrane
   C. mitochondria
   D. cytoplasm
7. Which describes the activities of a cell that include cellular growth and cell division?
   A. chromatin **C.** mitosis
   B. cytoplasm **D.** cell cycle
8. As a cell's volume increases, what happens to the proportional amount of surface area?
   A. increases
   B. decreases
   C. stays the same
   D. reaches its limit

Constructed Response

9. MAINIDEA Why are cellular transport and cellular communication factors that limit cell size?
10. **Short Answer** Summarize the relationship between surface area and volume as a cell grows.
11. **Short Answer** What types of activities are going on in a cell during interphase?

Think Critically

12. **Criticize** this statement: Interphase is a "resting period" for the cell before it begins mitosis.
13. **Explain** the relationship of DNA, a chromosome, and chromatin.

SECTION 2

Vocabulary Review

Complete the concept map using vocabulary terms from the Study Guide page.

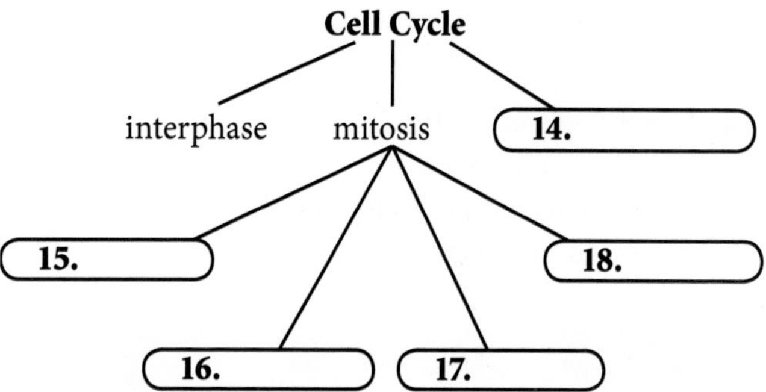

Understand Main Ideas

19. Starting with one cell that underwent six divisions, how many cells would result?
   A. 13 **C.** 48
   B. 32 **D.** 64

The following graph shows a cell over the course of its cell cycle. Use this graph to answer questions 20 and 21.

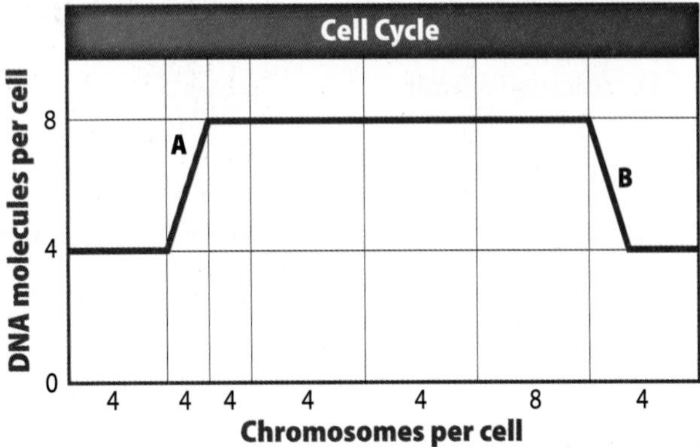

20. What stage occurred in the area labeled A?
A. prophase
B. G_1 stage
C. S stage
D. G_2 stage

21. What process occurred in the area labeled B?
A. interphase
B. cytokinesis
C. mitosis
D. metabolism

22. The cancer drug vinblastine interferes with synthesis of microtubules. In mitosis, this would interfere with what?
A. spindle formation
B. DNA replication
C. carbohydrate synthesis
D. disappearance of the nuclear envelope

Constructed Response

23. MAINIDEA During the cell cycle, when would a chromosome consist of two identical sister chromatids?

24. Short Answer In the following image of a section of onion root tip, identify a cell in each of the following stages: interphase, prophase, metaphase, anaphase, and telophase.

Stained LM Magnification: 60×

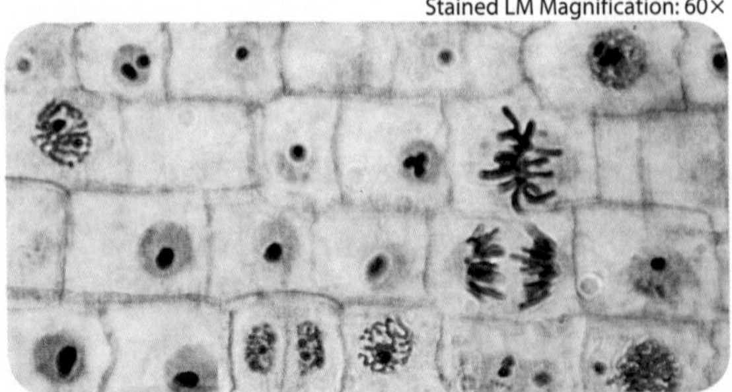

25. Short Answer Describe the events that occur in telophase.

Think Critically

26. Evaluate While looking through a microscope, you see a cell plate forming. This cell is most likely what type of cell?

27. MATH IN ▶ Biology A biologist examines a series of cells and counts 90 cells in interphase, 13 cells in prophase, 12 cells in metaphase, 3 cells in anaphase, and 2 cells in telophase. If a complete cycle for this type of cell requires 24 hours, what is the average duration of mitosis?

SECTION 3

Vocabulary Review

The sentences below include term(s) that have been used incorrectly. Replace the incorrect term(s) with vocabulary terms from the Study Guide page to make the sentences true.

28. Stem cells undergo uncontrolled, unrestrained growth and division because their genes have been changed.

29. Cancer is a cell response to DNA damage that results in cell death.

30. Cyclins are substances that cause cancer.

Understand Main Ideas

31. What is the role of cyclins in a cell?
A. to control the movement of microtubules
B. to signal for the cell to divide
C. to stimulate the breakdown of the nuclear membrane
D. to cause the nucleolus to disappear

32. What substances form the cyclin-cyclin dependent kinase combinations that control the stages in the cell cycle?
A. fats and proteins
B. carbohydrates and proteins
C. proteins and enzymes
D. fats and enzymes

Steven P. Lynch

33. Which is a characteristic of cancer cells?
   A. controlled cell division
   B. contain multiple genetic changes
   C. cytokinesis stage is skipped
   D. cell cyclins function normally

34. Which describes apoptosis?
   A. occurs in all cells
   B. is a programmed cell death
   C. disrupts the normal development of an organism
   D. is a response to hormones

35. Why have some stem cell researchers experienced roadblocks in their studies?
   A. Stem cells cannot be found.
   B. There are ethical concerns about obtaining stem cells.
   C. There are no known uses for stem cells.
   D. Stem cells do not become specialized cells.

Constructed Response

Refer to the diagram to answer question 36.

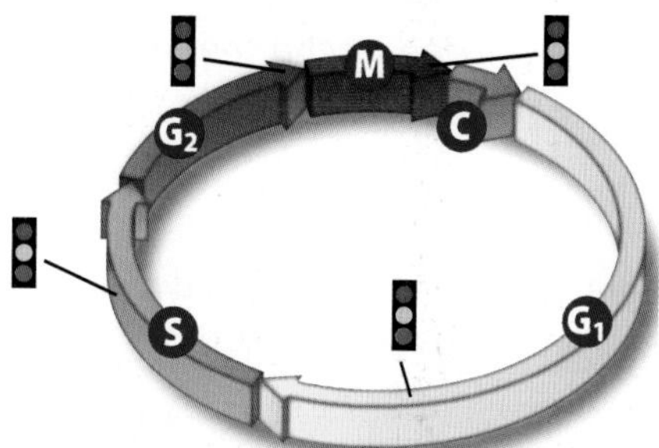

36. **THEME FOCUS** Explain the relationship between cancer cells and the cell cycle.

37. **Short Answer** Distinguish between mitosis and apoptosis.

Think Critically

38. **Describe** how stem cells might be used to help a patient who has a damaged spinal cord.

39. **MAINIDEA** **Explain** how the lack of cyclins would affect the cell cycle.

40. **Apply** Hundreds of millions of dollars are spent annually in the U.S. on the research and treatment of cancer, with much less being spent on cancer prevention. Compose a plan that would increase cancer prevention knowledge.

Summative Assessment

41. **BIGIDEA** Besides reproduction, what factors cause cells to complete the cycle of interphase, mitosis, and cytokinesis?

42. **WRITINGIN▶Biology** Write a skit using props and people to demonstrate mitosis.

43. Research chemicals that are carcinogens and write about how these chemicals can damage DNA.

DBQ Document–Based Questions

Dr. Chang and co-workers evaluated the risk of pancreatic cancer by studying its occurrence in a population group. Their data included age at diagnosis. The graph below shows cancer diagnosis rates for African-American men and women.

Data obtained from: Chang, K. J. et al. 2005. Risk of pancreatic adenocarcinoma. Cancer 103: 349–357.

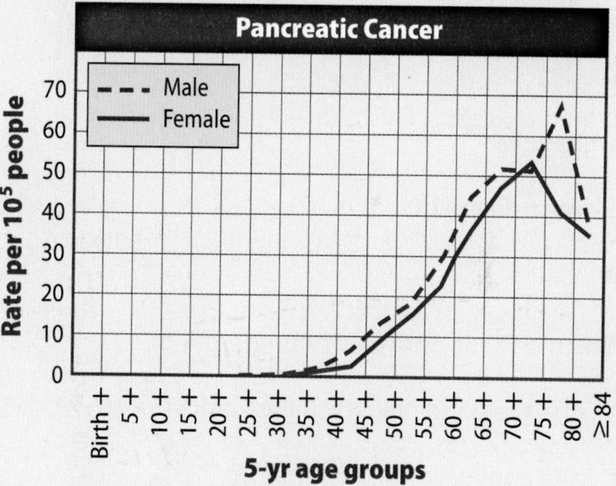

44. Summarize the relationship between the occurrence of cancer and age.

45. Considering what you know about cancer and the cell cycle, explain why incidences of cancer increase with age.

46. Compare the ages of men and women who are diagnosed with cancer.

47. At what age does diagnosis of pancreatic cancer decline?

CUMULATIVE

MULTIPLE CHOICE

1 Which carbon-containing compound is the product of glycolysis?

A acetyl CoA

B glucose

C lactic acid

D pyruvate

Use the diagram below to answer question 2.

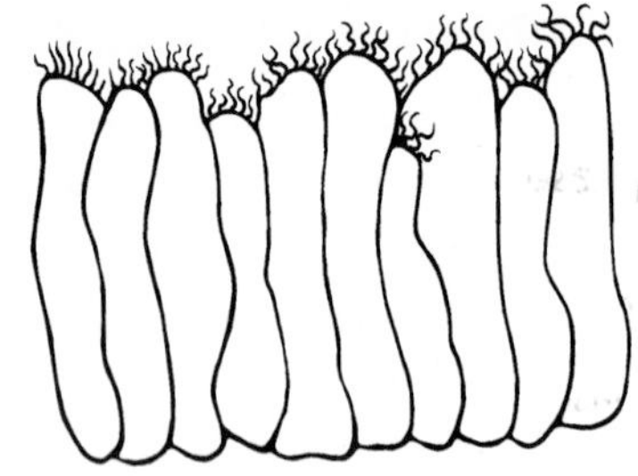

2 What are the structures projecting from the cells in the diagram?

A cilia

B flagella

C microfilaments

D villi

3 Which cellular process stores energy?

A the breaking of lipid chains

B the conversion of ADP to ATP

C the synthesization of proteins from RNA codons

D the transportation of ions across the membrane

4 Which contributes to the selective permeability of cell membranes?

A carbohydrates

B ions

C minerals

D proteins

SHORT ANSWER

Use the diagram below to answer questions 5–7.

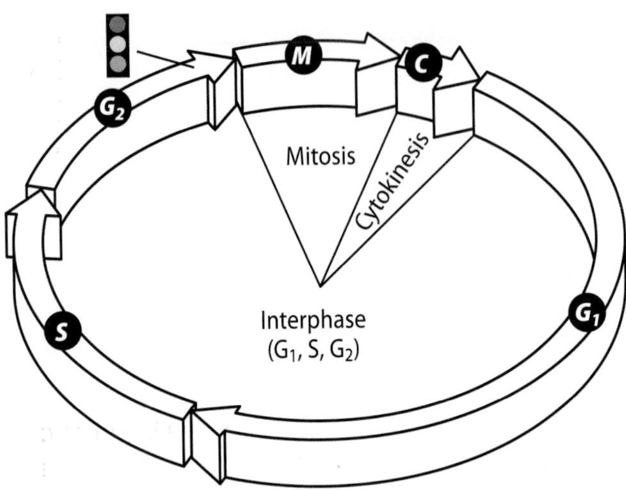

5 In the past, interphase often was called the "resting" phase of the cell cycle. Explain why this is inaccurate.

6 Explain what the cell does at the checkpoint indicated by the stoplight in the diagram.

7 Use the diagram to compare the relative rates at which mitosis and cytokinesis occur.

8 Hypothesize how an organism could be both a heterotroph and an autotroph.

9 Suppose you had ink, pebbles, and table salt. Describe what kind of mixture each one of these would make if mixed with water. Explain your answers.

10 Name two enzymes involved in photosynthesis, and describe their roles.

11 Infer how the ratio of surface area to volume changes as a cell grows larger.

EXTENDED RESPONSE

Use the diagram below to answer questions 12 and 13.

12 Analyze the diagram and describe the importance of the spindle fibers to chromatids during prophase.

13 Describe the function of the centromere and predict what might happen if cells did NOT have centromeres.

ESSAY QUESTION

The same organelles are found in many different types of cells in an animal's body. However, there are differences in the number of organelles present, depending on the function of the different cells. For instance, the cells that require a great amount of energy to carry out their work would contain more mitochondria.

Using the information in the paragraph above, answer the following question in essay format.

14 How do you think two types of animal cells would differ in terms of the kinds of organelles they contain? Write a hypothesis about the cellular differences between two types of animal cells and then design an experiment to test your hypothesis.

TEST PRACTICE

Use the diagram below to answer questions 15 and 16.

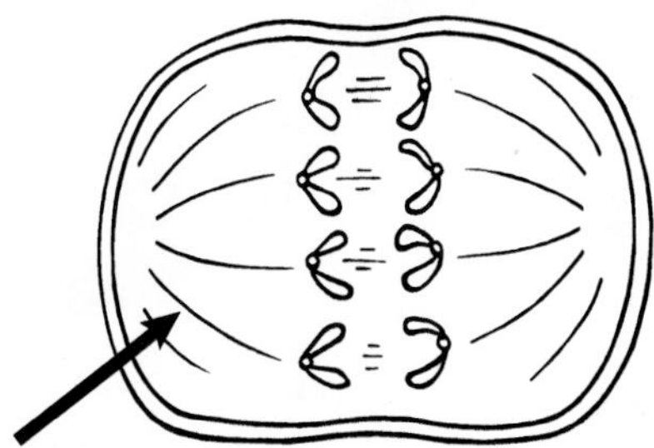

15 Which stage of mitosis is shown in this diagram?

A anaphase

B interphase

C metaphase

D telophase

16 To which structure does the arrow in the diagram point?

A centromere

B chromosome

C nucleolus

D spindle

17 If data from repeated experiments support a hypothesis, which would happen next?

A A conclusion would be established.

B The data would become a law.

C The hypothesis would be rejected.

D The hypothesis would be revised.

NEED EXTRA HELP?																	
If You Missed Question . . .	1	2	3	4	5	6	7	8	9	10	11	12	13	14	15	16	17
Review Section . . .	8.3	7.3	8.1	7.2	9.1	9.1	8.2	8.1	6.3	8.2	9.1	9.2	9.2	7.3	9.2	9.2	1.3

UNIT 3

(bkgd)McGraw-Hill Education; (inset)Monty Rakusen/Cultura/Getty Images

CAREERS USING BIOLOGY

Career in Action Livestock breeders can use information from the DNA of cattle to help them make decisions about which animals to breed.

cutting-edge BIOLOGY

See **page 316** for more information about the importance of genetics in livestock breeding.

LIVESTOCK BREEDER

Livestock breeders use visual appraisal, information from genetic tests, and genealogy to produce offspring with desired traits. They have knowledge about the reproduction, growth, nutrition, and genetics of the animals. Livestock breeders need to be able to keep good records and should love working with animals.

Related Careers

beef cattle farmer
beef cattle nutritionist
embryologist
herdsman
farm assistant
veterinarian

Career Resources

WHAT'S THAT? Today, cattle are bred for both their hide and their beef. Ranchers and breeders use technology to produce the best tasting beef. They can predict how long an animal will live and how well it will put on weight. Genetic tests can determine how marbled and tender a cow's meat will be.

Investigate

Evaluate Identify the pros and cons associated with using DNA testing to identify cattle that will produce offspring with desired traits.

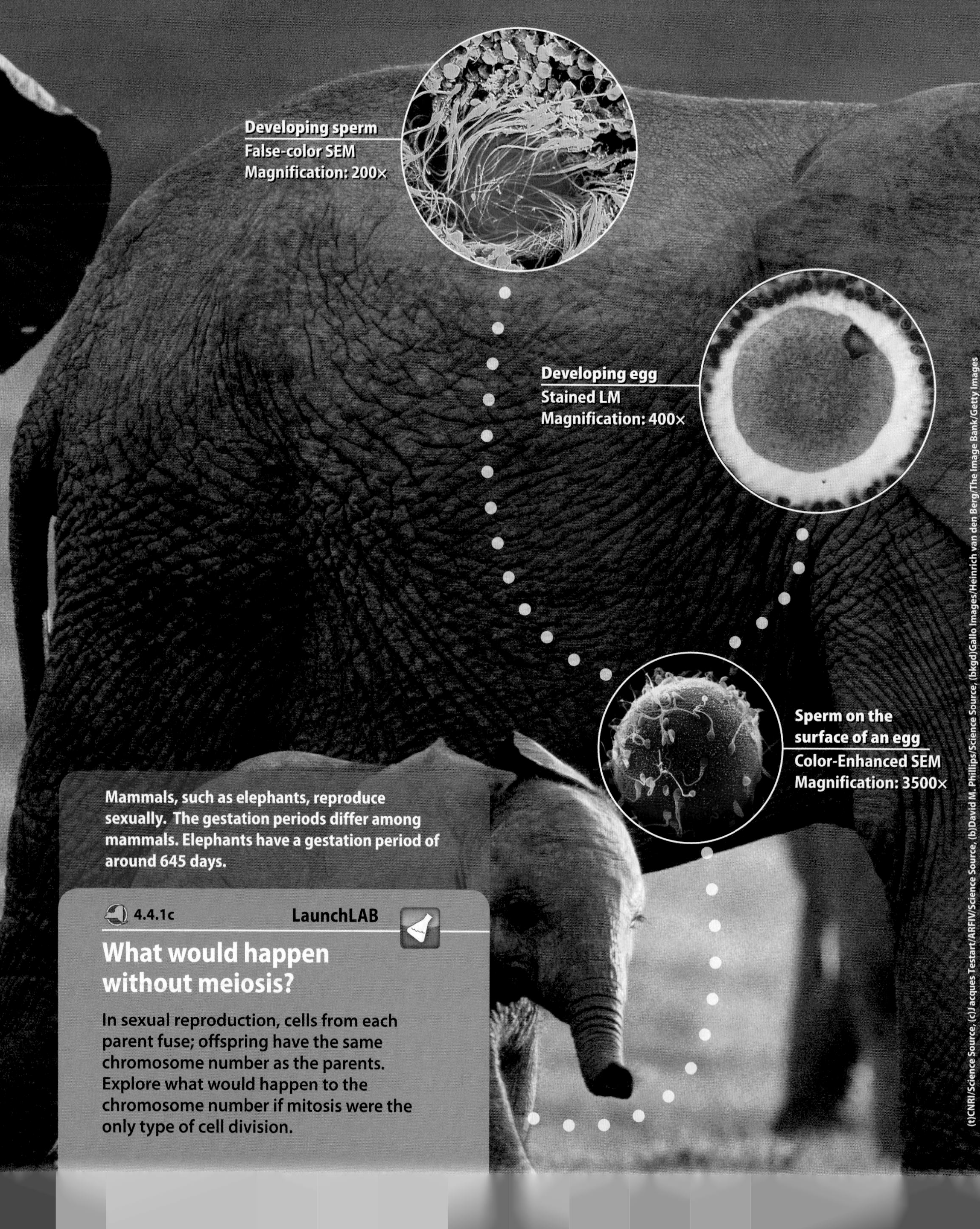

Mammals, such as elephants, reproduce sexually. The gestation periods differ among mammals. Elephants have a gestation period of around 645 days.

4.4.1c **LaunchLAB**

What would happen without meiosis?

In sexual reproduction, cells from each parent fuse; offspring have the same chromosome number as the parents. Explore what would happen to the chromosome number if mitosis were the only type of cell division.

(t)CNRI/Science Source, (c)Jacques Testart/ARFIV/Science Source, (b)David M. Phillips/Science Source, (bkgd)Gallo Images/Heinrich van den Berg/The Image Bank/Getty Images

CHAPTER 10

Sexual Reproduction and Genetics

THEMEFOCUS

Cause and effect The number of chromosomes changes to half the original number by the end of meiosis.

BIGIDEA

Reproductive cells, which pass on genetic traits from the parents to the child, are produced by the process of meiosis.

FOLDABLES® Study Organizer

Meiosis

Make a circle foldable using the titles shown. Use it to organize your notes on meiosis.

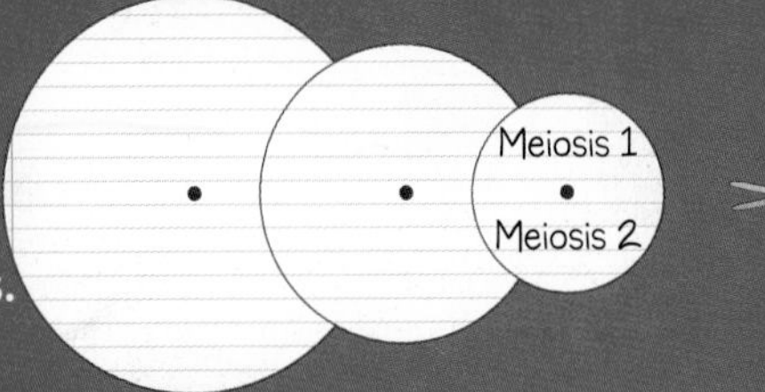

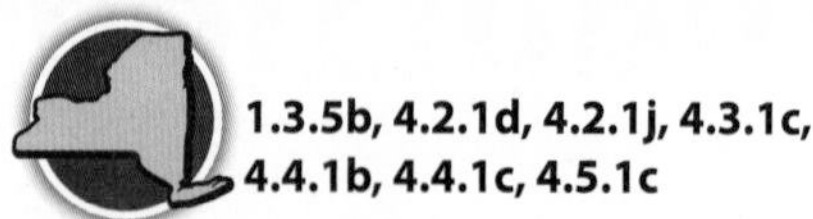

USE IT! Science Notebook

1 Meiosis

1.3.5b, 4.2.1d, 4.2.1j, 4.3.1c, 4.4.1b, 4.4.1c, 4.5.1c

MAIN IDEA
Meiosis produces haploid gametes.

Essential Questions

- How does the reduction in chromosome number occur during meiosis?
- What are the stages of meiosis?
- What is the importance of meiosis in providing genetic variation?

BIOLOGY 4U

Look around your biology class. You might notice that the students in your class do not look the same. The variety of characteristics is a result of two sex cells combining during sexual reproduction.

Review Vocabulary

chromosome: cellular structure that contains DNA

New Vocabulary

gene
homologous chromosome
gamete
haploid
fertilization
diploid
meiosis
crossing over

Multilingual eGlossary

Chromosomes and Chromosome Number

Each student in your biology class has characteristics passed on to them by their parents. Each characteristic, such as hair color, height, or eye color, is called a trait. The instructions for each trait are located on chromosomes, which are found in the nucleus of cells. The DNA on chromosomes is arranged in segments called **genes** that control the production of proteins. Each chromosome consists of hundreds of genes, each gene playing an important role in determining the characteristics and functions of the cell.

Homologous chromosomes Human body cells have 46 chromosomes. Each parent contributes 23 chromosomes, resulting in 23 pairs of chromosomes. The chromosomes that make up a pair, one chromosome from each parent, are called **homologous chromosomes.** As shown in **Figure 1,** homologous chromosomes in body cells have the same length and the same centromere position, and they carry genes that control the same inherited traits. For instance, the gene for earlobe type will be located at the same position on both homologous chromosomes. Although these genes each code for earlobe type, they might not code for the exact same type of earlobe.

Figure 1 Homologous chromosomes carry genes for any given trait at the same location. The genes that code for earlobe type might not code for the exact same type of earlobe.

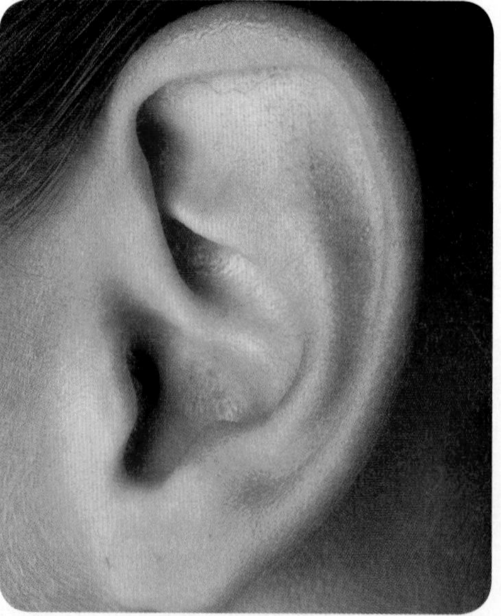

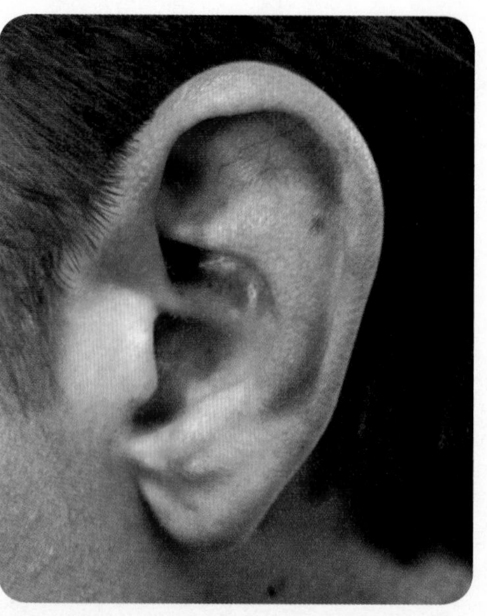

(l)Will & Deni McIntyre/Science Source, (r)Davies & Davies/Getty Images

Haploid and diploid cells In order to maintain the same chromosome number from generation to generation, an organism produces **gametes,** which are sex cells that have half the number of chromosomes. Although the number of chromosomes varies from one species to another, in humans each gamete contains 23 chromosomes. The symbol n can be used to represent the number of chromosomes in a gamete. A cell with n number of chromosomes is called a **haploid** cell. Haploid comes from the Greek word *haploos,* meaning *single.*

The process by which one haploid gamete combines with another haploid gamete is called **fertilization.** As a result of fertilization, the cell now will contain a total of $2n$ chromosomes—n chromosomes from the female parent plus n chromosomes from the male parent. A cell that contains $2n$ number of chromosomes is called a **diploid** cell.

Notice that n also describes the number of pairs of chromosomes in an organism. When two human gametes combine, 23 pairs of homologous chromosomes are formed.

Meiosis I

Gametes are formed during a process called **meiosis,** which is a type of cell division that reduces the number of chromosomes; therefore, it is referred to as a reduction division. Meiosis occurs in the reproductive structures of organisms that reproduce sexually. While mitosis maintains the chromosome number, meiosis reduces the chromosome number by half through the separation of homologous chromosomes. A cell with $2n$ number of chromosomes will have gametes with n number of chromosomes after meiosis, as illustrated in **Figure 2.** Meiosis involves two consecutive cell divisions called meiosis I and meiosis II.

FOLDABLES®
Incorporate information from this section into your Foldable.

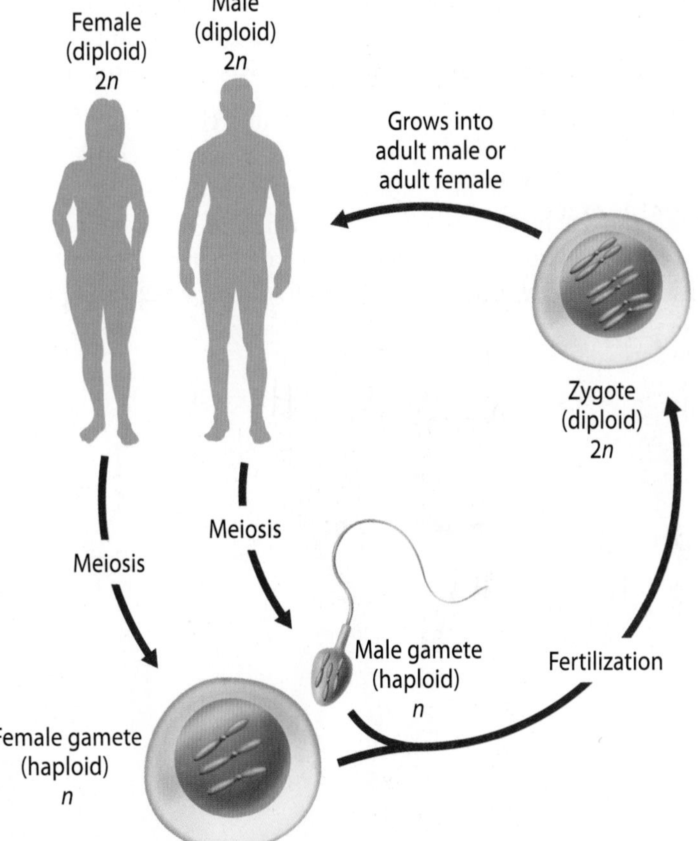

■ **Figure 2** The sexual life cycle in animals involves meiosis, which produces gametes. When gametes combine in fertilization, the number of chromosomes is restored.

Describe ***what happens to the number of chromosomes during meiosis.***

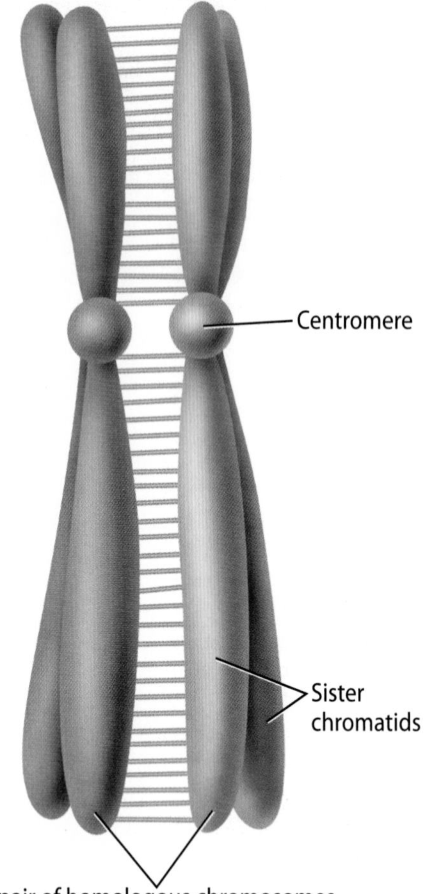

■ **Figure 3** The homologous chromosomes are physically bound together during synapsis in prophase I.

Interphase Recall that the cell cycle includes interphase prior to mitosis. Cells that undergo meiosis also go through interphase as part of the cell cycle. Cells in interphase carry out various metabolic processes, including the replication of DNA and the synthesis of proteins.

Prophase I As a cell enters prophase I, the replicated chromosomes become visible. As in mitosis, the replicated chromosomes consist of two sister chromatids. As the homologous chromosomes condense, they begin to form pairs in a process called synapsis. The homologous chromosomes are held tightly together along their lengths, as illustrated in **Figure 3.** Notice that in **Figure 4** the pink and green chromosomes have exchanged segments. This exchange occurs during synapsis. **Crossing over** is a process during which chromosomal segments are exchanged between a pair of homologous chromosomes.

As prophase I continues, centrioles move to the cell's opposite poles. Spindle fibers form and bind to the sister chromatids at the centromere.

Metaphase I In the next phase of meiosis, the pairs of homologous chromosomes line up at the equator of the cell, as illustrated in **Figure 5.** In meiosis, the spindle fibers attach to the centromere of each homologous chromosome. Recall that during metaphase in mitosis, the individual chromosomes, which consist of two sister chromatids, line up at the cell's equator. During metaphase I of meiosis, the homologous chromosomes line up as pairs at the cell's equator. This is an important distinction between mitosis and meiosis.

Anaphase I During anaphase I, the homologous chromosomes separate, which is also illustrated in **Figure 5.** Each member of the pair is guided by spindle fibers and moves toward opposite poles of the cell. The chromosome number is reduced from $2n$ to n when the homologous chromosomes separate. Recall that in mitosis, the sister chromatids split during anaphase. During anaphase I of meiosis, however, each homologous chromosome still consists of two sister chromatids.

Telophase I The homologous chromosomes, consisting of two sister chromatids, reach the cell's opposite poles. Each pole contains only one member of the original pair of homologous chromosomes. Notice in **Figure 5** that each chromosome still consists of two sister chromatids joined at the centromere. The sister chromatids might not be identical because crossing over might have occurred during synapsis in prophase I.

■ **Figure 4** The results of crossing over are new combinations of genes.
Determine ***which chromatids exchanged genetic material.***

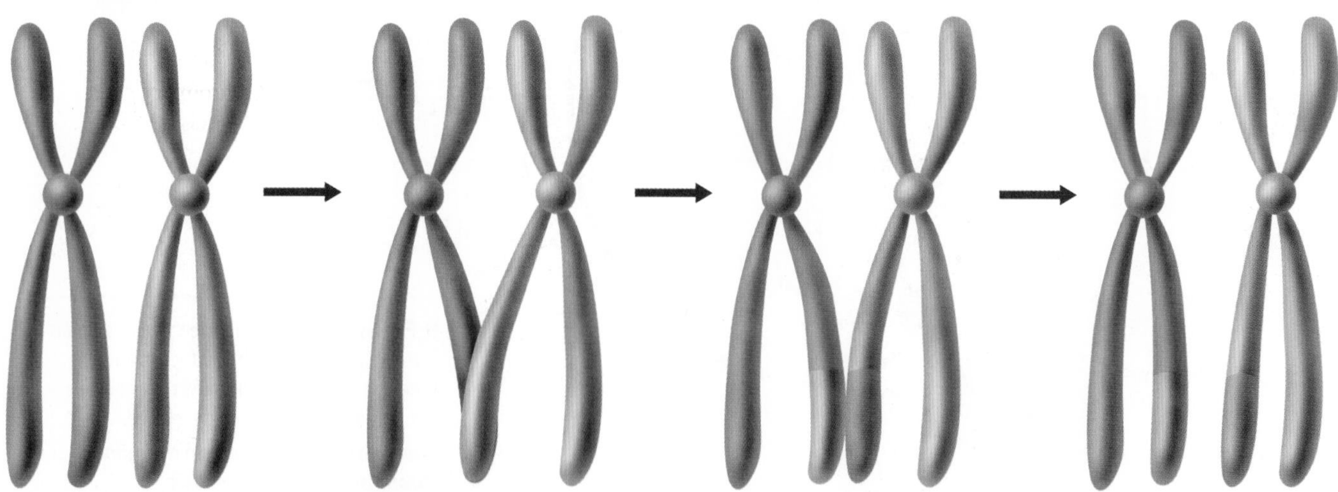

VISUALIZING Meiosis

Figure 5 Follow along the stages of meiosis I and meiosis II, beginning with interphase at the left.

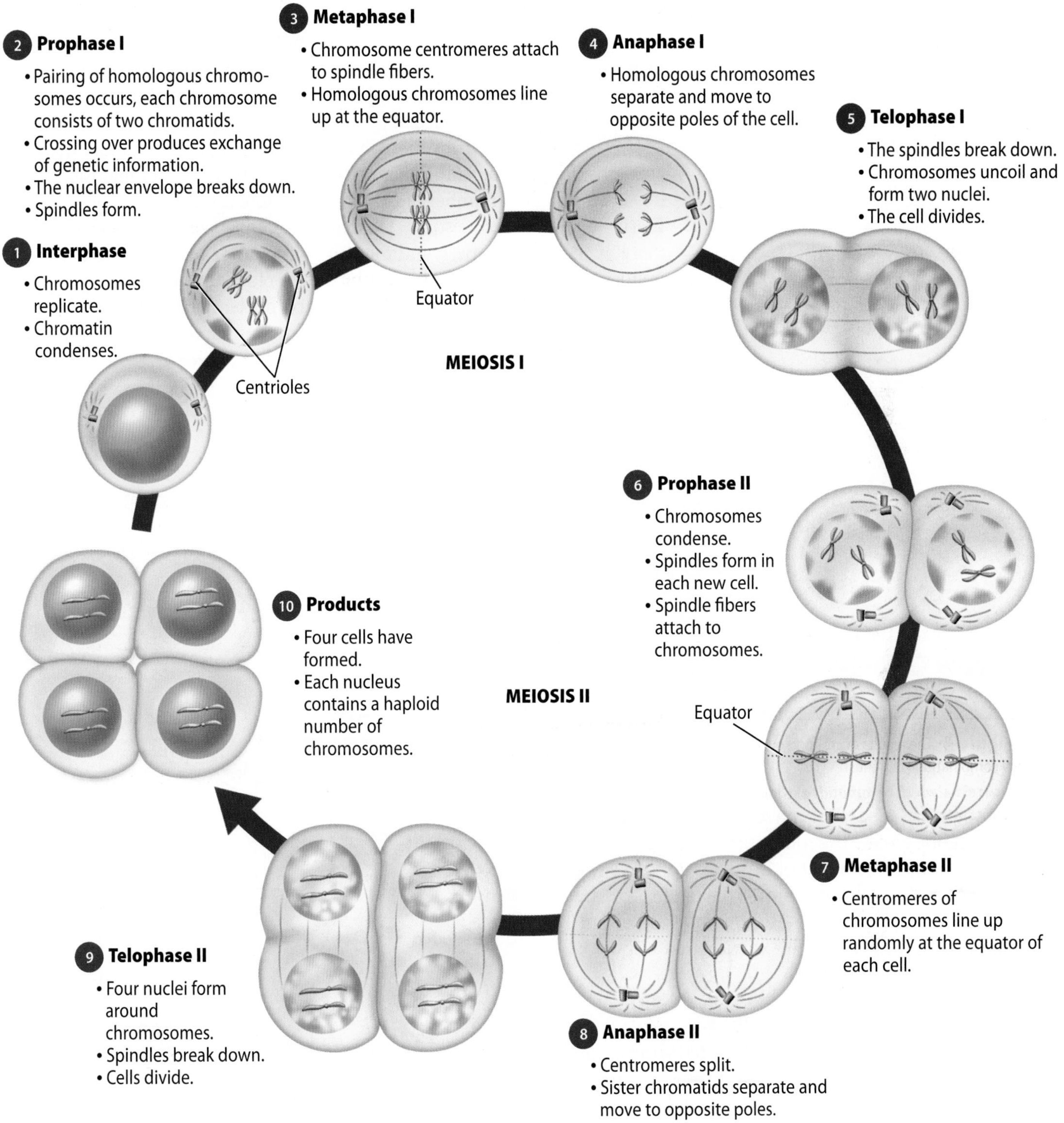

MEIOSIS I

1 Interphase
- Chromosomes replicate.
- Chromatin condenses.

Centrioles

2 Prophase I
- Pairing of homologous chromosomes occurs, each chromosome consists of two chromatids.
- Crossing over produces exchange of genetic information.
- The nuclear envelope breaks down.
- Spindles form.

3 Metaphase I
- Chromosome centromeres attach to spindle fibers.
- Homologous chromosomes line up at the equator.

Equator

4 Anaphase I
- Homologous chromosomes separate and move to opposite poles of the cell.

5 Telophase I
- The spindles break down.
- Chromosomes uncoil and form two nuclei.
- The cell divides.

MEIOSIS II

6 Prophase II
- Chromosomes condense.
- Spindles form in each new cell.
- Spindle fibers attach to chromosomes.

Equator

7 Metaphase II
- Centromeres of chromosomes line up randomly at the equator of each cell.

8 Anaphase II
- Centromeres split.
- Sister chromatids separate and move to opposite poles.

9 Telophase II
- Four nuclei form around chromosomes.
- Spindles break down.
- Cells divide.

10 Products
- Four cells have formed.
- Each nucleus contains a haploid number of chromosomes.

CAREERS IN BIOLOGY

Medical Geneticist A medical geneticist researches how diseases are inherited, how to diagnose genetic conditions, and treatments for genetic diseases.

During telophase I, cytokinesis usually occurs, forming a furrow by pinching in animal cells and by forming a cell plate in plant cells. Following cytokinesis, the cells may go into interphase again before the second set of divisions. However, the DNA is not replicated again during this interphase. In some species, the chromosomes uncoil, the nuclear membrane reappears, and nuclei re-form during telophase I.

Meiosis II

Meiosis is only halfway completed at the end of meiosis I. During prophase II, a second set of phases begins as the spindle apparatus forms and the chromosomes condense. During metaphase II, the chromosomes are positioned at the equator by the spindle fibers, as shown in **Figure 5.** During metaphase of mitosis, a diploid number of chromosomes line up at the equator. During metaphase II of meiosis, however, a haploid number of chromosomes line up at the equator. During anaphase II, the sister chromatids are pulled apart at the centromere by the spindle fibers, and the sister chromatids move toward the opposite poles of the cell. The chromosomes reach the poles during telophase II, and the nuclear membrane and nuclei reform. At the end of meiosis II, cytokinesis occurs, resulting in four haploid cells, each with *n* number of chromosomes, as illustrated in **Figure 5.**

Launch Lab

Review Based on what you have read about meiosis, how would you now answer the analysis questions?

GET IT? **Infer** Why are the two phases of meiosis important for gamete formation?

Data Analysis LAB 1

Based on Real Data*

Draw Conclusions

How do motor proteins affect cell division? Many scientists think that motor proteins play an important role in the movement of chromosomes in both mitosis and meiosis. To test this hypothesis, researchers have produced yeast that cannot make the motor protein called Kar3p. They also have produced yeast that cannot make the motor protein called Cik1p, which many think moderates the function of Kar3p. The results of their experiment are shown in the graph to the right.

Think Critically

1. **Evaluate** whether Cik1p seems to be important for yeast meiosis. Explain.
2. **Assess** whether Kar3p seems to be necessary for yeast meiosis. Explain.
3. **Conclude** whether all motor proteins seem to play a vital role in meiosis. Explain.

Data and Observations

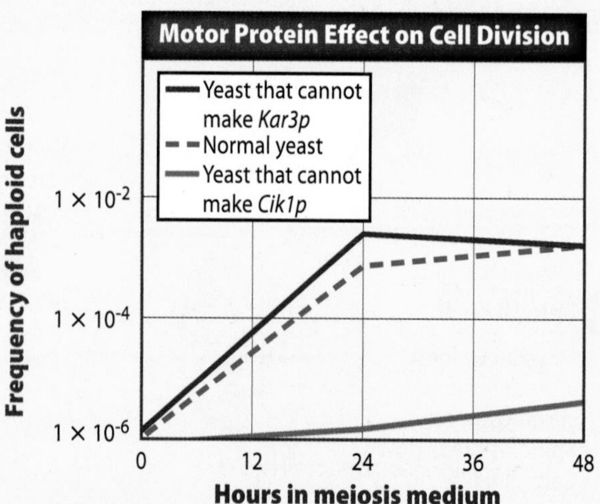

*Data obtained from: Shanks, et al. 2001. The Kar3-Interacting protein Cik1p plays a critical role in passage through meiosis I in *Saccharomyces cerevisiae.* Genetics 159: 939–951.

The Importance of Meiosis

Table 1 shows a comparison of mitosis and meiosis. Recall that mitosis consists of only one set of division phases and produces two identical diploid daughter cells. Meiosis, however, consists of two sets of divisions and produces four haploid daughter cells that are not identical. Meiosis is important because it results in genetic variation.

Table 1 Mitosis and Meiosis — Interactive Table

Mitosis	Meiosis
One division occurs during mitosis.	Two sets of divisions occur during meiosis: meiosis I and meiosis II.
DNA replication occurs during interphase.	DNA replication occurs once before meiosis I.
Synapsis of homologous chromosomes does not occur.	Synapsis of homologous chromosomes occurs during prophase I.
Two identical cells are formed per cell cycle.	Four haploid cells *(n)* are formed per cell cycle.
The daughter cells are genetically identical.	The daughter cells are not genetically identical because of crossing over.
Mitosis occurs only in body cells.	Meiosis occurs only in reproductive cells.
Mitosis is involved in growth and repair.	Meiosis is involved in the production of gametes and providing genetic variation in organisms.

MITOSIS

Parent cell
(before chromosome replication)

MEIOSIS

Meiosis I

Prophase

Duplicated chromosome (two sister chromatids)

Chromosome replication

Chromosome replication

Crossing over

Prophase I

Synapsis and crossing over of homologous chromosomes

$2n = 4$

Metaphase

Chromosomes line up at the equator

Homologous pairs line up at the equator

Metaphase I

Anaphase I
Telophase I

Anaphase
Telophase

Sister chromatids separate during anaphase

Homologous chromosomes separate during anaphase I; sister chromatids remain together

Daughter cells of meiosis I

Haploid
$n = 2$

Meiosis II

$2n$ $2n$

Daughter cells of mitosis

n n n n

Daughter cells of meiosis II

Chromosomes do not replicate again; sister chromatids separate during anaphase II

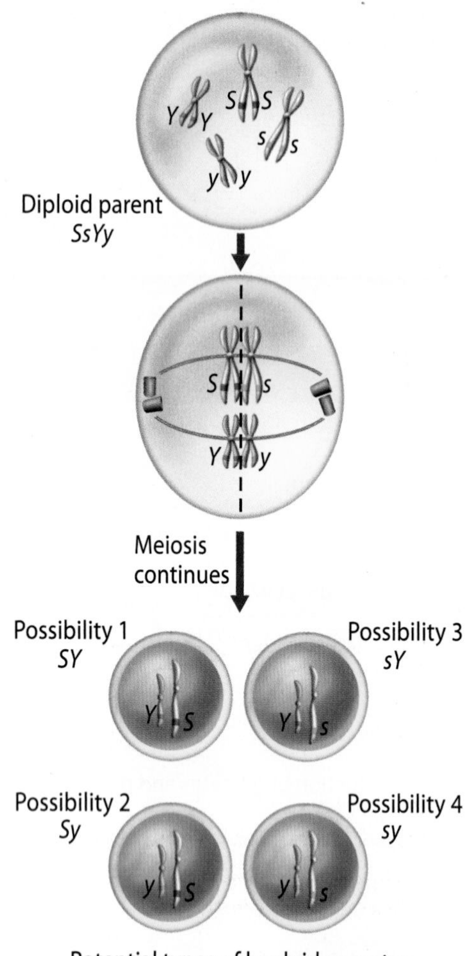

■ **Figure 6** The order in which the homologous pairs line up explains how a variety of sex cells can be produced.

Meiosis provides variation Recall that pairs of homologous chromosomes line up at the equator during prophase I. How the chromosomes line up at the equator is a random process that results in gametes with different combinations of chromosomes, such as the ones in **Figure 6.** Depending on how the chromosomes line up at the equator, four gametes with four different combinations of chromosomes can result.

Notice that the first possibility shows which chromosomes were on the same side of the equator and therefore traveled together. Different combinations of chromosomes were lined up on the same side of the equator to produce the gametes in the second possibility. Genetic variation also is produced during crossing over and during fertilization, when gametes randomly combine.

Sexual Reproduction v. Asexual Reproduction

Some organisms reproduce by asexual reproduction, while others reproduce by sexual reproduction. The life cycles of still other organisms might involve both asexual and sexual reproduction. During asexual reproduction, the organism inherits all of its chromosomes from a single parent. Therefore, the new individual is genetically identical to its parent. Bacteria reproduce asexually, whereas most protists reproduce both asexually and sexually, depending on environmental conditions. Most plants and many of the more simple animals can reproduce both asexually and sexually, compared to more advanced animals that reproduce only sexually.

Why do some species reproduce sexually while others reproduce asexually? Recent studies with fruit flies have shown that the rate of accumulation of beneficial mutations is faster when species reproduce sexually than when they reproduce asexually. In other words, when reproduction occurs sexually, the beneficial genes multiply faster over time than they do when reproduction is asexual.

REVIEW IT! Meiosis

Section Summary

- DNA replication takes place only once during meiosis, and it results in four haploid gametes.
- Meiosis consists of two sets of divisions.
- Meiosis produces genetic variation in gametes.

Self Check

Understand Main Ideas

1. MAINIDEA **Analyze** how meiosis produces haploid gametes.
2. **Indicate** how metaphase I is different from metaphase in mitosis.
3. **Describe** how synapsis occurs.
4. **Diagram** a cell with four chromosomes going through meiosis.
5. **Assess** how meiosis contributes to genetic variation, while mitosis does not.

Think Critically

6. **Compare and contrast** mitosis and meiosis, using **Figure 5** and **Table 1,** by creating a Venn diagram.

WRITING IN ▶ Biology

7. Imagine you are a chromosome going through meiosis. Describe what happens to you and the other chromosomes.

USE IT! Science Notebook

2 Mendelian Genetics

1.1.1b, 4.2.1b, 4.2.1c

MAINIDEA

Mendel explained how a dominant allele can mask the presence of a recessive allele.

Essential Questions

- What is the significance of Mendel's experiments to the study of genetics?
- What is the law of segregation and the law of independent assortment?
- What are the possible offspring from a cross using a Punnett square?

BIOLOGY 4U

There are many different breeds of dogs, such as Labrador retrievers, dachshunds, German shepherds, and poodles. You might like a certain breed of dog because of its appearance. These traits are passed from generation to generation.

Review Vocabulary

segregation: the separation of allelic genes that typically occurs during meiosis

New Vocabulary

genetics	genotype
allele	phenotype
dominant	law of segregation
recessive	hybrid
homozygous	law of independent assortment
heterozygous	

■ **Figure 7** Gregor Mendel is known as the father of genetics.

How Genetics Began

In 1866, Gregor Mendel, an Austrian monk and a plant breeder, published his findings on the method of inheritance in garden pea plants. The passing of traits to the next generation is called inheritance, or heredity. Mendel, shown in **Figure 7,** was successful in sorting out the mystery of inheritance because of the organism he chose for his study—the pea plant. Pea plants are true-breeding, meaning that they consistently produce offspring with only one form of a trait.

Pea plants usually reproduce by self-fertilization. A common occurrence in many flowering plants, self-fertilization occurs when a male gamete within a flower combines with a female gamete in the same flower. Mendel also discovered that pea plants could easily be cross-pollinated by hand. Mendel performed cross-pollination by transferring a male gamete from the flower of one pea plant to the female reproductive organ in a flower of another pea plant.

Connection to History Mendel rigorously followed various traits in the pea plants he bred. He analyzed the results of his experiments and formed hypotheses concerning how the traits were inherited. The study of **genetics,** which is the science of heredity, began with Mendel, who is regarded as the father of genetics.

GET IT? **Infer** why it is important that Mendel's experiments used a true-breeding plant.

The Inheritance of Traits

Mendel noticed that certain varieties of garden pea plants produced specific forms of a trait, generation after generation. For instance, he noticed that some varieties always produced green seeds and others always produced yellow seeds. In order to understand how these traits are inherited, Mendel performed cross-pollination by transferring male gametes from the flower of a true-breeding green-seed plant to the female organ of a flower from a true-breeding yellow-seed plant. To prevent self-fertilization, Mendel removed the male organs from the flower of the yellow-seed plant. Mendel called the green-seed plant and the yellow-seed plant the parent generation—also known as the P generation.

Figure 8 The results of Mendel's cross involving true-breeding pea plants with yellow seeds and green seeds are shown here.

***Explain** why the seeds in the F_1 generation were all yellow.*

 **Animation**

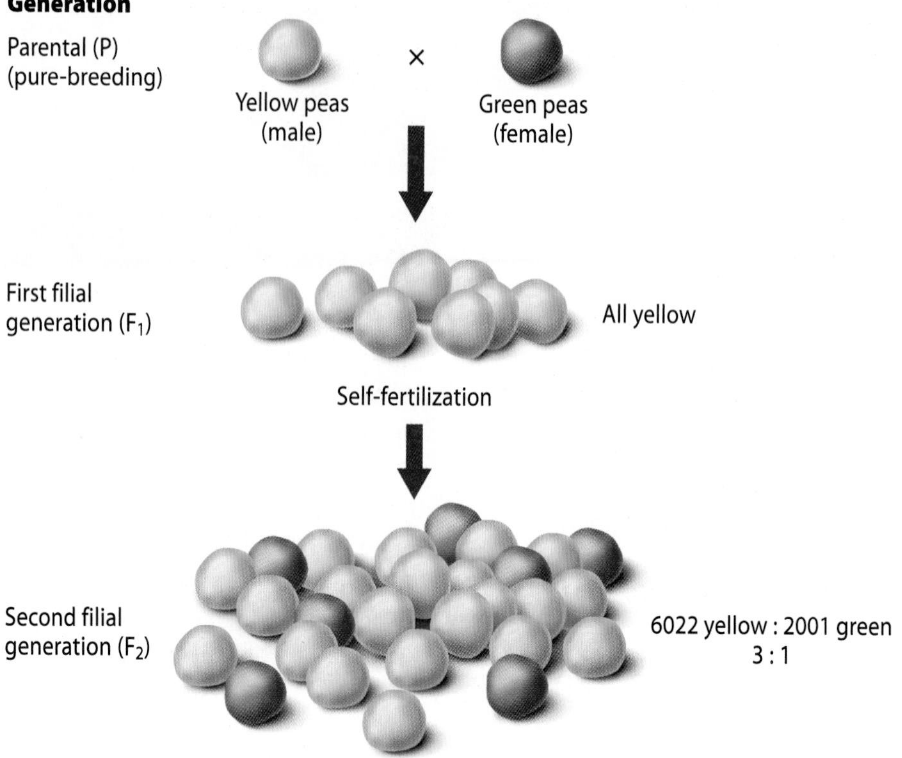

F_1 and F_2 generations When Mendel grew the seeds from the cross between the green-seed and yellow-seed plants, all of the resulting offspring had yellow seeds. The offspring of this P cross are called the first filial (F_1) generation. The green-seed trait seemed to have disappeared in the F_1 generation, and Mendel decided to investigate whether the trait was no longer present or whether it was hidden, or masked.

BrainPOP 

Mendel planted the F_1 generation of yellow seeds, allowed the plants to grow and self-fertilize, and then examined the seeds from this cross. The results of the second filial (F_2) generation—the offspring from the F_1 cross—are shown in **Figure 8.** Of the seeds Mendel collected, 6022 were yellow and 2001 were green, which almost is a perfect 3:1 ratio of yellow to green seeds.

Mendel studied seven different traits—seed or pea color, flower color, seed pod color, seed shape or texture, seed pod shape, stem length, and flower position—and found that the F_2 generation plants from these crosses also showed a 3:1 ratio.

CAREERS IN BIOLOGY

Genetics Laboratory Technician
A technician in a genetics laboratory assists a researcher by conducting experiments and helping to maintain the lab.

Genes in pairs Mendel concluded that there must be two forms of the seed trait in the pea plants—yellow-seed and green-seed—and that each was controlled by a factor, which now is called an allele. An **allele** is defined as an alternative form of a single gene passed from generation to generation. Therefore, the gene for yellow seeds and the gene for green seeds are each different forms of a single gene.

Mendel concluded that the 3:1 ratio observed during his experiments could be explained if the alleles were paired in each of the plants. He called the form of the trait that appeared in the F_1 generation **dominant** and the form of the trait that was masked in the F_1 generation **recessive.** In the cross between yellow-seed plants and green-seed plants, the yellow seed was the dominant form of the trait and the green seed was the recessive form of the trait.

Dominance When he allowed the F_1 generation to self-fertilize, Mendel showed that the recessive allele for green seeds had not disappeared but was masked. Mendel concluded that the green-seed form of the trait did not show up in the F_1 generation because the yellow-seed form of the trait is dominant and masks the allele for the green-seed form of the trait.

When modeling inheritance, the dominant allele is represented by a capital letter, and the recessive allele is represented by a lowercase letter. An organism with two of the same alleles for a particular trait is **homozygous** (ho muh ZI gus) for that trait. Homozygous, yellow-seed plants are *YY* and green-seed plants are *yy*. An organism with two different alleles for a particular trait is **heterozygous** (heh tuh roh ZY gus) for that trait, in this case *Yy*. When alleles are present in the heterozygous state, the dominant trait will be observed.

Genotype and phenotype A yellow-seed plant could be homozygous or heterozygous for the trait form. The outward appearance of an organism does not always indicate which pair of alleles is present. The organism's allele pairs are called its **genotype.** In the case of plants with yellow seeds, their genotypes could be *YY* or *Yy*. The observable characteristic or outward expression of an allele pair is called the **phenotype.** The phenotype of pea plants with the genotype *yy* will be green seeds.

Mendel's law of segregation Mendel used homozygous yellow-seed and green-seed plants in his P cross. In **Figure 9(A),** the top drawing shows that each gamete from the yellow-seed plant contains one *Y*. Recall that the chromosome number is divided in half during meiosis. The resulting gametes contain only one of the pair of seed-color alleles.

The bottom drawing in **Figure 9(A)** shows that each gamete from the green-seed plant contains one *y* allele. Mendel's **law of segregation** states that the two alleles for each trait separate during meiosis. During fertilization, two alleles for that trait unite.

The third drawing in **Figure 9(B)** shows the alleles uniting to produce the genotype *Yy* during fertilization. All resulting F_1 generation plants will have the genotype *Yy* and will have yellow seeds because yellow is dominant to green. These heterozygous organisms are called **hybrids.**

VOCABULARY

WORD ORIGIN

Homozygous and **Heterozygous** come from the Greek words *homos,* meaning *the same; hetero,* meaning *other* or *different;* and *zygon,* meaning *yoke.*

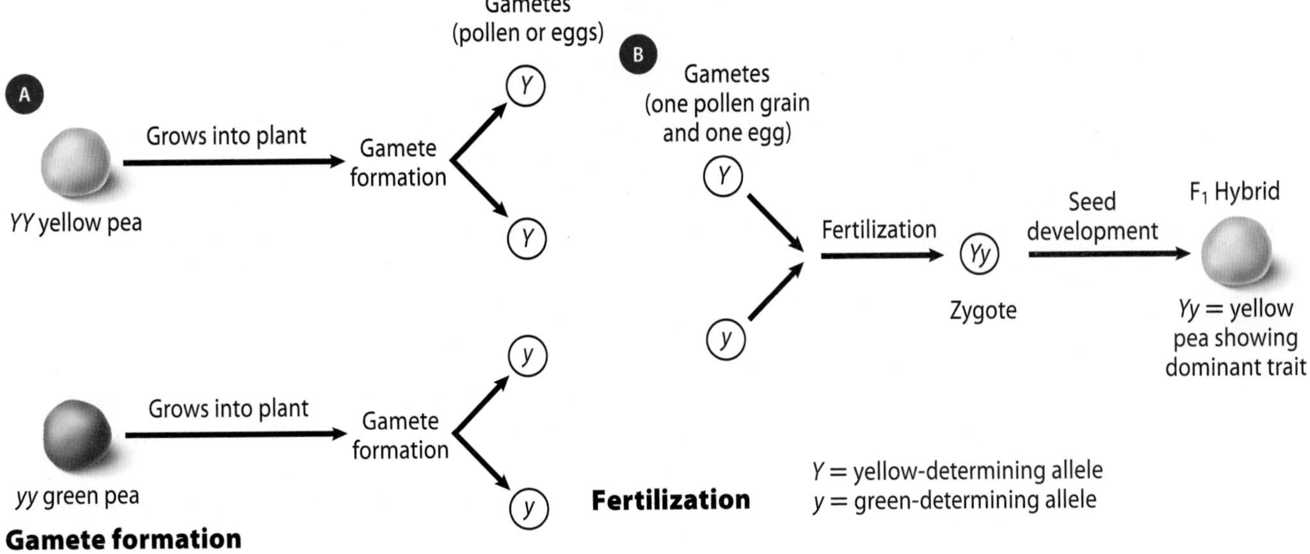

■ **Figure 9** During gamete formation in the *YY* or *yy* plant, the two alleles separate, resulting in *Y* or *y* in the gametes. Gametes from each parent unite during fertilization.

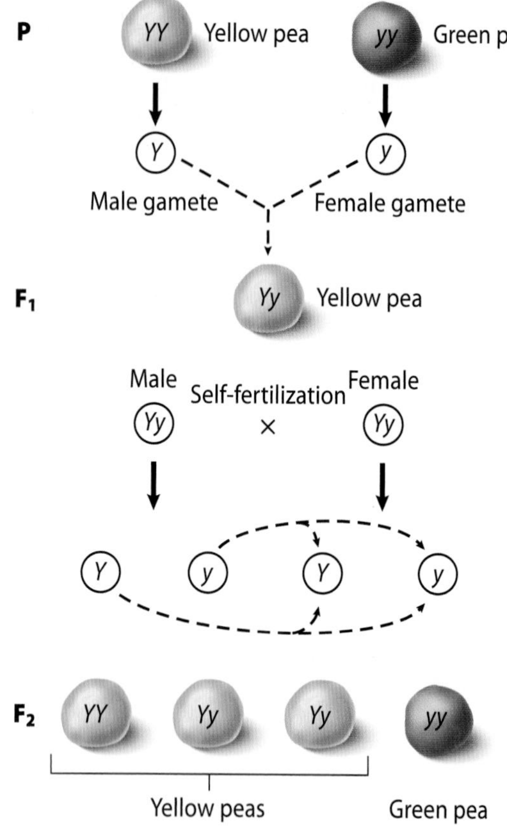

■ **Figure 10** During the F_1 generation self-fertilization, the male gametes randomly fertilize the female gametes.

■ **Figure 11** The law of independent assortment is demonstrated in the dihybrid cross by the equal chance that each pair of alleles (*Yy* and *Rr*) can randomly combine with each other.

***Predict** how many possible gamete types are produced.*

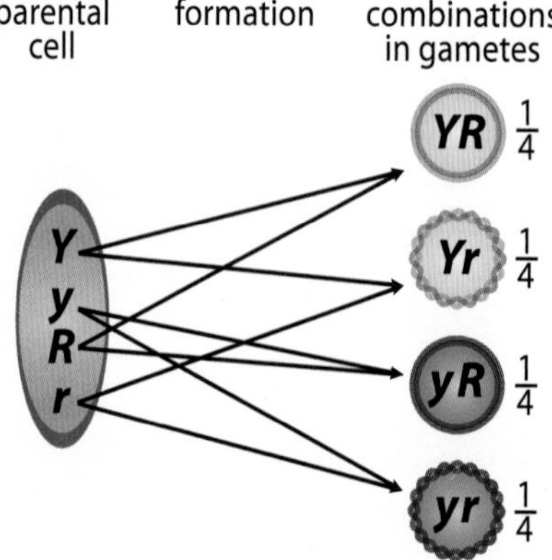

Monohybrid cross The diagram in **Figure 10** shows how Mendel continued his experiments by allowing the *Yy* plants to self-fertilize. A cross such as this one that involves hybrids for a single trait is called a monohybrid cross. The *Yy* plants produce two types of gametes—male and female—each with either the *Y* or *y* allele. The combining of these gametes is a random event. This random fertilization of male and female gametes results in the following genotypes—*YY, Yy, Yy,* or *yy,* as shown in **Figure 10.** Notice that the dominant *Y* allele is written first, whether it came from the male or female gamete. In Mendel's F_1 cross, there are three possible genotypes: *YY, Yy,* and *yy;* and the genotypic ratio is 1:2:1. The phenotypic ratio is 3:1—yellow seeds to green seeds.

Dihybrid cross Once Mendel established inheritance patterns of a single trait, he began to examine simultaneous inheritance of two or more traits in the same plant. In garden peas, round seeds *(R)* are dominant to wrinkled seeds *(r)*, and yellow seeds *(Y)* are dominant to green seeds *(y)*. If Mendel crossed homozygous yellow, round-seed pea plants with homozygous green, wrinkle-seed pea plants, the P cross could be represented by *YYRR* × *yyrr.* The F_1 generation genotype would be *YyRr*—yellow, round-seed plants. These F_1-generation plants are called dihybrids because they are heterozygous for both traits.

Law of independent assortment Mendel allowed F_1 pea plants with the genotype *YyRr* to self-fertilize in a dihybrid cross. Mendel calculated the genotypic and phenotypic ratios of the offspring in both the F_1 and F_2 generations. From these results, he developed the **law of independent assortment,** which states that a random distribution of alleles occurs during gamete formation. Genes on separate chromosomes sort independently during meiosis.

As shown in **Figure 11,** the random assortment of alleles results in four possible gametes: *YR, Yr, yR* or *yr,* each of which is equally likely to occur. When a plant self-fertilizes, any of the four allele combinations could be present in the male gamete, and any of the four combinations could be present in the female gamete. The results of Mendel's dihybrid cross included nine different genotypes: *YYRR, YYRr, YYrr, YyRR, YyRr, Yyrr, yyRR, yyRr,* and *yyrr.* He counted and recorded four different phenotypes: 315 yellow round, 108 green round, 101 yellow wrinkled, and 32 green wrinkled. These results represent a phenotypic ratio of approximately 9:3:3:1.

GET IT? **Evaluate** How can the random distribution of alleles result in a predictable ratio?

Punnett Squares

In the early 1900s, Dr. Reginald Punnett developed what is known as a Punnett square to predict the possible offspring of a cross between two known genotypes. Punnett squares make it easier to keep track of the possible genotypes involved in a cross.

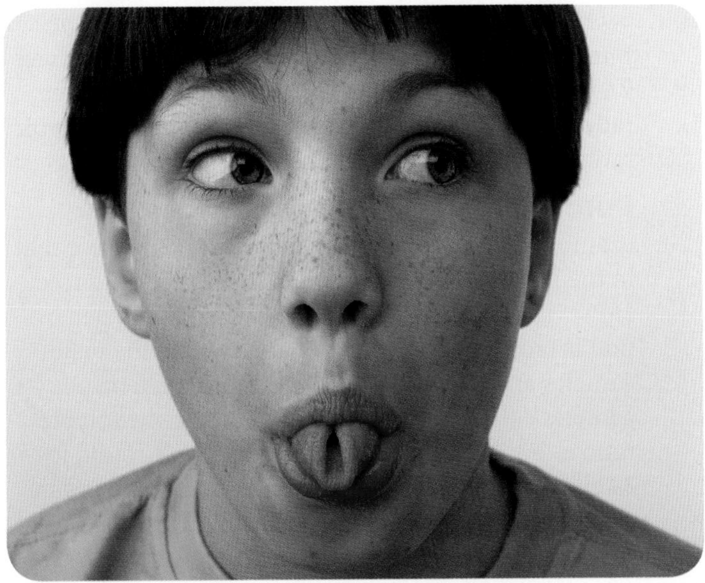

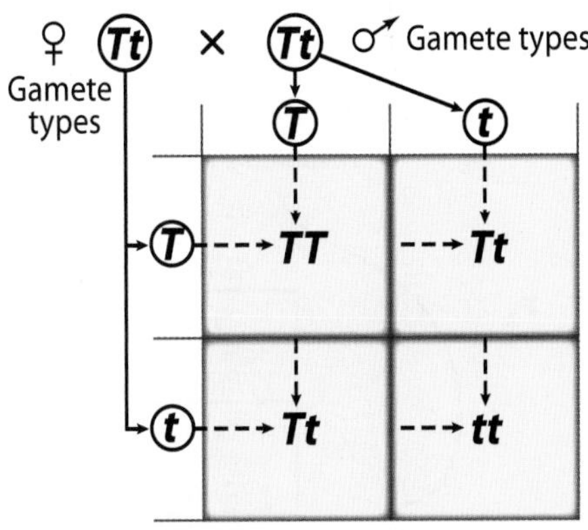

■ **Figure 12** The ability to roll one's tongue is a dominant trait. The Punnett square is a visual summary of the possible combinations of the alleles for the tongue-rolling trait.

 **Personal Tutor**

Punnett square—monohybrid cross Can you roll your tongue like the person pictured in **Figure 12?** Tongue-rolling ability is a dominant trait, which can be represented by *T*. Suppose both parents can roll their tongues and are heterozygous *(Tt)* for the trait. What possible phenotypes could their children have?

Examine the Punnett square in **Figure 12.** The number of squares is determined by the number of different types of alleles—*T* or *t*—produced by each parent. In this case, the square is 2 squares × 2 squares because each parent produces two different types of gametes. Notice that the male gametes are written across the horizontal side and the female gametes are written on the vertical side of the Punnett square. The possible combinations of each male and female gamete are written on the inside of each corresponding square.

 **Virtual Lab**

MiniLAB 1

Predict Probability in Genetics

How can an offspring's traits be predicted? A Punnett square can help predict ratios of dominant traits to recessive traits in the genotype of offspring. This lab involves two parents who are both heterozygous for free earlobes (E), which is a dominant trait. The recessive trait is attached earlobes (e).

Procedure

1. Read and complete the lab safety form.
2. Determine the gamete genotype(s) for this trait that each parent contributes.
3. Draw a Punnett square that has the same number of columns and the same number of rows as the number of alleles contributed for this trait by the gametes of each parent.
4. Write the alphabetical letter for each allele from one parent just above each column, and write the alphabetical letter for each allele from the other parent just to the left of each row.
5. In the boxes within the table, write the genotype of the offspring resulting from each combination of male and female alleles.

Analysis

1. **Summarize** the possible offspring phenotypes that could occur.
2. **Evaluate** the phenotypic ratio of the possible offspring. What is the genotypic ratio of the possible offspring?

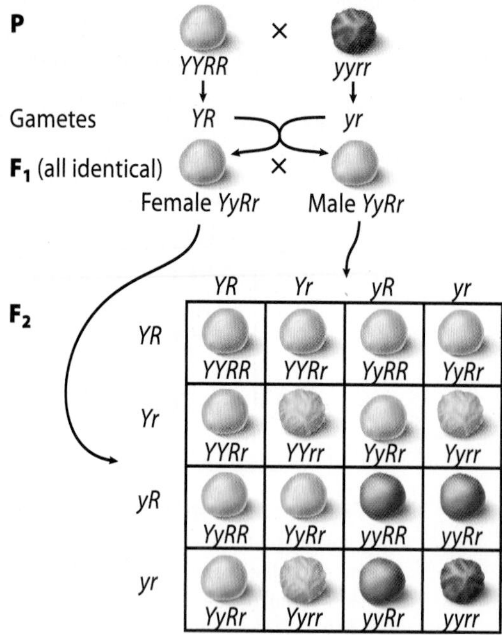

Type	Genotype	Phenotype	Number	Phenotypic Ratio
Parental	Y_R_	yellow round	315	9:16
Recombinant	yyR_	green round	108	3:16
Recombinant	Y_rr	yellow wrinkled	101	3:16
Parental	yyrr	green wrinkled	32	1:16

■ **Figure 13** The dihybrid Punnett square visually presents the possible combinations of the possible alleles from each parent.

How many different genotypes are found in the Punnett square? One square has *TT,* two squares have *Tt,* and one square has *tt.* Therefore, the genotypic ratio of the possible offspring is 1:2:1. The phenotypic ratio of tongue rollers to non-tongue rollers is 3:1.

Punnett square—dihybrid cross Now examine the Punnett square in **Figure 13.** Notice that in the P cross, only two types of alleles are produced. However, in the dihybrid cross—when the F_1 generation is crossed—four types of alleles from the male gametes and four types of alleles from the female gametes can be produced. The resulting phenotypic ratio is 9:3:3:1—9 yellow round to 3 green round to 3 yellow wrinkled to 1 green wrinkled. Mendel's data closely matched the outcome predicted by the Punnett square.

Probability

The inheritance of genes can be compared to the probability of flipping a coin. The probability of the coin landing on heads is 1 out of 2, or 1/2. If the same coin is flipped twice, the probability of it landing on heads is 1/2 each time or 1/2 × 1/2, or 1/4 both times.

Actual data might not perfectly match the predicted ratios. You know that if you flip a coin you might not get heads 1 out of 2 times. Mendel's results were not exactly a 9:3:3:1 ratio. However, the larger the number of offspring involved in a cross, the more likely it will match the results predicted by the Punnett square.

REVIEW IT! Mendelian Genetics

Section Summary

- The study of genetics began with Gregor Mendel, whose experiments with garden pea plants gave insight into the inheritance of traits.
- Mendel developed the law of segregation and the law of independent assortment.
- Punnett squares help predict the offspring of a cross.

Self Check

Understand Main Ideas

1. **MAINIDEA Diagram** Use a Punnett square to explain how a dominant allele masks the presence of a recessive allele.
2. **Apply** the law of segregation and the law of independent assortment by giving an example of each.
3. **Use a Punnett square** In fruit flies, red eyes *(R)* are dominant to pink eyes *(r).* What is the phenotypic ratio of a cross between a heterozygous male and a pink-eyed female?

Think Critically

4. **Evaluate** the significance of Mendel's work to the field of genetics.

MATH IN ▶ Biology

5. What is the probability of rolling a 2 on a six-sided die? What is the probability of rolling two 2s on two six-sided die? How is probability used in the study of genetics?

3 Gene Linkage and Polyploidy

4.2.1j, 4.3.1c

MAINIDEA
The crossing over of linked genes is a source of genetic variation.

Essential Questions

- How does the process of meiosis produce genetic recombination?
- How can gene linkage be used to create chromosome maps?
- Why is polyploidy important to the field of agriculture?

BIOLOGY 4U
You might have seen many varieties of roses at a garden center that range in color from red to pink to white. Plant breeders use scientists' knowledge of genes to vary certain characteristics in an effort to make their roses unique.

REVIEW VOCABULARY

protein: large, complex polymer essential to all life that provides structure for tissues and organs and helps carry out cell metabolism

NEW VOCABULARY Multilingual eGlossary

genetic recombination
polyploidy

Genetic Recombination

Connection to Math The new combination of genes produced by crossing over and independent assortment is called **genetic recombination.** The possible combinations of genes due to independent assortment can be calculated using the formula $2n$, where n is the number of chromosome pairs. For example, pea plants have seven pairs of chromosomes. For seven pairs of chromosomes, the possible combinations are 2^7, or 128 combinations. Because any possible male gamete can fertilize any possible female gamete, the number of possible combinations after fertilization is 16,384 (128 × 128). In humans, the possible number of combinations after fertilization would be $2^{23} \times 2^{23}$, or more than 70 trillion. This number does not include the amount of genetic recombination produced by crossing over.

Gene Linkage

Chromosomes contain multiple genes that code for proteins. Genes that are located close to each other on the same chromosome are said to be linked and usually travel together during gamete formation. Follow closely related genes A and B in **Figure 14** through the process of meiosis. The linkage of genes on a chromosome results in an exception to Mendel's law of independent assortment because linked genes usually do not segregate independently.

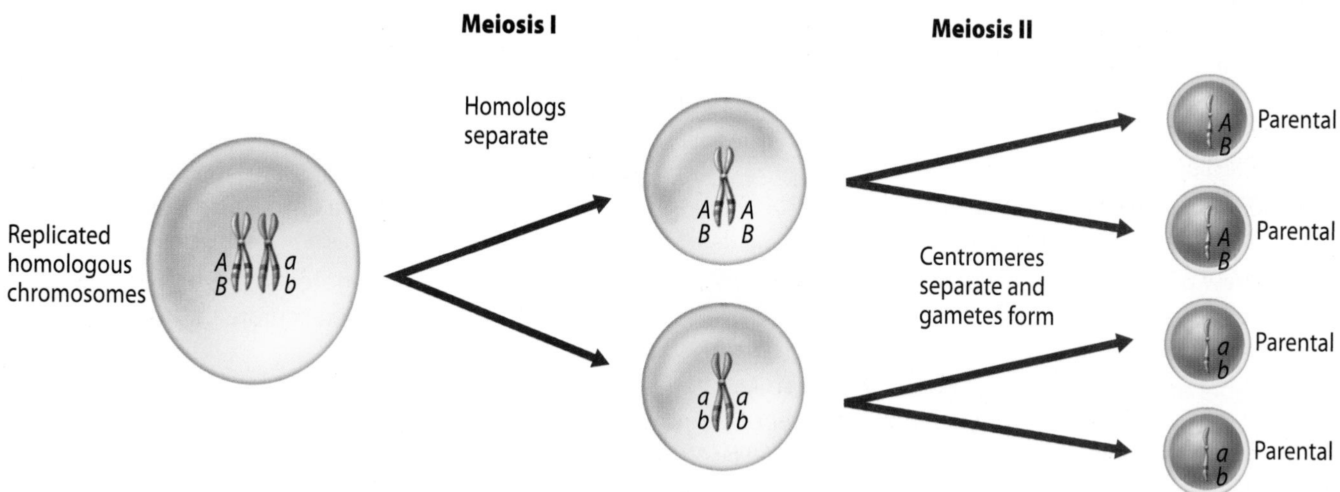

Figure 14 Genes that are linked together on the same chromosome usually travel together in the gamete.
***Calculate** the number of possible combinations if two or three of these gametes were to combine.*

■ **Figure 15** This chromosome map of the X chromosome of the fruit fly *Drosophila melanogaster* was created in 1913.

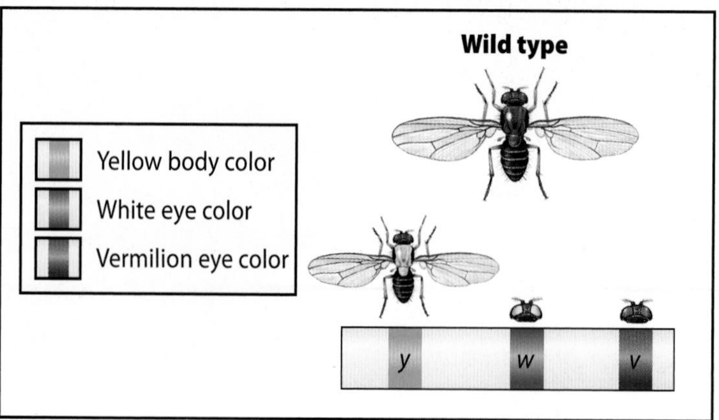

Gene linkage was first studied using the fruit fly *Drosophila melanogaster.* Thousands of crosses confirmed that linked genes usually traveled together during meiosis. However, some results revealed that linked genes do not always travel together during meiosis. Scientists concluded that linked genes can separate during crossing over.

Chromosome maps Crossing over occurs more frequently between genes that are far apart than those that are close together. A drawing called a chromosome map shows the sequence of genes on a chromosome and can be created by using crossover data. The very first chromosome maps were published in 1913 using data from thousands of fruit fly crosses. Chromosome map percentages are not actual chromosome distances, but they represent relative positions of the genes. **Figure 15** shows the first chromosome map created using fruit fly data. Notice that the higher the crossover frequency, the farther apart the two genes are.

MiniLAB 2

Map Chromosomes

Where are genes located on a chromosome? The distance between two genes on a chromosome is related to the crossover frequency between them. By comparing data for several gene pairs, a gene's relative location can be determined.

Procedure

1. Read and complete the lab safety form.
2. Obtain a table of the gene-pair crossover frequencies from your teacher.
3. Draw a line on a piece of paper and make marks every 1 cm. Each mark will represent a crossover frequency of 1 percent.
4. Label one mark near the middle of the line *A.* Find the crossover frequency between Genes A and B on the table, and use this data to label *B* the correct distance from A.
5. Use the crossover frequency between genes A and C and genes B and C to infer the position of gene C.
6. Repeat steps 4–5 for each gene, marking their positions on the line.

Analysis

1. **Evaluate** whether it is possible to know the location of a gene on a chromosome if only one other gene is used.
2. **Consider** why using more crossover frequencies would result in a more accurate chromosome map.

Strawberries (8*n*)

Coffee (4*n*)

■ **Figure 16** Various commercial plants, such as strawberries and coffee, are polyploids.

In a cross, the exchange of genes is directly related to the crossover frequency between them. This frequency correlates with the relative distance between the two genes. One map unit between two genes is equivalent to 1 percent of the crossing over occurring between them. Genes that are farther apart would have a greater frequency of crossing over.

Polyploidy

Most species have diploid cells, but some have polyploid cells. **Polyploidy** is the occurrence of one or more extra sets of all chromosomes in an organism. A triploid organism, for instance, would be designated $3n$, which means that it has three complete sets of chromosomes. Polyploidy rarely occurs in animals. In humans, polyploidy is always lethal.

Roughly one in three species of known flowering plants are polyploid. Polyploid plants are selected by plant growers for their desirable characteristics. Commercially grown bread wheat ($6n$), oats ($6n$), and sugar cane ($8n$) are polyploid crop plants. Polyploid plants, such as the ones shown in **Figure 16,** often have increased vigor and size.

REVIEW IT! Gene Linkage and Polyploidy

Section Summary

- Genetic recombination involves both crossing over and independent assortment.
- Early chromosome maps were created based on the linkage of genes on the chromosome.
- Polyploid organisms have one or more extra sets of all chromosomes.

Self Check

Understand Main Ideas

1. MAINIDEA **Analyze** how crossing over is related to variation.
2. **Draw** Suppose genes *C* and *D* are linked on one chromosome and genes *c* and *d* are linked on another chromosome. Assuming that crossing over does not take place, sketch the daughter cells resulting from meiosis, showing the chromosomes and position of the genes.
3. **Describe** how polyploidy is used in the field of agriculture.

Think Critically

4. **Construct** a chromosome map for genes *A, B, C* and *D* using the following crossing over data: *A* to *D* = 25 percent; *A* to *B* = 30 percent; *C* to *D* = 15 percent; *B* to *D* = 5 percent; *B* to *C* = 20 percent.
5. **Evaluate** what advantage polyploidy would give to a plant breeder.

WRITING IN ▶ Biology

6. Write a short story describing a society with no genetic variation in humans.

BIOdiscoveries

1.1.3b

A new treatment for Parkinson's Disease?

One morning, actor Michael J. Fox woke up to find his pinky finger twitching. At first he ignored this strange symptom. But a year later he was diagnosed with early-onset Parkinson's disease (PD), a debilitating illness that, among other symptoms, causes loss of control over the body's movements. On average, the disease strikes people around age 60; however, Fox was only 30 when he was diagnosed.

The Parkinson's Disease Foundation (PDF) along with other PD foundations, raise funds for PD research. A recent PDF-funded project studied a new treatment that might alleviate symptoms of the disease—with the help of an afflicted person's own skin cells.

What is PD? Parkinson's disease is an illness that kills or damages neurons in the brain. These neurons control muscle movement via a neurotransmitter called dopamine, which relays messages between neurons. In addition to problems controlling their muscles, people who have PD have trouble with muscle stiffness, balance, and coordination. The disease's symptoms are often subtle at first and worsen over time. Currently, there is no cure. Scientists do not know what causes PD. Some cases have been linked to mutated genes, the appearance of protein clumps in brain cells, and environmental factors.

Search for treatments Doctors usually treat PD symptoms with combinations of medications, brain surgery, and physical, speech, and other therapies. Recently, scientists investigated using stem cells, unspecialized cells that can develop into specialized cells under the right conditions, to replace brain neurons lost to PD. Scientists on the PDF-funded study are working to create stem cells from skin cells of PD patients.

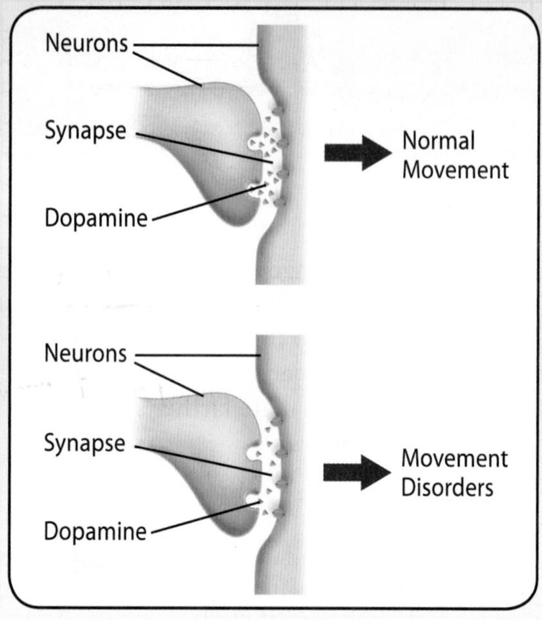

Lower levels of dopamine are an indicator of Parkinson's disease. Dopamine controls the movement of muscles.

These stem cells could be used to produce neurons that produce dopamine. Doctors could surgically introduce the newly created neurons into the brain. Because the stem cells came from the patient's own body, the immune system would not reject the cells, as sometimes happens with cells or organs donated by another person.

This stem-cell research is in its early stages with a pilot study that uses Rhesus monkeys as the patients. Scientists hope that their work will one day help alleviate the symptoms that make PD such a devastating illness.

COMMUNITY INVOLVEMENT

Volunteer Interview an administrator at a local agency who understands the needs of PD patients. Perhaps some people who have PD need help running errands or doing chores, such as yardwork. Compile a list of these needs to present to a local volunteer organization. If possible, volunteer to help people who have PD.

WebQuest

BioLAB DESIGN YOUR OWN

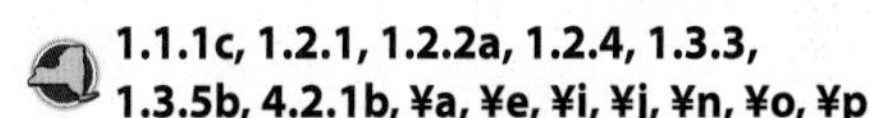

1.1.1c, 1.2.1, 1.2.2a, 1.2.4, 1.3.3, 1.3.5b, 4.2.1b, ¥a, ¥e, ¥i, ¥j, ¥n, ¥o, ¥p

How can the phenotype of offspring help determine parental genotype?

Background: The traits of most plants have dominant and recessive alleles. Analysis of plants grown from seeds can be a good indicator of the expected genotypes of offspring as well as phenotypes and genotypes of the parent plants.

Question: *Can the phenotypes and genotypes of parent organisms be determined from the phenotype of the offspring?*

Materials

Choose materials that would be appropriate for this lab.

two groups of plant seeds
potting soil
small flowerpots or other growing containers
watering can or bottle
small gardening trowel

Safety Precautions

Plan and Perform the Experiment

1. Read and complete the lab safety form.
2. Develop your own questions about phenotypes and genotypes and try to answer them in this lab.
3. Hypothesize whether the phenotype of offspring could be used to infer the genotypes of the parents.
4. Design an experiment to test your hypothesis.
5. Decide what data you need to collect.
6. Create a data table to record your observations.
7. Make certain your teacher has approved your experiment before you proceed.
8. Conduct your experiment.
9. **Cleanup and Disposal** Properly dispose of seeds or plants considered to be invasive species in your area. Never release invasive species into the environment.

Analyze and Conclude

1. **Collect and Organize Data** Count the number of seedlings of the different phenotypes in each group of plants. Prepare a graph of your data.
2. **Calculate** the ratio of different seedlings for each of your groups of seeds.
3. **Identify** two or more possible crosses that could have resulted in your observed ratio of seedlings.
4. **Analyze** Make a Punnett square for each cross you identified in question 3. Determine whether each possible cross could have resulted in the data you collected.
5. **Evaluate** how the combined data from the two seed groups affect the ratio of seedlings.
6. **Draw Conclusions** Based on the data from your two groups of seeds, list the genotype and phenotype of the parent plants.
7. **Error Analysis** Compare your calculated ratios to those of another student. Describe any differences. Combine your data with another group's data. Infer how increasing the number of seeds analyzed affects the outcome of the experiment.

COMMUNICATE

Poster Session Prepare a poster that describes the experiment you conducted and displays the data you collected. When posters are complete, have a poster session during which you examine each others' work and compare your results.

CHAPTER 10 STUDY GUIDE

BIGIDEA **Reproductive cells, which pass on genetic traits from the parents to the child, are produced by the process of meiosis.**

SECTION 1 Meiosis

MAINIDEA Meiosis produces haploid gametes.

- DNA replication takes place only once during meiosis, and it results in four haploid gametes.
- Meiosis consists of two sets of divisions.
- Meiosis produces genetic variation in gametes.

VOCABULARY

- **gene**
- **homologous chromosome**
- **gamete**
- **haploid**
- **fertilization**
- **diploid**
- **meiosis**
- **crossing over**

SECTION 2 Mendelian Genetics

MAINIDEA Mendel explained how a dominant allele can mask the presence of a recessive allele.

- The study of genetics began with Gregor Mendel, whose experiments with garden pea plants gave insight into the inheritance of traits.
- Mendel developed the law of segregation and the law of independent assortment.
- Punnett squares help predict the offspring of a cross.

VOCABULARY

- **genetics**
- **allele**
- **dominant**
- **recessive**
- **homozygous**
- **heterozygous**
- **genotype**
- **phenotype**
- **law of segregation**
- **hybrid**
- **law of independent assortment**

SECTION 3 Gene Linkage and Polyploidy

MAINIDEA The crossing over of linked genes is a source of genetic variation.

- Genetic recombination involves both crossing over and independent assortment.
- Early chromosome maps were created based on the linkage of genes on the chromosome.
- Polyploid organisms have one or more extra sets of all chromosomes.

VOCABULARY

- **genetic recombination**
- **polyploidy**

CHAPTER 10 ASSESSMENT

SECTION 1

Vocabulary Review

Use what you know about the terms in the Study Guide to answer the following questions.

1. When two cells with *n* number of chromosomes fuse, what type of cell results?
2. During which process are gametes formed?
3. What process results in an exchange of genes between homologous chromosomes?

Understand Main Ideas

4. How many chromosomes would a cell have during metaphase I of meiosis if it has 12 chromosomes during interphase?
   A. 6
   B. 12
   C. 24
   D. 36

Use the diagram below to answer questions 5 and 6.

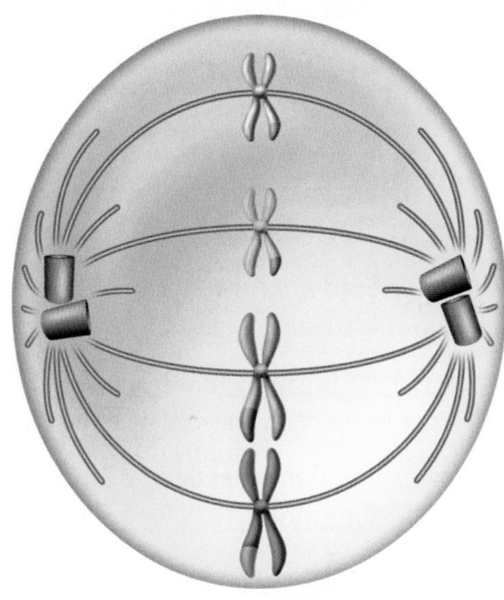

5. Which stage of meiosis is illustrated above?
   A. prophase I
   B. prophase II
   C. metaphase I
   D. metaphase II
6. What is the next step for the chromosomes illustrated above?
   A. They will experience replication.
   B. They will experience fertilization.
   C. Their number per cell will be halved.
   D. They will divide into sister chromatids.
7. Which is not a characteristic of homologous chromosomes?
   A. Homologous chromosomes have the same length.
   B. Homologous chromosomes have the same centromere position.
   C. Homologous chromosomes have the exact same type of allele at the same location.
   D. Homologous chromosomes pair up during meiosis I.

Constructed Response

8. **MAIN IDEA** Relate the terms meiosis, gametes, and fertilization in one or two sentences.
9. **Open Ended** Plant cells do not have centrioles. Hypothesize why plant cells might not need centrioles for mitosis or meiosis.

Think Critically

10. **Analyze** A horse has 64 chromosomes and a donkey has 62. Using your knowledge of meiosis, evaluate why a cross between a horse and a donkey produces a mule, which usually is sterile.
11. **Hypothesize** In bees, the female queen bee is diploid but male bees are haploid. The fertilized eggs develop into female bees and the unfertilized eggs develop into males. How might gamete production in male bees differ from normal meiosis?

SECTION 2

Vocabulary Review

Explain the differences between the vocabulary terms in the following sets.

12. dominant, recessive
13. genotype, phenotype

Understand Main Ideas

14. If a black guinea pig *(Bb)* were crossed with a white guinea pig *(bb)* what would be the resulting phenotypic ratio?
    A. 0:1 black to white
    B. 1:0 black to white
    C. 1:1 black to white
    D. 3:1 black to white

15. In garden peas, purple flowers *(P)* are dominant to white *(p)* flowers, and tall plants *(T)* are dominant to short plants *(t)*. If a purple tall plant *(PpTt)* is crossed with a white short plant *(pptt)*, what is the resulting phenotypic ratio?
    A. 1:1:1:1 purple tall to purple short to white tall to white short
    B. 3:2 purple tall to purple short
    C. 9:3:3:1 purple tall to purple short to white tall to white short
    D. all purple tall

Use the figure below to answer questions 16 and 17.

16. The unusual cat shown was crossed with a cat with noncurled ears. All the kittens born from that cross had noncurled ears. Later, when these offspring were crossed with each other, the phenotypic ratio was 3:1 noncurled to curled ears. What conclusions can be made about the inheritance of curled ears?
    A. Curled ears are a result of crossing over.
    B. It is a dominant trait.
    C. It is a recessive trait.
    D. More crosses need to be done to determine how the trait is inherited.

Constructed Response

17. **MAIN IDEA** What might occur in the F_3 generation of the curly-eared cat shown above if the F_2 generation all reproduce with cats that have noncurly ears?

18. **Short Answer** If there are five boys and no girls born into a family, does that increase the likelihood that the sixth offspring will be a girl? Explain.

Think Critically

Use the figure below to answer question 19.

19. **Predict** There are two types of American rat terrier dogs—those without hair and those with hair, as shown in the figure. The presence of hair is a genetically determined trait. Some female rat terriers with hair produce only puppies with hair, whereas other females produce rat terrier puppies without hair. Explain how this can occur.

20. **MATH IN ▶ Biology** What is the probability of a couple giving birth to five girls in a row?

SECTION 3

Vocabulary Review

Replace the underlined words with the correct vocabulary term from the Study Guide page.

21. Human growth hormone has been used in agriculture to increase the size of flowers.

22. Crossing over and independent assortment produce chromosomes.

Understand Main Ideas

23. Which does not contribute to genetic variation?
    A. chromosome number
    B. crossing over
    C. meiosis
    D. random mating

24. Which concept is considered an exception to Mendel's law of independent assortment?
    A. crossing over
    B. gene linkage
    C. polyploidy
    D. law of segregation

Use the figure below to answer questions 25 and 26.

Sergejs Nescereckis/Alamy

25. A housefly, shown in the photo above, has six pairs of chromosomes. If two houseflies are crossed, how many possible types of fertilized eggs could result from the random lining up of the pairs?
A. 256 **C.** 4096
B. 1024 **D.** 16,384

26. For the housefly with its six pairs of chromosomes, how many possible combinations of gametes can be produced by the random lining up of pairs in meiosis?
A. 32 **C.** 64
B. 48 **D.** 120

Constructed Response

27. **THEME FOCUS** What three processes increase genetic variation?

28. **Open Ended** Hypothesize how a plant breeder might create a polyploid plant.

29. **Short Answer** How is chromosome gene linkage an exception to the law of independent assortment?

Think Critically

30. **CAREERS IN ▶ Biology** Horticulturists grow thousands of genetically identical plants by using cuttings. Cuttings do not involve sexual reproduction. Discuss the benefits and drawbacks of using cuttings to reproduce a certain type of plant.

31. **MAIN IDEA** Crossing over provides genetic variation, eventually changing the gene pool in a population. Yet some sexually reproducing organisms do not seem to display recombination mechanisms. Why might it be advantageous for these organisms to reduce genetic recombination?

Summative Assessment

32. **BIG IDEA** The process of meiosis produces gametes. What other actions result in variation and diversity in the offspring?

33. **WRITING IN ▶ Biology** Imagine you are Gregor Mendel and create a journal entry for one of the days that you made a significant breakthrough. Describe your breakthrough and your next step.

34. In sheep, white wool is dominant and black wool is recessive. Suppose some sheep belonging to a certain flock are heterozygous for wool color. Write a plan indicating how a flock of pure-breeding white sheep could be developed.

35. In pigeons, the checker pattern of feathers *(P)* is dominant to the nonchecker pattern *(p)*. Suppose a checker pigeon with the genotype *Pp* mates with a nonchecker pigeon. Use a Punnett square to predict the genotypic ratio of their offspring.

DBQ Document-Based Questions

The paragraphs below were obtained from Mendel's publication.

Data obtained from: Mendel, Gregor. 1866. *Experiments in Plant Hybridization.* Originally translated by Bateson, William, 1901: 2.

"The hybrids of such plants must, during the flowering period, be protected from the influence of all foreign pollen, or be easily capable of such protection."

36. Mendel made the above rule for his experimental plants. Summarize why this rule was important for the success of his experiments.

Ibid: 4

"The object of the experiment was to observe these variations in the case of each pair of differentiating characters, and to deduce the law according to which they appear in successive generations. The experiment resolves itself therefore into just as many separate experiments. There are constantly differentiating characters presented in the experimental plants."

37. Describe Mendel's purpose for conducting plant breeding experiments.

CUMULATIVE

MULTIPLE CHOICE

1 Which process divides a cell's nucleus and nuclear material?

A cell cycle

B cytokinesis

C interphase

D mitosis

2 Which is the source of electrons in the electron transport chain stage of respiration?

A formation of acetyl CoA during the Krebs cycle

B creation of NADH and $FADH_2$ during the Krebs cycle

C fermentation of lactic acid

D breaking of bonds in glycolysis

3 What causes the movement of calcium and sodium ions in and out of cardiac cells?

A charged particles in the phospholipid bilayer

B cholesterol molecules in the phospholipid bilayer

C diffusion channels in the cell membrane

D transport proteins in the cell membrane

4 In a cell undergoing meiosis, during which stage do the sister chromatids separate from each other?

A anaphase I

B anaphase II

C telophase I

D telophase II

SHORT ANSWER

Use the diagram below to answer questions 5 and 6.

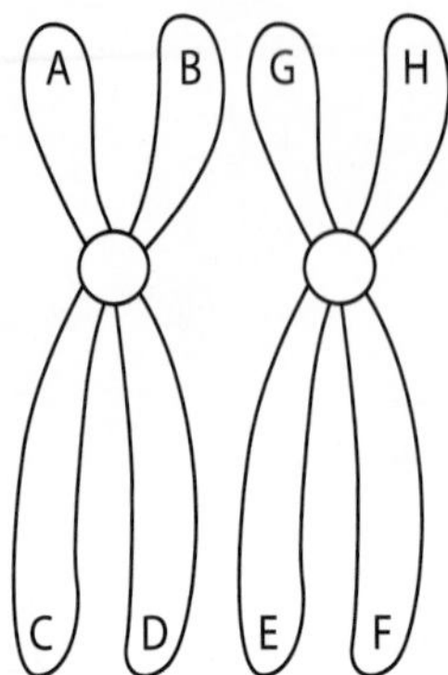

5 The diagram above shows a pair of chromosomes with different regions on the chromosomes labeled. Explain where crossing over could occur on this pair of chromosomes.

6 When is crossing over most likely to occur?

7 Suppose the concentration of CO_2 in a greenhouse decreases. Explain how the photosynthesis process could be affected by that change. Predict the overall effect on plants.

8 How does the process of meiosis promote genetic variation in a species?

9 Describe how the chromosomes change during the S phase.

10 Hypothesize why meiosis occurs in two stages—meiosis I and meiosis II.

11 Explain how factors in the environment can cause cancer to develop.

TEST Practice

EXTENDED RESPONSE

Use the diagram below to answer question 12.

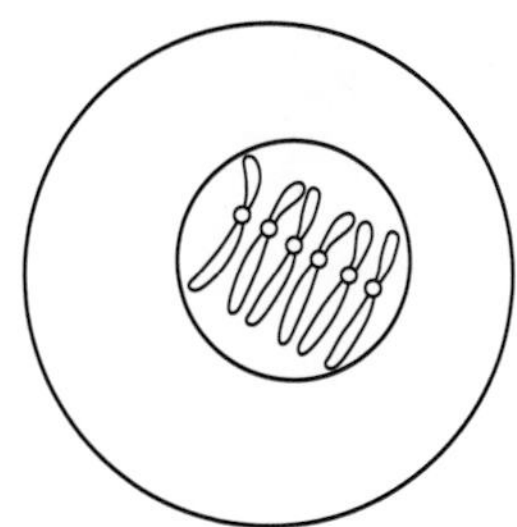

12 The diagram above shows the chromosomes found in the sex cells of a particular animal. Based on this diagram, describe what happens during fertilization in this species.

13 Assess what might happen if mitosis were NOT an extremely precise process.

ESSAY QUESTION

Stem cells are cells that are not specialized for a particular function. Like other cells, stem cells contain all of the genetic material found in the organism. Stem cells, if given the correct signal, can become any type of specialized cell. There are two different types of stem cells. Embryonic stem cells are found in embryos, while adult stem cells are found in small quantities in mature tissues. The process of conducting research using stem cells, especially using embryonic stem cells, is controversial because of ethical concerns.

Using the information in the paragraph above, answer the following question in essay format.

14 Do you think medical researchers should be allowed to use stem cells as research material? Judge what you think are the benefits or risks of stem cell research.

TEST PRACTICE

Use the illustration below to answer question 15.

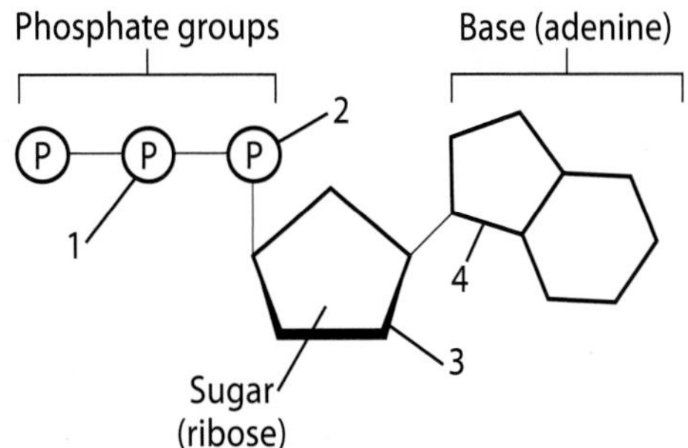

15 To release energy for use in the organism, the bond between which two groups in the ATP molecule must be broken?

A 1 and 2

B 2 and 3

C 2 and 4

D 3 and 4

Use the illustration below to answer question 16.

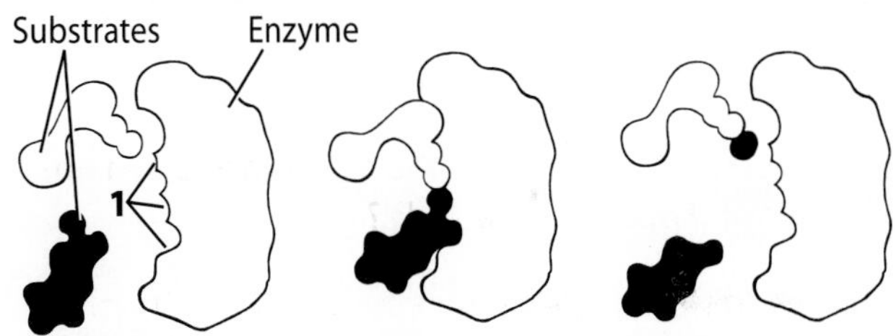

16 Which is the role of "1" in the activity of the enzyme?

A to make a reaction happen more slowly

B to make more reactants available to the substrate

C to provide a unique spot for substrate binding

D to raise the activation energy for the reaction

NEED EXTRA HELP?																
If You Missed Question . . .	1	2	3	4	5	6	7	8	9	10	11	12	13	14	15	16
Review Section . . .	9.1	8.3	7.2, 7.4	10.1	10.1	10.1	8.2	10.1, 10.3	9.2	10.2	9.3	10.1	9.2	9.2	8.2	6.2

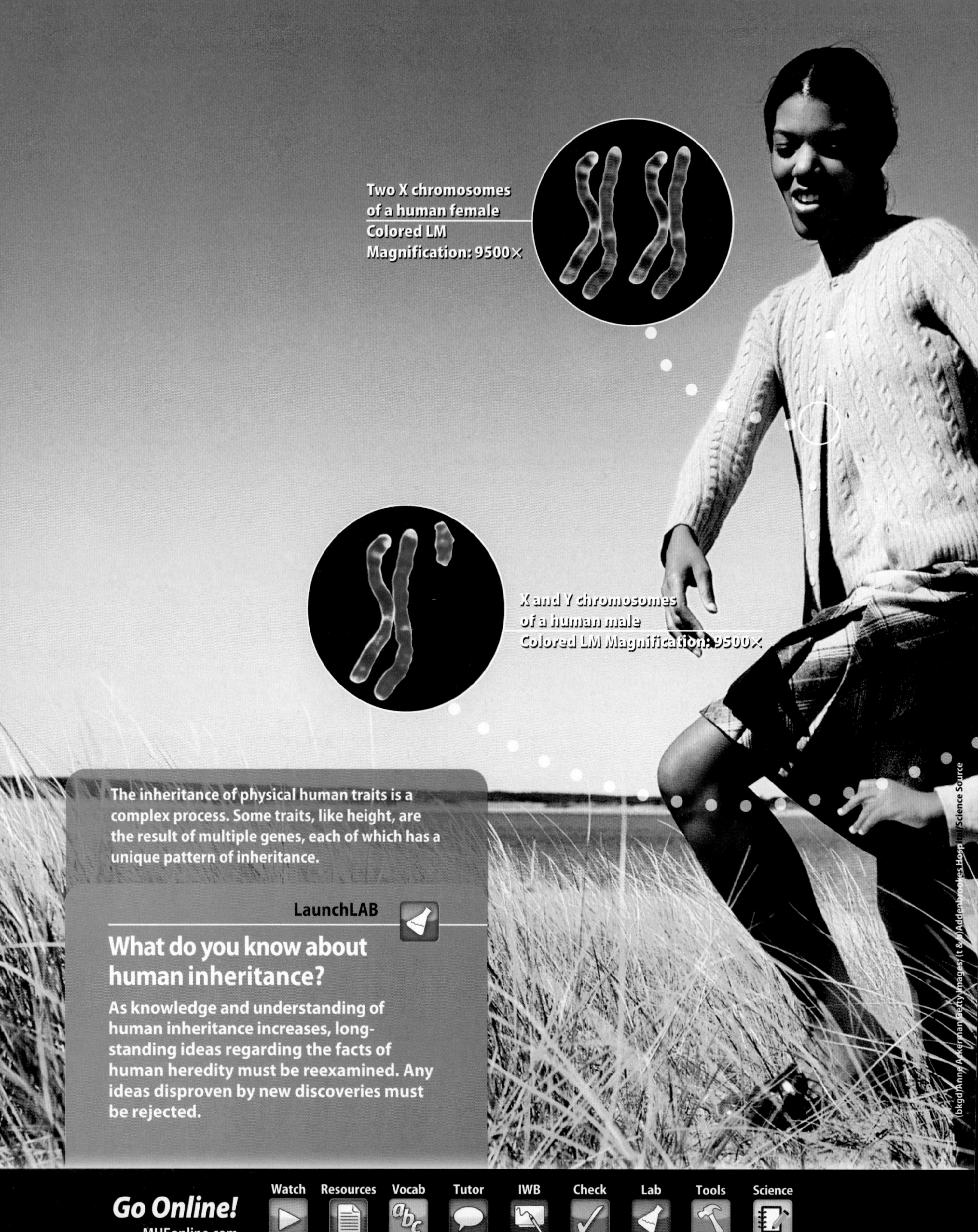

The inheritance of physical human traits is a complex process. Some traits, like height, are the result of multiple genes, each of which has a unique pattern of inheritance.

LaunchLAB

What do you know about human inheritance?

As knowledge and understanding of human inheritance increases, long-standing ideas regarding the facts of human heredity must be reexamined. Any ideas disproven by new discoveries must be rejected.

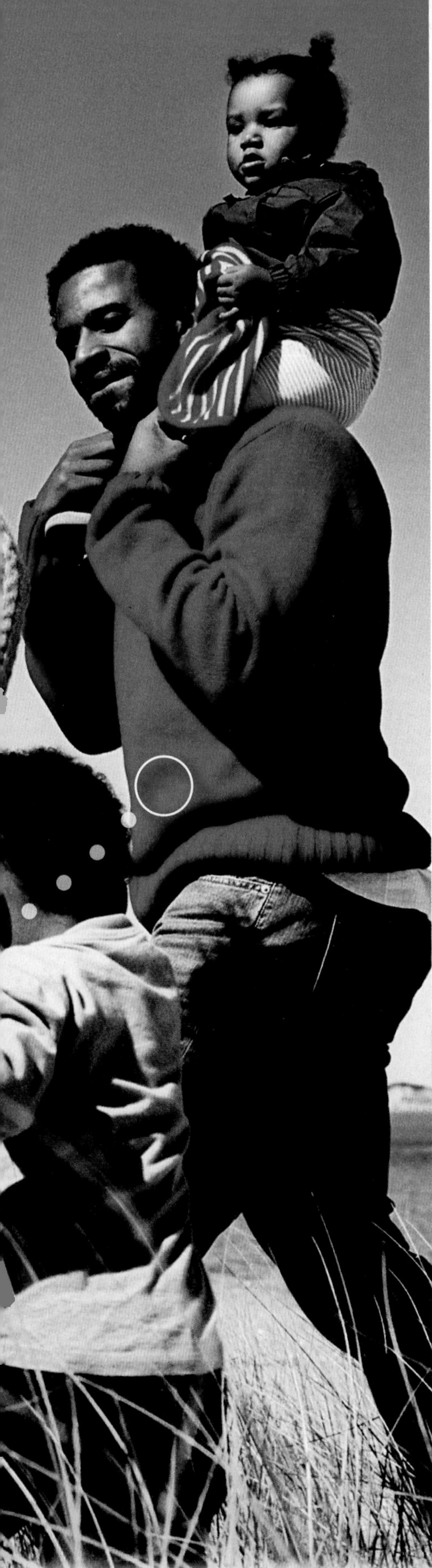

CHAPTER 11

Complex Inheritance and Human Heredity

1 Basic Patterns of Human Inheritance

4.2.1c

2 Complex Patterns of Inheritance

4.2.1c, 4.2.1h, 4.2.1k

3 Chromosomes and Human Heredity

4.2.1e, 4.3.1c, 4.4.1c, ¥a

THEMEFOCUS

Patterns Complex inheritance patterns account for some of the vast genetic diversity in humans.

BIGIDEA

Human inheritance does not always follow Mendel's laws.

Genetic Disorders

Make a vocabulary book and label each tab with the name of a different genetic disorder. Use it to organize your notes on genetic disorders.

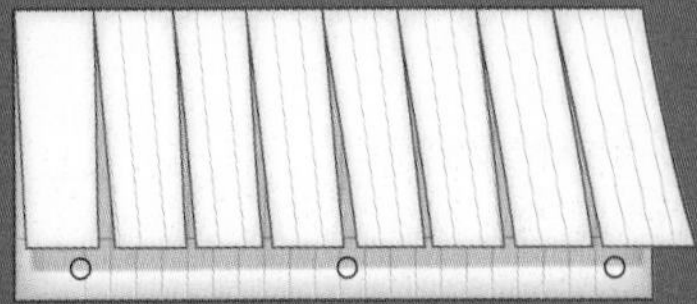

USE IT! Science Notebook

1 Basic Patterns of Human Inheritance

4.2.1c

MAINIDEA

The inheritance of a trait over several generations can be shown in a pedigree.

Essential Questions

- How can genetic patterns be analyzed to determine dominant or recessive inheritance patterns?
- What are examples of dominant and recessive disorders?
- How can human pedigrees be constructed from genetic information?

BIOLOGY 4U

Knowing a purebred dog's ancestry can help the owner know health problems that are common to that dog. Similarly, tracing human inheritance can show how a trait was passed down from one generation to the next.

REVIEW VOCABULARY

genes: segments of DNA that control the production of protein

NEW VOCABULARY

Multilingual eGlossary

carrier
pedigree

Recessive Genetic Disorders

Connection to History Gregor Mendel's work was ignored for more than 30 years. During the early 1900s, scientists began to take an interest in heredity, and Mendel's work was rediscovered. About this time, Dr. Archibald Garrod, an English physician, became interested in a disorder linked to an enzyme deficiency called alkaptonuria (al kap tuh NYUR ee uh), which results in black urine. It is caused by acid excretion into the urine. Dr. Garrod observed that the condition appeared at birth and continued throughout the patient's life, ultimately affecting bones and joints. He also noted that alkaptonuria ran in families. With the help of another scientist, he determined that alkaptonuria was a recessive genetic disorder.

Today, progress continues to help us understand genetic disorders. Review **Table 1,** and recall that a recessive trait is expressed when the individual is homozygous recessive for that trait. Therefore, those with at least one dominant allele will not express the recessive trait. An individual who is heterozygous for a recessive disorder is called a **carrier.** Review **Table 2** as you read about several recessive genetic disorders.

Table 1 Review of Terms — Interactive Table

Term	Example	Definition
Homozygous	True-breeding yellow-seed pea plants would be *YY,* and green-seed pea plants would be *yy.*	An organism with two of the same alleles for a particular trait is said to be homozygous for that trait.
Heterozygous	A plant that is *Yy* would be a yellow-seed pea.	An organism with two different alleles for a particular trait is said to be heterozygous for that trait. When alleles are present in the heterozygous state, the dominant trait will be observed.

Table 2 Recessive Genetic Disorders in Humans

Interactive Table

Disorder	Occurrence in the U.S.	Cause	Effect	Cure/Treatment
Cystic fibrosis	1 in 3500	The gene that codes for a membrane protein is defective.	• Excessive mucous production • Digestive and respiratory failure	• No cure • Daily cleaning of mucous from the lungs • Mucous-thinning drugs • Pancreatic enzyme supplements
Albinism	1 in 17,000	Genes do not produce normal amounts of the pigment melanin.	• No color in the skin, eyes and hair • Skin susceptible to UV damage • Vision problems	• No cure • Protect skin from the Sun and other environmental factors • Visual rehabilitation
Galactosemia	1 in 50,000 to 70,000	Absence of the gene that codes for the enzyme that breaks down galactose	• Mental disabilities • Enlarged liver • Kidney failure	• No cure • Restriction of lactose/galactose in the diet
Tay-Sachs disease	1 in 2500 (affects people of Jewish descent)	Absence of a necessary enzyme that breaks down fatty substances	• Buildup of fatty deposits in the brain • Mental disabilities	• No cure or treatment • Death by age 5

Cystic fibrosis One of the most common recessive genetic disorders among Caucasians is cystic fibrosis, which affects the mucus-producing glands, digestive enzymes, and sweat glands. Chloride ions are not properly transported out of cells of a person with cystic fibrosis. Because of the high concentration of chloride ions in cells, water does not diffuse from cells. This causes a secretion of thick mucus that affects many areas of the body. The thick mucus clogs the ducts in the pancreas, interrupts digestion, and blocks the tiny respiratory pathways in the lungs. Patients with cystic fibrosis are at a higher risk of infection because of excess mucus in their lungs.

Treatment for cystic fibrosis currently includes physical therapy, medication, special diets, and the use of replacement digestive enzymes. Genetic tests are available to determine whether a person is a carrier, indicating they are carrying the recessive gene.

FOLDABLES®
Incorporate information from this section into your Foldable.

Albinism In humans, albinism is caused by altered genes, resulting in the absence of the skin pigment melanin in hair and eyes. Albinism is found in other animals as well. A person with albinism has white hair, very pale skin, and pink pupils. The absence of pigment in eyes can cause problems with vision. Although we all must protect our skin from the Sun's ultraviolet radiation, those with albinism need to be especially careful.

Tay-Sachs disease Tay-Sachs (TAY saks) disease is a recessive genetic disorder. Its gene is found on chromosome 15. Often identified by a cherry-red spot on the back of the eye, Tay-Sachs disease (TSD) seems to be predominant among Jews of eastern European descent.

VOCABULARY

ACADEMIC VOCABULARY

Decline
to gradually waste away; or a downward slope
His health declined because of the disease.

TSD is caused by the absence of the enzymes responsible for breaking down fatty acids called gangliosides. Normally, gangliosides are made and then dissolved as the brain develops. However, in a person affected by Tay-Sachs disease, the gangliosides accumulate in the brain, inflating brain nerve cells and causing mental deterioration.

Galactosemia Galactosemia (guh lak tuh SEE mee uh) is characterized by the inability of the body to digest galactose. During digestion, lactose from milk breaks down into galactose and glucose. Glucose is the sugar used by the body for energy and circulates in the blood. Galactose must be broken down into glucose by an enzyme named GALT. Persons who lack or have defective GALT cannot digest galactose. Persons with galactosemia should avoid milk products.

Dominant Genetic Disorders

Not all genetic disorders are caused by recessive inheritance. As described in **Table 3,** some disorders, such as the rare disorder Huntington's disease, are caused by dominant alleles. That means those who do not have the disorder are homozygous recessive for the trait.

Huntington's disease The dominant genetic disorder Huntington's disease affects the nervous system and occurs in one out of 10,000 people in the U.S. The symptoms of this disorder first appear in affected individuals between the ages of 30 and 50 years old. The symptoms include a gradual loss of brain function, uncontrollable movements, and emotional disturbances. Genetic tests are available to detect this dominant allele. However, no preventive treatment or cure for this disease exists.

Achondroplasia An individual with achondroplasia (a kahn droh PLAY zhee uh) has a small body size and limbs that are comparatively short. Achondroplasia is the most common form of dwarfism. A person with achondroplasia will have an adult height of about four feet and will have a normal life expectancy.

Interestingly, 75 percent of individuals with achondroplasia are born to parents of average size. When children with achondroplasia are born to parents of average size, the conclusion is that the condition occurred because of a new mutation or a genetic change.

GET IT? **Compare** the chances of inheriting a dominant disorder to the chances of inheriting a recessive disorder if you have one parent with the disease.

Table 3 Dominant Genetic Disorders in Humans — Interactive Table

Disorder	Occurrence in the U.S.	Cause	Effect	Cure/Treatment
Huntington's disease	1 in 10,000	A gene affecting neurological function is defective.	• Decline of mental and neurological functions • Ability to move deteriorates	• No cure or treatment
Achondroplasia	1 in 25,000	A gene that affects bone growth is abnormal.	• Short arms and legs • Large head	• No cure or treatment

Key to Symbols

○	Normal female	□	Normal male
●	Female who expresses the trait being studied	■	Male who expresses the trait being studied
◐	Female who is a carrier for the particular trait	◧	Male who is a carrier for the particular trait
|	Generation		Roman numerals—Generations
—	Parents		Arabic numerals—Individuals in a certain generation
┌┬┐	Siblings		

Example Pedigree

I
1 2
II
1 2 3 4

■ **Figure 1** A pedigree uses standard symbols to indicate what is known about the trait being studied.

Personal Tutor

Pedigrees

In organisms such as peas and fruit flies, scientists can perform crosses to study genetic relationships. In the case of humans, a scientist studies a family history using a **pedigree,** a diagram that traces the inheritance of a particular trait through several generations. A pedigree uses symbols to illustrate inheritance of the trait. Males are represented by squares, and females are represented by circles, as shown in **Figure 1.** One who expresses the trait being studied is represented by a dark, or filled, square or circle, depending on their gender. One who does not express the trait is represented by an unfilled square or circle.

A horizontal line between two symbols shows that these individuals are the parents of the offspring listed below them. Offspring are listed in descending birth order from left to right and are connected to each other and their parents.

A pedigree uses a numbering system in which Roman numerals represent generations, and individuals are numbered by birth order using Arabic numbers. For example, in **Figure 1,** individual II1 is a female who is the firstborn in generation II.

Analyzing Pedigrees

A pedigree illustrating Tay-Sachs disease is shown in **Figure 2.** Recall from **Table 2** that Tay-Sachs disease is a recessive genetic disorder caused by the lack of an enzyme involved in lipid metabolism. The missing enzyme causes lipids to build up in the central nervous system, which can lead to death.

Examine the pedigree in **Figure 2.** Note that two unaffected parents, I1 and I2, have an affected child—II3, indicating that each parent has one recessive allele—they both are heterozygous and carriers for the trait. The half-filled square and circle show that both parents are carriers.

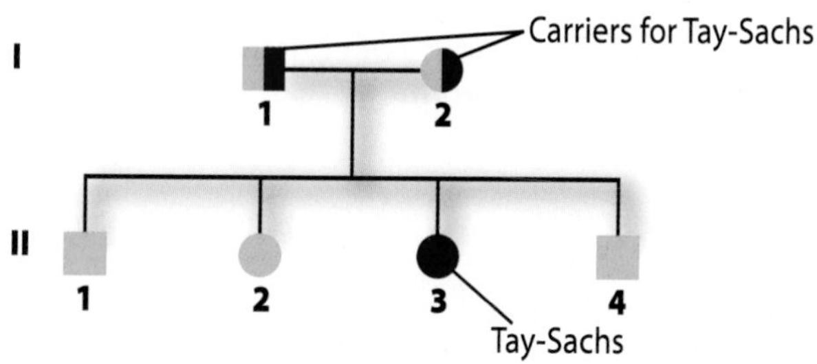

■ **Figure 2** This pedigree illustrates the inheritance of the recessive disorder Tay-Sachs disease. Note that two unaffected parents (I1 and I2) can have an affected child (II3).

■ **Figure 3** This pedigree illustrates the inheritance of a dominant disorder. Note that affected parents can pass on their genes (II2, II5), but unaffected parents cannot have an affected child (III2).

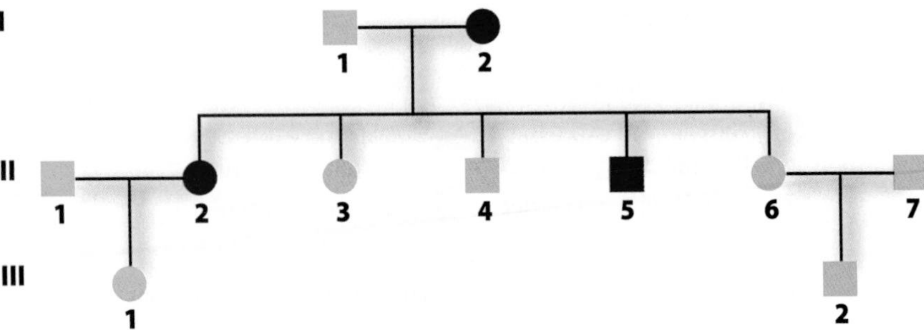

The pedigree in **Figure 3** shows the inheritance of the dominant genetic disorder polydactyly (pah lee DAK tuh lee). People with this disorder have extra fingers and toes. Recall that with dominant inheritance the trait is expressed when at least one dominant allele is present.An individual with an unaffected parent and a parent with polydactyly could be either heterozygous or homozygous recessive for the trait. Each unaffected person would be homozygous recessive for the trait.

For example, in **Figure 3,** individual I2 has polydactyly, indicated by the dark circle. Because she shows the trait, she is either homozygous dominant or heterozygous. It can be inferred that she is heterozygous—having one dominant gene and one recessive gene—because offspring II3 and II4 do not have the disorder. Notice that II6 and II7, two unaffected parents, have an unaffected offspring—III2. What can be inferred about II2, based on the phenotype of her parents and her offspring?

MiniLAB 1

Investigate Human Pedigrees

Where are the branches on the family tree? Unlike some organisms, humans reproduce slowly and produce few offspring at one time. One method used to study human traits is pedigree analysis.

Procedure

1. Read and complete the lab safety form.
2. Imagine that you are a geneticist interviewing a person about his or her family concerning the hypothetical trait of hairy earlobes.
3. From the transcript below, construct a pedigree. Use appropriate symbols and format.

   "My name is Scott. My great grandfather Walter had hairy earlobes (HEs), but great grandma Elsie did not. Walter and Elsie had three children: Lola, Leo, and Duane. Leo, the oldest, has HEs, as does the middle child, Lola; but the youngest child, Duane, does not. Duane never married and has no children. Leo married Bertie, and they have one daughter, Patty. In Leo's family, he is the only one with HEs. Lola married John, and they have two children: Carolina and Luetta. John does not have HEs, but both of his daughters do."

Analysis

1. **Assess** In what ways do pedigrees simplify the analysis of inheritance?
2. **Think Critically** Using this lab as a frame of reference, how can we put to practical use our understanding of constructing and analyzing human pedigrees?

Inferring genotypes Pedigrees are used to infer genotypes from the observation of phenotypes. By knowing physical traits, genealogists can determine what genes an individual is most likely to have. Phenotypes of entire families are analyzed in order to determine family genotypes, as symbolized in **Figure 3.**

Pedigrees help genetic counselors determine whether inheritance patterns are dominant or recessive. Once the inheritance pattern is determined, the genotypes of the individuals can largely be resolved through pedigree analysis. To analyze pedigrees, one particular trait is studied, and a determination is made as to whether that trait is dominant or recessive. Dominant traits are easier to recognize than recessive traits because dominant traits are exhibited in the phenotype.

A recessive trait will not be expressed unless the person is homozygous recessive for the trait. That means that a recessive allele is passed on by each parent. When recessive traits are expressed, the ancestry of the person expressing the trait is followed for several generations to determine which parents and grandparents were carriers of the recessive allele.

CAREERS IN BIOLOGY

Genealogist A genealogist studies or traces the descent of individuals or families. Many professional genealogists are board-certified and accredited.

Predicting disorders If good records have been kept within families, disorders in future offspring can be predicted. However, more accuracy can be expected if several individuals within the family can be evaluated. The study of human genetics is difficult, because scientists are limited by time, ethics, and circumstances. For example, it takes decades for each generation to mature and then to have offspring when the study involves humans. Therefore, good record keeping, where it exists, helps scientists use pedigree analysis to study inheritance patterns, to determine phenotypes, and to ascertain genotypes within a family.

REVIEW IT! Basic Patterns of Human Inheritance

Section Summary

- Genetic disorders can be caused by dominant or recessive alleles.
- Cystic fibrosis is a genetic disorder that affects mucus and sweat secretions.
- Individuals with albinism do not have melanin in their skin, hair, and eyes.
- Huntington's disease affects the nervous system.
- Achondroplasia sometimes is called dwarfism.
- Pedigrees are used to study human inheritance patterns.

Self Check

Understand Main Ideas

1. MAINIDEA **Construct** a family pedigree of two unaffected parents with a child who suffers from cystic fibrosis.
2. **Explain** the type of inheritance associated with Huntington's disease and achondroplasia.
3. **Interpret** Can two parents with albinism have an unaffected child? Explain.
4. **Diagram** Suppose both parents can roll their tongues but their son cannot. Draw a pedigree showing this trait, and label each symbol with the appropriate genotype.

Think Critically

MATH IN Biology

5. Phenylketonuria (PKU) is a recessive genetic disorder. If both parents are carriers, what is the probability of this couple having a child with PKU? What is the chance of this couple having two children with PKU?
6. **Determine** When a couple requests a test for the cystic fibrosis gene, what types of questions might the physician ask before ordering the tests?

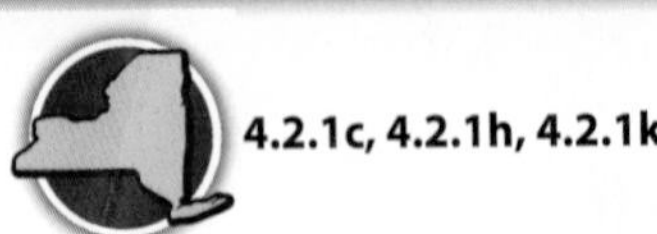

2 Complex Patterns of Inheritance

4.2.1c, 4.2.1h, 4.2.1k

MAIN IDEA

Complex inheritance of traits does not follow inheritance patterns described by Mendel.

Essential Questions

- What are the differences between various complex inheritance patterns?
- How can sex-linked inheritance patterns be analyzed?
- How can the environment influence the phenotype of an organism?

BIOLOGY 4 U

Imagine that you have red-green color blindness. In bright light, red lights do not stand out against surroundings. At night, green lights look like white streetlights. To help those with red-green color blindness, traffic lights always follow the same pattern. Red-green color blindness, however, does not follow the same pattern of inheritance described by Mendel.

Review Vocabulary

gamete: a mature sex cell (sperm or egg) with a haploid number of chromosomes

New Vocabulary

incomplete dominance
codominance
multiple alleles
epistasis
sex chromosome
autosome
sex-linked trait
polygenic trait

Multilingual eGlossary

Personal Tutor

Incomplete Dominance

Recall that when an organism is heterozygous for a trait, its phenotype will be that of the dominant trait. For example, if the genotype of a pea plant is *Tt* and *T* is the genotype for the dominant trait *tall,* then its phenotype will be tall. When red-flowered snapdragons (C^RC^R) are crossed with white-flowered snapdragons (C^WC^W), the heterozygous offspring have pink flowers (C^RC^W), as shown in **Figure 4.** This is an example of **incomplete dominance,** in which the heterozygous phenotype is an intermediate phenotype between the two homozygous phenotypes. When the heterozygous F_1 generation snapdragon plants are allowed to self-fertilize, as in **Figure 4,** the flowers are red, pink, and white in a 1:2:1 ratio, respectively.

Codominance

Recall that when an organism is heterozygous for a particular trait, the dominant phenotype is expressed. In a complex inheritance pattern called **codominance,** both alleles are expressed in the heterozygous condition. Sickle-cell disease provides a case study of codominant inheritance.

■ **Figure 4** The color of snapdragon flowers is a result of incomplete dominance. When a plant with white flowers is crossed with a plant with red flowers, the offspring have pink flowers. Red, pink, and white offspring will result from self-fertilization of a plant with pink flowers.

Predict ***what would happen if you crossed a pink flower with a white flower.***

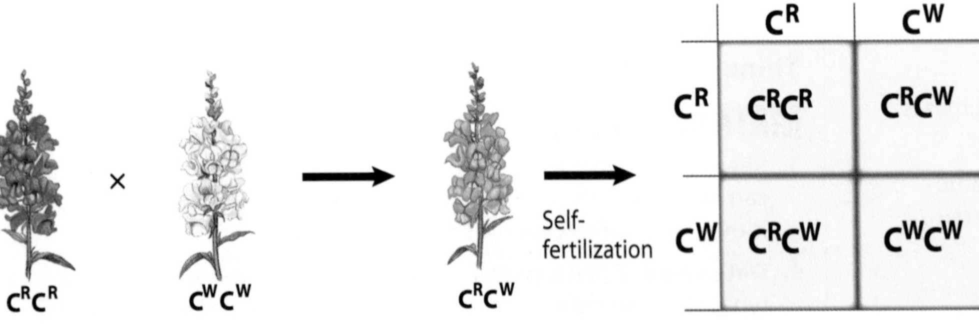

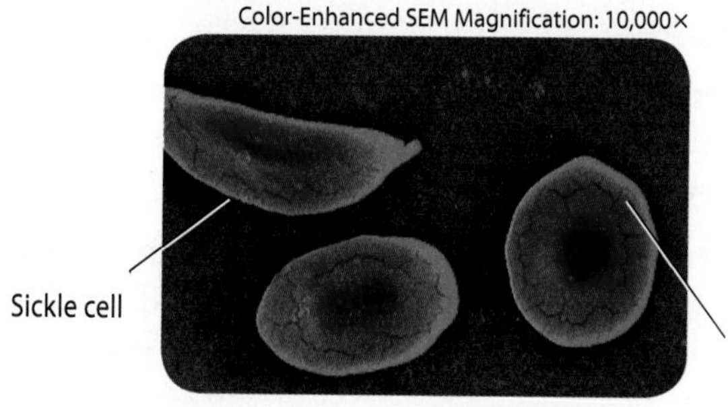

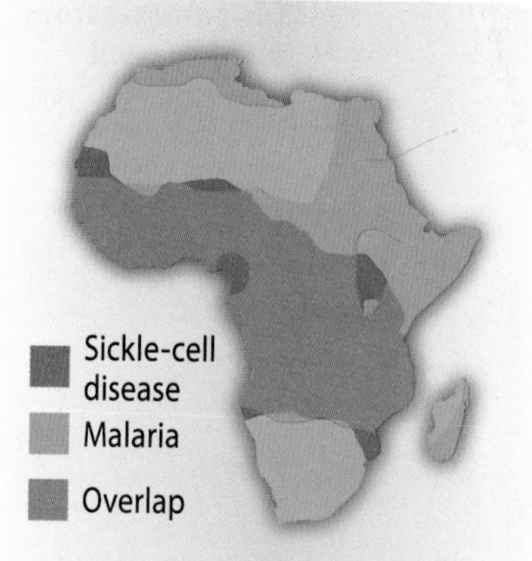

■ **Figure 5**
Left: Normal red blood cells are flat and disk-shaped. Sickle-shaped cells are elongated and C-shaped. They can clump, blocking circulation in small vessels.
Right: The sickle-cell allele increases resistance to malaria.

Sickle-cell disease The allele responsible for sickle-cell disease is particularly common in people of African descent, with about nine percent of African Americans having one form of the trait. Sickle-cell disease affects red blood cells and their ability to transport oxygen. The photograph in **Figure 5** shows the blood cells of an individual who is heterozygous for the sickle-cell trait. Changes in hemoglobin—the protein in red blood cells—cause those blood cells to change to a sickle, or C-shape. Sickle-shaped cells do not effectively transport oxygen because they block circulation in small blood vessels. Those who are heterozygous for the trait have both normal and sickle-shaped cells. These individuals can lead relatively normal lives, as the normal blood cells compensate for the sickle-shaped cells.

Sickle-cell disease and malaria Note in **Figure 5** the distribution of both sickle-cell disease and malaria in Africa. Some areas with sickle-cell disease overlap areas of widespread malaria. Why might such high levels of the sickle-cell allele exist in central Africa? Scientists have discovered that those who are heterozygous for the sickle-cell trait also have a higher resistance to malaria. The death rate due to malaria is lower where the sickle-cell trait is higher. Because less malaria exists in those areas, more people live to pass on the sickle-cell trait to offspring. Consequently, sickle-cell disease continues to increase in Africa.

Data Analysis LAB 1

Based on Real Data*

Interpret the Graph

What is the relationship between sickle-cell disease and other complications? Patients who have been diagnosed with sickle-cell disease face many symptoms, including respiratory failure and neurological problems. The graph shows the relationship between age and two different symptoms—pain and fever—during the two weeks preceding an episode of acute chest syndrome and hospitalization.

Think Critically

1. **State** which age group has the highest level of pain before being hospitalized.
2. **Describe** the relationship between age and fever before hospitalization.

Data and Observations

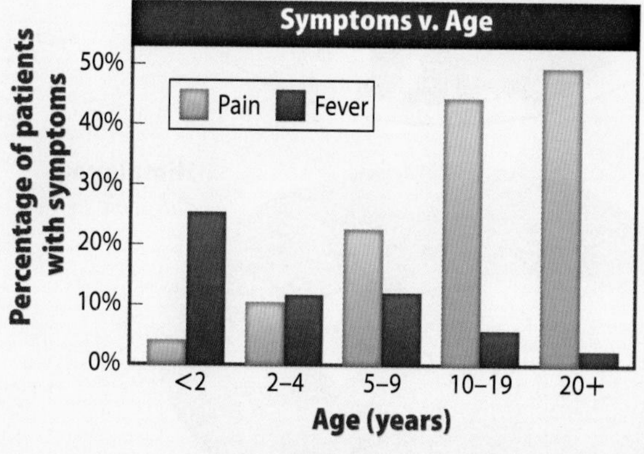

*Data obtained from: Walters, et al. 2002. Novel therapeutic approaches in sickle cell disease. *Hematology* 17: 10–34.

Kallista Images/Getty Images

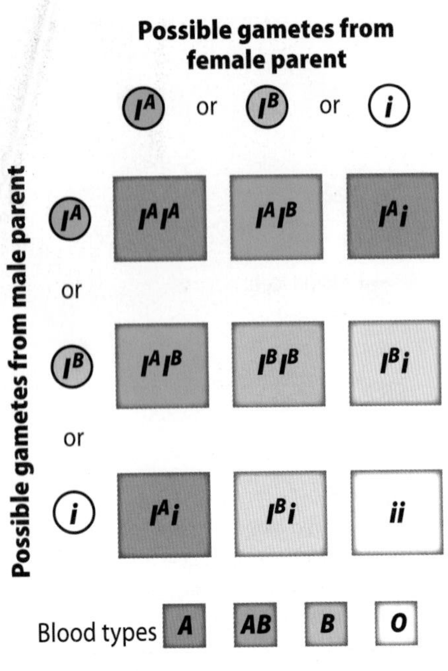

■ **Figure 6** There are three forms of alleles in the ABO blood group—I^A, I^B, and i.

Multiple Alleles

Not all traits are determined by two alleles. Some forms of inheritance are determined by more than two alleles referred to as **multiple alleles.** An example of such a trait is human blood group.

Blood groups in humans The ABO blood group, shown in **Figure 6,** has three forms of alleles, sometimes called AB markers: I^A is blood type A; I^B is blood type B; and i is blood type O. Type O is the absence of AB markers. Note that allele i is recessive to I^A and I^B. However, I^A and I^B are codominant; blood type AB results from both I^A and I^B alleles. Therefore, the ABO blood group is an example of both multiple alleles and codominance.

The Rh blood group includes Rh factors, inherited from each parent. Rh factors are either positive or negative (Rh+ or Rh–); Rh+ is dominant. The Rh factor is a blood protein named after the rhesus monkey because studies of the rhesus monkey led to discovery of that blood protein.

Coat color of rabbits Multiple alleles can demonstrate a hierarchy of dominance. In rabbits, four alleles code for coat color: C, c^{ch}, c^h, and c. Allele C is dominant to the other alleles and results in a full color coat. Allele c is recessive and results in an albino phenotype when the genotype is homozygous recessive. Allele c^{ch} is dominant to c^h, and allele c^h is dominant to c and the hierarchy of dominance can be written as $C > c^{ch} > c^h > c$. **Figure 7** shows the genotypes and phenotypes possible for rabbit-coat color. Full color is dominant over chinchilla, which is dominant over Himalayan, which is dominant over albino.

The presence of multiple alleles increases the possible number of genotypes and phenotypes. Without multiple-allele dominance, two alleles, such as T and t, produce only three possible genotypes—in this example TT, Tt, and tt—and two possible phenotypes. However, the four alleles for rabbit-coat color produce ten possible genotypes and four phenotypes, as shown in **Figure 7.** More variation in rabbit coat color comes from the interaction of the color gene with other genes.

■ **Figure 7** Rabbits have multiple alleles for coat color. The four alleles provide four basic variations in coat color.

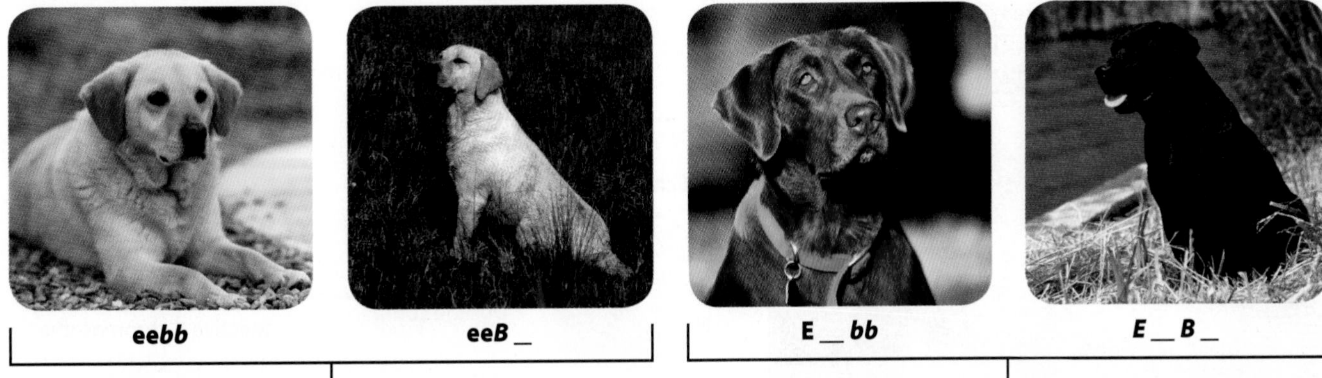

■ **Figure 8** The results of epistasis in coat color in Labrador retrievers show an interaction of two genes, each with two alleles. Note that an underscore in the genotype allows for either a dominant or recessive gene.

Epistasis

Coat color in Labrador retrievers can vary from yellow to black. This variety is the result of one allele hiding the effects of another allele, an interaction called **epistasis** (ih PIHS tuh sus). A Labrador's coat color is controlled by two sets of alleles. The dominant allele *E* determines whether the fur will have dark pigment. The fur of a dog with genotype *ee* will not have any pigment. The dominant B allele determines how dark the pigment will be. Study **Figure 8.** If the dog's genotype is *EEbb* or *Eebb,* the dog's fur will be chocolate brown. Genotypes *eebb, eeBb,* and *eeBB* will produce a yellow coat, because the *e* allele masks the effects of the dominant *B* allele.

Sex Determination

Each cell in your body, except for gametes, contains 46 chromosomes, or 23 pairs of chromosomes. One pair of these chromosomes, the **sex chromosomes,** determines an individual's gender. There are two types of sex chromosomes—X and Y. Individuals with two X chromosomes are female, and individuals with an X and a Y chromosome are male. The other 22 pairs of chromosomes are called **autosomes.** The offspring's gender is determined by the combination of sex chromosomes in the egg and sperm cell, as shown in **Figure 9.**

Color-Enhanced SEM Magnification: unavailable

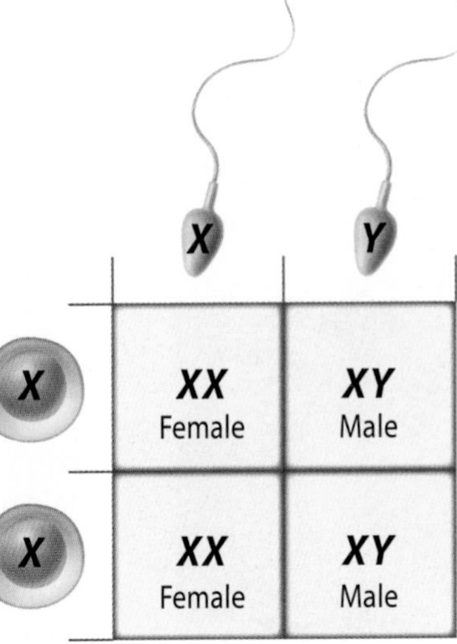

■ **Figure 9**
Left: The size and shape of the Y chromosome and the X chromosome are quite different from one another.
Right: The segregation of the sex chromosomes into gametes and the random combination of sperm and egg cells result in an approximately 1:1 ratio of males to females.

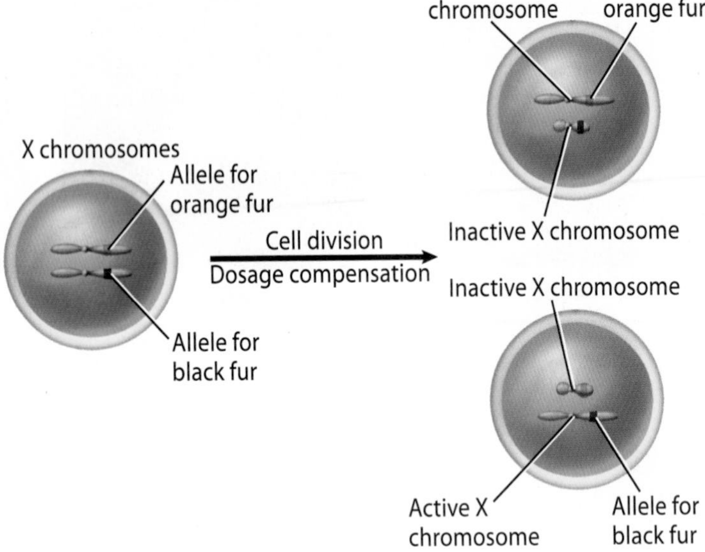

Figure 10 The calico coat of this cat results from the random inactivation of the X chromosomes in body cells. One X chromosome codes for orange fur, and one X chromosome codes for black fur, as illustrated on the right.

Dosage Compensation

Human females have 22 pairs of autosomes and one pair of X chromosomes. Males have 22 pairs of autosomes, along with one X and one Y chromosome. If you examine the X and Y chromosomes in **Figure 9,** you will notice that the X chromosome is larger than the Y chromosome. The X chromosome carries a variety of genes that are necessary for the development of both females and males. The Y chromosome mainly has genes that relate to the development of male characteristics.

Because females have two X chromosomes, it seems as though females get two doses of the X chromosome and males get only one dose. To balance the difference in the dose of X-related genes, one of the X chromosomes stops working in each of the female's body cells. This often is called dosage compensation or X-inactivation. Which X chromosome stops working in each body cell is a completely random event. Dosage compensation occurs in all mammals.

As a result of the Human Genome Project, the National Institutes of Health (NIH) has released new information on the sequence of the human X chromosome. Researchers now think that some genes on the inactivated X chromosome are more active than was previously thought.

Chromosome inactivation The coat colors of the calico cat shown in **Figure 10** are caused by the random inactivation of a particular X chromosome. The resulting colors depend on the X chromosome that is activated. The orange patches are formed by the inactivation of the X chromosome carrying the allele for black coat color. Similarly, the black patches are a result of the inactivation of the X chromosome carrying the allele for orange coat color.

Barr bodies The inactivated X chromosomes can be observed in cells. In 1949, Canadian scientist Murray Barr observed inactivated X chromosomes in female calico cats. He noticed a condensed, darkly stained structure in the nucleus. The darkly stained, inactivated X chromosomes, such as the one shown in **Figure 11,** are called Barr bodies. It was discovered later that only females, including human females, have Barr bodies in their cell nuclei.

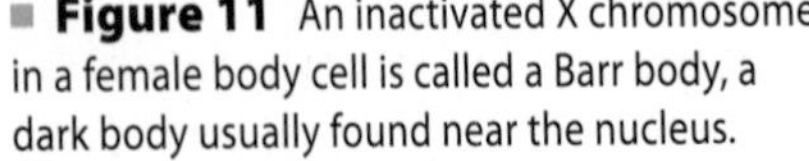

Figure 11 An inactivated X chromosome in a female body cell is called a Barr body, a dark body usually found near the nucleus.

Phase contrast LM Magnification: 1000×

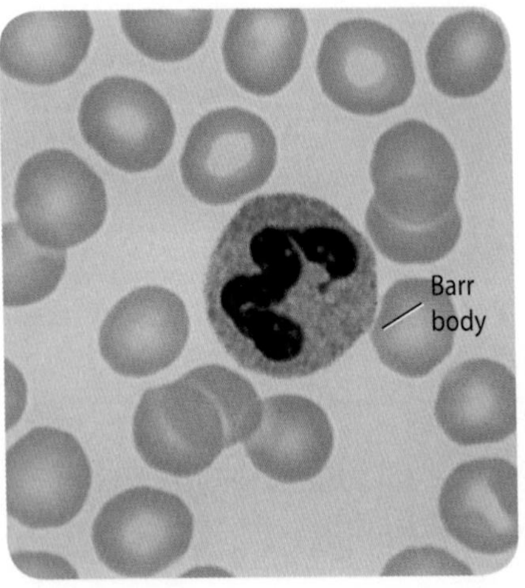

Sex-Linked Traits

Traits controlled by genes located on the X chromosome are called **sex-linked traits,** or X-linked traits. Because males have only one X chromosome, they are affected by recessive X-linked traits more often than are females. Females are less likely to express a recessive X-linked trait because the other X chromosome may mask the effect of the trait.

Some traits that are located on autosomes may appear to be sex-linked, even though they are not. This occurs when an allele appears to be dominant in one gender but recessive in the other. For example, the allele for baldness is recessive in females but dominant in males, causing hair loss that follows a typical pattern called male-pattern baldness. A male would be bald if he were heterozygous for the trait, while a female would be bald only if she were homozygous recessive.

Red-green color blindness The trait for red-green color blindness is a recessive X-linked trait. About 8 percent of males in the United States have red-green color blindness. The photos in **Figure 12** show how a person with red-green color blindness might view colors compared to a person who does not have red-green color blindness.

Study the Punnett square shown in **Figure 12.** The mother is a carrier for color blindness because she has the recessive allele for color blindness on one of her X chromosomes. The father is not color blind because he does not have the recessive allele. The sex-linked trait is represented by writing the allele on the X chromosome. Notice that the only offspring that can possibly have red-green color blindness is a male child. As a result of it being an X-linked trait, red-green color blindness is very rare in females.

■ **Figure 12** People with red-green color blindness view red and green as shades of gray.
Explain *why there are fewer females who have red-green color blindness than males.*

X^B = Normal
X^b = Red-green color blind
Y = Y chromosome

	X^B	Y
X^B	X^BX^B	X^BY
X^b	X^BX^b	X^bY

Queen Victoria's Pedigree

I
Edward Duke of Kent
Victoria Princess of Saxe-Coburg

II
Queen Victoria of England

III
(no affected descendants)
Leopold Duke of Albany
Alice
King Edward VII of England
Modern English royal family
Victoria
Emperor Frederick III of Germany
Beatrice

IV
Alice
Alix (Alexandra)
Tsar Nicholas II of Russia
Irene
Prince Henry of Prussia
King Alfonso XIII of Spain
Victoria

V
Rupert
Olga
Tatiana
Marie
Anastasia
Alexis
Russian royal family
German royal family

VI
Alfonso
Gonzalo
Spanish royal family

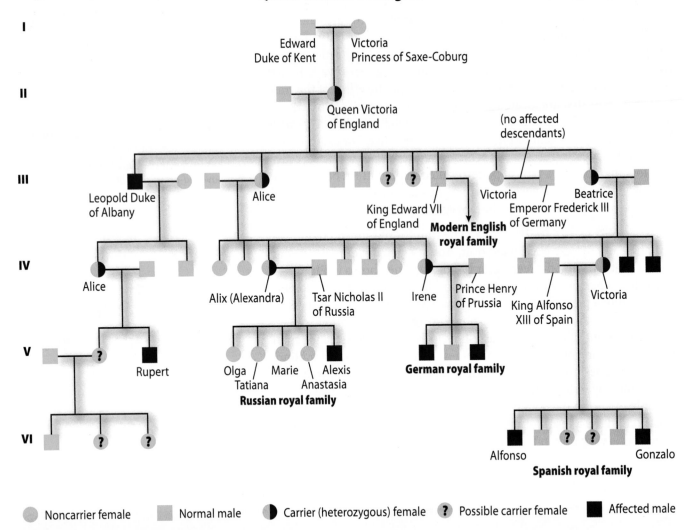

Noncarrier female | Normal male | Carrier (heterozygous) female | Possible carrier female | Affected male

■ **Figure 13** The pedigree above shows the inheritance of hemophilia in the royal families of England, Germany, Spain, and Russia, starting with the children of Queen Victoria.
Determine ***which of Alexandra's children inherited hemophilia.***

Hemophilia Hemophilia, another recessive sex-linked disorder, is characterized by delayed clotting of the blood. Like red-green color blindness, this disorder is more common in males than in females.

A famous pedigree of hemophilia is one that arose in the family of Queen Victoria of England (1819–1901). Her son Leopold died of hemophilia, and her daughters Alice and Beatrice, as illustrated in the pedigree in **Figure 13,** were carriers for the disease. Alice and Beatrice passed on the hemophilia trait to the Russian, German, and Spanish royal families. Follow the generations in this pedigree to see how this trait was passed through Queen Victoria's family. Queen Victoria's granddaughter Alexandra, who was a carrier for this trait, married sar Nicholas II of Russia. Irene, another granddaughter, passed the trait on to the German royal family. Hemophilia was passed to the Spanish royal family through a third granddaughter, whose name also was Victoria.

Virtual Lab 

Men with hemophilia usually died at an early age until the twentieth century when clotting factors were discovered and given to hemophiliacs. However, blood-borne viruses such as Hepatitis C and HIV were often contracted by hemophiliacs until the 1990s, when safer methods of blood transfusion were discovered.

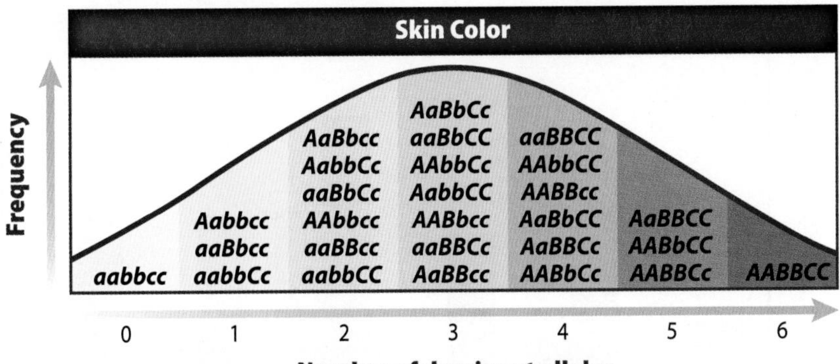

■ **Figure 14** This graph shows possible shades of skin color from three sets of alleles, although the trait is thought to involve more than three sets of alleles.

Predict ***Would more gene pairs increase or decrease the number of possible phenotypes?***

Polygenic Traits

You have examined traits determined by a pair of genes. Many phenotypic traits, however, arise from the interaction of multiple pairs of genes. Such traits are called **polygenic traits.** Traits such as skin color, height, eye color, and fingerprint pattern are polygenic traits. One characteristic of polygenic traits is that, when the frequency of the number of dominant alleles is graphed, as shown in **Figure 14,** the result is a bell-shaped curve. This shows that more of the intermediate phenotypes exist than do the extreme phenotypes.

 GET IT? **Infer** Why would a graph showing the frequency of the number of dominant alleles for polygenic traits be a bell-shaped curve?

Environmental Influences

The environment also has an effect on phenotype. For example, the tendency to develop heart disease can be inherited. However, environmental factors such as diet and exercise also can contribute to the occurrence and seriousness of the disease. Other ways in which environment influences phenotype are very familiar to you. You may not have thought of them in terms of phenotype, however. Sunlight, water, and temperature are environmental influences that commonly affect an organism's phenotype.

Sunlight and water Without enough sunlight, most flowering plants do not bear flowers. Many plants lose their leaves in response to water deficiency.

Temperature Most organisms experience phenotypic changes from extreme temperature changes. In extreme heat, for example, many plants suffer. Their leaves droop, flower buds shrivel, chlorophyll disappears, and roots stop growing. These are examples that probably do not surprise you, although you may have never thought of them as phenotypic changes. What other environmental factors affect the phenotypes of organisms? Temperature also influences the expression of genes. Notice the fur of the Siamese cat shown in **Figure 15.** The cat's tail, feet, ears, and nose are dark. These areas of the cat's body are cooler than the rest. The gene that codes for production of the color pigment in the Siamese cat's body functions only under cooler conditions. Therefore, the cooler regions are darker; and the warmer regions, where pigment production is inhibited by temperature, are lighter.

■ **Figure 15** Temperature affects the expression of color pigment in the fur of Siamese cats.

Carolyne A. McKeone/Science Source

■ **Figure 16** When a trait is found more often in both members of identical twins than in fraternal twins, the trait is presumed to have a significant inherited component.

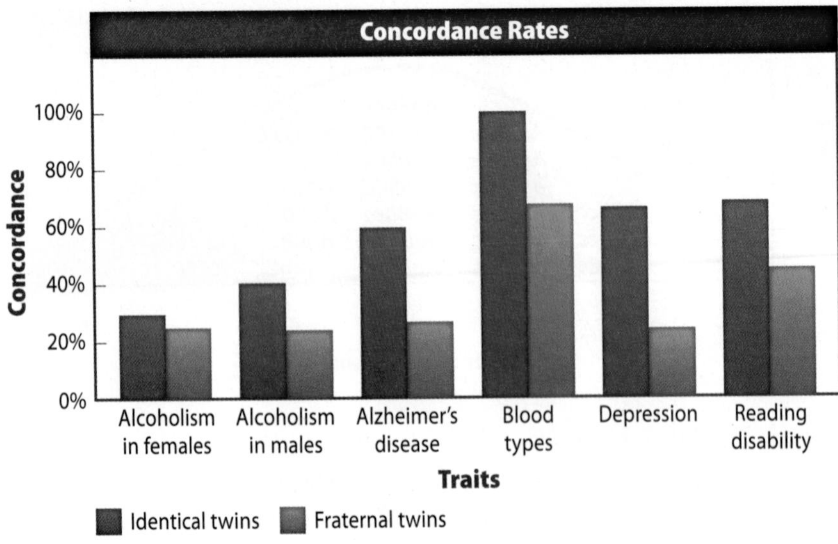

Launch Lab

Review Based on what you have read about human inheritance, how would you now answer the analysis questions?

Twin Studies

Another way to study inheritance patterns is to focus on identical twins, which helps scientists separate genetic contributions from environmental contributions. Identical twins are genetically the same. If a trait is inherited, both identical twins will have the trait. Scientists conclude that traits that appear frequently in identical twins are at least partially controlled by heredity. Also, scientists presume that traits expressed differently in identical twins are strongly influenced by environment. The percentage of twins who both express a given trait is called a concordance rate. Examine **Figure 16** for some traits and their concordance rates. A large difference between fraternal twins and identical twins shows a strong genetic influence.

REVIEW IT! Complex Patterns of Inheritance

Section Summary

- Some traits are inherited through complex inheritance patterns, such as incomplete dominance, codominance, and multiple alleles.
- Gender is determined by X and Y chromosomes. Some traits are linked to the X chromosome.
- Polygenic traits involve more than one pair of alleles.
- Both genes and environment influence an organism's phenotype.
- Studies of inheritance patterns of large families and twins give insight into complex human inheritance.

Self Check

Understand Main Ideas

1. MAINIDEA **Describe** two patterns of complex inheritance and explain how they are different from Mendelian patterns.
2. **Explain** What is epistasis, and how is it different from dominance?
3. **Determine** the genotypes of the parents if the father is blood type A, the mother is blood type B, the daughter is blood type O, one son is blood type AB, and the other son is blood type B.
4. **Analyze** how twin studies help to differentiate the effects of genetic and environmental influences.

Think Critically

5. **Evaluate** whether having sickle-cell disease would be advantageous or disadvantageous to a person living in central Africa.

MATH IN ▶ Biology

6. What is the chance of producing a son with normal vision if the father is color-blind and the mother is homozygous normal for the trait? Explain.

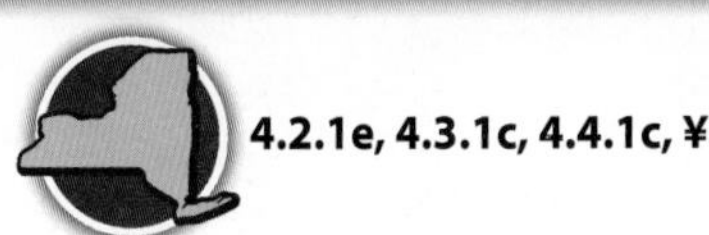

3 Chromosomes and Human Heredity

4.2.1e, 4.3.1c, 4.4.1c, ¥a

MAIN IDEA
Chromosomes can be studied using karyotypes.

Essential Questions

- How are karyotypes used to study genetic disorders?
- What is the role of telomeres?
- How is nondisjunction related to Down syndrome and other abnormal chromosome numbers?
- What are the benefits and risks of diagnostic fetal testing?

BIOLOGY 4U

Have you ever lost one of the playing pieces belonging to a game? You might not have been able to play the game because the missing piece was important. Just as a misplaced game piece affects a game, a missing chromosome has a significant impact on the organism.

Review Vocabulary

mitosis: a process in the nucleus of a dividing cell, including prophase, metaphase, anaphase, and telophase

New Vocabulary

karyotype
telomere
nondisjunction

Multilingual eGlossary

Karyotype Studies

The study of genetic material does not involve the study of genes alone. Scientists also study whole chromosomes by using images of chromosomes stained during metaphase. The staining bands identify or mark identical places on homologous chromosomes. During metaphase of mitosis, each chromosome has condensed greatly and consists of two sister chromatids. The pairs of homologous chromosomes are arranged in decreasing size to produce a micrograph called a **karyotype** (KER ee uh tipe). Karyotypes of a human male and a human female, each with 23 pairs of chromosomes, are shown in **Figure 17.** Notice that the 22 autosomes are matched together with one pair of nonmatching sex chromosomes.

Telomeres

Scientists have found that chromosomes end in protective caps called **telomeres.** Telomere caps consist of DNA associated with proteins. The cap serves a protective function for the structure of the chromosome. Scientists have discovered that telomeres also might be involved in both aging and cancer.

■ **Figure 17** Karyotypes arrange the pairs of homologous chromosomes from increasing to decreasing size.
Distinguish ***which two chromosomes are arranged separately from the other pairs.***

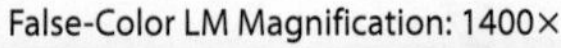
False-Color LM Magnification: 1400×

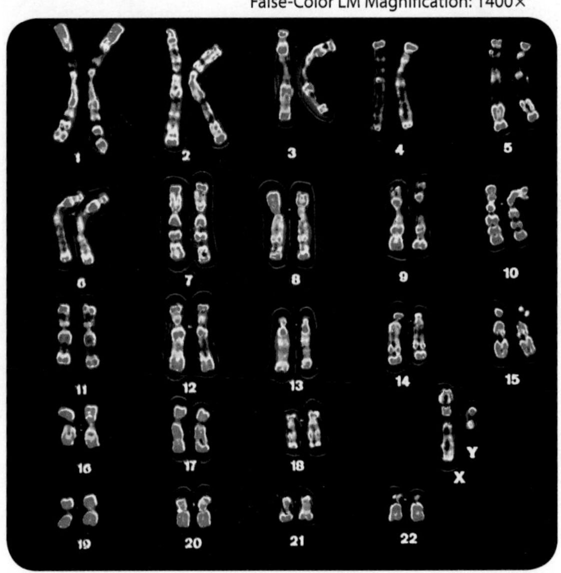

False-Color LM Magnification: 1400×

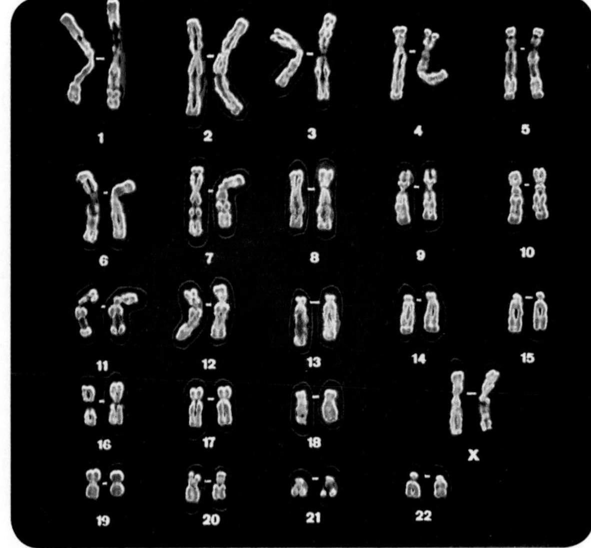

VISUALIZING Nondisjunction

Figure 18 Gametes with abnormal numbers of chromosomes can result from nondisjunction during meiosis. The orange chromosomes come from one parent, and the blue chromosomes come from the other parent.

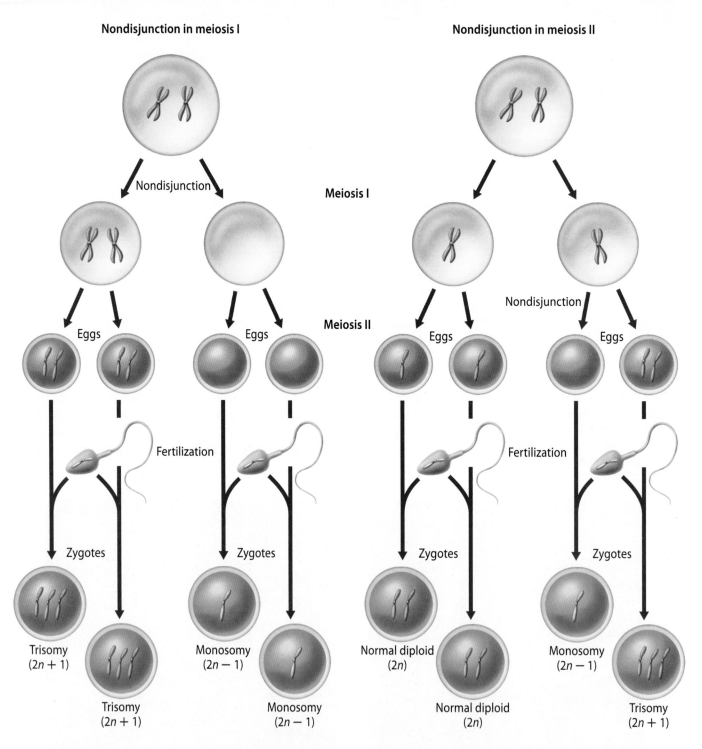

Nondisjunction

During cell division, the chromosomes separate, with one of each of the sister chromatids going to opposite poles of the cell. Therefore, each new cell has the correct number of chromosomes. Cell division during which sister chromatids fail to separate properly, which does happen occasionally, is called **nondisjunction.**

If nondisjunction occurs during meiosis I or meiosis II, as shown in **Figure 18,** the resulting gametes will not have the correct number of chromosomes. When one of these gametes fertilizes another gamete, the resulting offspring will not have the correct number of chromosomes. Notice that nondisjunction can result in extra copies of a certain chromosome or only one copy of a particular chromosome in the offspring. Having a set of three chromosomes of one kind is called trisomy (TRI so me). Having only one of a particular type of chromosome is called monosomy (MAH nuh so me). Nondisjunction can occur in any organism in which gametes are produced through meiosis. In humans, alterations of chromosome numbers are associated with serious human disorders, which are often are fatal.

Down syndrome One of the earliest known human chromosomal disorders is Down syndrome. It is the result of an extra chromosome 21. Therefore, Down syndrome often is called trisomy 21. Examine the karyotype of a child with Down syndrome, shown in **Figure 19.** Notice that she has three copies of chromosome 21. The characteristics of Down syndrome include distinctive facial features, as shown in **Figure 19,** short stature, heart defects, and mental disability. The frequency of children born with Down syndrome in the United States is approximately one out of 800. The frequency of Down syndrome increases with the age of the mother. Studies have shown that the risk of having a child with Down syndrome is about six percent in mothers who are 45 and older.

CAREERS IN **BIOLOGY**

Research Scientist Research scientists know and research a particular field of science, such as genetic disorders. Most research scientists begin their work in their undergraduate studies and continue on to a Master's degree or Ph.D.

■ **Figure 19** A person with Down syndrome has distinctive features and will have a karyotype that shows three copies of chromosome number 21.

False-Color LM Magnification: 1400×

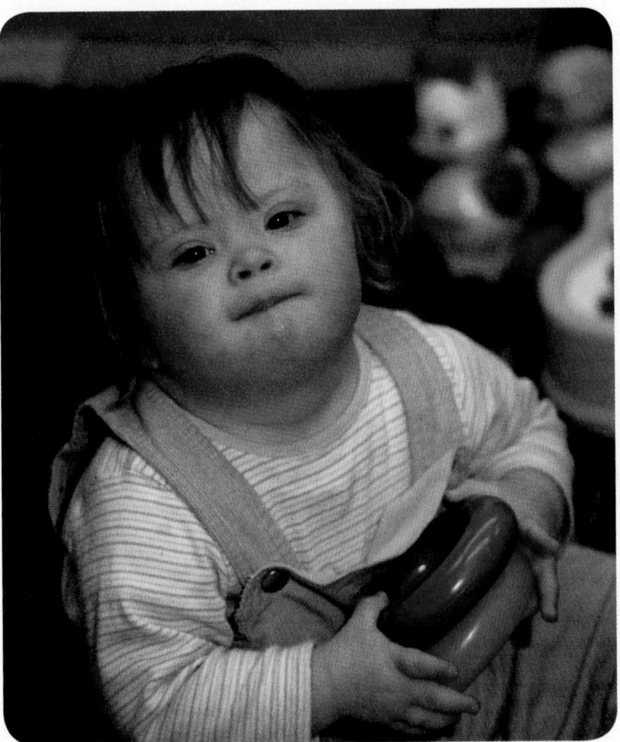

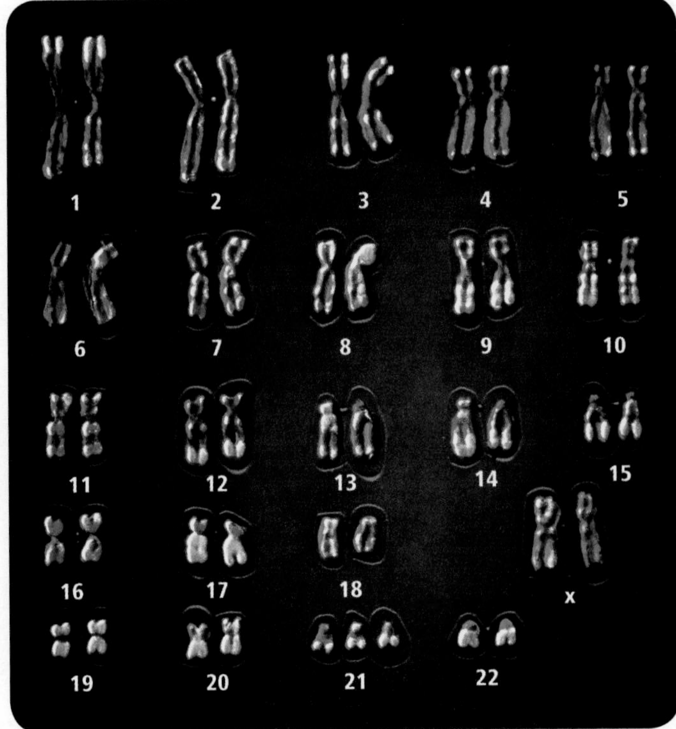

(l)Lauren Shear/Science Source, (r)CNRI/Science Source

Table 4 Nondisjunction in Sex Chromosomes — Interactive Table

Genotype	XX	XO	XXX	XY	XXY	XYY	OY
Example							
Phenotype	Normal female	Female with Turner's syndrome	Nearly normal female	Normal male	Male with Klinefelter's syndrome	Normal or nearly normal male	Results in death

Sex chromosomes Nondisjunction occurs in both autosomes and sex chromosomes. Some of the results of nondisjunction in human sex chromosomes are listed in **Table 4.** Note that an individual with Turner's syndrome has only one sex chromosome. This condition results from fertilization with a gamete that had no sex chromosome.

Fetal Testing

Couples who suspect they might be carriers for certain genetic disorders might want to have a fetal test performed. Older couples also might wish to know the chromosomal status of their developing baby, called the fetus. Various types of tests for observing both the mother and the baby are available.

MiniLAB 2

Explore the Methods of the Geneticist

How do geneticists learn about human heredity? Traditional methods used to investigate the genetics of plants, animals, and microbes are not suitable or possible to use on humans. A pedigree is one useful tool for investigating human inheritance. In this lab, you will explore yet another tool of the geneticist—population sampling.

Procedure

1. Read and complete the lab safety form.
2. Construct a data table as instructed by your teacher.
3. Survey your group for the hitchhiker's thumb trait.
4. Survey your group for other traits determined by your teacher.
5. Compile the class data, and analyze the traits that you investigated in the survey population. Determine which of the traits are dominant and which are recessive.

Analysis

1. **Interpret Data** What numerical clue did you look for to determine whether each trait surveyed was dominant or recessive?
2. **Think Critically** How could you check to see if you correctly identified dominant and recessive traits? Explain why you might have misidentified a trait.

Table 5 Fetal Tests — Interactive Table

Test	Benefit	Risk
Amniocentesis	• Diagnosis of chromosome abnormalities • Diagnosis of other defects	• Discomfort for expectant mother • Slight risk of infection • Risk of miscarriage
Chorionic villus sampling	• Diagnosis of chromosome abnormality • Diagnosis of certain genetic defects	• Risk of miscarriage • Risk of infection • Risk of newborn limb defects
Fetal blood sampling	• Diagnosis of genetic or chromosome abnormality • Checks for fetal blood problems and oxygen levels • Medications can be given to the fetus before birth	• Risk of bleeding from sample site • Risk of infection • Amniotic fluid might leak • Risk of fetal death

Connection to Health Many fetal tests can provide important information to the parents and the physician. **Table 5** describes the risks and benefits of some of the fetal tests that are available. Physicians must consider many factors when advising parents about such examinations. At least a small degree of risk is possible in any test or procedure. A physician would not want to advise tests that would endanger the mother or the fetus; therefore, when considering whether to recommend fetal testing, a physician would need to consider previous health problems of the mother and also the health of the fetus. If the physician and parents determine that any fetal test is needed, the health of both the mother and the fetus is closely monitored throughout the testing.

REVIEW IT! Chromosomes and Human Heredity

Section Summary

- Karyotypes are micrographs of chromosomes.
- Chromosomes terminate in a cap called a telomere.
- Nondisjunction results in gametes with an abnormal number of chromosomes.
- Down syndrome is a result of nondisjunction.
- Tests for assessing the possibility of genetic and chromosomal disorders are available.

Understand Main Ideas

1. MAINIDEA Explain how a scientist might use a karyotype to study genetic disorders.
2. **Summarize** the role of telomeres.
3. **Illustrate** Draw a sketch to show how nondisjunction occurs during meiosis.
4. **Analyze** Why might missing sections of the X or Y chromosome be a bigger problem in males than deletions would be in one of the X chromosomes in females?

Think Critically

5. **Create** a karyotype of a female organism in which $2n = 8$, showing trisomy of chromosome 3.
6. **Discuss** the benefits and risks of fetal testing.

WRITING IN Biology

7. Conduct research on the consequences of nondisjunction other than trisomy 21. Write a paragraph about your findings.

cutting-edge BIOLOGY

1.1.2a, 1.1.2b

Genetics and Beef Cattle

Inherited traits are not unique to humans. Genetic factors also determine the characteristics of livestock. Livestock geneticists study the genes of livestock animals, such as beef or dairy cattle, and seek to improve the quality of the livestock by identifying disease-causing genes and other factors that affect the characteristics of the animals and their offspring. In Texas and other beef-producing states, livestock geneticists work to improve the quality of beef cattle. DNA samples from beef cattle are collected from hair roots, blood, semen, and tissue for analysis, and data comparing the animals' physical traits to DNA sequences are analyzed.

Livestock geneticists perform genetic tests that can predict the characteristics of a cow's offspring.

Qualitative and Quantitative Traits When a livestock producer raises beef cattle for profit, there are certain characteristics that make the cattle more profitable or more desirable. Often, these characteristics are genetically determined. There are two general types of characteristics, qualitative and quantitative. A qualitative trait is a characteristic that is generally visible. Qualitative genetic traits include the color of the hair on the hide and the lack of horns on the head (polled). Quantitative genetic traits are not visible. These traits include marbling and tenderness of the meat, high weaning weights of the calves, milk production of cows, and rate of weight gain of calves after weaning. These traits are genetically determined, but they also depend on environmental factors.

Bovine Genetics Cattle, also called bovine, have a genome that is composed of 30 pairs of chromosomes and around 3 billion base pairs. Some genes act with other genes to produce dominant characteristics, such as hair color and polled or non-polled. These genes are called dominant genes. Other genes, called additive genes, can affect more than one trait. These genes produce characteristics that are important to producers, such as marbling and meat tenderness. The selection for these traits is determined by the amount of genetic variation produced by the genes.

Currently, genetic tests can determine which genes control some dominant characteristics, such as polled or non-polled or black or non-black (red). The chromosomal locations of additive genes have not been determined. So, cattle breeders must look for genetic markers in DNA. When the genetic markers are present in the DNA, the offspring have a high probability of exhibiting the characteristics predicted by the markers.

Beef producers from Texas and other states use DNA testing of cattle to determine parentage, disease or genetic defects, and other qualitative and quantitative inherited traits. The costs of DNA tests must be weighed against the improved qualities in the herd to determine the economic value of the genetic testing.

Investigate

Draw Inferences There are several companies that offer DNA testing services to beef producers. Research and find three or more companies that offer these services. Review their promotional materials and infer what genetic information their DNA tests provide, such as specific genes that control dominant traits or genetic markers that predict the traits of offspring. Create a brochure to present your results.

WebQuest

Getty Images/Image Source

BioLAB ¥o

What's in a face? Investigate Inherited Human Facial Characteristics

Background: Most people know that they inherit their hair color and their eye color from their parents. However, there are many other head and facial traits that humans inherit. In this lab, you will investigate a number of different inherited facial structures that combine to compose a human face.

Question: *What structures that comprise the human face are actually determined genetically?*

Materials

coins, 2 per team: heads=dominant trait, tails=recessive trait
table of inherited human facial characteristics provided by the teacher

Procedure

1. Read and complete the lab safety form.
2. Partner with a classmate.
3. One member of the team will represent the father, and one member will represent the mother. Decide which partner will represent the father and who will represent the mother.
4. Have the person representing the father flip a coin. If the coin lands *heads* facing up, the offspring is a female; if the coin lands *tails* facing up, the offspring is a male. Record the gender of the offspring.
5. Flip your coin at the same time as your partner. Flip the coins only once for each trait.
6. Continue to flip coins for each trait shown in the table. After each coin flip, record the trait of your offspring by placing a check in the appropriate box in the table.
7. Once the traits are determined, draw the offspring's facial features, give him or her a name, and be prepared to introduce the offspring to the rest of the class.

Analyze and Conclude

1. **Think Critically** Why did the partner representing the father flip the coin initially to determine the gender of the offspring?
2. **Calculate** What percent chance was there of producing male offspring? Female offspring? Explain.
3. **Recognize Cause and Effect** What are the possible genotypes of parents of the following three children: a boy with straight hair (hh), a daughter with wavy hair (Hh), and a son with curly hair (HH)?
4. **Observe and Infer** Which traits show codominance?
5. **Analyze and Conclude** Would you expect other student pairs in the class to have offspring exactly like yours? Explain.

WRITING IN ▶ Biology

Research Imagine that you write a science column for a large newspaper. A reader has written to you asking for a job description for a genetic counselor. Research this question; then write a short newspaper column answering the question.

CHAPTER 11 STUDY GUIDE

BIGIDEA **Human inheritance does not always follow Mendel's laws.**

SECTION 1 Basic Patterns of Human Inheritance

MAINIDEA The inheritance of a trait over several generations can be shown in a pedigree.

- Genetic disorders can be caused by dominant or recessive alleles.
- Cystic fibrosis is a genetic disorder that affects mucus and sweat secretions.
- Individuals with albinism do not have melanin in their skin, hair, and eyes.
- Huntington's disease affects the nervous system.
- Achondroplasia sometimes is called dwarfism.
- Pedigrees are used to study human inheritance patterns.

VOCABULARY
- **carrier**
- **pedigree**

SECTION 2 Complex Patterns of Inheritance

MAINIDEA Complex inheritance of traits does not follow inheritance patterns described by Mendel.

- Some traits are inherited through complex inheritance patterns, such as incomplete dominance, codominance, and multiple alleles.
- Gender is determined by X and Y chromosomes. Some traits are linked to the X chromosome.
- Polygenic traits involve more than one pair of alleles.
- Both genes and environment influence an organism's phenotype.
- Studies of inheritance patterns of large families and twins give insight into complex human inheritance.

VOCABULARY
- **incomplete dominance**
- **codominance**
- **multiple alleles**
- **epistasis**
- **sex chromosome**
- **autosome**
- **sex-linked trait**
- **polygenic trait**

SECTION 3 Chromosomes and Human Heredity

MAINIDEA Chromosomes can be studied using karyotypes.

- Karyotypes are micrographs of chromosomes.
- Chromosomes terminate in a cap called a telomere.
- Nondisjunction results in gametes with an abnormal number of chromosomes.
- Down syndrome is a result of nondisjunction.
- Tests for assessing the possibility of genetic and chromosomal disorders are available.

VOCABULARY
- **karyotype**
- **telomere**
- **nondisjunction**

SECTION 1

Vocabulary Review

Use what you know about the vocabulary terms from the Study Guide page to answer the questions.

1. Which term describes a person who is heterozygous for a recessive disorder?

2. How is the inheritance pattern between parents and offspring represented diagrammatically?

Understand Main Ideas

3. Which condition is inherited as a dominant allele?
   A. albinism
   B. cystic fibrosis
   C. Tay-Sachs disease
   D. Huntington's disease

4. Which is not a characteristic of a person with cystic fibrosis?
   A. chloride channel defect
   B. digestive problems
   C. lack of skin pigment
   D. recurrent lung infections

Use the diagram below to answer questions 5 and 6.

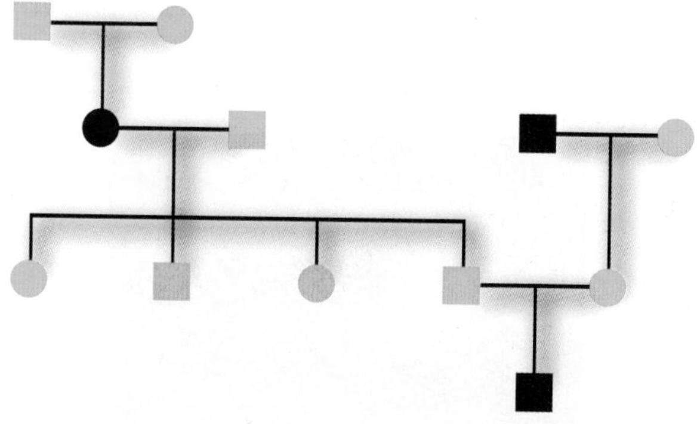

5. Which disorder could not follow the inheritance pattern shown?
   A. cystic fibrosis
   B. albinism
   C. Tay-Sachs disease
   D. Huntington's disease

6. **MAINIDEA** How many affected males and females are in the pedigree?
   A. 1 male, 2 females **C.** 1 male, 1 female
   B. 2 males, 1 female **D.** 2 males, 2 females

Constructed Response

Use the photo below to answer question 7.

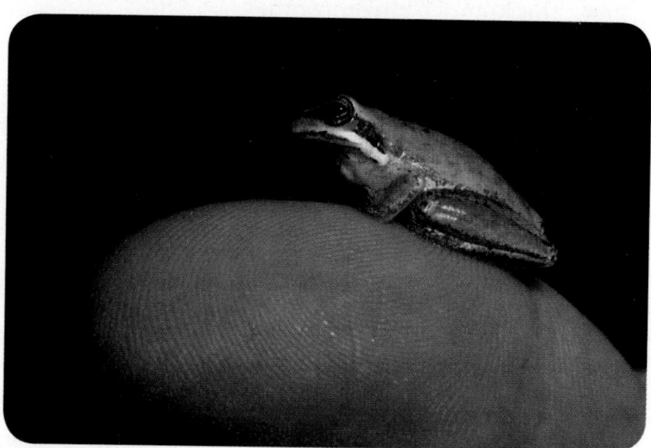

7. **Open Ended** Imagine that all animals have the same genetic disorders that humans have. What is the biological name of the genetic disorder that this dwarf tree frog would have? Describe the inheritance pattern of the genetic disorder.

8. **Short Answer** Predict the genotypes of the children of a father with Huntington's disease and an unaffected mother.

Think Critically

9. **Draw a conclusion** about the relationship of chloride ions to the excessively thick mucus in a patient suffering from cystic fibrosis.

SECTION 2

Vocabulary Review

Replace each underlined word with the correct vocabulary term from the Study Guide page.

10. <u>Codominance</u> is an inheritance pattern in which the heterozygous genotype results in an intermediate phenotype between the dominant and recessive phenotype.

11. A characteristic that has more than one pair of possible traits is said to be a(n) <u>epistasis</u>.

12. Genes found on the sex chromosomes are associated with <u>multiple alleles</u>.

Understand Main Ideas

13. What determines gender in humans?
    - **A.** the X and Y chromosomes
    - **B.** chromosome 21
    - **C.** codominance
    - **D.** epistasis
14. **MAIN**IDEA Which two terms best describe the inheritance of human blood types?
    - **A.** incomplete dominance and codominance
    - **B.** codominance and multiple alleles
    - **C.** incomplete dominance and multiple alleles
    - **D.** codominance and epistasis

Use the photos below to answer question 15.

15. **THEME FOCUS** In radishes, color is controlled by incomplete dominance. The figure above shows the phenotype for each color. What phenotypic ratios would you expect from crossing two heterozygous plants?
    - **A.** 2:2 red: white
    - **B.** 1:1:1 red: purple: white
    - **C.** 1:2:1 red: purple: white
    - **D.** 3:1 red: white

Constructed Response

16. **Short Answer** How does epistasis explain the differences in coat color in Labrador retrievers?
17. **Short Answer** Explain whether a male could be heterozygous for red-green color blindness.
18. **Short Answer** What types of phenotypes would one look for if a phenotype were a result of polygenic inheritance?

Think Critically

19. **Evaluate** why it might be difficult to perform genetic analysis in humans.
20. **Summarize** the meaning of the following information regarding trait inheritance: For a certain trait, identical twins have a concordance rate of 54 percent and fraternal twins have a rate of less than five percent.

SECTION 3

Vocabulary Review

Identify the vocabulary term from the Study Guide page described by each definition.

21. the protective ends of the chromosome
22. an error that occurs during cell division
23. a micrograph of stained chromosomes

Understand Main Ideas

24. **MAIN**IDEA What could explain a human karyotype showing 47 chromosomes?
    - **A.** monosomy
    - **B.** trisomy
    - **C.** codominance
    - **D.** dominant traits
25. Why does nondisjunction occur?
    - **A.** Cytokinesis does not occur properly.
    - **B.** The nucleoli do not disappear.
    - **C.** The sister chromatids do not separate.
    - **D.** The chromosomes do not condense properly.

Use the photo below to answer question 26.

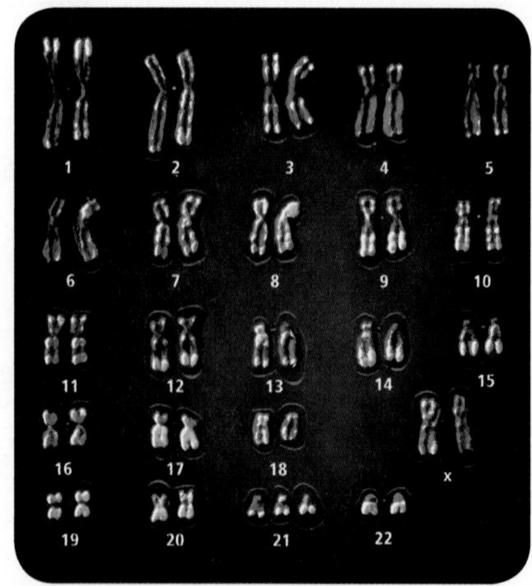

26. What disorder can be identified in the karyotype?
    - **A.** Turner's syndrome
    - **B.** Klinefelter's syndrome
    - **C.** Down syndrome
    - **D.** The karyotype shows no disorder.

27. Which statement concerning telomeres is not true?
   A. They are found on the ends of chromosomes.
   B. They consist of DNA and sugars.
   C. They protect chromosomes.
   D. They are involved with aging.

Constructed Response

Use the photo below to answer question 28.

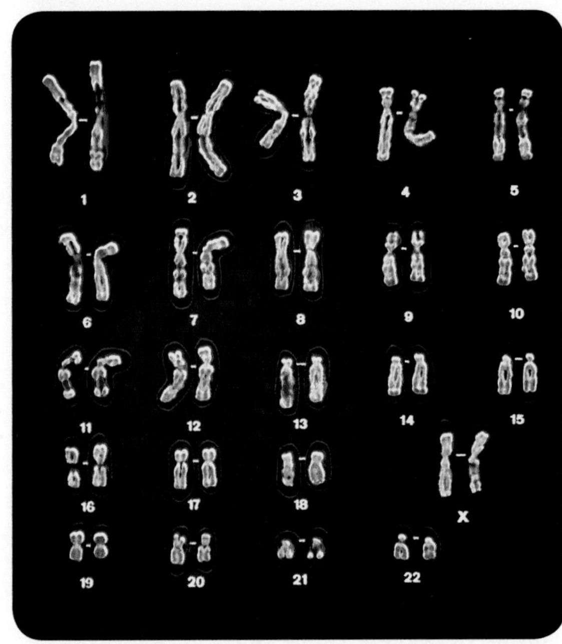

28. **Short Answer** Describe a fetal test that results in the karyotype shown above.

29. **Short Answer** What characteristics are associated with Down syndrome?

30. **Open Ended** Most cases of trisomy and monosomy in humans are fatal. Why might this be?

Think Critically

31. **Hypothesize** why chromosomes need telomeres.

32. **Explain** why a girl who has Turner's syndrome has red-green color blindness even though both of her parents have normal vision.

33. **Illustrate** what might have occurred to result in an extra chromosome in the following example: A technician is constructing a karyotype from male fetal cells. The technician discovers that the cells have one extra X chromosome.

CNRI/Science Source

Summative Assessment

34. **BIGIDEA** Give a specific example of an inheritable trait that does not follow Mendel's laws of inheritance. Apply Mendel's laws to that trait, and infer how the resulting genotypes and phenotypes would be different from what actually exists.

35. Describe how hemophilia is inherited.

36. Describe the cause of Down syndrome.

37. **WRITING IN ▶ Biology** Write a scenario for one of the genetic disorders described in **Table 2.** Then create a pedigree illustrating the scenario.

DBQ Document–Based Questions

Answer the questions below concerning the effect of environment on phenotype.

Data obtained from: Harnly, M.H. 1936. Genetics. *Journal of Experimental Zoology* 56: 363–379.

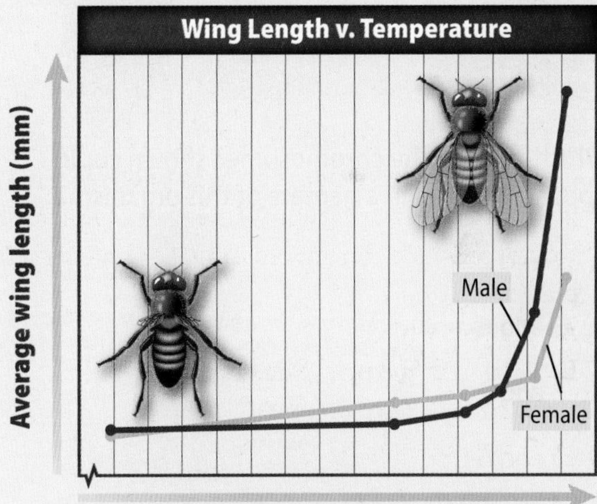

38. At which temperature is wing length the greatest?

39. Is male or female wing length more influenced by temperature? Explain.

40. What is the relationship between temperature and wing length for all flies?

CUMULATIVE
MULTIPLE CHOICE

Use the diagram below to answer questions 1 to 3.

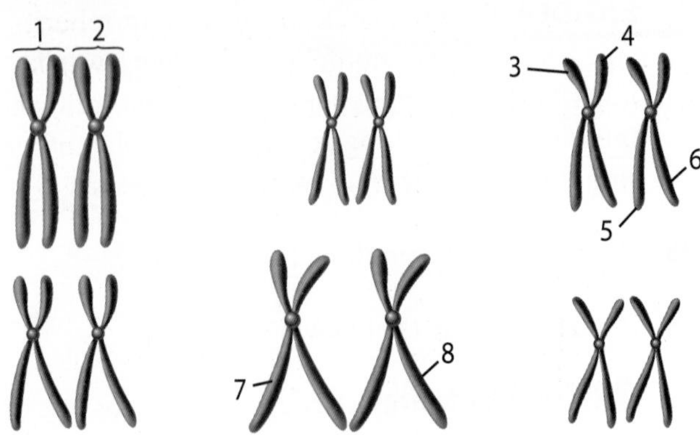

1 Which labeled structures represent a homologous pair?

A 1 and 2

B 3 and 4

C 3 and 6

D 7 and 8

2 Which parts of the chromosomes shown could appear together in a gamete of this organism?

A 1 and 2

B 3 and 6

C 3 and 7

D 5 and 6

3 If the diagram shows all the chromosomes from a body cell, how many chromosomes would be in a gamete of this organism at the end of meiosis I?

A 3

B 6

C 9

D 12

SHORT ANSWER

4 In pea plants, yellow seed color is the dominant trait, and green seed color is the recessive trait. Use a Punnett square to show the results of a cross between a heterozygous yellow-seed plant and a green-seed plant.

5 Based on your Punnett square from question 4, what percentage of the offspring would have a homozygous genotype? Explain your answer.

6 Because Huntington's disease is a dominant genetic disorder, it might seem that it would be selected out of a population naturally. Write a hypothesis that states why the disease continues to occur.

7 Explain how a cancerous tumor results from a disruption of the cell cycle.

8 Write, in order, the steps that must occur for cell division to result in an organism with trisomy.

9 Which function in metabolism is performed by both the thylakoid membrane and the mitochondrial membrane? Give a reason why this function might or might not be important.

10 Suppose two parents have a mild form of a genetic disease, but their child is born with a very severe form of the same disease. What kind of inheritance pattern took place for this disease?

11 Describe an example of each of the following: species diversity, genetic diversity, and ecosystem diversity.

EXTENDED RESPONSE

Use the diagram below to answer question 12.

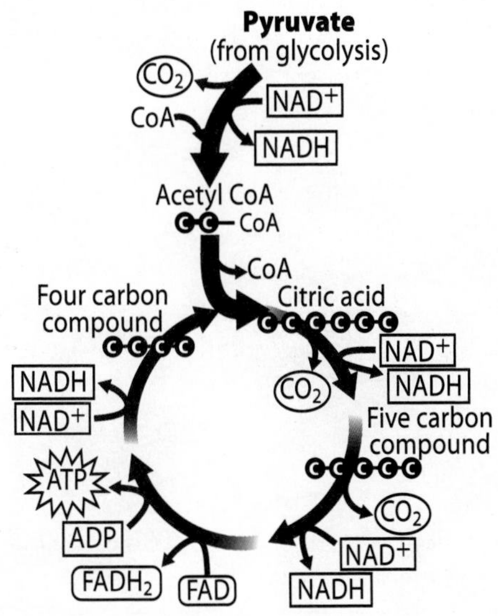

12 Identify the cycle in the figure and summarize the steps of the cycle.

13 Describe the function of microtubules, and predict what might happen if cells did NOT have microtubules.

ESSAY QUESTION

The type of pea plants that Mendel investigated had either purple flowers or white flowers. One flower-color trait is dominant, and the other is recessive.

Using the information in the paragraph above, answer the following question in essay format.

14 Explain what crosses Mendel would have performed to determine which color is the dominant trait.

TEST PRACTICE

Use the pedigree below to answer questions 15 and 16.

A researcher investigated generations of a family with a history of a genetic disease. She developed the following pedigree based on data collected.

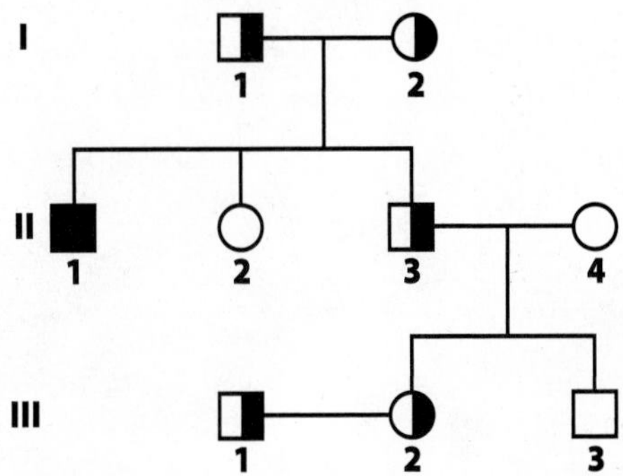

15 Analyze the results of the investigation. Which can you infer from the pedigree?

A I1 could develop symptoms of the disease.

B II1 could develop symptoms of the disease.

C II2 could develop symptoms of the disease.

D III2 could develop symptoms of the disease.

16 Analyze the results of the investigation and predict who is a carrier and cannot have children with the disease.

A I1

B II1

C II3

D III1

NEED EXTRA HELP?																
If You Missed Question . . .	1	2	3	4	5	6	7	8	9	10	11	12	13	14	15	16
Review Section . . .	10.1	10.1	10.1	10.2	10.2	11.1	9.3	11.3	8.2, 8.3	11.2	2.2	8.3	7.3	10.2	11.1	11.1

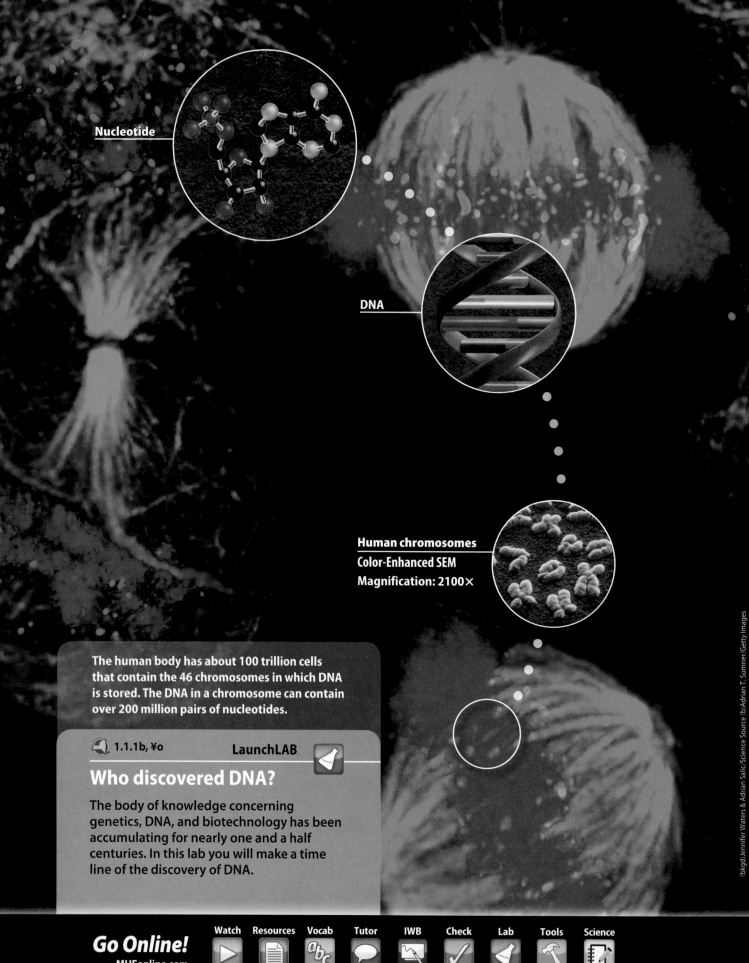

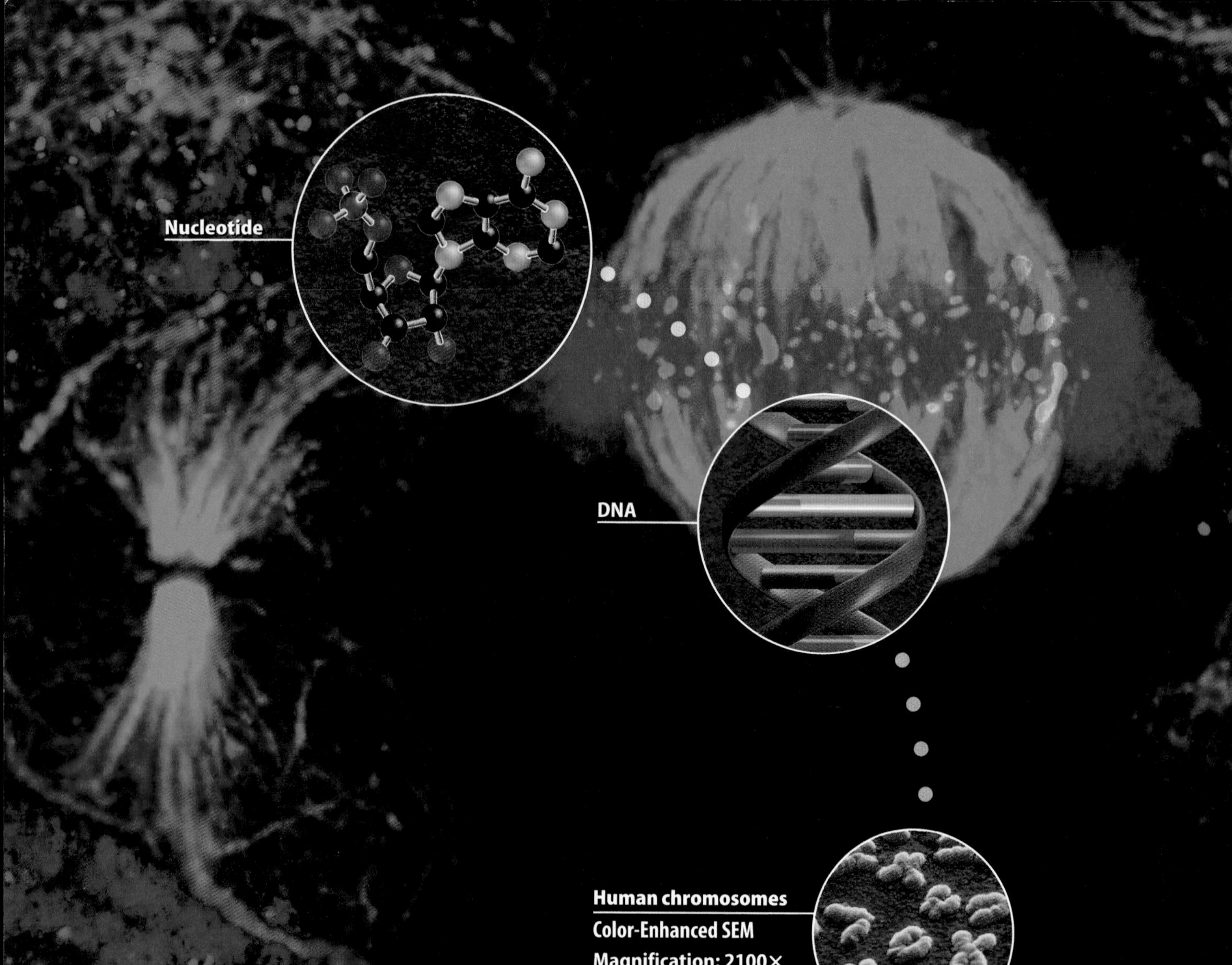

Nucleotide

DNA

Human chromosomes
Color-Enhanced SEM
Magnification: 2100×

(bkgd)Jennifer Waters & Adrian Salic/Science Source (b)Adrian T. Sumner/Getty Images

The human body has about 100 trillion cells that contain the 46 chromosomes in which DNA is stored. The DNA in a chromosome can contain over 200 million pairs of nucleotides.

1.1.1b, ¥o

LaunchLAB

Who discovered DNA?

The body of knowledge concerning genetics, DNA, and biotechnology has been accumulating for nearly one and a half centuries. In this lab you will make a time line of the discovery of DNA.

Watch  Resources  Vocab   Tutor  IWB  Check  Lab  Tools  Science Notebook

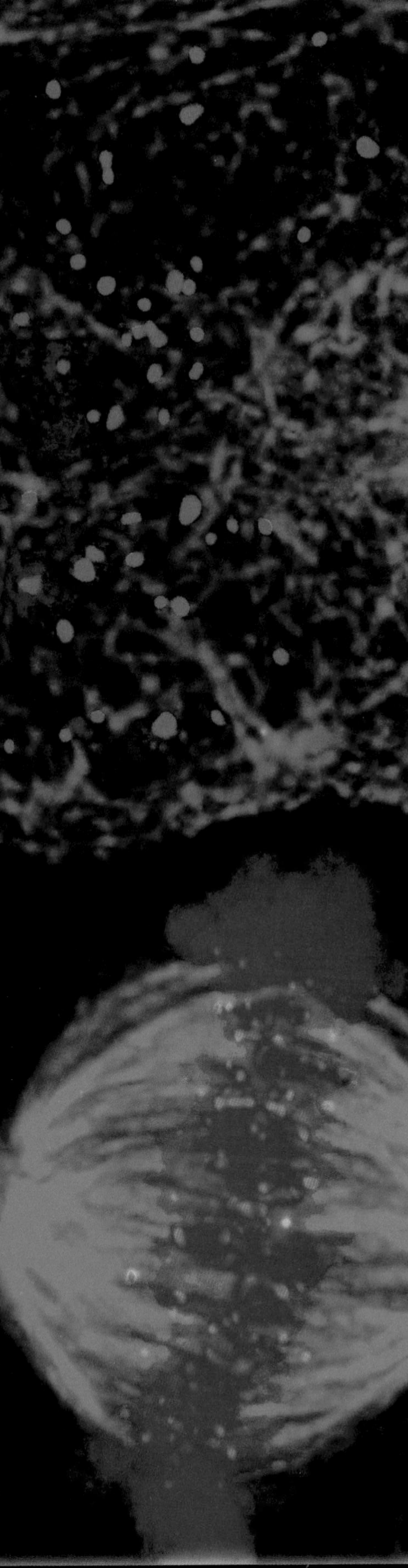

CHAPTER 12

Molecular Genetics

1 DNA: The Genetic Material

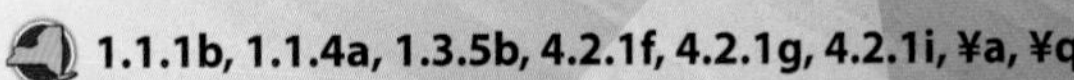

1.1.1b, 1.1.4a, 1.3.5b, 4.2.1f, 4.2.1g, 4.2.1i, ¥a, ¥q

2 Replication of DNA

4.5.1c, ¥a, ¥q

3 DNA, RNA, and Protein

4.1.2h, 4.2.1f, 4.2.1g, 4.2.2c, 4.5.1c, 4.5.1f, ¥o

4 Gene Regulation and Mutation

1.3.5b, 4.2.1a, 4.2.1f, 4.2.1g, 4.2.1h, 4.2.1i, 4.2.2c, 4.3.1d, 4.5.1f, 4.5.1g, ¥n, ¥o

THEMEFOCUS

Energy and matter Replication of DNA requires energy, as do all biosynthetic actions.

BIGIDEA

DNA is the genetic material that contains a code for proteins.

Transcription and Translation

Make a two-tab book using the labels shown. Use it to organize your notes about transcription and translation.

Transcription	Translation

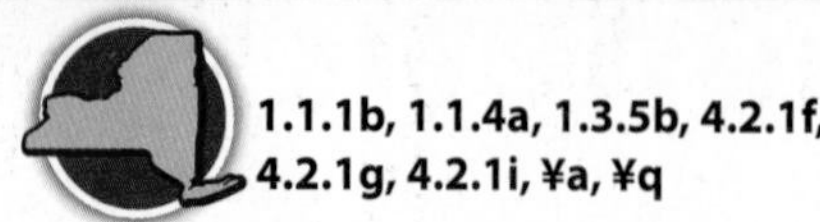

USE IT! Science Notebook

1 DNA: The Genetic Material

1.1.1b, 1.1.4a, 1.3.5b, 4.2.1f, 4.2.1g, 4.2.1i, ¥a, ¥q

MAINIDEA

The discovery that DNA is the genetic code involved many experiments.

Essential Questions

- Which experiments led to the discovery of DNA as the genetic material?
- What is the basic structure of DNA?
- What is the basic structure of eukaryotic chromosomes?

BIOLOGY 4U

Do you like to read mystery novels or watch people on television solve crimes? Detectives search for clues that will help them solve the mystery. Geneticists are detectives looking for clues in the mystery of inheritance.

Review Vocabulary

nucleic acid: complex biomolecule that stores cellular information in the form of a code

New Vocabulary

Multilingual eGlossary

double helix
nucleosome

Discovery of the Genetic Material

Once Mendel's work was rediscovered in the 1900s, scientists began to search for the molecule involved in inheritance. Scientists knew that genetic information was carried on the chromosomes in eukaryotic cells, and that the two main components of chromosomes are DNA and protein. For many years, scientists tried to determine which of these macromolecules—nucleic acid (DNA) or proteins—was the source of genetic information.

Griffith The first major experiment that led to the discovery of DNA as the genetic material was performed by Frederick Griffith in 1928. Griffith studied two strains of the bacteria *Streptococcus pneumoniae,* which causes pneumonia. He found that one strain could be transformed, or changed, into the other form.

Of the two strains he studied, one had a sugar coat and one did not. Both strains are shown in **Figure 1.** The coated strain causes pneumonia and is called the smooth (S) strain. The noncoated strain does not cause pneumonia and is called the rough (R) strain because, without the coat, the bacteria colonies have rough edges.

Follow Griffith's study described in **Figure 2.** Notice the live S cells killed the mouse in the study. The live R cells did not kill the mouse, and the killed S cells did not kill the mouse. However, when Griffith made a mixture of live R cells and killed S cells and injected the mixture into a mouse, the mouse died. Griffith isolated live bacteria from the dead mouse. When these isolated bacteria were cultured, the smooth trait was visible, suggesting that a disease-causing factor was passed from the killed S bacteria to the live R bacteria. Griffith concluded that there had been a transformation from live R bacteria to live S bacteria. This experiment set the stage for the search to identify the transforming substance.

SEM Magnification: 320×

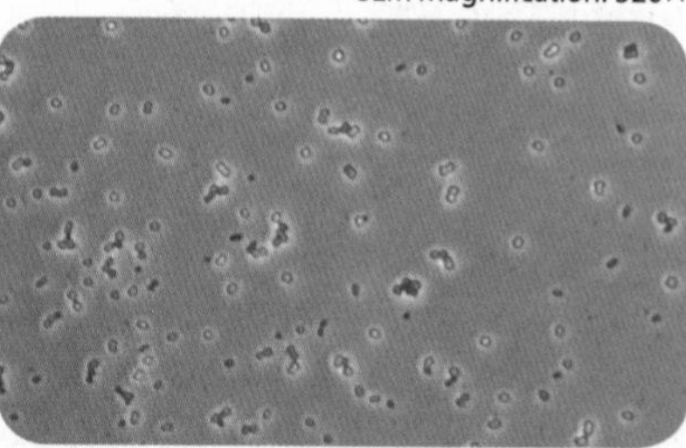

Smooth strain—*S. pneumoniae*

SEM Magnification: 800×

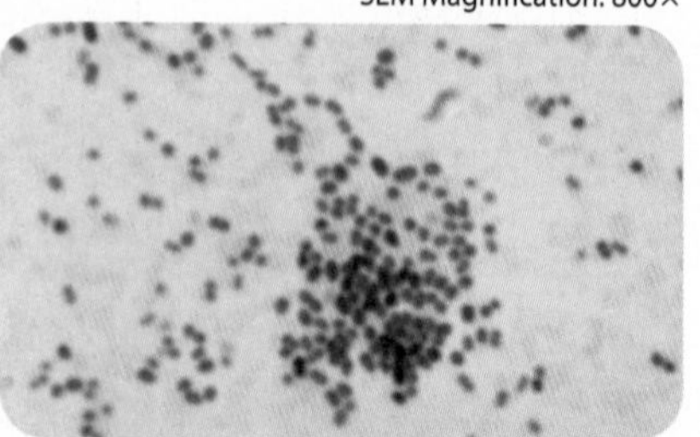

Rough strain—*S. pneumoniae*

(l & r)Michael Abbey/Science Source

■ **Figure 1** The smooth (S) strain of *S. pneumoniae* can cause pneumonia, though the rough (R) strain is not disease-causing.

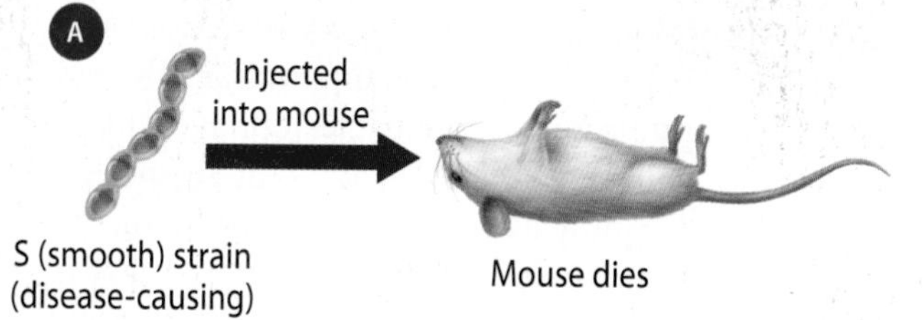

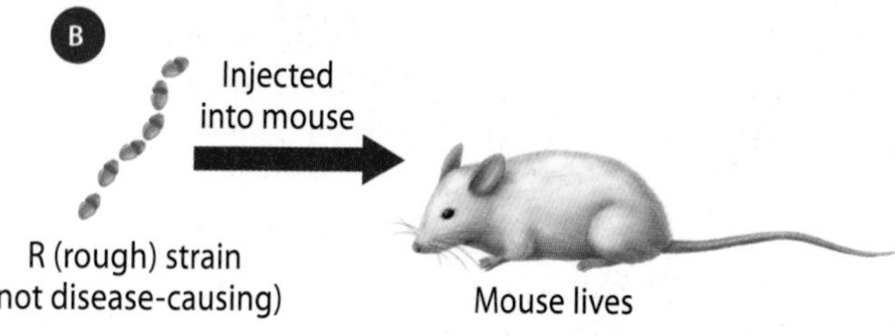

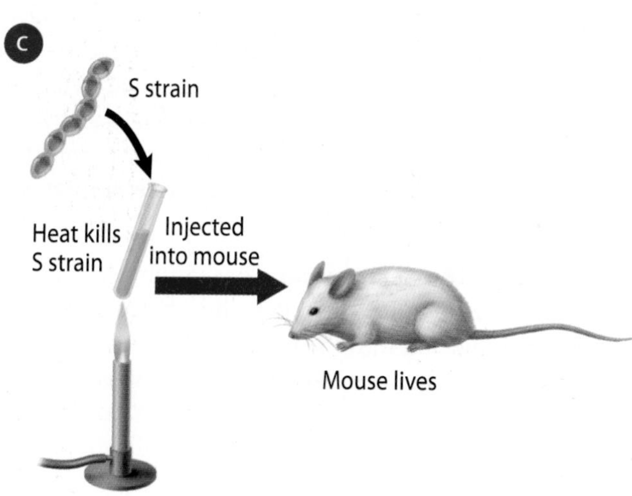

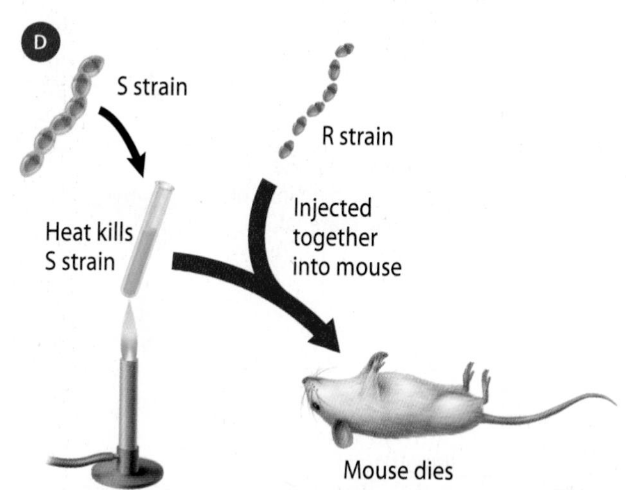

■ **Figure 2** Griffith's transformation experiment demonstrates the change of rough bacteria into smooth bacteria.

***Explain** why Griffith concluded there had been a change from live R bacteria to live S bacteria.*

Avery In 1944, Oswald Avery and his colleagues identified the molecule that transformed the R strain of bacteria into the S strain. Avery isolated different macromolecules, such as DNA, proteins, and lipids, from killed S cells. Then he exposed live R cells to the macromolecules separately. When the live R cells were exposed to the S strain DNA, they were transformed into S cells. Avery concluded that when the S cells in Griffith's experiments were killed, DNA was released. Some of the R bacteria incorporated this DNA into their cells, and this changed the bacteria into S cells. Avery's conclusions were not widely accepted by the scientific community, and many biologists continued to question and experiment to determine whether proteins or DNA were responsible for the transfer of genetic material.

GET IT? **Explain** how Avery discovered the transforming factor.

Hershey and Chase In 1952, Alfred Hershey and Martha Chase published results of experiments that provided definitive evidence that DNA was the transforming factor. These experiments involved a bacteriophage (bak TIHR ee uh fayj), a type of virus that attacks bacteria. Two components made the experiment ideal for confirming that DNA is the genetic material. First, the bacteriophage used in the experiment was made of DNA and protein. Second, viruses cannot replicate themselves. They must inject their genetic material into a living cell to reproduce. Hershey and Chase labeled both parts of the virus to determine which part was injected into the bacteria and, thus, which part was the genetic material.

VOCABULARY

ACADEMIC VOCABULARY

Transform
to cause a change in type or kind
Avery used DNA to transform bacteria.

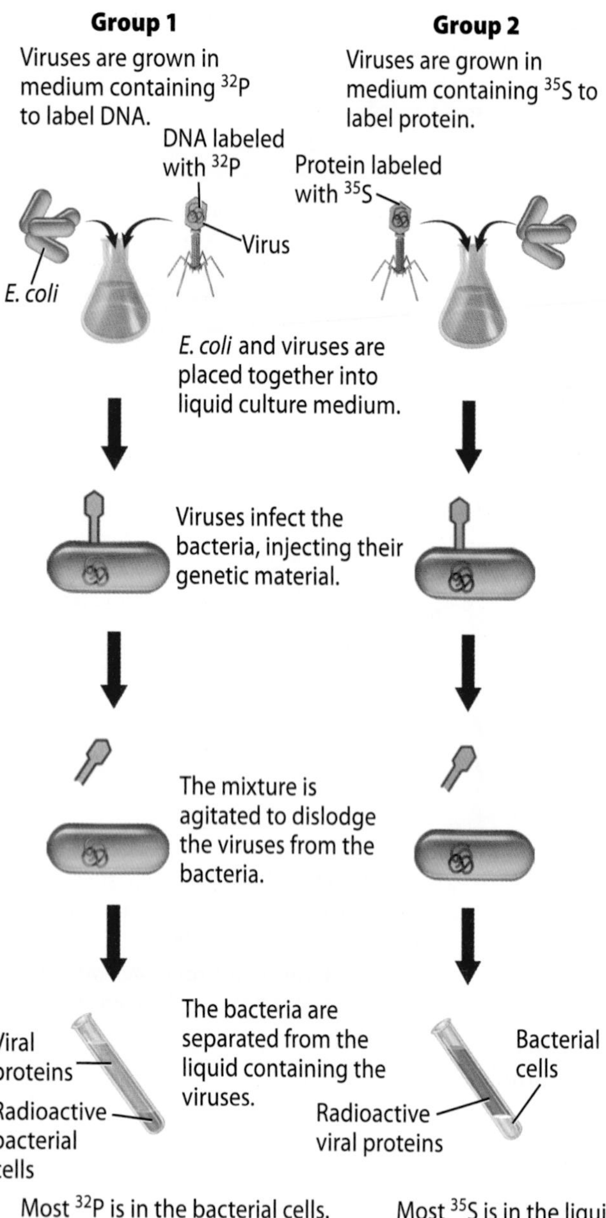
Group 1
Viruses are grown in medium containing ^{32}P to label DNA.
DNA labeled with ^{32}P
Virus
E. coli
Group 2
Viruses are grown in medium containing ^{35}S to label protein.
Protein labeled with ^{35}S
E. coli and viruses are placed together into liquid culture medium.
Viruses infect the bacteria, injecting their genetic material.
The mixture is agitated to dislodge the viruses from the bacteria.
The bacteria are separated from the liquid containing the viruses.
Viral proteins
Radioactive bacterial cells
Bacterial cells
Radioactive viral proteins
Most ^{32}P is in the bacterial cells.
Most ^{35}S is in the liquid with the viral proteins.

Figure 3 Hershey and Chase used radioactive labeling techniques to demonstrate that DNA is the genetic material in viruses.

Radioactive labeling Hershey and Chase used a technique called radioactive labeling to trace the fate of the DNA and protein as the bacteriophages infected bacteria and reproduced. Follow along in **Figure 3** as you continue learning about the Hershey-Chase experiment. They labeled one set of bacteriophages with radioactive phosphorus (^{32}P). Proteins do not contain phosphorous, so DNA and not protein in these viruses would be radioactive. Hershey and Chase labeled another set of bacteriophages with radioactive sulfur (^{35}S). Because proteins contain sulfur and DNA does not, proteins and not DNA would be radioactive.

Hershey and Chase infected bacteria with viruses from the two groups. When viruses infect bacteria, they attach to the outside of the bacteria and inject their genetic material. The infected bacteria then were separated from the viruses.

Tracking DNA Hershey and Chase examined Group 1 labeled with ^{32}P and found that the labeled viral DNA had been injected into the bacteria. Viruses later released from the infected bacteria contained ^{32}P, further indicating that DNA was the carrier of genetic information.

When examining Group 2 labeled with ^{35}S, Hershey and Chase observed that the labeled proteins were found outside of the bacterial cells. Viral replication had occurred in the bacterial cells, indicating that the viruses' genetic material had entered the bacteria, but no label (^{35}S) was found. **Table 1** summarizes the results of the Hershey-Chase experiment.

Based on their results, Hershey and Chase concluded that the viral DNA was injected into the cell and provided the genetic information needed to produce new viruses. This experiment provided powerful evidence that DNA, not protein, was the genetic material that could be passed from generation to generation in viruses.

GET IT? **Explain** why it is important that new viruses were produced in the bacteria.

Table 1 Summary of Hershey-Chase Results — Interactive Table

Group 1 (Viruses labeled with ^{32}P)		Group 2 (Viruses labeled with ^{35}S)	
Infected Bacteria	**Liquid with Viruses**	**Infected Bacteria**	**Liquid with Viruses**
• Labeled viral DNA (^{32}P) found in the bacteria • Viral replication occurred • New viruses contained ^{32}P	• No labeled DNA • No viral replication	• No labeled viral proteins (^{35}S) • Viral replication occurred • New viruses did not have a label	• Labeled proteins found • No viral replication

Nucleotide structure

Phosphate

Sugar

Base

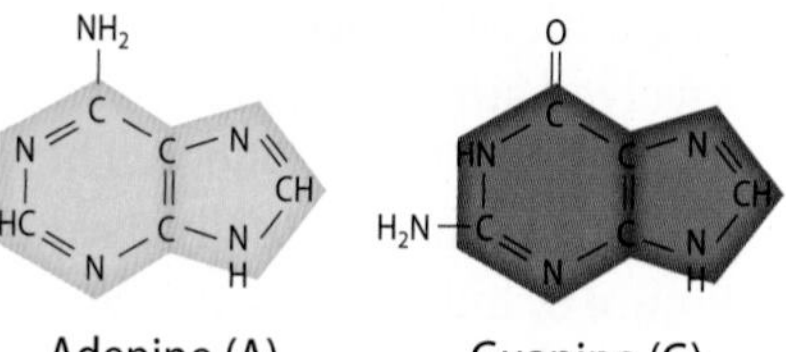

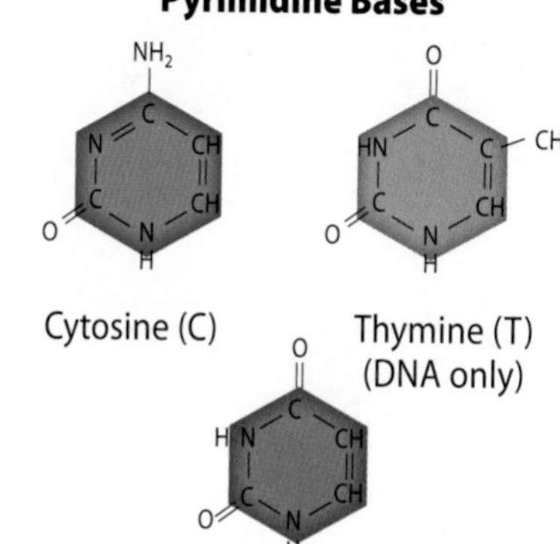

■ **Figure 4** Nucleotides are made of a phosphate, sugar, and a base. There are five different bases found in nucleotide subunits that make up DNA and RNA.

Identify ***the structural difference between purine and pyrimidine bases.***

DNA Structure

After the Hershey-Chase experiment, scientists were more confident that DNA was the genetic material. The clues had led to the identification of the genetic material, but the questions of how nucleotides came together to form DNA and how DNA could communicate information remained.

Nucleotides In the 1920s, the biochemist P. A. Levene determined the basic structure of nucleotides that make up DNA. Nucleotides are the subunits of nucleic acids and consist of a five-carbon sugar, a phosphate group, and a nitrogenous base. The two nucleic acids found in living cells are DNA and RNA. DNA nucleotides contain the sugar deoxyribose (dee ahk sih RI bos), a phosphate, and one of four nitrogenous bases: adenine (A duh neen), guanine (GWAH neen), cytosine (SI tuh seen), or thymine (THI meen). RNA nucleotides contain the sugar ribose, a phosphate, and one of four nitrogenous bases: adenine, guanine, cytosine, or uracil (YOO ruh sihl). Notice in **Figure 4** that guanine (G) and adenine (A) are double-ringed bases. This type of base is called a purine base. Thymine (T), cytosine (C), and uracil (U) are single-ringed bases called pyrimidine bases.

Chargaff Erwin Chargaff analyzed the amount of adenine, guanine, thymine, and cytosine in the DNA of various species. A portion of Chargaff's data, published in 1950, is shown in **Figure 5.** Chargaff found that the amount of guanine nearly equals the amount of cytosine, and the amount of adenine nearly equals the amount of thymine within a species. This finding is known as Chargaff's rule: C = G and T = A.

The structure question When four scientists joined the search for the DNA structure, the meaning and importance of Chargaff's data became clear. Rosalind Franklin, a British chemist; Maurice Wilkins, a British physicist; Francis Crick, a British physicist; and James Watson, an American biologist, provided information that was pivotal in answering the DNA structure question.

■ **Figure 5** Chargaff's data showed that though base composition varies from species to species, within a species C = G and A = T.

Chargaff's Data

	Base Composition (Mole Percent)			
Organism	A	T	G	C
Escherichia coli	26.0	23.9	24.9	25.2
Yeast	31.3	32.9	18.7	17.1
Herring	27.8	27.5	22.2	22.6
Rat	28.6	28.4	21.4	21.5
Human	30.9	29.4	19.9	19.8

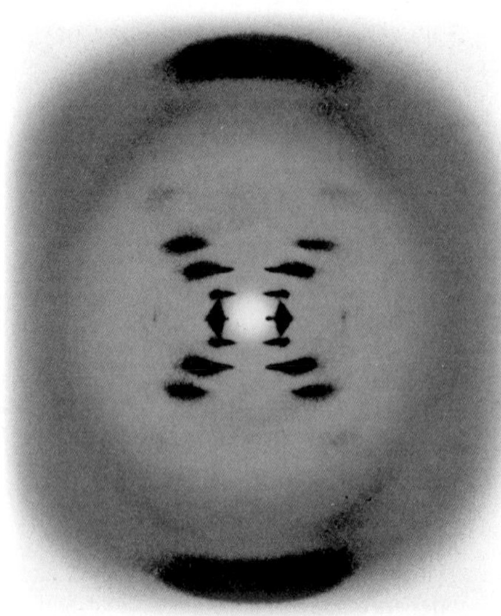

■ **Figure 6** Rosalind Franklin's Photo 51 and X-ray diffraction data helped Watson and Crick solve the structure of DNA. When analyzed and measured carefully, the pattern shows the characteristics of helix structure.

X-ray diffraction Wilkins was working at King's College in London, England, with a technique called X-ray diffraction, a technique that involved aiming X rays at the DNA molecule. In 1951, Franklin joined the staff at King's College. There she took the now famous Photo 51 and collected data eventually used by Watson and Crick. Photo 51, shown in **Figure 6,** indicated that DNA was a **double helix,** or twisted ladder shape, formed by two strands of nucleotides twisted around each other. The specific structure of the DNA double helix was determined later by Watson and Crick when they used Franklin's data and other mathematical data. DNA is the genetic material of all organisms, composed of two complementary, precisely paired strands of nucleotides wound in a double helix.

Watson and Crick Watson and Crick were working at Cambridge University in Cambridge, England, when they saw Franklin's X-ray diffraction picture. Using Chargaff's data and Franklin's data, Watson and Crick measured the width of the helix and the spacing of the bases. Together, they built a model of the double helix that conformed to the others' research. The model that they built is shown in **Figure 7.** Some important features of their proposed molecule include the following:

1. Two outside strands consist of alternating deoxyribose and phosphate.
2. Cytosine and guanine pair through three hydrogen bonds.
3. Thymine and adenine pair through two hydrogen bonds.

DNA structure DNA often is compared to a twisted ladder, with the rails of the ladder represented by the alternating deoxyribose and phosphate. The pairs of bases (cytosine–guanine or thymine–adenine) form the steps, or rungs, of the ladder. A purine base always binds to a pyrimidine base, ensuring a consistent distance between the two rails of the ladder. This proposed bonding of the bases also explains Chargaff's data, which suggested that the number of purine bases equaled the number of pyrimidine bases in a sample of DNA. Remember, cytosine and thymine are pyrimidine bases, adenine and guanine are purines, and C = G and A = T. Therefore, C + T = G + A, or purine bases equal pyrimidine bases. Complementary base pairing is used to describe the precise pairing of purine and pyrimidine bases between strands of nucleic acids. It is the characteristic of DNA replication through which the parent strand can determine the sequence of a new strand.

Launch Lab

Review Based on what you've read about the history of DNA experiments, how would you now answer the analysis questions?

GET IT? **Explain** why Chargaff's data was an important clue for putting together the structure of DNA.

■ **Figure 7** Using Chargaff's and Franklin's data, Watson and Crick, shown here, solved the puzzle of the structure of DNA.

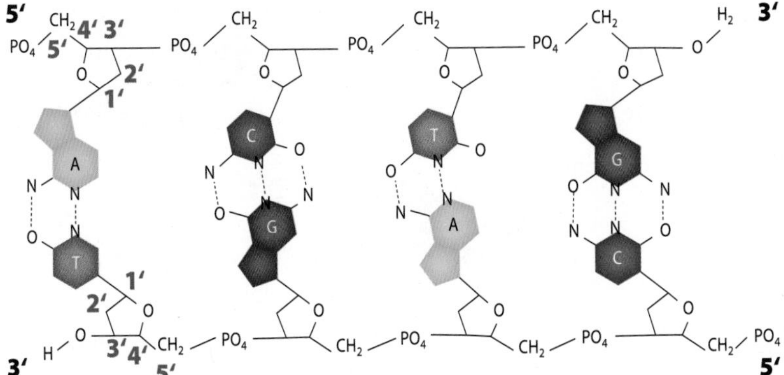

■ **Figure 8** Two strands of DNA running antiparallel make up the DNA helix.

Explain ***why the ends of the DNA strands are labeled 3′ and 5′.***

Animation

Orientation Another unique feature of the DNA molecule is the direction, or orientation, of the two strands. Carbon molecules can be numbered in organic molecules. **Figure 8** shows the orientation of the numbered carbons in the sugar molecules on each strand of DNA. On the top rail, the orientation of the sugar has the 5′ (read "five-prime") carbon on the left, and on the end of that rail, the 3′ (read "three-prime") carbon is on the right of the sugar-phosphate chain. The strand is said to be oriented 5′ to 3′. The strand on the bottom runs in the opposite direction and is oriented 3′ to 5′. This orientation of the two strands is called antiparallel. Another way to visualize antiparallel orientation is to take two pencils and position them so that the point of one pencil is next to the eraser of the other and vice versa.

The announcement In 1953, Watson and Crick surprised the scientific community by publishing a one-page letter in the journal *Nature* that suggested a structure for DNA and hypothesized a method of replication for the molecule deduced from the structure. In articles individually published in the same issue, Wilkins and Franklin presented evidence that supported the structure proposed by Watson and Crick. Still, the mysteries of how to prove DNA's replication and how it worked as a genetic code remained.

VOCABULARY

SCIENCE USAGE V. COMMON USAGE

Prime

Science usage: a mark located above and to the right of a character, used to identify a number or variable

Carbon molecules in organic molecules are numbered and labeled with a prime.

Common usage: first in value, excellence, or quality

The student found the prime seats in the stadium for watching the game.

MiniLAB 1

Model DNA Structure

What is the structure of the DNA molecule?
Construct a model to better understand the structure of the DNA molecule.

Procedure

1. Read and complete the lab safety form.
2. Construct a model of a short segment of DNA using the materials provided by your teacher.
3. Identify which parts of the model correspond to the different parts of a DNA molecule.

Analysis

1. **Describe** the structure of your DNA molecule.
2. **Identify** the characteristics of DNA that you focused on when constructing your model.
3. **Infer** in what way your model is different from your classmates' models. How does this relate to differences in DNA among organisms?

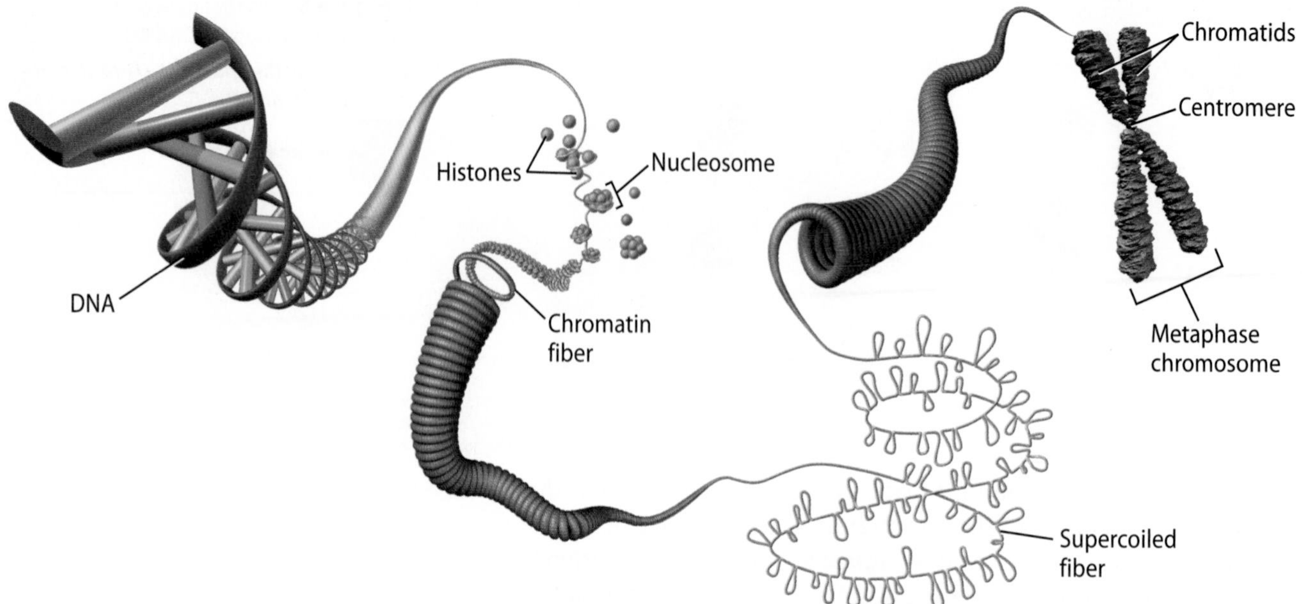

■ **Figure 9** DNA coils around histones to form nucleosomes, which coil to form chromatin fibers. The chromatin fibers supercoil to form chromosomes that are visible in the metaphase stage of mitosis.

Chromosome Structure

In prokaryotes, the DNA molecule is contained in the cytoplasm and consists mainly of a ring of DNA and associated proteins. Eukaryotic DNA is organized into individual chromosomes. The length of a human chromosome ranges from 51 million to 245 million base pairs. If a DNA strand 140 million nucleotides long was laid out in a straight line, it would be about five centimeters long. How does all of this DNA fit into a microscopic cell? In order to fit into the nucleus of a eukaryotic cell, the DNA tightly coils around a group of beadlike proteins called histones, as shown in **Figure 9.** The phosphate groups in DNA create a negative charge, which attracts the DNA to the positively charged histone proteins and forms a **nucleosome.** The nucleosomes then group together into chromatin fibers, which supercoil to make up the DNA structure recognized as a chromosome.

REVIEW IT! DNA: The Genetic Material

Section Summary

- Griffith's bacterial experiment and Avery's explanation first indicated that DNA is the genetic material.
- The Hershey-Chase experiment provided evidence that DNA is the genetic material of viruses.
- The work of Watson, Crick, Franklin, and Wilkins provided evidence of the double-helix structure of DNA.

Self Check

Understand Main Ideas

1. MAINIDEA **Summarize** the experiments of Griffith and Avery that indicated that DNA is the genetic material.
2. **Describe** the data used by Watson and Crick to determine the structure of DNA.
3. **Draw** and label a segment of DNA showing its helix and complementary base pairing.
4. **Compare and contrast** the structure of prokaryotic and eukaryotic chromosomes.

Think Critically

5. **Describe** two characteristics that DNA needs to fulfill its role as a genetic material.
6. **Evaluate** Hershey and Chase's decision to use radioactive phosphorus and sulfur for their experiments. Could they have used carbon or oxygen instead? Why or why not?

2 Replication of DNA

4.5.1c, ¥a, ¥q

MAIN IDEA

DNA replicates by making a strand that is complementary to each original strand.

Essential Questions

- What is the role of enzymes in the replication of DNA?
- How are leading and lagging strands synthesized differently?
- How does DNA replication compare in eukaryotes and prokaryotes?

BIOLOGY 4 U

When copies are made using a photocopy machine, they are expected to be exact copies of the original. Making a copy would not be very efficient if it contained errors that were not in the original. Think about how your body might make copies of DNA.

Review Vocabulary

template: a molecule of DNA that is a pattern for synthesis of a new DNA molecule

New Vocabulary

semiconservative replication
DNA polymerase
Okazaki fragment

Multilingual eGlossary

Semiconservative Replication

When Watson and Crick presented their model of DNA to the science community, they also suggested a possible method of replication called semiconservative replication. During **semiconservative replication,** parental strands of DNA separate, serve as templates, and produce DNA molecules that have one strand of parental DNA and one strand of new DNA. Recall that DNA replication occurs during interphase of mitosis and meiosis. An overview of semiconservative replication is in **Figure 10.** The process of semiconservative replication occurs in three main stages: unwinding, base pairing, and joining.

Unwinding DNA helicase, an enzyme, is responsible for unwinding and unzipping the double helix. When the double helix is unzipped, the hydrogen bonds between the bases are broken, leaving single strands of DNA. Then, proteins called single-stranded binding proteins associate with the DNA to keep the strands separate during replication. As the helix unwinds, another enzyme, RNA primase, adds a short segment of RNA, called an RNA primer, on each DNA strand.

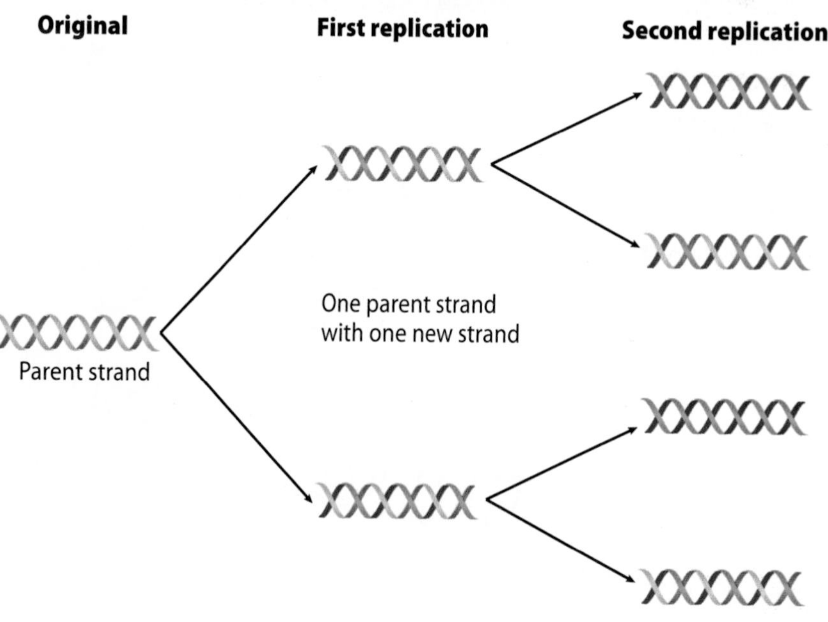

■ **Figure 10** In semiconservative replication, the parental DNA separates and serves as templates to produce two daughter DNA, which then can separate to produce four DNA.

MiniLAB 2

Model DNA Replication

How does the DNA molecule replicate? Use a model to better understand the replication of the DNA molecule.

Procedure

1. Read and complete the lab safety form.
2. Use your DNA model from **MiniLab 1** and extra pieces to model the replication of your segment of DNA.
3. Use your model to demonstrate DNA replication for a classmate, and identify the enzymes involved in each step.

Analysis

1. **Explain** how your model of DNA replication shows semiconservative replication.
2. **Infer** how DNA replication in a cell would be affected by an absence of DNA ligase.
3. **Identify** where errors could occur in the replication process.

Base pairing The enzyme **DNA polymerase** catalyzes the addition of appropriate nucleotides to the new DNA strand. The nucleotides are added to the 3′ end of the new strand, as illustrated in **Figure 11.** DNA polymerase continues adding new DNA nucleotides to the chain by adding to the 3′ end of the new DNA strand. Recall that each base binds only to its complement —A binds to T and C binds to G. In this way, the templates allow identical copies of the original double-stranded DNA to be produced.

Notice in **Figure 11** that the two strands are made in a slightly different manner. One strand is called the leading strand and is elongated as the DNA unwinds. This strand is built continuously by the addition of nucleotides to the 3′ end.

The other strand of DNA, called the lagging strand, elongates away from the replication fork. It is synthesized discontinuously into small segments, called **Okazaki fragments,** by the DNA polymerase in the 3′ to 5′ direction. These fragments are later connected by the enzyme DNA ligase. Each Okazaki fragment is about 100–200 nucleotides long in eukaryotes. Because one strand is synthesized continuously and the other is synthesized discontinuously, DNA replication is said to be semidiscontinuous as well as semiconservative.

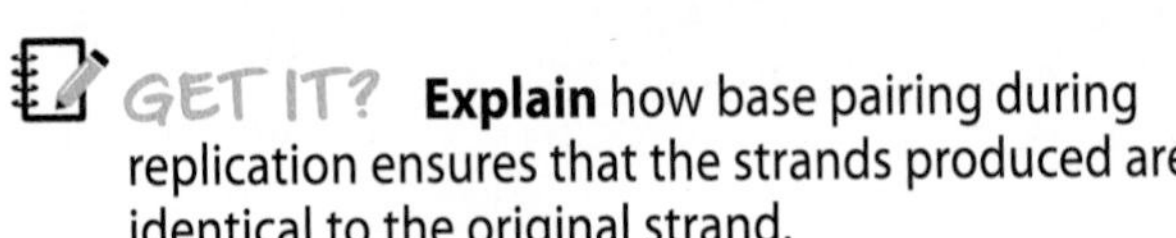

GET IT? **Explain** how base pairing during replication ensures that the strands produced are identical to the original strand.

■ **Figure 11** The DNA strands are separated during replication as each parent strand serves as a template for new strands.

Infer *why the lagging strand produces fragments instead of being synthesized continuously.*

Animation

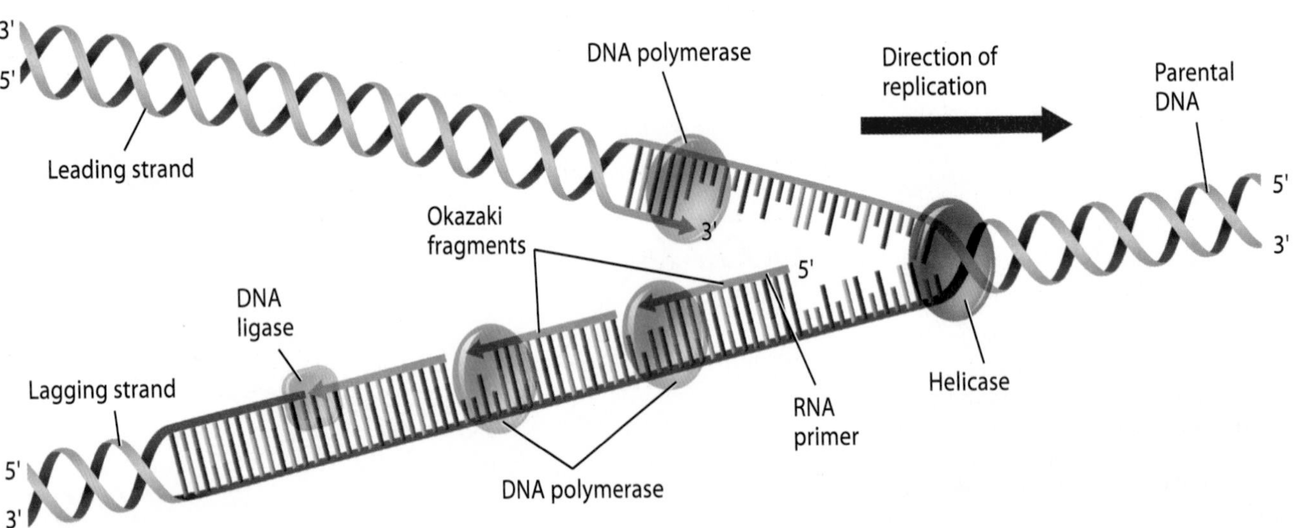

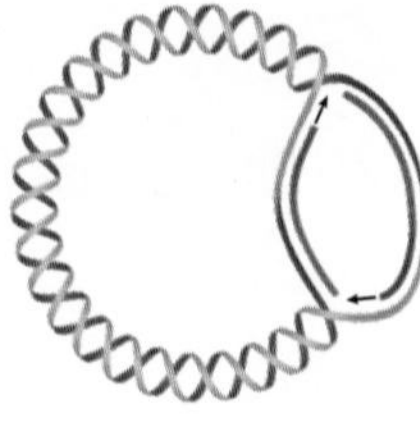

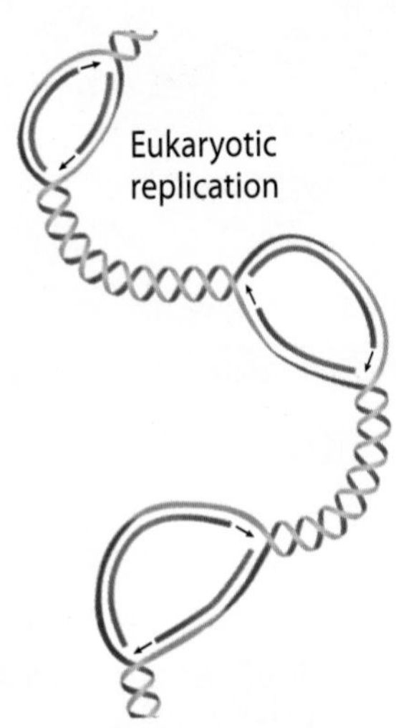

■ **Figure 12** Eukaryotes have many origins of replication. Bacteria have one origin of replication, with the DNA replicating in both directions when it unzips.

Joining Even though the leading strand is synthesized continuously, in eukaryotic DNA replication there often are many areas along the chromosome where replication begins. When the DNA polymerase comes to an RNA primer on the DNA, it removes the primer and fills in the place with DNA nucleotides. When the RNA primer has been replaced, DNA ligase links the two sections.

Comparing DNA Replication in Eukaryotes and Prokaryotes

Eukaryotic DNA unwinds in multiple areas as DNA is replicated. Each individual area of a chromosome replicates as a section, which can vary in length from 10,000 to one million base pairs. As a result, multiple areas of replication are occurring along the large eukaryotic chromosome at the same time. Multiple replication origins look like bubbles in the DNA strand, as shown in **Figure 12.**

In prokaryotes, the circular DNA strand is opened at one origin of replication, as shown in **Figure 12.** Notice in the figure that DNA replication occurs in two directions, just as it does in eukaryotes. Remember that prokaryotic DNA is typically shorter than eukaryotic DNA and remains in the cytoplasm, not packaged in a nucleus.

REVIEW IT! Replication of DNA

Section Summary

- The enzymes DNA helicase, RNA primase, DNA polymerase, and DNA ligase are involved in DNA replication.
- The leading strand is synthesized continuously, but the lagging strand is synthesized discontinuously, forming Okazaki fragments.
- Prokaryotic DNA opens at a single origin of replication, whereas eukaryotic DNA has multiple areas of replication.

Self Check

Understand Main Ideas

1. MAINIDEA **Indicate** the sequence of the template strand if a nontemplate strand has the sequence 5′ ATGGGGCGC 3′.
2. **Describe** the role of DNA helicase, DNA polymerase, and DNA ligase.
3. **Diagram** the way leading and lagging strands are synthesized.
4. **Explain** why DNA replication is more complex in eukaryotes than in bacteria.

Think Critically

MATH IN ▶ Biology

5. If the bacteria *E. coli* synthesize DNA at a rate of 100,000 nucleotides per min and it takes 30 min to replicate the DNA, how many base pairs are in an *E. coli* chromosome?

USE IT! **Science Notebook**

3 DNA, RNA, and Protein

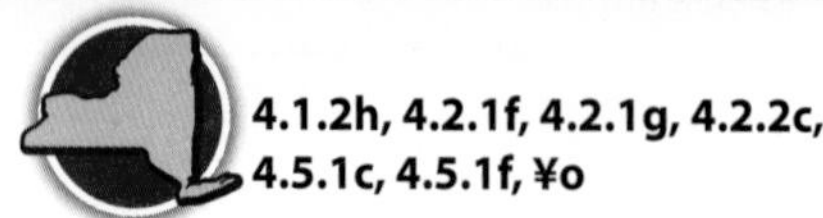

4.1.2h, 4.2.1f, 4.2.1g, 4.2.2c, 4.5.1c, 4.5.1f, ¥o

MAIN IDEA

DNA codes for RNA, which guides protein synthesis.

Essential Questions

- How are messenger RNA, ribosomal RNA, and transfer RNA involved in the transcription and translation of genes?
- What is the role of RNA polymerase in the synthesis of messenger RNA?
- How is the code of DNA translated into messenger RNA and utilized to synthesize a protein?

BIOLOGY 4 U

Computer programmers write their programs in a particular language, or code. The computer is designed to read the code and perform a function. Like the programming code, DNA contains a code that signals the cell to perform a function.

Review Vocabulary

synthesis: the composition or combination of parts to form a whole

New Vocabulary

RNA
messenger RNA
ribosomal RNA
transfer RNA
transcription
RNA polymerase
intron
exon
codon
translation

Multilingual eGlossary

Central Dogma

One of the important features of DNA that remained unresolved beyond the work of Watson and Crick was how DNA served as a genetic code for the synthesis of proteins. Recall that proteins function as structural building blocks for the cells and as enzymes.

Geneticists now accept that the basic mechanism of reading and expressing genes is from DNA to RNA to protein. This chain of events occurs in all living things—from bacteria to humans. Scientists refer to this mechanism as the central dogma of biology: DNA codes for RNA, which guides the synthesis of proteins.

RNA RNA is a nucleic acid that is similar to DNA. However, **RNA** contains the sugar ribose, the base uracil replaces thymine, and usually is single stranded. Three major types of RNA are found in living cells. **Messenger RNA** (mRNA) molecules are long strands of RNA nucleotides that are formed complementary to one strand of DNA. They travel from the nucleus to the ribosome to direct the synthesis of a specific protein. **Ribosomal RNA** (rRNA) is the type of RNA that associates with proteins to form ribosomes in the cytoplasm. The third type of RNA, **transfer RNA** (tRNA) are smaller segments of RNA nucleotides that transport amino acids to the ribosome. **Table 2** compares the structures and functions of the three types of RNA.

Table 2 Comparison of Three Types of RNA — Interactive Table

Name	mRNA	rRNA	tRNA
Function	Carries genetic information from DNA in the nucleus to direct protein synthesis in the cytoplasm	Associates with protein to form the ribosome	Transports amino acids to the ribosome
Example			

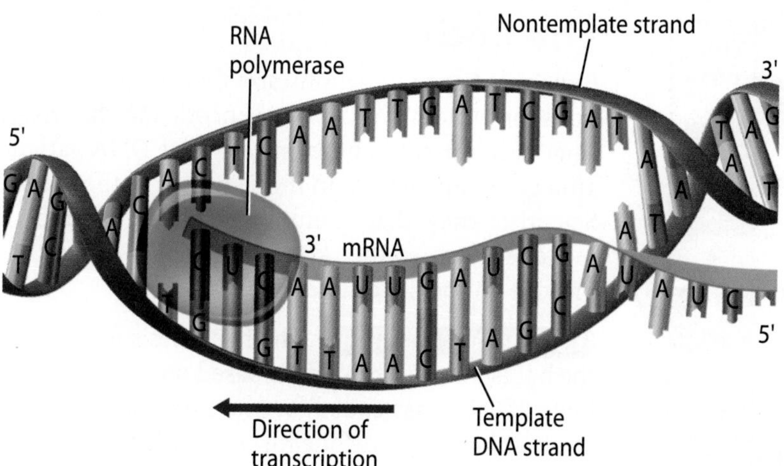

■ **Figure 13** RNA is grown in the 5′ to 3′ direction.

Identify ***which enzyme adds nucleotides to the growing RNA.***

Transcription The first step of the central dogma involves the synthesis of mRNA from DNA in a process called **transcription** (trans KRIHP shun). Through transcription, the DNA code is transferred to mRNA in the nucleus. The mRNA then can take the code into the cytoplasm for protein synthesis. Follow along with the process of transcription in **Figure 13.** The DNA is unzipped in the nucleus and **RNA polymerase,** an enzyme that regulates RNA synthesis, binds to a specific section where an mRNA will be synthesized. As the DNA strand unwinds, the RNA polymerase initiates mRNA synthesis and moves along one of the DNA strands in the 3′ to 5′ direction. The strand of DNA that is read by RNA polymerase is called the template strand, and mRNA is synthesized as a complement to the DNA nucleotides. The DNA strand not used as the template strand is called the nontemplate strand. The mRNA transcript is manufactured in a 5′ to 3′ direction, adding each new RNA nucleotide to the 3′ end. Uracil is incorporated instead of thymine as the mRNA molecule is made. Eventually, the mRNA is released, and the RNA polymerase detaches from the DNA. The new mRNA then moves out of the nucleus through nuclear pores into the cytoplasm.

FOLDABLES®
Incorporate information from this section into your Foldable.

GET IT? **Explain** the direction in which the mRNA transcript is manufactured.

Virtual Lab

RNA processing When scientists compared the coding region of the DNA with mRNA that ultimately coded for a protein, they found that the mRNA code is significantly shorter than the DNA code. Upon closer examination, they discovered that the code on the DNA is interrupted periodically by sequences that are not in the final mRNA. These sequences are called intervening sequences, or **introns.** The coding sequences that remain in the final mRNA are called **exons.** In eukaryotes, the original mRNA made in the nucleus is sometimes called pre-mRNA and contains all of the DNA code. Before the pre-mRNA leaves the nucleus, the introns are removed from it. Other processing of the pre-mRNA includes adding a protective cap on the 5′ end and adding a tail of many adenine nucleotides, called the poly-A tail, to the 3′ end of the mRNA. Research shows that the cap aids in ribosome recognition, though the significance of the poly-A tail remains unknown. The mRNA that reaches the ribosome has been processed.

First Base	Second Base: U	Second Base: C	Second Base: A	Second Base: G	Third Base
U	UUU phenylalanine	UCU serine	UAU tyrosine	UGU cysteine	U
U	UUC phenylalanine	UCC serine	UAC tyrosine	UGC cysteine	C
U	UUA leucine	UCA serine	UAA *stop*	UGA *stop*	A
U	UUG leucine	UCG serine	UAG *stop*	UGG tryptophan	G
C	CUU leucine	CCU proline	CAU histidine	CGU arginine	U
C	CUC leucine	CCC proline	CAC histidine	CGC arginine	C
C	CUA leucine	CCA proline	CAA glutamine	CGA arginine	A
C	CUG leucine	CCG proline	CAG glutamine	CGG arginine	G
A	AUU isoleucine	ACU threonine	AAU asparagine	AGU serine	U
A	AUC isoleucine	ACC threonine	AAC asparagine	AGC serine	C
A	AUA isoleucine	ACA threonine	AAA lysine	AGA arginine	A
A	AUG *(start)* methionine	ACG threonine	AAG lysine	AGG arginine	G
G	GUU valine	GCU alanine	GAU aspartate	GGU glycine	U
G	GUC valine	GCC alanine	GAC aspartate	GGC glycine	C
G	GUA valine	GCA alanine	GAA glutamate	GGA glycine	A
G	GUG valine	GCG alanine	GAG glutamate	GGG glycine	G

■ **Figure 14** This "dictionary" of the genetic code is helpful for knowing which codons code for which amino acids.

Determine ***the possible sequences that would produce the amino acid chain: start—serine—histidine—tryptophan—stop.***

The Code

Biologists began to hypothesize that the instructions for protein synthesis are encoded in the DNA. They recognized that the only way the DNA varied among organisms was in the sequence of the bases. Scientists knew that 20 amino acids were used to make proteins, so they knew that the DNA must provide at least 20 different codes.

Connection to Math The hypothesis for how the bases formed the code is based on math and logic. If each base coded for one amino acid, then the four bases could code for four amino acids. If each pair of bases coded for one amino acid, then the four bases could only code for 16 (4×4 or 4^2) amino acids. However, if a group of three bases coded for one amino acid, there would be 64 (4^3) possible codes. This provides more than the 20 codes needed for the 20 amino acids, but is the smallest possible combination of bases to provide enough codes for the amino acids.

This reasoning meant that the code was not contained in the base pairs themselves, but must run along a single strand of the DNA. Experiments during the 1960s demonstrated that the DNA code was indeed a three-base code. The three-base code in DNA or mRNA is called a **codon.** Each of the three bases of a codon in the DNA is transcribed into the mRNA code. **Figure 14** shows a "dictionary" of the genetic code. Notice that all but three codons are specific for an amino acid; these three are stop codons. Codon AUG codes for the amino acid methionine and also functions as the start codon.

Translation Once the mRNA is synthesized and processed, it moves to the ribosome. In eukaryotes, this means the mRNA must leave the nucleus and enter the cytoplasm. Once in the cytoplasm, the 5′ end of the mRNA connects to the ribosome. This is where the code is read and translated to make a protein through a process called **translation.** Follow along in **Figure 15** as you learn about translation.

In translation, tRNA molecules act as the interpreters of the mRNA codon sequence. The tRNA is folded into a cloverleaf shape and is activated by an enzyme that attaches a specific amino acid to the 3′ end. At the middle of the folded strand, there is a three-base coding sequence called the anticodon. Each anticodon is complementary to a codon on the mRNA. Though the code in DNA and RNA is read 5′ to 3′, the anticodon is read 3′ to 5′.

VISUALIZING Transcription and Translation

Figure 15 Transcription takes place in the nucleus. Translation occurs in the cytoplasm and results in the formation of polypeptides.

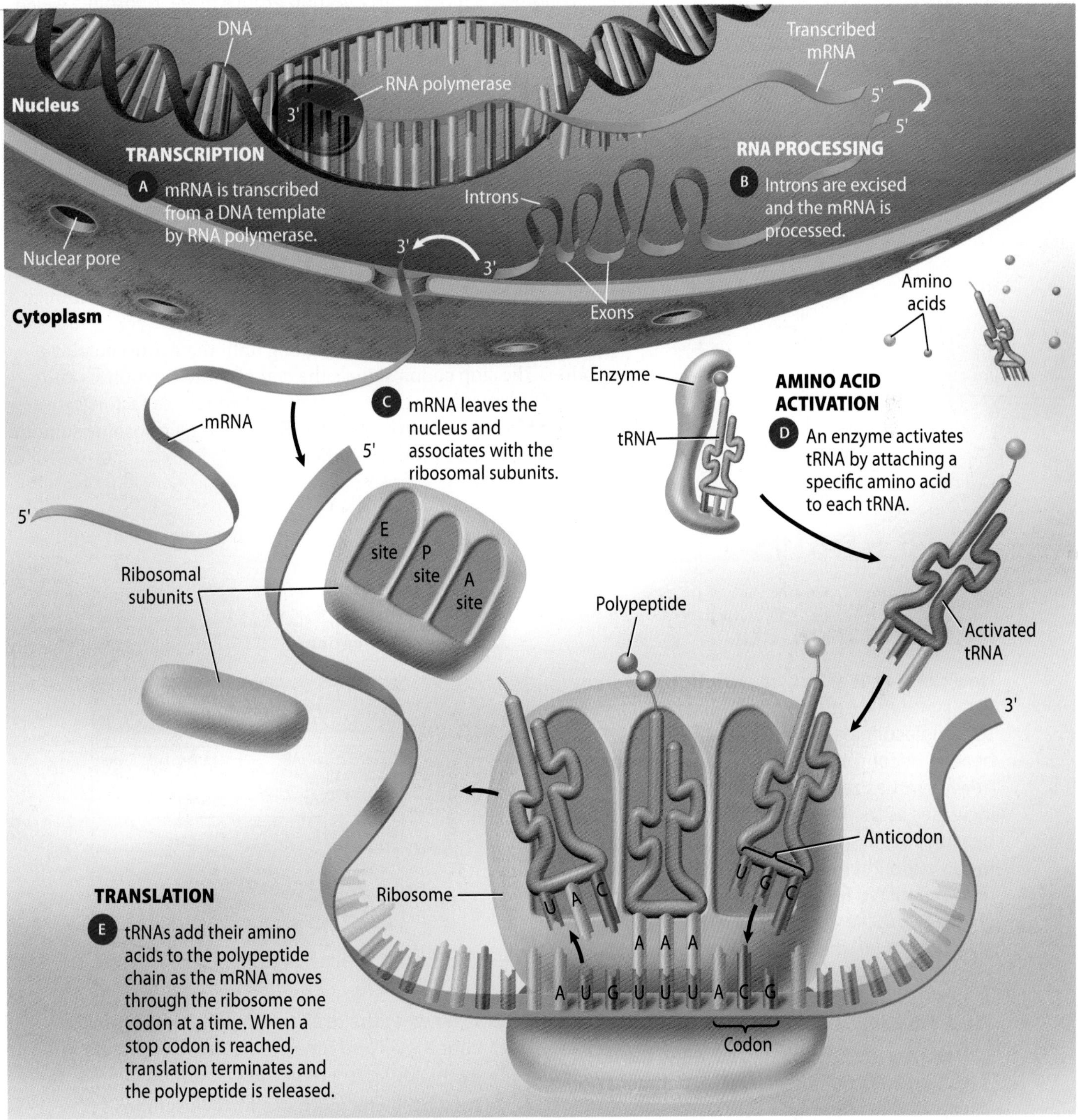

DNA

Nucleus

3'

RNA polymerase

Transcribed mRNA

5'

5'

TRANSCRIPTION

A mRNA is transcribed from a DNA template by RNA polymerase.

RNA PROCESSING

B Introns are excised and the mRNA is processed.

Introns

Nuclear pore

3'

3'

Exons

Cytoplasm

Amino acids

Enzyme

tRNA

AMINO ACID ACTIVATION

D An enzyme activates tRNA by attaching a specific amino acid to each tRNA.

mRNA

5'

C mRNA leaves the nucleus and associates with the ribosomal subunits.

5'

E site

P site

A site

Ribosomal subunits

Polypeptide

Activated tRNA

3'

Anticodon

U G C

U A C

A A A

Ribosome

A U G U U U A C G

Codon

TRANSLATION

E tRNAs add their amino acids to the polypeptide chain as the mRNA moves through the ribosome one codon at a time. When a stop codon is reached, translation terminates and the polypeptide is released.

The role of the ribosome The ribosome consists of two subunits, as shown in **Figure 15.** These subunits are not associated when they are not involved in protein translation. When the mRNA leaves the nucleus, the two parts of the ribosome come together and attach to the mRNA to complete the ribosome. Once the mRNA is associated with the ribosome, a tRNA with the anticodon CAU carrying a methionine will move in and bind to the mRNA start codon—AUG—on the 5′ end of the mRNA. The ribosome structure has a groove, called the P site, where the tRNA that is complementary to the mRNA moves in.

A second tRNA moves into a second groove in the ribosome, called the A site, and corresponds to the next codon of the mRNA. The next codon is UUU, so a tRNA with the anticodon AAA moves in, carrying the amino acid phenylalanine.

Part of the rRNA in the ribosome now acts as an enzyme catalyzing the formation of a bond between the new amino acid in the A site and the amino acid in the P site. As the two amino acids join, the tRNA in the P site is released to the third site, called the E site, where it exits the ribosome. The ribosome then moves so the tRNA found in Groove A is shifted to Site P, as shown in **Figure 15.** Now a new tRNA will enter the A site, complementing the next codon on the mRNA. This process will continue adding and linking amino acids in the sequence determined by the mRNA.

The ribosome continues to move along until the A site contains a stop codon. The stop codon signals the end of protein synthesis and does not complement any tRNA. Proteins called release factors cause the mRNA to be released from the last tRNA and the ribosome subunits to disassemble, ending protein synthesis.

STUDY TIP

FLOWCHART Draw a flowchart that connects the processes of DNA replication, transcription, and translation.

Data Analysis LAB 1

Based on Real Data*

Interpret the Data

How can a virus affect transcription? To study RNA synthesis, a group of scientists used a fluorescent molecular beacon to trace molecules. This beacon becomes fluorescent when it binds to newly synthesized RNA. The fluorescence increases as the RNA chain lengthens. Thus, the beacon can be used to follow RNA synthesis.
In this experiment, scientists added the antibiotic rifampin (rif) to RNA polymerase from a virus (T7 RNAP), *Escherchia coli (E. coli* RNAP*)*, and *Mycobacterium smegmatis (M. smegmatis* RNAP*)* and followed RNA synthesis.

Data and Observations

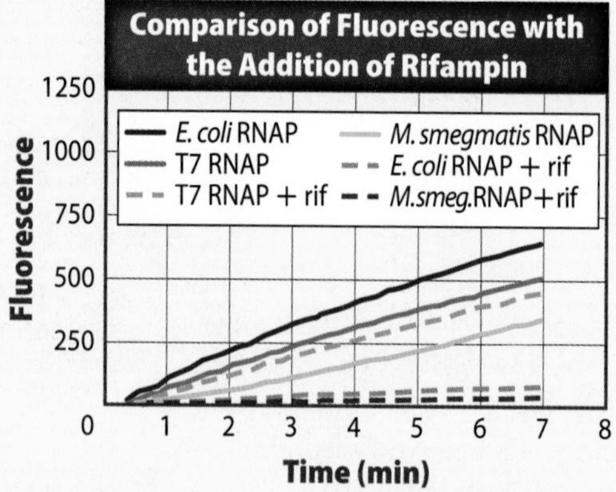

Think Critically

1. **Describe** the relationship between the fluorescence level and time in each experiment not exposed to rifampin.
2. **Infer** what the relationship between fluorescence level and time indicates is happening in each case where rifampin was added.
3. **Interpret** which organism's RNA synthesis is affected most by the antibiotic rifampin.

*Data obtained from: Marras, Salvatore A.E., et al. 2004. Real-time measurement of *in vitro* transcription. *Nucleic Acids Research* 32.9.e: 72.

One Gene—One Enzyme

Once scientists learned how DNA works as a code, they needed to learn the relationships between the genes and the proteins for which they coded. Experiments on the mold *Neurospora* were the first to demonstrate the relationship between genes and enzymes. In the 1940s, George Beadle and Edward Tatum provided evidence that a gene can code for an enzyme. They studied mold spores that were mutated by exposure to X-rays. Examine **Figure 16** to follow along with their experiment.

Normally, *Neurospora* can grow on an artificial medium that provides no amino acids. This type of medium is called minimal medium. Complete medium provides all the amino acids that *Neurospora* needs to function. In Beadle and Tatum's experiment, the spores were exposed to X-rays and grown on a complete medium. To test for a mutated spore, the scientists grew spores on a minimal medium. When a spore was unable to grow on the minimal medium, the mutant was tested to see what amino acid it lacked. When the mold-spore type grew on a minimal medium with a supplement such as arginine, Beadle and Tatum hypothesized that the mutant was missing the enzyme needed to synthesize arginine.

Beadle and Tatum came up with what is known as the "one gene—one enzyme" hypothesis. Today, because we know that polypeptides make up enzymes, their hypothesis has been modified slightly to refer to the fact that one gene codes for one polypeptide.

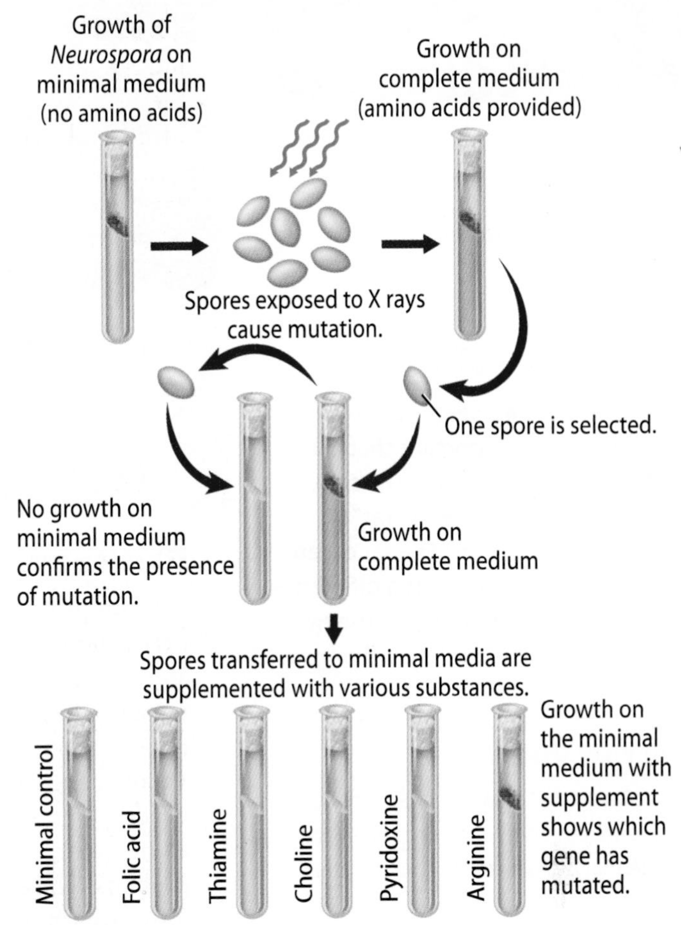

Figure 16 The Beadle and Tatum experiment showed that a gene codes for an enzyme. We now know that a gene codes for a polypeptide.

REVIEW IT! DNA, RNA, and Protein

Section Summary

- Three major types of RNA are involved in protein synthesis: mRNA, tRNA, and rRNA.
- The synthesis of the mRNA from the template DNA is called transcription.
- Translation is the process through which the mRNA attaches to the ribosome and a protein is assembled.
- In eukaryotes, mRNA contains introns that are excised before leaving the nucleus. A cap and poly-A tail are added to the mRNA.
- One gene codes for one polypeptide.

 Self Check

Understand Main Ideas

1. MAINIDEA **Summarize** the process by which the DNA code is made into a protein.
2. **Describe** the function of each of the following in protein synthesis: rRNA, mRNA, and tRNA.
3. **Differentiate** between codons and anticodons.
4. **Demonstrate** the role of RNA polymerase in mRNA synthesis during transcription.
5. **Conclude** why Beadle and Tatum's "one gene, one enzyme" hypothesis has been modified since they presented it in the 1940s.

Think Critically

MATH IN Biology

6. If the genetic code used four bases as a code instead of three, how many code units could be encoded?

4 Gene Regulation and Mutation

1.3.5b, 4.2.1a, 4.2.1f, 4.2.1g, 4.2.1h, 4.2.1i, 4.2.2c, 4.3.1d, 4.5.1f, 4.5.1g, ¥n, ¥o

MAINIDEA

Gene expression is regulated by the cell, and mutations can affect this expression.

Essential Questions

- How are bacteria able to regulate their genes by two types of operons?
- How do eukaryotes regulate the transcription of genes?
- What are the various types of mutations?

BIOLOGY 4U

When you type a sentence on a keyboard, it is important that each letter is typed correctly. The sentence "The fat cat ate the rat" is quite different from "The fat cat ate the hat." Though there is a difference of only one letter between the two sentences, the meaning is changed.

Review Vocabulary

prokaryote: organism that does not have membrane-bound organelles and DNA that is organized in chromosomes

New Vocabulary

gene regulation
operon
mutation
mutagen

Multilingual eGlossary

Prokaryote Gene Regulation

How do prokaryotic cells regulate which genes will be transcribed at particular times in the lifetime of an organism? **Gene regulation** is the ability of an organism to control which genes are transcribed in response to the environment. In prokaryotes, an operon often controls the transcription of genes in response to changes in the environment. An **operon** is a section of DNA that contains the genes for the proteins needed for a specific metabolic pathway. The parts of an operon include an operator, promoter, regulatory gene, and the genes coding for proteins. The operator is a segment of DNA that acts as an on/off switch for transcription. A second segment of DNA, called the promoter, is where the RNA polymerase first binds to the DNA. The bacteria *Escherichia coli (E. coli)* respond to tryptophan, which is an amino acid, and lactose, which is a sugar, through two operons.

The *trp* operon In bacteria, tryptophan synthesis occurs in a series of five steps, and each step is catalyzed by a specific enzyme. The five genes coding for these enzymes are clustered together on the bacterial chromosome with a group of DNA that controls whether or not they are transcribed. This cluster of DNA is called the tryptophan *(trp)* operon and is illustrated in **Figure 17.**

■ **Figure 17** The *trp* operon is an example of the gene expression of repressible enzymes.

Animation

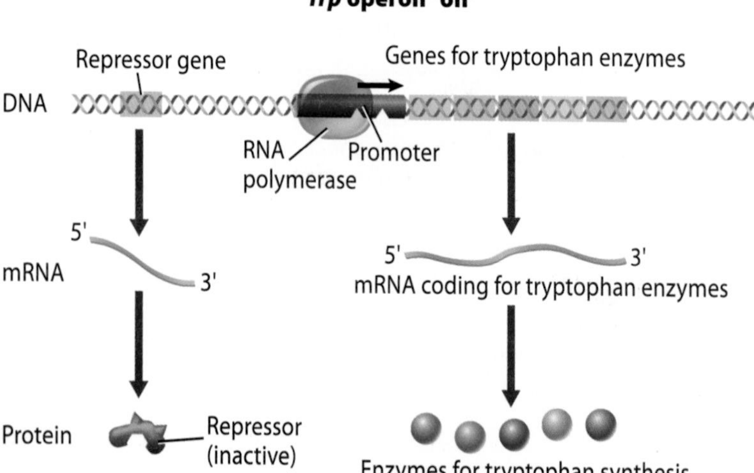

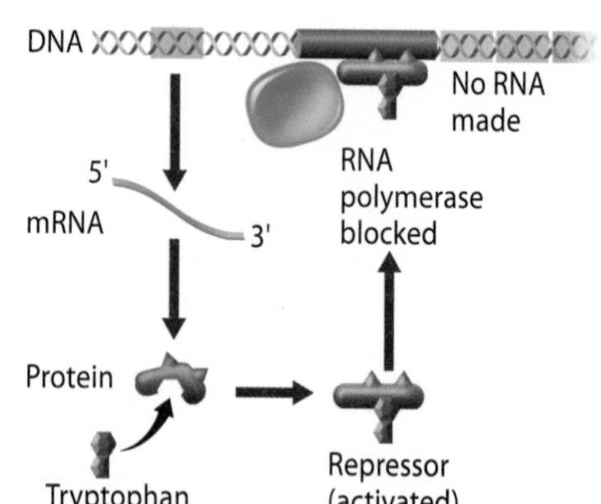

The *trp* operon is referred to as a repressible operon because transcription of the five enzyme genes normally is repressed, or turned off. When tryptophan is present in the cell's environment, the cell has no need to synthesize it and the *trp* repressor gene turns off, or represses, the transcription process by making a repressor protein. Tryptophan in *E. coli* combines with an inactive repressor protein to activate it, and the complex binds to the operator in the promoter sequence. If the repressor is bound to the operator, RNA polymerase cannot bind to it, which prevents the transcription of the enzyme genes. This prohibits the synthesis of tryptophan by the cell.

When tryptophan levels are low, the repressor is not bound to tryptophan and is inactive—it does not bind to the operator. The RNA polymerase is able to bind to the operator, turning on transcription of the five enzyme genes. This transcription enables the synthesis of tryptophan by the cell. Notice the location of the repressor protein in **Figure 17** when the operon is turned both off and on.

GET IT? **Summarize** the effect of tryptophan on the *trp* operon.

CAREERS IN BIOLOGY

Microbiologist Scientists who study microbes, primarily prokaryotes, are called microbiologists. They might research to learn about which genes control the production of particular proteins or how a protein affects the life of a cell.

The *lac* operon When lactose is present in the cell, *E. coli* makes enzymes that enable it to use lactose as an energy source. The lactose (*lac*) operon, illustrated in **Figure 18,** contains a promoter, an operator, a regulatory gene, and three enzyme genes that control lactose digestion. In the *lac* operon, the regulatory gene makes a repressor protein that binds to the operator in the promoter sequence and prevents the transcription of the enzyme genes.

When a molecule called an inducer is present, the inducer binds to the repressor and inactivates it. In the *lac* operon, the inducer is allolactose, a molecule that is present in food that contains lactose. Thus, when lactose is present, the allolactose binds to the repressor and inactivates it. With the repressor inactivated, RNA polymerase then can bind to the promoter and begin transcription. The *lac* operon is called an inducible operon because transcription is turned on by an inducer.

■ **Figure 18** The *lac* operon is an example of the gene expression of inducible enzymes.
Identify ***what the repressor is bound to when the lac operon is turned off.***

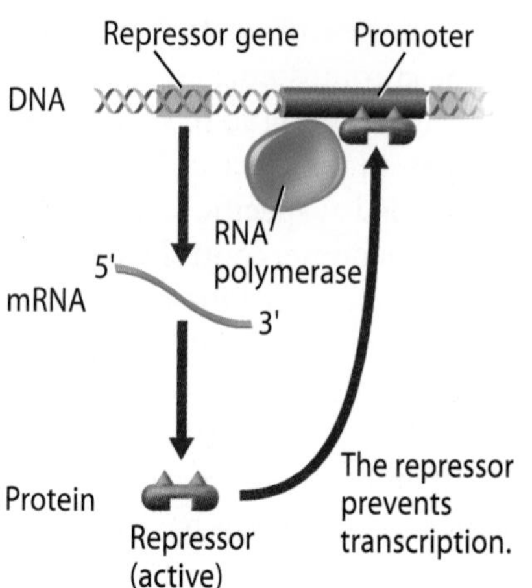

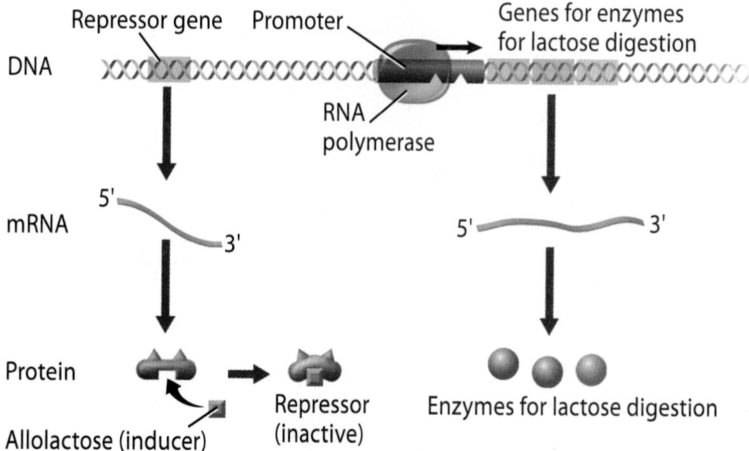

Adult *Drosophila*

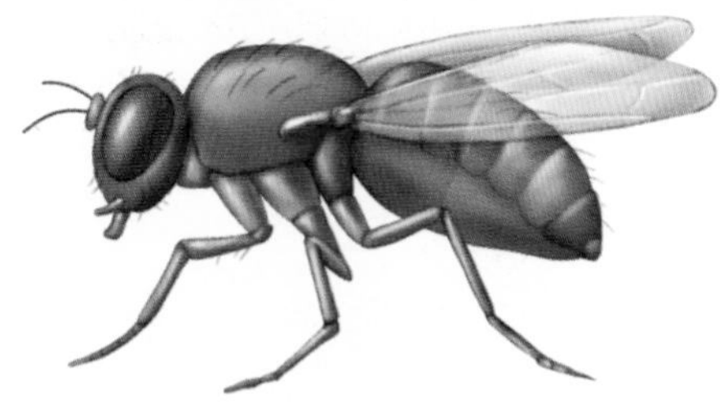

Drosophila embryo

Drosophila Hox genes

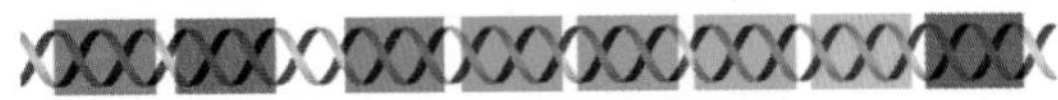

■ **Figure 19** Hox genes are responsible for the general body pattern of most animals. Notice that the order of the genes is the same as the order of the body sections the genes control.

Eukaryote Gene Regulation

Eukaryotic cells also must control gene expression—the transcription of DNA into RNA and translation of RNA into protein—during cell differentiation and in response to changes in the environment at different times in the organism's lifetime. In eukaryotic cells, many genes interact, requiring more elements than a single promoter and operator for a set of genes. The organization and structure of eukaryotic cells is more complex than in prokaryotic cells, increasing the complexity of the control system.

Controlling transcription One way that eukaryotes control gene expression is through proteins called transcription factors. Transcription factors ensure that a gene is used at the right time and that proteins are made in the right amounts. There are two main sets of transcription factors. One set of transcription factors forms complexes that guide and stabilize the binding of the RNA polymerase to a promoter. The other set includes regulatory proteins that help control the rate of transcription. For instance, proteins called activators fold DNA so that enhancer sites are close to the complex and increase the rate of gene transcription. Repressor proteins also bind to specific sites on the DNA and prevent the binding of activators.

The complex structure of eukaryotic DNA also regulates transcription. Recall that eukaryotic DNA is wrapped around histones to form nucleosomes. This structure provides some inhibition of transcription, although regulatory proteins and RNA polymerase still can activate specific genes even when they are packaged in the nucleosome.

Hox genes Gene regulation is crucial during development and cell differentiation. Differentiation is the process through which the cells become specialized in structure and function. One group of genes that controls differentiation has been discovered. These genes are called homeobox (Hox) genes. Hox genes are important for determining the body plan of an organism. They code for transcription factors and are active in zones of the embryo that are in the same order as the genes on the chromosome. For example, the colored regions of the fly and fly embryo in **Figure 19** correspond to the colored genes on the piece of DNA in the figure. These genes, transcribed at specific times, and located in specific places on the genome, control what body part will develop in a given location. One mutation in the Hox genes of fruit flies has yielded flies with legs growing where their antennae should be. Studying these flies has helped scientists understand more about how genes control the body plan of an organism. Similar clusters of Hox genes that control body plans have been found in all animals.

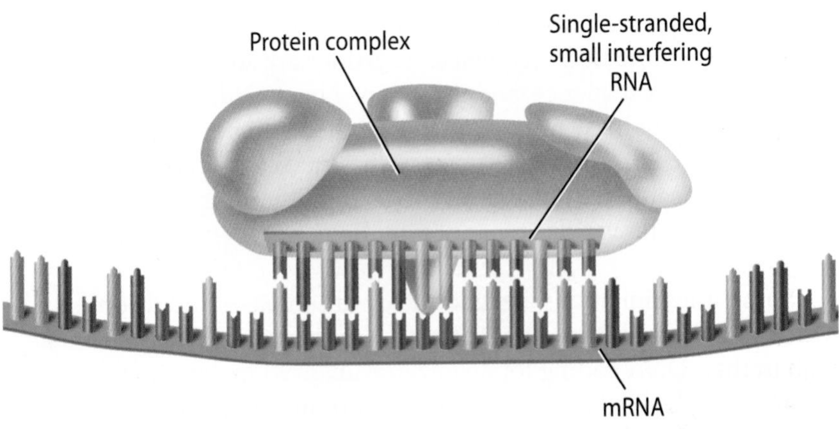

■ **Figure 20** RNA interference can stop the mRNA from translating its message.

Describe ***how the RNA-protein complex prevents the translation of the mRNA.***

RNA interference Another method of eukaryotic gene regulation is RNA interference (RNAi). Small pieces of double-stranded RNA in the cytoplasm of the cell are cut by an enzyme called dicer. The resulting double-stranded segments are called small interfering RNA. They bind to a protein complex that degrades one strand of the RNA. The resulting single-stranded small interfering RNA and protein complex bind to sequence-specific sections of mRNA in the cytoplasm, causing the mRNA in this region to be cut and thus preventing its translation. **Figure 20** shows the single-stranded small interfering RNA and protein complex binding to the mRNA. Research and clinical trials are being conducted to investigate the possibility of using RNAi to treat cancer, diabetes, and other diseases.

GET IT? **Explain** how RNA interference can regulate eukaryotic gene expression.

Mutations

Do you ever make mistakes when you are typing an assignment? When you type, sometimes you might strike the wrong key. Just as you might make a mistake when typing, cells sometimes make mistakes during replication. However, these mistakes are rare, and the cell has repair mechanisms that can repair some damage. Sometimes a permanent change occurs in a cell's DNA and this is called a **mutation.** Recall that one inheritance pattern that Mendel studied was round and wrinkled pea seeds. It is now known that the wrinkled phenotype is associated with the absence of an enzyme that influences the shape of starch molecules in the seeds. Because the mutation in the gene causes a change in the protein that is made, the enzyme is nonfunctional.

Types of mutations Mutations can range from changes in a single base pair in the coding sequence of DNA to the deletions of large pieces of chromosomes. Point mutations involve a chemical change in just one base pair and can be enough to cause a genetic disorder. A point mutation in which one base is exchanged for another is called a substitution. Most substitutions are missense mutations, where the DNA code is altered so that it codes for the wrong amino acid. Other substitutions, called nonsense mutations, change the codon for an amino acid to a stop codon. Nonsense mutations cause translation to terminate early. Nearly all nonsense mutations lead to proteins that cannot function normally.

VOCABULARY

ACADEMIC VOCABULARY

Substitution
the act of replacing one thing with another
The substitution of adenine for guanine in the DNA caused a dysfunctional protein.

Personal Tutor 

Another type of mutation that can occur involves the gain or loss of a nucleotide in the DNA sequence. Insertions are additions of a nucleotide to the DNA sequence, and the loss of a nucleotide is called a deletion. Both of these mutations change the multiples of three, from the point of the insertion or deletion. These are called frameshift mutations because they change the "frame" of the amino acid sequence. **Table 3** illustrates various types of mutations and their effect on the DNA sequence.

Sometimes mutations are associated with diseases and disorders. One example is alkaptonuria. Patients with this disorder have a mutation in their DNA coding for an enzyme involved in digesting the amino acid phenylalanine. This mutation results in the black-colored homogentisic acid that discolors the urine. Studies have shown that patients with alkaptonuria have a high occurrence of frameshift and missense mutations in a specific region of their DNA. **Table 3** lists some more examples of diseases associated with different types of mutations.

Table 3 Mutations — Interactive Table

Mutation Type	Analogy Sentence	Example of Associated Disease
Normal	THE BIG FAT CAT ATE THE WET RAT	
Missense (substitution)	THE BIZ FAT CAT ATE THE WET RAT	Achondroplasia: improper development of cartilage on the ends of the long bones of arms and legs resulting in a form of dwarfism
Nonsense (substitution)	THE BIG RAT	Muscular dystrophy: progressive muscle disorder characterized by the progressive weakening of many muscles in the body
Deletion (causing frameshift)	THB IGF ATC ATA TET HEW ETR AT	Cystic fibrosis: characterized by abnormally thick mucus in the lungs, intestines, and pancreas
Insertion (causing frameshift)	THE BIG ZFA TCA TAT ETH EWE TRA	Crohn's disease: chronic inflammation of the intestinal tract, producing frequent diarrhea, abdominal pain, nausea, fever, and weight loss
Duplication	THE BIG FAT FAT CAT ATE THE WET RAT	Charcot-Marie-Tooth disease (type 1A): damage to peripheral nerves leading to weakness and atrophy of muscles in hands and lower legs
Expanding mutation (tandem repeats) **Generation 1** **Generation 2** **Generation 3**	 THE BIG FAT CAT ATE THE WET RAT THE BIG FAT CAT CAT CAT ATE THE WET RAT THE BIG FAT CAT CAT CAT CAT CAT CAT ATE THE WET RAT	Huntington's disease: a progressive disease in which brain cells waste away, producing uncontrolled movements, emotional disturbances, and mental deterioration

Large portions of DNA can also be involved in a mutation. A piece of an individual chromosome containing one or more genes can be deleted or moved to a different location on the chromosome, or even to a different chromosome. Such rearrangements of the chromosome often have drastic effects on the expression of these genes.

Connection to Health In 1991, a new kind of mutation was discovered that involves an increase in the number of copies of repeated codons, called tandem repeats. The increase in repeated sequences seems to be involved in a number of inherited disorders. The first known example was fragile X syndrome—a syndrome that results in a number of mental and behavioral impairments. Near the end of a normal X chromosome, there is a section of CGG codons that repeat about 30 times. Individuals with fragile X have CGG codons that repeat hundreds of times. The syndrome received its name because the repeated area on the tip of the X chromosomes appears as a fragile piece hanging off the X chromosome, as illustrated in **Figure 21.** Currently, the mechanism by which the repeats expand from generation to generation is not known.

■ **Figure 21** Fragile X syndrome is due to many extra repeated CGG units near the end of the X chromosome, making the lower tip of the X chromosome appear fragile.

GET IT? **Describe** three types of mutations.

Protein folding and stability You might expect that large changes in the DNA code, such as frameshift mutations or changes in position, lead to genetic disorders. However, small changes like substitutions also can lead to genetic disorders. The change of one amino acid for another can change the sequence of amino acids in a protein enough to change both the folding and stability of the protein, as illustrated in **Figure 22.**

An example of a genetic disorder caused by a single point mutation is sickle-cell disease. In the case of sickle-cell disease, the codon for a glutamic acid (GAA) has been changed to a valine (GUA) in the protein. This change in composition changes the structure of hemoglobin and is the cause of this disorder.

■ **Figure 22** A single amino acid substitution can cause the genetic disorder sickle-cell disease.
Recall ***what happens to the protein with the substituted amino acid.***

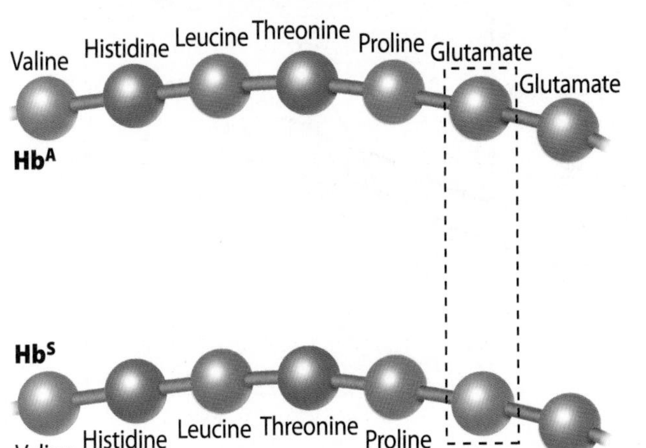

SEM Magnification: 400×

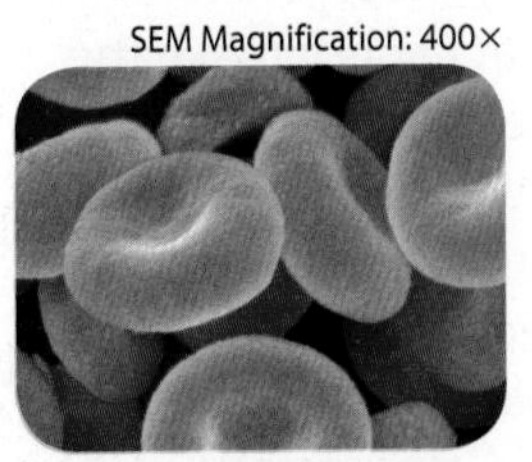

Normal shape of red blood cell

False-Color SEM Magnification: 1655×

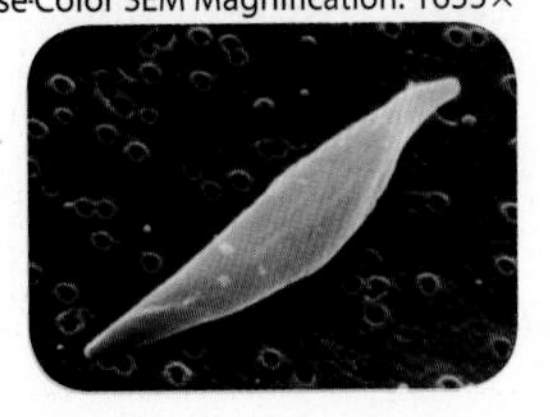

Sickle shape of red blood cell

Hemoglobin is made of four polypeptide chains, which are two sets of two identical chains. The molecule also contains a large carbon-ring structure that binds iron called the heme group. The substituted glutamic acid is located near the start of one set of chains, as shown in **Figure 22.** Glutamic acid is a polar amino acid, but the valine that substitutes for it in sickle-cell disease is nonpolar. Because of the charge difference, the sickle-cell hemoglobin folds differently than normal hemoglobin. The abnormal folding of the protein caused by the mutation results in a change to the sickle shape of the red blood cell. Numerous other diseases involve problems with protein folding, including Alzheimer's disease, cystic fibrosis, diabetes, and cancer.

Causes of mutation Some mutations, especially point mutations, can occur spontaneously. During replication, DNA polymerase sometimes adds the wrong nucleotides. Because the DNA polymerase has a proofreading function, the wrong nucleotide gets added only for one in one hundred thousand bases; it goes unfixed in less than one in one billion.

VOCABULARY
WORD ORIGIN
Mutagen
comes from the Latin word *mutare,* meaning *to change* and from the Greek word *genes,* meaning *born*

Certain chemicals and radiation also can damage DNA. Substances which cause mutations are called **mutagens** (MYEW tuh junz). Many different chemicals have been classified as mutagens. Some of these chemicals affect DNA by changing the chemical structure of the bases. Often these changes cause bases to mispair, or bond, with the wrong base. Other chemical mutagens have chemical structures that resemble nucleotides so closely that they can substitute for them. Once these imposter bases are incorporated into the DNA, it can not replicate properly. This type of chemical has become useful medically, especially in the treatment of HIV—the virus that causes AIDS. Many drugs used to treat HIV and other viral infections mimic various nucleotides. Once the drug is incorporated in the viral DNA, the DNA cannot copy itself properly.

Data Analysis LAB 2

Based on Real Data*

Interpret the Graph

How can we know if a compound is a mutagen? The Ames test is used to identify mutagens. The test uses a strain of bacteria that cannot make the amino acid histidine. The bacteria are exposed to a suspected mutagen and grow on a medium without histidine. The bacteria that grow have a mutation called a reversion because they reverted to the natural condition of making histidine. The compounds in the graph were Ames tested.

Data and Observations

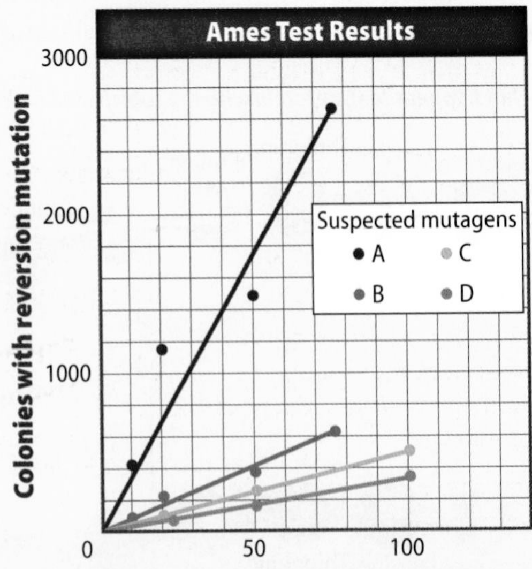

Think Critically

1. **Describe** the relationship between the amount of the compound and the mutation.
2. **Analyze** which compound is the strongest mutagenic compound.

*Data obtained from: Ames. B.N. 1979. Identifying environmental chemicals causing mutations and cancer. *Science.* 204: 587–593

High-energy forms of radiation, such as X-rays and gamma rays, are highly mutagenic. When the radiation reaches the DNA, electrons absorb the energy. The electrons can escape their atom, leaving behind a free radical. Free radicals are charged atoms with unpaired electrons that react violently with other molecules, including DNA. Ultraviolet (UV) radiation from the Sun contains less energy than X-ray radiation and does not cause electrons to be ejected from the atoms. However, UV radiation can cause adjacent thymine bases to bind together, disrupting the structure of DNA, as shown in **Figure 23.** DNA with this structure disruption, or kink, are unable to replicate properly unless repaired.

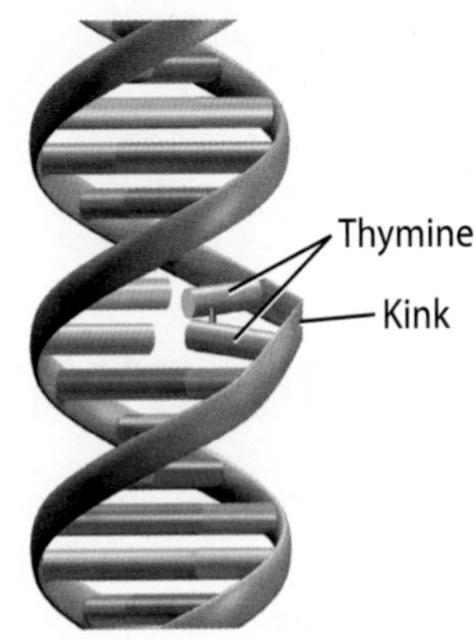

■ **Figure 23** Ultraviolet radiation can cause adjacent thymines to bind to each other instead of to their complementary bases, making the DNA "kink" and preventing replication.

Body-cell v. sex-cell mutation When a mutation in a body cell, also called a somatic cell, escapes the repair mechanism, it becomes part of the genetic sequence in that cell and in future daughter cells. Somatic cell mutations are not passed on to the next generation. In some cases, the mutations do not cause problems for the cell. They could be sequences not used by the adult cell when the mutation occurred, the mutation might have occurred in an exon, or the mutation might not have changed the amino acid for which it was coded. These mutations are called neutral mutations. When the mutation results in the production of an abnormal protein, the cell might not be able to perform its normal function, and cell death might occur. Recall that mutations in body cells that cause the cell cycle to be unregulated can lead to cancer. All of these effects are contained within the cells of the organism as long as only body cells are affected.

When mutations occur in sex cells, also called germ-line cells, the mutations are passed on to the organism's offspring and will be present in every cell of the offspring. In many cases, these mutations do not affect the function of cells in the organism, though they might affect the offspring drastically. When the mutations result in an abnormal protein in the sex cell, the offspring is impacted. However, the offspring is not impacted when an abnormal protein is produced in an isolated body cell.

REVIEW IT! Gene Regulation and Mutation

Section Summary

- Prokaryotic cells regulate their protein synthesis through a set of genes called operons.
- Eukaryotic cells regulate their protein synthesis using various transcription factors, eukaryotic nucleosome structures, and RNA interference.
- Mutations range from point mutations to the deletion or movement of large sections of the chromosome.
- Mutagens, such as chemicals and radiation, can cause mutations.

Self Check

Understand Main Ideas

1. MAINIDEA **Relate** gene regulation and mutations.
2. **Identify** the two main types of mutagens.
3. **Diagram** how adding lactose to a culture affects the *lac* operon of *E. coli*.
4. **Evaluate** how a point mutation can affect the overall protein shape and function, using hemoglobin as an example.
5. **Compare and contrast** prokaryotic and eukaryotic gene regulation.

Think Critically

6. **Explain** why most mutations in eukaryotes are recessive.
7. **Hypothesize** why DNA replication has such accuracy.

WRITING IN ▶ Biology

8. Write an article describing how Hox genes regulate development in animals.

BIOLOGY & society

Who owns genes?

Can a company own parts of the human body? That is an ethical debate that has raged since 1977, when universities and private companies first started seeking patents on genes. To date, about 20 percent of all human genes have been patented. This issue has made headlines since a company patented the BRCA1 and BRCA2 genes, mutations of which have been linked to breast cancer and ovarian cancer.

Agricultural gene patents have also sparked fierce debate. In recent decades, companies have modified the genes in many plants to incorporate them with desirable traits, such as resistance to diseases and pests. Companies have received patents on these modified plant genes.

What is a patent? A patent grants the exclusive right to make a profit from the sale of an invention. Often, people or businesses have invested years and large amounts of money researching and developing an invention. The profits they receive from holding patents help them recoup their investments, as well as provide money for future research.

A patent on nature Opponents argue that patenting genes will hinder free and open scientific research and will harm patients seeking medical care. If companies own patents on genes, they can refuse to allow other scientists to use the genes in their work, possibly preventing important discoveries. The high cost of genetic testing and therapies related to patented genes can deter patients from receiving treatments.

Agricultural implications Agricultural gene patents pose an additional problem for farmers. If winds or animals bring seeds containing patented genes to the fields of a farmer who has not bought the rights to use those seeds, the company who holds the patent can sue the farmer.

In the past, farmers have lost these court cases, even though it is impossible to stop natural forces from transferring seeds.

Soybeans

Corn

Around the world, the amount of land devoted to the cultivation of genetically modified plants is rising. Soybeans and corn are two crops that are often genetically modified.

As companies continue to seek patents on genes, the debate is certain to continue. For now, the patenting of genes is legal. But in the future, ethical and practical considerations might swing the pendulum the other way.

Investigate

Research List the various forms of agriculture in New York. Do any of the forms of agriculture you listed have gene patents? Have students further research gene patenting in the New York agricultural industry.

WebQuest

(t)Jamey Stillings/Getty Images; (b)Photo by Bob Nichols, USDA-ARS

BioLAB

1.1.1c, ¥a

FORENSICS: How is DNA extracted?

Background: DNA tests are important for biologists, doctors, and even detectives. Imagine that you are working in a lab where someone has brought a sample of corn from a crime scene to be analyzed. You decide to test the DNA of the corn to look for genes to identify the type of corn. Before the DNA sequence can be examined, the DNA must be extracted.

Question: *How can DNA be extracted?*

Materials

corn kernels (50 g)
beakers (2)
blender
cheesecloth (4 squares—30 cm on each edge)
rubber band
glass spooling hook
homogenization medium (100–150 mL)
plastic centrifuge tube (30–50 mL)
contact lens cleaning tablet (containing papain)
95% ethanol (12 mL)
distilled water (3 mL)
test tube
container of ice
water bath at 60°C
stirring rod
timer or clock

Safety Precautions

Procedure

1. Read and complete the lab safety form.
2. Carefully weigh out 50 g of corn kernels.
3. Place the corn kernels into a beaker and cover with homogenization medium that has been warmed to 60°C. Place the beaker in a 60°C water bath for 10 min. Gently stir every 45 s.
4. Remove the beaker from the water bath and chill quickly in an ice bath for 5 min.
5. Pour the mixture into a blender and homogenize, or blend, to achieve a consistent texture.
6. Filter the homogenized mixture through four layers of cheesecloth into a clean large beaker on ice.
7. Pour 15 mL of the filtrate into a 30–50 mL plastic centrifuge tube.
8. Dissolve one contact lens cleaning tablet in 3 mL of distilled water in a test tube. Add this to the filtrate tube and mix gently.
9. Hold the filtrate tube at an angle and slowly pour 12 mL of cold 95% ethanol down the side of the tube.
10. Observe the DNA rising into the alcohol layer as a cloudy suspension of white strings. Use a hooked glass rod to spool the DNA, and allow it to dry.
11. **Cleanup and Disposal** Clean your lab area, disposing of chemicals and materials as directed by your teacher. Be sure to wash your hands when you are finished.

Analyze and Conclude

1. **Describe** the appearance of the DNA in suspension and once it has dried.
2. **Explain** why you put the corn kernels into the blender.
3. **Think Critically** Why is it important not to contaminate a sample of DNA that is to be sequenced? How would you know if you had contaminated your sample?

WRITING IN ▶ Biology

Report Imagine you are the first researcher to extract DNA from corn. Write a report detailing your methods and possible applications of your discovery.

CHAPTER 12 STUDY GUIDE

BIGIDEA **DNA is the genetic material that contains a code for proteins.**

SECTION 1 DNA: The Genetic Material

MAINIDEA The discovery that DNA is the genetic code involved many experiments.

- Griffith's bacterial experiment and Avery's explanation first indicated that DNA is the genetic material.
- The Hershey-Chase experiment provided evidence that DNA is the genetic material of viruses.
- The work of Watson, Crick, Franklin, and Wilkins provided evidence of the double-helix structure of DNA.

VOCABULARY
- **double helix**
- **nucleosome**

SECTION 2 Replication of DNA

MAINIDEA DNA replicates by making a strand that is complementary to each original strand.

- The enzymes DNA helicase, RNA primase, DNA polymerase, and DNA ligase are involved in DNA replication.
- The leading strand is synthesized continuously, but the lagging strand is synthesized discontinously, forming Okazaki fragments.
- Prokaryotic DNA opens at a single origin of replication, whereas eukaryotic DNA has multiple areas of replication.

VOCABULARY
- **semiconservative replication**
- **DNA polymerase**
- **Okazaki fragment**

SECTION 3 DNA, RNA, and Protein

MAINIDEA DNA codes for RNA, which guides protein synthesis.

- Three major types of RNA are involved in protein synthesis: mRNA, tRNA, and rRNA.
- The synthesis of the mRNA from the template DNA is called transcription.
- Translation is the process through which the mRNA attaches to the ribosome and a protein is assembled.
- In eukaryotes, mRNA contains introns that are excised before leaving the nucleus. A cap and poly-A tail are added to the mRNA.
- One gene codes for one polypeptide.

VOCABULARY
- **RNA**
- **messenger RNA**
- **ribosomal RNA**
- **transfer RNA**
- **transcription**
- **RNA polymerase**
- **intron**
- **exon**
- **codon**
- **translation**

SECTION 4 Gene Regulation and Mutation

MAINIDEA Gene expression is regulated by the cell, and mutations can affect this expression.

- Prokaryotic cells regulate their protein synthesis through a set of genes called operons.
- Eukaryotic cells regulate their protein synthesis using various transcription factors, eukaryotic nucleosome structures, and RNA interference.
- Mutations range from point mutations to the deletion or movement of large sections of the chromosome.
- Mutagens, such as chemicals and radiation, can cause mutations.

VOCABULARY
- **gene regulation**
- **operon**
- **mutation**
- **mutagen**

SECTION 1

Vocabulary Review

Each of the following sentences is false. Make the sentence true by replacing the underlined word with the correct vocabulary term from the Study Guide page.

1. The twisted ladder shape of DNA is called a <u>nucleotide</u>.

2. A <u>double helix</u> consists of DNA wrapped around the histone proteins.

Understand Main Ideas

3. What are the basic building blocks of DNA and RNA?
   A. ribose
   B. purines
   C. nucleotides
   D. phosphorus

4. If a section of DNA has 27 percent thymine, how much cytosine will it have?
   A. 23 percent
   B. 27 percent
   C. 46 percent
   D 54 percent

5. Which was a conclusion of Griffith's work with *Streptococcus pneumoniae?*
   A. DNA is the genetic material in viruses.
   B. The structure of DNA is a double helix.
   C. Bacteria exposed to DNA can incorporate the DNA and change phenotype.
   D. The amount of thymine equals the amount of adenine in DNA.

Refer to the figure below to answer questions 6 and 7.

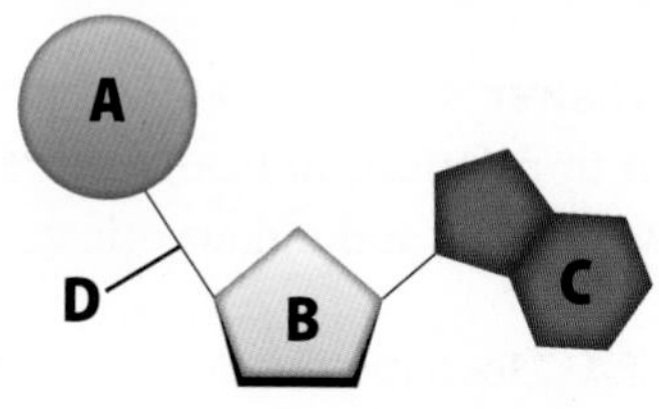

6. What is the entire labeled structure called?
   A. nucleotide
   B. RNA
   C. base
   D. phosphate

7. Which label represents the coding part of DNA?
   A. A
   B. B
   C. C
   D. D

Constructed Response

8. **Short Answer** Explain how DNA forms chromosomes in eukaryotic cells.

Use the figure below to answer question 9.

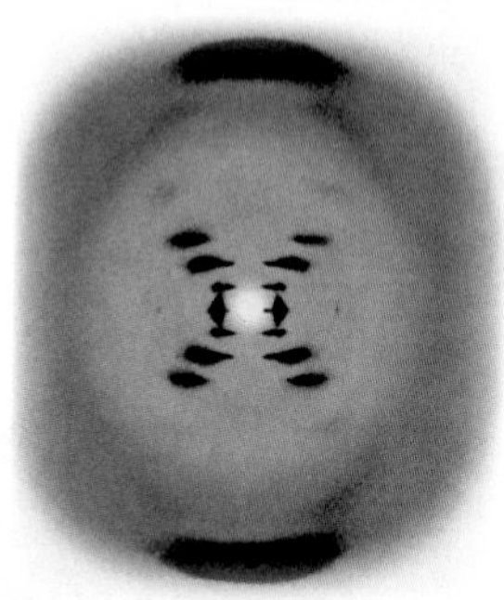

9. **THEME FOCUS** Summarize the experiments and data shown in the photo that led to the discovery of DNA.

Think Critically

10. **Design** How might you use radioactive phosphorus to demonstrate that the transforming compound of bacteria in Griffith's experiment was DNA?

11. **MAINIDEA** How would the results of the Hershey-Chase experiment have been different if protein were the genetic material?

SECTION 2

Vocabulary Review

Write a sentence defining each of the following vocabulary terms.

12. DNA polymerase

13. semiconservative replication

14. Okazaki fragment

Understand Main Ideas

15. With what does the synthesis of a new strand of DNA begin?
    A. RNA primer
    B. nucleotide unit
    C. messenger RNA
    D. transfer RNA

Omikron/Science Source

16. Which is true about the elongation of the lagging strand?
    A. does not require a template strand
    B. produces Okazaki fragments
    C. requires the action of RNA ligase
    D. proceeds by continually adding nucleotides to the 3′ end

Constructed Response

17. **Short Answer** List the enzymes involved in replication and describe their functions.

18. MAINIDEA Summarize the process of DNA replication in a diagram. Add labels to explain what is happening.

Think Critically

Use the figure below to answer questions 19 and 20.

19. **Determine** Imagine that you are a scientist looking at a cell through a microscope. You see DNA replicating in several areas. Determine what type of cell you are looking at based on the origins of replication.

20. **Hypothesize** why it is important for the DNA in the figure to have multiple origins of replication.

21. **Infer** how complementary base pairing is responsible for semiconservative replication.

SECTION 3

Vocabulary Review

Write a sentence that connects the vocabulary terms in each pair.

22. mRNA—tRNA

23. codon—RNA polymerase

24. intron—exon

Understand Main Ideas

25. Which correctly lists the changes to eukaryotic pre-mRNA to form mRNA?
    A. cap added, introns excised, and poly T tail added
    B. cap added, exons excised, and poly T tail added
    C. cap added, introns excised, and poly A tail added
    D. cap added, exons excised, and poly A tail added

Use the figure below to answer questions 26 and 27.

26. What is the mRNA sequence for the template strand DNA sequence in the figure?
    A. 5′ ATGTTTGATCTT 3′
    B. 5′ AUGUUUGAUCUU 3′
    C. 5′ TACAAACTAGAA 3′
    D. 5′ UACAAACUAGAA 3′

27. What is the sequence for the nontemplate strand of the DNA in the figure?
    A. 5′ ATGTTTGATCTT 3′
    B. 5′ AUGUUUGAUCUU 3′
    C. 5′ TACAAACTAGAA 3′
    D. 5′ UACAAACUAGAA 3′

Constructed Response

28. **Short Answer** Compare and contrast transcription and translation. Indicate where they occur in prokaryotic cells and eukaryotic cells.

29. MAINIDEA Describe the experiment that led to the One Gene–One Enzyme hypothesis.

Think Critically

30. **Identify** the mRNA sequence and orientation if the nontemplate strand has the sequence 5′ ATGCCAGTCATC 3′. Use **Figure 14** to determine the amino acid sequence coded by the mRNA.

SECTION 4

Vocabulary Review

Write the vocabulary term from the Study Guide page that describes each of the following processes.

31. regulation of a prokaryotic genome

32. control of the functional units of DNA

33. changes in DNA sequence

Understand Main Ideas

34. Which demonstrates an insertion mutation of the sequence 5′ GGGCCCAAA 3′?
A. 5′ GGGGCCAAA 3′
B. 5′ GGGCCAAA 3′
C. 5′ GGGAAACCC 3′
D. 5′ GGGCCCAAAAAA 3′

35. Which is true about eukaryotic gene regulation?
A. Eukaryotic gene regulation is exactly like prokaryotic gene regulation.
B. Replication factors guide the binding of eukaryotic RNA polymerase to the promoter.
C. Activator proteins fold DNA to enhancer sites that increase the rate of gene transmission.
D. Repressor proteins bind to activators, preventing them from binding to the DNA.

36. Which is not a type of mutation?
A. base substitutions
B. insertions
C. RNA interference
D. translocation

Constructed Response

37. Short Answer Illustrate the effect of adding tryptophan to a culture of *E. coli.*

38. Short Answer Describe the roles of DNA and RNA in eukaryotic cell differentiation.

Think Critically

39. Infer why base substitutions in the third position are least likely to cause a change in the amino acid for which it coded.

40. MAINIDEA Hypothesize how bacteria might respond to environmental stress by increasing the rate of mutations during cell division.

Summative Assessment

41. **BIGIDEA** Explain the central dogma of protein synthesis.

42. **WRITINGIN▶Biology** The discovery of DNA and its structure required many scientists to research, conduct experiments, and publish their findings. Write about a scientific event that required scientists to build on others' findings to produce results.

43. **WRITINGIN▶Biology** The book *Jurassic Park* by Michael Crichton presents the idea of isolating DNA from extinct organisms and "resurrecting" them. If this were possible, should this be done? Defend your opinion in an essay.

DBQ Document–Based Questions

Data obtained from: Watson, J.D. and Crick, F.H.. 1953. Molecular Structure of Nucleic Acids. Nature 171: 737–738.

The following excerpts are from Watson and Crick's description of the structure of DNA.

"The novel feature of the structure is the manner in which the two chains are held together by the purine and pyrimidine bases. The planes of the bases are perpendicular to the fibre axis. They are joined together in pairs, a single base from one chain being hydrogen-bonded to a single base from the other chain so that the two lie side by side with identical z-co-ordinates. One of the pair must be a purine and the other a pyrimidine for bonding to occur."

"It has not escaped our notice that the specific pairing we have postulated immediately suggests a possible copying mechanism for the genetic material."

44. Draw a diagram of DNA structure based on the description above.

45. According to the description, how are the bases joined together?

46. What did Watson and Crick see as a possible copying mechanism?

CUMULATIVE

MULTIPLE CHOICE

1 Which macromolecule can be formed using the sugars produced by plants during photosynthesis?

A cellulose

B DNA

C lipid

D protein

Use the diagram below to answer questions 2 and 3.

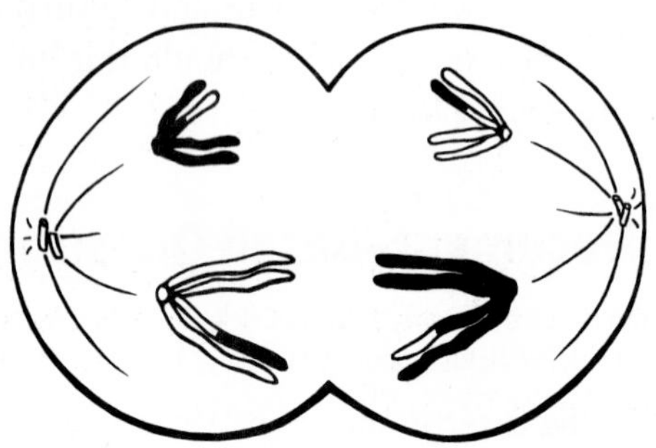

2 Which stage of meiosis is represented in the diagram?

A anaphase I

B anaphase II

C metaphase I

D metaphase II

3 Which process can take place during the stage of meiosis that follows the stage in the diagram?

A change to diploid

B crossing over

C cytokinesis

D DNA replication

SHORT ANSWER

4 Using the law of independent assortment, describe a dihybrid cross of heterozygous yellow, round-seed pea plants (YyRr). Include a Punnett square and phenotype ratios in your response.

5 Give an example of a technological development, and explain how it contributed to scientists' understanding of the structure of DNA.

6 Which probably causes the coat color variations that occur only in the females of a certain animal? Give a reason to support your conclusion.

7 Suppose you perform a dihybrid cross between two organisms with the genotype RrYy. What percentage of the offspring would be homozygous for both traits? Explain how you determined the answer.

8 Why do you think Mendel's work preceded the search for molecules involved in inheritance?

9 Suppose an organism (with a chromosome number of $2n = 6$) has monosomy of chromosome 3. How many chromosomes are in the organism's karyotype? Explain your answer.

10 Explain why the number of bases in a strand of mRNA can be different from the number in the DNA from which it was synthesized.

11 Explain why a hypothesis must be testable.

EXTENDED RESPONSE

Use the figure below to answer question 12.

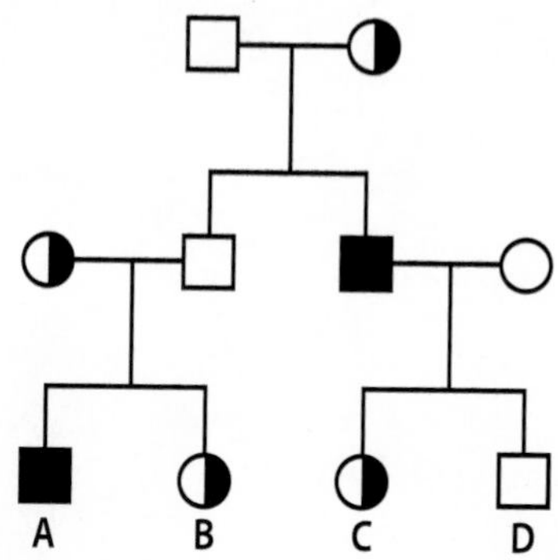

12 Describe the pattern of inheritance of the disease tracked in the pedigree above.

13 Human nerve cells seldom divide after they are formed. Evaluate how this might affect a person with a spinal cord injury.

14 Explain the role that publication of findings had in the discovery of DNA's structure.

ESSAY QUESTION

For certain kinds of research studies, scientists recruit pairs of twins to be participants or subjects of the research. They might recruit identical or fraternal twins, depending on the focus of the study. Twins can be particularly helpful in studies about genetics and heredity.

Using the information in the paragraph above, answer the following question in essay format.

15 Imagine you are a research scientist. Write a plan for a research study that would require participants to be twins. Explain what you are trying to learn, whether you are looking for identical or fraternal twins, and why it is important to have twins as subjects for your study.

TEST PRACTICE

TEST Practice

16 What enzyme is responsible for "unzipping" the DNA strand during replication?

A DNA helicase

B DNA ligase

C DNA polymerase

D RNA primase

Use the illustration below to answer question 17.

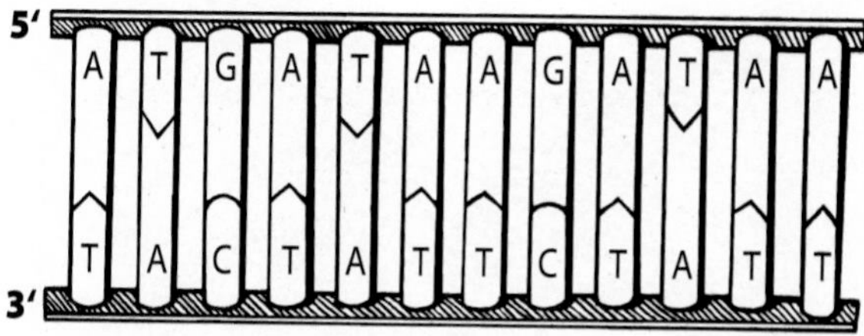

17 Which sequence is possible for mRNA formed from the DNA strand shown in the illustration?

A 5′ AATAGAATAGTA 3′

B 5′ AAUAGAAUAGUA 3′

C 5′ ATGATAAGATAA 3′

D 5′ AUGAUAAGAUAA 3′

18 Which cells would likely undergo apoptosis?

A cells between fingers

B cells reproducing normally

C cells reproducing slowly

D cells surrounding the heart

NEED EXTRA HELP?																		
If You Missed Question . . .	1	2	3	4	5	6	7	8	9	10	11	12	13	14	15	16	17	18
Review Section . . .	8.2	10.1	10.1	11.2	12.2	11.2	10.2	12.2	11.3	11.2	12.3	11.1	9.1	12.1	11.2	12.2	12.3	9.3

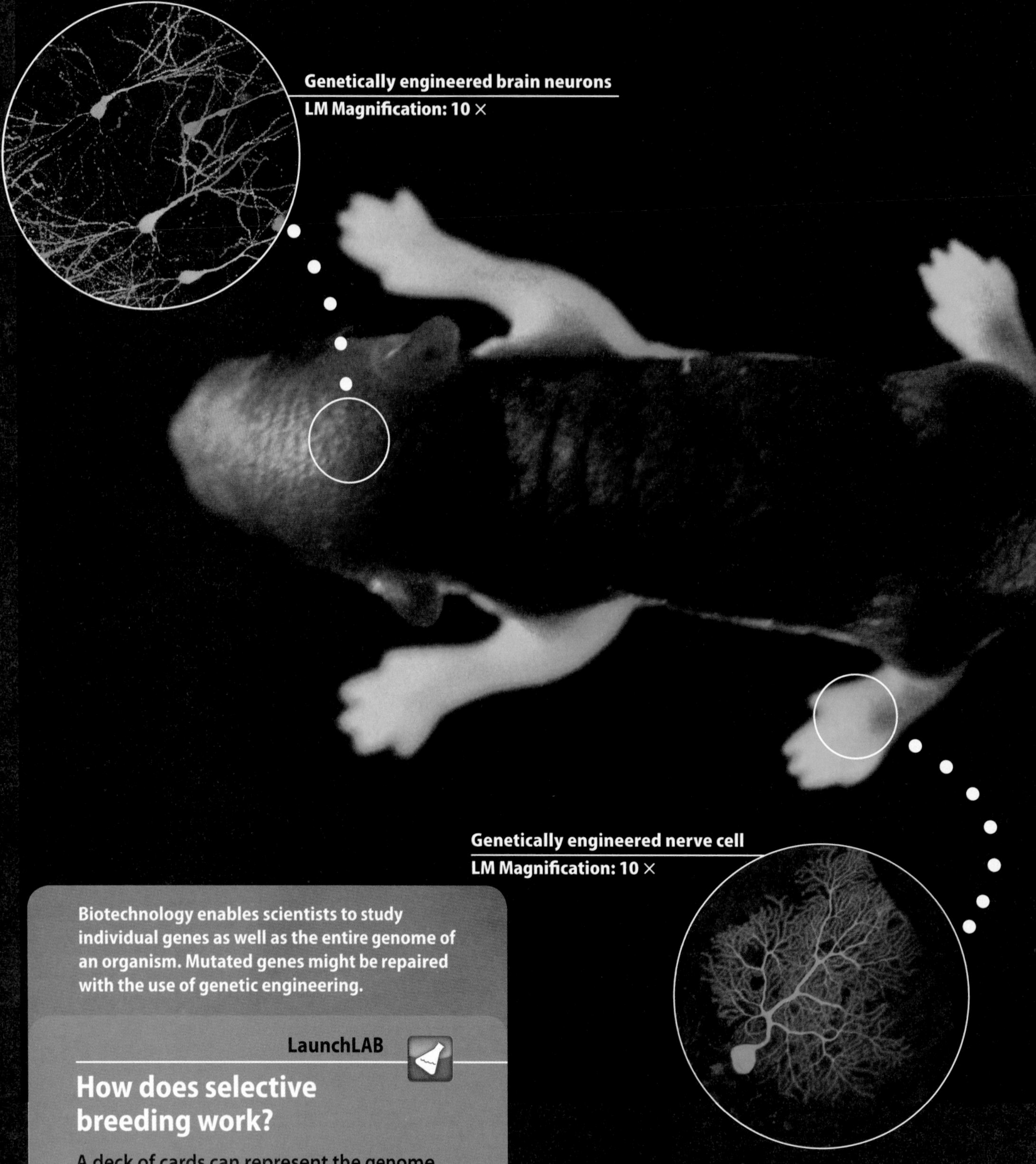

Genetically engineered brain neurons

LM Magnification: 10 ×

Genetically engineered nerve cell

LM Magnification: 10 ×

Biotechnology enables scientists to study individual genes as well as the entire genome of an organism. Mutated genes might be repaired with the use of genetic engineering.

LaunchLAB

How does selective breeding work?

A deck of cards can represent the genome of a population of organisms. In this lab, you will model selective breeding to create a population of cards with similar suits.

Go Online!
MHEonline.com

Watch

Resources

Vocab

Tutor

IWB

Check

Lab

Tools

Science Notebook

CHAPTER 13

Genetics and Biotechnology

1 Applied Genetics

4.2.2a, ¥a, ¥q

2 DNA Technology

1.1.3b, 4.2.2b, 4.4.1b, ¥a, ¥q

3 The Human Genome

1.1.1b, 1.1.3b, 1.1.4a, 4.2.1f, 4.2.1i, 4.2.2d, 4.5.2e, 4.7.3a

THEMEFOCUS

Stability and change Vectors provide a stable environment in which DNA and genes are inserted into gene therapy patients.

BIGIDEA

Genetic technology improves human health and quality of life.

Making Recombinant DNA

Make a three tab book and label it as shown. Use it to organize your notes about DNA tools.

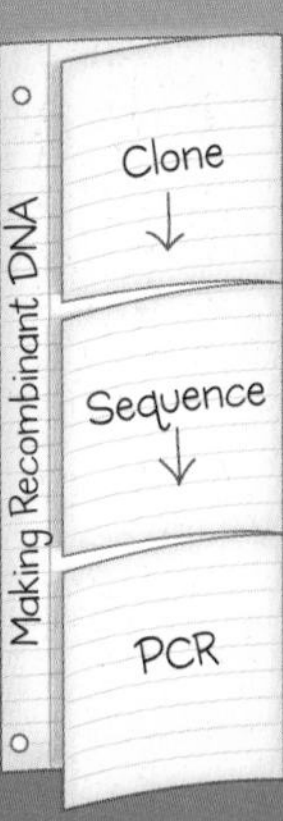

Science Notebook

1 Applied Genetics

4.2.2a, ¥a, ¥q

MAINIDEA

Selective breeding is used to produce organisms with desired traits.

Essential Questions

- How is selective breeding used to produce organisms with desired traits?
- What are similarities and differences between inbreeding and hybridization?
- How does a Punnett square test cross help assess the genotypes of organisms?

BIOLOGY 4 U

Coin collectors separate rare coins from all other coins because the rare ones are more valuable. Just as certain coins are selected for their value, certain plants and animals have been selected and bred to produce organisms with traits that are valuable to humans.

Review Vocabulary

hybrid: organism that is heterozygous for a particular trait

New Vocabulary

selective breeding
inbreeding
test cross

Multilingual eGlossary

Selective Breeding

You might be familiar with different breeds of dogs, such as Saint Bernards, huskies, and German shepherds. Observe some of the phenotypic traits of these breeds in **Figure 1.** All three have strong, muscular bodies. Saint Bernards have traits such as a keen sense of smell that make them good rescue dogs. Huskies are endurance runners and pull sleds long distances. German shepherds are highly trainable for special services.

Since ancient times, humans have bred animals with certain traits to obtain offspring that have desired traits. As a result, these traits become more common. Breeding for desired traits is not restricted to animals alone. Plants also are bred to produce desired traits, such as larger fruits and shorter growing times. The process by which desired traits of certain plants and animals are selected and passed on to their future generations is called **selective breeding.** Through the processes of hybridization and inbreeding, desired traits can be passed on to future generations.

■ **Figure 1** Dogs have traits that make them suited for different tasks: Saint Bernard—keen sense of smell; husky—endurance to run long distances; and German shepherd—high trainability.

Saint Bernard
Rescue dog

Husky
Sled dog

German shepherd
Service dog

Hybridization Recall that crossing parent organisms with different forms of a trait to produce offspring with specific traits results in hybrids. Farmers, animal breeders, scientists, and gardeners often use the production of hybrids, also known as hybridization. They select traits that will give hybrid organisms a competitive edge. These hybrid organisms can be bred to be more disease-resistant, to produce more offspring, or to grow faster. For example, plant breeders might choose to cross two different varieties of tomato plants in order to produce a hybrid that has both the disease resistance of one parent and the fast growth rate of the other parent.

Care must be taken to identify organisms with desired traits and successfully cross them to yield the right combination of traits from both parents. A disadvantage of hybridization is that it is time consuming and expensive. For example, it took rice breeders three decades to produce hybrid rice varieties that can produce higher yields than nonhybrid varieties. Because hybrids can be bred to be more nutritious, to have the ability to adapt to a wide range of changes in the environment, and to produce greater numbers of offspring, the advantages of hybridization sometimes outweigh the disadvantages.

Inbreeding Once a breeder observes a desired trait in an organism, a process is needed to ensure that the trait is passed on to future generations. This process, in which two closely related organisms are bred to have the desired traits and to eliminate the undesired ones in future generations, is called **inbreeding.**

Pure breeds are maintained by inbreeding. Clydesdale horses, Angus cattle, and German shepherd dogs are all examples of organisms produced by inbreeding. You might have seen Clydesdale horses at parades and petting zoos. Horse breeders first bred the Clydesdale horse in Scotland hundreds of years ago for use as a farm horse. Because of their strong build, agility, and obedient nature, Clydesdales originally were inbred and used extensively for pulling heavy loads.

A disadvantage of inbreeding is that harmful recessive traits also can be passed on to future generations. Inbreeding increases the chance of homozygous recessive offspring. If both parents carry the recessive allele, the harmful trait likely will not be eliminated.

GET IT? **Describe** the disadvantages associated with hybridization and inbreeding.

MiniLAB 1

Model Hybridization

How are hybrid lilies produced? In this lab, you will examine techniques used by both professional plant breeders and amateur gardeners to produce the wide variety of lilies you might see growing in landscaped areas.

Procedure

1. Read and complete the lab safety form.
2. Obtain a **labeled drawing of a lily flower** and a **fresh open lily flower.** Examine the flower with a **hand lens** and identify the male anthers and the female pistil.
3. Use a **cotton swab** to gently rub an anther to pick up pollen.
4. Trade flowers with another lab group and, using the cotton swab, gently apply the pollen from your flower to the stigma of the pistil of the new flower.

Analysis

1. **Infer** When breeders hybridize lilies, they transfer pollen to the stigma of an unopened lily flower and then cover the stigma with a foil cap. Why do you think this would be necessary?
2. **Think Critically** A breeder produces a hybrid lily which then is allowed to grow and produce seeds naturally. When these seeds are planted, the new lily plants do not have the same characteristics as the hybrid parent. Hypothesize why this would occur.

Launch Lab

Review Based on what you have read about selective breeding, how would you now answer the analysis questions?

Homozygous white grapefruit

Homozygous red grapefruit

	W	*W*
w	*Ww*	*Ww*
w	*Ww*	*Ww*

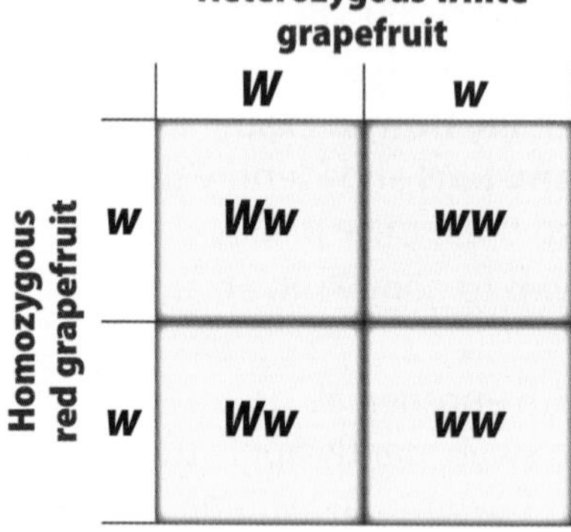

■ **Figure 2** The genotype of a white grapefruit tree can be determined by the results of a test cross with a homozygous red grapefruit.

Test Cross

An important thing a breeder has to determine when producing a hybrid is the genotype of the hybrid. Once a breeder observes the desired trait, if the trait is dominant, then the genotype of the organism could be homozygous dominant or heterozygous. The exact genotype is determined by performing a test cross. A **test cross** involves breeding an organism that has the unknown genotype with one that is homozygous recessive for the desired trait. If the parent's genotype is homozygous dominant, all the offspring will have the dominant phenotype; if it is heterozygous, the offspring will show a 1:1 phenotypic ratio.

Performing a test cross Suppose a breeder wants to produce hybrid white grapefruits. In grapefruit trees, white fruit color is the dominant trait, while red is recessive. Therefore, the red grapefruit trees in the orchard must be homozygous recessive (*ww*). The genotype of the hybrid white grapefruit tree obtained by the breeder can be homozygous dominant (*WW*) or heterozygous (*Ww*) for the white color. Therefore, the breeder has to perform a test cross to determine the genotype of the white grapefruit tree. Remember when performing a cross, pollen from the flower of one plant is transferred to the female organ in a flower of another plant.

Results As shown in the top Punnett square in **Figure 2,** if the white grapefruit tree is homozygous dominant (*WW*) and is crossed with a red grapefruit tree (*ww*), then all the offspring will be heterozygous (*Ww*) and white in color. In this case, all of the offspring will have the dominant phenotype. However, as shown in the second Punnett square in **Figure 2,** if the white grapefruit tree is heterozygous (*Ww*), then half the number of offspring will be white and half will be red, and the phenotypic ratio will be 1:1. Review the results in the Punnett squares in **Figure 2.** If the white grapefruit tree is homozygous, all offspring will be heterozygous—white in color. If the tree is heterozygous, half of the test-cross offspring will be white and half will be red.

REVIEW IT! Applied Genetics

Section Summary

- Selective breeding is used to produce organisms with traits that are considered desirable.
- Hybridization produces organisms with desired traits from parent organisms with different traits.
- Inbreeding creates pure breeds.
- A test cross can be used to determine an organism's genotype.

Self Check

Understand Main Ideas

1. MAINIDEA **Assess** the effect of selective breeding on food crops.
2. **Describe** three traits that might be desired in sheep. How can these traits be passed on to the next generation? Explain.
3. **Compare and contrast** inbreeding and hybridization.
4. **Predict** the phenotype of offspring from a test cross between a seedless orange (*ss*) and an orange with seeds (*Ss*).

Think Critically

5. **Evaluate** Should a cow and a bull that both carry recessive alleles for a mutation that causes decreased milk production be bred? Why or why not?

MATH IN Biology

6. A breeder performs a test cross to determine the genotype of a black cat. He crosses the black cat (*BB* or *Bb*) with a white cat (*bb*). If 50 percent of the offspring are black, what is the genotype of the black cat?

 USE IT! Science Notebook

2 DNA Technology

1.1.3b, 4.2.2b, 4.4.1b, ¥a, ¥q

MAIN IDEA

Researchers use genetic engineering to manipulate DNA.

Essential Questions

- What are the different tools and processes used in genetic engineering?
- How does genetic engineering manipulate recombinant DNA?
- What are the similarities between selective breeding and genetic engineering?
- How can genetic engineering and biotechnology be used to improve human life?

BIOLOGY 4 U

Have you seen a handmade patchwork quilt? Patchwork quilts are created by combining different pieces of fabric. Scientists use a similar process and combine DNA from different sources to create an organism with unique traits.

Review Vocabulary

DNA: the genetic material of all organisms, composed of two complementary chains of nucleotides wound in a double helix

New Vocabulary

genetic engineering
genome
restriction enzyme
gel electrophoresis
recombinant DNA
plasmid
DNA ligase
transformation
cloning
polymerase chain reaction
transgenic organism

Multilingual eGlossary

Genetic Engineering

By about 1970, researchers had discovered the structure of DNA and had determined the central dogma that information flowed from DNA to RNA and from RNA to proteins. However, scientists did not know much about the function of individual genes. Suppose your friend told you the final score of a high school football game but did not tell you how each player contributed to the game. Your curiosity about the details of the game is similar to the curiosity scientists experienced because they did not know how each gene contributed to a cell's function.

The situation changed when scientists began using **genetic engineering,** technology that involves manipulating the DNA of one organism in order to insert exogenous DNA (the DNA of another organism). For example, researchers have inserted a gene for a bioluminescent protein called green fluorescent protein (GFP) into various organisms. GFP, which is a substance naturally found in jellyfishes that live in the north Pacific Ocean, emits a green light when it is exposed to ultraviolet light. Organisms that have been genetically engineered to synthesize the DNA for GFP, such as the mosquito larvae shown in **Figure 3,** can be easily identified in the presence of ultraviolet light. The GFP DNA is attached to exogenous DNA to verify that the DNA has been inserted into the organism. These genetically engineered organisms are used in various processes, such as studying the expression of a particular gene, investigating cellular processes, studying the development of a certain disease, and selecting traits that might be beneficial to humans.

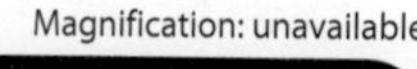

Magnification: unavailable

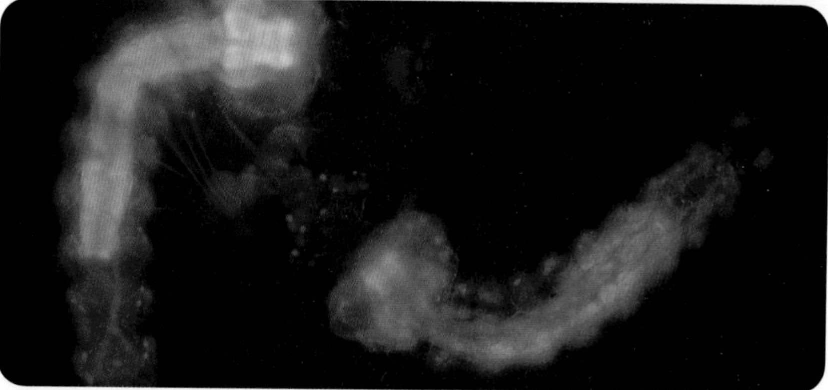

Genetically engineered mosquito larvae

■ **Figure 3** The gene for green fluorescent protein (GFP) was introduced into mosquito larvae so that researchers could verify that exogenous DNA was inserted.

Predict ***how genetic engineering might be used in the future by the medical field.***

Carolyn A. McKeone/Science Source

DNA Tools

Vocabulary

Academic Vocabulary

Manipulate
to manage or utilize skillfully
Scientists use technology to manipulate genetic information in order to test scientific hypotheses.

You have learned that selective breeding is used to produce plants and animals with desired traits. Genetic engineering can be used to increase or decrease the expression of specific genes in selected organisms. It has many applications from human health to agriculture.

An organism's **genome** is the total DNA present in the nucleus of each cell. As you will learn in the next section, genomes, such as the human genome, can contain millions and millions of nucleotides. In order to study a specific gene, DNA tools can be used to manipulate DNA and to isolate genes from the rest of the genome.

Restriction enzymes Some types of bacteria contain powerful defenses against viruses. These cells contain proteins called **restriction enzymes** that recognize and bind to specific DNA sequences and cleave the DNA within that sequence. A restriction enzyme, also called an endonuclease (en doh NEW klee ayz), cuts the viral DNA into fragments after it enters the bacteria. Since their discovery in the late 1960s, scientists have identified and isolated hundreds of restriction enzymes. Restriction enzymes are used as powerful tools for isolating specific genes or regions of the genome. When the restriction enzyme cleaves genomic DNA, it creates fragments of different sizes that are unique to every individual.

EcoRI One restriction enzyme that is used widely by scientists is known as *EcoR*I. As illustrated in **Figure 4,** *EcoR*I specifically cuts DNA containing the sequence GAATTC. The ends of the DNA fragments created by *EcoR*I are called sticky ends because they contain single-stranded DNA that is complementary. The ability of some restriction enzymes to create fragments with sticky ends is important because these sticky ends can be joined together with other DNA fragments that have complementary sticky ends.

GET IT? **Generalize** how restriction enzymes are used.

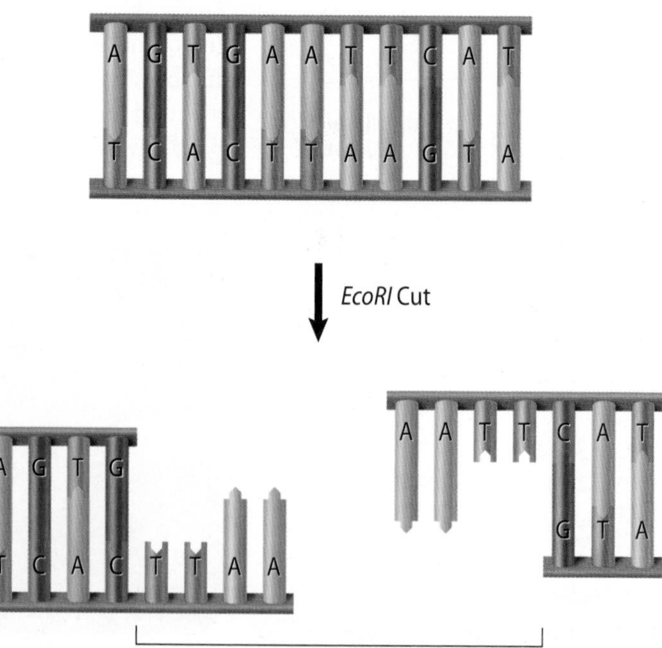

Figure 4 DNA containing the sequence GAATTC can be cut by the restriction enzyme *EcoRI* to produce sticky ends.

Animation

Loading the gel Solution containing DNA is dropped into holes at one end of the gel with a pipette.

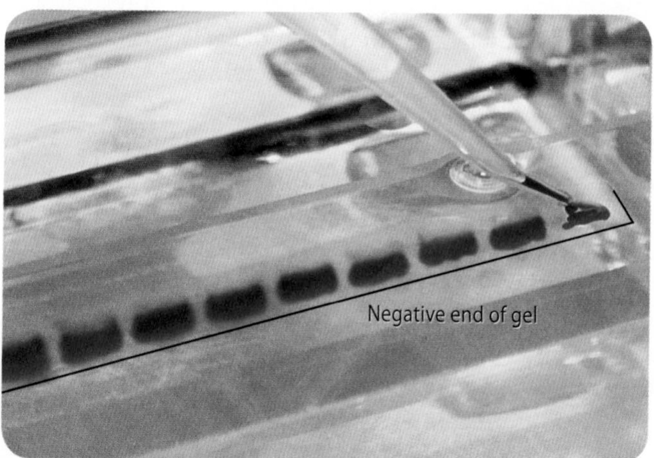

Fragment pattern A staining solution binds to the separated DNA fragments in the gel, making them visible under ultraviolet light.

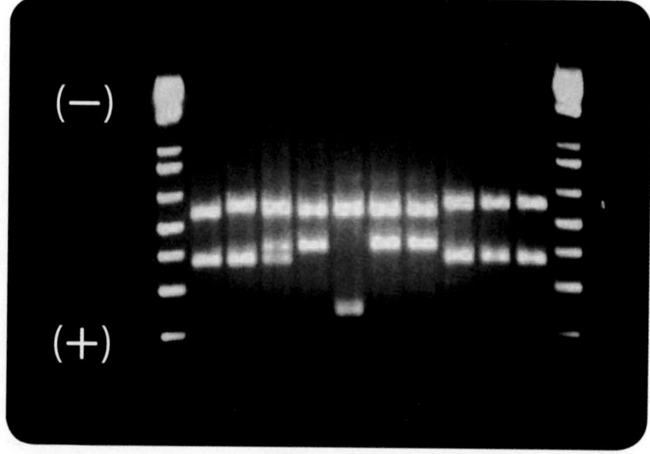

■ **Figure 5** When the loaded gel is placed in an electrophoresis tank and the electric current is turned on, the DNA fragments separate.

However, not all restriction enzymes create sticky ends. Some enzymes produce fragments containing blunt ends—created when the restriction enzyme cuts straight across both strands. Blunt ends do not have regions of single-stranded DNA and can join to any other DNA fragment with blunt ends.

Connection to Physics **Gel electrophoresis** An electric current is used to separate DNA fragments according to the size of the fragments in a process called **gel electrophoresis.** **Figure 5** shows how the DNA fragments are loaded on the negatively charged end of a gel. When an electric current is applied, the DNA fragments move toward the positive end of the gel. The smaller fragments move farther faster than the larger ones. The unique pattern created based on the size of the DNA fragment can be compared to known DNA fragments for identification. Also, portions of the gel containing each band can be removed for further study.

MiniLAB 2

Model Restriction Enzymes

How are sticky ends modeled? Use scissors and tape to produce paper DNA fragments with sticky ends and a recombinant DNA plasmid.

Procedure

1. Read and complete the lab safety form.
2. Obtain one **straight paper DNA sequence** from your teacher, which will represent genomic DNA, and one **circular paper DNA sequence,** which will represent a plasmid.
3. Find each GAATTC sequence recognized by the restriction enzyme *EcoRI* and cleave the genome and plasmid DNA using **scissors.**
4. Use **tape** to make a recombinant DNA plasmid.

Analysis

1. **Compare** your plasmid to those made by other lab groups. How many different recombinant plasmids could be made using this particular genomic sequence? Explain.
2. **Infer** what enzyme was represented by the scissors. Explain.

(l)Klaus Guldbrandsen/Science Source, (r)NOAA

Recombinant DNA Technology

When DNA fragments have been separated by gel electrophoresis, fragments of a specific size can be removed from the gel and combined with DNA fragments from another source. This newly generated DNA molecule, with DNA from different sources, is called **recombinant DNA.** Recombinant DNA technology has revolutionized the way scientists study DNA because it enables individual genes to be studied.

Large quantities of recombinant DNA molecules are needed in order to study them. A carrier, called a vector, transfers the recombinant DNA into a bacterial cell called the host cell. Plasmids and viruses are commonly used vectors. **Plasmids**—small, circular, double-stranded DNA molecules that occur naturally in bacteria and yeast cells—can be used as vectors because they can be cut with restriction enzymes. If a plasmid and a DNA fragment obtained from another genome have been cleaved by the same restriction enzyme, the ends of each DNA fragment will be complementary and can be combined, as shown in **Figure 6.** An enzyme normally used by cells in DNA repair and replication, called **DNA ligase,** joins the two DNA fragments chemically. Ligase joins DNA fragments that have sticky ends as well as those that have blunt ends.

Examine **Figure 6** again. Notice that the resulting circular DNA molecule contains the plasmid DNA and the DNA fragment isolated from another genome. This recombinant plasmid DNA molecule now can be inserted into a host cell so that large quantities of this type of recombinant DNA can be made.

GET IT? **Relate** restriction enzymes to recombinant DNA.

■ **Figure 6** Recombinant DNA is created by joining together DNA from two different sources.

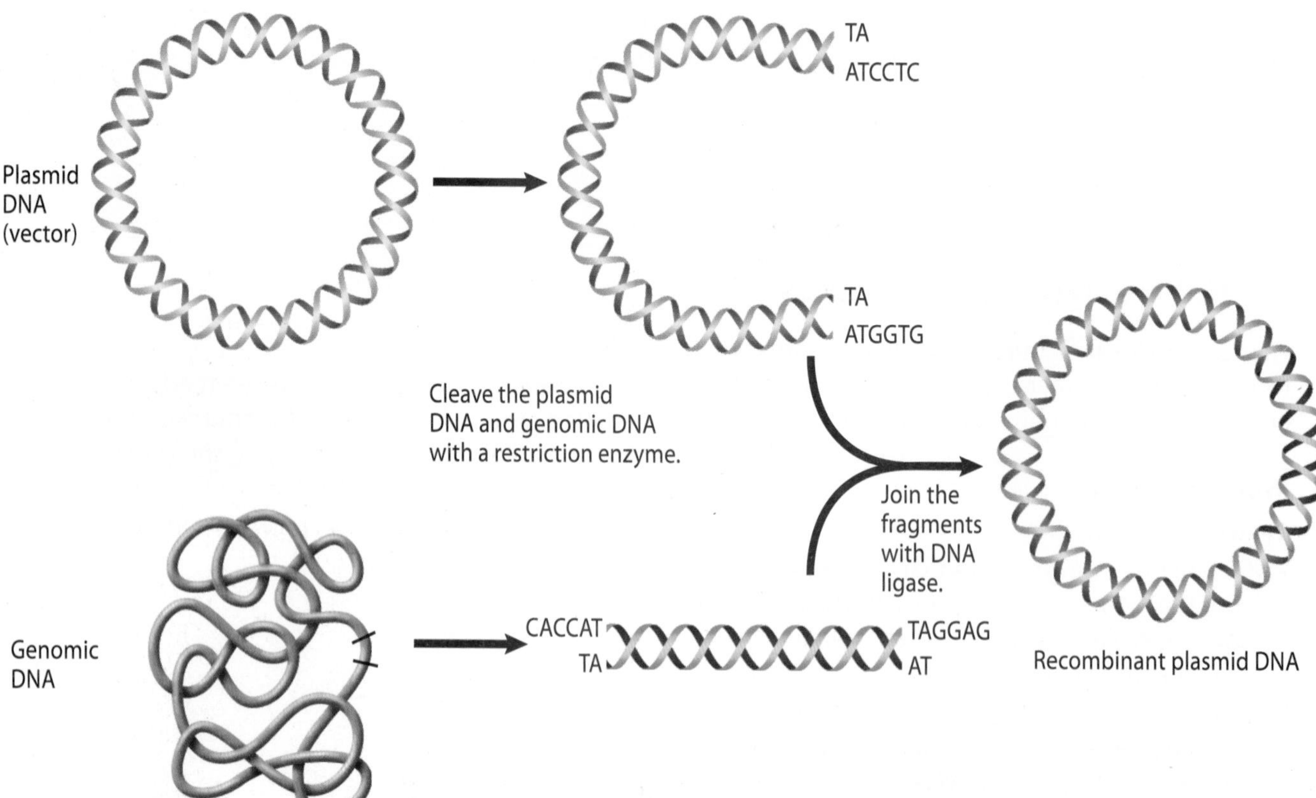

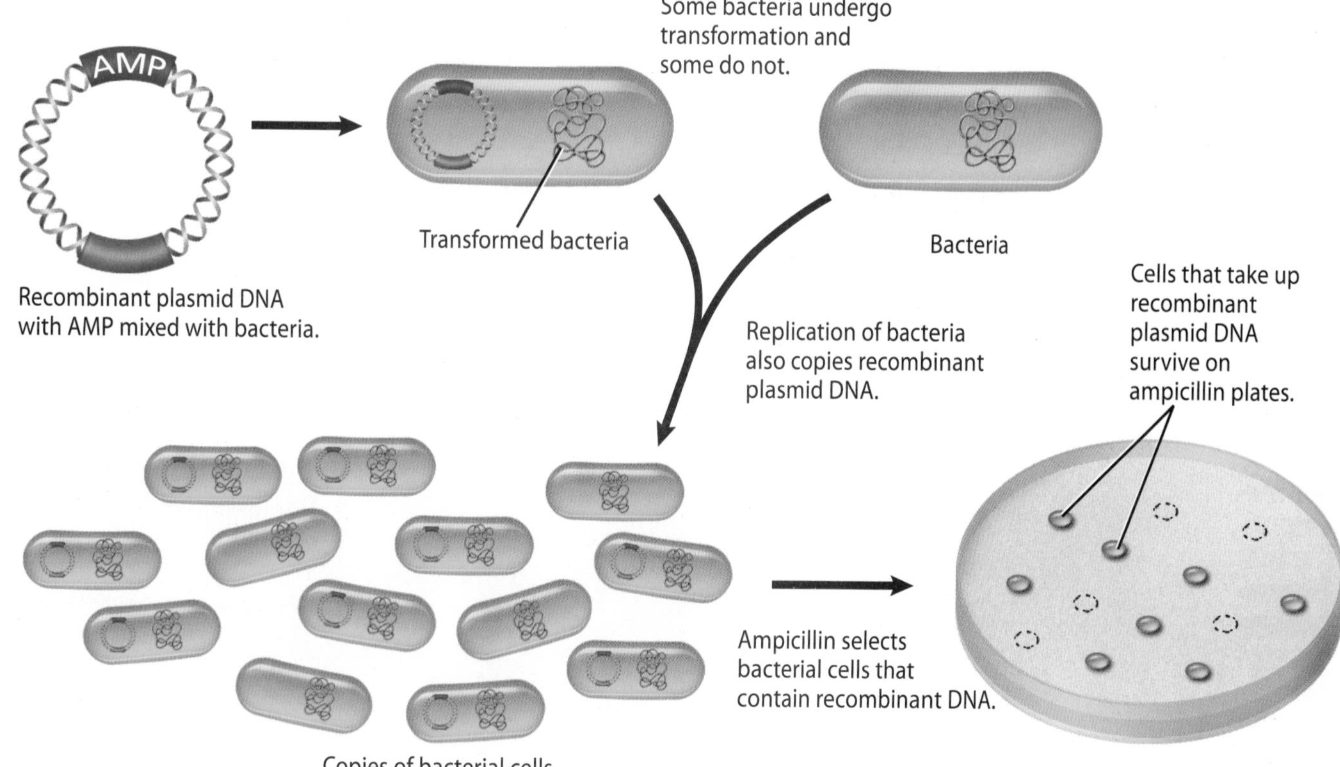
AMP
Recombinant plasmid DNA with AMP mixed with bacteria.
Some bacteria undergo transformation and some do not.
Transformed bacteria
Bacteria
Replication of bacteria also copies recombinant plasmid DNA.
Cells that take up recombinant plasmid DNA survive on ampicillin plates.
Ampicillin selects bacterial cells that contain recombinant DNA.
Copies of bacterial cells

■ **Figure 7** Clones containing copies of the recombinant DNA can be identified and used for further study when the bacterial cells that do not contain recombinant DNA die.

Gene cloning To make a large quantity of recombinant plasmid DNA, bacterial cells are mixed with recombinant plasmid DNA. Some of the bacterial cells take up the recombinant plasmid DNA through a process called **transformation,** as shown in **Figure 7.** Bacterial cells can be transformed using electric pulsation or heat. Recall that all cells, including bacterial cells, have plasma membranes. A short electric pulse or a brief rise in temperature temporarily creates openings in the plasma membrane of the bacteria. These temporary openings allow small molecules, such as the recombinant plasmid DNA, to enter the bacterial cell. The bacterial cells make copies of the recombinant plasmid DNA during cell replication. Large numbers of identical bacteria, each containing the inserted DNA molecules, can be produced through this process called **cloning.**

Recombinant plasmid DNA contains a gene that codes for resistance to an antibiotic such as ampicillin (AMP). Researchers use this gene to distinguish between bacterial cells that have taken up the recombinant plasmid DNA and those that have not. Notice in **Figure 7** that when the transformed bacterial cells are exposed to the specific antibiotic, only the bacterial cells that have the plasmid survive.

DNA sequencing The sequence of the DNA nucleotides of most organisms is unknown. Knowing the sequence of an organism's DNA or of a cloned DNA fragment provides scientists with valuable information for further study. The sequence of a gene can be used to predict the function of the gene, to compare genes with similar sequences from other organisms, and to identify mutations or errors in the DNA sequence. Because the genomes of most organisms are made up of millions of nucleotides, the DNA molecules used for sequencing reactions first must be cut into smaller fragments using restriction enzymes.

VOCABULARY

SCIENCE USAGE V. COMMON USAGE

Transformation

Science usage: process by which one type of bacterium takes up the DNA from another source

Transformation of bacteria involves the uptake of plasmid DNA.

Common usage: the act of change

The transformation of the room was complete with the addition of new drapes.

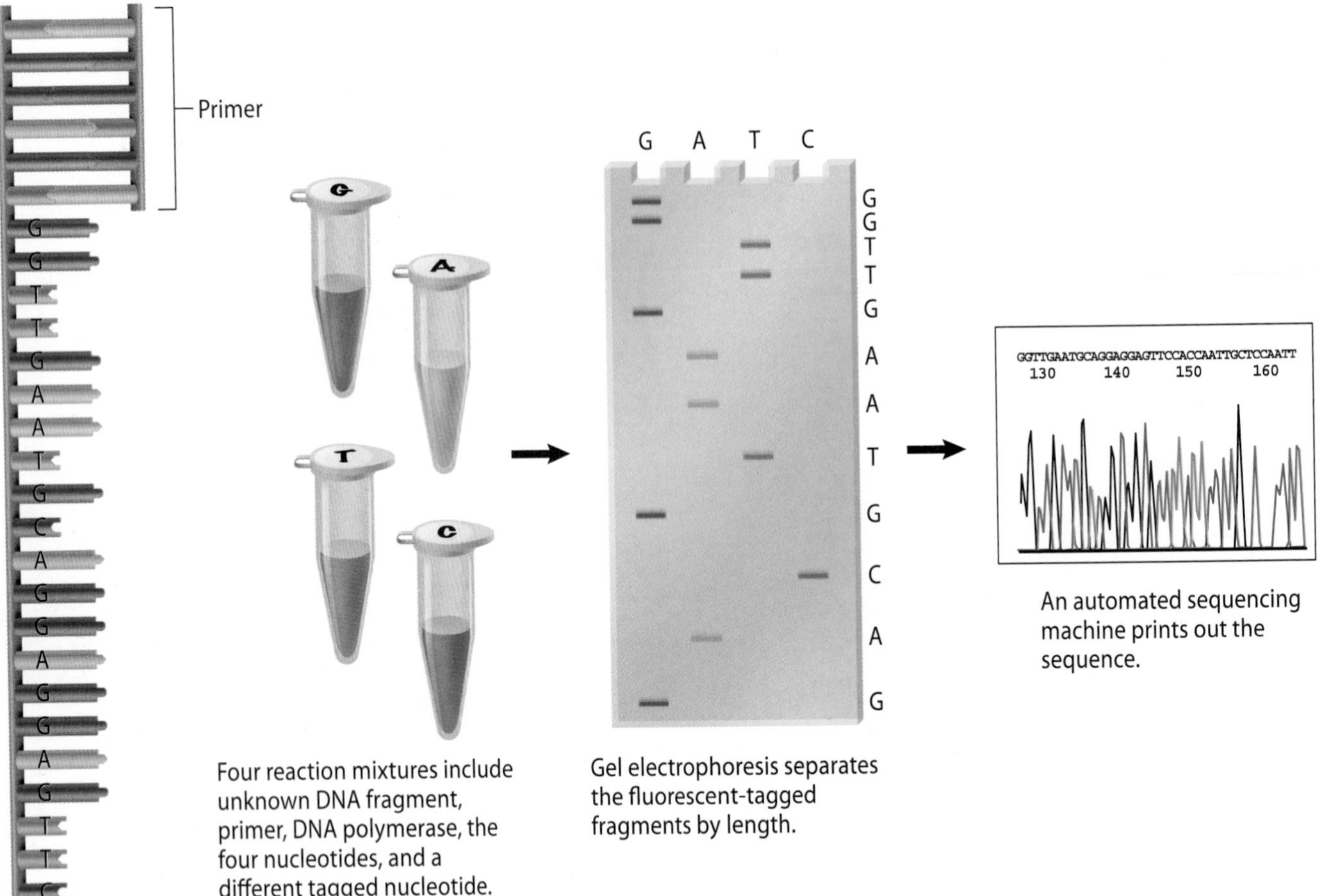
Primer
G
A
T
C
G A T C
G
G
T
T
G
A
A
T
G
C
A
G
GGTTGAATGCAGGAGGAGTTCCACCAATTGCTCCAATT
130 140 150 160
Four reaction mixtures include unknown DNA fragment, primer, DNA polymerase, the four nucleotides, and a different tagged nucleotide.
Gel electrophoresis separates the fluorescent-tagged fragments by length.
An automated sequencing machine prints out the sequence.

■ **Figure 8** DNA can be sequenced using fluorescent-tagged nucleotides.

Describe ***how the sequence of the original DNA template is determined.***

Follow **Figure 8** to understand how DNA is sequenced. Scientists mix an unknown DNA fragment, DNA polymerase, and the four nucleotides—A, C, G, T—in a tube. A small amount of each nucleotide is tagged with a different color of fluorescent dye, which also modifies the structure of the nucleotide. Every time a modified fluorescent-tagged nucleotide is incorporated into the newly synthesized strand, the reaction stops. This produces DNA strands of different lengths. The sequencing reaction is complete when the tagged DNA fragments are separated by gel electrophoresis. The gel is then analyzed in an automated DNA sequencing machine that detects the color of each tagged nucleotide. The sequence of the original DNA template is determined from the order of the tagged fragments.

Polymerase chain reaction Once the sequence of a DNA fragment is known, a technique called the **polymerase chain reaction** (PCR) can be used to make millions of copies of a specific region of a DNA fragment. PCR is extremely sensitive and can detect a single DNA molecule in a sample. PCR is useful because this single DNA molecule then can be copied, or amplified, numerous times to be used for DNA analysis. Follow **Figure 9** as you read about the steps of PCR.

Step 1 PCR is performed by placing the DNA fragment to be copied, DNA polymerase, the four DNA nucleotides, and two short single-stranded pieces of DNA called primers in a tube. The primers are complementary to the ends of the DNA fragment that will be copied and used as starting points for DNA synthesis. PCR begins when the tube is heated.

Step 2 The heat separates the two strands of the template DNA fragment. When the tube is cooled, the primers can bind to each strand of the template DNA. An automated machine called a thermocycler is used to cycle the tube containing all of the components involved in PCR through various hot and cool temperatures.

Step 3 As shown in **Figure 9,** each primer is made to bind to one strand of the DNA fragment. Once the primers are bound, DNA polymerase incorporates the correct nucleotides between the two primers as in DNA replication. This process of heating, cooling, and nucleotide incorporation is repeated 20 to 40 times, resulting in millions of copies of the original fragment. Because the separation of DNA strands requires heat, the DNA polymerase used in PCR has to be able to withstand high temperatures. This special DNA polymerase was isolated from a thermophilic, or heat-loving, bacterium such as those found living in the hot springs of Yellowstone National Park.

Because PCR can detect a single DNA molecule in a sample, it has become one of the most powerful tools used by scientists. PCR is not used only by researchers in laboratories, but also by forensic scientists to identify suspects and victims in crime investigations, and by doctors to detect infectious diseases, such as AIDS.

GET IT? **Describe** the polymerase chain reaction using an analogy.

■ **Figure 9** PCR is a biological version of a copy machine. During each PCR cycle, the reaction mixture is heated to separate the DNA strands and then cooled to allow primers to bind to complementary sequences. The DNA polymerase then adds nucleotides to form new DNA molecules.

Animation

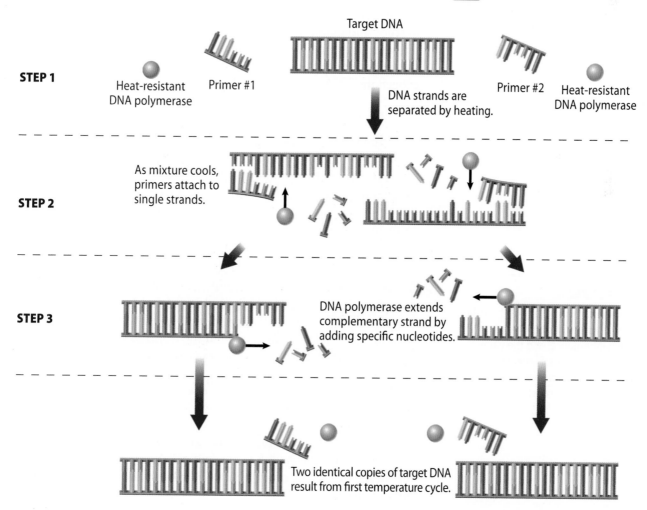

Target DNA

STEP 1

Heat-resistant DNA polymerase

Primer #1

DNA strands are separated by heating.

Primer #2

Heat-resistant DNA polymerase

STEP 2

As mixture cools, primers attach to single strands.

STEP 3

DNA polymerase extends complementary strand by adding specific nucleotides.

Two identical copies of target DNA result from first temperature cycle.

Table 1 Genetic Engineering — Interactive Table

Tool/Process	Function	Applications
Restriction enzymes Ex: *EcoRI*	Cut DNA strands into fragments	Used to create DNA fragments with sticky ends or blunt ends that can join with other DNA fragments
Gel electrophoresis	Separates DNA fragments by size	Used to study DNA fragments of various sizes
Recombinant DNA technology	Combines a DNA fragment with DNA from another source (exogenous DNA)	Used to create recombinant DNA to be used to study individual genes and genetically engineered organisms, and in the treatment of certain diseases
Gene cloning	Produces large numbers of identical recombinant DNA molecules	Used to create large amounts of recombinant DNA to be used in genetically engineered organisms
DNA sequencing	Identifies the DNA sequence of cloned recombinant DNA molecules for further study	Used to identify errors in the DNA sequence, to predict the function of a particular gene, and to compare to other genes with similar sequences from different organisms
Polymerase chain reaction (PCR)	Makes copies of specific regions of sequenced DNA	Used to copy DNA for any scientific investigation, including forensic analysis and medical testing

Genetic engineering uses powerful tools, summarized in **Table 1,** to study and manipulate DNA. Although researchers investigate many different problems, their experimental procedures often include cleavage by a restriction enzyme, isolation of fragments, combination with exogenous DNA, cloning or PCR, and identification of sequences.

Biotechnology

Biotechnology—the use of genetic engineering to find solutions to problems—makes it possible to produce organisms that contain individual genes from another organism. Recall that organisms such as the mosquito larvae shown in **Figure 3** have a gene from another organism. Such organisms, genetically engineered by inserting a gene from another organism, are called **transgenic organisms.** Transgenic animals, plants, and bacteria are used not only for research, but also for medical and agricultural purposes.

CAREERS IN BIOLOGY

Geneticist Using many of the DNA tools, a geneticist might research genes, inheritance, and the variations of organisms. Some geneticists are medical doctors who diagnose and treat genetic conditions.

Transgenic animals Currently, scientists produce most transgenic animals in laboratories for biological research. Mice, fruit flies, and the roundworm *Caenorhabditis elegans,* also called *C. elegans,* are widely used in research laboratories around the world to study diseases and develop ways to treat them. Some transgenic organisms, such as transgenic livestock, have been produced to improve the food supply and human health. Transgenic goats have been engineered to secrete a protein called antithrombin III, which is used to prevent human blood from forming clots during surgery. Researchers are working to produce transgenic chickens and turkeys that are resistant to diseases. Several species of fishes also have been genetically engineered to grow faster. In the future, transgenic organisms might be used as a source of organs for organ transplants.

■ **Figure 10** This researcher is examining cotton plant leaves. The leaf on the left has been genetically engineered to resist insect infestation.

Transgenic plants Many species of plants have been genetically engineered to be more resistant to insect or viral pests. In 2006, about 69.9 million hectares grown by 7 million farmers in 18 countries were planted with transgenic crops. These crops included herbicide- and insecticide-resistant soybeans, corn, cotton, and canola. Scientists now are producing genetically engineered cotton, as shown in **Figure 10,** that resists insect infestation of the bolls. Researchers also are developing peanuts and soybeans that do not cause allergic reactions.

Other crops are being grown commercially and being field-tested. These crops include sweet-potato plants that are resistant to a virus that could kill most of the African harvest, rice plants with increased iron and vitamins that could decrease malnutrition in Asian countries, and a variety of plants able to survive extreme weather conditions. Prospective crops include bananas that produce vaccines for infectious diseases, such as hepatitis B, and plants that produce biodegradable plastics.

Transgenic bacteria Insulin, growth hormones, and substances that dissolve blood clots are made by transgenic bacteria. Transgenic bacteria also slow the formation of ice crystals on crops to protect them from frost damage, clean up oil spills more efficiently, and decompose garbage.

REVIEW IT! DNA Technology

Section Summary

- Genetic engineering is used to produce organisms that are useful to humans.
- Recombinant DNA technology is used to study individual genes.
- DNA fragments can be separated using gel electrophoresis.
- Clones can be produced by transforming bacteria with recombinant DNA.
- The polymerase chain reaction is used to make copies of small DNA sequences.
- Transgenic organisms are being created to increase the quality of human life.

Self Check

Understand Main Ideas

1. MAINIDEA **Sequence** how recombinant DNA is made and manipulated.
2. **Explain** why some plasmids contain a gene for resistance to an antibiotic.
3. **Describe** how genetic engineering can improve human health.
4. **Contrast** one major difference between selective breeding and genetic engineering.

Think Critically

5. **Evaluate** Several popular movies and books involve mutated organisms. Are these transgenic organisms a possibility? Why or why not?

WRITING IN ▶ Biology

6. Why would a business synthesize and sell DNA? Who would their customers be? Write a list of possible uses for DNA that is synthesized in a laboratory.

USE IT! Science Notebook

3 The Human Genome

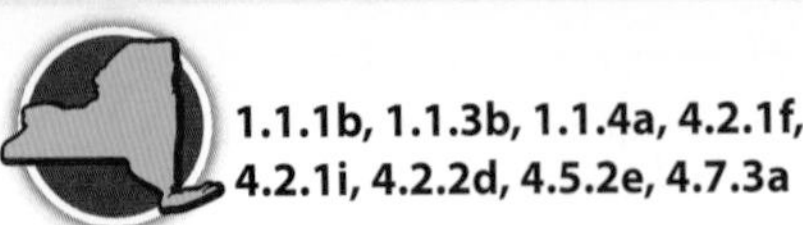

1.1.1b, 1.1.3b, 1.1.4a, 4.2.1f, 4.2.1i, 4.2.2d, 4.5.2e, 4.7.3a

MAINIDEA

Genomes contain all of the information needed for an organism to grow and survive.

Essential Questions

- What are the components of the human genome?
- How do forensic scientists use DNA fingerprinting?
- How can information from the human genome be used to treat human diseases?

BIOLOGY 4U

When you put together a jigsaw puzzle, you might first find all the border pieces and then fill in the other pieces. Sequencing the human genome can be compared to putting together a jigsaw puzzle. Just as you have to figure out which puzzle pieces fit together, scientists had to determine the sequence of the base pairs along the length of a human chromosome.

Review Vocabulary

codon: the triplet of bases in the DNA or mRNA

New Vocabulary

DNA fingerprinting
bioinformatics
DNA microarray
single nucleotide polymorphism
haplotype
pharmacogenomics
gene therapy
genomics
proteomics

Multilingual eGlossary

The Human Genome Project

The Human Genome Project (HGP) was an international project that was completed in 2003. A genome is the complete genetic information in a cell. The goal of the HGP was to determine the sequence of the approximately three billion nucleotides that make up human DNA and to identify all of the human genes. If all the nucleotides in the human genome were the size of the type on this page and fused together in one continuous line, the line would extend from Los Angeles, California, to Panama, as illustrated in **Figure 11.**

Though the HGP is finished, analysis of the data generated from this project will continue for many decades. To complete this huge task, researchers also have studied the genomes of several other organisms, including the fruit fly, the mouse, and *Escherichia coli*—the bacterium present in the human intestines. Studies in nonhuman organisms help to develop the technology required to handle the large amounts of data produced by the Human Genome Project. These technologies help to interpret the function of newly identified human genes.

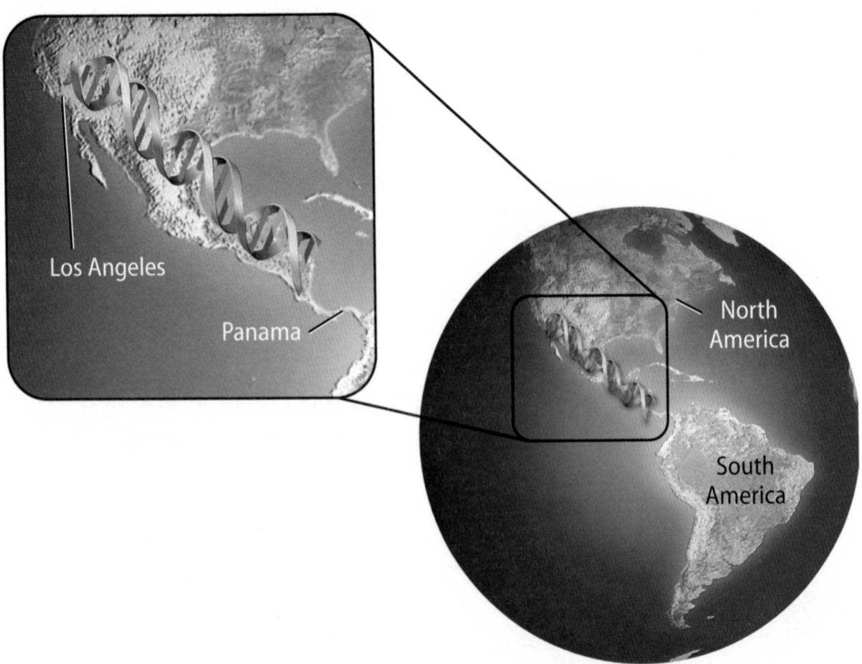

■ **Figure 11** If all the DNA in the human genome were fused together in one continuous line, it would stretch from California to Panama.

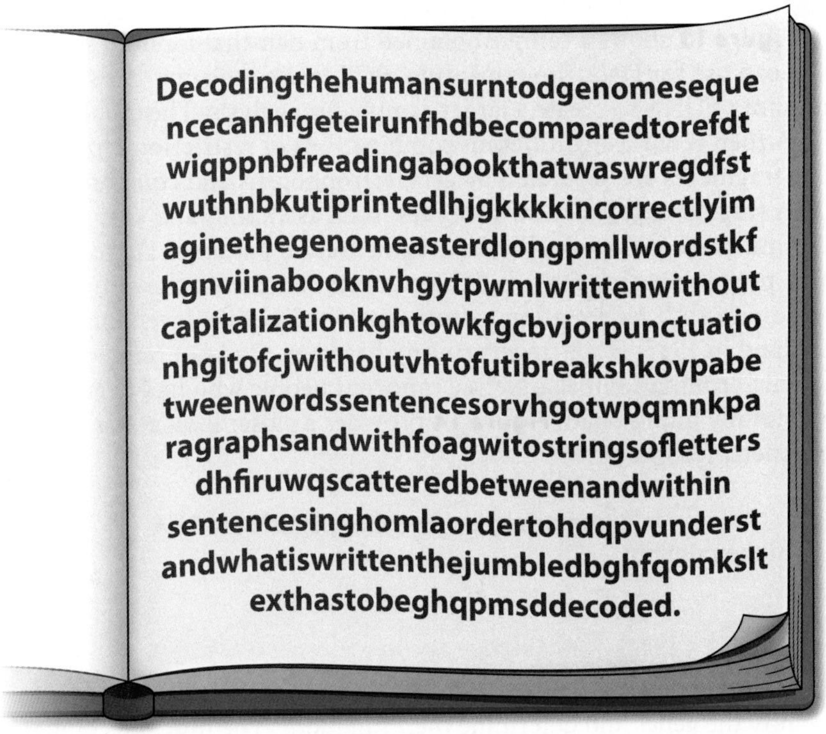

Decodingthehumansurntodgenomeseque ncecanhfgeteirunfhdbecomparedtorefdt wiqppnbfreadingabookthatwaswregdfst wuthnbkutiprintedlhjgkkkkincorrectlyim aginethegenomeasterdlongpmllwordstkf hgnviinabooknvhgytpwmlwrittenwithout capitalizationkghtowkfgcbvjorpunctuatio nhgitofcjwithoutvhtofutibreakshkovpabe tweenwordssentencesorvhgotwpqmnkpa ragraphsandwithfoagwitostringsofletters dhfiruwqscatteredbetweenandwithin sentencesinghomlaordertohdqpvunderst andwhatiswrittenthejumbledbghfqomkslt exthastobeghqpmsddecoded.

■ **Figure 12** The genetic information contained within the human genome has to be decoded in order to uncover important sequences.
Interpret ***the text by decoding the jumbled sentences.***

Sequencing the genome Human DNA is organized into 46 chromosomes. In order to determine one continuous human genome sequence, each of the 46 human chromosomes was cleaved. Several different restriction enzymes were used in order to produce fragments with overlapping sequences. These fragments were combined with vectors to create recombinant DNA, cloned to make many copies, and sequenced using automated sequencing machines. Computers analyzed the overlapping regions to generate one continuous sequence.

Decoding the sequence of the human genome can be compared to reading a book that was printed in code. Imagine the genome as words in a book written without capitalization, punctuation, or breaks between words, sentences, or paragraphs. Suppose there are strings of letters scattered between and within sentences. **Figure 12** illustrates how a page from such a book might look. In order to understand what is written, you have to decode the jumbled text. Similarly, scientists had to decode the genetic code in the human genome.

After sequencing the entire human genome, scientists observed that less than two percent of all of the nucleotides in the human genome code for all the proteins in the body. The genome is filled with long stretches of DNA that do not code for proteins. These regions are called noncoding sequences. Some of this noncoding DNA does function in the regulation of genes.

VOCABULARY
ACADEMIC VOCABULARY
Sequence (SEE kwens)
a continuous series
The sequence of colors formed a beautiful pattern.

Virtual Lab

DNA fingerprinting Unlike the protein-coding regions of DNA that are almost identical among individuals, the long stretches of noncoding regions of DNA are unique to each individual. When these regions are cut by restriction enzymes, as described earlier in this chapter, the set of DNA fragments produced is unique to every individual. **DNA fingerprinting** involves separating these DNA fragments using gel electrophoresis in order to observe the distinct banding patterns that are unique to every individual. Forensic scientists use DNA fingerprinting to identify suspects and victims in criminal cases, to determine paternity, and to identify soldiers killed in war.

CAREERS IN BIOLOGY
Forensic Scientist Genetic engineering is a technology used widely by forensic scientists. They use the various tools and processes, such as DNA fingerprinting, in criminal and archaeological investigations.

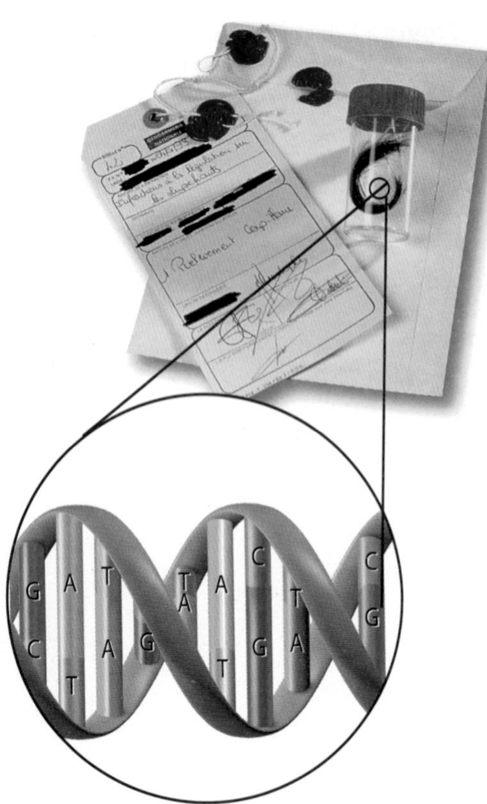

■ **Figure 13** People can be identified using the genetic information contained in blood, hair, semen, or skin.

Figure 13 shows a sample obtained from hair that forensic scientists can use for DNA fingerprinting. PCR is used to copy this small amount of DNA to create a larger sample for analysis. The amplified DNA then is cut using different combinations of restriction enzymes. The fragments are separated by gel electrophoresis and compared to DNA fragments from known sources, such as victims and suspects in a criminal case, to locate similar fragmentation patterns. There is a high probability that the two DNA samples came from the same person if two fragmentation patterns match. Since its development in England in 1985, DNA fingerprinting has been used not only to convict criminals but also to free innocent people who had been wrongfully imprisoned. **Figure 14** provides a closer look at the history of genetic technology.

GET IT? **Summarize** how forensic scientists use DNA fingerprinting.

Identifying Genes

Once the genome has been sequenced, the next step in the process is to identify the genes and determine their functions. The functions of many of the genes in the human genome are still unknown. Researchers use techniques that integrate computer analysis and recombinant DNA technology to determine the function of these genes.

For organisms such as bacteria and yeast, whose genomes do not have large regions of noncoding DNA, researchers have identified genes by scanning the sequence for open reading frames (or ORFs, pronounced "orphs"). ORFs are stretches of DNA containing at least 100 codons that begin with a start codon and end with a stop codon. While these sequences might indicate a gene, they will be tested to determine if these sequences produce functioning proteins.

■ **Figure 14** **Discoveries in Genetics**
Many studies in genetics have led to advances in biotechnology.

1960 1970 1980

1959 Down syndrome is the first chromosomal abnormality identified in humans.

1972 Paul Berg creates the first recombinant DNA molecules.

1973 Herbert Boyer, Annie Chang, Stanley Cohen, and Robert Helling discover that recombinant DNA reproduce if inserted into bacteria.

1983 Kary Mullis invents the polymerase chain reaction, for which he will be awarded the Nobel Prize in 1993.

(t)Pascal Goetgheluck/Science Source, (b)Pierre Roussel/Newscom

Recall that a codon is a group of three nucleotides that code for an amino acid. Researchers look for the start codon AUG and a stop codon such as UAA, UGA, or UAG. ORF analysis has been used to identify correctly over 90 percent of genes in yeast and bacteria. However, the identification of genes in more complex organisms such as humans requires more sophisticated computer programs called algorithms. These algorithms use information, such as the sequence of the genomes of other organisms, to identify human genes.

Bioinformatics

The completion of the HGP and the sequencing of the genomes of other organisms have resulted in large amounts of data. Not only has this enormous amount of data required careful storage, organization, and indexing of sequence information, but it also has created a new field of study. This field of study, called **bioinformatics,** involves creating and maintaining databases of biological information. The analysis of sequence information involves finding genes in DNA sequences of various organisms and developing methods to predict the structure and function of newly discovered proteins. Scientists also study the evolution of genes by grouping protein sequences into families of related sequences and comparing similar proteins from different organisms.

STUDY TIP

BIOJOURNAL As you read about the human genome, list several beneficial uses of this information.

DNA Microarrays

Analyzing all the expressed genes from a given organism or a specific cell type can be useful. This analysis can be done using **DNA microarrays,** which are tiny microscope slides or silicon chips that are spotted with DNA fragments. DNA microarrays can contain a few genes, such as the genes that control the cell cycle, or all of the genes of the human genome. Therefore, a large amount of information can be stored in one small slide or chip. DNA microarrays help researchers determine whether the expression of certain genes is caused by genetic factors or environmental factors.

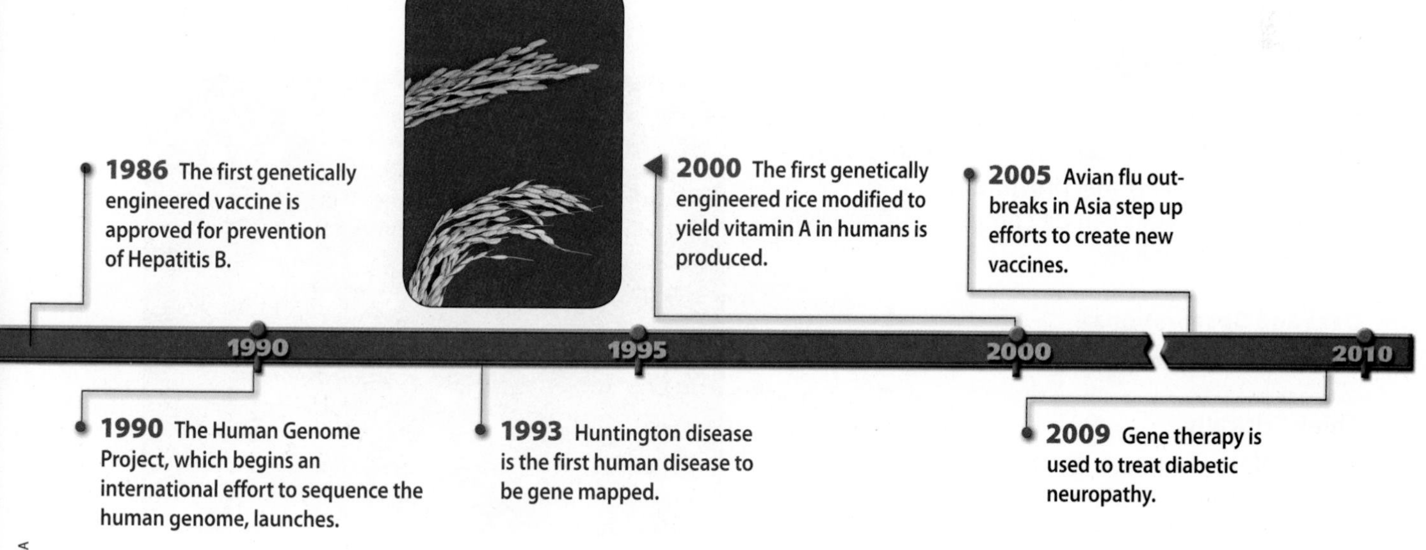

1986 The first genetically engineered vaccine is approved for prevention of Hepatitis B.

1990 The Human Genome Project, which begins an international effort to sequence the human genome, launches.

1993 Huntington disease is the first human disease to be gene mapped.

2000 The first genetically engineered rice modified to yield vitamin A in humans is produced.

2005 Avian flu outbreaks in Asia step up efforts to create new vaccines.

2009 Gene therapy is used to treat diabetic neuropathy.

Scott Bauer/USDA

Follow the steps involved in doing the DNA microarray experiment shown in **Figure 15.** mRNA from two different populations of cells is isolated and converted into complementary DNA (cDNA) strands using an enzyme called reverse transcriptase. The complementary DNA from each cell population is labeled with a specific fluorescent dye—for example, red for cancer cells and green for normal cells. Both pools of complementary DNA are combined on the microarray slide and incubated.

Figure 15 shows the fluorescent signals that are produced when the microarray slide is analyzed. When the expression of a gene is the same in both the normal and cancer cells, a yellow spot is produced on the chip. If the expression of a gene is higher in cancer cells, then the spot formed is red. However, if the expression is higher in normal cells, then the spot formed is green.

Because one DNA microarray slide can contain thousands of genes, researchers can examine changes in the expression patterns of multiple genes at the same time. Scientists also are using DNA microarrays to identify new genes and to study changes in the expression of proteins under different growth conditions.

The Genome and Genetic Disorders

Although more than 99 percent of all nucleotide base sequences are exactly the same in all people, sometimes there are variations that are linked to human diseases. These variations in the DNA sequence that occur when a single nucleotide in the genome is altered are called **single nucleotide polymorphisms** or SNPs. For a variation to be considered an SNP, it must occur in at least one percent of the population. Many SNPs have no effect on cell function, but scientists hypothesize that SNP maps will help identify many genes associated with many different types of genetic disorders.

Data Analysis LAB 1

Based on Real Data*

Apply Concepts

How can DNA microarrays be used to classify types of prostate cancer? The gene expression profiles between normal prostate cells and prostate cancer cells can be compared using DNA microarray technology.

Data and Observations

The diagram shows a subset of the data obtained.

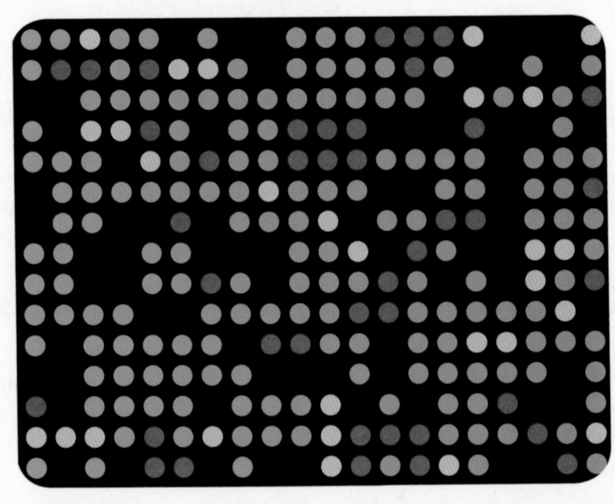

Think Critically

1. **Calculate** the percentage of spots that are yellow. Then calculate the percentage of green spots and red spots.
2. **Explain** why some of the spots are black.
3. **Apply Concepts** How would you choose a gene to study as a cause of prostate cancer?

*Data obtained from: Lapointe, et al. 2004. Gene expression profiling identifies clinically relevant subtypes of prostate cancer. *PNAS* 101: 811–816.

VISUALIZING Microarray Analysis

Figure 15 In this experiment, the expression of thousands of human genes was detected by DNA microarray analysis. Each spot on the microarray chip represents a gene. A red spot indicates the expression of a gene is higher in cancer cells compared to normal cells. A green spot indicates the expression in normal cells is higher. Yellow spots indicate no difference in the expression between cancer cells and normal cells.

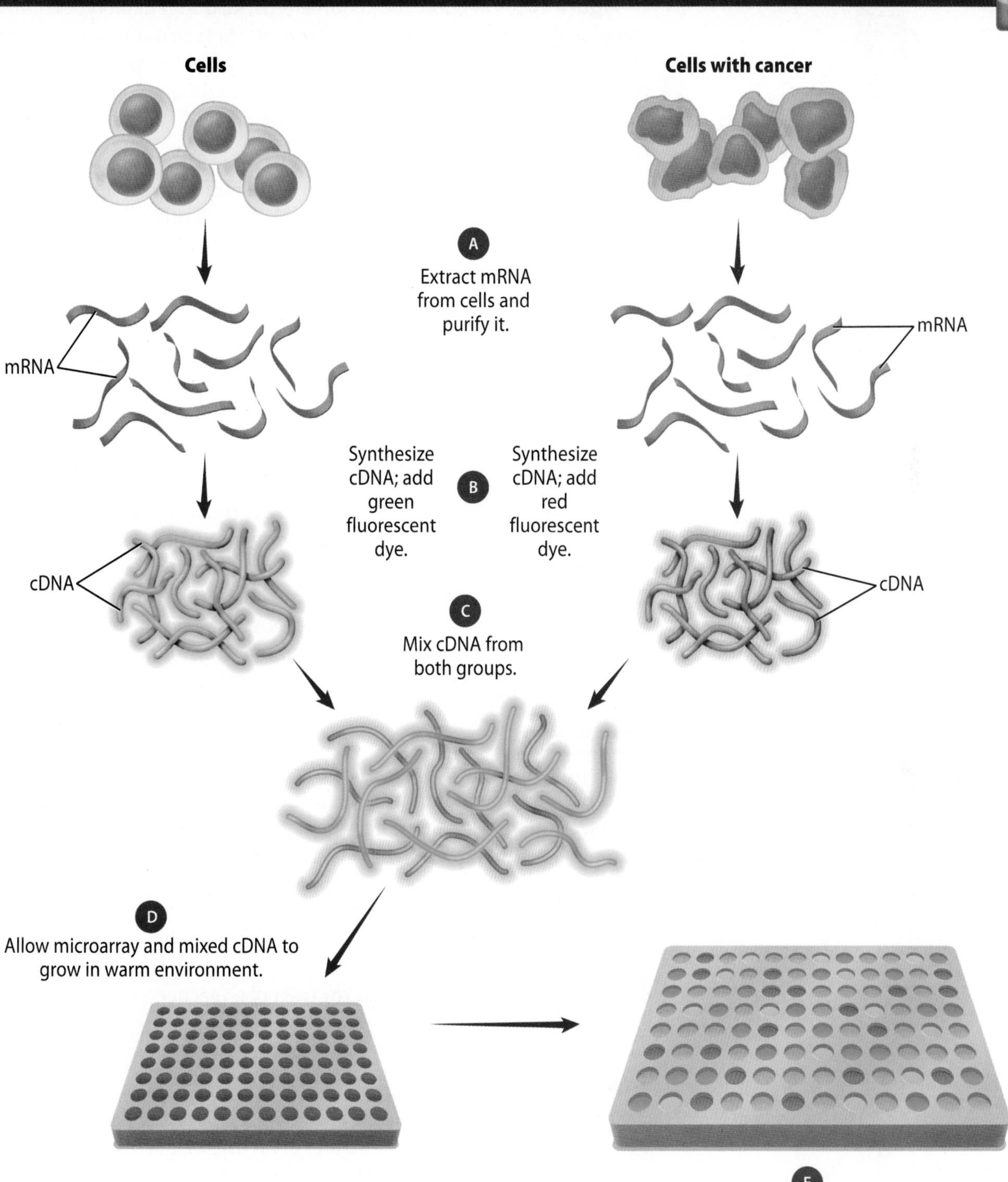

Cells
Cells with cancer
A
Extract mRNA from cells and purify it.
mRNA
mRNA
Synthesize cDNA; add green fluorescent dye.
B
Synthesize cDNA; add red fluorescent dye.
cDNA
cDNA
C
Mix cDNA from both groups.
D
Allow microarray and mixed cDNA to grow in warm environment.
E
Examine completed DNA microarray.

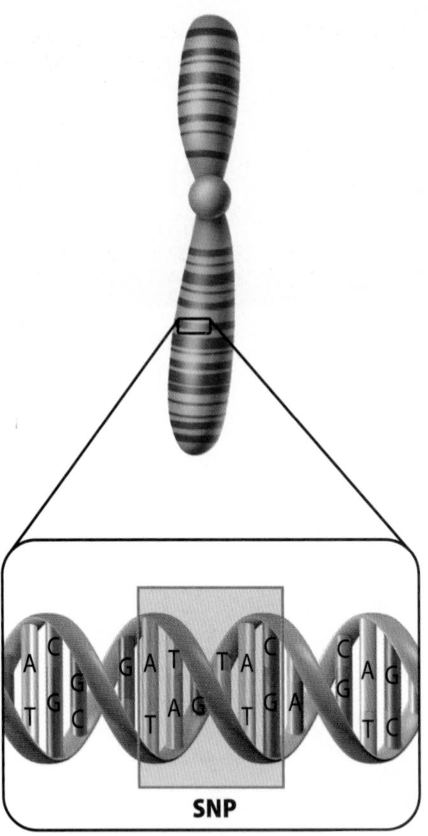

■ **Figure 16** The HapMap project involves grouping all adjacent SNPs that are inherited together into haplotypes.

The HapMap project An international group of scientists is creating a catalog of common genetic variations that occur in humans. Linked genes are inherited together and similarly, genetic variations located close together also tend to be inherited together. Therefore, regions of linked variations in the human genome, known as **haplotypes,** can be located. The project to create this catalog is called the haplotype map, or HapMap project. Assembling the HapMap involves identifying groups of SNPs in a specific region of DNA.

Figure 16 shows how the genome is divided into haplotypes. Once completed, the HapMap will describe what these variations are, where they occur in our DNA, and how they are distributed among people within populations and among populations in different parts of the world. This information will help researchers find genes that cause disease and affect an individual's response to drugs.

Pharmacogenomics Sequencing the human genome combines the knowledge of genes, proteins, and SNPs with other areas of science. The study of how genetic inheritance affects the body's response to drugs is called **pharmacogenomics** (far muh koh jeh NAW mihks). The benefits of pharmacogenomics include more accurate dosing of drugs that are safer and more specific. Researchers hope that pharmacogenomics will allow for drugs to be custom-made for individuals based on their genetic makeups. Prescribing drugs based on an individual's genetic makeup will increase safety, speed recovery, and reduce side effects. Perhaps one day when you are sick, your doctor will read your genetic code and prescribe medicine tailor-made for you.

Gene therapy A technique aimed at correcting mutated genes that cause human diseases is called **gene therapy.** Scientists insert a normal gene into a chromosome to replace a dysfunctional gene. In most gene therapy studies, inserting a normal gene into a viral vector, like the one in **Figure 17,** produces recombinant DNA. Target cells in the patient are infected with the virus and the recombinant DNA material is released into the affected cells. Once deposited into cells, the normal gene inserts itself into the genome and begins functioning.

Connection to Health In 1990, the first clinical gene therapy trial at the National Institutes of Health was conducted on a four-year-old child with severe combined immunodeficiency (SCID). The Food and Drug Administration (FDA) monitors new medical trials, including gene therapy. Gene therapy has seen its share of setbacks, but the possibilities are endless when it comes to new treatments. Recent gene therapy trials include work with diabetes, cancer, retinal disease, Parkinson's disease, and others.

■ **Figure 17** DNA can be encapsulated in a virus and delivered into a patient to replace a defective gene. Once the virus enters the cells, the genetic information is released into the nucleus and inserted into the genome.

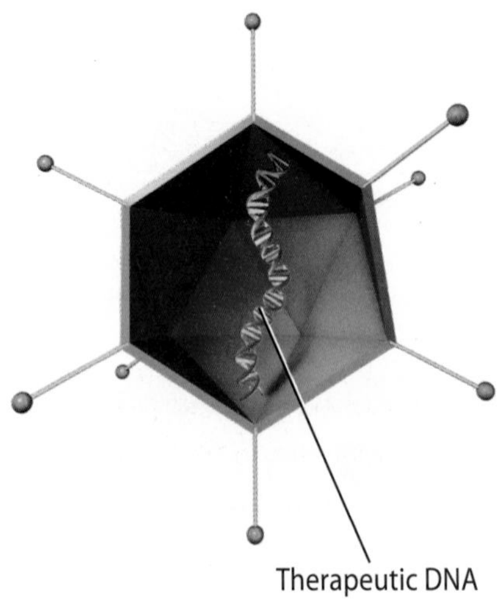

GET IT? **Compare and contrast** pharmacogenomics to gene therapy.

Genomics and Proteomics

Sequencing the human genome began what researchers call "the genomic era." **Genomics** is the study of an organism's genome. Genomics has become one of the most powerful strategies for identifying human genes and interpreting their functions. In addition to the mass of data obtained from sequencing the genomes of multiple organisms, scientists also are investigating the proteins produced by these genes.

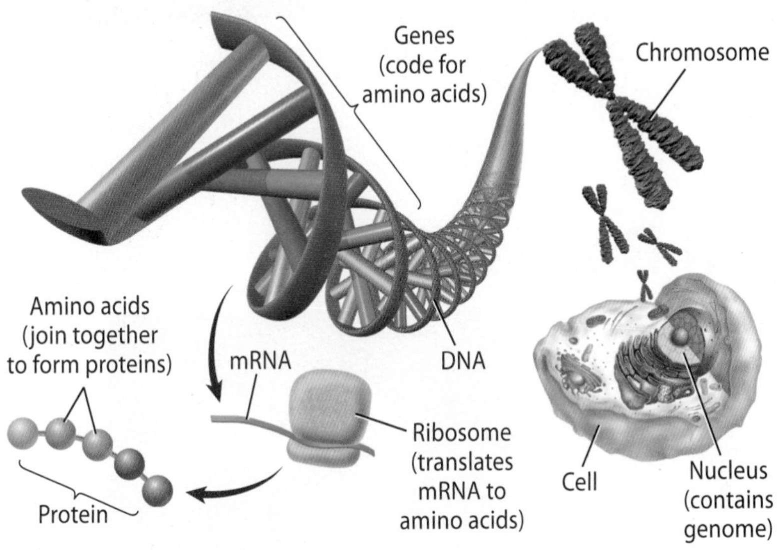

Figure 18 The central dogma is that the information in genes flows from DNA to RNA and RNA to proteins.

Genes are the primary information storage units, whereas proteins are the machines of a cell. Recall that when a gene is expressed, a protein is produced, as illustrated in **Figure 18.** Therefore, an understanding of how proteins function also is important. For instance, if the genome represents the words in a dictionary, the proteome, which represents all the proteins found in a cell, provides the definition of these words and how to use these words in a sentence. The large-scale study and cataloging of the structure and function of proteins in the human body is called **proteomics.** Proteomics allows researchers to look at hundreds or thousands of proteins at the same time. This type of broad analysis will better define both normal and disease states. Scientists anticipate that proteomics will revolutionize the development of new drugs to treat diseases such as Type II diabetes, obesity, and atherosclerosis.

What's BIOLOGY Got To Do With It?

REVIEW IT! The Human Genome

Section Summary

- Researchers who worked on the HGP sequenced all nucleotides in the human genome.
- DNA fingerprinting can be used to identify individuals.
- DNA microarrays allow researchers to study all the genes in the genome simultaneously.
- Gene therapy might be used in the future to correct genetic disorders.
- Genomics is the study of an organism's genome and proteomics is the study of the proteins in the human body.

Understand Main Ideas

1. MAINIDEA **Relate** the human genome to blueprints for a house.
2. **Analyze** the role of DNA fingerprinting in criminal investigations.
3. **Indicate** why the HapMap project is useful in diagnosing human disease.
4. **Explain** the process of gene therapy. What is the ultimate goal of gene therapy?

Think Critically

5. **Analyze, evaluate, and critique** The human genome consists of coding and noncoding DNA. Research and summarize current investigations into the functions of noncoding DNA.

MATH IN ▶ Biology

6. If 1.5 percent of the human genome consists of protein-coding sequences, and the entire genome has 3.2×10^9 nucleotides, how many codons are in the human genome? Remember that a codon is three nucleotides in length.

IN THE FIELD

1.1.1b, 1.1.2a, 1.1.2b, 1.1.3b

Career: Biomedical Research

Illuminating Medical Research

Have you ever watched fireflies glow on a summer evening? A chemical reaction in firefly cells produces light through a process called bioluminescence. Many marine organisms, like the jellyfish shown in the image, are also bioluminescent. The jellyfish species *Aequorea victoria* has emerged as a hero to biomedical researchers. This jellyfish produces a substance called green fluorescent protein (GFP), which makes parts of its body shine with an emerald green light.

Green fluorescent protein was first observed in bioluminescent jellyfishes.

Shining Light on Cell Functions Found off the west coast of North America, the diminutive *Aequorea victoria* is only five to ten centimeters in diameter. Its cells contain aequorin, a bioluminescent protein that emits a deep blue light. GFP absorbs this light and converts it into a glowing emerald green. In the early 1990s, scientists removed the GFP gene from *Aequorea victoria* and cloned it. Today, biomedical researchers can fuse GFP to other proteins inside cells of living organisms. When illuminated with light of a specific frequency, these marked proteins glow, making it possible to observe their behavior during cell processes.

Biological Marking at Work GFP allows scientists to determine where proteins are located during different stages of a cell's life, and to observe how proteins interact to produce disease. Researchers can attach GFP to a virus and observe the spread of the virus throughout the host.

By injecting tumor cells marked with GFP, scientists can analyze how they develop, spread, and destroy healthy cells over time. Bioluminescent imaging can be used to evaluate the effectiveness of various treatments on these types of tumors. Ultimately, scientists hope to incorporate GFP directly into human tumor cells, then use bioluminescence to identify the mass as a separate cell population within the body. Easily differentiated from healthy cells and tissues, the glowing cancerous cells would be marked for treatment.

WRITING IN ▶ Biology

Research and Communicate GFP is used to investigate the effectiveness of gene therapy, vaccines, and cancer treatments. Research how GFP is used in cancer studies and share your findings with classmates.

WebQuest

BioLAB

1.1.1c, 1.1.2a, 1.1.2b, 1.1.3b, ¥a, ¥e, ¥i, ¥m, ¥n, ¥o

Forensics: How can genetic engineering be used to solve a crime?

Background: Although all humans are similar genetically, variations do occur in certain segments of DNA. When cut with restriction enzymes, the variety of sizes of these fragments can be used to determine the source of a sample of DNA. In this lab, DNA from suspects will be analyzed.

Question: *Based on the DNA samples, were any of the suspects at the scene?*

Materials

various DNA samples
electrophoresis chamber
power source
micropipette and tips
prepared agarose gels
restriction enzyme
microcentrifuge tubes and rack
sample-loading dye
nontoxic dye
staining and destaining containers
DNA fragments of known size (control)
ruler
ice in foam container
water bath at 37°C

Safety Precautions

Procedure

1. Read and complete the lab safety form.
2. Read the entire procedure.
3. Label your DNA samples.
4. Design and construct a data table you can use to record your observations when you perform gel electrophoresis of your samples.
5. Your teacher will instruct you how to prepare your samples, set up the gel electrophoresis equipment, load your samples, and run the electrophoresis.
6. Use the gel-staining dye to detect the location of DNA fragments in the gel for each of your samples.
7. Use a ruler to measure (in mm) the distance of each migrated DNA band from the wells with precision and accuracy. Record this information in your table.
8. **Cleanup and Disposal** Wash and return all reusable materials. Dispose of gels and other reagents in properly labeled containers. Wash your hands thoroughly.

Analyze and Conclude

1. **Interpret Data** Based on your observations, predict which suspect is incriminated by the DNA evidence.
2. **Think Critically** While the amount of DNA needed for electrophoresis is not large, the amount that can be extracted from a few hairs might not be enough. How might forensic scientists solve this problem?
3. **Error Analysis** DNA fingerprints have a very high level of accuracy if they are run correctly. What are some sources of error that could lead to inaccurate results?
4. **Plan Ahead** Suggest ways that you could improve your procedure and methods to avoid the sources of error listed in your answer for question 3. Try out your plans.

WRITING IN ▶ Biology

Plan a procedure. Find a news article describing the use of DNA fingerprinting in investigations such as a criminal investigation or identifying a bacterium involved in a disease outbreak. Write a mock lab that explains the techniques and steps that might be taken in the situation described by the article.

CHAPTER 13 STUDY GUIDE

BIGIDEA **Genetic technology improves human health and quality of life.**

SECTION 1 Applied Genetics

MAINIDEA Selective breeding is used to produce organisms with desired traits.

- Selective breeding is used to produce organisms with traits that are considered desirable.
- Hybridization produces organisms with the desired traits from parent organisms with different traits.
- Inbreeding creates pure breeds.
- A test cross can be used to determine an organism's genotype.

VOCABULARY

- **selective breeding**
- **inbreeding**
- **test cross**

SECTION 2 DNA Technology

MAINIDEA Researchers use genetic engineering to manipulate DNA.

- Genetic engineering is used to produce organisms that are useful to humans.
- Recombinant DNA technology is used to study individual genes.
- DNA fragments can be separated using gel electrophoresis.
- Clones can be produced by transforming bacteria with recombinant DNA.
- The polymerase chain reaction is used to make copies of small DNA sequences.
- Transgenic organisms are being created to increase the quality of human life.

VOCABULARY

- **genetic engineering**
- **genome**
- **restriction enzyme**
- **gel electrophoresis**
- **recombinant DNA**
- **plasmid**
- **DNA ligase**
- **transformation**
- **cloning**
- **polymerase chain reaction**
- **transgenic organism**

SECTION 3 The Human Genome

MAINIDEA Genomes contain all of the information needed for an organism to grow and survive.

- Researchers who worked on the HGP sequenced all nucleotides in the human genome.
- DNA fingerprinting can be used to identify individuals.
- DNA microarrays allow researchers to study all the genes in the genome simultaneously.
- Gene therapy might be used in the future to correct genetic disorders.
- Genomics is the study of an organism's genome and proteomics is the study of the proteins in the human body.

VOCABULARY

- **DNA fingerprinting**
- **bioinformatics**
- **DNA microarray**
- **single nucleotide polymorphism**
- **haplotype**
- **pharmacogenomics**
- **gene therapy**
- **genomics**
- **proteomics**

SECTION 1

Vocabulary Review

Fill in the blanks with the correct term from the Study Guide page.

1. A ________ is used to determine the genotype of a plant or animal.

2. The offspring produced by ________ are homozygous for most traits.

Understand Main Ideas

Use the illustration below to answer questions 3 and 4.

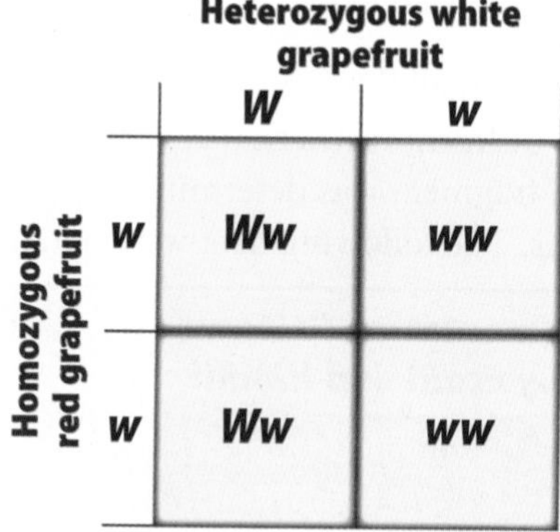

3. What is the genotypic ratio of the offspring in the cross above?
A. 1:2:1
B. 1:1
C. All are homozygous recessive.
D. All are heterozygous.

4. The cross above could be used to determine the genotype of a parent with a dominant phenotype. What is this type of cross called?
A. a homozygous cross
B. a heterozygous cross
C. a test cross
D. a parental cross

Constructed Response

5. **THEME FOCUS** Predict the phenotype of the parent plants of hybrid tomato plants that grow fast and are resistant to pesticides. Explain.

6. **Short Answer** How do polygenic traits affect selective breeding?

7. **MAIN**IDEA Discuss the advantages and disadvantages of selective breeding.

Think Critically

8. **Explain** why purebred animals do not exist in the wild.

9. **Determine** Suppose a phenotype is controlled by more than one gene. Can a test cross be used to determine the genotype? Why or why not?

SECTION 2

Vocabulary Review

Fill in the blank with the correct vocabulary term from the Study Guide page.

10. Transgenic animals are produced by ________.

11. Biologists use ________ to join two DNA molecules together.

12. During ________, a cell takes in DNA from outside the cell.

13. Small, circular DNA molecules that are found in bacterial cells are called ________.

Understand Main Ideas

Use the illustration below to answer question 14.

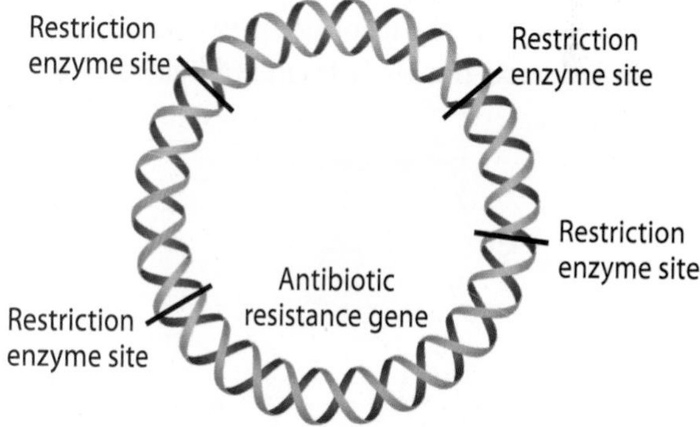

14. What is the role of the molecule above in DNA cloning?
A. to carry the foreign DNA into the host cell
B. to identify the source of DNA as foreign
C. to identify the host cell that has taken up the gene of interest
D. to make the foreign DNA susceptible to digestion with enzymes

15. Based on the sequences below, which enzyme produces a blunt end? *The cut site is indicated by the *.*

A. *Eag*I	C*GGCC G G CCGG*C
B. *Eco*RV	GAT*ATC CTA*TAG
C. *Nsi*I	A TGCA*T T*ACGT A
D. *Taq*I	T*CG A A GC*T

16. Why is the polymerase chain reaction used?
   A. to amplify DNA
   B. to cut DNA
   C. to ligate DNA
   D. to separate DNA

Constructed Response

17. MAINIDEA Predict what effect genetic engineering will have on the evolution of a species.

18. **Short Answer** Suppose you transform bacteria with a recombinant DNA plasmid and by mistake grow the transformed cells without an antibiotic. What result would you observe? Why?

19. **Interpret the Figure** Refer to **Figure 9** to make a flowchart diagramming the steps in the PCR.

Think Critically

20. **Conclude** A recombinant DNA molecule was created by joining a plasmid vector and a DNA fragment. Gel electrophoresis verified that the plasmid and the DNA fragment ligated.

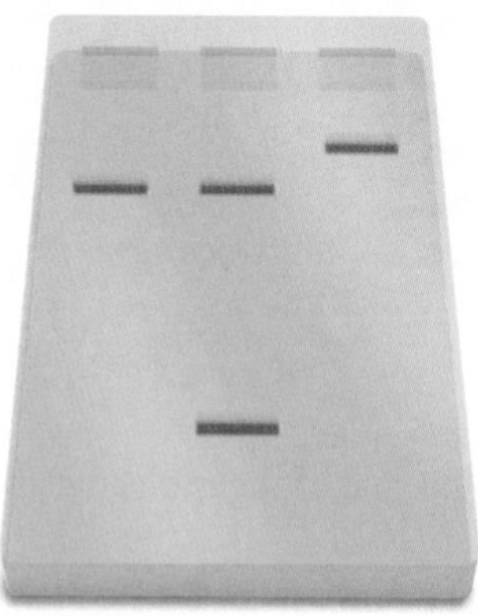

   A. Which lane in the gel corresponds to the recombinant DNA?
   B. Which lane corresponds to the plasmid?
   C. Which lane represents cleaving using a restriction enzyme of the recombinant DNA molecule?

21. **Differentiate** The plasmid below was cut to produce the five fragments shown in the diagram. The fragments then were separated by gel electrophoresis. Draw a diagram of a gel and the location of each fragment. Label ends as positive or negative.

1633 base pairs (bp)

257 bp

1108 bp

1400 bp

601 bp

22. **Assess** A small DNA molecule was cleaved with several different restriction enzymes, and the size of each fragment was determined by gel electrophoresis. The following data were obtained.

DNA Fragmentation Patterns Created by *Eco*RI and *Hind*III

Enzyme	Number of Fragments	Fragment Size (kilobases)
*Eco*RI	2	1.5 kb 1.5 kb
*Hind*III	1	3.0 kb
*Eco*RI + *Hind*III	3	0.8 kb 0.7 kb 1.5 kb

   A. Is the original DNA linear or circular?
   B. Draw a restriction-site map showing distances consistent with the data.

SECTION 3

Vocabulary Review

Fill in the blanks with the correct vocabulary term from the Study Guide page.

23. The field of __________ uses computers to index and organize information created by sequencing the human genome.

24. Genetic variations that are located close together are called __________.

Understand Main Ideas

25. Which statement about the human genome is false?
    A. The human genome contains approximately 25,000 genes.
    B. The human genome contains long stretches of DNA with no known function.
    C. The human genome was sequenced by scientists from around the world.
    D. The human genome contains nucleotide sequences that all code for proteins.

26. What are variations in specific nucleotides that are linked to human diseases called?
    A. proteomes
    B. haplotypes
    C. single nucleotide polymorphisms
    D. genomes

27. For what purpose is DNA fingerprinting used?
    A. to sequence DNA from bacteria
    B. to separate DNA fragments
    C. to identify individuals who have committed crimes
    D. to identify single nucleotide polymorphisms

Constructed Response

28. **Short Answer** Discuss the advantages and disadvantages of using DNA microarrays.

29. **Short Answer** List three ways patients will benefit from pharmacogenomics.

30. **MAIN IDEA** What impact does sequencing the human genome have on diagnosing and treating diseases?

Think Critically

31. **Describe** how DNA microarrays and DNA sequencing can be used to identify a defective gene.

32. **CAREERS IN Biology** A forensic scientist finds a strand of hair at a crime scene. Draw a flowchart and explain the steps that the forensic scientist has to take to determine the identity of the person to whom the hair belongs.

Summative Assessment

33. **BIG IDEA** Explain the importance of the completion of the human genome project. What are some health discoveries that are a result of this project?

34. **WRITING IN Biology** Write a paragraph discussing the approach you would take to create a transgenic organism and the drawbacks to creating it.

DBQ Document-Based Questions

The data below were obtained during a study on mosquito biting patterns. DNA fingerprints were obtained from individuals A, B, and C who were bitten by mosquitoes. In order to determine which mosquitoes bit each individual, a group of mosquitoes was collected and their DNA fingerprints were obtained. The mosquitoes were numbered 1–8.

Use the data to answer the questions below.

Data obtained from: Michael, et al. 2001. Quantifying mosquito biting patterns on humans by DNA fingerprinting of blood meals. *American Journal of Tropical Medicine and Hygiene* 65(6): 722–728.

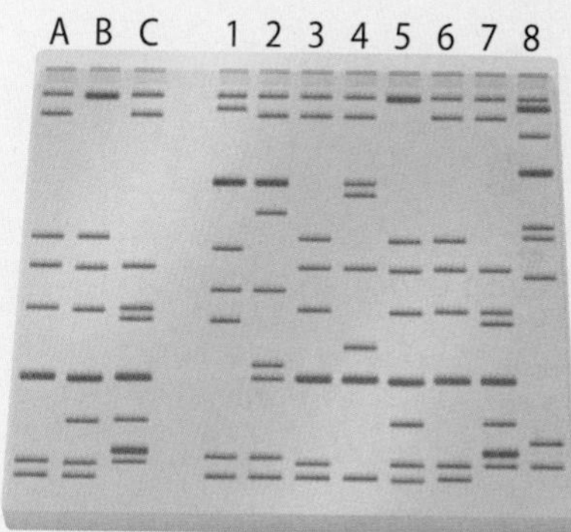

35. Examine the banding patterns and match each individual with the mosquito(es) that bit him or her.

36. What can researchers gain by knowing which mosquito bit which individual?

37. Based on your answer to question 35, what is a disadvantage of using this DNA fingerprinting to identify disease-carrying mosquitoes in the environment?

CHAPTER 13 BIOLOGY Review

CUMULATIVE MULTIPLE CHOICE

1 Which correctly lists the following terms in order from smallest to largest: DNA, chromatin, chromosomes, nucleosomes?

A chromatin, chromosomes, DNA, nucleosomes

B chromosomes, DNA, chromatin, nucleosomes

C DNA, nucleosomes, chromatin, chromosomes

D nucleosomes, DNA, chromatin, chromosomes

Use the figure below to answer question 2.

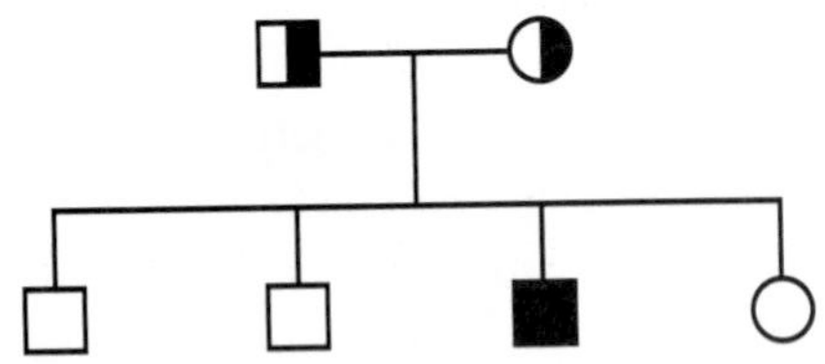

2 In a particular family, one child out of four is born with Tay-Sachs disease. Which pair of symbols represents the parents of these offspring?

A

B

C

D

3 Which is a stop codon in mRNA?

A AUG

B AUU

C CAU

D UAA

4 In a triploid organism, how many alleles are present for each gene per cell?

A 1

B 3

C 6

D 9

SHORT ANSWER

Use the figure below to answer question 5.

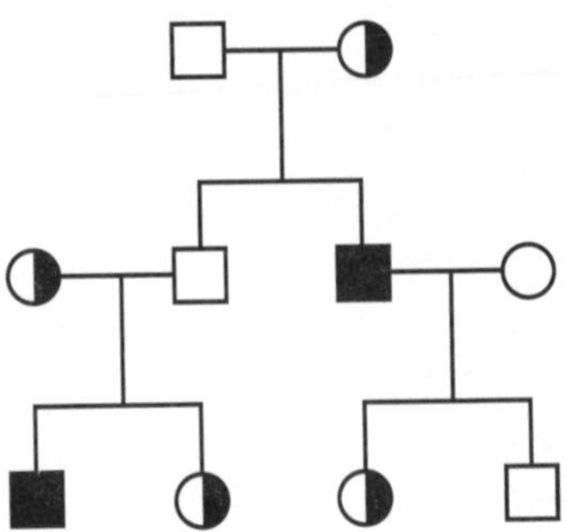

5 The pedigree in the figure tracks a recessive, sex-linked genetic disease. Explain the meaning of the symbols in the last generation.

6 Why are the protein-coding regions of most human genomes identical?

7 If hemophilia is a sex-linked recessive gene, what is the chance that a father with hemophilia and a mother who is a carrier for hemophilia will have a boy with hemophilia? Explain.

8 Compare and contrast the two major processes in protein synthesis.

9 List three genetic disorders; classify them as dominant or recessive; and name the affected organ systems.

10 Why might it take many generations to develop a purebred animal?

11 List the purine bases and the pyrimidine bases in DNA; explain their importance in DNA structure.

EXTENDED RESPONSE

12 Give the names of two DNA mutations, and illustrate how each one would change the following DNA sequence.

CGATTGACGTTTTAGGAT

13 Chemosynthetic autotrophs might have evolved long before the photosynthetic ones that currently are more common on Earth. Propose an explanation for this difference in evolution.

14 Explain how the noncoding sequences in the human genome make it difficult to interpret the DNA code.

15 Even though chloroplasts and mitochondria perform different functions, their structures are similar. Relate the similarity of their structures to their functions.

ESSAY QUESTION

Suppose a scientist uses gel electrophoresis to separate the DNA extracted from a cell line. After performing the experiment, the scientist observes that several bands are missing and that other bands have traveled to the far end of the gel.

Using the information in the paragraph above, answer the following question in essay format.

16 Using what you know about DNA separation and gel electrophoresis, explain what might have gone wrong with the experiment. Then, describe how to adjust the experimental procedures to test your explanation.

TEST PRACTICE

Use the illustration below to answer questions 17 and 18.

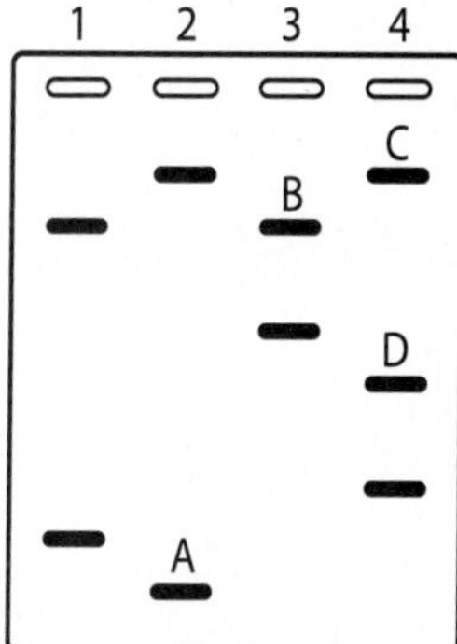

17 The figure above shows bands of DNA that were separated using gel electrophoresis. Which band contains the smallest DNA fragments?

A Band A

B Band B

C Band C

D Band D

18 What could the results of this gel electrophoresis show to a scientist?

A the amount of noncoding DNA present

B the fingerprint of a person's DNA

C the number of genes in a piece of DNA

D the random patterns of DNA

NEED EXTRA HELP?																		
If You Missed Question . . .	1	2	3	4	5	6	7	8	9	10	11	12	13	14	15	16	17	18
Review Section . . .	12.1	11.1	12.3	10.3	11.1	13.3	11.3	12.3	11.2	13.1	12.1	12.4	2.2	13.3	7.3	13.2	13.2	13.3

UNIT 4

(bkgd) McGraw-Hill Education, (inset) John Mitchell/Science Source

CAREERS USING BIOLOGY

Career in Action Paleontologists may have to conduct field work to excavate newly discovered fossils.

BIOdiscoveries

See **page 408** for more information about important fossil discoveries.

◀ PALEONTOLOGIST

Paleontologists study fossils and other remains to learn about prehistoric life and environments. They look at anatomical features, similarities to modern organisms, and the positions of fossils to learn more about them. Some paleontologists work in the field to uncover new fossils, while others work in the lab to learn more about fossils that have already been discovered. Paleontologists may work at universities or museums.

Related Careers

archaeologist

museum curator

paleontologist

geologist

 **Career Resources**

WHAT'S THAT? Columbian mammoths and other prehistoric animals roamed the earth thousands of years ago. Their fossils have been found throughout the southwestern United States. Many are on display in museums, such as this one in The Texas Memorial Museum in Austin. At the nearby Waco Mammoth Site, paleontologists found remains from 25 mammoths, a saber-toothed cat, a camel and another unidentified mammal.

Investigate

Communicate Research an important fossil find made in New York. Why was the fossil important? What did the fossil tell scientists about the past environment in New York? Present your findings to the class.

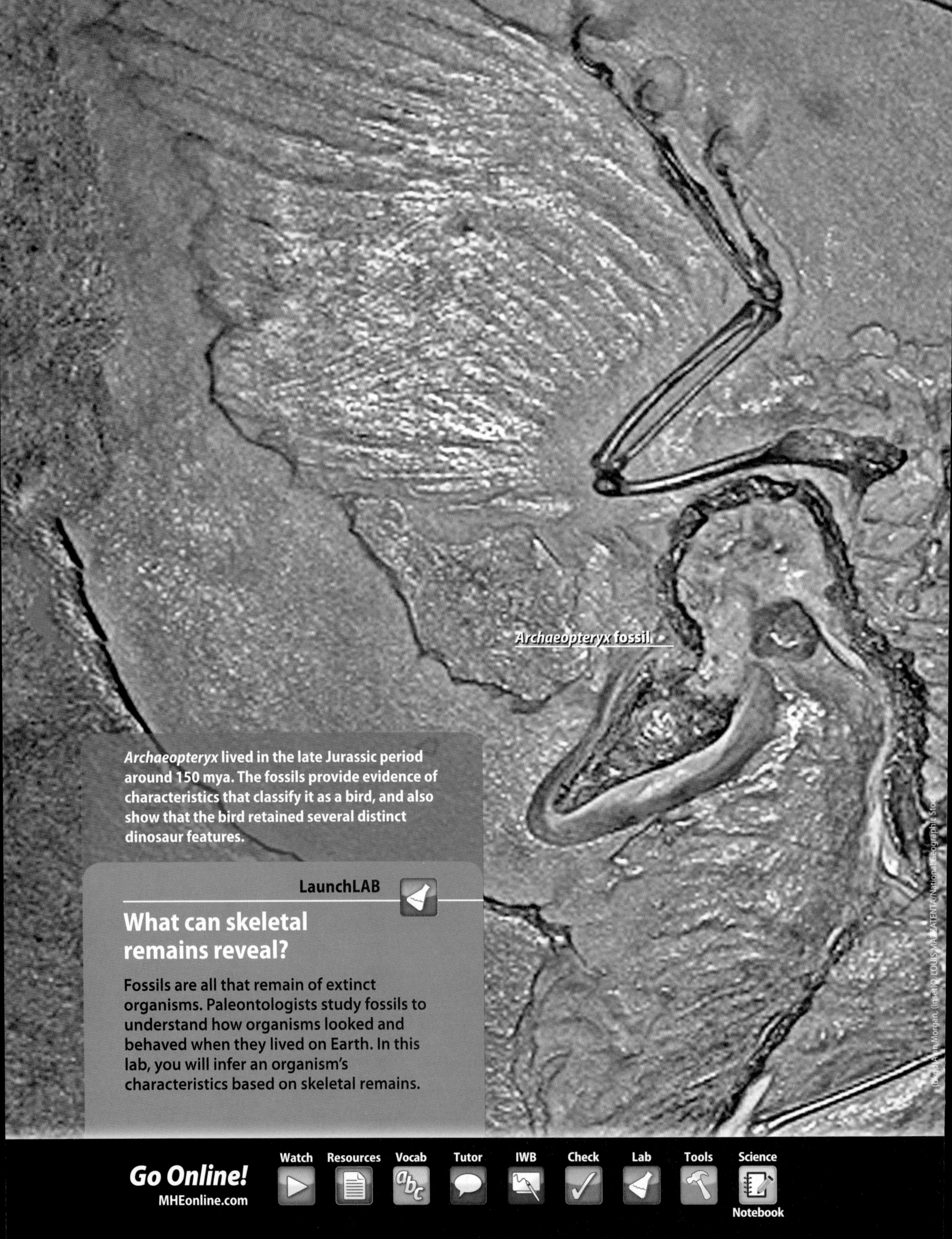

Archaeopteryx lived in the late Jurassic period around 150 mya. The fossils provide evidence of characteristics that classify it as a bird, and also show that the bird retained several distinct dinosaur features.

LaunchLAB

What can skeletal remains reveal?

Fossils are all that remain of extinct organisms. Paleontologists study fossils to understand how organisms looked and behaved when they lived on Earth. In this lab, you will infer an organism's characteristics based on skeletal remains.

Go Online! MHEonline.com

Watch Resources Vocab Tutor IWB Check Lab Tools Science Notebook

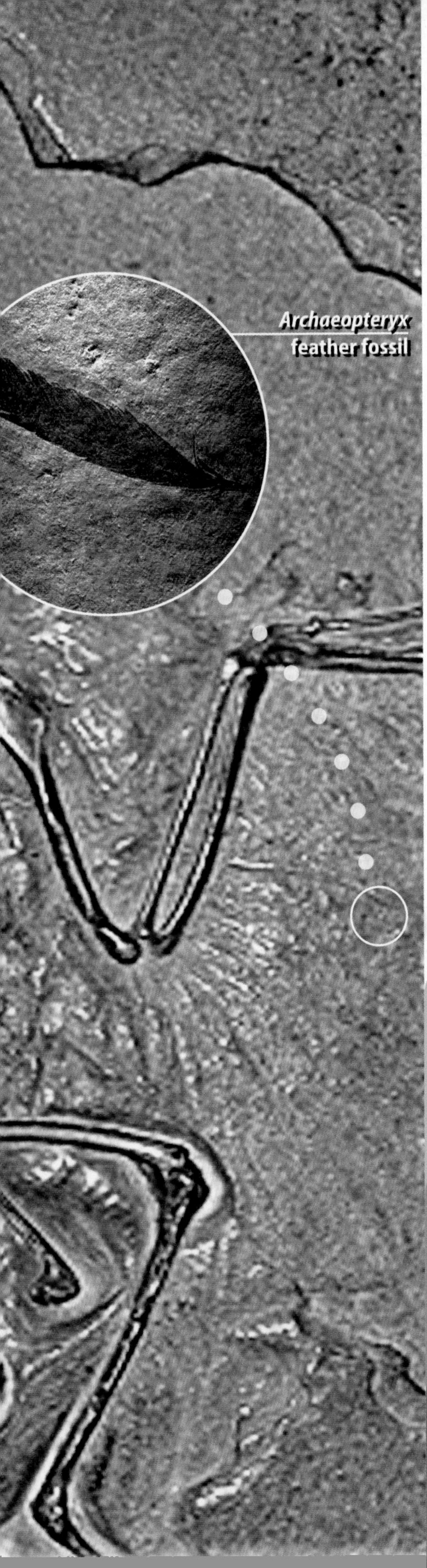

CHAPTER 14

The History of Life

1 Fossil Evidence of Change

1.1.1a, 1.3.5b, 4.3.1e, ¥a

2 The Origin of Life

1.1.1a, 1.1.1b, 1.3.5b

THEME FOCUS

Energy and matter Energy from lightning is thought to be involved in the origin of life.

BIG IDEA

Fossils provide key evidence for understanding the origin and the history of life on Earth.

FOLDABLES®
Study Organizer

Scientists

Make a folded chart using the titles shown. Use it to organize your notes on the scientists.

Redi	Pasteur	Miller and Urey

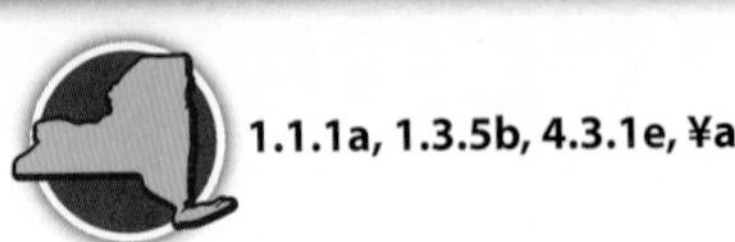

1 Fossil Evidence of Change

1.1.1a, 1.3.5b, 4.3.1e, ¥a

MAINIDEA

Fossils provide evidence of the change in organisms over time.

Essential Questions

- What are the similarities and differences between Earth's early environment and Earth's current environment?
- What is a typical sequence of events in fossilization?
- How are the different techniques for dating fossils used?
- What are the major events on the geologic time scale?

BIOLOGY 4U

Did you know that when you look at the stars at night you are looking into the past? The stars are so far away that the light you see left the stars thousands and sometimes millions of years ago. You also are looking into the past when you look at rocks. The rocks formed thousands or even millions of years ago. Rocks can tell us what Earth was like in the distant past, and sometimes they can tell us what lived during that time.

Review Vocabulary

extinction: the death of all individuals of a species

New Vocabulary

fossil
paleontologist
relative dating
law of superposition
radiometric dating
half-life
geologic time scale
epoch
period
era
eon
Cambrian explosion
K-T boundary
plate tectonics

Multilingual eGlossary

Earth's Early History

What were the conditions on Earth as it formed, and how did life arise on a lifeless planet? Because there were no people to witness Earth's earliest history, it might seem that this is an unsolvable mystery. Like any good mystery, however, it left clues behind. Each clue to Earth's history and life's origin is open to investigation by the scientists who study the history of the Earth.

Land environments By studying other planets in the solar system and rocks on Earth, scientists conclude that Earth was a molten body when it formed about 4.6 billion years ago. Gravity pulled the densest elements to the center of the planet. After about 500 million years, a solid crust formed on the surface, much like the crust that forms on the top of lava, shown in **Figure 1.** The surface was rich in lighter elements, such as silicon. From the oldest rocks remaining today, scientists infer that Earth's young surface included a number of volcanic features. In addition, the cooling interior radiated much more heat to the surface than it does today. Meteorites would have caused additional heating as they crashed into Earth's surface. If there had been any life on Earth, it most likely would have been consumed by the intense heat.

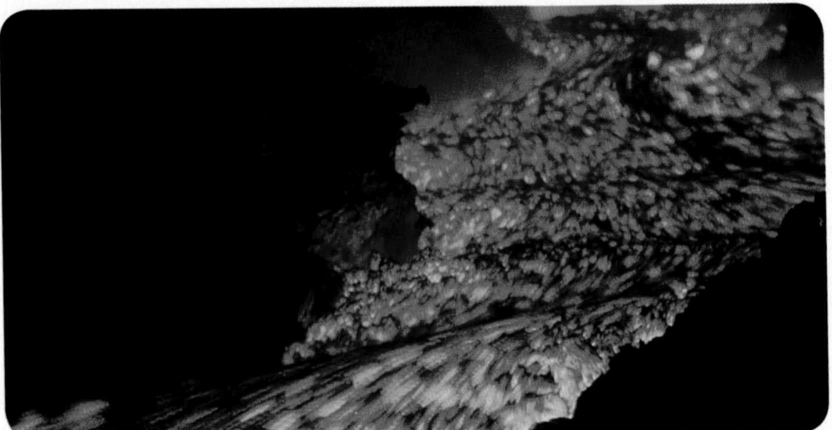

Molten lava flow

■ **Figure 1** Lava, molten rock ejected from volcanoes, forms a crust as it cools.
***Infer** the importance of the crust to the origin of life on Earth.*

Atmosphere Because of its gravitational field, Earth is a planet that is able to maintain an atmosphere. However, no one can be certain about the exact composition of Earth's early atmosphere. The gases that likely made up the atmosphere are those that were expelled by volcanoes. Volcanic gases today include water vapor (H_2O), carbon dioxide (CO_2), sulfur dioxide (SO_2), carbon monoxide (CO), hydrogen sulfide (H_2S), hydrogen cyanide (HCN), nitrogen (N_2), and hydrogen (H_2). Scientists infer that the same gases would have been present in Earth's early atmosphere. The minerals in the oldest known rocks suggest that the early atmosphere, unlike today's atmosphere, had little or no free oxygen.

Clues in Rocks

Earth eventually cooled to the point where liquid water formed on its surface, which became the first oceans. It was a short time after this—maybe as little as 500 million years—that life first appeared. The earliest clues about life on Earth date to about 3.5 billion years ago.

The fossil record A **fossil** is any preserved evidence of an organism. Six categories of fossils are shown in **Table 1.** Plants, animals, and even bacteria can form fossils. Although there is a rich diversity of fossils, the fossil record is like a book with many missing pages. Perhaps more than 99 percent of the species that ever have lived are now extinct, but only a tiny percentage of these organisms are preserved as fossils.

Most organisms decompose before they have a chance to become fossilized. Only those organisms that are buried rapidly in sediment are readily preserved. This occurs more frequently with organisms living in water because the sediment in aquatic environments is constantly settling, covering, and preserving the remains of organisms.

VOCABULARY

WORD ORIGIN

Fossil
from the Latin word *fossilis,* meaning *dug up*

What's BIOLOGY Got To Do With It?

Table 1 Categories of Fossil Types

Interactive Table

Category	Trace fossil	Molds and casts	Replacement	Petrified or permineralized	Amber	Original material
Example						
Formation	A trace fossil is any indirect evidence left by an organism. Footprints, burrows, and fossilized feces are trace fossils.	A mold is an impression of an organism. A cast is a mold filled with sediment.	The original material of an organism is replaced with mineral crystals that can leave detailed replicas of hard or soft parts.	Empty pore spaces are filled in by minerals, such as in petrified wood.	Tree sap traps an entire organism. The sap hardens into amber and preserves the trapped organism.	Mummification or freezing preserves original organisms.

■ **Figure 2** **(A)** Organisms usually become fossilized after they die and are buried by sediment. **(B)** Sediments build up in layers, eventually encasing the remains in sedimentary rock. **(C)** Minerals replace, or fill in the pore space of, the bones and hard parts of the organism. **(D)** Erosion can expose the fossils.

Fossil formation Fossils do not form in igneous (IHG nee us) or metamorphic (meh tuh MOR fihk) rocks. Igneous rocks form when magma from Earth's interior cools. Metamorphic rocks form when rocks are exposed to extreme heat and pressure. Fossils usually do not survive the heat or pressure involved in the formation of either of these kinds of rocks.

Nearly all fossils are formed in sedimentary rock through the process illustrated in **Figure 2.** The organism dies and is buried in sediments. The sediments build up until they cover the organism's remains. In some cases, minerals replace the organic matter or fill the empty pore spaces of the organism. In other cases, the organism decays, leaving behind an impression of its body. The sediments eventually harden into rock.

A **paleontologist** (pay lee ahn TAH luh jist) is a scientist who studies fossils. He or she attempts to read the record of life left in rocks. From fossil evidence, paleontologists infer the diet of an organism and the environment in which it lived. In fact, paleontologists often can create images of extinct communities.

STUDY TIP

BACKGROUND KNOWLEDGE CHECK Based on what you know, predict the meaning of each new vocabulary term before reading the section. As you read, check the actual meaning compared to your prediction.

Connection to Earth Science When geologists began to study rock layers, or strata, in different areas, they noticed that layers of the same age tended to have the same kinds of fossils no matter where the rocks were found. The geologists inferred that all strata of the same age contained similar collections of fossils. This led to the establishment of a relative age scale for rocks all over the world.

Dating fossils **Relative dating** is a method used to determine the age of rocks by comparing them with those in other layers. Relative dating is based on the **law of superposition,** illustrated in **Figure 3,** which states that younger layers of rock are deposited on top of older layers. The process is similar to stacking newspapers in a pile as you read them each day. Unless you disturb the newspapers, the oldest ones will be on the bottom.

Figure 3 According to the law of superposition, rock layers are deposited with the youngest undisturbed layers on top.

Infer ***which layer shows that an aquatic ecosystem replaced a land ecosystem.***

Virtual Lab

BrainPOP

Radiometric dating uses the decay of radioactive isotopes to measure the age of a rock. Recall that an isotope is a form of an element that has the same atomic number but a different mass number. The method requires that the **half-life** of the isotope, which is the amount of time it takes for half of the original isotope to decay, is known. The relative amounts of the radioactive isotope and its decay product must also be known.

One radioactive isotope that is commonly used to determine the age of rocks is Uranium 238. Uranium 238 (U^{238}) decays to Lead 206 (Pb^{206}) with a half-life of 4510 million years. When testing a rock sample, scientists calculate the ratio of the parent isotope to the daughter isotope to determine the age of the sample.

Radiometric dating is not useful for dating sedimentary rocks because the minerals in sedimentary rocks were formed from pre-existing rocks. Igneous or metamorphic rocks that are found in layers closely associated with sedimentary rocks often can be used for assigning relative ages to sedimentary layers and the fossils within.

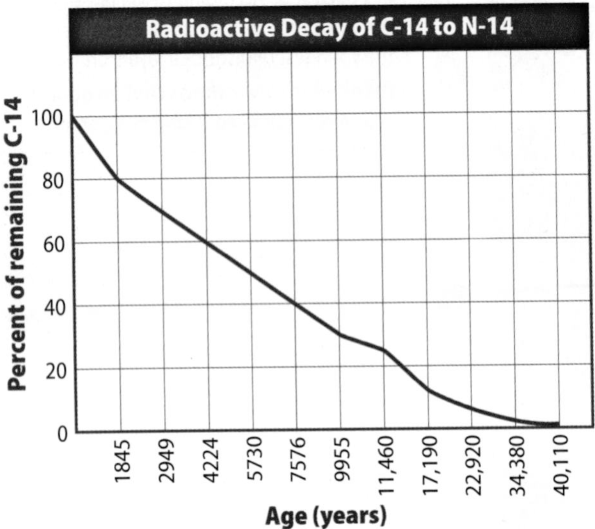

■ **Figure 4** The graph shows how the percent of carbon-14 remaining in a sample indicates age.

Interpret the graph ***What would the age of a bone be if it contained only 10 percent of C-14?***

Materials, such as mummies, bones, and tissues, can be dated directly using carbon-14 (C-14). Given the half-life of carbon-14, shown in **Figure 4,** only materials less than 60,000 years old can be dated accurately with this isotope.

The Geologic Time Scale

Think of geologic time as a ribbon that is 4.6 m long. If each meter represents one billion years, each millimeter represents one million years. Earth was formed at one end of the ribbon, and humans appear at the tip of the opposite end.

The **geologic time scale** is a record of Earth's history. Major geological and biological events in Earth's history can be identified within the geologic time scale. Because geologic time spans more than 4 billion years, subdivisions of time are used to identify how many millions of years ago (mya) an event occurred. The geologic time scale is divided into two segments—Precambrian time and the Phanerozoic eon.

Epochs, which last several million years, are the smallest units of geologic time. **Periods,** which last tens of millions of years, are divisions of geologic time consisting of two or more epochs. An **era,** which lasts hundreds of millions of years, is a unit of geologic time consisting of two or more periods. An **eon** is the longest unit of time in the geologic time scale and can include billions of years. **Figure 5** shows a portion of the geologic time scale that includes the Phanerozoic eon.

 GET IT? **Explain** why C-14 would not be useful for dating something from the Precambrian.

MiniLAB 1

Correlate Rock Layers Using Fossils

How can paleontologists establish relative age? Scientists use fossils from many locations to piece together the sequence of Earth's rock layers. This is the process of correlation.

Procedure

1. Read and complete the lab safety form.
2. Your teacher will assign you to a group and will give your group a **container** with layers of material embedded with fossils.
3. Carefully remove each layer, noting any embedded materials.
4. Make a sketch of the cross section, and label each layer and any materials contained within it.
5. Collect copies of sketches from the other groups and use them to determine the sequence of all the layers the class has studied.

Analysis

1. **Describe** the materials in each cross section. What patterns did you observe?
2. **Explain** how your analysis would be different if different layers contained the same materials. What if some of the layers didn't overlap?
3. **Critique** relative dating of fossils by rock layers. Include all sides of scientific evidence relating to relative dating. Consider how relative dating may be supported by other dating methods.

VISUALIZING the Geologic Time Scale

Figure 5 This figure illustrates the Phanerozoic Eon of the geologic time scale. The major biologic events during the Phanerozoic Eon are described in the figure. All of the times listed are approximate and as in all science fields, continuing research and discoveries might result in future revisions.

Eon	Era	Period	Epoch	MYA	Biological events
Phanerozoic	Cenozoic	Quaternary	Holocene		• Humans form civilizations
			Pleistocene	0.01	• Ice ages occur • Modern humans appear
		Neogene	Pliocene	2.6	• Hominins appear • Flowering plants are dominant 
			Miocene	5.3	• Apes appear • Climate is cooler
			Oligocene	23.0	• Monkeys appear • Climate is mild
		Paleogene	Eocene	33.9	• Flowering plants diversify • Most mammal orders exist 
			Paleocene	55.8	• Mammals, birds, and insects diversify • Climate is tropical
			Mass extinction (K-T Boundary)		
	Mesozoic	Cretaceous		65.5	• Flowering plants appear • Dinosaur population peaks 
		Jurassic		145.5	• First birds appear • Dinosaurs diversify • Forests are lush 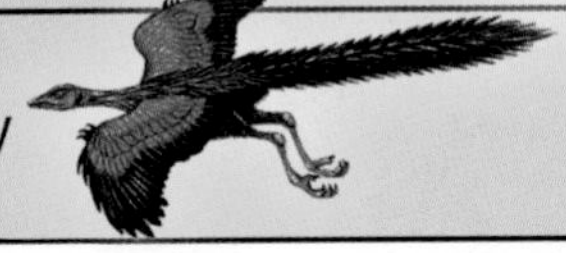
			Mass extinction		
		Triassic		199.6	• Gymnosperms are dominant • Dinosaurs appear • First mammals appear 
			Mass extinction		
	Paleozoic	Permian		251.0	• Reptiles diversify • Gymnosperms appear 
		Carboniferous		299.0	• Ferns and evergreens make up forests • Amphibians appear • Insects diversify 
			Mass extinction		
		Devonian		359.2	• Sharks and bony fishes appear • Tetrapods appear 
		Silurian		416.0	• Coral and other invertebrates are dominant • Land plants and insects appear
			Mass extinction		
		Ordovician		443.7	• First vertebrates appear • First plants appear
		Cambrian		488.3	• Cambrian explosion • All body plans arise 

■ **Figure 6** Fossils much like these stromatolites are found in rocks almost 3.5 billion years old.

Explain ***the importance of the organisms that left these stromatolites.***

Precambrian The first 4 billion years of Earth's history make up the Precambrian. This is nearly 90 percent of Earth's entire history, stretching from the formation of Earth to the beginning of the Paleozoic Era about 542 million years ago. During the Precambrian, Earth formed and life first appeared. Eventually, autotrophic prokaryotes, much like the cyanobacteria that made the stromatolites in **Figure 6,** enriched the atmosphere with oxygen. Eukaryotic cells also emerged, and by the end of the Precambrian, life was flourishing and the first animals had appeared.

Extensive glaciation marked the second half of the Precambrian. This might have delayed the further evolution of life until the ice receded at the beginning of the Ediacaran (ee dee UH kur uhn) Period. The Ediacaran Period was added to the time scale in 2004. It was the first new period added to the time scale since 1891 and reflects new knowledge of Earth's history. The Ediacaran Period lasted from about 635 million years ago to about 542 million years ago, representing about three quarters of a meter on the time ribbon at the end of the Precambrian. Simple organisms, such as the fossil in **Figure 7,** inhabited Ediacaran marine ecosystems. Food chains probably were short, and were dominated by animals that consumed tiny particles suspended in the water and by animals that ate debris on the bottom of the sea.

GET IT? **Infer** the process by which early autotrophic prokaryotes produced oxygen.

The Paleozoic Era A drastic change in the history of animal life on Earth marked the start of the Paleozoic (pay lee uh ZOH ihk) Era. In the space of just a few million years, the ancestors of most major animal groups diversified in what scientists call the **Cambrian explosion.** Not all major groups of organisms evolved rapidly at this time, and paleontologists still do not know when the rapid changes started or ended.

Major changes in ocean life occurred during the Paleozoic. More importantly, it seems the first life on land emerged during this era. Life in the oceans continued to evolve through the Cambrian Period. Fish, land plants, and insects appeared during the Ordovician and Silurian Periods. Organisms of many kinds, including huge insects, soon flourished in swampy forests that dominated the land, as shown in **Figure 8.** Tetrapods, the first land vertebrates (animals with backbones), emerged in the Devonian Period. By the end of the Carboniferous Period, the first reptiles were roaming the forests.

■ **Figure 7** Paleontologists disagree about scarce Ediacaran fossils such as this one. Some paleontologists suggest that they are relatives of today's living invertebrates such as segmented worms, while others think they represent an evolutionary dead end of giant protists or simple metazoans.

■ **Figure 8** During the Carboniferous Period, swamp forests covered much of Earth's land surface. Insects dominated the air, and tetrapods flourished in freshwater pools.
Infer ***how the plants of the Paleozoic Era were different from those of today.***

A mass extinction ended the Paleozoic Era at the end of the Permian Period. Recall that a mass extinction is an event in which many species become extinct in a short time. Mass extinctions have occurred every several million years with varying frequencies. Between 60 and 75 percent of the species alive went extinct in each of these events. During the Permian mass extinction, 90 percent of marine organisms disappeared. Geologists disagree about the cause of the Permian extinction, but most agree that geological forces, including increased volcanic activity, would have disrupted ecosystems or changed the climate.

The Mesozoic Era At the beginning of the Triassic Period, the ancestors of early mammals were the dominant land animals. Mammals and dinosaurs first appeared late in the Triassic Period, and flowering plants evolved from nonflowering plants. Birds evolved from a group of predatory dinosaurs in the middle Jurassic Period. For the rest of the Mesozoic, reptiles, such as the dinosaurs illustrated in **Figure 9,** were the dominant organisms on the planet. Then, about 65 million years ago, a meteorite struck Earth.

The primary evidence for this meteorite impact is found in a layer of material between the rocks of the Cretaceous (krih TAY shus) Period and the rocks of the Paleogene Period, the first period of the Cenozoic Era. Paleontologists call this layer the **K-T boundary.** Within this layer, scientists find unusually high levels of an element called iridium. Iridium is rare on Earth, but relatively common in meteorites. Therefore, the presence of iridium on Earth indicates a meteorite impact.

Many scientists think that this impact is related to the mass extinction at the end of the Mesozoic Era, which eliminated all dinosaurs, with the exception of their avian and reptilian descendents, many marine invertebrates, and numerous plant species. The meteorite did not wipe out all of these species, but the debris from the impact probably stayed in the atmosphere for months or even years, affecting global climate. Species that could not adjust to the changing climate disappeared.

GET IT? **Recall** the dominant land animals in the Triassic and Jurassic Periods.

■ **Figure 9** The dominant organisms during the Mesozoic Era were dinosaurs. A mass extinction occurred at the end of the Mesozoic Era that eliminated approximately 60 percent of all species living during the Mesozoic Era.

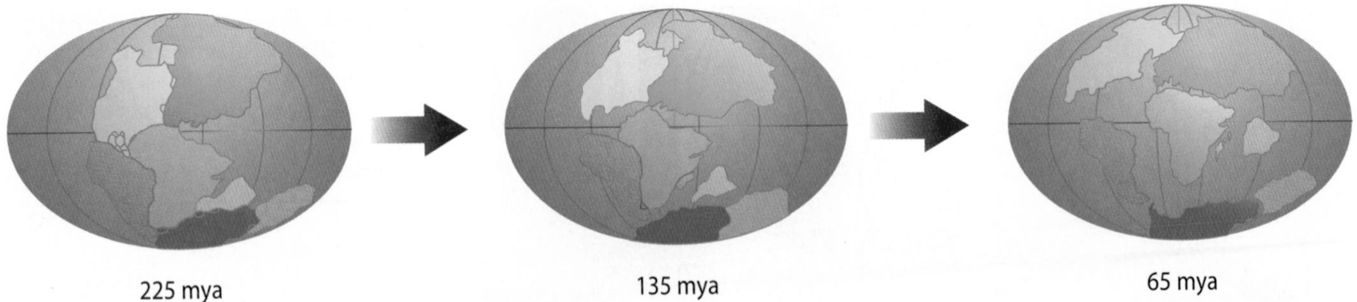

■ **Figure 10** These illustrations show the movement of Earth's major tectonic plates from about 225 million years ago, when all of the continents were joined into one landmass called Pangaea, to 65 million years ago.

 **Animation**

Scientists also think that the course of evolution in the Cenozoic Era was shaped by the massive geological changes shown in **Figure 10** that characterized the Mesozoic Era. While it might appear to us that continents are immobile, they have been moving since they formed. Alfred Wegener, a German scientist, presented the first evidence for continental drift in the 1920s. Continental drift has since become part of the theory of plate tectonics. **Plate tectonics** describes the movement of several large plates that make up the surface of Earth. These plates, some of which contain continents, move atop a partially molten layer of rock underneath them.

The Cenozoic Era The most recent era is the one in which mammals became the dominant land animals. At the beginning of the Cenozoic (sen uh ZOH ihk) Era, which means "recent life," most mammals were small and resembled shrews. After the mass extinction at the end of the Mesozoic Era, mammals began to diversify into distinct groups, including primates—the group to which you belong. Humans appeared very recently, near the end of the geologic time scale, in the current Quaternary Period. Humans survived the last ice age, but many species of mammals did not. To get an idea of how recently modern humans have appeared, you need to remove about two threads at the end of your geologic time ribbon. These threads represent the time that humans have existed on Earth.

REVIEW IT! Fossil Evidence of Change

Section Summary

- Fossils provide evidence of past life.
- Relative dating and radiometric dating are two methods used to determine the age of fossils.
- The geologic time scale is divided into eras, periods, and epochs.
- Major events in the geological time scale include both biological and geological changes.

Understand Main Ideas

1. MAINIDEA **Discuss** how fossils provide evidence of change from the earliest life-forms to those alive today.
2. **Diagram** a typical sequence of events in fossilization.
3. **Discuss** two ways that radiometric dating can be used to establish the age of a fossil. What are the limitations of this method of dating?
4. **Examine** scientific explanations regarding the sudden appearance or stasis of organisms in the fossil record.

Think Critically

5. **Infer** what changes in the fossil record might indicate a mass extinction.

MATH IN ▶ Biology

6. Out of the total of Earth's history (approximately 4.6 billion years), modern humans have existed for only 200,000 years. To put this in perspective, calculate the percentage of Earth's history that modern humans have existed.

2 The Origin of Life

MAINIDEA

Evidence indicates that a sequence of chemical events preceded the origin of life on Earth and that life has evolved continuously since that time.

Essential Questions

- What are the differences between spontaneous generation and biogenesis?
- What might have been the sequence of events that led to cellular life?
- What is the endosymbiont theory?

BIOLOGY 4U

In a recipe, some steps can be out of order, but some steps have to occur earlier than others or the end result will be different from what was intended. In the same way, to arrive at the pattern of life that is seen today, events leading to the emergence of life had to occur in specific ways.

Review Vocabulary

amino acid: building blocks for proteins

New Vocabulary

spontaneous generation
theory of biogenesis
endosymbiont theory

Multilingual eGlossary

Origins: Early Ideas

Perhaps one of the oldest ideas about the origin of life is spontaneous generation. **Spontaneous generation** is the idea that life arises from nonlife. For example, at one time people thought that mice could be created by placing damp hay and corn in a dark corner, or that mud could give rise to worms, insects, and fish. These ideas might seem humorous to us today, but before much was known about reproduction, it is easy to see how someone might form these conclusions.

One of the first recorded investigations of spontaneous generation came in 1668. Francesco Redi, an Italian scientist, tested the idea that flies arose spontaneously from rotting meat. He hypothesized that flies—not meat—produced other flies. In his experiment, illustrated using present-day equipment in **Figure 11,** Redi observed that maggots, the larvae of flies, appeared only in flasks that were open to flies. Closed flasks had no flies and no maggots. The results of his experiments failed to convince everyone, however. Although people were beginning to use the microscope during Redi's time and knew that organisms invisible to the naked eye could be found almost everywhere, some thought that these tiny organisms must arise spontaneously, even if flies did not.

■ **Figure 11** Francesco Redi showed that flies and maggots did not arise spontaneously from rotting meat.
Infer ***the purpose of the covered flask in Redi's experiment.***

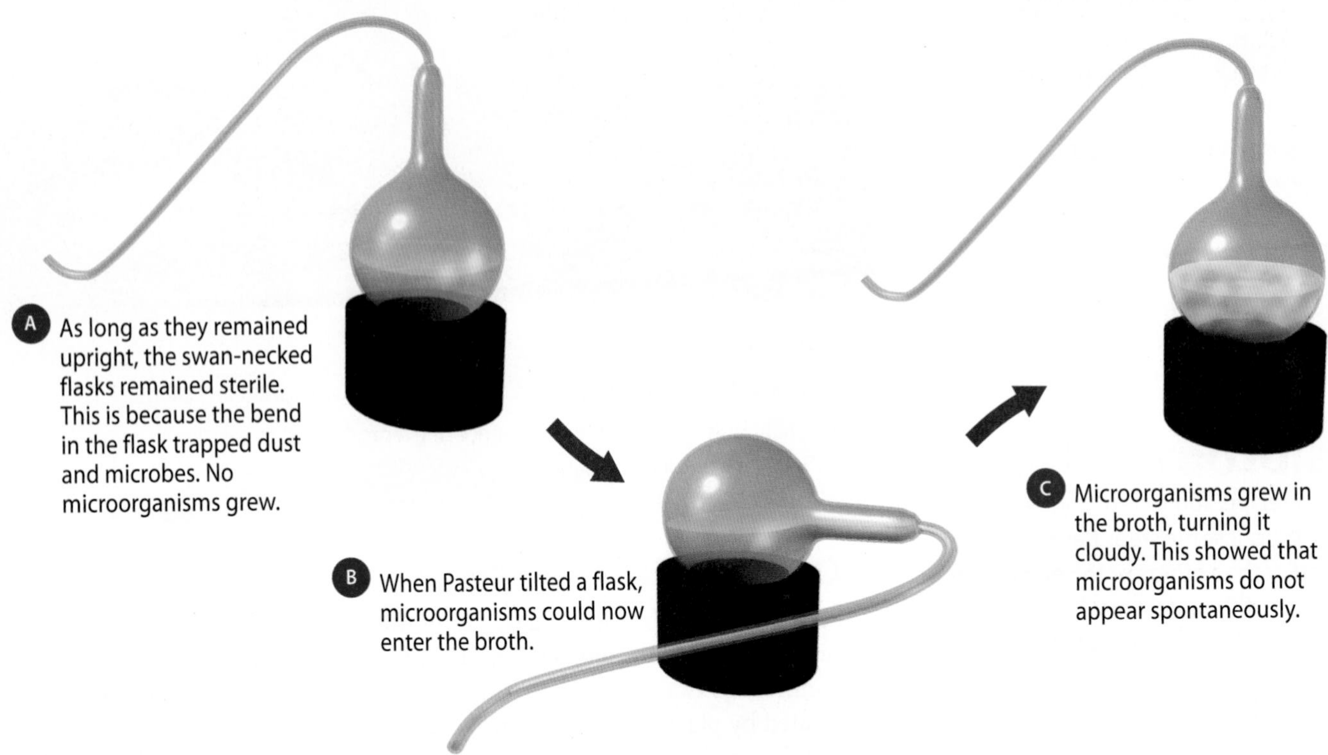

A As long as they remained upright, the swan-necked flasks remained sterile. This is because the bend in the flask trapped dust and microbes. No microorganisms grew.
B When Pasteur tilted a flask, microorganisms could now enter the broth.
C Microorganisms grew in the broth, turning it cloudy. This showed that microorganisms do not appear spontaneously.

■ **Figure 12** Pasteur's experiment showed that sterile broth remained free of microorganisms until exposed to air.

FOLDABLES® Incorporate information from this section into your Foldable.

The idea of spontaneous generation was not completely rejected until the mid-1800s. It was replaced by the **theory of biogenesis** (bi oh JEN uh sus), which states that only living organisms can produce other living organisms. Louis Pasteur designed an experiment to show that biogenesis was true even for microorganisms. Pasteur's experiment is illustrated in **Figure 12.** In one flask, only air was allowed to contact a sterile nutrient broth. Nutrient broth supports the growth of microorganisms. In another flask, both air and microorganisms were allowed to contact the broth. No microorganisms grew in the first container. They did, however, grow in the second container.

Origins: Modern Ideas

If life can arise only from preexisting life, then how did the first life-form appear? Most biologists agree that life originated through a series of chemical events early in Earth's history. During these events, complex organic molecules were generated from simpler ones. Eventually, simple metabolic pathways developed. Such pathways allowed molecules to be synthesized or broken down more efficiently. These pathways might have led to the emergence of life as we know it. How this happened is a topic of ongoing research among scientists today.

Simple organic molecule formation The primordial soup hypothesis was an early hypothesis about the origin of life. Scientists Alexander Oparin and John Haldane suggested this hypothesis in the 1920s. They thought that if Earth's early atmosphere had a mix of certain gases, organic molecules could have been synthesized from simple reactions involving those gases in the early oceans. UV light from the Sun and electric discharge in lightning might have been the primary energy sources. They thought that these organic molecules would have eventually supplied the precursors to life.

Connection to Chemistry In 1953, American scientists Stanley Miller and Harold Urey were the first to show that simple organic molecules could be made from inorganic compounds, as proposed by Oparin and Haldane. Miller and Urey built a glass apparatus, illustrated in **Figure 13,** to simulate the early Earth conditions hypothesized by Oparin. They filled the apparatus with water and the gases that they thought had made up the early atmosphere. The water was boiled and electric discharges were used to simulate lightning as an energy source. Upon examination, the resulting mixture contained a variety of organic compounds including amino acids. Because amino acids are the building blocks of proteins, this discovery supported the primordial soup hypothesis.

Later, other scientists found that hydrogen cyanide could be formed from even simpler molecules in simulated early Earth environments. Hydrogen cyanide can react with itself to eventually form adenine, one of the nucleotide bases in the genetic code. Many other experiments have since been carried out under conditions that probably reflect the atmosphere of early Earth more accurately. The final reaction products in these experiments were amino acids and sugars as well as nucleotides.

Some scientists suggest that the organic reactions that preceded life's emergence began in the hydrothermal volcanic vents of the deep sea, where sulfur forms the base of a unique food chain. Still others think that meteorites brought the first organic molecules to Earth.

CAREERS IN BIOLOGY

Evolutionary Biochemist Scientists who study chemistry and how it relates to life are biochemists. Evolutionary biochemists specifically study the structure and function of molecules from Earth's early history.

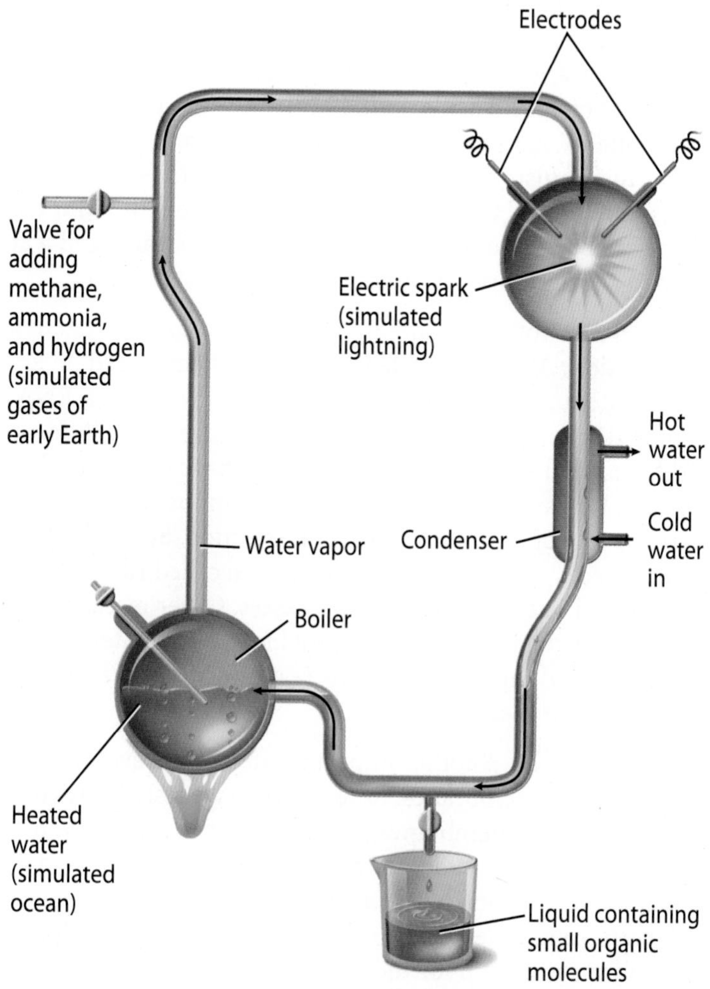

Animation

■ **Figure 13** The Miller-Urey experiment showed for the first time that organic molecules could be produced from gases proposed to have made up the atmosphere of early Earth.

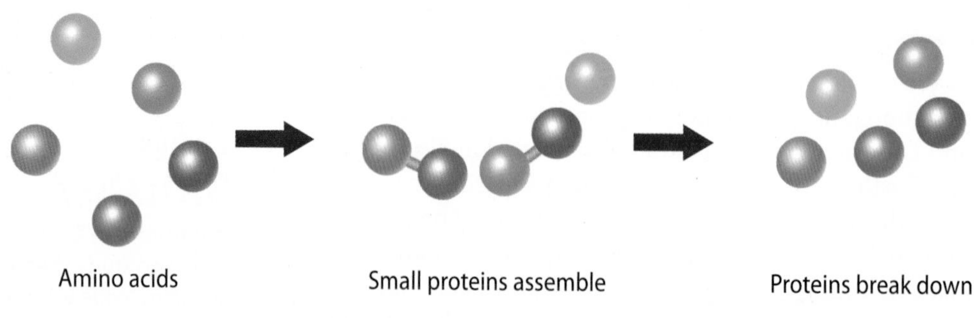

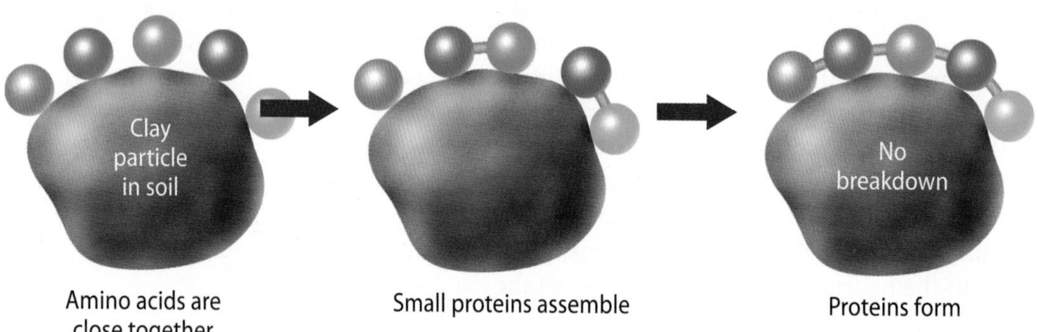

■ **Figure 14** Without clay, amino acids could have formed small, unstable proteins. In the presence of clay, amino acids might have come together in a more stable manner.

Personal Tutor

Making proteins Wherever the first organic molecules originated, it is clear that the next critical step was the formation of proteins. Amino acids alone are not sufficient for life. Life requires proteins, which are chains of amino acids. In the Miller-Urey experiment, amino acids could bond to one another, but they could separate just as quickly. One possible mechanism for the formation of proteins would be if amino acids were bound to a clay particle, as illustrated in **Figure 14.** Clay would have been a common sediment in early oceans, and it could have provided a framework for protein assembly.

Genetic code Another requirement for life is a coding system for protein production. All modern life has such a system, based on either RNA or DNA. Because all DNA-based life-forms also contain RNA, and because some RNA sequences appear to have changed very little through time, many biologists consider RNA to have been life's first coding system. Researchers have been able to demonstrate that RNA systems are capable of evolution by natural selection. Some RNAs also can behave like enzymes. These RNA molecules, called ribozymes, could have carried out some early life processes. Other researchers have proposed that clay crystals could have provided an initial template for RNA replication, and that eventually the resulting molecules developed their own replication mechanism.

VOCABULARY

ACADEMIC VOCABULARY

Mechanism
an instrument or process by which something is done or comes into being
The mechanism for protein synthesis was unknown for a long time.

Molecules to cells Another important step in the evolution of life was the formation of membranes. Researchers have tested ways of enclosing molecules in membranes, allowing early metabolic and replication pathways to develop. In these studies, as in other origin-of-life research, the connection between the various chemical events and the overall path from molecules to cells remains unresolved. However, scientists continue to search for the connection.

Cellular Evolution

What were the earliest cells like? Scientists don't know because the first life left no fossils. The earliest fossils are 3.5 billion years old. Chemical markings in rocks as old as 3.8 billion years suggest that life was present at that time even though no fossils remain. Scientists recently announced the discovery of what appeared to be fossilized microbes in rock that is 3.5 billion years old. This suggests that cellular activity had become established very early in Earth's history.

The first cells Scientists hypothesize that the first cells were prokaryotes. Recall that prokaryotic cells are much smaller than eukaryotic cells, and they lack a defined nucleus and most other organelles. Many scientists think that modern prokaryotes called archaea (ar KEE uh) are the closest relatives of Earth's first cells. These organisms often live in extreme environments, such as the hot springs of Yellowstone Park or the volcanic vents in the deep sea, such as the one shown in **Figure 15.** These are environments similar to the environment that might have existed on early Earth.

Figure 15 Some archaea live near deep-sea hydrothermal vents. They use energy from inorganic molecules to form the base of the vent food web.

Infer ***why some scientists think archaea most resemble the first cells.***

Photosynthesizing prokaryotes Scientists think that oxygen was absent from Earth's earliest atmosphere until about 1.8 billion years ago. Any oxygen that appeared earlier than 1.8 billion years ago likely bonded with free ions of iron as oxygen does today. Evidence that iron oxide was formed by oxygen generated by early life is found in unique sedimentary rock formations, such as those shown in **Figure 16,** that are between about 1.8 billion and 2.5 billion years old. Scientists hypothesize that after 1.8 billion years ago, the early Earth's free iron was saturated with oxygen, and oxygen instead began accumulating in the atmosphere.

Many scientists think that photosynthesizing prokaryotes evolved not long after the archaea—very early in life's history. Fossil evidence of these primitive prokaryotes, called cyanobacteria, has been found in rocks as old as 3.5 billion years. Cyanobacteria eventually produced enough oxygen to support the formation of an ozone layer. Once an ozone shield was established, conditions would be right for the appearance of eukaryotic cells.

GET IT? **Create** a list of the steps that led to the formation of the ozone layer in Earth's atmosphere.

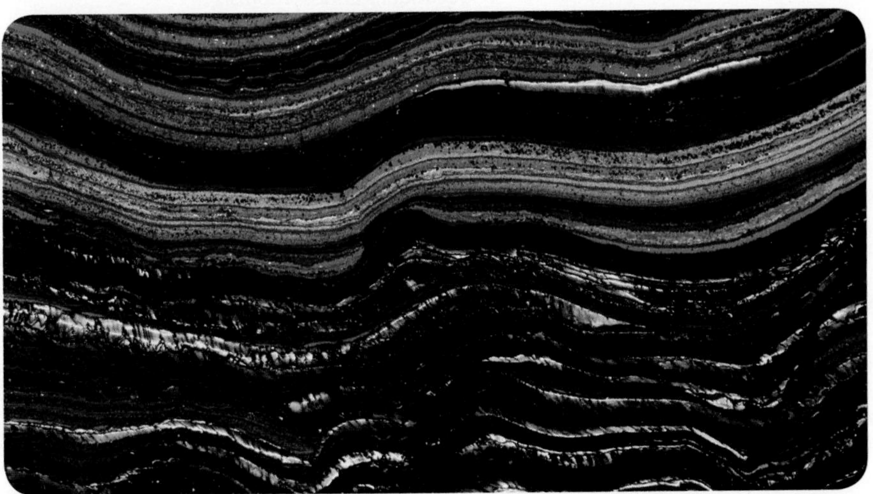

Figure 16 These rock formations, called banded iron formations, or BIFs, are unique sedimentary deposits. These rocks formed as a result of free oxygen production by photosynthetic bacteria billions of years ago. Because this deposit is a result of an organism, BIFs are considered trace fossils.

The endosymbiont theory Eukaryotic cells appeared in the fossil record about 1.8 billion years ago, around two billion years after life first formed. Eukaryotic cells have complex internal membranes, which enclose various organelles, including mitochondria and, in plant cells, chloroplasts. Mitochondria metabolize food through cellular respiration, and chloroplasts are the site of photosynthesis. Both mitochondria and chloroplasts are about the size of prokaryotic cells and contain similar prokaryote features. This led some scientists to speculate that prokaryotic cells were involved in the evolution of eukaryotic cells.

In 1966, biologist Lynn Margulis proposed the endosymbiont theory. According to the **endosymbiont theory,** the ancestors of eukaryotic cells lived in association with prokaryotic cells. In some cases, prokaryotes even might have lived inside eukaryotes. Prokaryotes could have entered a host cell as undigested prey, or they could have been internal parasites. Eventually, the relationship between the cells became mutually beneficial, and the prokaryotic symbionts became organelles in eukaryotic cells. This theory explains the origin of chloroplasts and mitochondria, as illustrated in **Figure 17.**

Evidence for the endosymbiont theory When Margulis first proposed the endosymbiont theory, many scientists were hesitant to accept it. There is evidence, however, that at least mitochondria and chloroplasts formed by endosymbiosis. For example, mitochondria and chloroplasts contain their own DNA. It is arranged in a circular pattern, just as it is in prokaryotic cells. Mitochondria and chloroplasts also have ribosomes that more closely resemble those in prokaryotic cells than those in eukaryotic cells. Finally, like prokaryotic cells, mitochondria and chloroplasts reproduce by fission, independent from the rest of the cell.

Data Analysis LAB 1

Based on Real Data*

Analyze Scientific Illustrations

How did plastids evolve? Chloroplasts belong to a group of organelles called plastids, which are found in plants and algae. Chloroplasts perform photosynthesis. Other plastids store starch and make substances needed as cellular building blocks or for plant function.

Think Critically

1. **Summarize** the process described in the diagram. Include the definition of phagocytosis in your description.
2. **Compare** secondary endosymbiosis to the endosymbiont theory described in **Figure 17.**
3. **Analyze and critique** the endosymbiont theory for the evolution of plastids. Include all sides of scientific evidence for the explanation.

Data and Observations

The illustration shows a way these plastids might have evolved.

Plastid origin

Secondary Endosymbiosis

*Data obtained from: Dyall, S.D., et al. 2004. Ancient invasions: from endosymbionts to organelles. *Science* 304: 253–257.

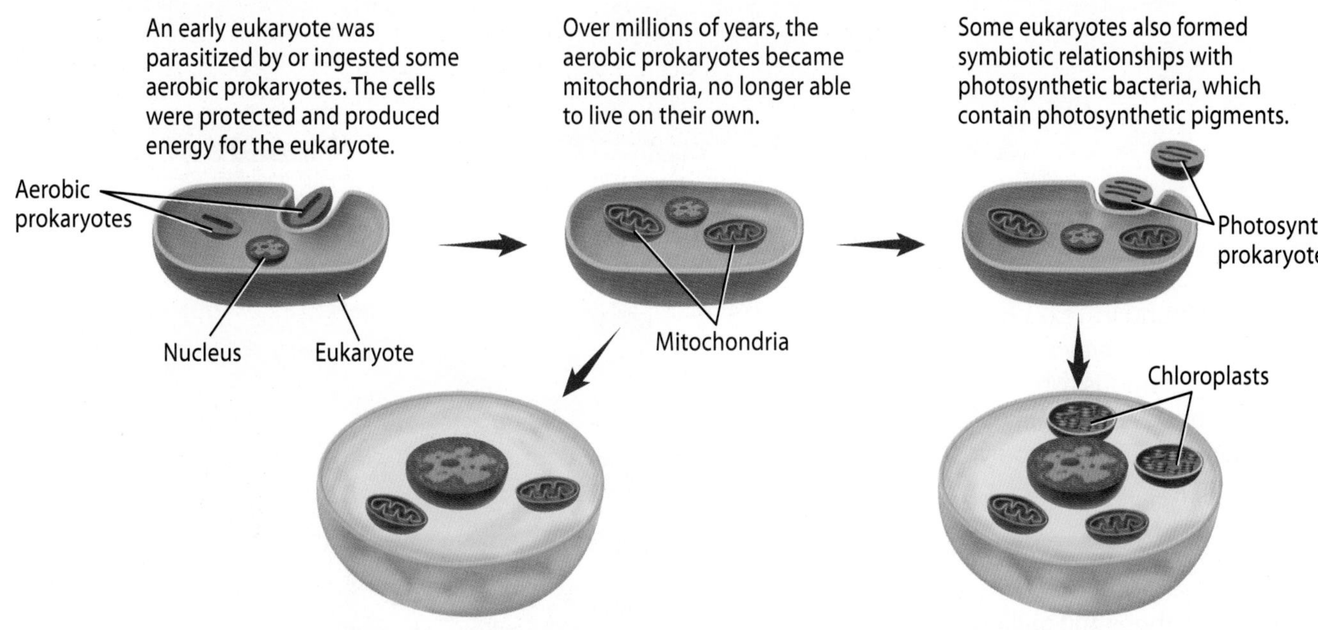

An early eukaryote was parasitized by or ingested some aerobic prokaryotes. The cells were protected and produced energy for the eukaryote.
Over millions of years, the aerobic prokaryotes became mitochondria, no longer able to live on their own.
Some eukaryotes also formed symbiotic relationships with photosynthetic bacteria, which contain photosynthetic pigments.
Aerobic prokaryotes
Nucleus
Eukaryote
Mitochondria
Photosynthetic prokaryotes
Chloroplasts
The aerobic prokaryotes became mitochondria in all eukaryotic cells.
The photosynthetic bacteria became chloroplasts in protist or plant cells.

■ **Figure 17** This illustration shows how Margulis hypothesized that eukaryotic cells and their organelles evolved.

Animation

Though the endosymbiont theory is widely endorsed, it is important to understand that scientists do not know the early steps that led to the emergence of life or to its early evolution. It is unlikely that any traces of the first life will ever be found. What scientists do know is that the conditions on Earth shortly after it took shape allowed the precursors of life to form.

The evolution of life is better understood than how the first life appeared. Fossil, geologic, and biochemical evidence supports many of the proposed steps in life's subsequent evolution. However, future discoveries might alter any or all of these steps. Scientists will continue to evaluate new evidence and test new theories in years to come.

REVIEW IT! The Origin of Life

Section Summary

- Spontaneous generation was disproved in favor of biogenesis.
- The origin of life is hypothesized to be a series of chemical events.
- Organic molecules, such as amino acids, might have been formed from simpler molecules on early Earth.
- The first cells probably were autotrophic and prokaryotic.
- The endosymbiont theory explains how eukaryotic cells might have evolved from prokaryotic cells.

Self Check

Understand Main Ideas

1. MAINIDEA **Infer** why scientists hypothesize that chemical events preceded the origin of life on Earth.
2. **Compare and contrast** spontaneous generation and biogenesis.
3. **Discuss** why prokaryotic cells probably appeared before eukaryotic cells.
4. **Hypothesize** whether prokaryotic cells might have been symbiotic before the evolution of eukaryotic cells.

Think Critically

5. **Describe** the hypothesized sequence of chemical and biological events that preceded the origin of eukaryotic cells.

WRITING IN ▶ Biology

6. Write a persuasive paragraph that explains why many scientists accept the endosymbiont theory.

BIOdiscoveries

A Fantastic Find! 4.3.1e

Tiny fossils found in Texas have changed what we know about the evolutionary history of the world's most famous fish. The fossils were identified as a new species and family of coelacanth. The fossils date back 100 million years and represent the youngest coelacanth ever found in North America.

A Famous Fish Coelacanths are one of the oldest types of fish in the world. They first appeared in the fossil record about 400 million years ago—over 100 million years before the dinosaurs. At one time, there were many different coelacanth species. They left an extensive fossil record around the world. Then, they seemed to disappear from the fossil record. Scientists believed that they went extinct with the dinosaurs about 65 million years ago until one was found in 1938 off the coast of South Africa. The finding made headlines around the world. Today, there are two known living species.

The Missing Link The newly-discovered Texas specimen is important because it links the living species of coelacanths with older, extinct species. Older coelacanth species tended to occupy freshwater environments, while the younger species tended to occupy marine environments.

Coelacanths have extended, lobed fins with bony support which is believed to be an early step in the evolution of limbs used for walking on land. Although paleontologists disagree about the exact placement of coelacanths in evolutionary history, they generally agree that they are related to an early ancestor of tetrapods.

The Texas specimen was found in marine sediments in the Duck Creek Formation in north Texas. 100 million years ago, the area was covered by the Western Interior Seaway, a wide shallow sea.

Coelacanths are sometimes called "living fossils" because they have changed very little over the past 400 million years.

The tiny fossils were part of the coelacanth's skull and jaw. When they were discovered by amateur fossil collector, Robert Reid, in the 1980's he had no idea how significant they were. He donated them to Southern Methodist University in Dallas to have them identified. The paleontologists at the University knew immediately that the bones were from a coelacanth, but it was not until recently that they were confirmed to be from a new species and family.

The new species was named *Reidus hilli* after both Robert Reid, its discoverer, and Robert T. Hill, the "Father of Texas Geology." During the late 1800's, Hill published several research papers describing Texas geology.

Investigate

Research Paper *Reidus hilli* lived during the Cretaceous Period. What species lived in New York during the Cretaceous? What was the environment like? How do you know?

WebQuest

Peter Scoones/Getty Images

BioLAB

1.1.1b, 1.1.1c, 1.3.5b, ¥a, ¥b1, ¥b2, ¥b3, ¥b4, ¥b5, ¥e, ¥i, ¥m

Is spontaneous generation possible?

Background: In the mid-1800s, Louis Pasteur conducted an experiment that showed that living organisms come from other living organisms—not from nonliving material. Pasteur's classic experiment, which disproved the notion of spontaneous generation, laid an essential foundation for modern biology by supporting the concept of biogenesis. In this lab, you will carry out an experiment based on Pasteur's work.

Question: *How can the idea of spontaneous generation be disproved?*

Materials

beef broth
graduated cylinder
Erlenmeyer flask (2)
ring stand (2)
wire gauze (2)
string
rubber stopper (2)
Bunsen burner (2)
5 cm of plastic tubing
30 cm of plastic tubing

Safety Precautions

Procedure

1. Read and complete the lab safety form.
2. Study the description of Louis Pasteur's classic experiment that disproved spontaneous generation.
3. Design and construct a data table to record changes in color, smell, and the presence of sediments.
4. Label the flasks "A" and "B." Flask A will be capped with a stopper holding a 5-cm piece of tubing. Flask B will be capped with a stopper holding a 30-cm piece of tubing.
5. Place 50 mL of beef broth in each flask. Cap each flask with the appropriate stopper.
6. Put each flask on a wire gauze on a ring stand over a Bunsen burner.
7. Bend the tubing on Flask B until it forms a U-shape. The bottom of the U should be near the base of the flask. Tie the end of the tubing to the ring stand to hold the U-shape.
8. Boil the broth in each flask for 30 min.
9. After the equipment and broth cool, move the apparatuses to an area of the lab where they will not be disturbed.
10. Observe the flasks over the next two weeks. Record your observations in your data table.
11. **Cleanup and Disposal** Dispose of beef broth according to your teacher's instructions. Clean and return all equipment to the appropriate location.

Analyze and Conclude

1. **Describe** the experimental procedure you followed. How does it compare to the steps followed by Louis Pasteur?
2. **Compare** your findings to Pasteur's findings.
3. **Describe** why it is important for scientists to verify one another's data.
4. **Think Critically** Explain how Pasteur's findings disprove spontaneous generation.
5. **Error Analysis** If your results did not match Pasteur's results, explain a possible reason for the difference.

WRITING IN ▶ Biology

Pasteur's experiment resulted in wide acceptance of biogenesis by the scientific community. Write an essay explaining how Pasteur's work contributed to some of the central ideas of biology.

CHAPTER 14 STUDY GUIDE

BIGIDEA **Fossils provide key evidence for understanding the origin and the history of life on Earth.**

SECTION 1 Fossil Evidence of Change

MAINIDEA Fossils provide evidence of the change in organisms over time.

- Fossils provide evidence of past life.
- Relative dating and radiometric dating are two methods used to determine the age of fossils.
- The geologic time scale is divided into eras, periods, and epochs.
- Major events in the geologic time scale include both biological and geological changes.

VOCABULARY
- **fossil**
- **paleontologist**
- **relative dating**
- **law of superposition**
- **radiometric dating**
- **half-life**
- **geologic time scale**
- **epoch**
- **period**
- **era**
- **eon**
- **Cambrian explosion**
- **K-T boundary**
- **plate tectonics**

SECTION 2 The Origin of Life

MAINIDEA Evidence indicates that a sequence of chemical events preceded the origin of life on Earth and that life has evolved continuously since that time.

- Spontaneous generation was disproved in favor of biogenesis.
- The origin of life is hypothesized to be a series of chemical events.
- Organic molecules, such as amino acids, might have been formed from simpler molecules on early Earth.
- The first cells probably were autotrophic and prokaryotic.
- The endosymbiont theory explains how eukaryotic cells might have evolved from prokaryotic cells.

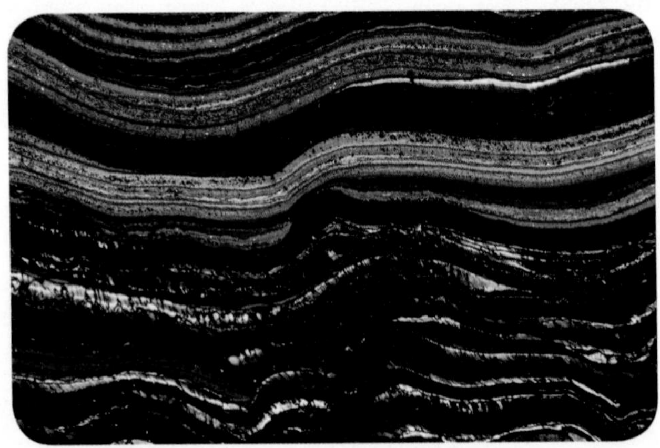

VOCABULARY
- **spontaneous generation**
- **theory of biogenesis**
- **endosymbiont theory**

(t)Biophoto Associates/Science Source, (b)Francois Gohier/Science Source

CHAPTER 14 ASSESSMENT

SECTION 1

Vocabulary Review

Choose the vocabulary term from the Study Guide page that best describes each of the following phrases.

1. determining the age of a fossil by radioactive elements

2. the remains or evidence of an organism

3. scientist who studies fossils

Understand Main Ideas

Use the table below to answer questions 4 and 5.

Radioactive Isotope	Product of Decay	Half-Life (Years)
Carbon-14	Nitrogen-14	5730
Chlorine-36	Argon-36	300,000
Beryllium-10	Boron-10	1.52 million
Uranium-235	Lead-207	700 million

4. According to the table above, if one-fourth of the original radioactive carbon is present in a fossil, what is the fossil's age?
   A. 2857.5 years old
   B. 5730 years old
   C. 11,460 years old
   D. 17,145 years old

5. Which isotope would be best for measuring the age of a rock layer estimated to be about one million years old?
   A. beryllium-10
   B. carbon-14
   C. chlorine-36
   D. uranium-235

6. Which fossil type provides the most anatomical information to paleontologists?
   A. trace
   B. molds
   C. replacement
   D. amber

Use the graph below to answer questions 7 and 8.

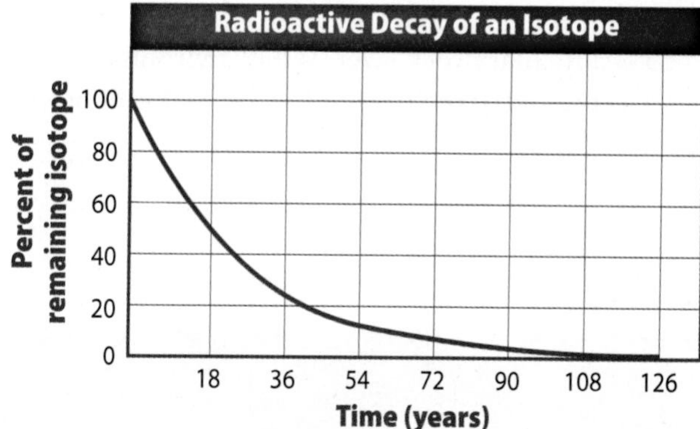

7. Which is the half-life of the radioactive isotope shown in the graph?
   A. 18 years **C.** 54 years
   B. 36 years **D.** 72 years

8. Assuming that you can only date material that has at least one percent of the radioisotope remaining, which age would be too old to date with this isotope?
   A. 35 years **C.** 75 years
   B. 50 years **D.** 125 years

9. What era followed the mass extinction at the end of the Permian Period?
   A. Cambrian
   B. Mesozoic
   C. Paleozoic
   D. Neogene

10. Nearly all fossils occur in what kind of rocks?
   A. batholithic
   B. igneous
   C. metamorphic
   D. sedimentary

Constructed Response

11. **Short Answer** How does the law of superposition help paleontologists?

12. **Explain** the geologic time scale using examples of data showing stasis and sudden appearances of organisms in the fossil record.

13. **Short Answer** Calculate the percentage of Earth's existence occupied by the Cenozoic Era.

Think Critically

14. **Infer** Imagine that you found a piece of amber in a sedimentary rock layer. What environment likely was present at the time of the fossil's formation?

15. **Describe** a fossil type and how it helps paleontologists understand an organism's anatomy.

Use the photo below to answer question 16.

16. MAINIDEA If you found the above fossil of a flowering plant in a layer of rock, what would you conclude about the age of the layer? Would you look in layers above or below the layer with the flower to learn about the Permian mass extinction?

SECTION 2

Vocabulary Review

Replace the underlined words with the correct vocabulary term from the Study Guide page.

17. The belief that organisms originate from nonliving matter was disproven by Redi and Pasteur.

18. The explanation that bacteria might have lived inside prokaryotes and eventually became organelles was proposed by Lynn Margulis.

Understand Main Ideas

19. Pasteur's experiments led to which theory?
    A. biogenesis theory
    B. endosymbiont theory
    C. evolution theory
    D. spontaneous generation theory

Use the illustration below to answer questions 20 and 21.

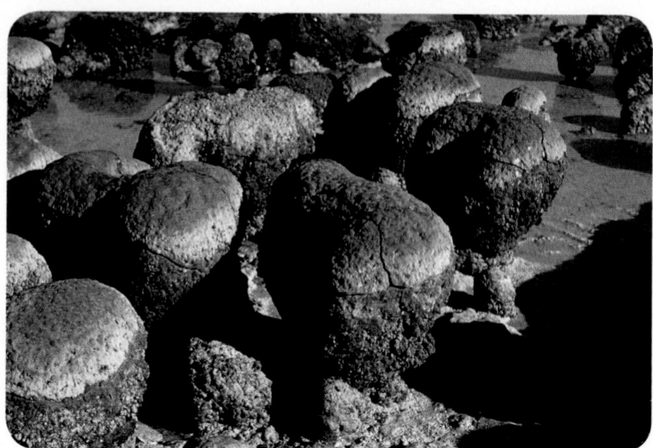

20. The organisms represented in the photo above had which effect on early Earth?
    A. produced the first amino acids
    B. increased oxygen in the atmosphere
    C. became the first mitochondria
    D. consumed the first heterotrophs

21. When did the fossils of organisms like those in the photo first appear in the fossil record?
    A. 1.0 million years ago
    B. 2.0 million years ago
    C. 3.5 billion years ago
    D. 4.5 billion years ago

22. Clay most likely was involved in which process?
    A. producing the first oxygen in the atmosphere
    B. forming the first plasma membranes
    C. providing a framework for amino acid chains
    D. capturing prokaryotes for chloroplast evolution

23. Scientists have fossil evidence for which idea for the origin of life?
    A. first amino acids
    B. first RNA
    C. first cells
    D. first autotrophs

24. Banded iron formations are important evidence for which idea in the early evolution of life?
    A. photosynthetic autotrophs
    B. endosymbiont organelles
    C. heterotrophic prokaryotes
    D. heterotrophic eukaryotes

Constructed Response

25. **Open Ended** What would you expect the first step to be in the emergence of life from nonliving matter?

26. MAINIDEA Analyze the importance of the Miller-Urey experiments in understanding the formation of organic molecules.

27. **Open Ended** Which evidence do you think is most important for the endosymbiont hypothesis? Why?

Think Critically

28. **Sequence** the hypothesized events that led from a lifeless Earth to the presence of eukaryotic cells.

29. **Compare** the contributions of Redi and Pasteur in disproving spontaneous generation.

Use the photo below to answer question 30.

30. THEME FOCUS How is the hot spring shown above similar to conditions on early Earth? What kind of organisms can survive in this type of environment?

31. **Infer** How was evolution affected by the increase in oxygen caused by the first photosynthetic organisms?

32. **CAREERS IN Biology** How could a biochemist studying DNA sequences provide evidence for the endosymbiont theory?

33. **Analyze and critique** the endosymbiont theory. What are its strengths and weaknesses?

NPS Photo by Jim Peaco

Summative Assessment

34. **BIG IDEA** There are six major fossil types discussed in **Table 1.** Create a hierarchy of the fossil types in **Table 1** based on the amount and type of information obtained from the fossil. Write a paragraph supporting your hierarchy.

35. **WRITING IN Biology** Assume that you are a scientist searching for the cause of a mass extinction. Several causes have been hypothesized. Write a paragraph that explains how you could use dating methods to accept or reject them.

36. **WRITING IN Biology** Explain the importance of a particular fossil being found in both South America and Africa.

37. Make a list of requirements for the existence of life. Put them in the order in which you think that they had to occur in order for life to begin successfully.

38. Explain why paleontologists find radiometric dating important.

39. Based on what you know about laws and theories, could the endosymbiont theory become a law? Explain your answer.

DBQ Document–Based Questions

"Probably all of the organic beings which have ever lived on this Earth have descended from some one primordial form."
Charles Darwin in *The Origin of Species,* 1859.

40. If Darwin was alive today, do you think he would include proteins among "organic beings"? Why or why not?

41. Use the quote above to support why you think Darwin would or would not have supported the endosymbiont theory.

42. Discuss what Darwin might have meant by the phrase, "...descended from some one primordial form."

CUMULATIVE

MULTIPLE CHOICE

Use the illustration below to answer questions 1 and 2.

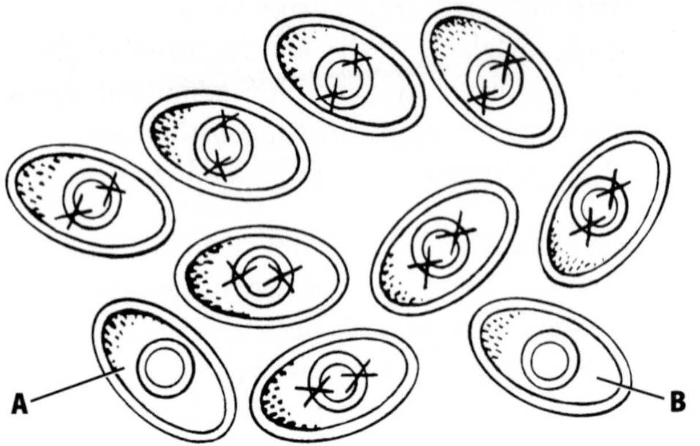

1 The bacterial cells in the figure above were transformed after they were mixed with recombinant DNA—represented by "XX" in the diagram. Which is one possible reason that Cells A and B do not have the new recombinant DNA plasmid?

A Cells A and B are resistant to antibiotics.

B Cells A and B do not have plasma membranes.

C Cells A and B did not take up the DNA fragment.

D Cells A and B initially had different plasmids.

2 In the figure, which step is likely to happen after the transformation of bacterial cells?

A Cells with the new plasmid will die after exposure to an antibiotic.

B Cells with the new plasmid will replicate quicker.

C Cells without the new plasmid will die after exposure to an antibiotic.

D Cells without the new plasmid will replicate more quickly.

SHORT ANSWER

Use the illustration below to answer questions 3 and 4.

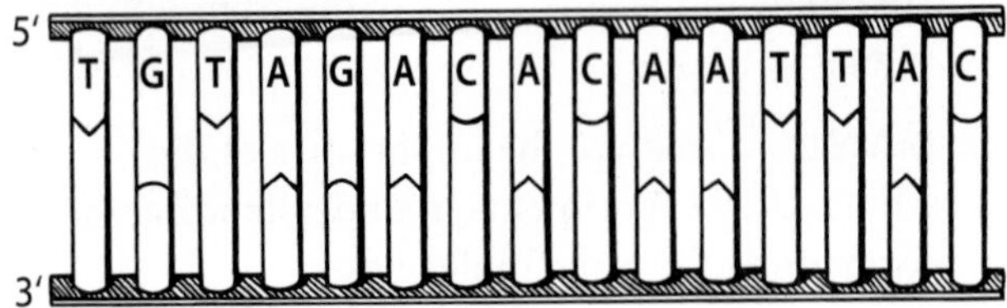

3 The diagram shows a molecule of DNA. What is the complementary DNA strand base code? Be sure to indicate the orientation of the strand.

4 Suppose the adjacent thymine bases in the figure formed a dimer after being exposed to ultraviolet radiation. How would the dimer affect the structure of the DNA molecule?

5 Describe the difference between petrified and replacement fossils.

6 Describe why scientists infer that oxygen was absent from the early atmosphere on Earth.

7 Use a chart to show the role that different enzymes play in the replication of DNA. Be sure to put the steps in the correct order.

8 What are restriction enzymes? Assess why they are an important tool for genetic engineering.

9 How does a paleontologist use geologic principles for the relative dating of fossils?

10 What causes DNA fragments to separate during gel electrophoresis?

EXTENDED RESPONSE

11 How is selective breeding related to genetic engineering?

12 Appraise how your body temperature is related to homeostasis.

13 Explain the three steps that take place in a polymerase chain reaction (PCR).

ESSAY QUESTION

Some genes contain instructions for controlling when our cells grow, divide, and die. Certain genes that promote cell division are called oncogenes. Others that slow down cell division, or cause cells to die at the right time, are called tumor suppressor genes. It is known that cancers can be caused by DNA mutations (changes) that "turn on" oncogenes or "turn off" tumor suppressor genes.

The BRCA genes (BRCA1 and BRCA2) are tumor suppressor genes. When they are mutated, they no longer function to suppress abnormal growth and breast cancer is more likely to develop. Certain inherited DNA changes can result in a high risk for the development of breast cancer in people who carry these genes and are responsible for the cancers that run in some families.

Using the information in the paragraph above, answer the following question in essay format.

14 How could oncogenes and tumor suppressor genes play a part in the development of breast cancer? Use what you know about molecular genetics to write an essay explaining how these genes might contribute to the formation of tumors.

TEST PRACTICE

Use the graph below to answer question 15.

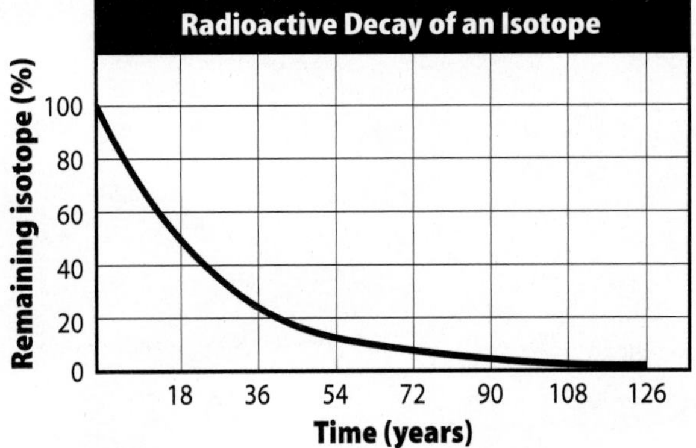

15 How much of the original isotope remains after 10 years?

A 50 percent

B 75 percent

C 10 percent

D 30 percent

16 Which of the following is NOT a reason why some scientists support the endosymbiont theory?

A Mitochondria and chloroplasts are found living outside eukaryotic cells.

B Mitochondria and chloroplasts reproduce by fission.

C The size and structure of mitochondria and chloroplasts are similar to prokaryotic cells.

D The genetic material in mitochondria and chloroplasts is circular.

NEED EXTRA HELP?																
If You Missed Question...	1	2	3	4	5	6	7	8	9	10	11	12	13	14	15	16
Review Section...	13.2	13.2	12.2	12.4	14.1	14.2	12.3	13.2	14.1	13.2	13.2, 12.2	1.1	13.2	12.3, 12.4	14.1	14.2

The bee and the orchid in this photo have each changed through many generations. Observation of such changes provides data in support the theory of evolution.

LaunchLAB

How does selection work?

Predators can cause changes in populations by choosing certain organisms as prey. In this lab, you will look at how prey populations might respond to a predator.

CHAPTER 15
Evolution

1 Darwin's Theory of Evolution by Natural Selection

1.1.1b, 4.3.1e, 4.3.1f, 4.3.1g, 4.3.1i, ¥o

2 Evidence of Evolution

1.3.5b, 4.3.1a, 4.3.1e, 4.3.1f, 4.3.1g, 4.3.1i, ¥a, ¥e

3 Shaping Evolutionary Theory

1.1.1a, 1.1.4a, 1.3.5b, 4.3.1b, 4.3.1d, 4.3.1e, 4.3.1f, 4.3.1k, 4.3.1g, 4.6.1g

THEMEFOCUS

Stability and change Populations may evolve due to a long-term disruption in homeostasis.

BIGIDEA

The theory of evolution is supported by natural selection and explains the diversity of life.

Natural Selection

Make a four-door book and label each door with one of the four principal ideas of natural selection. Use it to organize your notes on natural selection.

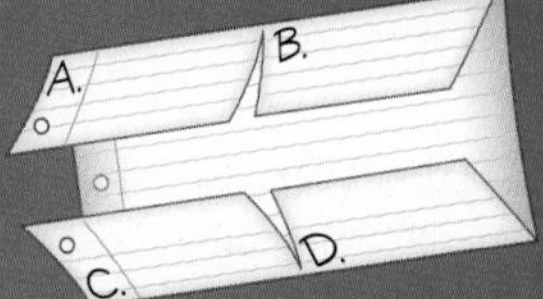

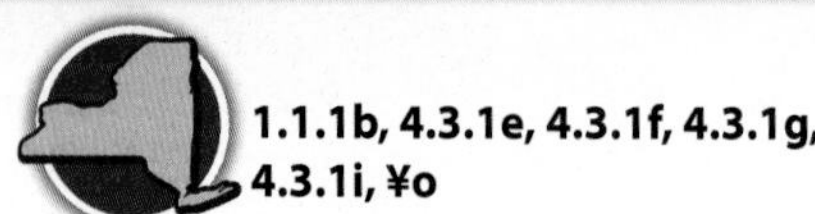

1 Darwin's Theory of Evolution by Natural Selection

1.1.1b, 4.3.1e, 4.3.1f, 4.3.1g, 4.3.1i, ¥o

MAINIDEA

Charles Darwin developed a theory of evolution based on natural selection.

Essential Questions

- What evidence convinced Darwin that species could change over time?
- What are the four principles of natural selection?
- How can natural selection change a population?

BIOLOGY 4U

Today, a jet can travel from London to New York in hours. Imagine how different things were when it took almost five years for Charles Darwin to circle the globe aboard a small, cramped ship.

REVIEW VOCABULARY

selective breeding: the process by which a breeder develops a plant or animal to have certain traits

NEW VOCABULARY

artificial selection
natural selection
evolution

Multilingual eGlossary

■ **Figure 1** Charles Darwin (1809–1882) posed for this portrait shortly after he returned from his voyage aboard the HMS *Beagle.*

Developing the Theory of Evolution

When Charles Darwin, shown in **Figure 1,** boarded the HMS *Beagle* in 1831, the average person thought that the world was about 6000 years old. Almost everyone, including the young Darwin, thought that animals and plants were unchanging. The concept of gradual change over time was still years away.

Darwin on the HMS *Beagle* The primary mission of the *Beagle* was to survey the coast of South America. In 1831, the *Beagle* set sail from England for Maderia and then proceeded to South America, as shown on the map in **Figure 2.** Darwin's role on the ship was as a naturalist and companion to the captain. His job was to collect biological and geological specimens during the ship's travels. Darwin had a degree in theology from Christ's College, Cambridge, although he previously had studied medicine and the sciences.

Over the course of the ship's five-year voyage, Darwin made extensive collections of rocks, fossils, plants, and animals. He also read a copy of Charles Lyell's *Principles of Geology*—a book proposing that Earth was millions of years old. This book influenced his thinking as he observed fossils of marine life at high elevations in the Andes, unearthed giant fossil versions of smaller living mammals, and saw how earthquakes could lift rocks great distances very quickly.

The Galápagos Islands In 1835, the *Beagle* arrived in the Galápagos (guh LAH puh gus) Islands off the coast of South America. Darwin was initially disappointed by the stark barrenness of these volcanic islands. However, as he began to collect mockingbirds, finches, and other animals on the four islands that he visited, he noticed that the different islands seemed to have their own, slightly different varieties of animals. These differences, however, only sparked a mere curiosity. He took little notice of the comment from the colony's vice governor that the island origins of the giant tortoises could be identified solely by the appearance of the tortoises' shells.

GET IT? **Summarize** some of the experiences or observations that influenced Darwin during his voyage on the Beagle.

AKG/Science Source

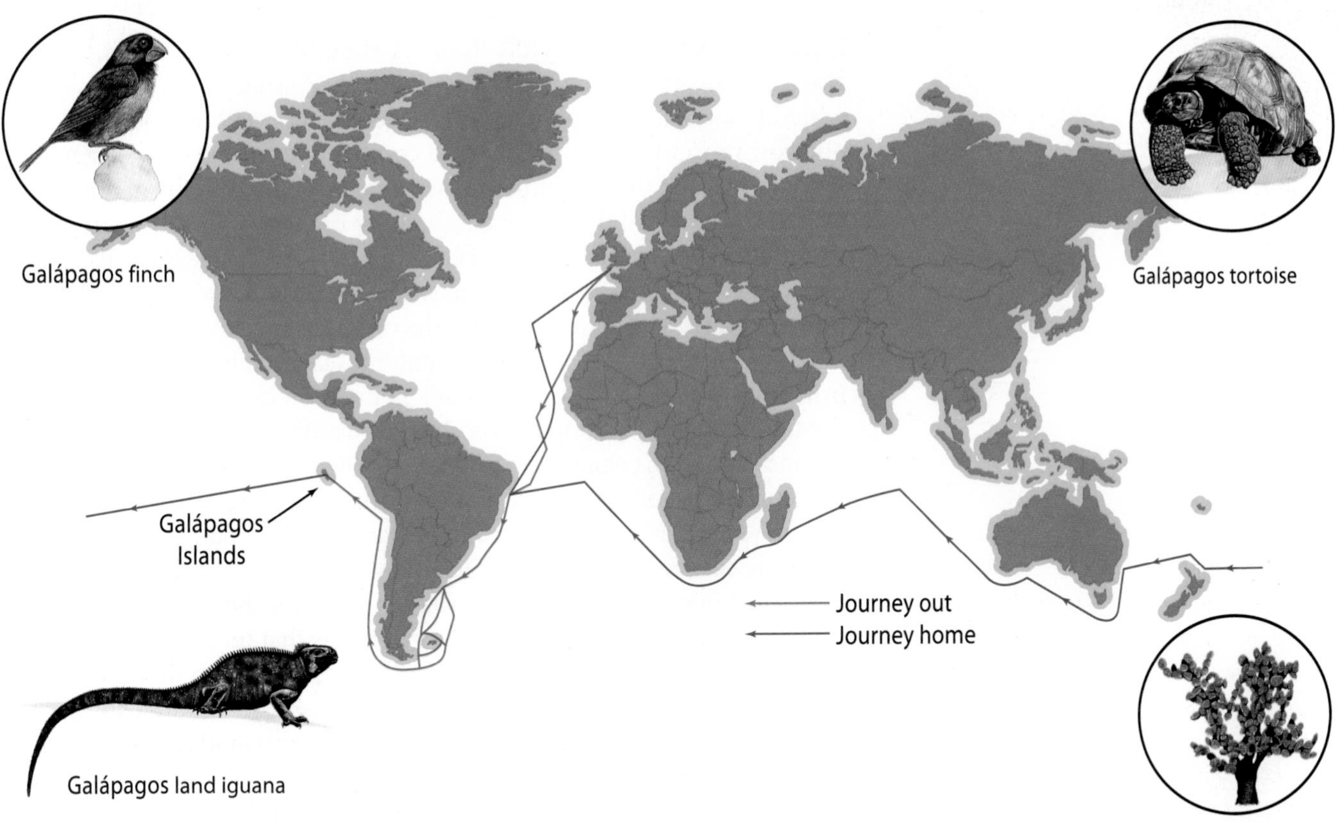

■ **Figure 2** The map shows the route of the *Beagle's* voyage. The species shown are all unique to the Galápagos Islands.

Infer ***How did the first organisms reach the Galápagos Islands?***

A few years after Darwin returned to England, he began reconsidering his observations. He took note of the work of John Gould, an ornithologist who was classifying the birds Darwin brought back from the Galápagos. Gould discovered that the Galápagos finches were separate species and determined that the finches of the Galápagos did not live anywhere else in South America. In fact, almost every specimen that Darwin had collected on the islands was new to European scientists. These new species most closely resembled species from mainland South America, although the Galápagos and the mainland had different environments. Island and mainland species should not have resembled one another so closely unless, as Darwin began to suspect, populations from the mainland changed after reaching the Galápagos.

Darwin continued his studies Darwin hypothesized that new species could appear gradually through small changes in ancestral species, but he could not see how such a process would work. To understand it better, he turned to animal breeders—pigeon breeders in particular.

Different breeds of pigeons have certain distinctive traits that also are present in these breeds' offspring. A breeder can promote these traits by selecting and breeding pigeons that have the most exaggerated expressions of those traits. For example, to produce pigeons with fan-shaped tails, the breeder will breed pigeons with the most fan-shaped tails. The process of directed breeding to produce offspring with desired traits, referred to as selective breeding was called **artificial selection** by Darwin.

Artificial selection also occurs when humans develop new breeds of dogs or new strains of crop plants. Darwin inferred that if humans could change species by artificial selection, then perhaps the same process could work in nature. Further, Darwin thought that, given enough time, perhaps this process could produce new species.

Natural selection While thinking about artificial selection, Darwin read an essay by economist Thomas Malthus. The essay suggested that the human population, if unchecked, eventually would outgrow its food supply, leading to a competitive struggle for existence. Darwin realized that Malthus's ideas could be applied to the natural world. He reasoned that some competitors in the struggle for existence would be better equipped for survival than others. Those less equipped would die. This is the process of **natural selection.** Here, finally, was the framework for a new theory about the origin of species.

Darwin's theory of evolution by natural selection has four basic principles that explain how traits of a population can change over time. First, individuals in a population show differences, or variations. Second, variations can be inherited, meaning that they are passed down from parent to offspring. Third, organisms have more offspring than can survive on available resources. The average cardinal, for example, lays nine eggs each summer. If each baby cardinal survived and reproduced just once, it would take only seven years for the first pair to have produced one million birds. Finally, variations that increase reproductive success will have a greater chance of being passed on than those that do not increase reproductive success. If having a fantail helps a pigeon reproduce successfully, future generations would include more pigeons with fan-shaped tails.

FOLDABLES® Incorporate information from this section into your Foldable.

Given enough time, natural selection could modify a population enough to produce a new species. Natural selection is now considered the mechanism by which evolution takes place. **Figure 3** shows how natural selection might modify a population of sunflowers.

GET IT? **Explain** the four principles of natural selection.

Data Analysis LAB 1

Based on Real Data*

Interpret the Data

How did artificial selection change corn? Plant breeders have made many changes to crops. In one of the longest experiments ever conducted, scientists selected maize (corn) for oil content in kernels.

Data and Observations

Look at the graph and compare the selection in the different plant lines.

Line IHO was selected for high oil content, and line ILO was selected for low oil content. The direction of selection was reversed in lines RHO (started from IHO) and RLO (started from ILO) at generation 48. In line SHO (derived from RHO), selection was switched back to high oil content at generation 55.

*Data obtained from: Hill, W. G. 2005. A century of corn selection. *Science* 307: 683–684.

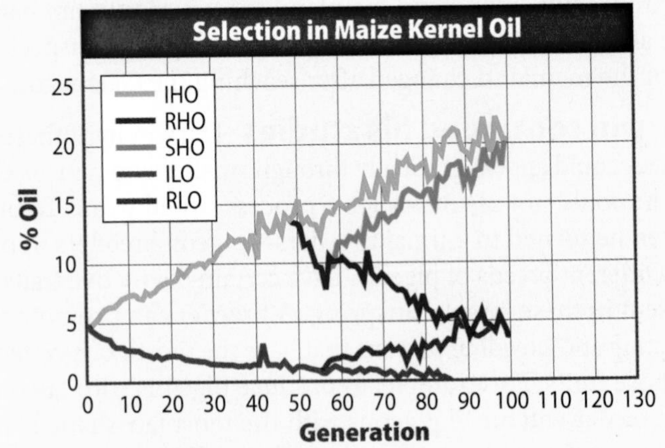

Think Critically

1. **Measure** What were the highest and lowest percentages of oil seen in the experiment?
2. **Predict** If the trend continues for line RHO, approximately how many generations will it take until the oil content reaches zero percent?

VISUALIZING
VISUALIZING

VISUALIZING Natural Selection

Figure 3 Natural selection is the mechanism by which, if given enough time, a population—in this case, a population of sunflowers—could be modified to produce a new species. There are four principles of natural selection that explain how this can occur: variation, heritability, overproduction, and reproductive advantage.

Variation Individuals in a population differ from one another. For example, some sunflowers are taller than others.

Heritability Variations are inherited from parents. Tall sunflowers produce tall sunflowers, and short sunflowers produce short sunflowers.

Overproduction Populations produce more offspring than can survive. Each sunflower has hundreds of seeds, most of which will not germinate.

Reproductive Advantage Some variations allow the organism that possesses them to have more offspring than the organism that does not possess them. For example, in this habitat, shorter sunflowers reproduce more successfully.

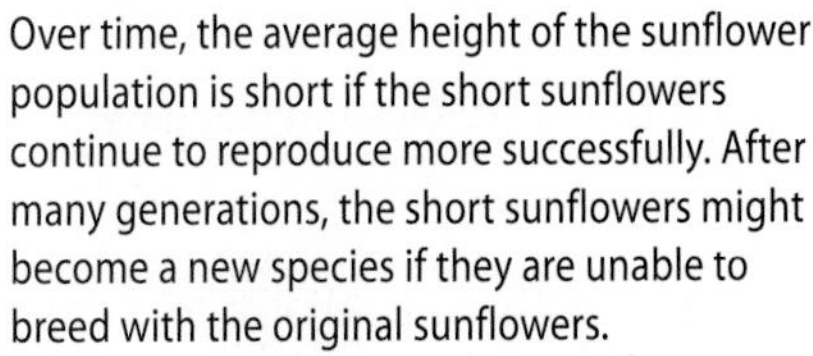

Over time, the average height of the sunflower population is short if the short sunflowers continue to reproduce more successfully. After many generations, the short sunflowers might become a new species if they are unable to breed with the original sunflowers.

Table 1 Basic Principles of Natural Selection — Interactive Table

Principle	Example
Individuals in a population differ from one another.	The students in a classroom all look different.
Variations are inherited.	You look similar to your parents.
Animals have more young than can survive on the available resources.	The average cardinal lays nine eggs per summer. If each cardinal lived only one year and all offspring survived, in seven years there would be a million cardinals.
Variations that increase reproductive success will be more common in the next generation.	If having a fan-shaped tail increases the reproductive success of pigeons, then more pigeons in the next generation will have fan-shaped tails.

The Origin of Species

Darwin had likely formulated his theory of evolution by natural selection by about 1840. Soon after, he began writing a multivolume book compiled of evidence for evolution and explaining how natural selection might provide a mechanism for the origin of species. **Table 1** summarizes the principles of natural selection described in Darwin's work. He continued to compile evidence in support of his theory for many years. For example, he spent eight years studying relationships among barnacles.

In 1858, Alfred Russel Wallace, another English naturalist, proposed a theory that was almost identical to Darwin's theory. Both men's ideas were presented to the Linnean Society of London. One year later, Darwin published *On the Origin of Species by Means of Natural Selection*—a condensed version of the book he had started many years before.

In his book, Darwin used the term *evolution* only on the last page. Today, biologists use the term **evolution** to define cumulative changes in groups of organisms through time. Natural selection is not synonymous with evolution; it is a mechanism by which evolution occurs.

VOCABULARY

WORD ORIGIN

Evolve
comes from the Latin word *evolvere*, meaning *unroll* or *unfold*

REVIEW IT! Darwin's Theory of Evolution by Natural Selection

Section Summary

- Darwin drew from his observations on the HMS *Beagle* and later studies to develop his theory of evolution by natural selection.
- Natural selection is based on ideas of variation, inheritance, excess reproduction, and advantages of certain traits in certain environments.
- Darwin reasoned that the process of natural selection eventually could result in the appearance of new species.

Self Check

Understand Main Ideas

1. MAINIDEA **Describe** the evidence Charles Darwin gathered that led to his theory of evolution.
2. **Explain** how the idea of artificial selection contributed to Darwin's ideas on natural selection.
3. **Identify** the four principles of natural selection and provide examples not used in this section.
4. **Discuss** Wallace's contribution to the theory of evolution by natural selection.

Think Critically

5. **Infer** the consequences for evolution if species did not vary.

WRITING IN Biology

6. Write a short story about what it might have been like to visit the Galápagos Islands with Darwin.

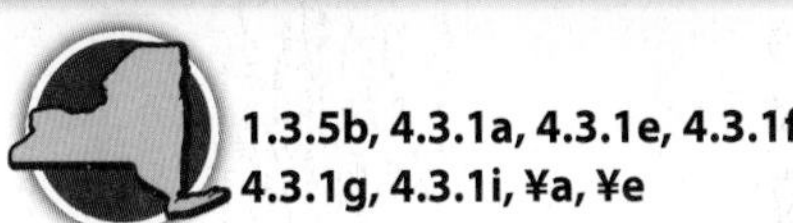 Science Notebook

2 Evidence of Evolution

1.3.5b, 4.3.1a, 4.3.1e, 4.3.1f, 4.3.1g, 4.3.1i, ¥a, ¥e

MAIN IDEA
Multiple lines of evidence support the theory of evolution.

Essential Questions

- How do fossils provide evidence of evolution?
- How does morphology provide evidence of evolution?
- How does biochemistry provide evidence of evolution?

BIOLOGY 4U

The evidence for evolution is like a set of building blocks. Just as you cannot build something with only one building block, one piece of evidence does not make a theory. The evidence for evolution is more convincing when it is supported by many pieces of evidence, just as a structure is more sturdy when it is built with many blocks.

Review Vocabulary

fossil: remains of an organism or its activities

New Vocabulary

derived trait
ancestral trait
homologous structure
vestigial structure
analogous structure
embryo
biogeography
fitness
camouflage
mimicry

Multilingual eGlossary

Support for Evolution

Darwin's book *On the Origin of Species* demonstrated how evolution might happen. The book also provided evidence that evolution has occurred on our planet. The concepts of natural selection and evolution are different, though related. Darwin's theory of evolution by natural selection is part of the larger theory of evolution. Recall that a theory provides an explanation for a natural phenomenon based on observations. Theories explain available data and suggest further areas for experimentation. The theory of evolution states that all organisms on Earth have descended from a common ancestor.

The fossil record Fossils provide a record of species that lived long ago, and they supply some of the most significant evidence of evolutionary change. This record can show how ancient species are similar to current species, as illustrated in **Figure 4.** Fossils also show that some species, such as the horseshoe crab, have remained unchanged for millions of years. The fossil record is an important source of information for determining the ancestry of organisms and patterns of evolution.

■ **Figure 4** The giant armadillo-like glyptodont, *Glyptodon,* is an extinct animal that Darwin thought must have been related to living armadillos.
Observe ***What features of the 2000-kg glyptodont are similar to those of the 4-kg armadillo?***

Glyptodont

Armadillo

(r)John and Karen Hollingsworth/USFWS

■ **Figure 5** This artist's rendering of *Archaeopteryx* shows that it shares many features with modern birds while retaining ancestral dinosaur features.

Connection to Earth Science Although Darwin recognized the limitations of the fossil record, he predicted the existence of fossils intermediate in form between species. Today, scientists studying evolutionary relationships have found hundreds of thousands of transitional fossils that contain features shared by different species. For example, certain dinosaur fossils show feathers of modern birds and teeth and bony tails of reptiles. **Figure 5** shows an artist's rendering of *Archaeopteryx,* one of the first birds. *Archaeopteryx* fossils provide evidence of characteristics that classify it as a bird, and also show that the bird retained several distinct dinosaur features.

Researchers consider two major classes of traits when studying transitional fossils: derived traits and ancestral traits. **Derived traits** are newly evolved features, such as feathers, that do not appear in the fossils of common ancestors. **Ancestral traits,** on the other hand, are more primitive features, such as teeth and tails, that do appear in ancestral forms. Transitional fossils provide detailed patterns of evolutionary change for the ancestors of many modern animals, including mollusks, horses, whales, and humans.

VOCABULARY

WORD ORIGIN

Homologous

comes from the Greek words *homos,* meaning *same,* and *logos,* meaning *relation* or *reasoning*

Comparative anatomy

Why do the vertebrate forelimbs shown in **Figure 6** have different functions but appear to be constructed of similar bones in similar ways? Evolutionary theory suggests that the answer lies in shared ancestry.

Homologous structures Anatomically similar structures inherited from a common ancestor are called **homologous structures.** Evolution predicts that an organism's body parts are more likely to be modifications of ancestral body parts than they are to be entirely new features. The limbs illustrated in **Figure 6** move animals in different ways, yet they share similar construction. Bird wings and reptile limbs are another example. Although birds use their wings to fly and reptiles use their limbs to walk, bird wings and reptile forelimbs are similar in shape and construction, which indicates that they were inherited from a common ancestor. While homologous structures alone are not evidence of evolution, they are an example for which evolution is the best available explanation for the biological data.

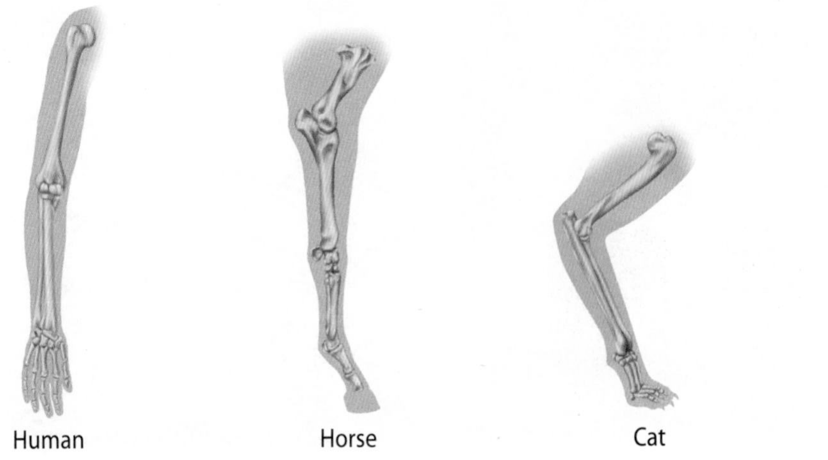

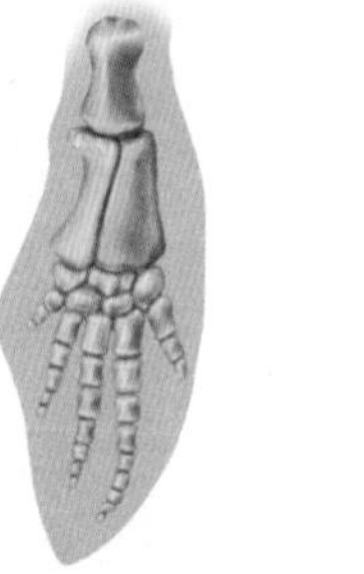

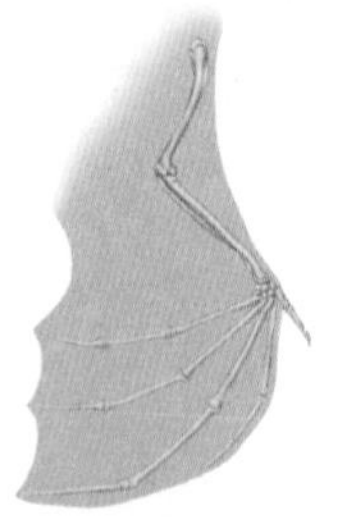

■ **Figure 6** The forelimbs of vertebrates illustrate homologous structures. Each limb is adapted for different uses, but they all have similar bones.

Infer ***which of the forelimbs shown would most likely resemble a whale's pectoral fin.***

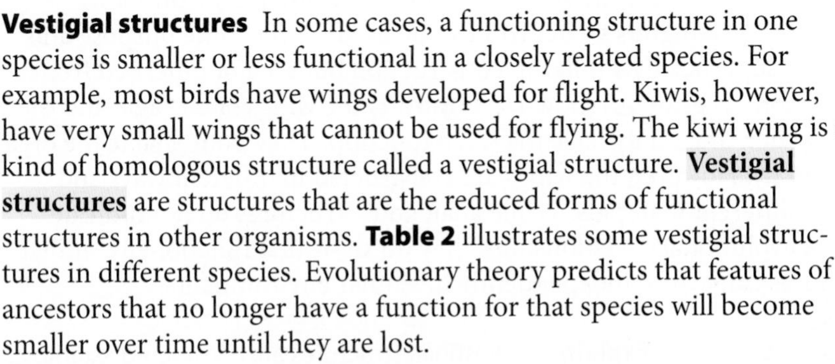

Vestigial structures In some cases, a functioning structure in one species is smaller or less functional in a closely related species. For example, most birds have wings developed for flight. Kiwis, however, have very small wings that cannot be used for flying. The kiwi wing is a kind of homologous structure called a vestigial structure. **Vestigial structures** are structures that are the reduced forms of functional structures in other organisms. **Table 2** illustrates some vestigial structures in different species. Evolutionary theory predicts that features of ancestors that no longer have a function for that species will become smaller over time until they are lost.

Table 2 Vestigial Structures — Interactive Table

Trait	Example	Description
Snake pelvis	Ribs; Pelvic bone; Femur; Hind limb claw; Vertebrae	The pelvis is the attachment point for legs and is therefore nonfunctional in an animal without legs.
Kiwi wings		The wings of kiwis are too small to be of any use in flight.
Human appendix	Appendix	This is a 5- to 15-cm-long structure that is important for digestion in many mammals, but is of limited use in humans and some apes.

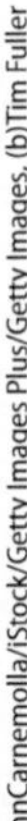

Bald eagle

Flame Skimmer

■ **Figure 7** Eagles and beetles use their wings to fly, but their wing structures are different.

Explain ***how scientists know that the wings of eagles and beetles are analogous structures.***

Not all anatomically similar features are evidence of common ancestry. **Analogous structures** can be used for the same purpose and can be superficially similar in construction but are not inherited from a common ancestor. As shown in **Figure 7,** the wings of an eagle and the wings of a dragon fly have the same function. They both enable the organism to fly. However, the wings are constructed in different ways and from different materials. While analogous structures do not indicate close evolutionary relationships, they do show that functionally similar features can evolve independently in similar environments.

GET IT? **Explain** why vestigial structures are considered examples of homologous structures.

Comparative embryology Vertebrate embryos provide more glimpses into evolutionary relationships. An **embryo** is an early, pre-birth stage of an organism's development. Scientists have found that vertebrate embryos exhibit homologous structures during certain phases of development but become totally different structures in the adult forms. The embryos shown in **Figure 8,** like all vertebrate embryos, have a tail and paired structures called pharyngeal pouches. In fish, the pouches develop into gills. In reptiles, birds, and mammals, these structures become parts of the ears, jaws, and throats. Although the adult forms differ, the shared features in the embryos suggest that vertebrates evolved from a shared ancestor.

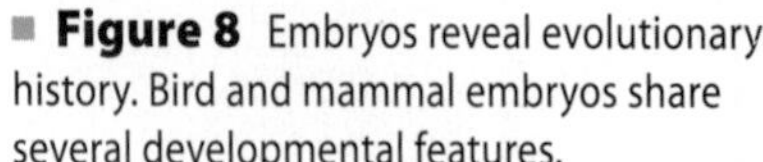

■ **Figure 8** Embryos reveal evolutionary history. Bird and mammal embryos share several developmental features.

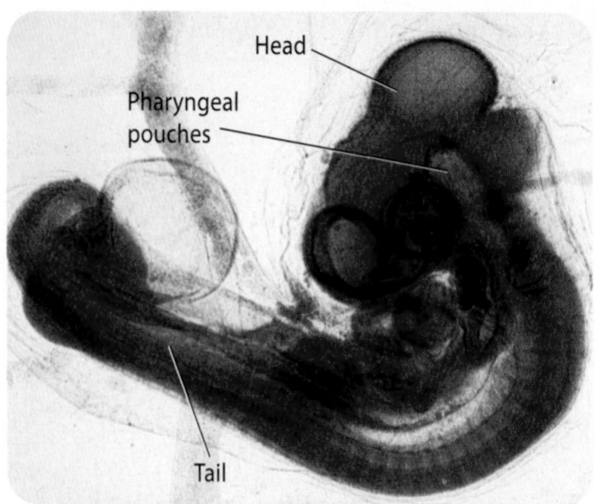

Bird embryo

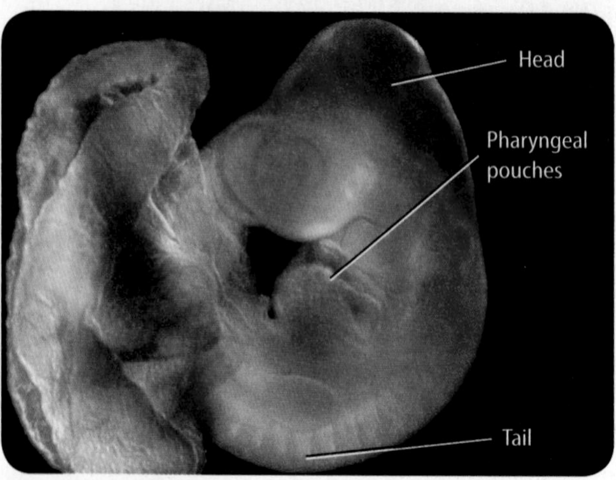

Mammal embryo

(tl)Alan & Sandy Carey/Getty Images, (tr)USFWS Photo by Cyndi Souza, (bl)Biophoto Associates/Science Source, (br)©Clouds Hill Imaging Ltd./Corbis

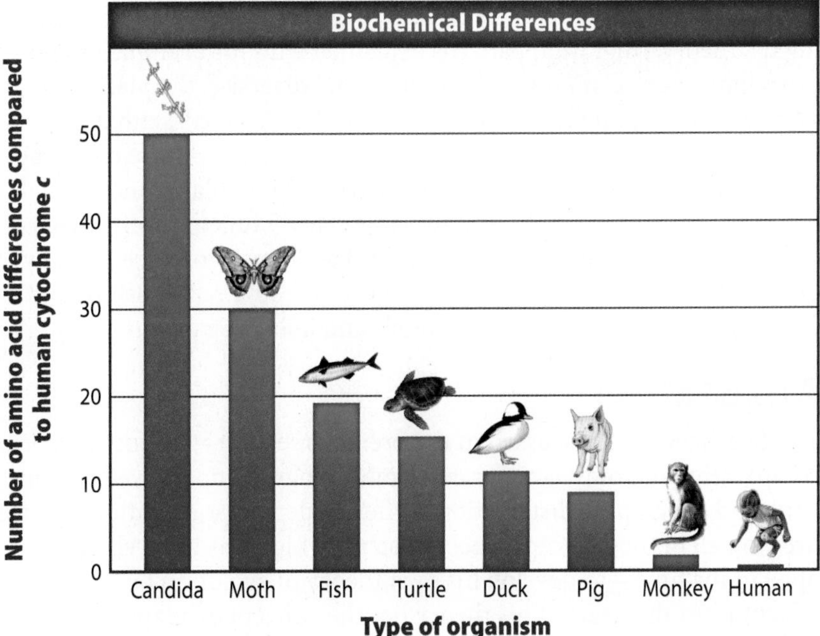

Figure 9 This illustration compares amino acid sequences of cytochrome *c* in humans and other organisms.

Infer ***Would the cytochrome c of a reptile or a bird be expected to have more amino acid differences when compared with that of a human? Explain.***

Comparative biochemistry Scientific data also show that common ancestry can be seen in the complex metabolic molecules that many different organisms share. Cytochrome *c* is an enzyme that is essential for respiration and is highly conserved in animals. This means that despite slight variations in its amino acid sequence, the molecule has changed very little over time.

Evolutionary theory predicts that molecules in species with a recent common ancestor should share certain ancient amino acid sequences. The more closely related the species are, the greater the number of sequences that will be shared. This predicted pattern is what scientists find to be true in cytochrome *c*. For example, as illustrated in **Figure 9,** the cytochrome *c* in the pig and in the monkey share more amino acid sequences with humans than the cytochrome *c* in the duck shares with humans.

Connection to Chemistry Scientists have found similar biochemical patterns in other proteins, as well as in DNA and RNA. DNA and RNA form the molecular basis of heredity in all living organisms. The fact that many organisms have the same complex molecules suggests that these molecules evolved early in the history of life and were passed on through the life-forms that have lived on Earth. Comparisons of the similarities in these molecules across species reflect evolutionary patterns seen in comparative anatomy and in the fossil record. Organisms with closely related morphological features have more closely related molecular features.

Geographic distribution The distribution of plants and animals that Darwin saw during his South American travels first suggested evolution to Darwin. He observed that animals on the South American mainland were more similar to other South American animals than they were to animals living in similar environments in Europe. The South American mara, for example, inhabited a niche that was occupied by the English rabbit. You can compare a mara and an English rabbit in **Figure 10.** Darwin realized that the mara was more similar to other South American species than it was to the English rabbit because it shared a closer ancestor with the South American animals.

Figure 10 The mara *(Dolichotis patagonum)* exists in a niche similar to that of the English rabbit *(Oryctolagus cuniculus).*

Mara

English rabbit

Patterns of migration were critical to Darwin when he was developing his theory. Migration patterns explained why, for example, islands often have more plant diversity than animal diversity: the plants are more able to migrate from the closest mainland as seeds, either by wind or on the backs of birds. Since Darwin's time, scientists have confirmed and expanded Darwin's study of the distribution of plants and animals around the world in a field of study now called **biogeography.** Evolution is intimately linked with climate and geological forces, especially plate tectonics, which helps explain many ancestral relationships and geographic distributions seen in fossils and living organisms today.

Adaptation

The five categories discussed in the previous section—the fossil record, comparative anatomy, comparative embryology, comparative biochemistry, and geographic distribution—offer evidence for evolution. Darwin drew on all of these except biochemistry—which was not well developed in his time—to develop his own theory of evolution by natural selection. At the heart of his theory lies the concept of adaptation.

Types of adaptation An adaptation is a trait shaped by natural selection that increases an organism's reproductive success. One way to determine how effectively a trait contributes to reproductive success is to measure fitness. **Fitness** is a measure of the relative contribution that an individual trait makes to the next generation. It often is measured as the number of reproductively viable offspring that an organism produces in the next generation.

VOCABULARY

SCIENCE USAGE V. COMMON USAGE

Adaptation

Science usage: a trait shaped by natural selection to increase the survival or reproductive success of an organism
The prehensile tail of monkeys is an adaptation for life in trees.

Common usage: adjustment or change
The movie script is an adaptation of the original play.

The better an organism is adapted to its environment, the greater its chances of survival and reproductive success. This concept explains the variations Darwin observed in the finches' beaks on the Galápagos Islands. Because the environments differed on each island, different beak characteristics were selected for.

Camouflage Some species have evolved morphological adaptations that allow them to blend in with their environments. This is called **camouflage** (KA muh flahj). Camouflage allows organisms to become almost invisible to predators, as shown in **Figure 11.** As a result, more of the camouflaged individuals survive and reproduce.

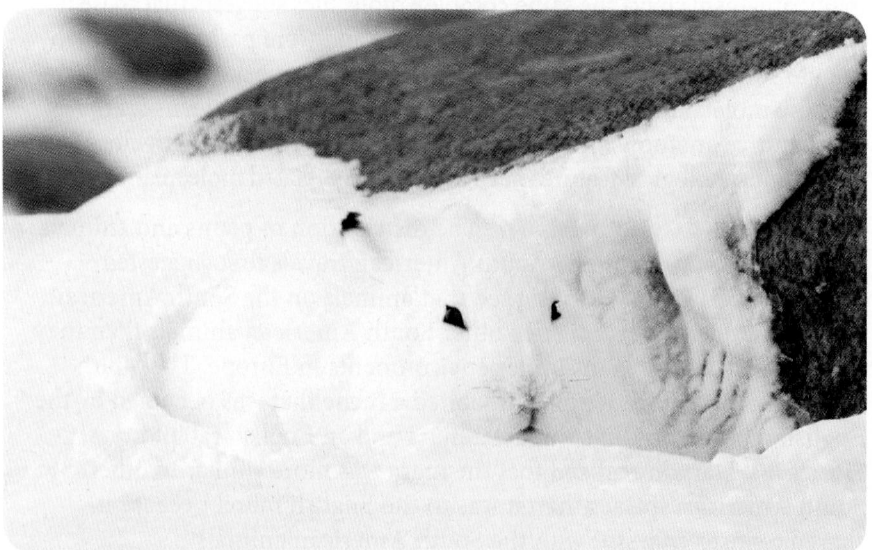

VisualCommunications/Getty Images

■ **Figure 11** It would be easy for a predator to overlook a white Arctic Hare, *Lepus arcticus*, in the winter snow because of the animal's effective camouflage.

California kingsnake

Eastern coral snake

■ **Figure 12** Predators avoid the harmless California kingsnake because it has color patterns similar to those of the poisonous eastern coral snake.

Mimicry Another type of morphological adaptation is mimicry. In **mimicry,** one species evolves to resemble another species. You might expect that mimicry would make it difficult for individuals in one species to find and breed with other members of their species, thus decreasing reproductive success. However, mimicry often increases an organism's fitness. Mimicry can occur in a harmless species that has evolved to resemble a harmful species, such as the example shown in **Figure 12.** Sometimes mimicry benefits two harmful species. In both cases, the mimics are protected because predators can't always tell the mimic from the animal that it is mimicking, so they learn to avoid them both.

GET IT? **Compare** mimicry and camouflage.

Antimicrobial resistance Species of bacteria that originally were killed by penicillin and other antibiotics have developed drug resistance. For almost every antibiotic, at least one species of resistant bacteria exists. One unintended consequence of the continued development of antibiotics is that some diseases, which were once thought to be contained, such as tuberculosis, have re-emerged in more harmful forms.

MiniLAB 1

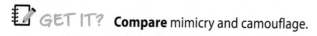

Investigate Mimicry

Why do some species mimic the features of other species? Mimicry is the process of natural selection that shapes one species of organism to look similar to another species. Natural selection has shaped the nontoxic viceroy butterfly to look like the toxic monarch butterfly. Investigate the mimicry displayed during this lab.

Procedure

1. Read and complete the lab safety form.
2. Create a data table for recording your observations and measurements of the **monarch** and **viceroy butterflies.**
3. Observe the physical characteristics of both butterfly species and record your observations in your data table.

Analysis

1. **Compare and contrast** the physical characteristics of the two butterfly species.
2. **Hypothesize** why the viceroy butterflies have bright colors that are highly visible.

(l)Design Pics/Jack Goldfarb, (r)©Jason Ondreicka/Alamy

■ **Figure 13** Spaces between arches set in a square to support a dome are called spandrels and are often decorative. Some features in organisms might be like spandrels, a consequence of another adaptation.

Consequences of adaptations Not all features of an organism are necessarily adaptive. Some features might be consequences of other evolved characteristics. Biologists Stephen Jay Gould and Richard Lewontin made this point in 1979 in a paper claiming that biologists tended to overemphasize the importance of adaptations in evolution.

Spandrel example To illustrate this concept, they used an example from architecture. Building a set of four arches in a square to support a dome means that spaces called spandrels will appear between the arches, as illustrated in **Figure 13.** Because spandrels are often decorative, one might think that spandrels exist for decoration. In reality, they are an unavoidable consequence of arch construction. Gould and Lewontin argued that some features in organisms are like spandrels because even though they are prominent, they do not increase reproductive success. Instead, they likely arose as an unavoidable consequence of prior evolutionary change.

Human example A biological example of a spandrel is the helplessness of human babies. Humans give birth at a much earlier developmental stage than other primates do. This causes them to need increased care early in their lives. Many scientists think that the helplessness of human babies is a consequence of the evolution of big brains and upright posture. To walk upright, humans need narrow pelvises, which means that babies' heads must be small enough to fit through the pelvic opening at birth. In contrast, scientists previously thought that the helplessness of human infants provided an adaptive advantage, such as increased attention from parents and more learning.

REVIEW IT! Evidence of Evolution

Section Summary

- Fossils provide strong direct evidence to support evolution.
- Homologous and vestigial structures indicate shared ancestry.
- Examples of embryological and biochemical traits provide insight into the evolution of species.
- Biogeography can explain why certain species live in certain locations.
- Natural selection gives rise to features that increase reproductive success.

Self Check

Understand Main Ideas

1. MAINIDEA **Analyze and evaluate** how the fossil record provides evidence of common ancestry.
2. **Explain** what natural selection predicts about mimicry, camouflage, homologous structures, and vestigial structures.
3. **Indicate** how biogeography provides evidence of common ancestry.
4. **Analyze and evaluate** the morphological, biochemical, and developmental evidence supporting evolution.

Think Critically

5. **Hypothesize** Evidence suggests that the bones in bird wings share a number of features with the bones of dinosaur arms. Based on this evidence, what hypothesis could you make about the evolutionary relationship between birds and dinosaurs?
6. **Apply** Research has shown that if a prescribed dose of an antibiotic is not taken completely, some bacteria might not be killed and the disease might return. How does natural selection explain this phenomenon?

Steve Raymer/National Geographic Stock

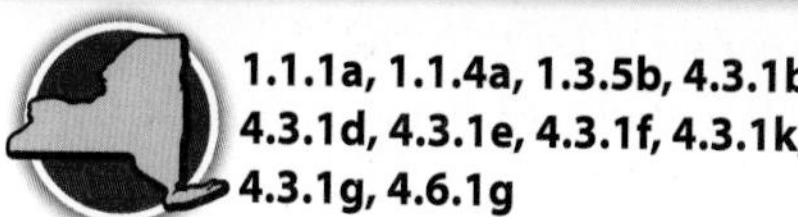

3 Shaping Evolutionary Theory

1.1.1a, 1.1.4a, 1.3.5b, 4.3.1b, 4.3.1d, 4.3.1e, 4.3.1f, 4.3.1k, 4.3.1g, 4.6.1g

MAIN IDEA

The theory of evolution continues to be refined as scientists learn new information.

Essential Questions

- What are the conditions of the Hardy-Weinberg principle?
- What patterns can be observed in evolution?
- What factors influence speciation?

BIOLOGY 4U

The longer you operate a complicated piece of electronics, the better you understand how it works. The device does not change, but you become more familiar with its functions. Scientists have been studying evolution for almost 150 years, yet they are still learning new ways in which evolution leads to changes in species.

Review Vocabulary

allele: alternate forms of a character trait that can be inherited

New Vocabulary

Hardy-Weinberg principle
genetic drift
founder effect
bottleneck
stabilizing selection
directional selection
disruptive selection
sexual selection
prezygotic isolating mechanism
postzygotic isolating mechanism
allopatric speciation
sympatric speciation
adaptive radiation
gradualism
punctuated equilibrium

Multilingual eGlossary

Mechanisms of Evolution

Natural selection remains a central theme in evolution. It explains how organisms adapt to their environments and how variations can give rise to adaptations within species. Scientists now know that natural selection is not the only mechanism of evolution. Studies in population genetics and molecular biology led to the development of evolutionary theory. At the center is the understanding that evolution occurs at the population level, with genes as the raw material.

Population genetics At the turn of the twentieth century, genes had not been discovered. However, the allele was understood to be one form of an inherited character trait, such as eye color, that gets passed down from parent to offspring. Scientists did not understand why dominant alleles would not simply overpower recessive alleles in a population.

In 1908, English mathematician Godfrey Hardy and German physician Wilhelm Weinberg independently came up with the same solution to this problem. They showed mathematically that evolution will not occur in a population unless allelic frequencies are acted upon by forces that cause change. In the absence of these forces, the allelic frequency remains the same and evolution doesn't occur. According to this idea, which is now known as the **Hardy-Weinberg principle,** when allelic frequencies remain constant, a population is in genetic equilibrium. This concept is illustrated in **Figure 14.**

Figure 14 According to the Hardy-Weinberg principle, even though the number of owls doubled, the ratio of gray to red owls remained the same.

CAREERS IN BIOLOGY

Biometrician Almost all scientific research papers include some statistics. Many researchers consult biometricians—people who specialize in statistics related to biology—to help design studies and analyze study results.

Connection to Math To illustrate the Hardy-Weinberg principle, consider a population of 100 humans. Forty people are homozygous dominant for earlobe attachment *(EE)*. Another 40 people are heterozygous *(Ee)*. Twenty people are homozygous recessive *(ee)*. In the 40 homozygous dominant people, there are 80 *E* alleles (2 *E* alleles × 40); and in the 20 homozygous recessive people, there are 40 *e* alleles (2 *e* alleles × 20). The heterozygous people have 40 *E* alleles and 40 *e* alleles. Summing the alleles, we have 120 *E* alleles and 80 *e* alleles for a total of 200 alleles. The *E* allele frequency is 120/200, or 0.6. The *e* allele frequency is 80/200, or 0.4.

The Hardy-Weinberg principle states that the allele frequencies in populations should be constant. This often is expressed as $p + q = 1$. For our example, p can represent the E allele frequency and q can represent the *e* allele frequency.

Squaring both sides of the equation yields the new equation $p^2 + 2pq + q^2 = 1$. This equation allows us to determine the equilibrium frequency of each genotype in the population: homozygous dominant (p^2), heterozygous ($2pq$), and homozygous recessive (q^2). From the above example, $p = 0.6$, and $q = 0.4$, so $(0.6)(0.6) + 2(0.6)(0.4) + (0.4)(0.4) = 1$. In the example population, the equilibrium frequency for homozygous dominant will be 0.36, the equilibrium frequency of heterozygous will be 0.48, and the equilibrium frequency of homozygous recessive will be 0.16. Note that the sum of these frequencies equals one.

GET IT? **Determine** when a population is in equilibrium.

Conditions According to the Hardy-Weinberg principle, a population in genetic equilibrium must meet five conditions: there must be no genetic drift, no gene flow, no mutation, mating must be random, and there must be no natural selection. Populations in nature might meet some of these requirements, but hardly any population meets all five conditions for long periods of time. If a population is not in genetic equilibrium, at least one of the five conditions has been violated. These five conditions, listed in **Table 3,** are known mechanisms of evolutionary change.

Table 3 The Hardy-Weinberg Principle

Interactive Table

Condition	Violation	Consequence
The population is very large.	Many populations are small.	Chance events can lead to changes in population traits.
There is no immigration or emigration.	Organisms move in and out of the population.	The population can lose or gain traits with movement of organisms.
Mating is random.	Mating is not random.	New traits do not pass as quickly to the rest of the population.
Mutations do not occur.	Mutations occur.	New variations appear in the population with each new generation.
Natural selection does not occur.	Natural selection occurs.	Traits in a population change from one generation to the next.

Genetic drift Any change in the allelic frequencies in a population that results from chance is called **genetic drift.** Recall that for simple traits, only one of a parent's two alleles passes to the offspring, and that this allele is selected randomly through independent assortment. In large populations, enough alleles "drift" to ensure that the allelic frequency of the entire population remains relatively constant from one generation to the next. In smaller populations, however, the effects of genetic drift become more pronounced, and the chance of losing an allele becomes greater.

Founder effect The founder effect is an extreme example of genetic drift. The **founder effect** can occur when a small sample of a population settles in a location separated from the rest of the population. Because this sample is a random subset of the original population, the sample population carries a random subset of the population's genes. Alleles that were uncommon in the original population might be common in the new population, and the offspring in the new population will carry those alleles. Such an event can result in large genetic variations in the separated populations.

The founder effect is evident in the Amish and Mennonite communities in the United States, in which the people rarely marry outside their own communities. The Old Order Amish have a high frequency of six-finger dwarfism. All affected individuals can trace their ancestry back to one of the founders of the Order.

STUDY TIP

CONCEPT MAP Make a concept map, placing the term *evolution* in the top oval. The second row of ovals should contain the following terms: *genetic drift, gene flow, nonrandom mating, mutation,* and *natural selection.* As you read the chapter, fill in definitions and write examples that illustrate each term.

Bottleneck Another extreme example of genetic drift is a **bottleneck,** which occurs when a population declines to a very low number and then rebounds. The gene pool of the rebound population often is genetically similar to that of the population at its lowest level, that is, it has reduced diversity. Researchers think that cheetahs in Africa experienced a bottleneck 10,000 years ago, and then another one about 100 years ago. Throughout their current range, shown in **Figure 15,** cheetahs are so genetically similar that they appear inbred. Inbreeding decreases fertility, and might be a factor in the potential extinction of this endangered species.

GET IT? **Explain** how genetic drift affects populations.

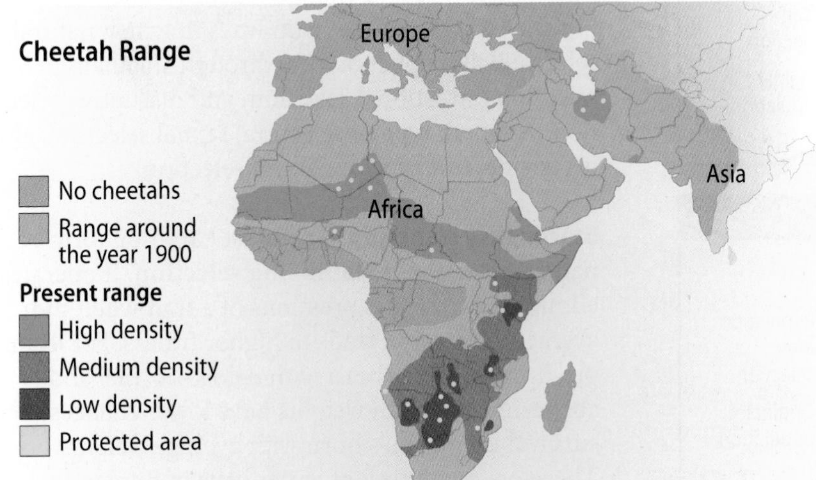

Figure 15 The map shows the present range of cheetahs in Africa. It is believed that cheetahs had a much larger population until a bottleneck occurred.

Apply Concepts ***What effect has the bottleneck had on the reproductive rate of cheetahs?***

Gene flow A population in genetic equilibrium experiences no gene flow. It is a closed system, with no new genes entering the population and no genes leaving the population. In reality, few populations are isolated. The random movement of individuals between populations, or migration, increases genetic variation within a population and reduces differences between populations.

Nonrandom mating Rarely is mating completely random in a population. Usually, organisms mate with individuals in close proximity. This promotes inbreeding and could lead to a change in allelic proportions favoring individuals that are homozygous for particular traits.

Mutation Recall that a mutation is a random change in genetic material. The cumulative effect of mutations in a population might cause a change in allelic frequencies and thus violate genetic equilibrium. Although many mutations cause harm or are lethal, occasionally a mutation provides an advantage to an organism. This mutation will then be selected for and become more common in subsequent generations. In this way, mutations provide the raw material upon which natural selection works.

GET IT? **Summarize** how mutation violates the Hardy-Weinberg principle.

Natural selection The Hardy-Weinberg principle requires that all individuals in a population be equally adapted to their environment and thus contribute equally to the next generation. As you have learned, this rarely happens. Natural selection acts to select the individuals that are best adapted for survival and reproduction. Natural selection acts on an organism's phenotype and changes allelic frequencies. **Figure 16** shows three main ways in which natural selection alters phenotypes: through stabilizing selection, directional selection, and disruptive selection. A fourth type of selection, sexual selection, also is considered a type of natural selection.

Stabilizing selection The most common form of natural selection is **stabilizing selection.** It operates to eliminate extreme expressions of a trait when the average expression leads to higher fitness. For example, human babies born with below-normal and above-normal birth weights have lower chances of survival than babies born with average weights. Therefore, birth weight varies little in human populations.

Personal Tutor

Figure 16 Natural selection can alter allele frequencies of a population in three ways. The bell-shaped curve shown as a dotted line in each graph indicates the trait's original variation in a population. The solid line indicates the outcome of each type of selection pressure.

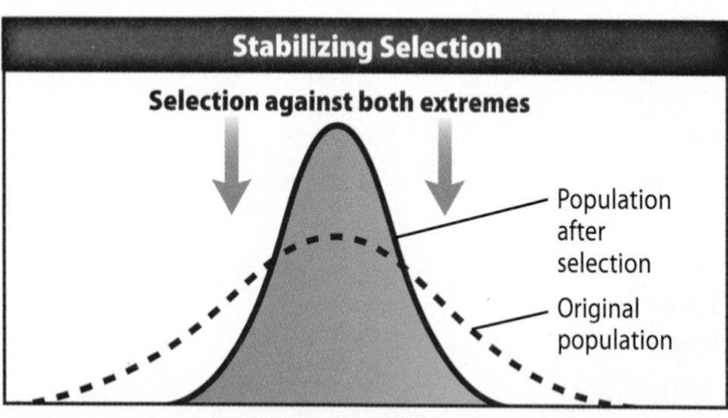

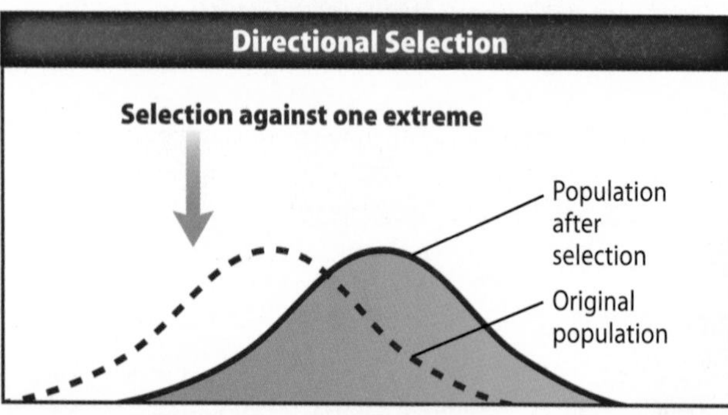

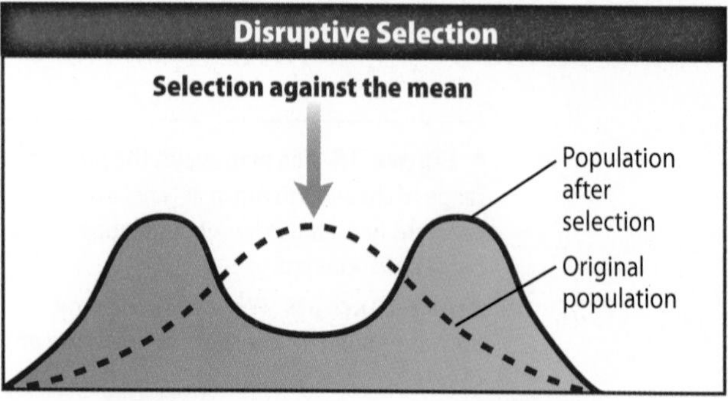

Directional selection If an extreme version of a trait makes an organism more fit, **directional selection** might occur. This form of selection increases the expression of the extreme versions of a trait in a population. One example is the evolution of moths in industrial England. The peppered moth has two color forms, or morphs, as shown in **Figure 17.** Until the mid-1850s, nearly all peppered moths in England had light-colored bodies and wings. Beginning around 1850, however, dark moths began appearing. By the early 1900s, nearly all peppered moths were dark. Why? Industrial pollution favored the dark-colored moths at the expense of the light-colored moths. The darker the moth, the more it matched the sooty background of its tree habitat, and the harder it was for predators to see. Thus, more dark moths survived, adding more genes for dark color to the population. This conclusion was reinforced in the mid-1900s, when the passage of air pollution laws led to the resurgence of light-colored moths. This phenomenon is called industrial melanism.

Directional selection also can be seen in Galápagos finches. For three decades in the latter part of the twentieth century, Peter and Rosemary Grant studied populations of these finches. The Grants found that during drought years, food supplies dwindled and the birds had to eat the hard seeds that they normally ignored. Birds with the largest beaks were more successful in cracking the tough seed coatings than were birds with smaller beaks. As a result, over the duration of the drought, birds with larger beaks came to dominate the population. In rainy years, however, the directional trend was reversed, and the population's average beak size decreased.

■ **Figure 17** The peppered moth exists in two forms: light-colored and dark-colored.
Infer ***how natural selection might have caused a change in the frequencies of the two forms.***

Data Analysis LAB 2

Based on Real Data*

Interpret the Graph

How does pollution affect melanism in moths? The changing frequencies of light-colored and dark-colored moths have been studied for decades in the United States. The percentage of the melanic, or dark, form of the moth was low prior to the Industrial Revolution. It increased until it made up nearly the entire population in the early 1900s. After antipollution laws were passed, the percentage of melanic moths declined, as shown in the graph.

Think Critically

1. **Interpret** the percent decrease in Pennsylvania melanic moth population.
2. **Hypothesize** why the percentage of melanic moths might have remained at a relatively low level in Virginia.

Data and Observations

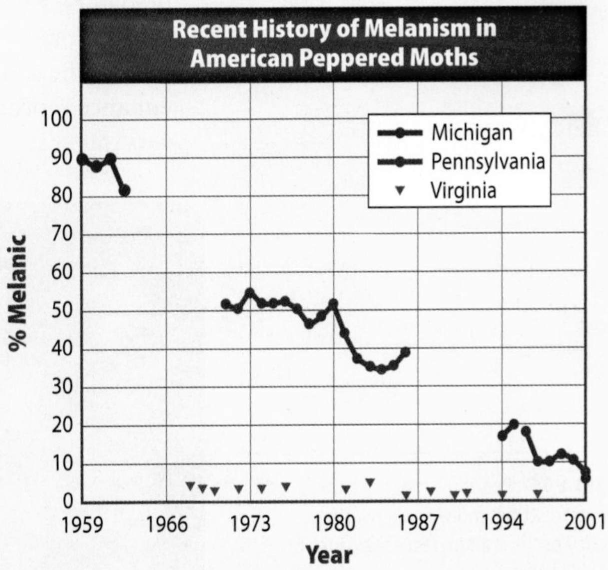

*Data obtained from: Grant, B. S. and L. L. Wiseman. 2002. Recent history of melanism in American peppered moths. *Journal of Heredity* 93: 86–90.

■ **Figure 18** Northern water snakes have two different color patterns, depending on their habitats. Intermediate color patterns would make them more visible to predators.

Disruptive selection Another type of natural selection, **disruptive selection,** is a process that splits a population into two groups. It tends to remove individuals with average traits but retain individuals expressing extreme traits at both ends of a continuum. Northern water snakes, illustrated in **Figure 18,** are an example. Snakes living on the mainland shores inhabit grasslands and have mottled brown skin. Snakes inhabiting rocky island shores have gray skin. Each is adapted to its particular environment. A snake with intermediate coloring would be disadvantaged because it would be more visible to predators.

Launch Lab

Review Based on what you have learned about adaptation, how would you now answer the analysis questions?

Sexual selection Another type of natural selection, in which change in frequency of a trait is based on the ability to attract a mate is called **sexual selection.** This type of selection often operates in populations in which males and females differ significantly in appearance. Usually in these populations, males are the largest and most colorful of the group. The bigger the tail of a male peacock, as shown in **Figure 19,** the more attractive the bird is to females. Males also evolve threatening characteristics that intimidate other males; this is common in species, such as elk and deer, where the male keeps a harem of females.

Darwin wondered why some qualities of sexual attractiveness appeared to be the opposite of qualities that might enhance survival. For example, the peacock's tail, while attracting females, is large and cumbersome, and it might make the peacock a more likely target for predators. Although some modern scientists think that sexual selection is not a form of natural selection, others think that sexual selection follows the same general principle: brighter colors and bigger bodies enhance reproductive success, whatever the chances are for long-term survival.

■ **Figure 19** Peacocks that have the largest tails tend to attract more peahens. The frequency of this trait increases because of sexual selection.

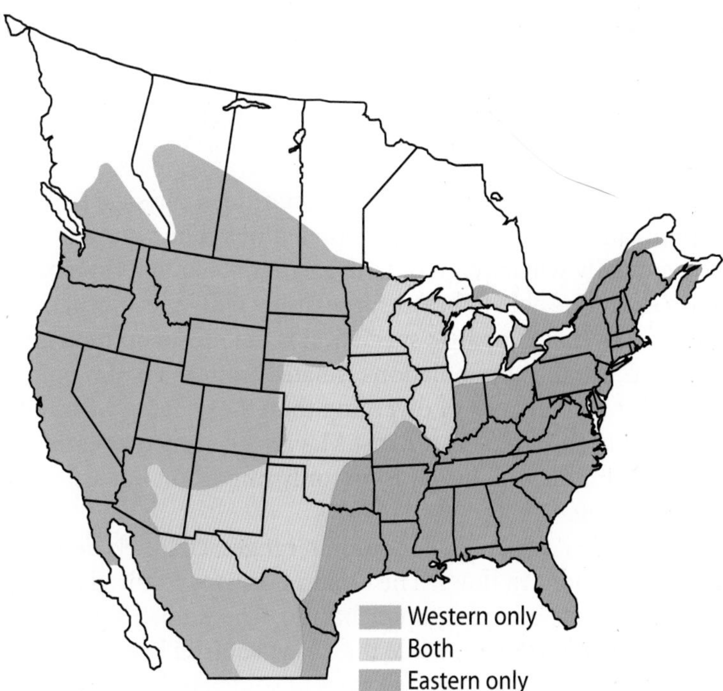

■ **Figure 20** The map shows the overlapping ranges of the Eastern meadowlark and Western meadowlark. While the two are similar in appearance, their songs separate them behaviorally.

Infer ***how different songs prevent the meadowlarks from breeding.***

Reproductive Isolation

Mechanisms of evolution—genetic drift, gene flow, nonrandom mating, mutation, and natural selection—violate the Hardy-Weinberg principle. To what extent each mechanism contributes to the origin of new species is a major topic of debate in evolutionary science today. Most scientists define speciation as the process whereby some members of a sexually reproducing population change so much that they can no longer produce fertile offspring with members of the original population. Two types of reproductive isolating mechanisms prevent gene flow among populations. **Prezygotic isolating mechanisms** operate before fertilization occurs. **Postzygotic isolating mechanisms** operate after fertilization has occurred to ensure that the resulting hybrid remains infertile.

Virtual Lab

Prezygotic isolation Prezygotic isolating mechanisms prevent reproduction by making fertilization unlikely. These mechanisms prevent genotypes from entering a population's gene pool through geographic, ecological, behavioral, or other differences. For example, the Eastern meadowlark and the Western meadowlark, pictured in **Figure 20,** have overlapping ranges and are similar in appearance. These two species, however, use different mating songs and do not interbreed. Time is another factor in maintaining a reproductive barrier. Closely related species of fireflies mate at different times of night, just as different species of trout live in the same stream but breed at different times of the year.

Postzygotic isolation When fertilization has occurred but a hybrid offspring cannot develop or reproduce, postzygotic isolation has occurred. Postzygotic isolating mechanisms prevent offspring survival or reproduction. A lion and a tiger are considered separate species because even though they can mate, the offspring—a tigon, shown in **Figure 21**—is sterile.

■ **Figure 21** The offspring of a male tiger and a lioness is a tigon. Tigons are sterile.

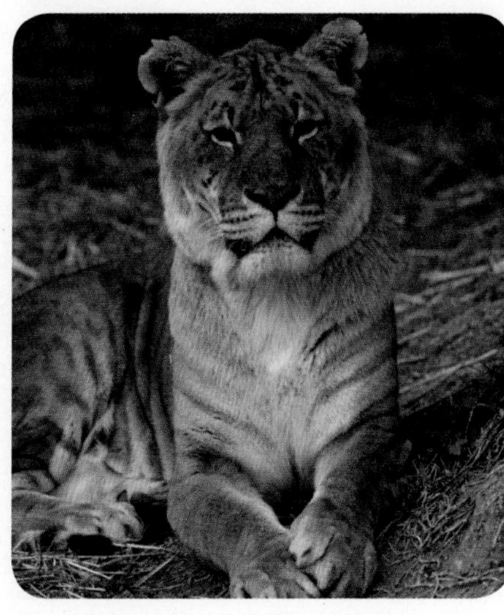

Speciation

For speciation to occur, a population must diverge and then be reproductively isolated. Biologists usually recognize two types of speciation: allopatric and sympatric.

Allopatric speciation In **allopatric speciation,** a physical barrier divides one population into two or more populations. The separate populations eventually will contain organisms that, if enough time has passed, will no longer be able to breed successfully with one another. Most scientists think that allopatric speciation is the most common form of speciation. Small subpopulations isolated from the main population have a better chance of diverging than those living within it. This was the conclusion of biologist Ernst Mayr, who argued as early as the 1940s that geographic isolation was not only important but also was required for speciation.

Geographic barriers can include mountain ranges, channels between islands, wide rivers, and lava flows. The Grand Canyon, pictured in **Figure 22,** is an example of a geographic barrier. The Kaibab squirrel is found on the canyon's north rim, while the Abert squirrel lives on the south rim. Scientists think that the two types of squirrels diverged from an ancestral species and today are reproductively isolated by the width of the canyon. While these animals officially belong to the same species, they demonstrate distinct differences and, in time, they might diverge enough to be classified as separate species.

VOCABULARY

ACADEMIC VOCABULARY

Isolation
the condition of being separated from others
After infection, a patient is kept in isolation from other patients to prevent the infection from spreading.

Sympatric speciation In **sympatric speciation,** a species evolves into a new species without a physical barrier. The ancestor species and the new species live side-by-side during the speciation process. Evidence of sympatric evolution can be seen in several insect species, including apple maggot flies, which appear to be diverging based on the type of fruit they eat. Scientists think that sympatric speciation happens fairly frequently in plants, especially through polyploidy. Recall that polyploidy is a mutation that increases a plant's chromosome number. As a result, the plant is no longer able to interbreed with the main population.

Figure 22 The Grand Canyon is a geographic barrier separating the Abert and Kaibab squirrels.

(l)Rick & Nora Bowers/Alamy, (c)Terry Moore/Stocktrek Images/Getty Images, (r)Emmanuel Rondeau/Alamy

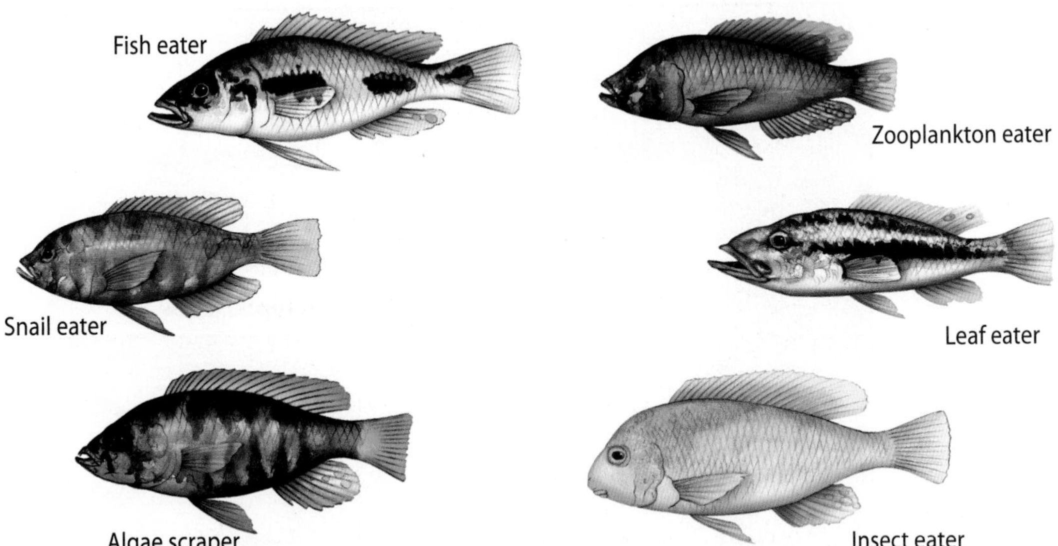

Patterns of Evolution

Many details of the speciation process remain unresolved. Relative to the human life span, speciation is a long process, and first-hand accounts of speciation are expected to be rare. However, evidence of speciation is visible in patterns of evolution.

Adaptive radiation More than 300 species of cichlid fish, six of which are illustrated in **Figure 23,** once lived in Africa's Lake Victoria. Data show that these species diverged from a single ancestor within the last 14,000 years. This is a dramatic example of a type of speciation called **adaptive radiation.** Adaptive radiation, also called divergent evolution, can occur in a relatively short time when one species gives rise to many species in response to the creation of a new habitat or another ecological opportunity. Likely, a combination of factors caused the explosive radiation of the cichlids, including the appearance of a unique double jaw, which allowed these fish to exploit various food sources. Adaptive radiation often follows large-scale extinctions. Adaptive radiation of mammals at the beginning of the Cenozoic era following the extinction of dinosaurs likely produced the diversity of mammals visible today.

■ **Figure 23** More than 300 species of cichlid fishes once lived in Lake Victoria. Their adaptive radiation is remarkable because it is thought to have occurred in less than 14,000 years.

Coevolution Many species evolve in close relationship with other species. The relationship might be so close that the evolution of one species affects the evolution of other species. This is called coevolution. Mutualism is one form of coevolution. Mutualism occurs when two species benefit each other. For example, comet orchids and the moths that pollinate them have coevolved an intimate dependency: the foot-long flowers of the orchid perfectly match the foot-long tongue of the moth, shown in **Figure 24.**

In another form of coevolution, one species can evolve a parasitic dependency on another species. This type of relationship is often called a coevolutionary arms race. The classic example is a plant and an insect pathogen that is dependent on the plant for food. The plant population evolves a chemical defense against the insect population. The insects, in turn, evolve the biochemistry to resist the defense. The plant then steps up the race by evolving new defenses, the insect escalates its response, and the race goes on. Complex coevolutionary relationships like these might reflect thousands of years of evolutionary interaction.

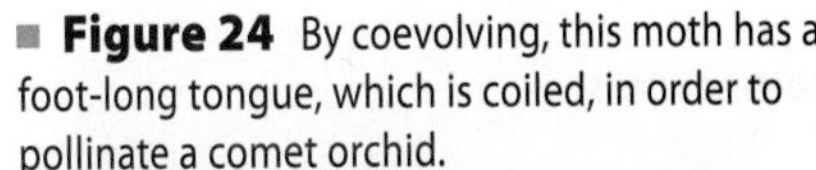
■ **Figure 24** By coevolving, this moth has a foot-long tongue, which is coiled, in order to pollinate a comet orchid.

NHPA/SuperStock

Table 4 Convergent Evolution

Interactive Table

Niche	Placental Mammals	Australian Marsupials
Burrower	Mole	Marsupial mole
Anteater	Lesser anteater	Numbat (anteater)
Mouse	Mouse	Marsupial mouse
Glider	Flying squirrel	Flying phalanger
Wolf	Wolf	Tasmanian wolf

Convergent evolution Sometimes unrelated species evolve similar traits even though they live in different parts of the world. This is called convergent evolution. Convergent evolution occurs in environments that are geographically far apart but have similar ecology and climate. The mara and rabbit discussed in Section 2 provide an example of convergent evolution. The mara and the rabbit are unrelated, but because they inhabit similar niches, they have evolved similarities in morphology, physiology, and behavior. **Table 4** shows examples of convergent evolution between Australian marsupials and the placental mammals on other continents.

Rate of speciation Evolution is a dynamic process. In some cases, as in a coevolutionary arms race, traits might change rapidly. In other cases, traits might remain unchanged for millions of years. Most scientists think that evolution proceeds in small, gradual steps. This is a theory called **gradualism.** A great deal of evidence favors this theory. However, the fossil record contains instances of abrupt transitions. For example, certain species of fossil snails looked the same for millions of years, and then the shell shape changed dramatically in only a few thousand years. The theory of **punctuated equilibrium** attempts to explain such abrupt transitions in the fossil record. According to this theory, rapid spurts of genetic change cause species to diverge quickly; these periods punctuate much longer periods when the species exhibit little change.

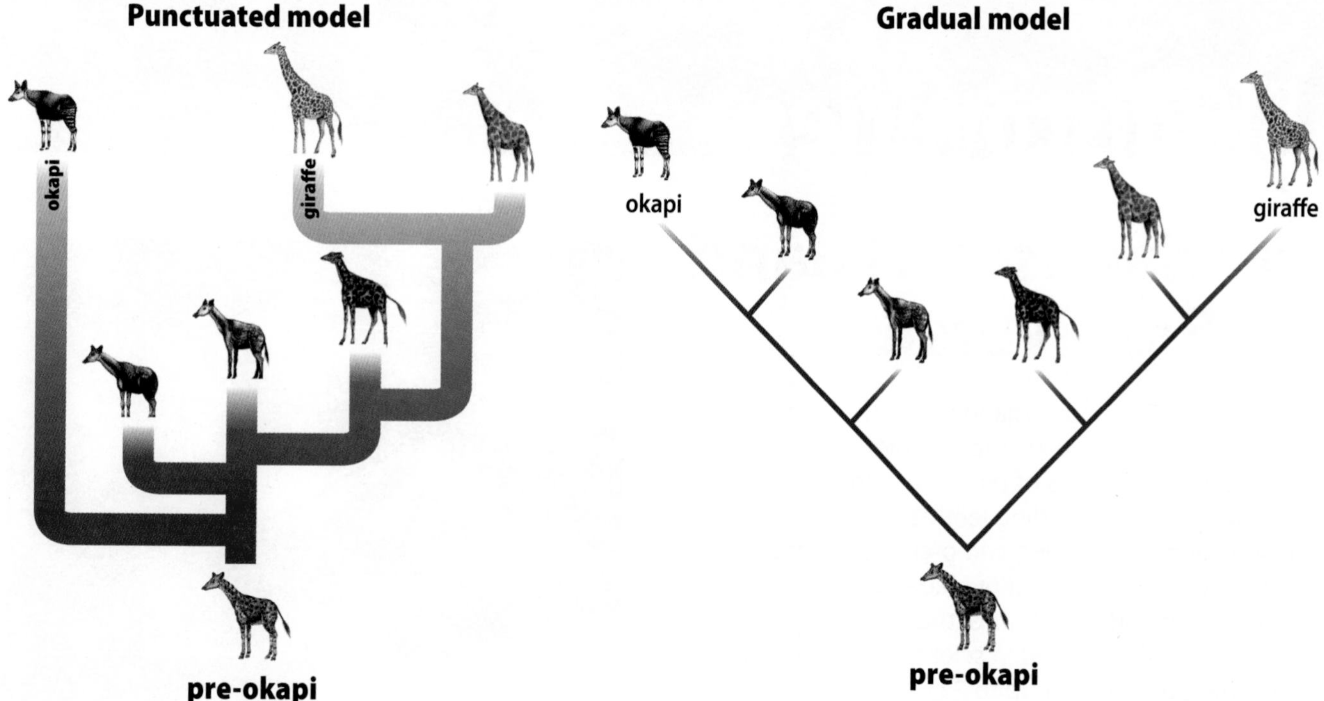

■ **Figure 25** Gradualism and punctuated equilibrium are two competing models describing the tempo of evolution.

Animation

The two theories for the tempo of evolution are illustrated in **Figure 25.** The tempo of evolution is an active area of research in evolutionary theory today. Does most evolution occur gradually or in short bursts? Fossils can show only morphological structures. Changes in internal anatomy and function go unnoticed. How, then, does one examine the past for evidence?

The question of the tempo of evolution is an excellent illustration of how science works. Solving this puzzle requires insights from a variety of disciplines using a variety of methods. Like many areas of scientific endeavor, evolution offers a complex collection of evidence, and it does not yield easily to simple analysis.

REVIEW IT! Shaping Evolutionary Theory

Section Summary

- The Hardy-Weinberg principle describes the conditions within which evolution does not occur.
- Speciation often begins in small, isolated populations.
- Selection can operate by favoring average or extreme traits.
- Punctuated equilibrium and gradualism are two models that explain the tempo of evolution.

Self Check

Understand Main Ideas

1. MAINIDEA **Describe** one new mechanism of evolution that scientists learned after Darwin's book was published.
2. **Identify** three of the conditions of the Hardy-Weinberg principle.
3. **Discuss** factors that can lead to speciation.
4. **Indicate** which pattern of evolution is shown by the many species of finches on the Galápagos Islands.

Think Critically

5. **Apply** what you have learned about gene flow, genetic drift, mutation, and recombination in order to analyze and evaluate their effects.

MATH IN ▶ Biology

6. What type of mathematical results would you expect from the experiment you designed above if the two populations diverged only recently?

BIOdiscoveries

4.3.1g

Madagascar: Island of Biodiversity

Move over, Galàpagos Islands—another island is emerging as a prime example of biodiversity. Thousands of species of rare plants and animals live on Madagascar, including lemurs, frogs, geckos, chameleons, butterflies, and orchids. Scientists estimate that 80 percent of Madagascar's plants and animals are endemic, that is, they do not live anywhere else in the world. A scientific study published in 2009 reported that up to 221 new species of frogs had been found on Madagascar, which nearly doubles the number of amphibians found on the island so far.

Giant leaf-tailed gecko One of the reptile species is the giant leaf-tailed gecko *(Uroplatus fimbriatus)*. As the name indicates, the tails of these nocturnal geckos are shaped like leaves, which helps camouflage them from predators. If a predator grabs a gecko's tail, it breaks off so the gecko can escape. The tail will grow back, but it might have a different appearance. These geckos' colorings also help them blend with their rainforest home, as they have some ability to change color to better blend with the trees.

Giant leaf-tailed geckos have other fascinating characteristics. They do not have eyelids, so they use their tongues to lick their eyeballs clean. Their toes are equipped with tiny bristles that allow them to run up smooth, vertical surfaces. And when these geckos are startled, they lift their heads and tails, open their mouths, and bark or scream.

Pygmy mouse lemur Lemurs are a group of primates that are endemic to Madagascar. There are 88 species of lemurs on the island, and the smallest is the pygmy mouse lemur *(Microcebus myoxinus)*, the tiniest primate in the world.

The giant leaf-tailed gecko (above) and the pygmy mouse lemur (right) are both species that live only on Madagascar.

The pygmy mouse lemur is just 6 centimeters long with a 13 centimeter tail. It weighs only 30 grams. These nocturnal animals live mainly in trees and eat insects and fruit. The pygmy mouse lemur has large ears that it uses to listen for predators.

New species are discovered on Madagascar every year. As larger numbers of scientists turn their attention to this island, its status as one of the most important areas of biodiversity on the planet is likely to grow.

PUBLIC SPEAKING AND SOCIAL NETWORKING

Scavenger Hunt Your teacher will divide your class into several groups, giving each group a list of five species that are endemic to Madagascar. With your group, research the species. Present your findings to the class.

WebQuest

(t)DEA/C.DANI/I.JESKE/De Agostini/Getty Images; (b)Bikeadventure

BioLAB 1.3.5b, 4.3.1i, ¥a, ¥o, ¥q

Can scientists model natural selection?

Background: Natural selection is the mechanism that Darwin proposed to explain evolution. Through natural selection, traits that allow individuals to have the most offspring in a given environment tend to increase in the population over time.

Question: *How can natural selection be modeled in a laboratory setting?*

Materials

small, medium, and large beads
forceps
short-nosed pliers
tray or pan
stopwatch

Safety Precautions

Procedure

1. Read and complete the lab safety form.
2. Divide into groups of three. One student will use forceps to represent one adult member of a predator population, one will use pliers to represent another adult member of the predator population, and the third will keep time and score.
3. Mix prey items (beads) on a tray or pan.
4. In 20 seconds, try to pick up all possible beads using forceps or pliers.
5. After 20 seconds, assign three points for each large bead, two points for each medium bead, and one point for each small bead.
6. Add up the points and use the following rules: survival requires 18 points, and the ability to produce a new offspring requires an additional 10 points.
7. Determine the number of survivors and the number of offspring.
8. Repeat the procedure 10 times and combine your data with the other groups.

Analyze and Conclude

1. **Calculate** Combining all of the trials of all of the groups, determine the percentage of forceps and pliers that survived.
2. **Evaluate** Using data from the entire class, determine the total number of offspring produced by the forceps adult and the plier adult.
3. **Summarize** The original population was divided evenly between the forceps adult and the plier adult. If all of the adults left, what would be the new population ratio? Use the results from the entire class.
4. **Infer** Given the survival and reproduction data, predict what will happen to the two organisms in the study. Which adult—the forceps or the pliers—is better adapted to produce more offspring?
5. **Conclude** Using the principles of natural selection, how is this population changing?

APPLY YOUR SKILL

Make Inferences Given the results of the experiment, how will the prey populations (beads) change as the predator population changes? Explain your inference.

CHAPTER 15 STUDY GUIDE

BIGIDEA **The theory of evolution is supported by natural selection and explains the diversity of life.**

SECTION 1 Darwin's Theory of Evolution by Natural Selection

MAINIDEA Charles Darwin developed a theory of evolution based on natural selection.

- Darwin drew from his observations on the HMS *Beagle* and later studies to develop his theory of evolution by natural selection.
- Natural selection is based on ideas of excess reproduction, variation, inheritance, and advantages of certain traits in certain environments.
- Darwin reasoned that the process of natural selection eventually could result in the appearance of new species.

VOCABULARY

- **artificial selection**
- **natural selection**
- **evolution**

SECTION 2 Evidence of Evolution

MAINIDEA Multiple lines of evidence support the theory of evolution.

- Fossils provide strong direct evidence to support evolution.
- Homologous and vestigial structures indicate shared ancestry.
- Examples of embryological and biochemical traits provide insight into the evolution of species.
- Biogeography can explain why certain species live in certain locations.
- Natural selection gives rise to features that increase reproductive success.

VOCABULARY

- **derived trait**
- **ancestral trait**
- **homologous structure**
- **vestigial structure**
- **analogous structure**
- **embryo**
- **biogeography**
- **fitness**
- **camouflage**
- **mimicry**

SECTION 3 Shaping Evolutionary Theory

MAINIDEA The theory of evolution continues to be refined as scientists learn new information.

- The Hardy-Weinberg principle describes the conditions within which evolution does not occur.
- Speciation often begins in small, isolated populations.
- Selection can operate by favoring average or extreme traits.
- Punctuated equilibrium and gradualism are two models that explain the tempo of evolution.

VOCABULARY

- **Hardy-Weinberg principle**
- **genetic drift**
- **founder effect**
- **bottleneck**
- **stabilizing selection**
- **directional selection**
- **disruptive selection**
- **sexual selection**
- **prezygotic isolating mechanism**
- **postzygotic isolating mechanism**
- **allopatric speciation**
- **sympatric speciation**
- **adaptive radiation**
- **gradualism**
- **punctuated equilibrium**

SECTION 1

Vocabulary Review

Replace the underlined portions of the sentences below with words from the Study Guide to make each sentence correct.

1. Natural selection is a mechanism for species change over time.
2. Selective breeding was used to produce purebred Chihuahuas and cocker spaniels.
3. Differential survival by members of a population with favorable adaptations is a mechanism for a theory developed by Charles Darwin.

Understand Main Ideas

4. Which best describes the prevailing view about the age of Earth and evolution before Darwin's voyage on the HMS *Beagle?*
   A. Earth and life are recent and have remained unchanged.
   B. Species evolved rapidly during the first six thousand to a few hundred thousand years.
   C. Earth is billions of years old, but species have not evolved.
   D. Species have evolved on Earth for billions of years.

Use the photo below to answer question 5.

5. Which statement about the tortoise above would be part of an explanation for tortoise evolution based on natural selection?
   A. All tortoises look like the above tortoise.
   B. Tortoises with domed shells have more young than tortoises with flat shells.
   C. All the tortoises born on the island survive.
   D. The tortoise shell looks nothing like the shell of either parent.

Constructed Response

6. **MAIN IDEA** Summarize Darwin's theory of evolution by using an example.
7. **Short Answer** How is artificial selection similar to natural selection?

Think Critically

8. **Sequence** Sequence events leading to evolution by natural selection.
9. **Recognize Cause and Effect** What is the likely evolutionary effect on a species of an increase in global temperatures over time?

SECTION 2

Vocabulary Review

The sentences below include terms that have been used incorrectly. Make the sentences true by replacing the italicized word with a vocabulary term from the Study Guide page.

10. Anatomical parts that have a reduced function in an organism are *analogous structures.*
11. *Biogeography* is a measure of the relative contribution an individual trait makes to the next generation.
12. *Camouflage* occurs when two or more species evolve adaptations to resemble each other.

Understand Main Ideas

Use the photos below to answer question 13.

13. These organisms have similar features that are considered what kind of structures?
   A. vestigial
   B. homologous
   C. analogous
   D. comparative

Use the photo below to answer question 14.

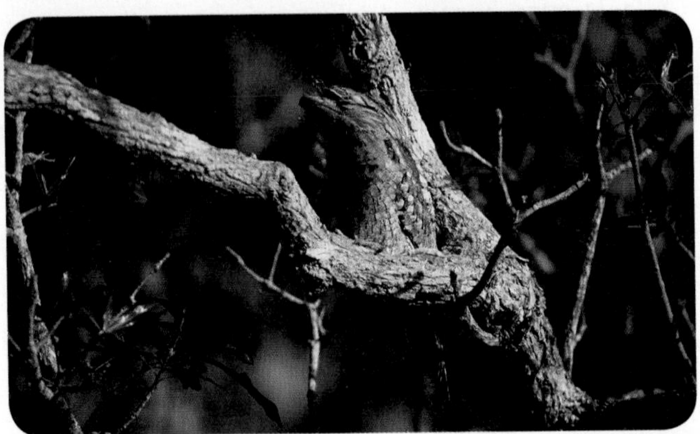

14. The photo of the bird above shows what kind of morphological adaptation?
    - A. vestigial organ
    - B. camouflage
    - C. mimicry
    - D. analogous structure

15. Which is not an example of a morphological adaptation?
    - A. Cytochrome *c* is similar in monkeys and humans.
    - B. Butterflies evolve similar color patterns.
    - C. A harmless species of snake resembles a harmful species.
    - D. Young birds have adaptations for blending into the environment.

16. Industrial melanism could be considered a special case of which of the following?
    - A. embryological adaptation
    - B. mimicry
    - C. physiological adaptation
    - D. structural adaptation

17. Which sets of structures are homologous?
    - A. a butterfly's wing and a bat's wing
    - B. a moth's eyes and a cow's eyes
    - C. a beetle's leg and a horse's leg
    - D. a whale's pectoral fin and a bird's wing

Constructed Response

18. **Short Answer** Describe how cytochrome *c* provides evidence of evolution.

19. **Short Answer** What can be concluded from the fact that many insects are resistant to certain pesticides?

20. **MAINIDEA** Why are fossils considered to provide the strongest evidence supporting evolution?

Think Critically

21. **THEME FOCUS** How could you design an experiment to show that a species of small fish has the ability to evolve a camouflage color pattern?

22. **CAREERS IN Biology** An evolutionary biologist is studying several species of closely related lizards found on Cuba and surrounding islands. Each species occupies a somewhat different niche, but in some ways they all look similar to the green anole lizard found in Florida. Suggest the pattern of lizard evolution.

SECTION 3

Vocabulary Review

Choose the vocabulary term from the Study Guide page that best matches each of the following descriptions.

23. one species evolves over millions of years to become two different but closely related species

24. a species evolves into a new species without a physical barrier

25. the random changes in gene frequency found in small populations

Understand Main Ideas

Use the figure below to answer question 26.

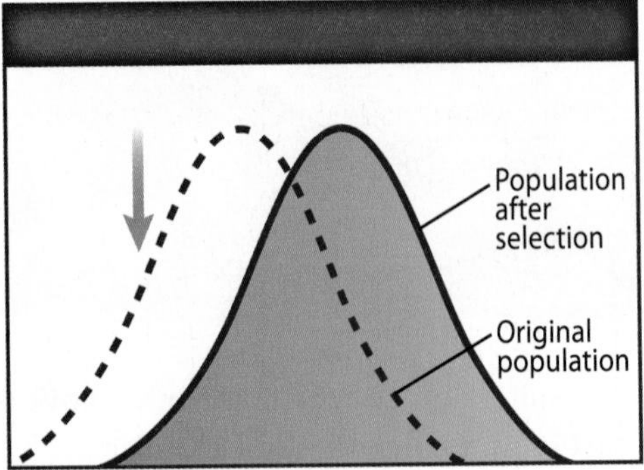

26. The graph above best represents which kind of selection?
    - A. directional
    - B. disruptive
    - C. sexual
    - D. stabilizing

A.N.T./Science Source

Use the photo below to answer question 27.

27. The plant in the above illustration looks like a cactus but is classified in a completely separate group of plants. This would be an example of which mechanism?
    A. adaptive radiation
    B. disruptive selection
    C. convergent evolution
    D. punctuated equilibrium

Constructed Response

28. Open Ended Discuss why the Hardy-Weinberg principle is often violated in real populations.

29. Open Ended Sea stars eat clams by pulling apart the two halves of a clam's shell. Discuss how this could result in directional selection of clam muscle size.

30. Short Answer Compare and contrast genetic drift and natural selection as mechanisms of evolution.

Think Critically

31. Make and Use Graphs Draw a graph that would illustrate a population that has a wide variation of color from light to dark brown. Then draw on the same graph what that population would look like after several years of stabilizing selection. Label your graph.

32. MAINIDEA What would you conclude about the evolutionary process that produces two unrelated species that share similar niches on different continents?

Summative Assessment

33. BIGIDEA Imagine that there has been a major climate shift. Most of Earth is covered in ice, and the equatorial regions are temperate. Describe how plant and animal distribution might change over time through natural selection. Also, describe new available niches that could develop and the types of organisms that may fill them.

34. WRITING IN ▶ Biology Imagine that you are Charles Darwin and write a letter to your father detailing your observations aboard the Beagle.

35. WRITING IN ▶ Biology Write a paragraph that explains why a genetic bottleneck can be an important evolutionary factor for a species.

36. Choose three lines of evidence that support evolution. Give an example of each.

DBQ Document–Based Questions

Darwin,Charles. 1859. *On the Origin of Species by Means of Natural Selection, or the Preservation of Favoured Races in the Struggle for Life.*

Naturalists continually refer to external conditions, such as climate, food, etc., as the only possible cause of variation. In one very limited sense, as we shall hereafter see, this may be true; but it is preposterous to attribute to mere external conditions, the structure, for instance, of the woodpecker, with its feet, tail, beak, and tongue, so admirably adapted to catch insects under the bark of trees.

37. In Darwin's time, most naturalists considered only external conditions as causes of variation. What nonexternal mechanism did Darwin propose as a cause of variation?

38. How would modern scientists explain the nonexternal mechanisms that Darwin proposed?

39. Consider Darwin's example of the woodpecker. Explain the role that natural selection has producing a bird species with a woodpeckerlike beak.

CUMULATIVE

MULTIPLE CHOICE

1 Which experimental setup did Francesco Redi use to test the idea of spontaneous generation?

A a flask filled with all the chemicals present on early Earth

B mice sealed in jars with lit candles and jars with unlit candles

C rotten meat in covered jars and uncovered jars

D special flasks that were filled with broth

Use the Punnett square below to answer question 2.

	B	?
b		
b		

2 A test cross, shown in the Punnett square above, is used to determine the genotype of an animal that is expressing a dominant gene (B) for a particular characteristic. If the animal is homozygous for the dominant trait, which percentage of its offspring will have the dominant gene?

A 25%

B 50%

C 75%

D 100%

3 What prevents the two strands of DNA from immediately coming back together after they unzip?

A addition of binding proteins

B connection of Okazaki fragments

C parting of leading and lagging strands

D use of multiple areas of replication

SHORT ANSWER

Use the diagram of Miller and Urey's experiment below to answer questions 4 and 5.

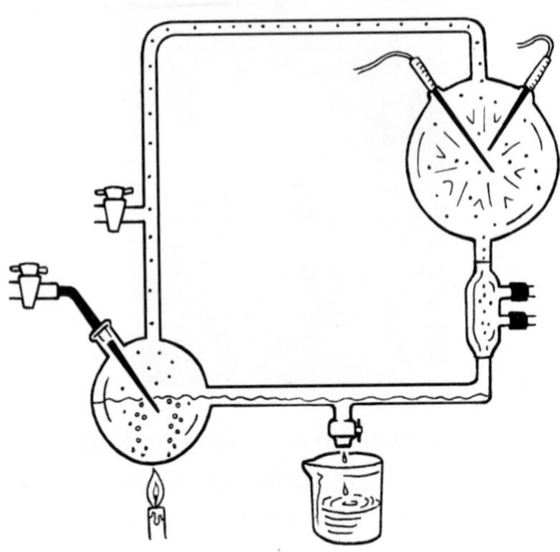

4 What are the possible consequences of a different mix of gases in the apparatus?

5 Some scientists think that lightning might not have been present on Earth in the past. What other energy sources might have caused these reactions?

6 Describe briefly how scientists could use a particular kind of bacteria to synthesize a specific protein.

7 Predict two positive outcomes and two negative outcomes of using transgenic plants for agricultural purposes.

8 Explain the connection between excess reproduction and the concept of natural selection as formulated by Darwin.

9 How would a primitive cell benefit from a symbiotic relationship with a mitochondrion?

TEST Practice

EXTENDED RESPONSE

Use the diagram below to answer questions 10 and 11.

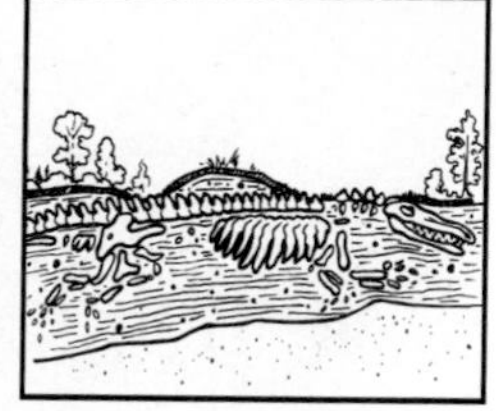

10 Describe the process illustrated in the figure.

11 Explain why a fossil is more likely to form in a wet environment than in a dry environment.

ESSAY QUESTION

Scientists think that archaea living today are similar to ancient archaea. Many archaea today are found in places such as hot springs, deep-ocean hydrothermal vents, polar ice, and other extreme environments. The organisms living in these environments might be similar to organisms that existed in the distant past.

Using the information in the paragraph above, answer the following question in essay format.

12 Scientists also study organisms in extreme environments to help identify where life might exist on other planets. Why would understanding the origins of life on Earth help with discovering life on other planets?

TEST PRACTICE

Use the illustration below of tortoises on two different islands to answer questions 13 and 14.

Large Island

Small Island

13 The above illustrates which principle of natural selection?

A inheritance

B variation

C differential reproduction

D overproduction of offspring

14 Tortoises that have shells with higher openings can eat taller plants. Others can only reach vegetation close to the ground. Judging from the differences in the tortoises' shells, what kind of vegetation would you expect to find on the large and small islands?

A Both islands have a dense ground cover of low-growing plants.

B Both islands have similar plants, but vegetation is more spread out on the large island.

C On the large island, the land is mostly dry, and only tall trees grow.

D The small island is less grassy, and plants grow with their leaves farther above ground.

NEED EXTRA HELP?														
If You Missed Question . . .	1	2	3	4	5	6	7	8	9	10	11	12	13	14
Review Section . . .	14.2	10.2	12.2	14.2	14.2	13.2	13.2	15.1	14.2	14.1	14.1	14.2	15.1, 15.3	15.1

The primates pictured here have several of the traits common to all primates. As primates have evolved, the specific traits of each species have become increasingly specialized.

4.5.3b **LaunchLAB**

What are the characteristics of primates?

If you've been to the zoo or seen pictures of African wildlife, you have probably observed monkeys, chimpanzees, and gorillas. Maybe you've even seen pictures of lemurs. What makes these animals primates? What makes you a primate? In this lab, you will investigate the features that you share with these other primates.

CHAPTER 16

Primate Evolution

THEMEFOCUS

Stability and change Natural selection has resulted in changes in primates over long periods of time.

BIGIDEA

Evolutionary change in a group of small, tree-living mammals eventually led to a diversity of species that includes modern humans.

Monkeys

Make a three-tab book with the labels shown. Use it to organize your notes on monkeys.

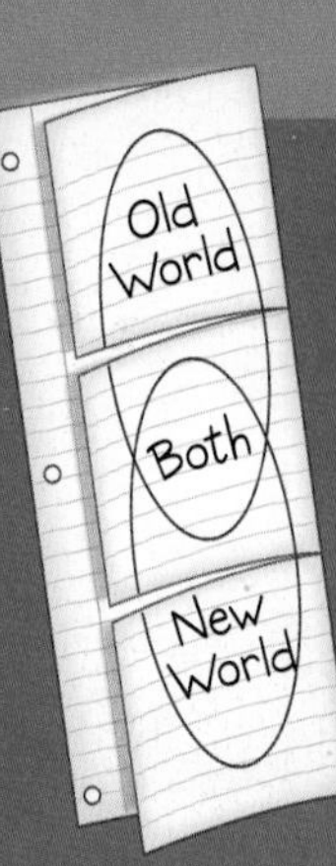

USE IT! **Science Notebook**

1 Primates

4.3.1e, ¥o

MAINIDEA

Primates share several behavioral and biological characteristics, which indicates that they evolved from a common ancestor.

Essential Questions

- What are the characteristics of primates?
- What are the similarities and differences between major primate groups?
- How can the evolution of primates be traced?

BIOLOGY 4 U

You can often tell that your aunts, uncles, or cousins are related to you. Perhaps they have the same color hair or similar features, or they are as tall as you are. Just as you can tell that you are related to your biological family, characteristics of primates show that they are also a related family.

Review Vocabulary

extinction: the disappearance of a species when the last of its members dies

New Vocabulary

opposable first digit	arboreal
binocular vision	anthropoid
diurnal	prehensile tail
nocturnal	hominin

■ **Figure 1** This squirrel monkey is using its opposable digits to hold its dinner—a lantern fly.
Infer ***other ways that a primate might use an opposable digit.***

Characteristics of Primates

Humans, apes, monkeys, and lemurs belong to a group of mammals called primates. Though primates are highly diverse, they share some general features. Some primates have a high level of manual dexterity, which is the ability to manipulate or grasp objects with their hands. They usually also have keen eyesight and long, highly movable arms. Compared to other animals, they have large brains. The primates with the largest brains, which includes humans, have the capacity to reason.

Manual dexterity Primates are distinguished by their flexible hands and feet. All primates typically have five digits on each hand and foot; as you know, humans have fingers and toes. Most have flat nails and sensitive areas on the ends of their digits. The first digits on most primates' hands are opposable, and the first digit on many primates' feet are opposable. An **opposable first digit,** either a thumb or a great toe, is set apart from the other digits. This digit can be brought across the palm or foot so that it touches or nearly touches the other digits. This action allows the primate to grasp an object in a powerful grip. Some primates also have lengthened first digits that provide added dexterity. **Figure 1** shows a monkey using its opposable thumbs to grasp its food.

Senses Though there are exceptions, primates rely more on vision and less on their sense of smell than other mammals do. Their eyes, protected by bony eye sockets, are on the front of their face. This creates overlapping fields of vision, often called **binocular vision.** Forward-looking eyes allow for a greater field of depth perception and enable primates to judge relative distance and movement of an object.

Most primates are **diurnal** (di YUR nul), which means they are active during the day. Because these primates are active in daylight, most also have color vision. Primates that are **nocturnal** (nahk TUR nul) are active at night. They see only in black and white. An increased sense of vision is generally accompanied by a decreased sense of smell. Nocturnal primates' snouts are smaller and their faces tend to be flattened, which increases the degree of binocular vision. Their teeth are reduced in size and usually are unspecialized, meaning that they are suitable for many different types of diets.

Gary Retherford/Science Source

Locomotion Another characteristic of primates is their flexible bodies. Primates have limber shoulders and hips and primarily rely on hind limbs for locomotion. Most primates live in trees and have developed an extraordinary ability to move easily from branch to branch. When on the ground, all primates except humans walk on all four limbs. Many primates can walk upright for short distances, and many have a more upright posture compared to four-legged animals.

Launch Lab

Review Based on what you have read about primate characteristics, how would you now answer the analysis questions?

Complex brains and behaviors Primates tend to have large brains in relation to their body size. Their brains have fewer areas devoted to smell and more areas devoted to vision. They also tend to have larger areas devoted to memory and the coordination of arm and leg movement. Along with larger brains, many primates have problem-solving abilities and well-developed social behaviors, such as grooming and communicating. Most diurnal primates spend a great deal of time socializing by spending time grooming each other. In addition, many primates have complex ways of communicating to each other, which include a wide range of facial expressions.

Reproductive rate Most primates have fewer offspring than other animals. Usually, primates give birth to one offspring at a time. Compared to other mammals, pregnancy is long, and newborns are dependent on their mothers for an extended period of time. For many primates, this time period allows for the increased learning of complex social interactions. A low reproductive rate, the loss of tropical habitats, and human predation has threatened some primate populations. Many are endangered. **Figure 2** illustrates the tropical areas of the world, such as Africa and Southeast Asia, where primates live.

■ **Figure 2** Nonhuman primates live in a broad area spanning most of the world's tropical regions. Use this map as you read about the different primates.

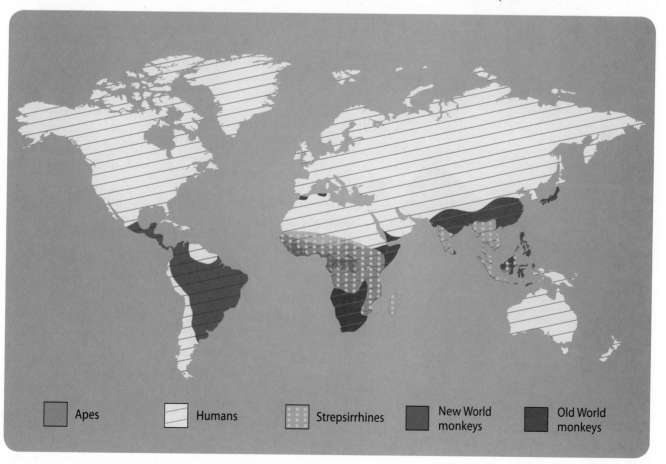

Apes
Humans
Strepsirrhines
New World monkeys
Old World monkeys

VISUALIZING Primates

Figure 3 Primates are members of a highly diverse order of mammals. Most primates share common features such as binocular vision and opposable digits.

Ⓐ The strepsirrhines are relatively small, have large eyes, and are nocturnal. They resemble the earliest primates.

Ⓑ New World monkeys are characterized by relatively long tails. Many have prehensile tails.

Ⓒ Old World monkeys resemble New World monkeys but lack prehensile tails. Some have reduced tails.

Ⓓ Asian apes are long-armed and inhabit tropical rain forests. Apes lack tails.

Ⓔ African apes live in family groups or small bands and display complex social behavior.

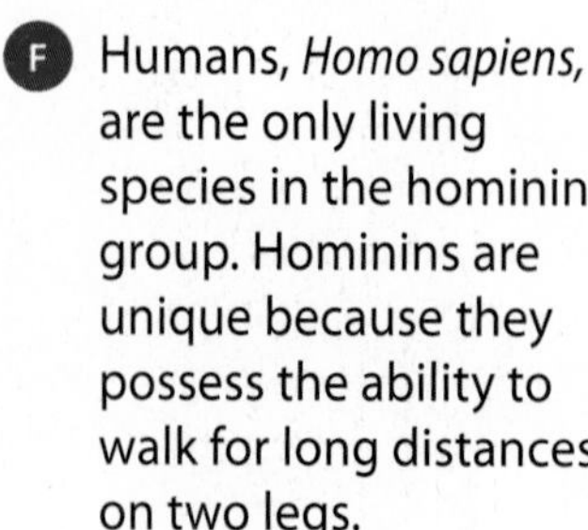

Ⓕ Humans, *Homo sapiens,* are the only living species in the hominin group. Hominins are unique because they possess the ability to walk for long distances on two legs.

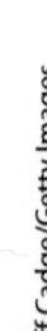

Jeff Cadge/Getty Images

Primate Groups

Primates are a large, diverse group of more than 200 living species. Examine **Figure 3** as you read about this diverse group. Most primates are **arboreal** (ar BOHR ee uhl), or tree-dwelling. Arboreal primates live in the world's tropical and subtropical forests. Primates that live on the ground are considered terrestrial primates.

Primates are classified into two subgroups based on characteristics of their noses, eyes, and teeth. The most basic subgroup is the strepsirrhines (STREP sihr ines) (also called "wet-nosed primates"), such as the lemur. The second subgroup consists of the haplorhines (HAP lohr ines), also called "dry-nosed primates." The haplorhines include the **anthropoids** (AN thruh poydz), a group of large-brained, diurnal monkeys and hominoids.

GET IT? **Differentiate** between strepsirrhines and haplorhines.

Strepsirrhines

Strepsirrhines can be identified by their large eyes and ears. However, they are the only primates that rely predominantly on smell for hunting and social interaction. Some members of this primate group can be found in tropical Africa and Asia. Most are found in Madagascar and nearby islands. As Madagascar drifted away from the African mainland, these animals evolved which left them reproductively isolated. This isolation resulted in their diversification. **Table 1** lists characteristics of some strepsirrhine groups.

VOCABULARY

WORD ORIGIN

Lemur
comes from Latin, meaning *spirit of the night*.

Table 1 Characteristics of Strepsirrhines

Interactive Table

Group	Lemurs	Aye-Ayes	Lorises	Galagos
Example				
Active Period	Large—diurnal Small—nocturnal	Nocturnal	Nocturnal	Mostly nocturnal
Range	Madagascar	Madagascar	Africa and Southeast Asia	Africa
Characteristics	• Vertical leaper • Uses long bushy tail for balance • Herbivores and omnivores	• Taps bark, listens, fishes out grubs with long third finger	• Small and slow climber, solitary • Lack tails • Some have toxic secretions	• Small and fast leaper • No opposable digit • Long tail

■ **Figure 4** Lemurs vary in their size and color. Some lemurs, like this sifaka, spend time on the ground.

Most small lemurs are nocturnal and solitary. Only a few large species, such as the sifaka shown in **Figure 4,** are diurnal and social. The indri is unique because it does not have a tail, unlike most lemurs that use their bushy tails for balance as they jump from branch to branch. Lorises are similar to lemurs but are found primarily in India and Southeast Asia. Galagos (ga LAY gohs), also called bushbabies, are found only in Africa.

Haplorhines

The second group of primates is a much larger group. The haplorhines include tarsiers, monkeys, and apes. The apes, in turn, include gibbons, orangutans, gorillas, chimpanzees, and humans.

The tarsier is found only in Borneo and the Philippines. It is a small, nocturnal creature with large eyes. It has the ability to rotate its head 180 degrees like an owl. It lives in trees, where it climbs and leaps among the branches. The tarsier shares characteristics with both lemurs and monkeys. Scientists once classified it with the lemurs, but new evidence suggests that it is more closely related to anthropoids, which makes it part of the haplorhine group.

Anthropoids are generally larger than strepsirrhines, and they have large brains relative to their body size. They are more likely to be diurnal, with eyes adapted to daylight and sometimes to color. Anthropoids also have more complex social interactions. They tend to live longer than lemurs and other strepsirrhines. The anthropoids are split into the New World monkeys and the Old World monkeys. "New World" refers to the Americas; "Old World" refers to Africa, Asia, and Europe.

FOLDABLES® Incorporate information from this section into your Foldable.

New World monkeys The New World monkeys are a group of about 60 species of arboreal monkeys that inhabit the tropical forests of Mexico, Central America, and South America. New World monkeys include the marmosets and tamarins. These are among the smallest and most unique primates. Neither species has fingernails or opposable digits.

The New World monkeys also include the squirrel monkeys, spider monkeys, and capuchin monkeys. Some of these monkeys have opposable digits, and most are diurnal and live together in social bands. Most are also distinguished by their prehensile (pree HEN sul) tails. A **prehensile tail** functions like a fifth limb. It can grasp tree branches or other objects and support a monkey's weight, as shown in **Figure 5.**

■ **Figure 5** This spider monkey uses its prehensile tail as a fifth limb.

Old World monkeys Old World monkeys live in a wide variety of habitats throughout Asia and Africa, from snow-covered mountains in Japan to arid grasslands in Africa. Some Old World monkeys live in Gibraltar, which is located at the southern tip of Spain. There are about 80 species in this group, including macaques and baboons in one subgroup, and colobus and proboscis monkeys in another. Old World monkeys are similar to New World monkeys in many ways. They are diurnal and live in social groups. However, their noses tend to be narrower and their bodies are usually larger. They also spend more time on the ground. None have prehensile tails, and some have no tails. Most Old World monkeys have opposable digits.

Apes Only a handful of ape species exist today. Apes generally have larger brains in proportion to their body size than monkeys. They also have longer arms than legs, barrel-shaped chests, no tails, and flexible wrists. They are often highly social and have complex vocalizations. They are classified into two subcategories: the lesser apes, which include the gibbons and siamangs, and the great apes, which include orangutans, gorillas, chimpanzees, and humans.

Lesser apes The Asian gibbons and their close relatives, the larger siamangs, are the arboreal gymnasts of the ape family. Though they have the ability to walk on either two or four legs like all great apes, they generally move from branch to branch using a hand-over-hand swinging motion called brachiation. This motion, as shown in **Figure 6,** enables an adult gibbon to move almost 3 m in one swing.

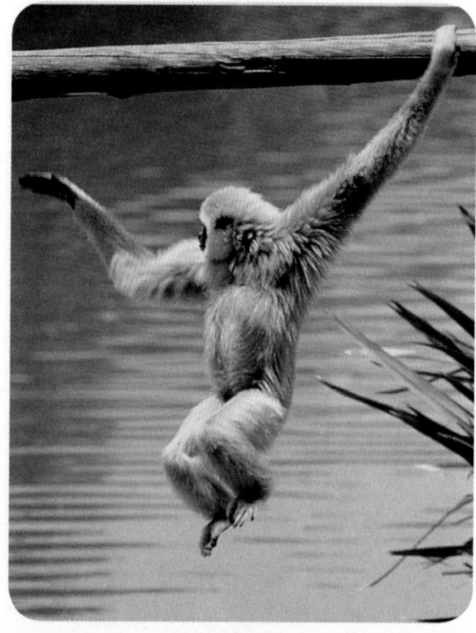

■ **Figure 6** Lesser apes, such as this gibbon, move through trees primarily by brachiation—a hand-over-hand swinging motion.

Great apes Orangutans are the largest arboreal primates and the only great ape species that lives exclusively in Asia. Orangutans are large enough that the males are often more comfortable on the ground, though they are not efficient walkers. Female orangutans give birth once every eight years and nurse their young for up to six years. A male orangutan, with prominent cheek pads, and a female orangutan with her offspring are shown in **Figure 7.**

The gorillas are the largest of the primates. Like all great apes, they are predominantly terrestrial animals. They walk on all four limbs, supporting themselves by their front knuckles. Also, like other great apes, they use sticks as simple tools in the wild, and some living in captivity have been taught to recognize written characters and numbers.

■ **Figure 7** Male orangutans are much larger and more solitary than females. The females spend most of their time raising their offspring.

(t)Tom McHugh/Science Source, (bl)PhotoLink/Photodisc/Getty Images, (br)©Renee Lynn/Corbis

■ **Figure 8** The bonobo is slightly smaller than the chimpanzee. Like the chimpanzee, it is structurally and behaviorally similar to humans.

Chimpanzees and their close relatives, the bonobos, are also knuckle-walkers. They have well-developed communication systems, such as body positions and gestures, and social behavior, and they live in a wide variety of habitats. They are more like humans in their physical structure and behavior than any other primates are. The bonobo, shown in **Figure 8,** is slightly smaller than the chimpanzee. It was once called the "pygmy chimpanzee," but it now is considered a separate species.

Humans are included in the great ape family. They are then classified in a separate subcategory of hominids called hominins. **Hominins** are humanlike primates that appear to be more closely related to present-day humans than they are to present-day chimpanzees and bonobos. Though many species of hominins have existed on Earth, only one species—the group to which you belong—survives today. The diagram in **Figure 9** illustrates evolutionary relationships among primates.

Primate Evolution

Most primates today are arboreal. Prehensile tails, long limbs, binocular vision, brachiation, and opposable digits are traits that help them take full advantage of their forest environments.

Arboreal adaptation Some scientists suggest that primates evolved from ground-dwelling animals that searched for food in the top branches of forest shrubbery. They then evolved into additional food-gathering niches in trees. For example, the flexible hand with its opposable digits evolved not to grasp tree branches but to catch insects. Other scientists suggest that the rise of flowering plants provided new niche opportunities, and that arboreal adaptations allowed primates to take advantage of the fruits and flowers of trees.

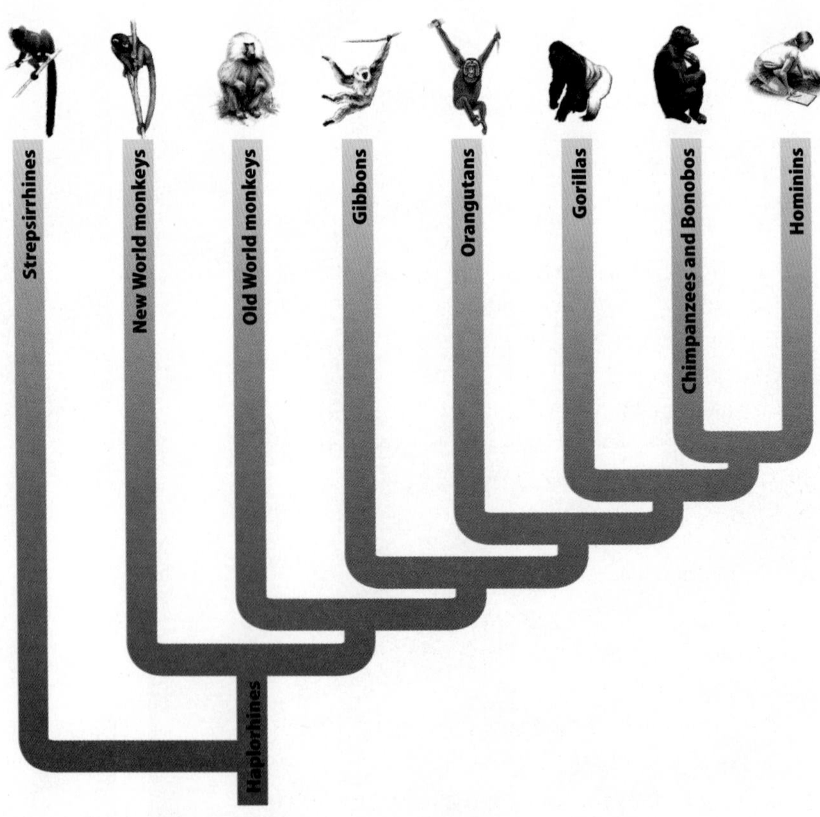

■ **Figure 9** This branching diagram illustrates the diverging pattern of primate evolution.

Interpret ***Which primate was the earliest to diverge?***

Primate ancestors Genetic data suggest that the first primates probably lived about 85 mya, when dinosaurs still roamed Earth. However, the earliest primate fossils do not appear in the fossil record until the beginning of the Eocene epoch, about 60 mya. One of the earliest fossil primates, called *Altiatlasius* (al tee aht lah SEE us), was a small, nocturnal animal that ate insects and fruits using its hands and feet for grasping. It might have resembled the tiny tree shrew in **Figure 10,** but it had some features similar to those of lemurs today. Learn more about the early evolution of primates in **Data Analysis Lab 1.**

■ **Figure 10** The earliest primate ancestor might have looked like this tree shrew.

Diverging primates Lemurlike primates were widespread by about 50 mya, and many species existed on all continents except Australia and Antarctica. Sometime around 50 mya, and possibly earlier, the anthropoids diverged from the tarsiers; this might have occurred in Asia, where the tarsiers are found today. The earliest anthropoids leaped less and walked more than the strepsirrhines and tarsiers, but they were still tiny and their brains were still small. By the end of the Eocene, 30–35 mya, the anthropoids had diverged and spread widely.

Displacement Many early strepsirrhines appear to have become extinct by the end of the Eocene. This might have been caused by a change in climate. Many major geological events took place at the end of the Eocene and temperatures became cooler. Or, it could have been caused by the divergence of the anthropoids. The anthropoids of this time generally were larger and had bigger brains than the strepsirrhines did. Thus, the anthropoids might have outcompeted some of the strepsirrhines for resources. This idea is supported by the observation that today, the nocturnal strepsirrhines do not interact with the diurnal anthropoids when the habitats of these two groups overlap.

Data Analysis LAB 1

Based on Real Data*

Interpret Scientific Illustrations

When did early primate lineages diverge?
The fossil record for primate evolution is sparse. In the simplified primate evolutionary tree at right, the green diagram shows the present divergence according to known fossils. The red diagram shows the time line with presumed fossils filling the gaps. Use the diagrams to answer the following questions.

Think Critically

1. **Summarize** why lemurs, lorises, and bushbabies are considered descendants of the earliest primates.
2. **Extrapolate** how far back the divergence of the lemurs might have occurred.
3. **Infer** whether tarsiers are more closely related to apes or to lemurs.

Data and Observations

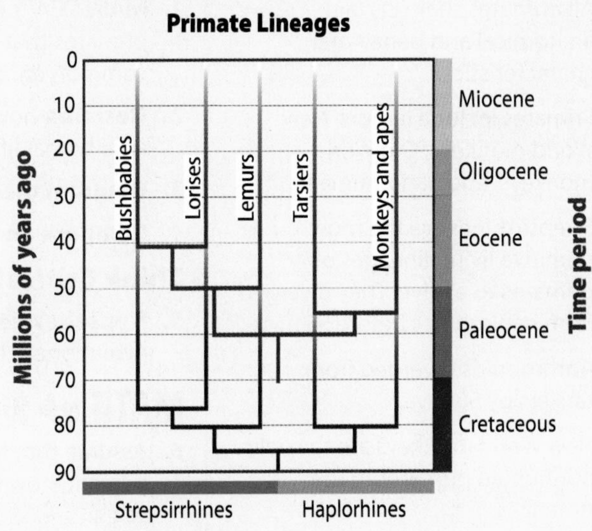

*Data obtained from: Martin, Robert D. 2003. Paleontology: combing the primate record. *Nature* 422: 388–391.

Monkeys The end of the Eocene also saw the appearance of the monkeys. Early monkeys had larger brains than their anthropoid ancestors did, and their eyes were more forward-looking. Their snouts were less pointed and they relied less on smell. Scientists hypothesize that the New World monkeys diverged from the line that gave rise to the Old World monkeys sometime between 35 and 25 mya in Africa. While the Old World monkeys continued to evolve in Africa, the New World monkeys developed distinct characteristics in South America. By this time, Africa and South America had separated into two continents. How, then, did the New World monkeys arrive in South America?

Journey to South America Many scientists hypothesize that the New World monkeys evolved from an isolated group of ancestral anthropoids that somehow drifted to South America from Africa, perhaps on rafts of vegetation and soil, much like how the ancestors of lemurs might have drifted to Madagascar from the African mainland. Some scientists suggest that the New World monkeys might have diverged from the anthropoid lineage and made their journey millions of years earlier, when sea levels were lower and the continents were closer.

VOCABULARY

ACADEMIC VOCABULARY

Diverge
to become different in character or form
Their ideas diverged so much that they could not come to an agreement.

Aegyptopithecus In Africa and Asia, anthropoids continued to evolve. Many anthropoid fossils have been found at a site in present-day Egypt called the Fayum Basin. Now a desert, the Fayum was predominantly tropical when dozens of anthropoid species lived there 36–31 mya. The largest among them was *Aegyptopithecus* (ee gypt oh PIH thuh kus), often called the dawn ape. Some scientists hypothesize that this arboreal animal, which was about the size of a domestic cat, was ancestral to the apes. It might have been part of the anthropoid line that split from the Old World monkeys and might have given rise to orangutans, gorillas, chimpanzees, and humans.

REVIEW IT! Primates

Section Summary

- All primates share certain anatomical and behavioral characteristics.
- Primates include lemurs, New World monkeys, Old World monkeys, apes, and humans.
- Strepsirrhines are the most primitive living lineages of primates to evolve. They diverged from haplorhines before 55 mya.
- Anthropoids diverged from tarsiers by 50 mya.
- New World monkeys are the only nonhuman primates in the Americas.

Self Check

Understand Main Ideas

1. MAINIDEA **List** four characteristics that are representative of most primates that led paleoanthropologists to conclude that primates share a common ancestry.
2. **Describe** how the characteristics of primates make them well-adapted for an arboreal lifestyle.
3. **Diagram** the evolutionary relationships of primates.
4. **Compare and contrast** major primate groups.

Think Critically

5. **Hypothesize** how the breakup of Pangaea might have contributed to the evolutionary history of primates.

MATH IN Biology

6. Assume that life on Earth began 3.5 billion years ago. To the nearest percent, how much of this time have anthropoids been living?

USE IT! Science Notebook

2 Hominoids to Hominins

1.1.1b, ¥a

MAINIDEA

Hominins, a subgroup of the hominoids, likely evolved in response to climate changes of the Miocene epoch.

BIOLOGY 4U

Have you ever tried to put together a puzzle that is missing some of its pieces? Human evolution is like that puzzle. Scientists who try to understand how humans evolved are slowed by the holes in the fossil record. Recent advances in genetics and molecular biology have helped, but the puzzle that is human evolution remains only partially assembled.

Essential Questions

- What are the features of hominoids and hominins?
- How can hominoid evolution be traced from *Proconsul* to *Homo?*
- What are the similarities between the various australopithecine species?

Review Vocabulary

savanna: a flat grassland of tropical or subtropical regions

New Vocabulary

Multilingual eGlossary

hominoid
bipedal
australopithecine

Hominoids

Hominoids (HAH mih noydz) include all nonmonkey anthropoids—the living and extinct gibbons, orangutans, chimpanzees, gorillas, and humans. The fossil transition from early anthropoid to ape is not clear; very few fossils from the late Oligocene epoch exist. The earliest hominoid fossils appear in the fossil record only about 25 mya, at the beginning of the Miocene epoch. These hominoids retained some ancestral primate features. For example, most had bodies adapted for brachiation. There is evidence that they had relatively large brains and had shoulders and hips that moved freely, and some might even have had the ability to stand on two legs.

Connection to Chemistry Scientists use fossils to help them determine when ancestral hominoids diverged into the hominoids that exist today. However, because the fossil record for hominoids is so sparse, scientists also turn to biochemical data to help them with this task. By comparing the DNA of living hominoid species, researchers conclude that gibbons likely diverged first from an ancestral anthropoid, followed by orangutans, gorillas, chimpanzees and bonobos, and finally, humans. **Figure 11** shows the potential divergence of these species. Chimpanzees and bonobos are the closest living relatives to humans. All three share at least 96 percent of their DNA sequences.

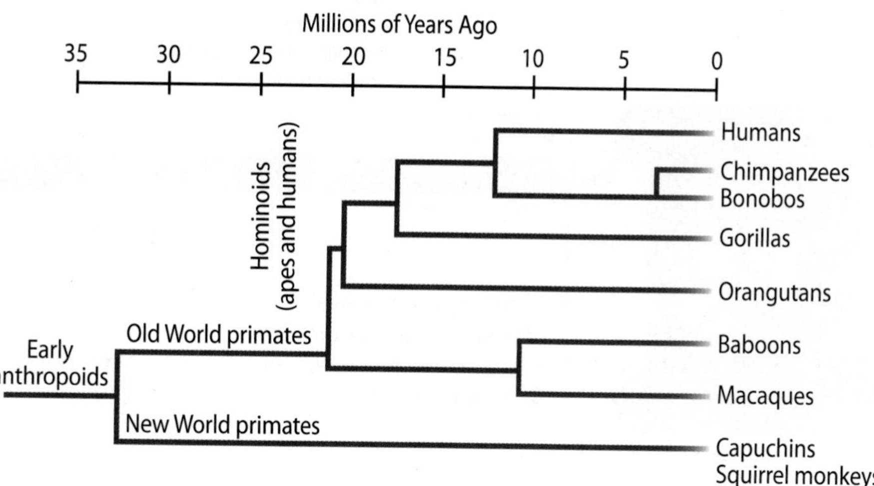

■ **Figure 11** Orangutans, gorillas, bonobos, and chimpanzees all diverged from an ancestral anthropoid.

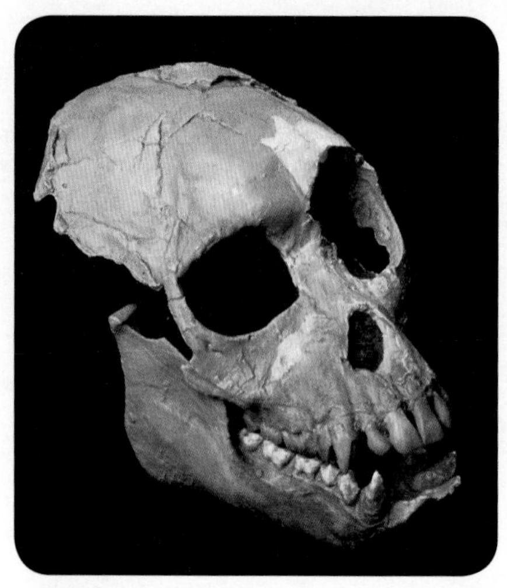

■ **Figure 12** *Proconsul* was an early, small-brained hominoid that might have been a human ancestor.

Hominoid characteristics Hominoids are the largest of the primates, and they have the largest brain size in relation to their body size. They tend to have broad pelvises, long fingers, no tail, and flexible arm and shoulder joints. They also have semi-upright or upright posture, and, except for hominins, their arms are longer than their legs. Their teeth are less specialized than those of other animals, and their molars have a distinctive pattern that scientists use to distinguish hominoid fossils from other primate fossils.

Hominoid biogeography During the Miocene epoch (24–5 mya), the world's climate became warmer and drier. As a result, tropical rain forests in Africa began to shrink. Many new animals, including new hominoids, evolved as they adapted to the changing environments. Between about 23 and 14 mya, perhaps as many as 100 hominoid species existed. Early hominoids were more diverse than the modern apes, and they migrated from Africa to Europe and Asia.

Proconsul The best-known hominoid fossils, and some of the oldest, are those from the genus *Proconsul*. **Figure 12** shows a fossil skull of one *Proconsul* species discovered by Mary Leakey in Kenya in 1948. This *Proconsul* species generally had the smallest brains of the hominoids. Most had freely moving arms and legs, and while they lived predominantly in trees, some might have had the ability to walk upright. Some scientists think that this *Proconsul* species is a human ancestor, but others suggest that one of the European hominoids—whose fossils are in some ways more humanlike than *Proconsul*—might have returned to Africa at the end of the Miocene and given rise to the human line.

Hominins

The lineage that most likely led to humans split off from the other African apes sometime between 8 and 5 mya. The hominins include humans and all their extinct relatives. These extinct relatives are more closely related to humans than to chimpanzees. The time line in **Figure 13** highlights some important hominin discoveries.

■ **Figure 13** **Hominin Evolution**
Discoveries have shaped our understanding of how *Homo sapiens* evolved from hominoids.

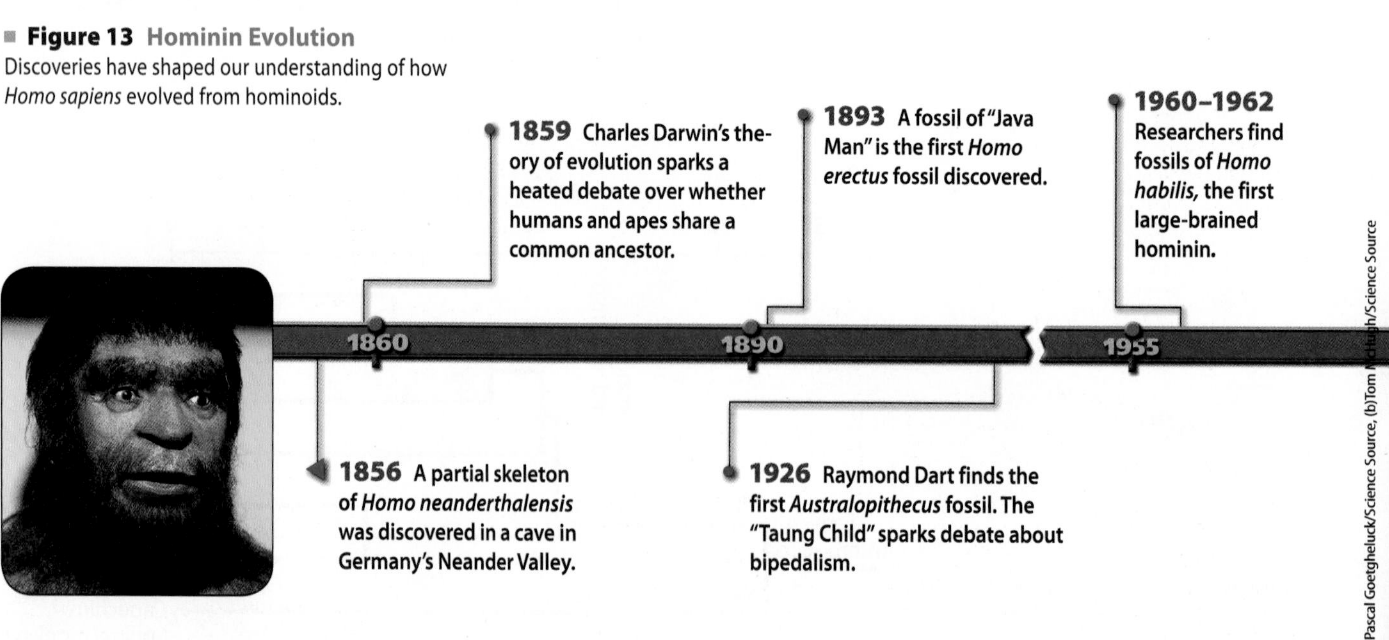

1859 Charles Darwin's theory of evolution sparks a heated debate over whether humans and apes share a common ancestor.
1893 A fossil of "Java Man" is the first Homo erectus fossil discovered.
1960–1962 Researchers find fossils of Homo habilis, the first large-brained hominin.
1860
1890
1955
1856 A partial skeleton of Homo neanderthalensis was discovered in a cave in Germany's Neander Valley.
1926 Raymond Dart finds the first Australopithecus fossil. The "Taung Child" sparks debate about bipedalism.

Chimpanzee	Hominin
Skull attaches posteriorly	Skull attaches inferiorly
Spine slightly curved	S-shaped spine
Arms longer than legs and used for walking	Arms shorter than legs and not used for walking
Long, narrow pelvis	Bowl-shaped pelvis
Femur angled outward	Femur angled inward

■ **Figure 14** A comparison between chimpanzee and hominin skeletons illustrates evolutionary changes leading to bipedalism.

Observe and Infer ***What differences in the lengths of the arms and the legs do you detect?***

Hominin characteristics Hominins have bigger brains than other hominoids, with more complexity in parts of the brain where high-level thought occurs. The hominin face is thinner and flatter than those of other hominoids. Hominin teeth are also smaller. With lengthened thumbs and more flexible wrists, hominins have high manual dexterity. Hominins are also **bipedal,** which means that they can walk upright on two legs.

Examine **Figure 14,** which illustrates anatomical differences in a quadruped and a biped. When becoming bipedal, hominins developed a fully upright stance, shortened arms, restructured pelvic bones and foot bones, and a change in the position of the head on the spinal cord. In quadrupedal animals, or those that walk on all four limbs, the foramen magnum—the hole in the skull where the spine extends from the brain—is located at the back of the skull. In hominins, it is positioned at the base of the skull.

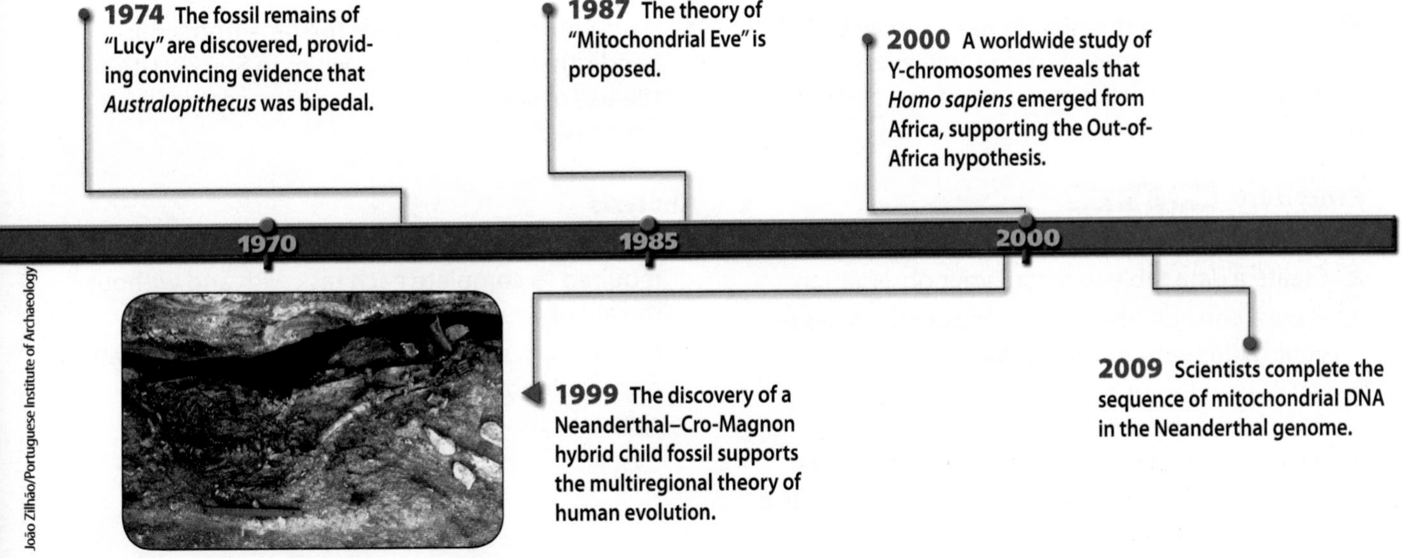

1974 The fossil remains of "Lucy" are discovered, providing convincing evidence that *Australopithecus* was bipedal.
1987 The theory of "Mitochondrial Eve" is proposed.
2000 A worldwide study of Y-chromosomes reveals that *Homo sapiens* emerged from Africa, supporting the Out-of-Africa hypothesis.
1970
1985
2000
1999 The discovery of a Neanderthal–Cro-Magnon hybrid child fossil supports the multiregional theory of human evolution.
2009 Scientists complete the sequence of mitochondrial DNA in the Neanderthal genome.
João Zilhão/Portuguese Institute of Archaeology

Disadvantages of bipedalism Bipedalism is not necessarily more efficient than quadrupedalism. Bipedal individuals are easier for predators to see, they might not run as fast, and bipedalism puts greater strain on the hips and back. Also, standing upright defies gravity and therefore requires more energy. Why, then, did hominins become bipedal when their ancestors were so well adapted to life in the trees?

Advantages of bipedalism There is no single answer to the question of why bipedalism developed. Bipedalism could have been selected for because it uses less energy than walking on all fours over long distances. Also, standing upright could have made it easier to see food sources. Walking upright for long distances might also have reduced the total area of the body exposed to sunlight and increased the area exposed to cooling winds.

One hypothesis explaining bipedalism is based on the idea that the African landscape was changing during the period when hominins evolved. Many scientists suggest that bipedalism was an adaptation to the new environment. The most successful hominins may have been those that evolved at the boundaries of the environments. Bipedalism would have allowed them to carry objects while walking through the forest, and to see above tall grasses to find food and avoid predators.

Another hypothesis, based on fossils of *Ardipithecus ramidus,* suggests that bipedalism evolved due to social structure. Fossils indicate that a social structure existed in which males cooperated with females to raise offspring. Males may have traveled through the forest to find food for their offspring. Bipedalism would have allowed *Ar. ramidus* to keep hands free while traveling with food or other objects.

GET IT? **Summarize** the advantages and disadvantages of bipedalism.

MiniLAB 1

Observe the Functions of an Opposable Thumb

How do opposable thumbs aid in everyday tasks? Explore the advantages of performing everyday activities with and without the aid of opposable thumbs.

Procedure 

1. Read and complete the lab safety form.
2. Create a data table to record your observations.
3. Have a partner tape your thumbs to the sides of your hands with **masking tape.**
4. Using your taped hands, perform the following tasks: pick up a **pen or pencil** and write your name on a **piece of paper,** tie your **shoelaces,** and open a **closed door.** Have your partner use a **stopwatch** to time each task.
5. Have your partner remove the tape from your hands, then repeat the activities in Step 4 with the use of your thumbs. Have your partner time each task.

Analysis

1. **Compare and contrast** the time and effort required to complete each task with and without the aid of your thumbs.
2. **Infer** the advantages that ancestral primates with opposable thumbs would have had over competitors without opposable thumbs.

Hominin fossils Bipedalism evolved before many other hominin traits, and it is often used to identify hominin fossils. The earliest fossils of species that show some degree of bipedalism are 6–7 million years old. Evidence of true bipedalism has been suggested by the fossilized remains of *Ar. ramidus* and the australopithecines (aw stray loh PIH thuh seens).

Australopithecines lived in the east-central and southern parts of Africa between 4.2 and 1 mya. They were small—the males were only about 1.5 m tall—and they had apelike brains and jaws. However, their teeth and limb joints were humanlike.

The Taung child Anthropologist Raymond Dart (1893–1988) identified the first australopithecine fossil, the "Taung child," in Africa in 1926. He called the species *Australopithecus africanus,* meaning "southern ape from Africa." *A. africanus* likely lived between 3.3 and 2.3 mya. The placement of the foramen magnum in the skull of the Taung child, shown in **Figure 15,** convinced Dart that *A. africanus* was bipedal. Not everyone agreed, because *A. africanus* had a small brain. Some scientists thought that larger brains evolved before bipedalism. The question continued to be debated for many years, even after the discovery of other African australopithecine fossils such as *A. bosei* and *A. robustus,* which indicated bipedalism and small brains.

■ **Figure 15** The Taung child skull convinced Raymond Dart that *A. africanus* walked upright.

Lucy In 1974 in Kenya, anthropologist Donald Johanson discovered an australopithecine skeleton that helped resolve the debate. Lucy is one of the most complete australopithecine fossils ever found. She was a member of the species *A. afarensis,* which lived between 4 and 2.9 mya.

Lucy was about the size of a chimpanzee. She had the typical australopithecine skull and small brain, and her arms were still somewhat long in proportion to her legs. She also had finger bones that were more curved than those of modern humans, which indicates that she was capable of arboreal activity. However, her hip and knee joints were humanlike. It was clear that she walked upright. A few years later, Mary Leakey uncovered further evidence that australopithecines were bipedal when she discovered fossilized australopithecine footprints. Lucy's skeleton and the footprints of her relatives are illustrated in **Figure 16.**

■ **Figure 16** Fossilized footprints indicate that Lucy was bipedal. Though incomplete, this skeleton of Lucy indicates that *A. afarensis* had a small brain but also had the ability to walk upright.

Infer ***what bones scientists would examine to determine if Lucy walked upright.***

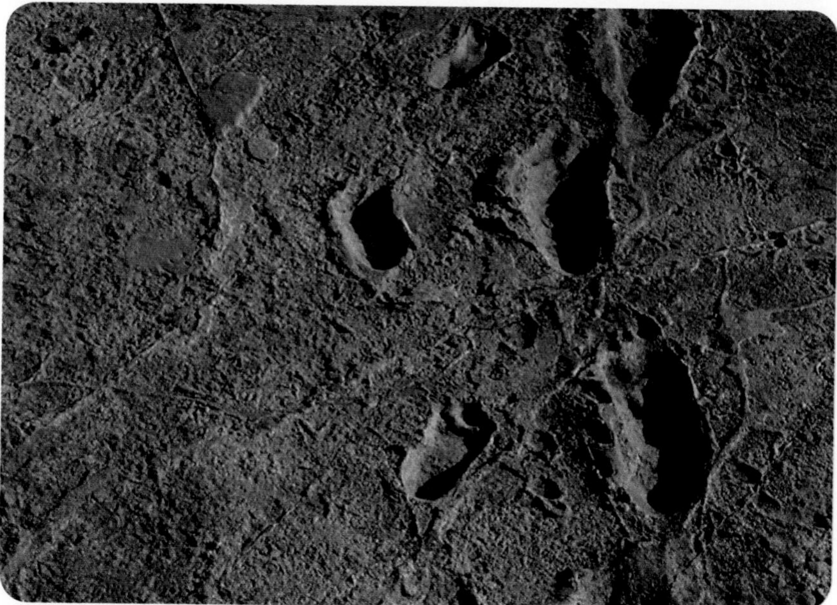

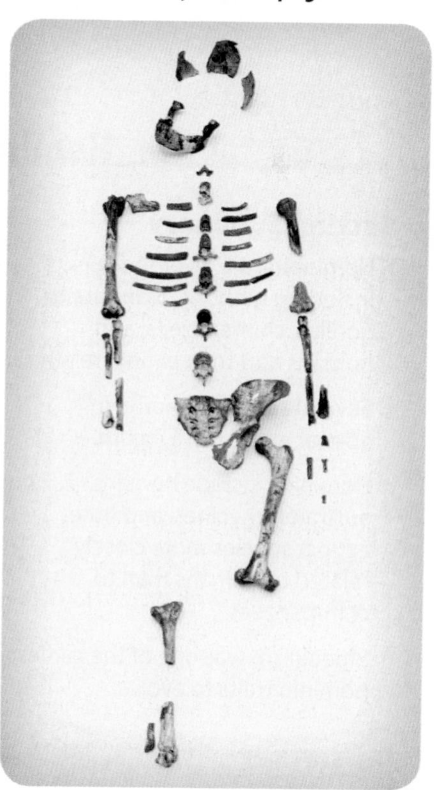

(t)Pascal Goetgheluck/Science Source; (bl & br) John Reader/Science Source

Vocabulary

Word origin

Australopithecine
from the Latin word *australis,* meaning *southern,* and the Greek word *pithekos,* meaning *ape*

Mosaic pattern Like other hominin fossils, Lucy and her relatives show a patchwork of human and apelike traits. In this way, they follow a mosaic pattern of evolution. Mosaic evolution occurs when different body parts or behaviors evolve at different rates. For example, hominins developed the ability to walk upright nearly two million years before they developed modern flat faces and larger brains.

Hominin evolution Within the last 30 years, scientists have discovered many more early hominin fossils. Some defy characterization and have led to new genus designations. Scientists have estimated that *Kenyanthropus platyops* (ken yan THROH pus • PLAT ee ops), for example, lived between 3.5 and 3.2 mya. Some scientists think that *K. platyops,* which means "flat-faced man," represents a completely new hominin genus.

Paranthropus There is also confusion about where *A. bosei* and *A. robustus* fit in the classification of hominins. Traditionally, these two species have been classified as robust forms of australopithecines, distinguished from the smaller, more slender forms by their size and muscular jaws. Today, many scientists prefer to put these primates in a separate genus called *Paranthropus.* Paranthropoids, which thrived between 2 and 1.2 mya, were an offshoot of the human line that lived alongside human ancestors but were not directly related.

Overlapping hominins However they are classified, these robust hominins appear to have lived alongside some of the slender australopithecines. They might have overlapped, for example, with *A. garhi,* an African australopithecine that was discovered in 1999. The illustration of the evolution of hominins is more like a bush than a tree. Many species lived successfully for years, often overlapping with earlier species and then—for unknown reasons—became extinct. By 1 mya, all australopithecines had disappeared from the fossil record. The only hominin fossils found after that time belong to the genus *Homo.*

REVIEW IT! Hominoids to Hominins

Section Summary

- Hominoids are all of the apes, including gibbons, orangutans, gorillas, chimpanzees, and humans and their extinct relatives.
- Several species of hominins appear in the fossil record.
- Hominins include humans, australopithecines, and other extinct species more closely related to humans than to chimpanzees.
- Bipedalism was one of the earliest hominin traits to evolve.

Self Check

Understand Main Ideas

1. MAINIDEA **Summarize** how the climate of the Miocene epoch impacted the evolution of hominins.
2. **Describe** characteristics unique to hominoids.
3. **Describe** characteristics unique to hominins.
4. **Outline** hominoid evolution from *Proconsul* to *Homo.*
5. **Compare** australopithecine species.

Think Critically

6. **Discuss** Do you think hominins would have evolved if the climate had not changed during the Miocene epoch? Why?
7. **Classify** If you found a primate skeleton with arms shorter than legs, in what general category would you place it?

USE IT! Science Notebook

3 Human Ancestry

BIOLOGY 4U

Have you ever heard anyone use the term "cave man" in an insulting way? Unfortunately, this term is used sometimes to indicate brutish behavior. However, the people who lived in caves 40,000 years ago were very much like modern humans. Their art was beautiful, and their tools were sophisticated.

MAIN IDEA

Tracing the evolution of the genus *Homo* is important for understanding the ancestry of humans, the only living species of *Homo*.

Essential Questions

- How can the species in the genus *Homo* be described?
- What is the Out-of-Africa hypothesis?
- What are the similarities and differences between Neanderthals and modern humans?

Review Vocabulary

mitochondrion: an organelle found in eukaryotic cells containing genetic material and responsible for cellular energy

New Vocabulary

Homo
Neanderthal
Cro-Magnon

Multilingual eGlossary

The Genus *Homo*

The African environment became considerably cooler between 3 and 2.5 mya. Forests became smaller in size, and the range of grasslands was extended. The genus ***Homo***, which includes living and extinct humans, first appeared during these years. Although the fossil record is lacking fossils, many scientists infer that they evolved from an ancestor of the australopithecines.

Homo species had bigger brains, lighter skeletons, flatter faces, and smaller teeth than their australopithecine ancestors. They are also the first species known to control fire and to modify stones for tool use. As they evolved, they developed language and culture.

***Homo habilis* used stone tools** The earliest known species that is generally accepted as a member of the genus *Homo* is *Homo habilis*, called "handy man" because of its association with primitive stone tools. This species lived in Africa between about 2.4 and 1.4 mya. **Figure 17** shows a scientific illustrator's idea of what *H. habilis* might have looked like.

H. habilis possessed a brain averaging 650 cm^3, about 20 percent larger than that of the australopithecines. It also had other *Homo* species traits, including a smaller brow, reduced jaw, flatter face, and more humanlike teeth. Like australopithecines, it was small, long-armed, and seems to have retained the ability to climb trees. Other *Homo* species might have coexisted with *H. habilis*, among them a species called *Homo rudolfensis*. Because few fossils of *H. rudolfensis* have been found, its exact relationship to the rest of the *Homo* line is uncertain.

Figure 17 Scientific illustrators use fossils and their knowledge of anatomy to create drawings of what *H. habilis* might have looked like.

■ **Figure 18** Models of nonliving species can be created from fossil remains. *H. ergaster* appeared in the fossil record about 1.8–1.3 mya.

***Homo ergaster* migrated** Within about 500,000 years of the appearance of *H. habilis,* another *Homo species, Homo ergaster,* emerged with an even larger brain. *H. ergaster,* illustrated in **Figure 18,** appeared only briefly in the fossil record, from about 1.8 to 1.3 mya. *H. ergaster* was taller and lighter than *H. habilis,* and had longer legs and shorter arms. Its brain averaged 1000 cm^3, and it had a rounded skull, reduced teeth, and what many scientists think was the first human nose (with the nostrils facing downward).

Tools Carefully made hand axes and other tools associated with *H. ergaster* fossils suggest to some scientists that *H. ergaster* was a hunter, but others think that *H. ergaster* was primarily a scavenger and used the tools to scrape the meat off scavenged bones.

MiniLAB 2

Explore Hominin Migration

Where did early hominins live? Scientists carefully record the locations where fossils are found. The latitude and longitude coordinates represent the known geographic points of each *Homo* species' range.

Procedure

1. Read and complete the lab safety form.
2. Plot the following fossil sites on the map that your teacher gives you. Use a different color for each species. When you are finished, lightly shade in the approximate boundaries.
   - *H. habilis* (2.4–1.4 million years ago): 37°E: 4°S, 36°E: 3°N, 36°E: 7°N, 43°E: 8°N
   - *H. erectus* (2 million–400,000 years ago): 112°E: 38°N, 13°E: 47°N, 7°W: 34°N, 112°E: 8°S
   - *H. neanderthalensis* (300,000–200,000 years ago): 8°E: 53°N, 66°E: 39°N, 5°W: 37°N, 36°E: 33°N
   - *H. sapiens* (195,000 years ago–present): 70°E: 62°N, 24°E: 30°S, 138°E: 34°S, 112°E: 38°N, 99°W: 19°N, 102°W: 32°N

Analysis

1. **Hypothesize** when was the earliest that hominins could have migrated out of Africa. Where did they go? Use the map you made for reference.
2. **Determine** what sets of fossils overlapped in geographic ranges. What does this suggest?

■ **Figure 19** *H. erectus* might have lived in caves, made tools, and used fire.

Explain ***some of the advantages* H. erectus *would have over* H. ergaster.**

Migration Both scavenging and hunting are associated with a migratory lifestyle, and *H. ergaster* appears to have been the first African *Homo* species to migrate in large numbers to Asia and possibly Europe, perhaps following the trail of migrating animals. The later Eurasian forms of *H. ergaster* are called *Homo erectus.* Because *H. ergaster* shares features with modern humans, scientists hypothesize that *H. ergaster* is an ancestor of modern humans.

***Homo erectus* used fire** *H. erectus,* illustrated in **Figure 19,** lived between 1.8 million and 400,000 years ago and appears to have evolved from *H. ergaster* as it migrated out of Africa. While some scientists consider *H. ergaster* and *H. erectus* a single species, *H. erectus* appears to have evolved traits that the early African *H. ergaster* species did not have. Members of this species seem to have been more versatile than their predecessors, and they adapted successfully to a variety of environments. *H. erectus* includes "Java Man," discovered in Indonesia in the 1890s, and "Peking Man," discovered in China in the 1920s.

In general, *H. erectus* was larger than *H. habilis* and had a bigger brain. It also had teeth that were more humanlike. Brain capacity ranged from about 900 cm^3 in early specimens to about 1100 cm^3 in later ones. It was as tall as *H. sapiens,* but it had a longer skull, lower forehead, and thicker facial bones than either *H. ergaster* or *H. sapiens.* It also had a more prominent browridge. Evidence indicates that *H. erectus* made sophisticated tools, used fire, and sometimes lived in caves.

***Homo floresiensis*—"The Hobbit"** In 2003 a curious set of fossils were discovered on the Indonesian island of Flores. These fossils, which are about 18,000 years old, are heavily debated in the scientific community. Some scientists think they might represent a species called *Homo floresiensis* (flor eh see EN sus). Others think that the fossils belong to early human dwarfs and do not warrant classification as a separate species. *H. floresiensis,* nicknamed "The Hobbit," was only about 1 m tall when fully grown. While it had brain and body proportions like all the australopithecines, primitive stone tools were found with its fossils. In 2007 a study showed that *H. floresiensis* had apelike wrist bones—further support for its status as a separate species. You can compare *H. floresiensis* and *H. sapiens* skulls in **Figure 20.**

GET IT? What are the evolutionary relationships among *H. habilis, H. ergaster,* and *H. erectus?*

■ **Figure 20** Scientists are debating whether *H. floresiensis* is a new species. The *H. floresiensis* skull on the left is smaller than the human skull on the right.

Infer ***what this skull comparison might predict about the evolutionary relationship between* H. floresiensis *and* H. sapiens.**

Homo heidelbergensis—traits The transition from *H. ergaster* to modern humans appears to have occurred gradually. Numerous transitional fossils have been found that display a mixture of *H. ergaster* and *H. sapiens* traits. These fossils are often categorized as *Homo heidelbergensis,* but some scientists put them in the category *Homo sapiens.* These humans generally had larger brains and thinner bones than *H. ergaster* did, but they still had browridges and receding chins.

GET IT? **Relate** *H. heidelbergensis* to *H. sapiens.*

Homo neanderthalensis built shelter A distinct human species called *Homo neanderthalensis,* or the **Neanderthals,** evolved exclusively in Europe and Asia about 200,000 years ago, likely from *H. erectus* or a *Homo* intermediary. Neanderthals were shorter but had more muscle mass than most modern humans do. Their brains were sometimes even larger than the brains of modern humans, though the brains might have been organized in different ways. Neanderthals had thick skulls, bony browridges, and large noses. They also had a heavily muscled, robust stature, as illustrated in **Figure 21.** Evidence of heavy musculature appears in the extremely large muscle attachments and the bowing of the long bones.

Neanderthals lived near the end of the Pleistocene ice age, a time of bitter cold. Their skeletons reflect lives of hardship; bone fractures and arthritis seem to have been common. There is evidence that they used fire and constructed complex shelters. They hunted and skinned animals, and it is possible that they had basic language. There is also some evidence that they cared for their sick and buried their dead.

Are Neanderthals our ancestors? In some areas of their range, particularly in the Middle East and southern Europe, Neanderthals and modern humans overlapped for as long as 10,000 years. Some scientists suggest that the two species interbred. However, some studies suggest that Neanderthals were a distinct species that likely did not contribute to the modern human gene pool. As new information is discovered, scientists continue to debate the interactions between Neanderthals and modern humans. Neanderthals became extinct about 30,000 years ago.

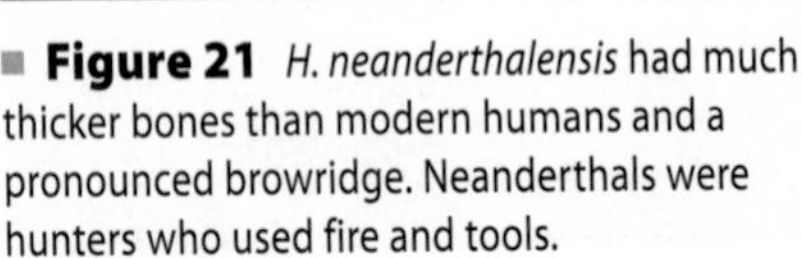

■ **Figure 21** *H. neanderthalensis* had much thicker bones than modern humans and a pronounced browridge. Neanderthals were hunters who used fire and tools.

Emergence of Modern Humans

The species that displaced the Neanderthals, *Homo sapiens*, is characterized by a more slender appearance than all other *Homo* species. They have thinner skeletons, rounder skulls, and smaller faces with prominent chins. Their brain capacity averages 1350 cm^3. *H. sapiens* first appeared in the fossil record, in what is now Ethiopia, about 195,000 years ago. These early *H. sapiens* made chipped hand axes and other sophisticated stone tools. They appear to have had the ability to use a range of resources and environments, and at some point they began migrating out of Africa. **Table 2** compares modern humans with other *Homo* species.

Table 2 Characteristics of the *Homo* species

Interactive Table

Species	Skull	Time in fossil record	Characteristics
Homo habilis		2.4–1.4 million years ago	• Average brain had a capacity of 650 cm^3 • Used tools
Homo ergaster		1.8–1.2 million years ago	• Average brain had a capacity of 1000 cm^3 • Had thinner skull bones • Had humanlike nose
Homo erectus		1.8 million–400,000 years ago	• Average brain had a capacity of 1000 cm^3 • Had thinner skull bones • Used fire
Homo neanderthalensis		300,000–200,000 years ago	• Average brain had a capacity of 1500 cm^3 • Buried their dead • Possibly had a language
Homo sapiens		195,000 years ago to present	• Average brain has a capacity of 1350 cm^3 • Does not have browridge • Has a small chin • Has language and culture

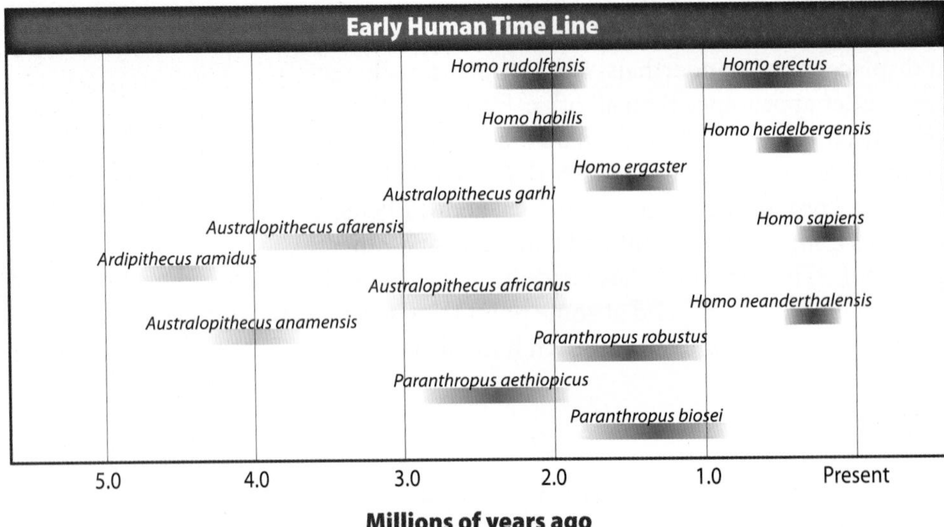

■ **Figure 22** The period of existence of several early hominins overlapped until about 30,000 years ago.

Out-of-Africa hypothesis The world's population 200,000 years ago looked significantly different from how it does today. It was inhabited by a morphologically diverse genus of hominins, including primitive humans, Neanderthals, and modern humans, as illustrated in **Figure 22.** By 30,000 years ago, however, only modern humans remained. Some scientists propose that these modern humans evolved from several dispersed populations of early *Homo* species at the same time in different areas of the world. According to this multiregional evolution model, modern races of humans arose in isolated populations by convergent evolution.

Most scientists explain the global dominance of modern humans with the African Replacement model or, more commonly, the Out-of-Africa hypothesis. According to this hypothesis, which was first proposed by Christopher Stringer and Peter Andrews of the British Museum of Natural History in 1988, modern humans evolved only once, in Africa, and then migrated to all parts of the world, eventually displacing other hominins.

"Mitochondrial Eve" The Out-of-Africa hypothesis was supported by mitochondrial DNA analysis of contemporary humans in the early 1990s. Mitochondrial DNA changes very little over time, and humans living today have nearly identical mitochondrial DNA. Researchers Allan Wilson and Rebecca Cann of the University of California, Berkeley, reasoned that the population with the most variation should be the population that has had the longest time to accumulate diversity. This was exactly what they found in the mitochondrial DNA of Africans. Because mitochondrial DNA is inherited only from the mother, this analysis suggested that *H. sapiens* emerged in Africa about 200,000 years ago from a hypothetical "Mitochondrial Eve."

Later, work by other scientists studying DNA sequences in the male Y chromosome yielded similar results. While some scientists think that a single movement of only a few hundred modern humans ultimately gave rise to the world's current population, others think the process occurred in phases, with some interbreeding among the species that humans displaced.

STUDY TIP

DISCUSSION GROUP Discuss with your classmates what you've learned about human evolution. What characteristics of early hominins have surprised you or your classmates?

GET IT? **Describe** evidence in support of the Out-of-Africa hypothesis.

■ **Figure 23** Cro-Magnons were known for their sophisticated cave paintings, tools, and weapons. The painting on the left was found in Lascaux Cave in France.

The beginning of culture The first evidence of complex human culture appeared in Europe only about 40,000 years ago, shortly before the Neanderthals disappeared. Unlike the Neanderthals, early modern humans expressed themselves symbolically and artistically in decorative artifacts and cave drawings, as illustrated in **Figure 23.** They developed sophisticated tools and weapons, including spears and bows and arrows. They were the first to fish, the first to tailor clothing, and the first to domesticate animals. These and many other cultural expressions marked the appearance of fully modern humans, the subspecies *Homo sapiens*. Some people call them **Cro-Magnons.** They represent the beginning of historic hunter-gatherer societies.

Connection to History Humans continued their migration throughout Europe and Asia. They probably reached Australia by boat and traveled to North America via a land bridge from Asia. From North America, they spread to South America. They adapted to new challenges along the way, leaving behind a trail of artifacts that we study today.

REVIEW IT! Human Ancestry

Section Summary

- The genus *Homo* is thought to have evolved from genus *Australopithecus.*
- Of the many species that have existed in the hominin group, only one species survives today.
- The first member of the genus *Homo* was *H. habilis.*
- The Out-of-Africa hypothesis suggests that humans evolved in Africa and migrated to Europe and Asia.
- *H. neanderthalensis* became extinct about 30,000 years ago, and *H. sapiens* moved into those areas inhabited by *H. neanderthalensis* at about the same time.

Self Check

Understand Main Ideas

1. MAINIDEA **Hypothesize** why only one genus and species remains in the hominin group.
2. **Describe** how *H. habilis* might have lived.
3. **Apply** what you have learned about the Out-of-Africa hypothesis to what you know about the arrival of *H. sapiens* in North America.
4. **Compare and contrast** *H. neanderthalensis* and *H. sapiens.*

Think Critically

5. **Classify** how you would classify a fossil that was found in France and dated at about 150,000 years old if the skull had a thick browridge, but in most other ways appeared human.

WRITING IN ▶ Biology

6. **Hypothesize** the importance of language to the early modern humans and how it might have contributed to their success.

BIOdiscoveries

1.1.1b, 1.1.2a, 1.1.2b

A New Species... or Something Else?

In 2003, scientists found a partial skeleton and fragments of six or more other skeletons in a cave on the island of Flores, Indonesia. The "hobbits," as the scientists dubbed them, were humanlike beings a little over three feet tall, with heads the size of grapefruits and chimpanzee-sized brains. Tests revealed that the partial skeleton and fragments ranged between 13,000 and 95,000 years old.

These little creatures are the cause of a big disagreement within the scientific community. Since their discovery, some scientists have claimed the "hobbits" are *Homo sapiens,* or modern humans, with a medical condition that caused their diminutive stature. Others insist that they are a new species, *Homo floresiensis.* Scientists on each side are using scientific methods to uncover the truth. Their different interpretations of the data are part of the collaborative scientific process.

Diseased modern humans? Scientists who doubt the "new species hypothesis" proposed several hypotheses to explain the tiny creatures' sizes and other characteristics. Some suggested that the "hobbits" were pygmies who suffered from microcephaly, a rare, sometimes genetic neurological disorder that results in a smaller-than-normal head. Other scientists have hypothesized that the miniature humans had hypothyroidism.

A new species? Most scientists who support the hypothesis that the "hobbits" are the new species *Homo floresiensis* think that they evolved from members of *Homo erectus,* a precursor to modern humans. Some, however, think that the "hobbits" evolved from an even earlier species of human called *Homo habilis.* Once on the island of Flores, scientists think that the organisms evolved to be dwarflike.

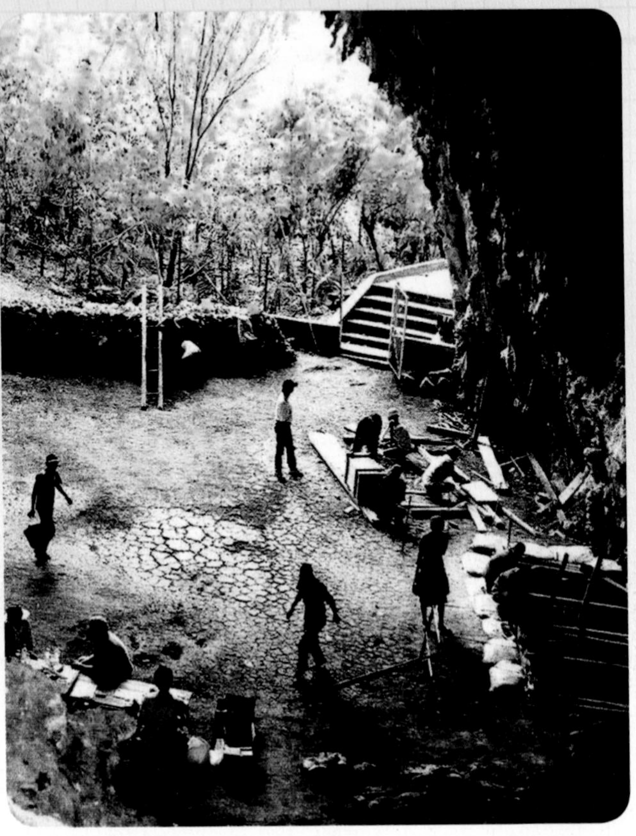

Scientists search for fossils at a cave site called Liang Bau on the island of Flores.

Structural differences Both groups of scientists are using the structural data provided by the bone fragments. These include the skull, wrist, foot, and shoulders. As more bone fragments are discovered and studied, more pieces are added to the puzzle.

WRITING IN ▶ Biology

Peer Review Research the controversial fossils found on Flores. Write an article as though you are one of the researchers. Include your hypothesis, evidence, and conclusions. Submit your article to your classmates for peer review.

WebQuest

BioLAB

What can you learn about bipedalism from comparing bones?

Background: Humans and chimpanzees have the same number of bones in the same places, but humans walk upright and chimpanzees do not. Can you identify the skeletal features that enable humans to walk upright on two legs? Assume that you are a paleontologist and have been given chimpanzee and human bones to identify and assemble. Then, you receive a third set. How is the mystery skeleton related to the human and chimpanzee skeletons?

Question: *What unique skeletal features did humans evolve to become bipedal?*

Materials

envelopes containing paper bones and clues (2)
paper, pencil, and ruler

Safety Precautions

Procedure

1. Read and complete the lab safety form.
2. Make a data table to help you compare the following characteristics of each of the three fossil sets you will examine: skull, rib cage, pelvis, arms, legs, and feet.
3. Make sure your teacher approves your table.
4. Open envelope #1.
5. Using the clues in your envelope, identify the bones, determine to which species they belong, and write down at least one distinguishing characteristic of each on your data table.
6. Open envelope #2.
7. Using the new set of clues, classify each new bone as chimpanzee, human, similar to both, similar to chimpanzee, or similar to human. Record the data in your table.

Analyze and Conclude

1. **List** features that a scientist might use to determine if a fossil organism was bipedal.
2. **Think Critically** Based on your knowledge, do you think the mystery fossil is bipedal? Why?
3. **Conclude** What organism do you think your mystery bones represent?
4. **Compare** your table with those of other students in the class. Did you arrive at the same conclusions? If not, discuss the differences.
5. **Experiment** Chimpanzees cannot completely straighten—or lock—their knees as humans can and must use more muscles when standing upright. Try standing for 10 s with your knees locked and for 10 s with your knees bent. Describe how your legs feel at the end.
6. **Reason,** from your mystery fossil bones, what it means to say that humans evolved in a mixed, or mosaic, pattern.

WRITING IN ▶ Biology

Research and discuss why bipedalism is often thought of as an evolutionary compromise. List skeletal injuries that humans suffer as a result of walking upright.

CHAPTER 16 STUDY GUIDE

BIGIDEA **Evolutionary change in a group of small, tree-living mammals eventually led to a diversity of species that includes modern humans.**

SECTION 1 Primates

MAINIDEA Primates share several behavioral and biological characteristics, which indicates that they evolved from a common ancestor.

- All primates share certain anatomical and behavioral characteristics.
- Primates include lemurs, New World monkeys, Old World monkeys, apes, and humans.
- Strepsirrhines are the most primitive living lineages of primates to evolve. They diverged from haplorhines before 55 mya.
- Anthropoids diverged from tarsiers by 50 mya.
- New World monkeys are the only nonhuman primates in the Americas.

VOCABULARY

- **opposable first digit**
- **binocular vision**
- **diurnal**
- **nocturnal**
- **arboreal**
- **anthropoid**
- **prehensile tail**
- **hominin**

SECTION 2 Hominoids to Hominins

MAINIDEA Hominins, a subgroup of the hominoids, likely evolved in response to climate changes of the Miocene epoch.

- Hominoids are all of the apes, including gibbons, orangutans, gorillas, chimpanzees, and humans and their extinct relatives.
- Several species of hominins appear in the fossil record.
- Hominins include humans, australopithecines, and other extinct species more closely related to humans than to chimpanzees.
- Bipedalism was one of the earliest hominin traits to evolve.

VOCABULARY

- **hominoid**
- **bipedal**
- **australopithecine**

SECTION 3 Human Ancestry

MAINIDEA Tracing the evolution of the genus *Homo* is important for understanding the ancestry of humans, the only living species of *Homo*.

- The genus *Homo* is thought to have evolved from the genus *Australopithecus*.
- Of the many species that have existed in the hominin group, only one species survives today.
- The first member of the genus *Homo* was *H. habilis*.
- The Out-of-Africa hypothesis suggests that humans evolved in Africa and migrated to Europe and Asia.
- *H. neanderthalensis* went extinct about 30,000 years ago and *H. sapiens* moved into those areas inhabited by *H. neanderthalensis* about the same time.

VOCABULARY

- ***Homo***
- **Neanderthal**
- **Cro-Magnon**

SECTION 1

Vocabulary Review

Replace each underlined word or phrase with the correct vocabulary term from the Study Guide page.

1. A fifth limb might be used by a primate to grip a limb while engaged in reaching for and eating food.
2. Primates that are active at night are "wet-nosed" primates.
3. Depth perception evolved as the faces of primates became flattened.

Understand Main Ideas

Use the figure below to answer question 4.

4. Which is the term for the movement demonstrated by this gibbon?
   A. brachiation
   B. knuckle-walking
   C. quadruped movement
   D. upright locomotion
5. Which group was the first to evolve?
   A. African apes
   B. hominins
   C. New World monkeys
   D. Old World monkeys
6. Which adaptation results in a better gripping ability?
   A. complex brain
   B. flexible forelimbs
   C. opposable digits
   D. prehensile tail
7. The first primates most resembled which animal?
   A. gibbon
   B. gorilla
   C. tamarin
   D. lemur

Constructed Response

8. **Open Ended** Describe the usefulness of binocular and color vision.
9. **Short Answer** Which groups of primates make up the anthropoids?

Think Critically

10. **Hypothesize** Why do you think primate fossils have not been found on Antarctica?
11. MAINIDEA Suppose that while on a trip to Brazil, you found a fossil of a primate that closely resembles a squirrel monkey. Into which group of anthropoids would the specimen be placed?

SECTION 2

Vocabulary Review

Define the following vocabulary terms in complete sentences.

12. australopithecine
13. bipedal
14. hominoid

Understand Main Ideas

15. Which hominin species made the fossilized footprints shown in **Figure 16?**
    A. *A. afarensis*
    B. *A. africanus*
    C. *Paranthropus*
    D. *Proconsul*
16. Which hominoid might be ancestral to apes and humans?
    A. *A. afarensis*
    B. *A. africanus*
    C. *Paranthropus*
    D. *Proconsul*

17. Which is the correct sequence of fossils as evidenced by the fossil record?
   A. *A. africanus, A. afarensis, Paranthropus, Proconsul*
   B. *Proconsul, A. afarensis, A. africanus, Paranthropus*
   C. *Proconsul, Paranthropus, A. afarensis, A. africanus*
   D. *Paranthropus, Proconsul, A. africanus, A. afarensis*

18. *A. afarensis* was bipedal but exhibited apelike traits. What type of evolutionary pattern might account for this?
   A. convergence
   B. mosaic
   C. divergence
   D. coevolution

Constructed Response

19. **Open Ended** Discuss the debate regarding the classification of *Paranthropus*.

Use the figure below to answer question 20.

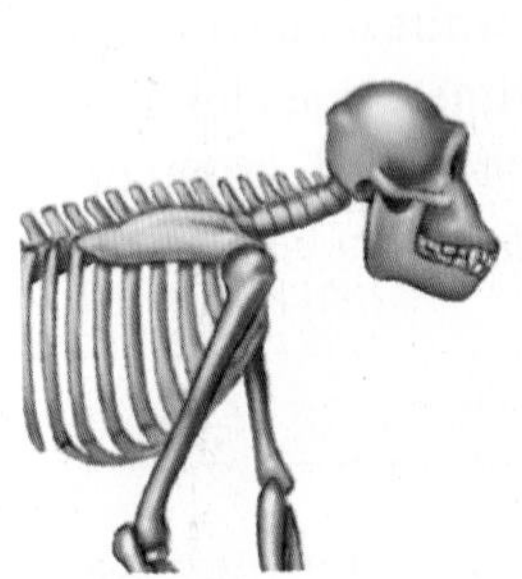

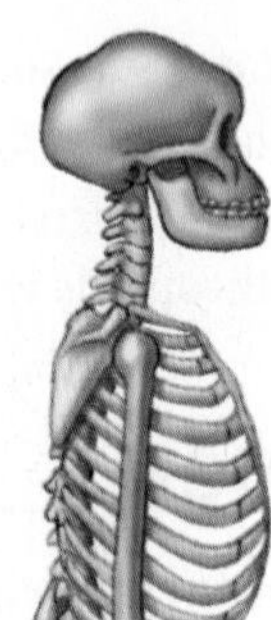

20. **Short Answer** Describe the relevance of the foramen magnum's location to bipedalism.

Think Critically

21. MAINIDEA Explain how climate change might have contributed to the evolution of bipedalism.

22. THEME FOCUS Why is biochemical evidence important in helping scientists learn about the divergence of primate groups?

SECTION 3

Vocabulary Review

Each of the following sentences is false. Make each sentence true by replacing the underlined word with a vocabulary term from the Study Guide page.

23. The genus *Australopithecus* is thought to be ancestral to the genus <u>*Proconsul*</u>.

24. <u>Cro-Magnons</u> were adapted to cold climates. They eventually were replaced by modern humans.

25. <u>*H. neanderthalensis*</u> is the scientific name for modern humans.

Understand Main Ideas

Use the figure below to answer question 26.

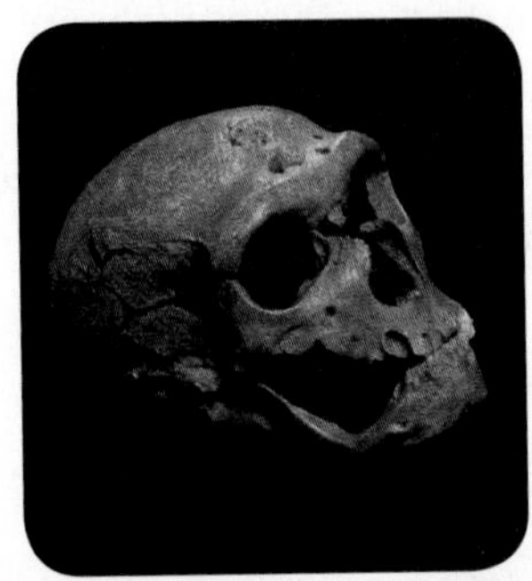

26. The large brain and thickened browridges illustrated by the skull above are characteristic of which species?
   A. Cro-Magnons
   B. modern *H. sapiens*
   C. Neanderthals
   D. *Proconsul*

27. The first undisputed member of the hominin group was which of the following?
   A. *A. africanus*
   B. *H. antecessor*
   C. *H. ergaster*
   D. *H. habilis*

28. Which hominin was likely the first to migrate long distances?
   A. *H. ergaster*
   B. *H. antecessor*
   C. *H. neanderthalensis*
   D. *H. sapiens*

29. Which hominin likely first used fire, lived in caves, and made tools?
   A. *H. ergaster*
   B. *H. erectus*
   C. *H. neanderthalensis*
   D. *H. sapiens*

30. *H. heidelbergensis* is generally considered part of which group?
   A. Neanderthals
   B. *H. sapiens*
   C. Cro-Magnons
   D. australopithecines

Use the figure below to answer questions 31 and 32.

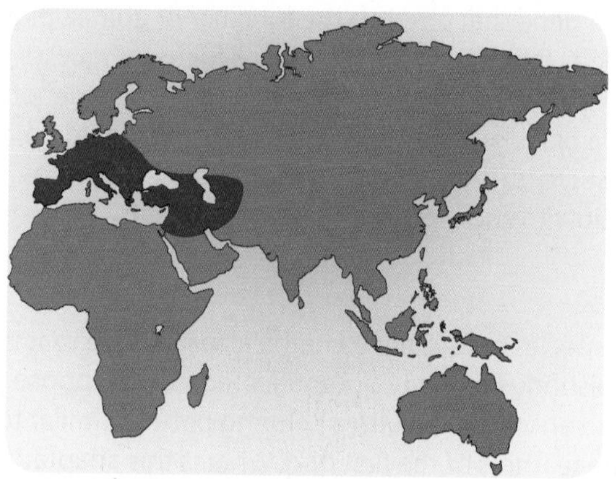

31. The map above represents the geographic range of which species?
A. *Homo erectus*
B. *Homo sapiens*
C. *Homo neanderthalensis*
D. *Homo heidelbergensis*

32. During what time did the species represented on the map live?
A. 300,000–200,000 years ago
B. 100,000–12,000 years ago
C. 2.4–1.4 million years ago
D. 1.8–1.2 million years ago

Constructed Response

33. MAINIDEA Describe the importance of *H. habilis* in human evolution.

34. Short Answer Describe the importance of fire to the migration of early *Homo* species.

35. Open Ended From what you have learned about the evolution of primates, do you think *Homo sapiens*, our species, will continue to evolve? Why?

Think Critically

36. Apply Concepts Explain why mitochondrial DNA instead of nuclear DNA is used to study the evolution of modern humans.

37. Predict If modern humans had not arrived in Europe, do you think Neanderthals would have persisted?

38. Hypothesize How might *H. floresiensis* have coexisted with modern humans?

Summative Assessment

39. BIGIDEA Identify three characteristics that modern humans share with other primates, and three that separate them from other primates. Infer why the three that separate humans from other primates are important.

40. WRITINGIN▶Biology Write a paragraph to describe what you imagine a day in the life of *A. afarensis* to have been like.

DBQ Document–Based Questions

Scientists generally consider walking, but not running, to be a key trait in the evolution of humans. Like apes, humans are poor sprinters when compared to quadruped animals such as horses and dogs. Unlike apes, but like some quadrupeds, humans are capable of endurance running (ER), running long distances over extended time periods. The graph below compares speed during ER to length of an organism's stride (two steps for a human).

Data obtained from: Bramble, D. and Lieberman, D. 2004. Endurance running and the evolution of *Homo*. *Nature* 432: 345–352.

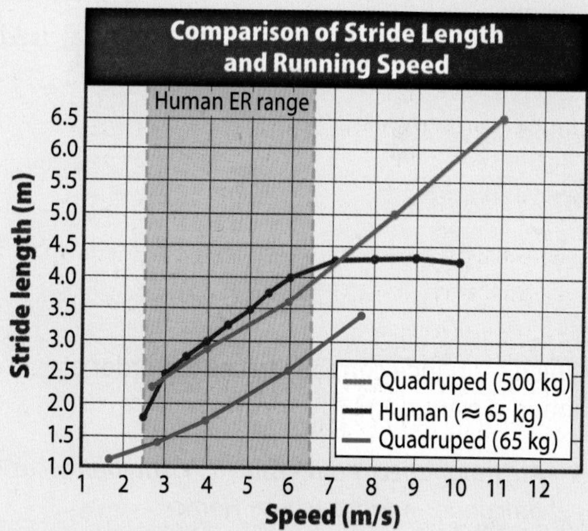

41. During ER, is the stride length of a human more like that of a 65-kg quadruped or a 500-kg quadruped?

42. Is a human more efficient at endurance running than a similar-sized quadruped, such as a cheetah or a leopard? Explain.

CUMULATIVE

MULTIPLE CHOICE

1 A scientific understanding of which natural process helped Darwin formulate the concept of natural selection?

A artificial selection

B continental drift

C group selection

D plant genetics

2 Which is a physiological adaptation?

A A beaver's teeth grow throughout its life.

B A chameleon's skin changes color to blend in with its surroundings.

C A human sleeps during the day in order to work at night.

D An insect does not respond to a chemical used as an insecticide.

3 Which sequence correctly traces the order of hominin evolution?

A *Australopithecus afarensis* → *Australopithecus africanus* → *Proconsul* → *Homo*

B *Australopithecus africanus* → *Australopithecus afarensis* → *Proconsul* → *Homo*

C *Homo* → *Australopithecus africanus* → *Australopithecus afarensis* → *Proconsul*

D *Proconsul* → *Australopithecus afarensis* → *Australopithecus africanus* → *Homo*

SHORT ANSWER

4 The gene that controls the fur color of guinea pigs codes for either dominant black fur (B) or recessive white fur (b). Suppose you want to find the genotype of a black guinea pig. Explain how you would do a test cross. Then use one or both Punnett squares below to show possible test-cross results.

5 A species of bird has a chemical in its tissue that is poisonous to many potential predators. Suppose you find another bird with a coloring pattern similar to the feathers of the first bird. What is this adaptation? Explain its importance.

6 Contrast the multiregional hypothesis and the Out-of-Africa hypothesis for human evolution.

7 Malathion is a pesticide used to control mosquitoes. Suppose a population of mosquitoes develops an ability to survive malathion spraying. How does this phenomenon fit with the ideas of variation and heritability in natural selection?

Use the figure below to answer question 8.

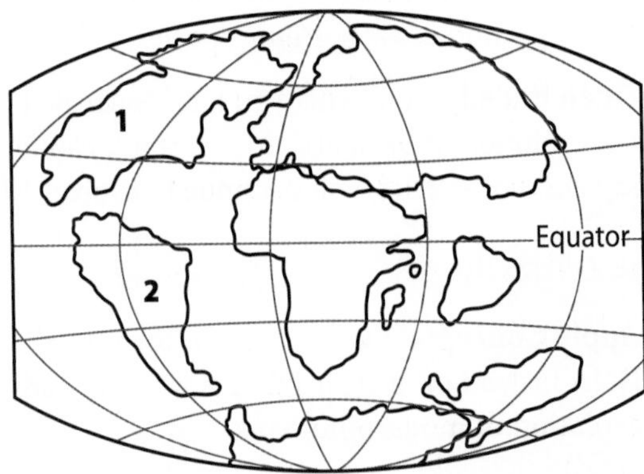

8 Discuss how land species and environments might change if the two numbered continents in the figure collided.

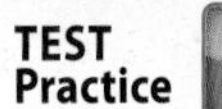

EXTENDED RESPONSE

9 Suppose you are explaining human evolution to someone who is unfamiliar with the topic. Hypothesize why *Homo sapiens* is the only surviving member of the human family.

10 Some aggressive bacterial infections are treated with combinations of antibiotics. How would such a treatment affect drug resistance?

ESSAY QUESTION

"If evolution almost always occurs by rapid speciation in small, peripheral isolates, then what should the fossil record look like? We are not likely to detect the event of speciation itself. It happens too fast, in too small a group, isolated too far from the ancestral range. Only after its successful origin will we first meet the new species as a fossil—when it reinvades the ancestral range and becomes a large central population in its own right. During its recorded history in the fossil record, we should expect no major change."

Gould, Stephen Jay. "Ladders, Bushes, and Human Evolution," Natural History 85 (April 1976): 30–31.

Using the information in the paragraph above, answer the following question in essay format.

11 Gould's research in evolution was devoted, in part, to explaining his theory of punctuated equilibrium. In an essay, explain why the fossil record is incomplete.

TEST PRACTICE

Use the diagram below to answer questions 12 and 13.

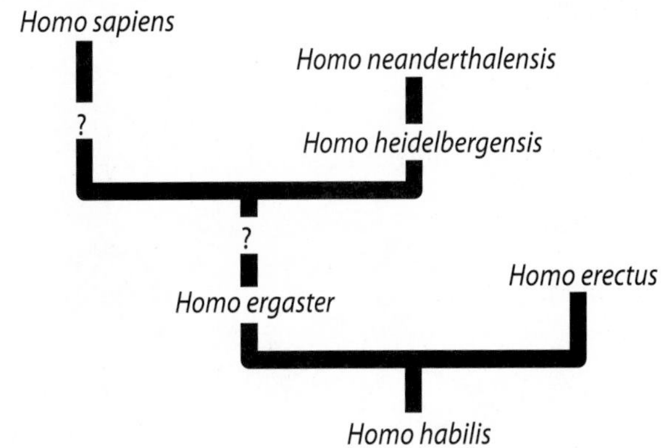

12 According to the diagram of the evolution of genus *Homo*, which is an ancestor of *Homo sapiens*?

A *Homo erectus*

B *Homo ergaster*

C *Homo neanderthalensis*

D *Homo rudolfensis*

13 Which scientific information might best support a hypothesis to test the relationships in the diagram?

A DNA sequences

B fossil tools

C carbon dating

D superposition

NEED EXTRA HELP?													
If You Missed Question . . .	1	2	3	4	5	6	7	8	9	10	11	12	13
Review Section . . .	15.1	15.2	16.2	13.1	15.3	16.3	15.1	14.1	16.3	15.2	15.3	16.3	16.3

The organisms in a single biome may share characteristics that allow them to survive similar conditions. These adaptations, such as those shared by desert organisms, can be used to create a system of classification.

LaunchLAB

How can desert organisms be grouped?

You might think of a desert as a place without much biodiversity, but a wide variety of species have adaptations for desert life. Some adaptations are useful for grouping these organisms. In this lab, you will develop a system for grouping desert organisms.

CHAPTER 17

Organizing Life's Diversity

1 The History of Classification

1.3.5b, ¥a, ¥d

2 Modern Classification

1.3.5b, 4.3.1j

3 Domains and Kingdoms

4.5.2b, 4.6.1g, ¥a, ¥c1, ¥c2, ¥c3, ¥c4, ¥e, ¥m, ¥n

THEMEFOCUS

Patterns Organisms are classified using genetics and phylogeny.

BIGIDEA

Evolution underlies the classification of life's diversity.

The Six Kingdoms

Make a layered look book Foldable. Label it as shown. Use it to organize your notes about the six kingdoms.

The Six Kingdoms
Bacteria
Archaea
Protista
Fungi
Plantae
Animalia

USE IT! Science Notebook

1 The History of Classification

MAIN IDEA

Biologists use a system of classification to organize information about the diversity of living things.

Essential Questions

- What are the similarities and differences between Aristotle's and Linnaeus's methods of classification?
- Using binomial nomenclature, how are scientific names written?
- What are the categories used in biological classification?

BIOLOGY 4 U

Think about how frustrating it would be if you went into a music store and all the CDs were in one big pile. You might need to go through all of them to find the one you want. Just as stores group CDs according to type of music and artist, biologists group living things by their characteristics and evolutionary relationships.

Review Vocabulary

morphology: the structure and form of an organism or one of its parts

New Vocabulary

classification
taxonomy
binomial nomenclature
taxon
genus
family
order
class
phylum
division
kingdom
domain

Multilingual eGlossary

Early Systems of Classification

Has anyone ever told you to get organized? You are probably expected to keep your room in order. Your teachers might have asked you to organize your notes or homework. Keeping items or information in order makes them easier to find and understand. Biologists find it easier to communicate and retain information about organisms when the organisms are organized into groups. One of the principal tools for this is biological classification. **Classification** is the grouping of objects or organisms based on a set of criteria.

Aristotle's system More than two thousand years ago, the Greek philosopher Aristotle (384–322 b.c.) developed the first widely accepted system of biological classification. Aristotle classified organisms as either animals or plants. Animals were classified according to the presence or absence of "red blood." Aristotle's "bloodless" and "red-blooded" animals nearly match the modern distinction of invertebrates and vertebrates. Animals were further grouped according to their habitats and morphology. Plants were classified by average size and structure as trees, shrubs, or herbs. **Table 1** shows how Aristotle might have divided some of his groups.

Table 1 Aristotle's Classification System — Interactive Table

Plants		
Herbs	**Shrubs**	**Trees**
Violets Rosemary Onions	Blackberry bush Honeysuckle Flannelbush	Apple Oak Maple
Animals with red blood		
Land	**Water**	**Air**
Wolf Cat Bear	Dolphin Eel Sea bass	Owl Bat Crow

Aristotle's system was useful for organizing, but it had many limitations. Aristotle's system was based on his view that species are distinct, separate, and unchanging. The idea that species are unchanging was common until Darwin presented his theory of evolution. Because of his understanding of species, Aristotle's classification did not account for evolutionary relationships. Additionally, many organisms do not fit easily into Aristotle's system, such as birds that do not fly or frogs that live both on land and in water. Nevertheless, many centuries passed before Aristotle's system was replaced by a new system that was better suited to the increased knowledge of the natural world.

Linnaeus's system In the eighteenth century, Swedish naturalist Carolus Linnaeus (1707–1778) broadened Aristotle's classification method and formalized it into a scientific system. Like Aristotle, he based his system on observational studies of the morphology and the behavior of organisms. For example, he organized birds into three major groups depending on their behavior and habitat. The birds in **Figure 1** illustrate these categories. The eagle is classified as a bird of prey, the heron as a wading bird, and the cedar waxwing is grouped with the perching birds.

Linnaeus's system of classification was the first formal system of taxonomic organization. **Taxonomy** (tak SAH nuh mee) is a discipline of biology primarily concerned with identifying, naming, and classifying species based on natural relationships. Taxonomy is part of the larger branch of biology called systematics. Systematics is the study of biological diversity with an emphasis on evolutionary history.

Binomial nomenclature Linnaeus's method of naming organisms, called binomial nomenclature, set his system apart from Aristotle's system and remains valid today. **Binomial nomenclature** (bi NOH mee ul • NOH mun klay chur) gives each species a scientific name that has two parts. The first part is the genus (JEE nus) name, and the second part is the specific epithet (EP uh thet), or specific name, that identifies the species. Latin is the basis for binomial nomenclature because Latin is an unchanging language, and, historically, it has been the language of science and education.

Figure 1 Linnaeus would have classified these birds based on their morphological and behavioral differences.
Infer ***in which group Linnaeus might have placed a robin.***

American bald eagle
Bird of prey

Great blue heron
Wading bird

Cedar waxwing
Perching bird

■ **Figure 2** *Cardinalis cardinalis* is a bird with many common names and is seen throughout much of the United States. It is the state bird of Illinois, Indiana, Kentucky, North Carolina, and Ohio.

Identify ***some other animals that have multiple common names.***

Biologists use scientific names for species because common names vary in useage. Many times the bird shown in **Figure 2** is called a redbird, sometimes it is called a cardinal, and other times it is called a Northern cardinal. In 1758, Linnaeus gave this bird its scientific name, *Cardinalis cardinalis.* The use of scientific names avoids the confusion that can be created with common names. Binomial nomenclature also is useful because common names can be misleading. If you were doing a scientific study on fish, you would not include starfish in your studies. Starfish are not fish. In the same way, great horned owls do not have horns and sea cucumbers are not plants.

VOCABULARY

WORD ORIGIN

Binomial nomenclature
comes from the Latin words *bi,* meaning *two; nomen,* meaning *name;* and *calatus,* meaning *list.*

When writing a scientific name, scientists follow these rules.

- The first letter of the genus name is always capitalized, but the rest of the genus name and all letters of the specific epithet are lowercase.
- If a scientific name is written in a printed book or magazine, it should be italicized.
- When a scientific name is written by hand, both parts of the name should be underlined.
- After the scientific name has been written once completely, the genus name often will be abbreviated to the first letter in later appearances. For example, the scientific name of *Cardinalis cardinalis* can be written *C. cardinalis.*

GET IT? **Explain** why Latin is the basis for many scientific names.

Modern classification systems The study of evolution in the 1800s added a new dimension to Linnaeus's classification system. Many scientists at that time, including Charles Darwin, Jean-Baptiste Lamarck, and Ernst Haeckel, began to classify organisms not only on the basis of morphological and behavioral characteristics. They also included inferred evolutionary relationships in their classification systems. Today, while modern classification systems remain rooted in the Linnaeus tradition, they have been modified to reflect new knowledge about evolutionary ancestry.

Taxonomic Categories

Think about how things are grouped in your favorite video store. How are the DVDs arranged on the shelves? They might be arranged according to genre—action, drama, or comedy—and then by title and year. Although taxonomists group organisms instead of DVDs, they also subdivide groups based on more specific criteria. The taxonomic categories used by scientists are part of a nested-hierarchical system—each category is contained within another, and they are arranged from broadest to most specific.

Species and genus A named group of organisms is called a **taxon** (plural, taxa). Taxa range from having broad diagnostic characteristics to having specific characteristics. The broader the characteristics, the more species the taxon contains. One way to think of taxa is to imagine nesting boxes—one fitting inside the other. You have already learned about two taxa used by Linnaeus—genus and species. Today, a **genus** (plural, genera) is defined as a group of species that are closely related and share a common ancestor.

Note the similarities and differences among the three species of bears in **Figure 3.** The scientific names of the American black bear *(Ursus americanus)* and Asiatic black bear *(Ursus thibetanus)* indicate that they belong to the same genus, *Ursus.* All species in the genus *Ursus* have massive skulls and similar tooth structures. Sloth bears *(Melursus ursinus),* despite their similarity to members of the genus *Ursus,* usually are classified in a different genus, *Melursus,* because they are smaller, have a different skull shape and size, and have two fewer incisor teeth than bears of the genus *Ursus.*

Family All bears, both living and extinct species, belong to the same family, Ursidae. A **family** is the next higher taxon, consisting of similar, related genera. In addition to the three species shown in **Figure 3,** the Ursidae family contains six other species: brown bears, polar bears, giant pandas, Sun bears, and Andean bears. All members of the bear family share certain characteristics. For example, they all walk flatfooted and have forearms that can rotate to grasp prey closely.

CAREERS IN BIOLOGY

Wildlife Biologist A scientist who studies organisms in the wild is called a wildlife biologist. Wildlife biologists might study populations of bears or work to educate the public about nature.

■ **Figure 3** All species in the genus *Ursus* have large body size and massive skulls. Sloth bears are classified in the genus *Melursus.*

Ursus americanus
American black bear

Ursus arctos horribilis
Grizzly bear

Melursus ursinus
Sloth bear

(l)Chad Graham/Getty Images, (c)Cleveland Metroparks Zoo/McGraw-Hill Education, (r)Joseph H. Bailey/Getty Images

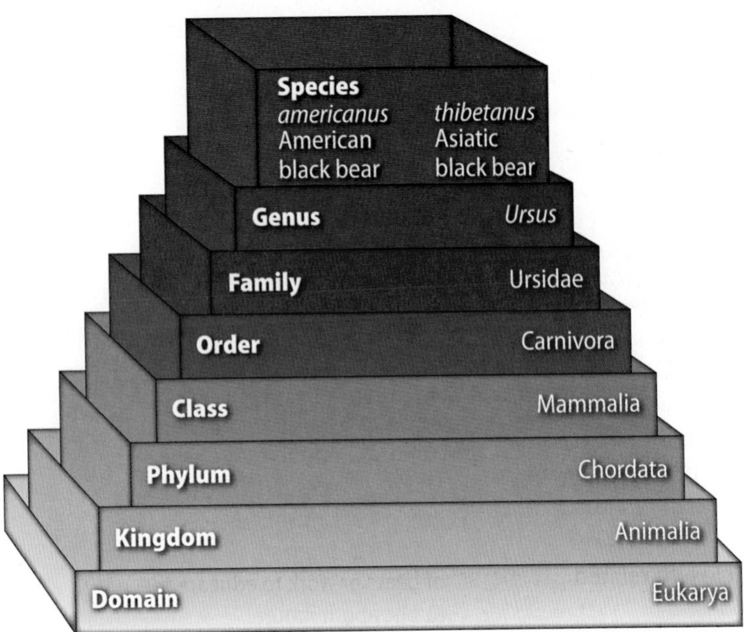

Figure 4 Taxonomic categories are contained within one another like nesting boxes. Notice that the American black bear and Asiatic black bear are different species; however, their classification is the same for all other categories.

Figure 4 shows how the taxa are organized into a hierarchical system. The figure also shows the complete classification from domain to species for the American black bear and the Asiatic black bear. Notice that the only difference in the classification of the two different bears is in the species category.

Higher taxa An **order** contains related families. A **class** contains related orders. The bears in **Figure 3** belong to the order Carnivora and class Mammalia. A **phylum** (FI lum) (plural, phyla) or **division** contains related classes. The term *division* is used instead of *phylum* for the classification of bacteria and plants. Sometimes scientists break the commonly used taxa into subcategories, such as subspecies, subfamilies, infraorders, and subphyla.

The taxon composed of related phyla or divisions is a **kingdom.** Bears are classified in phylum Chordata, Kingdom Animalia, and Domain Eukarya. The **domain** is the broadest of all the taxa and contains one or more kingdoms. The basic characteristics of the three domains and six kingdoms are described later in this chapter.

MiniLAB 1

Develop a Dichotomous Key

How can you classify items? Scientists group organisms based on their characteristics. These groups are the basis for classification tools called dichotomous keys. A dichotomous key consists of a series of choices that lead the user to the correct identification of an organism. In this lab, you will develop a dichotomous key as you group familiar objects.

Procedure

1. Read and complete the lab safety form.
2. Remove one **shoe** and make a shoe pile with other shoes from your group.
3. Write a question in your dichotomous key regarding whether the shoe has a characteristic of your choice. Divide the shoes into two groups based on that distinguishing characteristic.
4. Write another question for a different characteristic in your dichotomous key. Divide one of the subgroups into two smaller groups based on this distinguishing characteristic.
5. Continue dividing shoes into subgroups and adding questions to your key until there is only one shoe in each group. Make a branching diagram to identify each shoe with a distinctive name.
6. Use your diagram to classify your teacher's shoe.

Analysis

1. **Relate** taxa to the other groups you used to classify shoes. Which group relates to kingdom, phyla, and so on?
2. **Explain** how you were able to classify your teacher's shoe in Step 6.
3. **Critique** how your classification system could be modified to be more effective.

■ **Figure 5** This systematist is studying a cactus to determine if it is a new species.

Systematics Applications

Scientists who study classification provide detailed guides that help people identify organisms. Many times a field guide will contain a dichotomous (di KAHT uh mus) key, which is a key based on a series of choices between alternate characteristics. You can find out whether a plant or animal is poisonous by using a dichotomous key to identify it.

CAREERS IN ▸ Biology Systematists, like the one shown in **Figure 5** also work to identify new species and relationships among known species. They incorporate information from taxonomy, paleontology, molecular biology, and comparative anatomy in their studies. While the discovery of new species is exciting and important, learning a new connection between species also impacts science and society. For example, if a biologist knows that a certain plant such as the Madagascar periwinkle, *Catharanthus roseus,* produces a chemical that can be used to treat cancer, he or she knows that it is possible related plants also might produce the same or similar chemicals.

REVIEW IT! The History of Classification

Section Summary

- Aristotle developed the first widely accepted biological classification system.
- Linnaeus used morphology and behavior to classify plants and animals.
- Binomial nomenclature uses the Latin genus and species to give an organism a scientific name.
- Organisms are classified according to a nested hierarchical system.

 **Self Check**

Understand Main Ideas

1. MAINIDEA **Explain** why a biological classification system is important.
2. **Summarize** the rules for using binomial nomenclature.
3. **Compare and contrast** how modern classification systems differ from those used by Aristotle and Linnaeus.
4. **Classify** a giant panda, *Ailuropoda melanoleuca,* completely from domain to species level by referring to **Figure 4.**

Think Critically

WRITING IN ▸ Biology

5. Write a short story describing an application of biological classification.
6. **Consider** where you would expect to see more biodiversity: among members of a phyla or among members of a class. Why?
7. **Differentiate** between taxonomy and systematics.

USE IT! Science Notebook

2 Modern Classification

1.3.5b, 4.3.1j

MAINIDEA
Classification systems have changed over time as information has increased.

Essential Questions

- What are the similarities and differences between species concepts?
- What are the methods used to reveal phylogeny?
- How is a cladogram constructed?

BIOLOGY 4U
Did you ever try a new way of organizing your school notes? Just as you sometimes make changes in the way you do something based on a new idea or new information, scientists adjust systems and theories in science when new information becomes available.

REVIEW VOCABULARY
evolution: the historical development of a group of organisms

NEW VOCABULARY
phylogeny
character
molecular clock
cladistics
cladogram

Multilingual eGlossary

Determining Species

It is not always easy to define a species. Organisms that are different species by one definition might be the same species by a different definition. As knowledge increases, definitions change. The concept of a species today is much different than it was 100 years ago.

Typological species concept Aristotle and Linnaeus thought of each species as a distinctly different group of organisms based on physical similarities. This definition of species is called the typological species concept. It is based on the idea that species are unchanging, distinct, and natural types, as defined earlier by Aristotle. The type specimen was an individual of the species that best displayed the characteristics of that species. When another specimen was found that varied significantly from the type specimen, it was classified as a different species. For example, in **Figure 6** the color patterns on the butterflies' wings are all slightly different. At one time, they might have been classified as three different species because of these differences, but now they are classified as the same species.

Because we now know that species change over time, and because we know that members of some species exhibit tremendous variation, the typological species concept has been replaced. However, some of its traditions, such as reference to type specimens, remain.

■ **Figure 6** Although these tropical butterflies vary in their color patterns, they are classified as different varieties of the same species, *Heliconius erato*.
Describe ***why early taxonomists might have classified them as separate species.***

Barbara Strnadova/Photo Researchers

Biological species concept Theodosius Dobzhansky and Ernst Mayr, two evolutionary biologists, redefined the term species in the 1930s and 1940s. They defined a species as a group of organisms that is able to interbreed and produce fertile offspring in a natural setting. This is called the biological species concept, and it is the definition for species used throughout this textbook. Though the butterflies in **Figure 6** have variable color patterns, they can interbreed to produce fertile offspring and therefore are classified as the same species.

There are limitations to the biological species concept. For example, wolves and dogs, as well as many plant species, are known to interbreed and produce fertile offspring even though they are classified as different species. The biological species concept also does not account for extinct species or species that reproduce asexually. However, because the biological species concept works in most everyday experiences of classification, it is used often.

Phylogenetic species concept In the 1940s, the evolutionary species concept was proposed as a companion to the biological species concept. The evolutionary species concept defines species in terms of populations and ancestry. According to this concept, two or more groups that evolve independently from an ancestral population are classified as different species. More recently, this concept has developed into the phylogenetic species concept. **Phylogeny** (fi LAH juh nee) is the evolutionary history of a species. The phylogenetic species concept defines a species as a cluster of organisms that is distinct from other clusters and shows evidence of a pattern of ancestry and descent. When a phylogenetic species branches, it becomes two different phylogenetic species. For example, recall that when organisms become isolated—geographically or otherwise—they often evolve different adaptations. Eventually, they might become different enough to be classified as a new species.

This definition of a species solves some of the problems of earlier concepts because it applies to extinct species and species that reproduce asexually. It also incorporates molecular data. **Table 2** summarizes the three main species concepts.

STUDY TIP

NOTE DISCUSSIONS While you read, use self-adhesive notes to mark passages that you do not understand. In addition, mark passages you do understand and can explain to others with your own explanations, examples, and ideas. Then, discuss them with your classmates.

Launch Lab

Review Based on what you have read about classification systems, how would you now answer the analysis questions?

Table 2 Species Concepts — Interactive Table

Species Concept	Description	Limitation	Benefit
Typological species concept	Classification is determined by the comparison of physical characteristics with a type specimen.	Alleles produce a wide variety of features within a species.	Descriptions of type specimens provide detailed records of the physical characteristics of many organisms.
Biological species concept	Classification is determined by similar characteristics and the ability to interbreed and produce fertile offspring.	Some organisms, such as wolves and dogs that are different species, interbreed occasionally. It does not account for extinct species.	The working definition applies in most cases, so it is still used frequently.
Phylogenetic species concept	Classification is determined by evolutionary history.	Evolutionary histories are not known for all species.	Accounts for extinct species and considers molecular data.

VOCABULARY

SCIENCE USAGE V. COMMON USAGE

Character

Science usage: a feature that varies among species

Organisms are compared based on similar characters

Common usage: imaginary person in a work of fiction—a play, novel, or film

The queen was my favorite character in the book.

Characters

To classify a species, scientists often construct patterns of descent, or phylogenies, by using **characters**—inherited features that vary among species. Characters can be morphological or biochemical. Shared morphological characters suggest that species are related closely and evolved from a recent common ancestor. For example, because hawks and eagles share many morphological characters that they do not share with other bird species, such as keen eyesight, hooked beaks, and taloned feet, they should share a more recent common ancestor with each other than with other bird groups.

Morphological characters When comparing morphological characters, it is important to remember that analogous characters do not indicate a close evolutionary relationship. Remember that analogous structures are those that have the same function but different underlying construction. Homologous characters, however, might perform different functions but show an anatomical similarity inherited from a common ancestor.

Birds and dinosaurs Consider the oviraptor and the sparrow shown in **Figure 7.** At first you might think that dinosaurs and birds do not have much in common and do not share a close evolutionary relationship. A closer look at dinosaur fossils shows that they share many features with birds. Some fossil dinosaur bones, like those of the large, carnivorous theropod dinosaurs, show that their bones had large hollow spaces. Birds have bones with hollow spaces. In this respect, they are more like birds than most living reptiles, such as alligators, lizards, and turtles, which have dense bones. Also, theropods have hip, leg, wrist, and shoulder structures that are more similar to birds than to other reptiles. Recently, scientists have discovered some fossil dinosaur bones that suggest some theropods had feathers. The evidence provided by these morphological characters indicates that theropod dinosaurs are related more closely to modern birds than they are to other reptiles.

GET IT? **Explain** how morphological characters have influenced the classification of dinosaurs and birds.

■ **Figure 7** This artist's conception of *Oviraptor philoceratops* might not appear to be related to the sparrow *Zonotrichia leucophrys,* but these animals share many characteristics that indicate a shared evolutionary history.

Deduce ***which similarities might prompt you to think that these species are more closely related than was commonly thought.***

Oviraptor philoceratops

Zonotrichia leucophrys

■ **Figure 8** The representation of chromosome-banding patterns for these homologous chromosomes illustrates the evidence of a close evolutionary relationship among the chimpanzee, gorilla, and orangutan.

Biochemical characters Scientists use biochemical characters, such as amino acids and nucleotides, to help them determine evolutionary relationships among species. Chromosome structure and number is also a powerful clue for determining species similarities. For example, members of the mustard family (Cruciferae)—including broccoli, cauliflower, and kale—all look different in the garden, but these plants have almost identical chromosome structures. This is strong evidence that they share a recent common ancestor. Likewise, the similar appearance of chromosomes among chimpanzees, gorillas, and orangutans suggests a shared ancestry. **Figure 8** shows the similar appearance of a chromosome-banding pattern in these three primates.

DNA and RNA analyses are powerful tools for reconstructing phylogenies. Remember that DNA and RNA are made up of four nucleotides. The nucleotide sequences in DNA define the genes that direct RNA to make proteins. The greater the number of shared DNA sequences between species, the greater the number of shared genes—and the greater the evidence that the species share a recent common ancestor.

Scientists use a variety of techniques to compare DNA sequences when assessing evolutionary relationships. They can sequence and compare whole genomes of different organisms. They can compare genome maps made by using restriction enzymes. They also use a technique called DNA-DNA hybridization, during which single strands of DNA from different species are melted together. The success of the hybridization depends on the similarity of the sequences—complementary sequences will bind to each other, while dissimilar sequences will not bind. Comparing the DNA sequences of different species is an objective, quantitative way to measure evolutionary relationships.

VOCABULARY
ACADEMIC VOCABULARY
Corresponding
being similar or equivalent in character, quantity, origin, structure, or function
The corresponding sequences matched perfectly.

African elephant (savanna)

African elephant (forest)

Asiatic elephant

■ **Figure 9** The two populations of African elephants have been classified as the same species; however, DNA analysis shows that they might be separate species. The Asiatic elephant belongs to a separate genus.

A species example The classification of elephants is one example of how molecular data has changed traditional taxonomic organization. **Figure 9** shows pictures of elephants that live in the world today. Taxonomists have classified the Asiatic elephant *(Elephas maximus)* as one species and the African elephant *(Loxodonta africana)* as another for over 100 years. However, they have classified the two types of African elephant as the same species, even though the two populations look different. The forest-dwelling elephants are much smaller and have longer tusks and smaller ears than the savanna-dwelling elephants. Even so, scientists thought that the elephants interbred freely at the margins of their ranges. Recent DNA studies, however, show that the African elephants diverged from a common ancestor about 2.5 million years ago. Scientists have proposed renaming the forest-dwelling elephant *Loxodonta cyclotis.* Use **Data Analysis Lab 1** to explore molecular evidence for renaming the forest-dwelling elephant.

Data Analysis LAB 1

Based on Real Data*

Draw a Conclusion

Are African elephants a separate species?

Efforts to count and protect elephant populations in Africa were based on the assumption that all African elephants belong to the same species. Evidence from a project originally designed to trace ivory samples changed that assumption.

A group of scientists studied the DNA variation among 195 African elephants from 21 populations in 11 of the 37 nations in which African elephants range and from seven Asian elephants. They used biopsy darts to obtain plugs of skin from the African elephants. The researchers focused on a total of 1732 nucleotides from four nuclear genes that are not subject to natural selection. The following paragraph shows the results of the samples.

*Data obtained from: Roca, A.L., et al. 2001. Genetic evidence for two species of elephants in Africa. *Science* 293(5534): 1473–1477.

Data and Observations

"Phylogenetic distinctions between African forest elephant and savannah elephant population corresponded to 58% of the difference in the same genes between elephant genera Loxodonta (African) and Elephas (Asian)."

Think Critically

1. **Describe** the type of evidence used in the study.
2. **Explain** the evidence that there are two species of elephants in Africa.
3. **Propose** other kinds of data that could be used to support three different scientific names for elephants.
4. **Infer** Currently, *Loxodonta africana* is protected from being hunted. How might reclassification affect the conservation of forest elephants?

Molecular clocks You know that mutations occur randomly in DNA. As time passes, mutations accumulate, or build up, in the chromosomes. Some of these mutations do not affect the way cells function, and they are passed down from parent to offspring. Systematists can use these mutations to help them determine the degree of relationship among species. A **molecular clock** is a model that is used to compare DNA sequences from two different species to estimate how long the species have been evolving since they diverged from a common ancestor. **Figure 10** illustrates how a molecular clock works.

Scientists use molecular clocks to compare the DNA sequences or amino acid sequences of genes that are shared by different species. The differences between the genes indicate the presence of mutations. The more mutations that have accumulated, the more time that has passed since divergence. When the molecular clock technique was first introduced in the 1960s, scientists thought the rate of mutation within specific genes was constant. Hence, they used the clock as an analogy. However, scientists now know that the speed by which mutations occur is not always the same in a single gene or amino acid sequence.

The rate of mutation is affected by many factors, including the type of mutation, where it is in the genome, the type of protein that the mutation affects, and the population in which the mutation occurs. In a single organism, different genes might mutate, or "tick," at different speeds. This inconsistency makes molecular clocks difficult to read. Researchers try to compare genes that accumulate mutations at a relatively constant rate in a wide range of organisms. One such gene is the gene for cytochrome *c* oxidase, which is found in the mitochondrial DNA of most organisms.

Despite their limitations, molecular clocks can be valuable tools for determining a relative time of divergence of a species. They are especially useful when used in conjunction with other data, such as the fossil record.

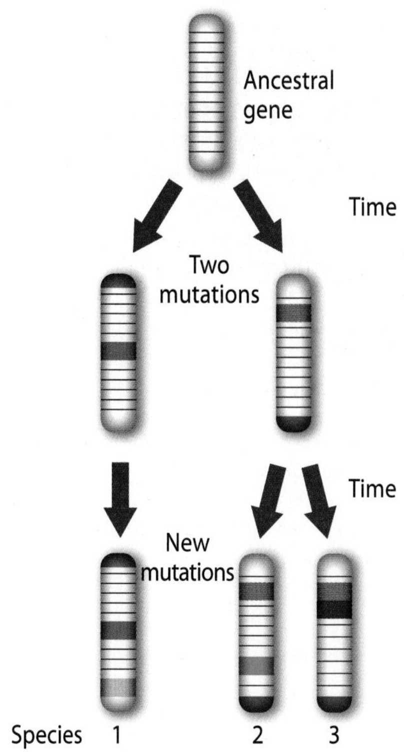

Figure 10 This molecular clock diagram shows how mutations might accumulate over time.

Infer ***why a clock is not a good analogy for this process.***

GET IT? **Explain** what the molecular clock model uses to compare DNA.

Phylogenetic Reconstruction

The most common systems of classification today are based on a method of analysis called cladistics. **Cladistics** (kla DIHS tiks) is a method that classifies organisms according to the order that they diverged from a common ancestor.

Vocabulary
Word Origin
Cladistics
comes from the Greek word *klados*, meaning *sprout* or *branch*

Character types Scientists consider two main types of characters when doing cladistic analyses. An ancestral character is found within the entire line of descent of a group of organisms. Derived characters are present in members of one group of the line but not in the common ancestor. For example, when considering the relationship between birds and mammals, a backbone is an ancestral character because both birds and mammals have a backbone and so did their shared ancestor. However, birds have feathers and mammals have hair. Therefore, having hair is a derived character for mammals because only mammals have an ancestor with hair. Likewise, having feathers is a derived character for birds.

CAREERS IN BIOLOGY

Evolutionary Geneticist An evolutionary geneticist uses genetic analysis to establish evolutionary relationships. Often, they work at colleges and universities where they teach and perform research.

Cladograms Sytematists use shared derived characters to make a cladogram. A **cladogram** (KLAD uh gram) is a branching diagram that represents the proposed phylogeny or evolutionary history of a species or group. A cladogram is a model similar to a pedigree. Just as a pedigree's branches show direct ancestry, a cladogram's branches indicate phylogeny. The groups used in cladograms are called clades. A clade is one branch of the cladogram.

Constructing a cladogram **Figure 11** is a simplified cladogram for some major plant groups. This cladogram was constructed in the following way. First, two species were identified, conifers and ferns, to compare with the lily species. Then, another species was identified that is ancestral to conifers and ferns. This species is called the outgroup. The outgroup is the species or group of species on a cladogram that has more ancestral characters with respect to the other organisms being compared. In the diagram below, the outgroup is moss. Mosses are more distantly related to ferns, conifers, and lilies.

The cladogram is constructed by sequencing the order in which derived characters evolved with respect to the outgroup. The closeness of clades in the cladogram indicate the number of characters shared. The group that is closest to the lily shares the most derived characters with lilies and thus shares a more recent common ancestor with lilies than with the groups farther away. The nodes where the branches originate represent a common ancestor. This common ancestor generally is not a known organism, species, or fossil. Scientists hypothesize its characters based on the traits of its descendants.

The primary assumption The primary assumption that systematists make when constructing cladograms is that the greater the number of derived characters shared by groups, the more recently the groups share a common ancestor. Thus, as shown in **Figure 11,** lilies and conifers have three derived characters in common and are presumed to share a more recent common ancestor than lilies and ferns, which share only two characters.

A cladogram also is called a phylogenetic tree. Detailed phylogenetic trees show relationships among many species and groups of organisms. **Figure 12** illustrates a phylogenetic tree that shows the relationships among the domains and kingdoms of the most commonly used classification system today.

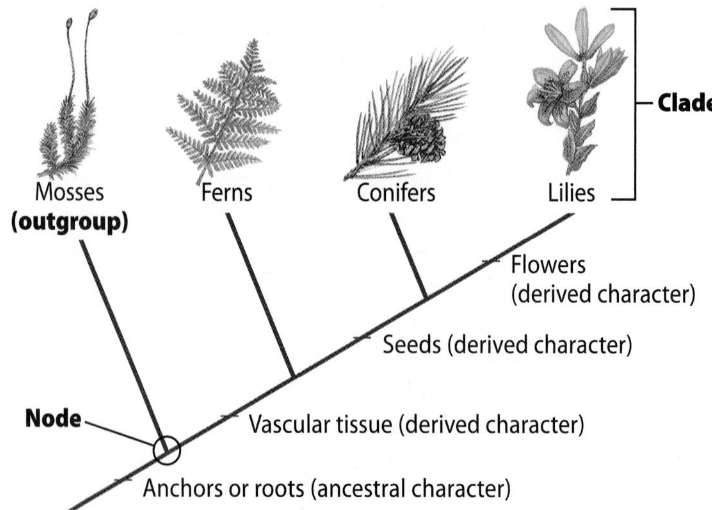

Animation

Personal Tutor

■ **Figure 11** This cladogram uses the derived characters of plant taxa to model its phylogeny. Groups that are closer to the lily on the cladogram share a more recent common ancestor.

Identify ***which clades have chloroplasts but do not produce seeds.***

VISUALIZING the Tree of Life

Figure 12 This phylogenetic tree shows the main branches in the "tree of life." Notice the three domains and the four kingdoms of Domain Eukarya. All of the branches are connected at the trunk, which is labeled *Common Ancestor.*

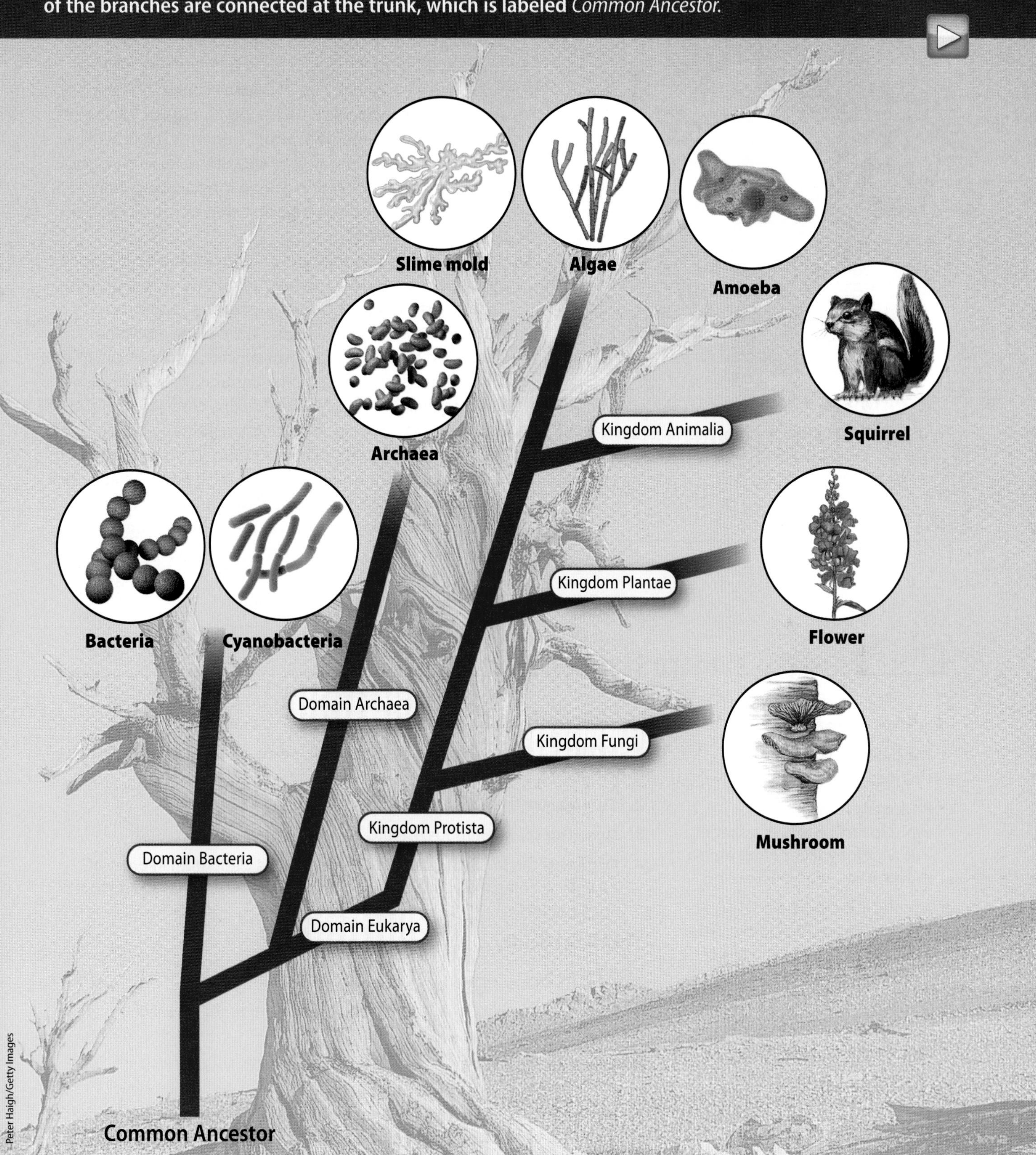

Peter Haigh/Getty Images

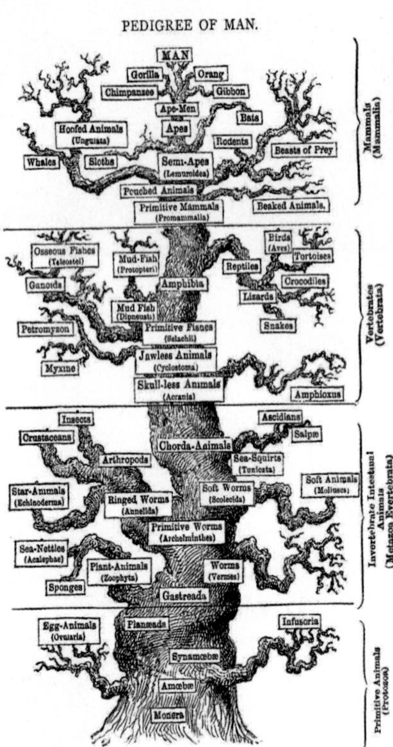

Figure 13 This illustration, made by Ernst Haeckel in the nineteenth century, was one of the first graphic depictions of evolutionary relationships.

Animation

Connection to History **The tree of life** In his book *On the Origin of Species,* Charles Darwin used the analogy of a tree to suggest that all of the species developed from one or a few species. He imagined the tree's trunk to represent ancestral groups and each of the branches to have similar species. From each branch, smaller and smaller branches grew. Finally, at the tips of the twigs of these branches were the leaves, consisting of individual living species. This concept was developed further, and the term *tree of life* was coined by German biologist Ernst Haeckel (1834–1919). **Figure 13** shows Haeckel's Genealogical Tree of Humanity. Haeckel was the first to represent phylogenies in the form of a tree, and while his phylogenies are no longer completely accurate, they represent the first step in the reconstruction of phylogenies.

The tree of life diagram in **Figure 13** is a representation of the diversity of living organisms. A tree of life that incorporates all known organisms is almost unimaginably large. Scientists have discovered and described nearly 1.75 million species, and they estimate that millions more remain unclassified. Assembling a comprehensive tree of life requires a convergence of data from phylogenetic and molecular analysis. It also requires collaboration among many scientists representing many disciplines, from molecular biology to Earth science to computer science. Many scientists think that the construction of a comprehensive tree of life, though an enormous task, is an important goal. Knowing how all organisms are related would benefit industry, agriculture, medicine, and conservation.

REVIEW IT! Modern Classification

Section Summary

- The definition of species has changed over time.
- Phylogeny is the inferred evolutionary history of a species, evidence for which comes from a variety of studies.
- A molecular clock uses comparisons of DNA sequences to estimate phylogeny and rate of evolutionary change.
- Cladistic analysis models evolutionary relationships based on sequencing derived characters.

Self Check

Understand Main Ideas

1. MAINIDEA **Describe** how the changing species concept has affected classification systems.
2. **Summarize** the different concepts of a species.
3. **Describe** some methods used to determine phylogeny.
4. **Organize** the following derived characters on a cladogram in order of ascending complexity: multicellular, hair, backbone, unicellular, and four appendages.

Think Critically

MATH IN Biology

5. **Describe** the mathematical challenges of counting the "ticks" of a molecular clock.
6. **Evaluate** the analogy of a tree for the organization of species based on phylogeny.
7. **Indicate** the hypothetical evolutionary relationship between two species if their DNA sequences share a 98 percent similarity.

Science Source

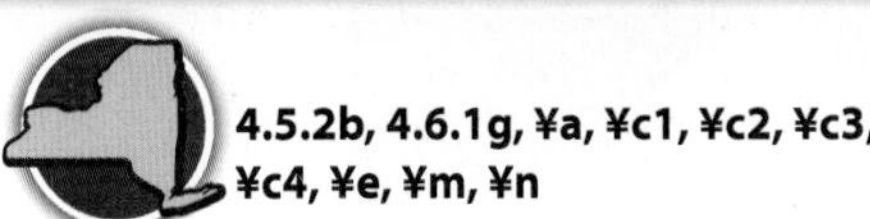

3 Domains and Kingdoms

4.5.2b, 4.6.1g, ¥a, ¥c1, ¥c2, ¥c3, ¥c4, ¥e, ¥m, ¥n

MAIN IDEA

The most widely used biological classification system has six kingdoms within three domains.

Essential Questions

- What are the major characteristics of the three domains?
- What are the differences among the six kingdoms?
- How are organisms classified at the kingdom level?

BIOLOGY 4U

What have you learned about the size of a kingdom as compared to a city, a village, or an individual home in your history classes? How does this knowledge help you understand the classification system?

REVIEW VOCABULARY

eukaryote: an organism composed of one or more cells containing a nucleus and membrane-bound organelles

NEW VOCABULARY

archaea
protist
fungus

Multilingual eGlossary

Virtual Lab

Grouping Species

The broadest category in the classification system used by most biologists is the domain. There are three domains: Bacteria, Archaea, and Eukarya. Within these domains are six kingdoms: Bacteria, Archaea, Protists, Fungi, Plantae, and Animalia. Organisms are classified into domains according to cell type and structure, and into kingdoms according to cell type, structure, and nutrition.

This three-domain, six-kingdom classification system has been in use for less than three decades. It was modified from a system that did not have domains but had five kingdoms after scientists discovered an entirely new kind of organism in the 1970s. These new organisms are unicellular prokaryotes that scientists named archaea (ar KEE uh). Subsequent biochemical studies found that archaea are significantly different from the only other prokaryotes then known—the bacteria—and, in 1990, they were renamed and a new classification scheme was proposed to accommodate them. Archaea are now members of their own domain.

Domain Bacteria

Connection to Chemistry Bacteria, members of Domain and Kingdom Bacteria, are prokaryotes whose cell walls contain peptidoglycan (pep tih doh GLY kan). Peptidoglycan is a polymer that contains two kinds of sugars that alternate in the chain. The amino acids of one sugar are linked to the amino acids in other chains, creating a netlike structure that is simple and porous, yet strong. Two examples of bacteria are shown in **Figure 14.**

Figure 14 Bacteria vary in their habitats and their methods of obtaining nourishment. The bacteria *Mycobacterium tuberculosis* that cause tuberculosis are heterotrophs. Cyanobacteria, such as *Anabaena,* are autotrophs.

Color-Enhanced SEM Magnification: 15,000×

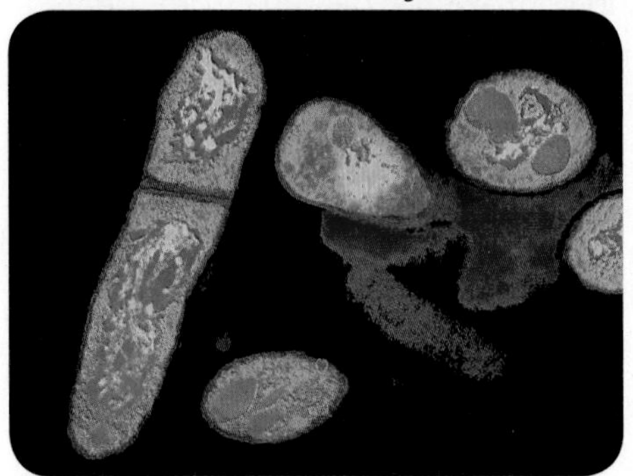

Mycobacterium tuberculosis

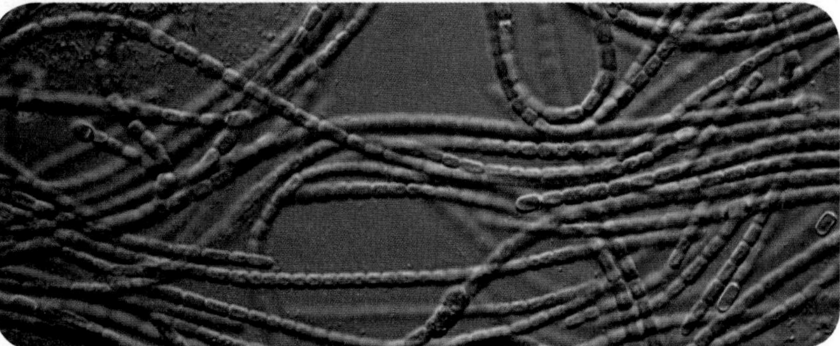

Anabaena

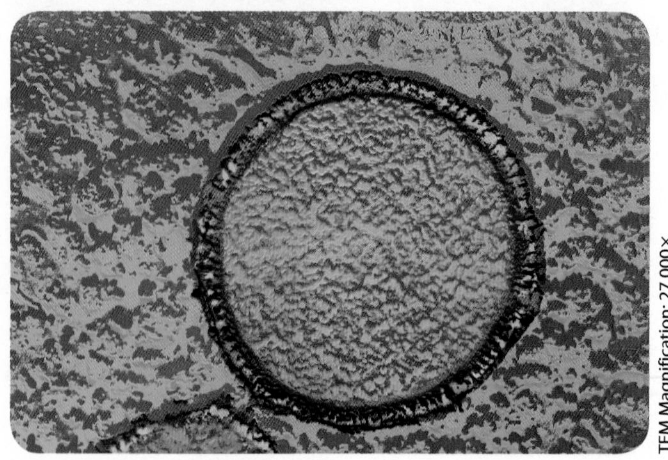

■ **Figure 15** This electron microscope image of *Staphylothermus marinus* shows the cell wall (green) and cell contents (pink). *S. marinus* is an extremophile found in deep ocean thermal vents.

Bacteria are a diverse group that can survive in many different environments. Some are aerobic organisms that need oxygen to survive, while others are anaerobic organisms that die in the presence of oxygen. Some bacteria are autotrophic and produce their own food, but most are heterotrophic and get their nutrition from other organisms. Bacteria are more abundant than any other organism. There are probably more bacteria in your body than there are people in the world. You can view some different types of bacteria in **MiniLab 2.**

VOCABULARY

WORD ORIGIN

Archaea
comes from the Greek word *archaios*, meaning *ancient* or *primitive*

Domain Archaea

Archaea (ar KEE uh), the species classified in Domain Archaea, are thought to be more ancient than bacteria and yet more closely related to eukaryote ancestors. Their cell walls do not contain peptidoglycan, and they have some of the same proteins that eukaryotes do. They are diverse in shape and nutrition requirements. Some are autotrophic, but most are heterotrophic. Archaea are called extremophiles because they can live in extreme environments. They have been found in boiling hot springs, salty lakes, thermal vents on the oceans' floors, and in the mud of marshes where there is no oxygen. The archaea *Staphylothermus marinus,* shown in **Figure 15,** is found in deep ocean thermal vents and can live in water temperatures up to 98°C.

MiniLAB 2

Compare Bacteria

How do the physical characteristics of various types of bacteria compare? Investigate the different features of bacteria by viewing prepared bacteria slides under the microscope.

Procedure

1. Read and complete the lab safety form.
2. Observe the prepared **slides of bacteria** with a **compound light microscope.**
3. Create a data table to compare the shapes and features of the bacteria you observe.
4. Compare and contrast the bacteria from the prepared slides. Record your observations and comparisons in your data table.

Analysis

1. **Compare and contrast** the shapes of the individual bacteria cells that you observed.
2. **Describe** whether any of your bacteria samples formed colonies. What does a colony look like?
3. **Design** a classification system for the bacteria that you observed based on the collected data.

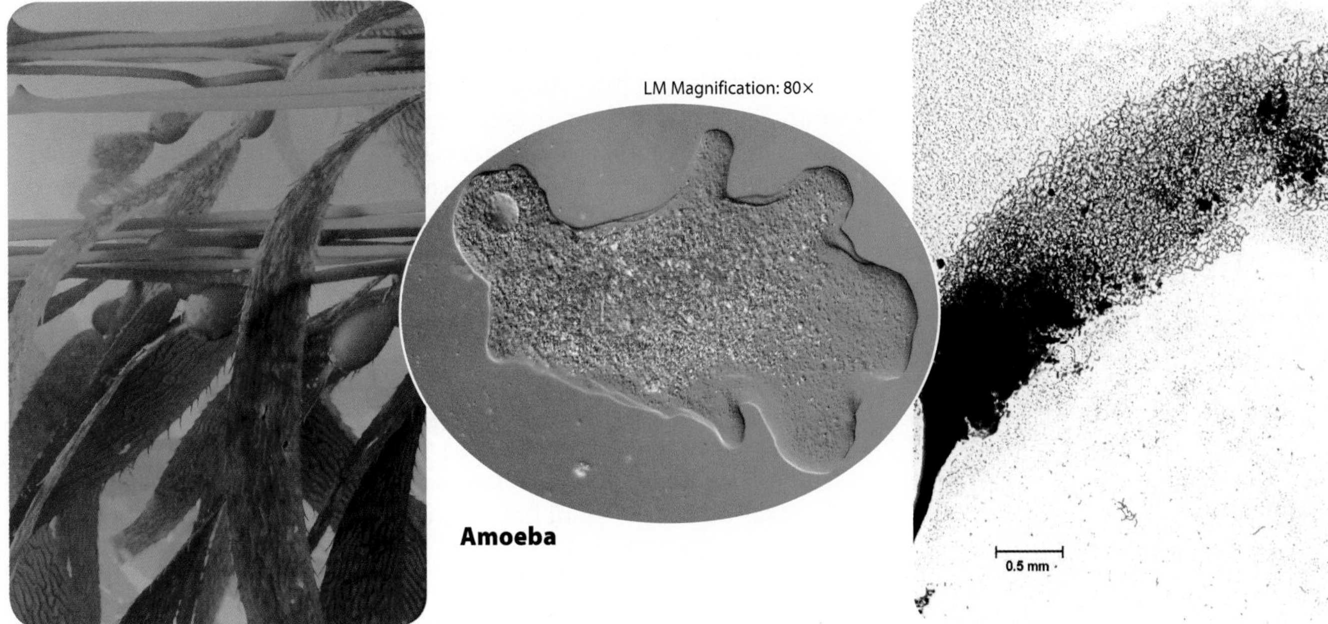

■ **Figure 16** These protists look different, but they all are eukaryotes, live in moist environments, and do not have organs.

Infer ***which of these protists are plantlike, animal-like, or funguslike.***

Domain Eukarya

Cells with a membrane-bound nucleus and other membrane-bound organelles are called eukaryotic cells. All organisms with these cells are called eukaryotes and are classified in Domain Eukarya. Domain Eukarya contains Kingdom Protista, Kingdom Fungi, Kingdom Plantae, and Kingdom Animalia.

Kingdom Protista The wide variety of species shown in **Figure 16** belong to Kingdom Protista. Members of Kingdom Protista are called protists. **Protists** are eukaryotic organisms that can be unicellular, colonial, or multicellular. Unlike plants or animals, protists do not have organs. Though protists are not necessarily similar to each other, they do not fit in any other kingdoms. They are classified into three broad groups.

The plantlike protists are called algae. All algae, such as kelp, are autotrophs that perform photosynthesis. Animal-like protists are called protozoans. Protozoans, such as amoebas, are heterotrophs. Funguslike protists include slime molds and mildews, and they comprise the third group of protists. Euglenoids (yoo GLEE noyds) are a type of protist that has both plantlike and animal-like characteristics. They usually are grouped with the plantlike protists because they have chloroplasts and can perform photosynthesis.

BrainPOP

Kingdom Fungi A **fungus** is a unicellular or multicellular eukaryote that absorbs nutrients from organic materials in its environment. Members of Kingdom Fungi are heterotrophic, lack motility—the ability to move—and have cell walls. Their cell walls contain a substance called chitin (KI tun)—a rigid polymer that provides structural support. A fungus consists of a mass of threadlike filaments called hyphae (HI fee). Hyphae are threadlike filaments that are responsible for the fungus's growth, feeding, and reproduction. Fungi fossils exist that are over 400 million years old, and there are more than 70,000 known species.

FOLDABLES®
Incorporate information from this section into your Foldable.

■ **Figure 17** Fungi come in a variety of sizes, from microscopic yeasts to multicellular forms, such as the mushrooms shown here.

Fungi, such as the mushrooms in **Figure 17,** are heterotrophic organisms. Some fungi are parasites—organisms that grow and feed on other organisms. Other fungi are saprobes—organisms that get their nourishment from dead or decaying organic matter. Unlike heterotrophs that digest their food internally, fungi secrete digestive enzymes into their food source and then absorb digested materials directly into their cells. Fungi that live in a mutualistic relationship with algae are called lichens. Lichens get their food from the algae that live among their hyphae.

Kingdom Plantae There are more than 250,000 species of plants in Kingdom Plantae (PLAN tuh). These organisms form the base of all terrestrial habitats. All plants are multicellular and have cell walls composed of cellulose. Most plants contain chloroplasts, where photosynthesis is carried out, but a few plants are heterotrophic. For example, the parasitic dodder plant has no green parts and extracts its food from host plants through suckers.

All plants possess cells that are organized into tissues, and many plants also possess organs such as roots, stems, and leaves. Like the fungi, plants lack motility. However, some plants do have reproductive cells that have flagella, which propel them through water. The characteristics of plants and members of the other five kingdoms are summarized in **Table 3.**

GET IT? **Describe** three characteristics of plants.

Table 3 Kingdom Characteristics — Interactive Table

Domain	Bacteria	Archaea	Eukarya			
Kingdom	Bacteria	Archaea	Protista	Fungi	Plantae	Animalia
Example	*Pseudomonas* SEM Magnification: 5500×	*Methanopyrus* TEM Magnification: 25,000×	*Paramecium* LM Magnification: 150×	Mushroom	Moss	Earthworm
Cell type	Prokaryote		Eukaryote			
Cell walls	Cell walls with peptidoglycan	Cell walls without peptidoglycan	Cell walls with cellulose in some	Cell walls with chitin	Cell walls with cellulose	No cell walls
Number of cells	Unicellular		Unicellular and multicellular	Most multicellular	Multicellular	
Nutrition	Autotroph or heterotroph			Heterotroph	Autotroph	Heterotroph

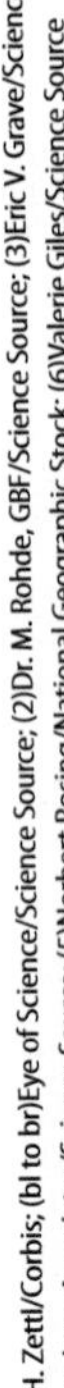

Coral

Fish

Rabbit

■ **Figure 18** Members of Kingdom Animalia can look very different from each other, even though they are in the same kingdom.

Kingdom Animalia Members of Kingdom Animalia are commonly called animals. More than one million animal species have been identified. All animals are heterotrophic, multicellular eukaryotes. Animal cells do not have cell walls. All animal cells are organized into tissues, and most tissues are organized into organs, such as skin, a stomach, and a brain. Animal organs often are organized into complex organ systems, like digestive, circulatory, or nervous systems. Animals range in size from a few millimeters to many meters. They live in the water, on land, and in the air. **Figure 18** shows some of the variety of organisms classified in Kingdom Animalia. Most animals are motile, although some, such as coral, lack motility as adults.

Viruses—an exception Have you ever experienced a cold or the flu? If so, you have had a close encounter with a virus. A virus is a nucleic acid surrounded by a protein coat. Viruses do not possess cells, nor are they cells, and are not considered to be living. Because they are nonliving, they usually are not placed in the biological classification system.

REVIEW IT! Domains and Kingdoms

Section Summary

- Domains Bacteria and Archaea contain prokaryotes.
- Organisms are classified at the kingdom level based on cell type, structures, and nutrition.
- Domain Eukarya contains four kingdoms of eukaryotes.
- Because viruses are not living, they are not included in the biological classification system.

Self Check

Understand Main Ideas

1. MAINIDEA **State** the three domains and the kingdoms in each.
2. **Compare and contrast** characteristics of the three domains.
3. **Explain** the difference between Kingdom Protista and Kingdom Fungi.
4. **Classify** to the kingdom level an organism that has organ systems, lacks cell walls, and ingests food.

Think Critically

5. **Summarize** the reasons why systematists separated Domain Bacteria from Domain Archaea.

WRITING IN ▶ Biology

6. Write an essay for or against including viruses in the biological classification system.

(l)Georgette Douwma/Getty Images, (c)Tim Laman/National Geographic/Getty Images, (r)U.S. Fish & Wildlife Service/Lewis Gorman

cutting-edge BIOLOGY

4.7.3a

DNA BAR CODES

Most people would find it odd if their friend collected vials containing muscles from 940 different species of fish—but then again most people have not undertaken a project as ambitious as this one.

DNA UPC Paul Herbert, a geneticist at the University of Guelph in Ontario, Canada, is trying to gather cell samples from all of the world's organisms. With small pieces of tissue no larger than the head of a pin, Herbert and his international colleagues are working to assign DNA bar codes to every living species.

Herbert has shown that the segment of mitochondrial DNA, called cytochrome *c* oxidase I, or COI, can be used as a diagnostic tool to tell animal species apart. The COI gene is simple to isolate and allows for identification of an animal. A different gene would need to be used for plants. Just like UPC codes, the DNA segment sequence could be stored in a master database that would allow for easy access to the material. A hand scanner, when supplied with a small piece of tissue, such as a scale, a hair, or a feather, could identify the species almost instantly.

Potential benefits This technology has several potential benefits. A doctor might use it to pinpoint disease-causing organisms quickly to prevent epidemics or to determine what antivenom to give a snakebite victim. Health inspectors could scan foods for plant and animal contaminants. People who are curious about their surroundings could learn what lives around them. Farmers would be able to identify pests and use species-specific methods for their removal.

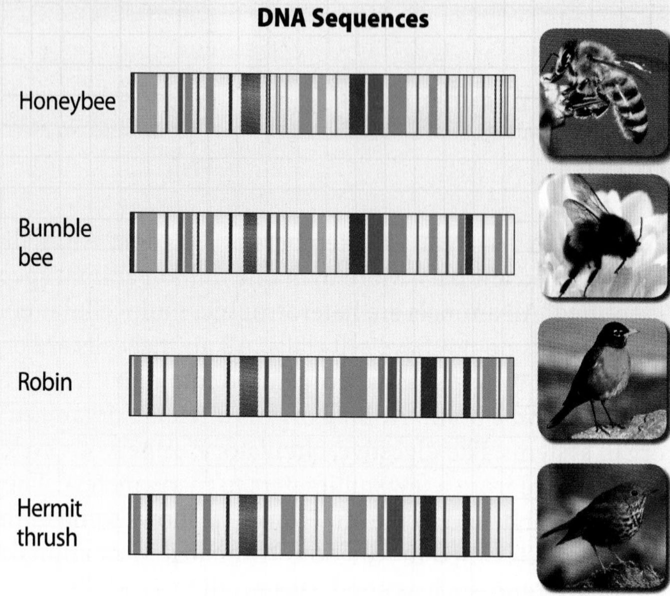

This representation of DNA barcodes shows that more closely related species would have more similar barcodes.

A new way to classify Using bioinformatics—a field of science in which biology, computer science, and information technology merge—to create a database of DNA barcodes allows taxonomists to classify more organisms quickly.

Currently, taxonomists have identified approximately 1.75 million species. Scientists estimate that anywhere between 10 and 100 million species exist. Historically, species have been classified using morphology, genetics, phylogeny, habitat, and behavior. While the bar codes would not replace classic taxonomic methods, they could supplement them by giving scientists another tool to use.

E-COMMUNICATION

Fact Finder Think of at least three questions you have about DNA bar coding. Research to find answers to your questions. Then, share your questions and answers with your class by e-mailing them to your teacher.

WebQuest

BioLAB 1.2.2a

How can organisms be grouped on a cladogram?

Background: When a cladogram is made, derived characters are used to divide the organisms into groups called clades. In this exercise, you will use simulated data to learn how to make a simple cladogram and then make your own cladogram.

Question: *How can you use organisms' characteristics to construct a cladogram?*

Materials

paper and pencil
examples of cladograms
photographs of various organisms
books describing characteristics of organisms

Procedure

1. Read and complete the lab safety form.
2. Examine the data table provided.
3. Compare the shared derived characteristics of the sample organisms. Assume that all the characteristics of your outgroup are ancestral. To make the data easier to compare, note that a "0" has been assigned to each ancestral character and a "1" to all derived characters.
4. Use the information to develop a cladogram that best shows the relationships of the organisms.
5. Make sure your teacher approves your cladogram before you proceed.
6. Choose four organisms from one of the domains you have studied that you believe are closely related.
7. Develop a table of derived characteristics of these organisms similar to the table you used in Step 2. Use your table to develop a cladogram that groups the organisms based on their shared derived characters.

Data Table for Cladistic Analysis

Organisms	Characters			
	1	2	3	4
A	b(1)	a(0)	a(0)	b(1)
B	b(1)	b(1)	b(1)	a(0)
C	b(1)	a(0)	b(1)	a(0)

Data obtained from: Lipscomb, D. 1998. Basics of cladistic analysis. George Washington University. http://www.gwu.edu/~clade/faculty/lipscomb/Cladistics.pdf

Analyze and Conclude

1. **Think Critically** How did you determine which were the ancestral and which were the derived characters of the organisms you examined?
2. **Explain** how you determined which characteristics to use to separate the clades.
3. **Explain** which organism is the outgroup on your cladogram. Why?
4. **Critique** Trade data tables with another lab group. Use their data to draw a cladogram. Compare the two cladograms and explain any differences.
5. **Error Analysis** What type of error would mistaking analogous structures as homologous introduce into a cladogram? Examine your second cladogram and determine if you have made this error.

APPLY YOUR SKILL

Construct Molecular data, such as the amino acid sequences of shared proteins, can be used to make cladograms. Research cytochrome *c*, a protein important in aerobic respiration, and decide how it could be used to construct a cladogram.

CHAPTER 17 STUDY GUIDE

BIGIDEA **Evolution underlies the classification of life's diversity.**

SECTION 1 The History of Classification

MAINIDEA Biologists use a system of classification to organize information about the diversity of living things.

- Aristotle developed the first widely accepted biological classification system.
- Linnaeus used morphology and behavior to classify plants and animals.
- Binomial nomenclature uses the Latin genus and species to give an organism a scientific name.
- Organisms are classified according to a nested hierarchical system.

VOCABULARY

- **classification**
- **taxonomy**
- **binomial nomenclature**
- **taxon**
- **genus**
- **family**
- **order**
- **class**
- **phylum**
- **division**
- **kingdom**
- **domain**

SECTION 2 Modern Classification

MAINIDEA Classification systems have changed over time as information has increased.

- The definition of species has changed over time.
- Phylogeny is the inferred evolutionary history of a species, evidence for which comes from a variety of studies.
- A molecular clock uses comparisons of DNA sequences to estimate phylogeny and rate of evolutionary change.
- Cladistic analysis models evolutionary relationships based on sequencing derived characters.

VOCABULARY

- **phylogeny**
- **character**
- **molecular clock**
- **cladistics**
- **cladogram**

SECTION 3 Domains and Kingdoms

MAINIDEA The most widely used biological classification system has six kingdoms within three domains.

- Domains Bacteria and Archaea contain prokaryotes.
- Organisms are classified at the kingdom level based on cell type, structures, and nutrition.
- Domain Eukarya contains four kingdoms of eukaryotes.
- Because viruses are not living, they are not included in the biological classification system.

VOCABULARY

- **archaea**
- **protist**
- **fungus**

SECTION 1

Vocabulary Review

Match each definition with the correct term from the Study Guide page.

1. system of naming species using two words
2. taxon of closely related species that share a recent common ancestor
3. branch of biology that groups and names species based on studies of their different characteristics

Understand Main Ideas

4. On what did Linnaeus base his classification?
   A. derived characters
   B. binomial nomenclature
   C. morphology and habitat
   D. evolutionary relationship

Use the table to answer questions 5 and 6.

Classification of Selected Mammals				
Kingdom	Animalia	Animalia	Animalia	Animalia
Phylum	Chordata	Chordata	Chordata	Chordata
Class	Mammalia	Mammalia	Mammalia	Mammalia
Order	Cetacea	Carnivora	Carnivora	Carnivora
Family	Mysticeti	Felidae	Canidae	Canidae
Genus	*Balenopora*	*Felis*	*Canis*	*Canis*
Species	*B. physalis*	*F. catus*	*C. latrans*	*C. lupus*
Common name	Blue whale	Domestic cat	Coyote	Wolf

5. Which animal is the most distant relative to the others?
   A. wolf
   B. coyote
   C. domestic cat
   D. blue whale

6. At which level does the domestic cat diverge from the coyote?
   A. family
   B. class
   C. order
   D. genus

Constructed Response

7. **THEME FOCUS** Explain the rules and uses of binomial nomenclature.

8. **Short Answer** Why is seahorse not a good scientific name?

Think Critically

9. **MAIN IDEA** How does the system of classification relate to the diversity of species?

SECTION 2

Vocabulary Review

Differentiate between the following pairs.

10. phylogeny, character
11. cladogram, molecular clock

Understand Main Ideas

Use the figure below to answer questions 12 and 13.

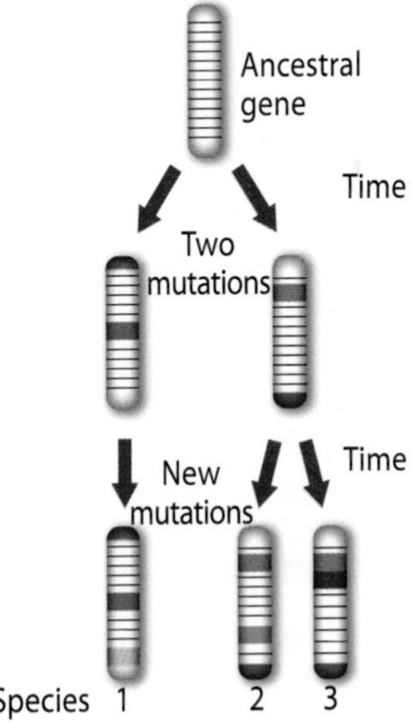

12. What does this figure represent?
    A. pedigree
    B. cladogram
    C. molecular clock
    D. phylogenetic tree

13. What do the colored bands in the figure represent?
    A. mutations
    B. derived characters
    C. ancestral characters
    D. genomes

14. Which species concept defines a species as a group of organisms that are able to reproduce successfully in the wild?
   A. typological species concept
   B. biological species concept
   C. evolutionary species concept
   D. phylogenetic species concept

Use the figure below to answer questions 15 and 16.

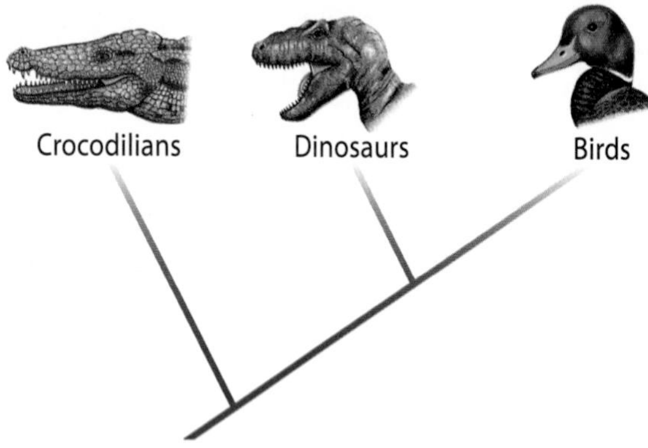

15. According to the figure, which organism diverged last?
   A. alligators
   B. birds
   C. crocodiles
   D. dinosaurs

16. Which is represented by the figure?
   A. pedigree
   B. cladogram
   C. molecular clock
   D. character

17. Which does not affect the rate of mutation in a molecular clock?
   A. type of mutation
   B. location of gene in genome
   C. the protein affected
   D. the time of divergence

Constructed Response

18. **Open Ended** Two scientists produce two different cladograms for the same groups of organisms. Explain how the differences are possible.

19. **Short Answer** Describe how to make a cladogram. Include the types of characters that are used and the judgments you must make about the characters.

20. **Short Answer** Summarize how biochemical characters can be used to determine phylogeny.

Think Critically

21. MAINIDEA Differentiate between the typological species concept and the phylogenetic species concept.

22. **Decide** How should molecular clocks be used if not all mutations occur at the same rate? Should they be considered reliable evidence of phylogeny? Explain your answer.

Use the figure below to answer question 23.

23. **Evaluate** evidence that suggests that the two organisms in the figure are closely related.

SECTION 3

Vocabulary Review

Replace the italicized words with the correct vocabulary terms from the Study Guide page.

24. Algae are a type of *archaea.*

25. *Bacteria* are called extremophiles because they grow in extreme environments.

26. Some types of *protists* are used to make food products like bread and cheese.

Understand Main Ideas

27. Which taxon contains one or more kingdoms?
   A. genus
   B. phylum
   C. family
   D. domain

28. In which kingdom would prokaryotes found living in acid runoff likely be classified?
   A. Bacteria
   B. Archaea
   C. Fungi
   D. Protista

Use the photograph below to answer question 29.

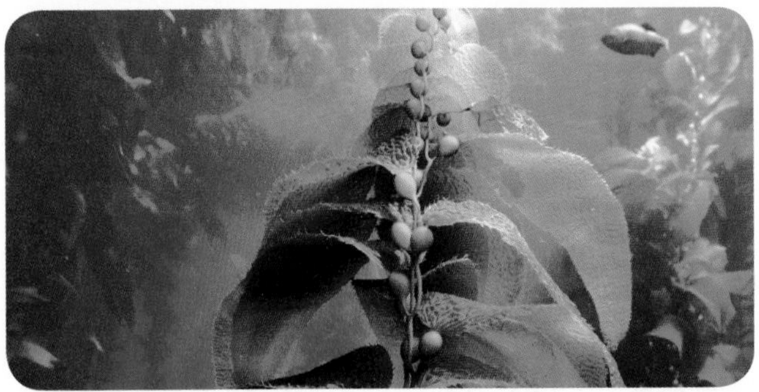

29. In which kingdom would this organism, which has chloroplasts, cell walls, but no organs, be classified?
    A. Plantae
    B. Animalia
    C. Protista
    D. Fungi

30. Which substance would most likely be in the cell walls of an organism with chloroplasts and tissues?
    A. peptidoglycan
    B. chitin
    C. hyphae
    D. cellulose

Constructed Response

31. **MAINIDEA** Indicate the relationship between domains and kingdoms.

32. **Short Answer** Predict in which domain a taxonomist would place a newly discovered photosynthetic organism that has cells without membrane-bound organelles and no peptidoglycan.

33. **Open Ended** Write an argument for or against including Bacteria and Archaea in the same domain. How would this affect the phylogenetic tree of life?

Think Critically

34. **Analyze** Using the model in **Figure 12,** decide which three of the kingdoms in Domain Eukarya evolved from the fourth.

35. **CAREERSIN ▶ Biology** A biologist studied two groups of frogs in the laboratory. The groups looked identical and produced fertile offspring when interbred. However, in nature, they do not interbreed because their reproductive calls are different and their territories do not overlap. Use your knowledge of species concepts and speciation to decide why they should or should not be placed in the same species.

Summative Assessment

36. **BIGIDEA** Life on Earth was organized by Aristotle into three categories. Why has the classification system become so complex since Aristotle's time?

37. Draw a cladogram or phylogenetic tree that displays the order of evolution of the six kingdoms. Explain the reasoning for your interpretation.

38. **WRITINGIN ▶ Biology** Suppose you found a cricket near your home. After a biologist from a local university studies your find, you learn that the cricket is a new species. Write a paragraph to explain how the biologist might have determined that the cricket is a new species.

DBQ Document–Based Questions

Data obtained from: Blaxter, M. 2001. Sum of the arthropod parts. Science 413:121–122.

Scientists continue to debate about evolutionary relationships among organisms. Groups of arthropods were thought to be related in the way shown on the left, but new molecular evidence suggests that the grouping on the right is more accurate.

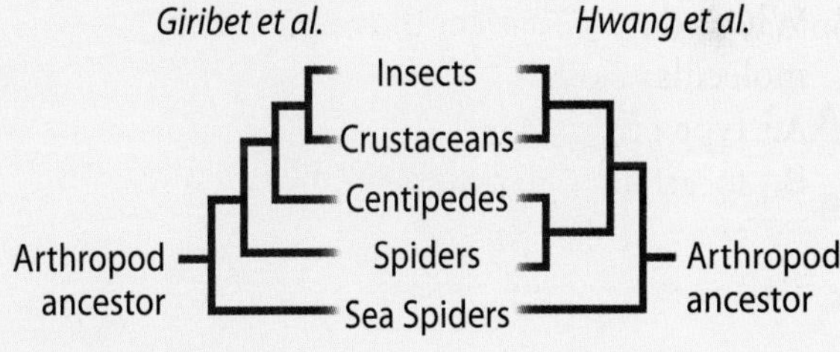

39. Compare and contrast the two cladograms. How did the molecular evidence change the relationship between centipedes and spiders?

40. To which group are crustaceans most closely related?

41. Which group in the cladogram appears to be the most ancestral?

CUMULATIVE
MULTIPLE CHOICE

1 According to the Hardy-Weinberg principle, which situation would disrupt genetic equilibrium?

A A large population of deer inhabits a forest region.

B A particular population of flies mates randomly.

C A population of flowering plants always has the same group of natural predators.

D A small population of birds colonizes a new island.

Use the diagram below to answer question 2.

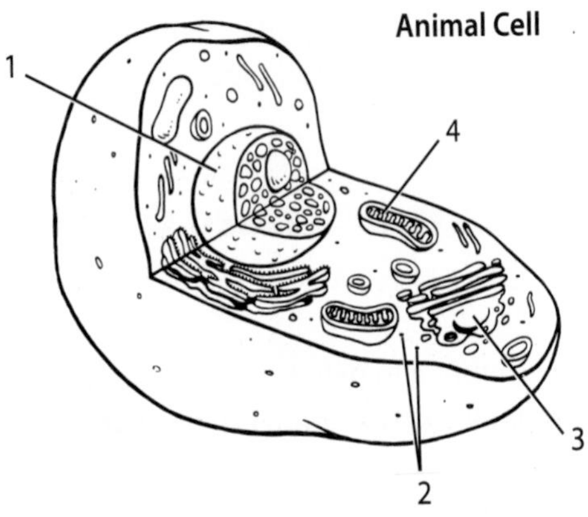

2 Which labeled structure contains the cell's genetic information?

A 1

B 2

C 3

D 4

3 According to the endosymbiont theory, which part of the eukaryotic cell evolved from a prokaryotic cell?

A chloroplast

B golgi apparatus

C nucleus

D ribosome

SHORT ANSWER

4 List three primate adaptations found in humans, and explain how each one relates to a tree-dwelling habitat.

5 Explain how molecular clocks are useful in investigating phylogeny in ways that morphological characteristics are not.

6 In terms of their evolution, how are homologous structures and analogous structures different?

7 Infer why Aristotle only used two kingdoms to classify living things.

8 Assess the significance of the discovery of the Lucy fossil.

Use the figure below to answer question 9.

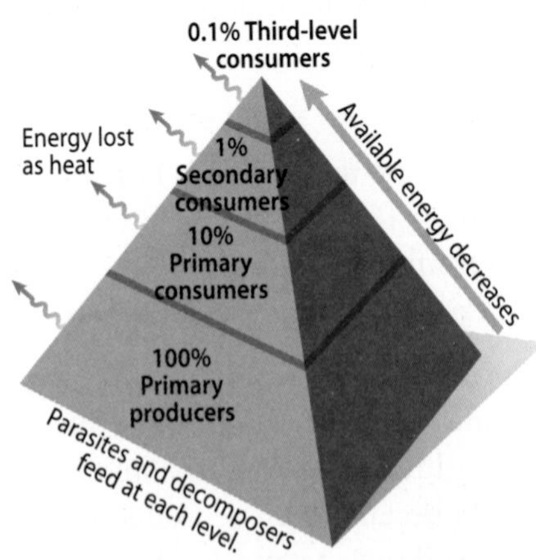

9 How much energy from one trophic level is available to organisms at the next higher trophic level?

EXTENDED RESPONSE

10 How could a mutagen cause a change in the protein for which a DNA strand is coding? Trace the effect of a specific mutation through the process of protein synthesis.

11 Assess the value of the binomial system of naming organisms.

12 Analyze, evaluate, and critique the advantage of bipedalism.

13 Contrast one of the characteristics of living things with the characteristics of nonliving things such as rocks.

14 Name two animals that you would expect to have similar chromosomal characters. Design an experiment to test whether they are similar.

ESSAY QUESTION

Scientists often use multiple types and sources of data in order to determine when different groups of organisms evolved. Taken together, the data can help construct an evolutionary history.

Using the information in the paragraph above, answer the following question in essay format.

15 What kind of evidence could help scientists determine whether bacteria or archaea evolved earlier on Earth? Write an essay that justifies what specific kinds of data would need to be collected to make this judgment.

TEST PRACTICE

Use the illustration below to answer questions 16 and 17.

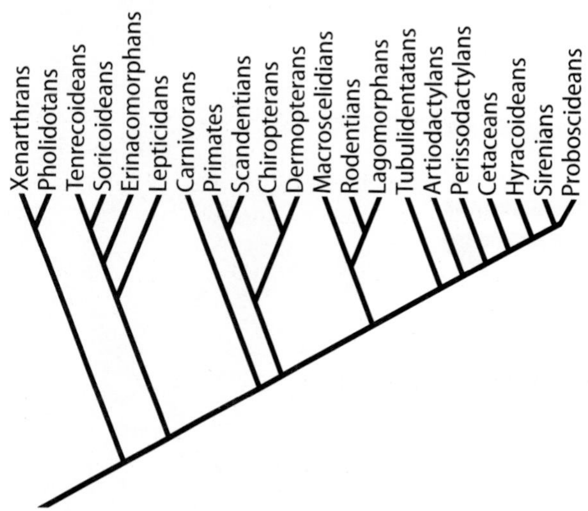

16 According to the cladogram of mammals, which two groups of animals have a more recent common ancestor?

A carnivorans and chiropterans

B cetaceans and hyracoideans

C dermopterans and carnivorans

D rodentians and lagomorphans

17 Which mammal is most closely related to bats (chiropterans)?

A carnivorans

B xenarthrans

C primates

D rodentians

NEED EXTRA HELP?																	
If You Missed Question . . .	1	2	3	4	5	6	7	8	9	10	11	12	13	14	15	16	17
Review Section . . .	15.3	16.2	14.2	16.1	7.2	15.2	17.1	16.2	2.2	12.3	17.1	16.2	1.1	17.2	17.2, 17.3	17.2	17.2

UNIT 5

WHAT'S THAT? Genetic research has helped us to better understand many human diseases. The Human Genome Project for example, was a collaborative research effort to map the genes of a human. The human genome was completely mapped in 2003, after 13 years of work. University research centers such as Baylor College of Medicine Human Genome Sequencing Center (BCM-HGSC) in Houston, Texas contributed greatly to this project. Researchers are now working to identify ways to use genomic information to diagnose diseases, develop vaccines and antibiotics, and customize treatments for diseases.

(bkgd)©Don Mason/Blend Images LLC, (inset)MedicalRF.com/Getty Images

CAREERS USING BIOLOGY

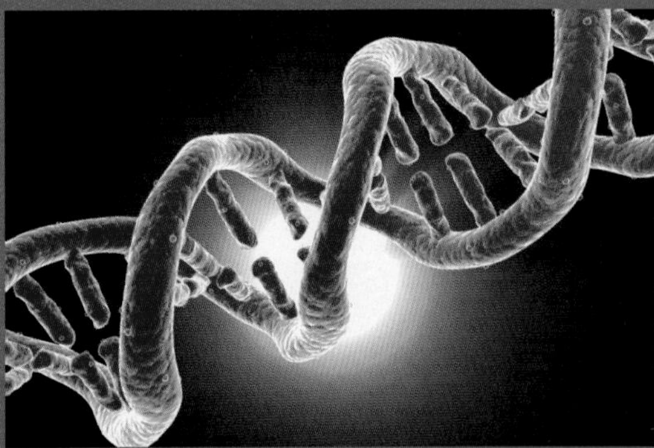

Applying the Science Dr. James Watson, one of the discoverers of the DNA double helix structure, was one of the first people to have his entire genome sequenced. Doctors were able to use his genetic information to customize his medication.

cutting-edge BIOLOGY

See **page 686** for more information about medical applications of Texas research.

◀ BIOETHICIST

Bioethics is a new and interdisciplinary field. Bioethicists consider the ethical issues that may arise by new biological and medical advancements. Bioethicists are trained in the healthcare field, policy, philosophy, and life sciences. Sequencing an individual's genome has ethical implications. For example, insurance companies may raise rates if they find that a patient has a disease that will be costly to treat. Bioethicists help to create safeguards to protect people from the negative impacts of new and emerging technologies.

Related Careers

- bioinformatics researcher
- biomedical engineer
- clinical laboratory scientist
- genealogist
- genetic counselor
- genetic laboratory tech
- physician

 **Career Resources**

Investigate

Evaluate What impact has the Human Genome Project had on society? How is the knowledge gained from the HGP being applied? What new projects have developed at the BCM-HGSC as a result of the HGP? **1.1.1b, 1.1.2a, 1.1.3b, 4.5.2e**

Homeostasis and the Human Body

4.1.2a, 4.1.2b, 4.1.2c, 4.1.2d, 4.1.2e, 4.1.2f, 4.2.1d, 4.5.3b, 4.6.1a, 4.6.1g, 4.6.3b

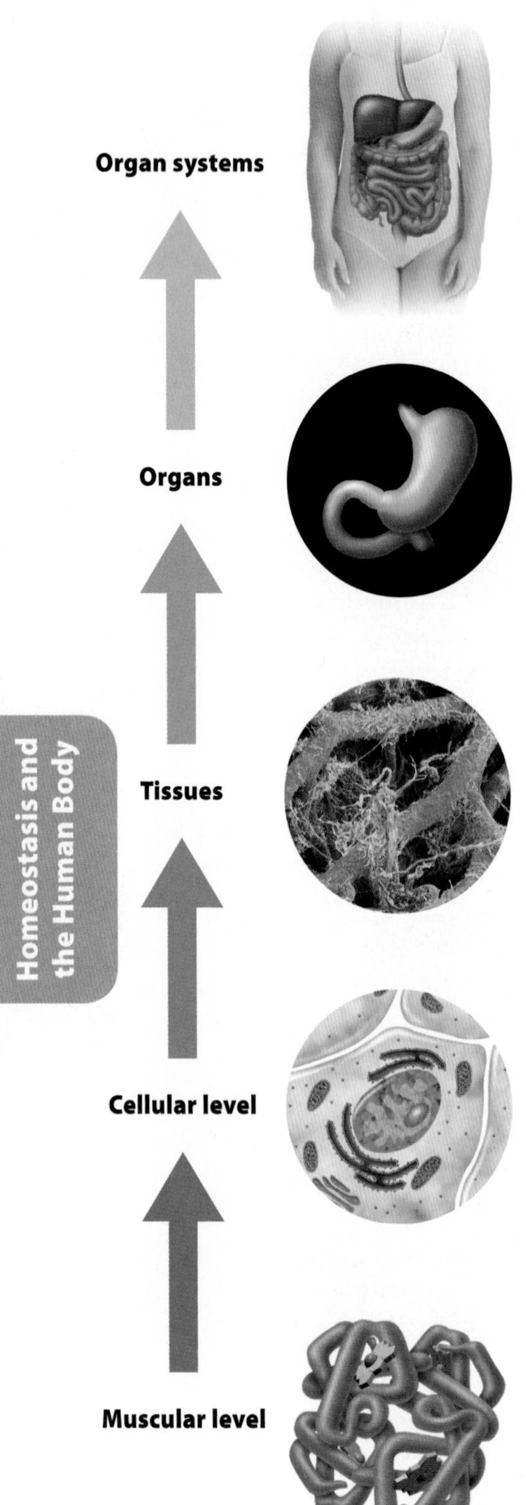

■ **Figure 1** Living things display levels of organization, and each level is necessary to maintain homeostasis.

Maintenance of Life

For a human body to function, its internal environment must remain relatively stable. Human body temperature averages 37°C, blood glucose concentration remains at about 100 mg/100 mL, blood pH is near 7.4, and blood pressure averages near 120/80 mm Hg. This ability of the body to maintain its internal environment within normal limits is called homeostasis. Because the human internal environment can remain stable within normal limits, humans can live in diverse habitats, ranging from the tropics to Arctic regions

Levels of Organization

To understand how the body maintains homeostasis, picture the human body as a hierarchy of levels with each level increasing in complexity, as shown in **Figure 1**. Each level works with the other levels to maintain dynamic equilibrium. As a result, all conditions affecting the body's internal environment are within normal limits.

Molecular level The first level of organization is the molecular level. At this level are carbon-based molecules such as carbohydrates, proteins, lipids, and nucleic acids. These molecules, also called macromolecules, provide structural support and energy to cells at the next level. Other substances, such as sodium ions and potassium ions, also play roles in cell processes

Cellular level The second level of organization is the cellular level. Cells in multicellular organisms, such as plants and animals, usually have specific functions. For example, the cells that make up human heart muscle are found only in the heart and function to keep the heart beating.

Tissue level A tissue is a group of cells that work together to perform a specific function. At the tissue level of organization, there are four basic types of tissue in the human body. Epithelial tissues cover the body and line organs, vessels, and body cavities. Muscular tissue is found attached to bones and in the walls of organs. Connective tissue is found throughout the body, providing support, binding, and storage. Nervous tissue, found throughout the body, sends signals to and from the brain and spinal cord

Organ level Organs form the next level of organization. Organs are formed when a group of tissues work together to perform a larger, more specific function. Organs in the human body include the heart, the brain, the stomach, and the urinary bladder.

Organ system level An organ system consists of a group of organs that work together to carry out a major life function. For example, the circulatory system, which consists of the heart, the blood vessels, and the blood, moves oxygen and nutrients throughout the body and removes wastes from cells. Organ systems work together to maintain homeostasis in the body

Feedback from the Levels of Organization

Homeostasis is maintained through an internal feedback system controlled by the nervous system and the endocrine system. Internal feedback loops provide responses or information to the nervous system and endocrine system about the body's processes. While feedback loops can be positive or negative, most of the feedback loops that maintain homeostasis are negative.

Negative feedback Blood glucose levels are constantly monitored and maintained by a negative feedback loop, illustrated in **Figure 2**. When blood glucose levels drop too low, the pancreas releases the hormone glucagon. Glucagon causes cells in the liver to break down glycogen—a storage form of glucose—and release glucose into the blood. As a result, blood glucose levels return to a normal level.

High levels of glucose in the blood signal the pancreas to release insulin. Insulin causes body cells to take in glucose, removing glucose from the blood and causing blood glucose levels to fall. As blood glucose levels fall, the pancreas is inhibited from releasing more insulin. Levels of glucose in the blood rise and fall over the course of the day. Based on feedback, homeostasis is maintained in order to keep blood glucose levels within a normal range.

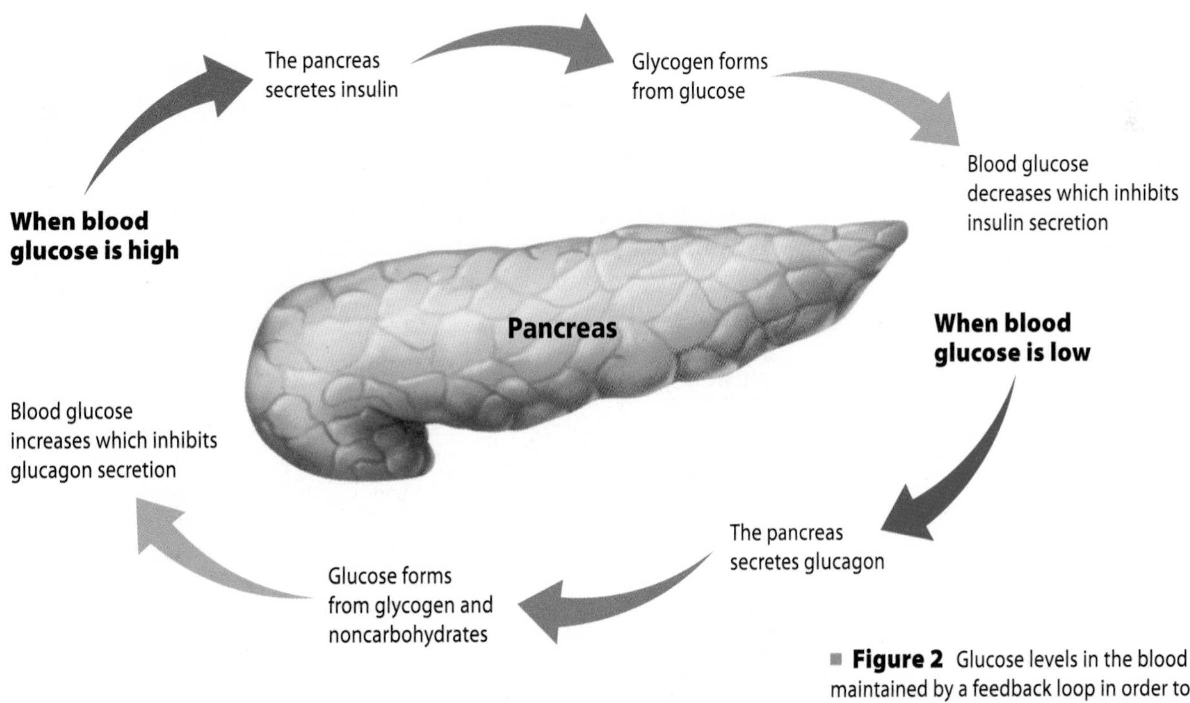
The pancreas secretes insulin
Glycogen forms from glucose
Blood glucose decreases which inhibits insulin secretion
When blood glucose is high
Pancreas
When blood glucose is low
Blood glucose increases which inhibits glucagon secretion
The pancreas secretes glucagon
Glucose forms from glycogen and noncarbohydrates

■ **Figure 2** Glucose levels in the blood are maintained by a feedback loop in order to help the pancreas maintain homeostasis.

■ **Figure 3** Metabolism involves the process that provides your body with energy

Maintaining homeostasis Homeostasis is maintained and regulated at all levels of organization. At the molecular level, the amounts of certain substances are monitored and adjusted to stay within a normal range. At the cellular level, cells respond to messages from the nervous system and hormones from the endocrine system to help maintain homeostasis. Some organs such as the pancreas, testes, and ovaries act as endocrine glands and release hormones. Organ systems, particularly the reproductive system, respond to hormones in order to undergo processes or produce certain substances

Metabolism

All the activities you carry out require energy. You know you need energy to play sports such as volleyball, as shown in **Figure 3**, or to make it through a day of classes. But your body also constantly needs energy even while you sleep. Metabolism is the term used to describe all of the chemical reactions that occur within an organism in order to maintain homeostasis. Metabolism includes using and storing the macromolecules, water, minerals, and vitamins digested from food for energy and to build essential substances such as proteins. Refer to **Table 1** to see some of the roles of macromolecules in the human body.

Energy production Metabolism involves all of the levels of organization. At the organ system level, the digestive system breaks down ingested food and absorbs carbohydrates, lipids, proteins, and other nutrients into the body. The circulatory system carries to the cell these substances, along with oxygen obtained by the respiratory system. Some of these substances are necessary for the production of ATP through the process of aerobic cellular respiration at the molecular level. ATP provides energy the body needs to maintain homeostasis.

Carbon dioxide produced by cellular respiration is removed from cells by the circulatory system and exhaled from the body by the respiratory system. Other waste products from metabolic processes are removed from cells by the circulatory system and removed from the body by the excretory system.

Table 1 Functions of Macromolecules

Molecule	Function
Carbohydrate	• Used as a source of energy • Used for DNA and RNA production
Protein	• Used to make muscle tissue, collagen, hormones, antibodies, enzymes, and hemoglobin
Lipid	• Stored by the body and used for energy, protection, and insulation • Used in the production of hormones and vitamin D

Heat production Metabolism is regulated by the nervous and endocrine systems. Interaction between these two systems results in the release of hormones that are needed to trigger metabolic processes, such as ATP production and the storage and subsequent breakdown of glycogen. Heat is released as metabolic reactions occur in the body. This internal heat, along with homeostasis, allows endotherms to maintain a constant internal body temperature, in a way similar to that shown in **Figure 4**. Body temperature in humans is maintained by a negative feedback system that involves the nervous system, circulatory system, integumentary system, muscular system, and endocrine system

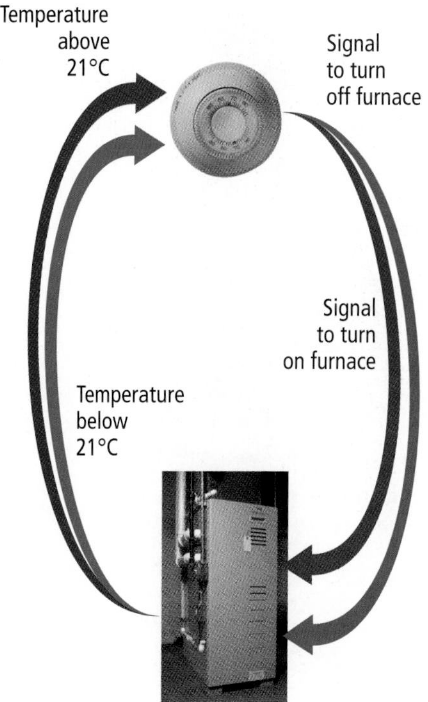

■ **Figure 4** Just as a thermostat regulates whether a furnace is on or off to maintain room temperature human body systems work together to control heat production from metabolism and internal body temperature.

Disruption of Homeostasis

When homeostasis is disrupted, the result is disease. Pathogens, genetics, the degeneration of body structure, or exposure to a carcinogen can cause disease. If homeostasis is permanently disrupted, damage or death can result. When a pathogen such as a bacterium or virus infects the body, the immune system plays an important role in restoring homeostasis. Different types of white blood cells work to destroy and remove invading microorganisms from the body.

Diabetes—an example Any condition that affects the ability of an organ, such as the liver, kidneys, or pancreas, to perform its function upsets homeostasis. For example, if the pancreas does not produce enough insulin or any insulin at all, the disease type 1 diabetes results. Blood glucose levels are regulated by a negative feedback loop that involves the release of two hormones from the pancreas—insulin and glucagon. Insulin helps control blood glucose levels by stimulating cells to take in glucose. In type 1 diabetes, there is not enough insulin and glucose is not taken into cells. This means that glucose remains at high levels in the blood and cells do not get the glucose they need to undergo cellular respiration and make ATP. This excess glucose is lost from the body in the urine.

Without glucose, cells use fatty acids for cellular respiration. When fatty acids are broken down, the blood becomes more acidic, lowering blood pH and upsetting homeostasis. If the pH of the blood drops too low, death can result. Because insulin is necessary for homeostasis, people with type 1 diabetes must take insulin shots to maintain normal blood glucose levels.

Type 2 diabetes results when the cells of the body become insensitive to insulin. It usually occurs after the age of 40. Type 2 diabetes is diagnosed in 70–80 percent of people diagnosed with diabetes. In either case, glucose levels in the blood must be monitored and maintained to help keep homeostasis in the body.

Functions of Human Body Systems

The human body is complex—it consists of many systems. Though each system performs a specific life function, they all interact to maintain homeostasis.

Digestion The digestive system, illustrated in **Figure 5**, functions to ingest food, digest food, absorb nutrients, and eliminate food that cannot be digested. Mechanical digestion of food begins in the mouth as the teeth tear food into smaller pieces. The teeth, tongue, and esophagus carry out the function of ingestion—food is chewed in the mouth and swallowed. Ingested food travels to the stomach via the esophagus. Chemical digestion can also begin in the mouth. An enzyme released by the salivary glands begins to break down starches. Continued digestion of food takes place in the stomach and small intestine.

Other digestive organs, including the liver, gallbladder, and pancreas, release enzymes that digest food. Nutrients from digested food are absorbed by the small intestine where they then enter the blood. In the large intestine, water is absorbed into the body. Undigested material in the large intestine becomes solid and is excreted from the body.

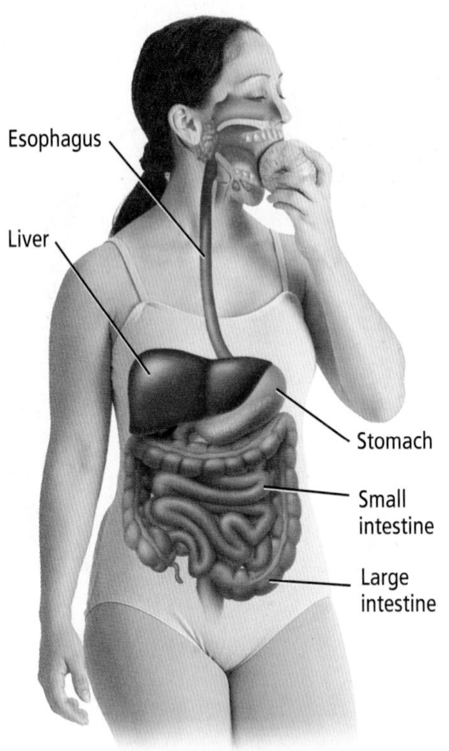

■ **Figure 5** Mechanical digestion begins in the mouth. Food travels to the stomach through the esophagus. Digestive organs chemically digest food and excrete undigested material from the body

Respiration As shown in Figure 6, the respiratory system includes the nasal passages, the pharynx, the larynx, the epiglottis, the trachea, bronchi, the lungs, and the diaphragm. The organs of the respiratory system function to exchange gases between the air and the blood. The exchange of oxygen and carbon dioxide helps maintain homeostasis. After air is inhaled through the nose or mouth, it travels to the lungs. It reaches aveoli, small saclike structures at the end of bronchioles, where oxygen diffuses across the thin walls into surrounding capillaries. Oxygen is then carried throughout the body in red blood cells from which it diffuses into the cells of the body.

Cells use oxygen as they undergo cellular respiration to make ATP. Carbon dioxide, a product of cellular respiration, diffuses out of capillaries back into the lungs and is expelled from the body during exhalation. The muscles of the diaphragm and ribs contract and relax as the lungs take in and release air during breathing.

■ **Figure 6** The respiratory system allows the exchange of oxygen and carbon dioxide tohelp maintain homeostasis in the body

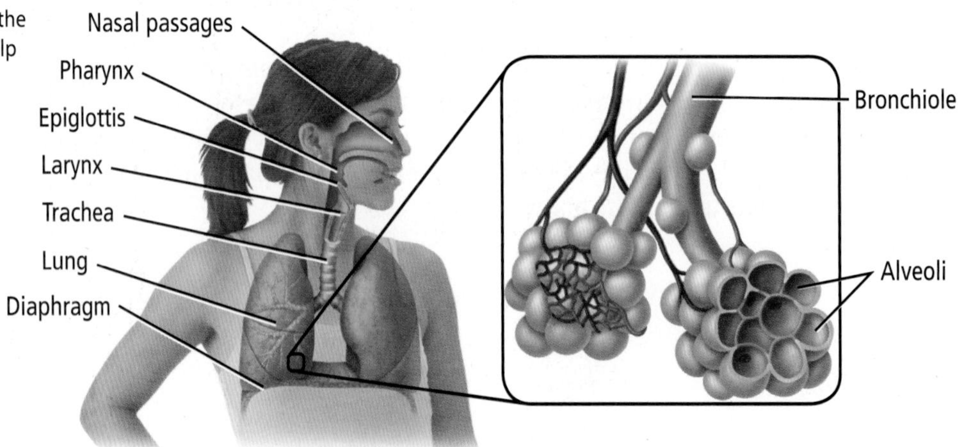

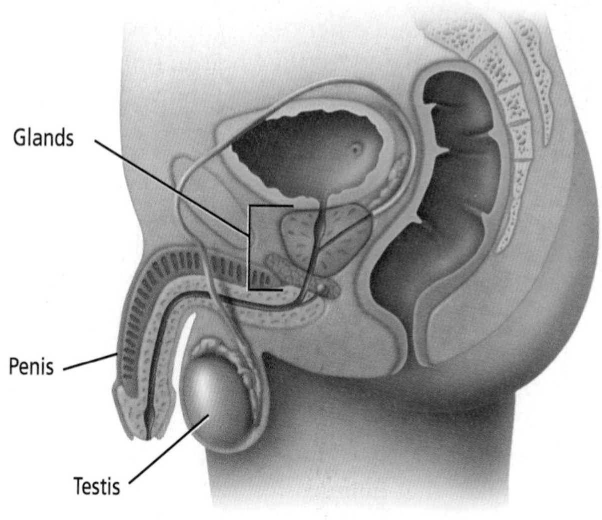
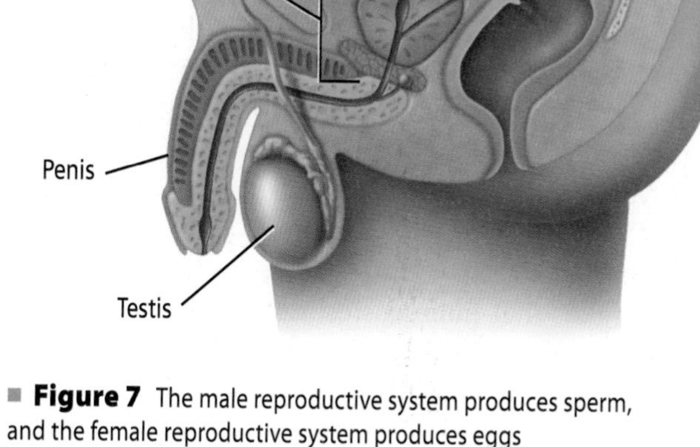

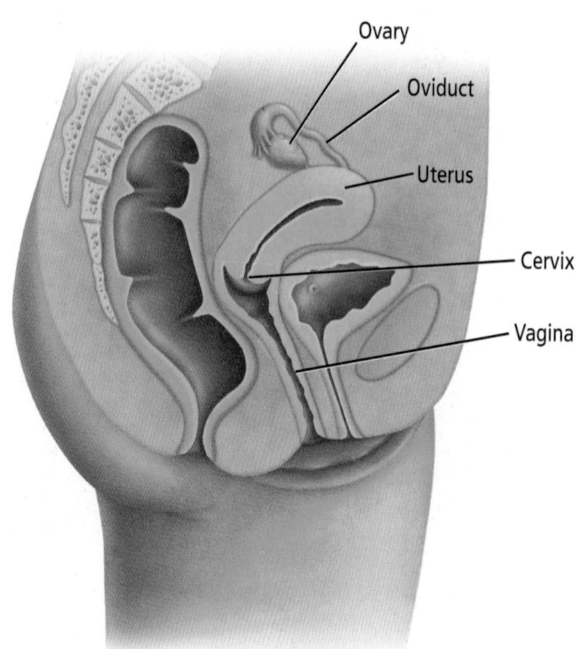

■ **Figure 7** The male reproductive system produces sperm, and the female reproductive system produces eggs

Reproduction

The male reproductive system includes the testes, the penis, and glands that produce seminal f luid. The female reproductive system is made up of the uterus, oviducts, ovaries, cervix, and the vagina. The main function of both the male and female reproductive systems, shown in **Figure 7**, is to produce gametes. Sperm are produced, maintained, and transferred to the female reproductive system by the male reproductive system. Eggs are produced and maintained by the female reproductive system, which also receives sperm and supports a developing fetus. Positive feedback and negative feedback loops maintain homeostasis as the fetus develops. Sperm and eggs are produced by the process of meiosis. Hormones play an important role in the functioning of both the male and female reproductive systems.

Circulation

The heart, blood vessels, the blood, and the lymphatic system make up the circulatory system. These structures move blood and lymph throughout the body, bringing oxygen and nutrients to cells and removing wastes, such as carbon dioxide, from cells. There are three types of blood vessels—arteries, veins, and capillaries. As illustrated in **Figure 8**, arteries carry oxygenated blood away from the heart. Veins carry deoxygenated blood back to the heart. Capillaries are microscopic vessels through which gases and nutrients diffuse to and from body cells.

■ **Figure 8** Oxygenated blood flows from the heart to the cells of the body; deoxygenated blood flows from the cells back to the heart

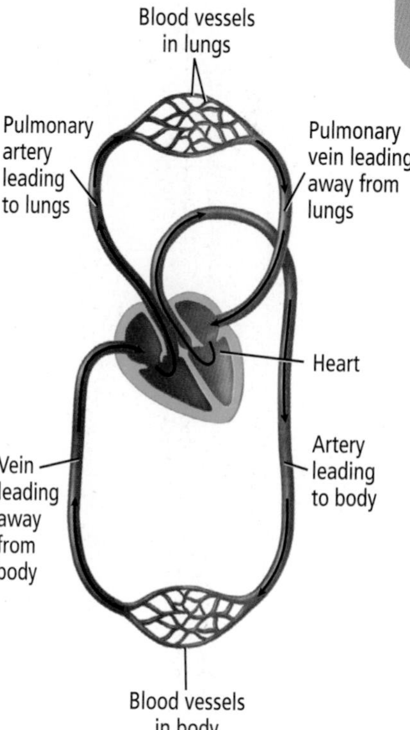

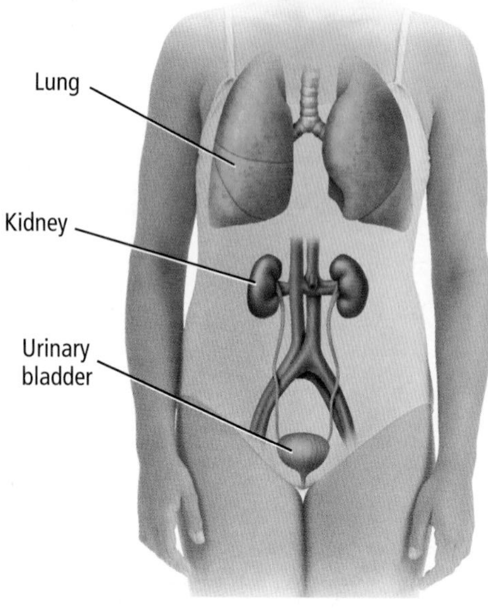

■ **Figure 9** Organs of the excretory system remove wastes from the body to help maintain homeostasis.

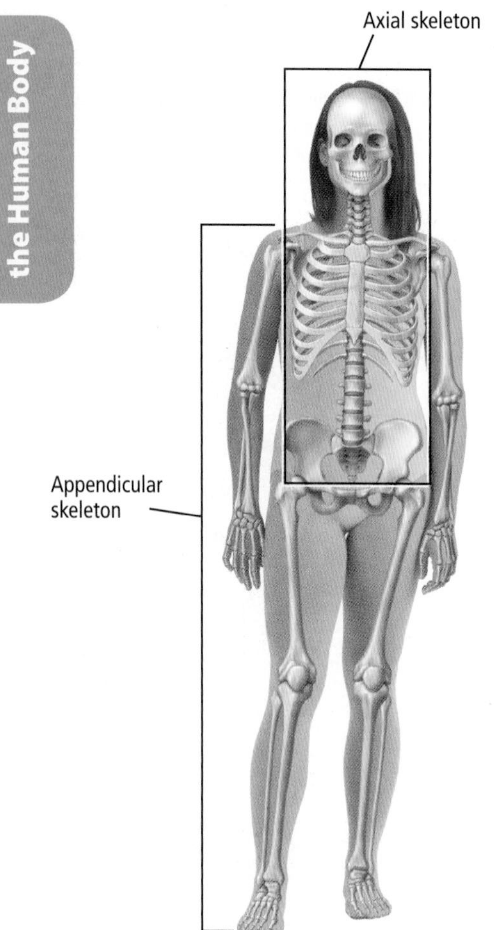

The blood also carries disease-fighting materials produced in the immune system. White blood cells and other cells fight infection and destroy foreign cells. Platelets help blood to clot when an injury occurs. The circulatory system also helps maintain a constant body temperature by distributing heat throughout the body

Excretion

The lungs, skin, kidneys, and urinary bladder all make up the excretory system, shown in **Figure 9**. In some capacity, each organ carries out the function of removing wastes from the body in order to maintain homeostasis. The lungs expel carbon dioxide, a product of cellular respiration, when the breath is exhaled. The skin excretes water and salt when the body sweats.

The kidneys form the major excretory organ in the body. The kidneys are bean-shaped organs that filter wastes, salts, and water from the blood. Through the excretion of hydrogen ions and the reabsorption of sodium ions, the kidneys help maintain the pH of blood within a normal range. Wastes, in the form of urine, travel from the kidneys to the urinary bladder through the ureters. Urine is excreted from the bladder through the urethra during urination

Movement and coordination

The coordination of the body's systems requires the response of the nervous system and the endocrine system. Movement of the body is a function of the skeletal system and the muscular system

The skeletal system Illustrated in **Figure 10**, the skeletal system is made up of all 206 bones in the body. It is divided into two sections—the axial skeleton and the appendicular skeleton. The main function of the skeletal system is to support the body. Bones protect organs from injury as well. For example, the brain is protected by the skull and the heart and lungs are protected by the ribs and sternum. Other functions of the skeletal system include the production of red blood cells, white blood cells, and platelets. Bones also store minerals such as calcium and phosphorus.

Bones are the surface to which muscles attach in order to move the body. Bones meet at joints which are classified based on the type of movement they allow and the shapes of their parts. The bones of joints are held together by ligaments, which are tough bands of connective tissue. Some joints, such as those in the skull, are not movable.

■ **Figure 10** The skeletal system is divided into the axial skeleton and the appendicular skeleton

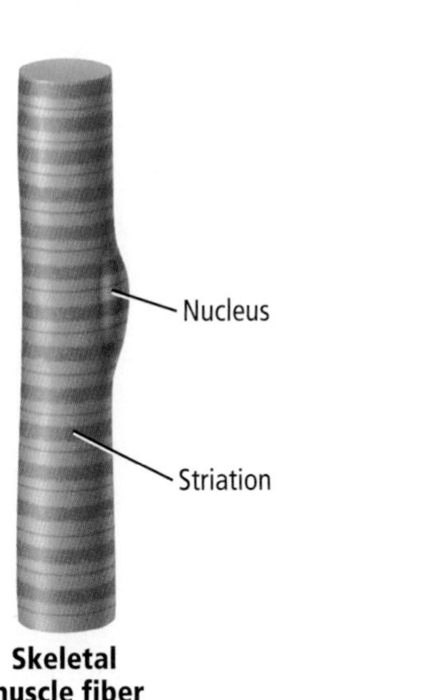

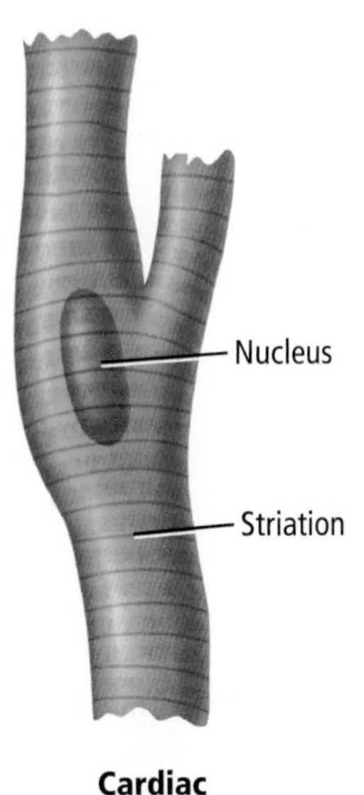

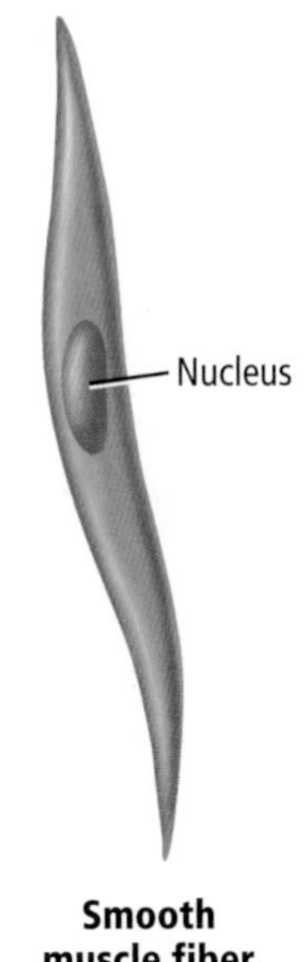

■ **Figure 11** Skeletal muscle is striated; cardiac muscle—found only in the heart—is also striated; smooth muscle is spindle shaped.

The muscular system The muscular system includes three types of muscle tissue—skeletal, smooth, and cardiac muscle, shown in **Figure 11**. Skeletal muscle is attached to bones by tendons. Skeletal muscles are voluntary muscles—ones that can be consciously controlled to perform body movement, such as walking, running, or typing on a keyboard.

Cardiac muscle is found only in the heart. This involuntary muscle tissue—muscle tissue that you cannot control—keeps the heart beating rhythmically and consistently. Smooth muscle, which lines many internal organs, also is involuntary. It helps move substances through organs. For example, smooth muscle that lines the organs of the digestive system helps move food through the esophagus, the stomach, and the small and the large intestines.

The nervous system Nerve cells, or neurons, the brain, and the spinal cord form the nervous system. Neurons transmit messages from the brain to cells in the body and back. Sensory neurons respond to stimuli from both outside and inside the body, and sends information to the brain. Interneurons in the brain and spinal cord carry impulses to motor neurons. Motor neurons carry impulses away from the brain and spinal cord back out to the body. This coordinates the body' reaction to the stimuli detected by the sensory neurons to help maintain homeostasis.

The nervous system has two divisions—the central nervous system and the peripheral nervous system. The central nervous system consists of the brain and spinal cord, and is illustrated in Figure 12. The peripheral nervous system consists of sensory and motor neurons that send information to and from the central nervous system

■ **Figure 12** The brain and spinal cord make up the central nervous system

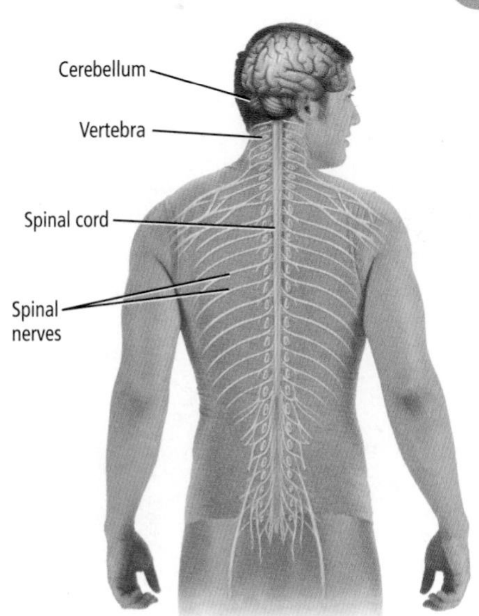

Homeostasis and the Human Body

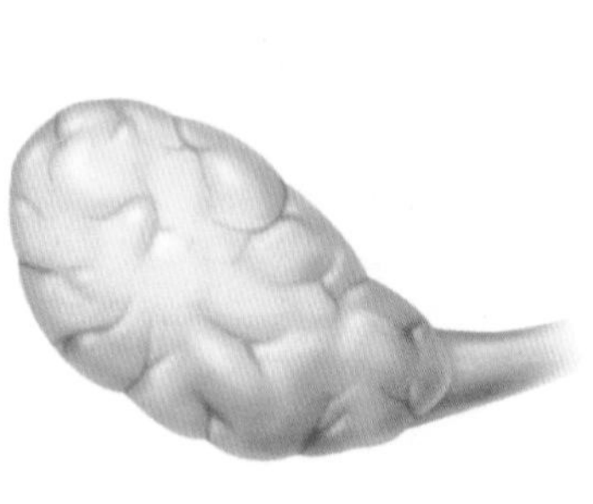

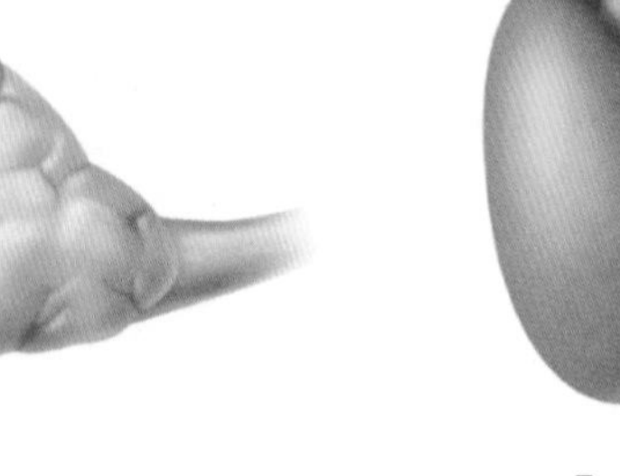

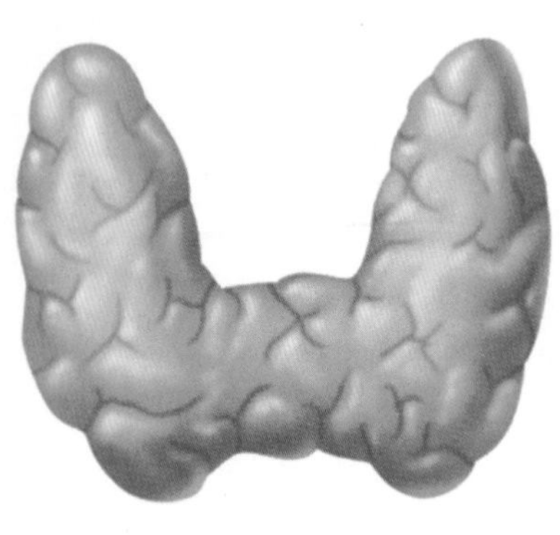

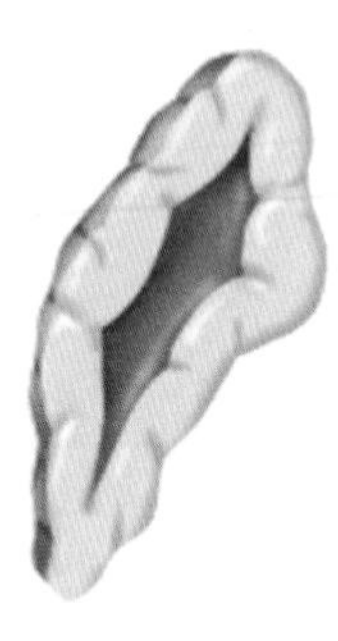

■ **Figure 13** Hormones released by the endocrine system glands communicate information to help maintain homeostasis

The endocrine system The endocrine system functions as a communication system. It is composed of glands, some of which are shown in **Figure 13**, that produce hormones in response to information from the internal feedback loops. The glands of the endocrine system include the pituitary gland, the thyroid gland, the parathyroid gland, the thymus gland, the pineal gland, the pancreas, the adrenal glands, the ovaries, and the testes. The hormones released by these glands help regulate homeostasis throughout the body. Blood calcium levels, blood glucose levels, and the body's water balance are all monitored and regulated by the endocrine system. Human growth hormone (hGH), released by the pituitary gland, acts on muscle and bone tissue. In these tissues, hGH stimulates cell division, which results in growth of the body. Hormones released by the testes and ovaries in males and females respectively stimulate puberty and regulate processes of the reproductive system.

Immunity

The body has many defenses that help fight invasion by a foreign substance. These defenses can be nonspecific—in the case of the integumentary system, and specific—in the case of the cells of the immune system.

Skin The integumentary system, illustrated in **Figure 14**, consists of the skin, hair, and nails. The skin covers the body and prevents microorganisms and other foreign substances from entering the body. The skin is the first line of defense against infection. Cells in the skin also protect the body against UV radiation and make skin waterproof. One of the main functions of the skin is to help maintain homeostasis by keeping the body's internal temperature within a normal range. The evaporation of sweat from the skin's surface helps cool the body as its internal temperature rises. If body temperature gets too low, capillaries in the skin narrow. Because the blood is not near the surface of the skin, heat loss decreases. The skin also acts as a sensory organ because it has nerve receptors for pain, pressure, and temperature changes that send information to the brain about these changes. Skin is also involved in the production of vitamin D—a vitamin that is important for proper bone formation

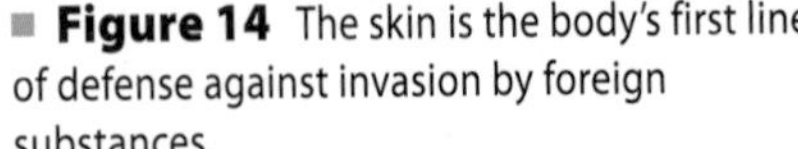
■ **Figure 14** The skin is the body's first line of defense against invasion by foreign substances.

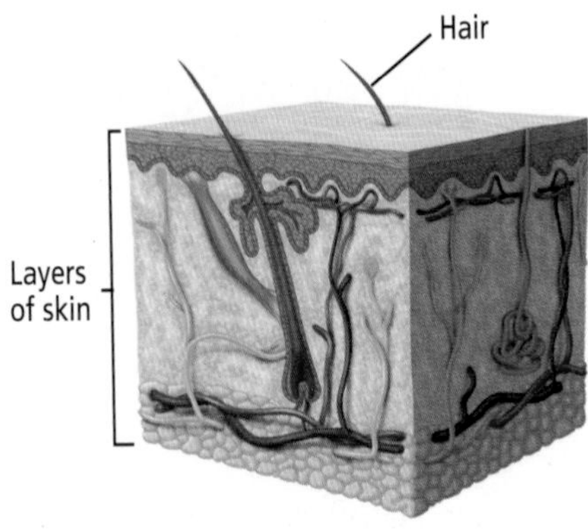

Cells of immune system Organs and substances that function as part of the body's immunity include the skin, mucus, and white blood cells. These structures are involved in nonspecific immunity and help protect the body from foreign substances and pathogens by physically blocking them from entering the body or by chemically destroying them if they do enter the body. Also, the lymphatic system works to filter and destroy pathogens. The lymphatic system includes the lymph nodes, tonsils, the spleen, the thymus gland, and lymphatic tissue in the mucous membranes of other organs in the body. Two types of lymphocytes—B cells and T cells—are involved in specific immunity. B cells produce antibodies in response to specific microorganisms and some act as memory cells in case the body is invaded by the same pathogen a second time.

Table 2 Structure and Function of Human Body Systems

Body System	Organs and Structures	Role in Maintaining Homeostasis
Digestive	Mouth, teeth, tongue, salivary glands, pharynx, esophagus, stomach, small intestine, large intestine, liver, gallbladder, pancreas	Ingest and digest food, absorb nutrients into blood, absorb water, excrete wastes
Respiratory	Nasal passages, pharynx, larynx, epiglottis, trachea, bronchi, lungs	Bring air into the body, gas exchange, remove wastes
Reproductive	Male: testes, penis, glands Female: ovaries, oviducts, uterus, cervix, vagina	Male: produce, maintain, and transfer sperm to female reproductive system Female: produce and maintain eggs, receive sperm, maintain developing fetus
Circulatory	Heart, blood vessels, blood	Transport oxygen, nutrients, carbon dioxide, and other wastes to and from body cells, distribute heat throughout body
Excretory	Kidneys, urinary bladder, lungs, skin	Remove toxins and wastes from the body
Skeletal	Bones, joints, ligaments	Support body, protect vital organs, produce blood cells, store minerals, allow for movement of the body
Muscular	Skeletal muscle, smooth muscle, cardiac muscle, tendons	Voluntary body movement, move substances through the body, maintain heartbeat
Nervous	Brain, spinal cord, neurons, sense organs	Transmit and interpret messages throughout the body, respond to internal and external stimuli, maintain homeostasis, control voluntary and involuntary body functions
Endocrine	Pituitary, thyroid, parathyroid, adrenal, pineal, thymus glands, pancreas, ovaries, testes	Secrete hormones, maintain homeostasis
Immune	Skin, mucus, white blood cells, lymphatic system	Protect body against foreign microorganisms, fight infection and disease
Integumentary	Skin, hair, nails	Protection, temperature regulation, vitamin production

The human body is made up of cells, tissues, organs, and systems. Muscles and bones work together to move the organism. Skin covers and protects the muscles and bones.

LaunchLAB

How is a chicken's wing like your arm?

Chickens have structures similar to ours. They have skin, muscles, and bones. In this lab, you will examine a chicken wing and begin to explore it.

CHAPTER 18

Integumentary, Skeletal, and Muscular Systems

THEMEFOCUS

Stability and change The integumentary system provides protection from outside pathogens and regulates body temperature.

BIGIDEA

These systems work together to maintain homeostasis by protecting, supporting, and moving the body.

FOLDABLES® Study Organizer

Skin

Make a layered look-book using the labels shown. Use it to organize your notes on skin.

Subcutaneous
Dermis
Epidermis
SKIN

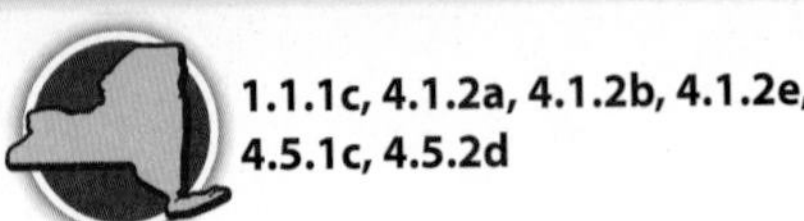

1 The Integumentary System

1.1.1c, 4.1.2a, 4.1.2b, 4.1.2e, 4.5.1c, 4.5.2d

MAINIDEA
Skin is a multilayered organ that covers and protects the body.

Essential Questions
- What are the four tissue types that are found in the integumentary system?
- What are the functions of the integumentary system?
- What are the two layers of skin composed of?
- What are the events that occur when skin is repaired?

BIOLOGY 4U
The skin on the tips of fingers and toes is thick and is composed of curving ridges that form the basis of fingerprints. Fingerprints were first used in criminal investigations in 1860 by Henry Faulds, a Scottish medical missionary. Your skin is not just a simple covering that keeps your body together. It is complex and is essential for your survival. Your ridges are uniquely yours!

Review Vocabulary
integument: an enveloping layer of an organism

New Vocabulary
epidermis
keratin
melanin
dermis
hair follicle
sebaceous gland

Multilingual eGlossary

Incorporate information from this section into your Foldable.

The Structure of Skin

The integumentary (ihn TEG yuh MEN tuh ree) system is the organ system that covers and protects the body. Skin is the main organ of the integumentary system and is composed of four types of tissues: epithelial tissue, connective tissue, muscle tissue, and nerve tissue. Epithelial tissue covers body surfaces, and connective tissue provides support and protection. Muscle tissue is involved in body movement. Nerve tissue forms the body's communication network. You will learn more about muscle tissue in Section 3.

The epidermis Refer to **Figure 1,** which illustrates the two main layers of skin as seen through a microscope. The outer superficial layer of skin is the **epidermis.** The epidermis consists of epithelial cells and is about 10 to 30 cells thick, or about as thick as this page. The outer layers of epidermal cells contain **keratin** (KER uh tun), a protein which waterproofs and protects the cells and tissues that lie underneath. These dead, outer cells are constantly shed. **Figure 2** shows that some of the dust in a house are dead skin cells. As much as an entire layer of skin cells can be lost each month.

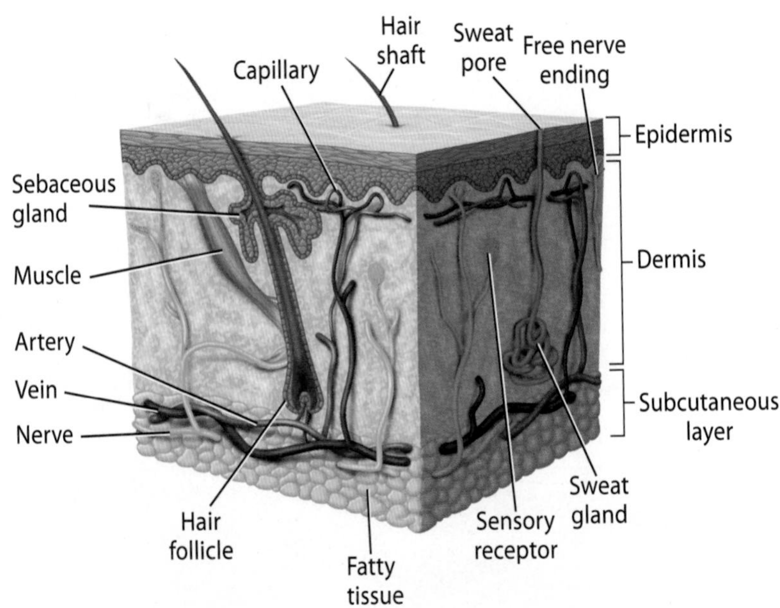

■ **Figure 1** Skin is an organ because it consists of different types of tissues joined together for specific purposes.
***Summarize** what types of tissues make up the skin.*

The inner layer of the epidermis contains cells that continually are dividing by mitosis to replace cells that are lost or die. Some cells in the inner layer of the epidermis provide protection from harmful ultraviolet radiation by making a pigment called melanin. **Melanin** is a pigment that absorbs light energy, which protects deeper cells from the damaging effects of ultraviolet rays of sunlight. The amount of melanin that is produced also influences the color of a person's skin. A suntan results when melanin is produced in response to exposure to the ultraviolet radiation in sunlight.

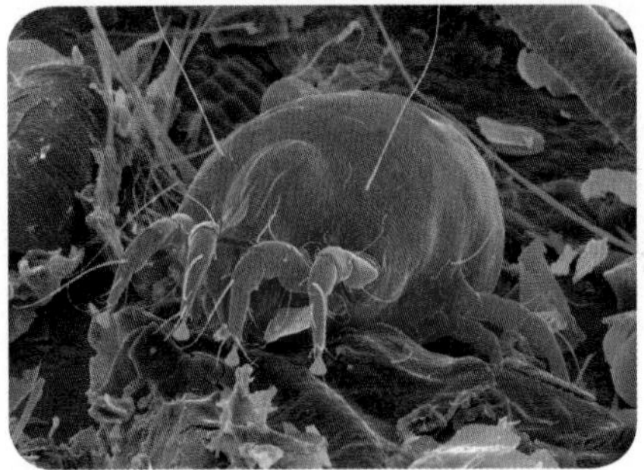

Figure 2 The dust mite pictured here is feeding on dead skin cells—a major component of dust.

The dermis Directly beneath the epidermis is the **dermis,** the second layer of skin. The thickness of the dermis varies but usually is 15–40 times thicker than the epidermis. The dermis consists of connective tissue, a type of tissue that prevents the skin from tearing and also enables the skin to return to its normal state after being stretched. This layer contains other structures including nerve cells, muscle fibers, sweat glands, oil glands, and hair follicles. Beneath the dermis is the subcutaneous layer, a layer of connective tissue that stores fat and helps the body retain heat.

Hair and nails Hair, fingernails, and toenails also are parts of the integumentary system. Both hair and nails contain keratin and develop from epithelial cells. Hair cells grow out of narrow cavities in the dermis called **hair follicles.** Cells at the base of a hair follicle divide and push cells away from the follicle, causing hair to grow.

Hair follicles usually have sebaceous or oil glands associated with them, as shown in **Figure 3. Sebaceous glands** lubricate skin and hair. When glands produce too much oil, the follicles can become blocked. The blockage can close the opening of a follicle, causing a whitehead, blackhead, or acne—an inflammation of the sebaceous glands.

STUDY TIP

CHART Make a chart with *Skin, Bones,* and *Muscles* as row labels, and *Components and structure* and *Function and purpose* as the column labels. Work in small groups to complete your chart as you review the text.

GET IT? **Summarize** the differences in structure and function of the epidermis and the dermis.

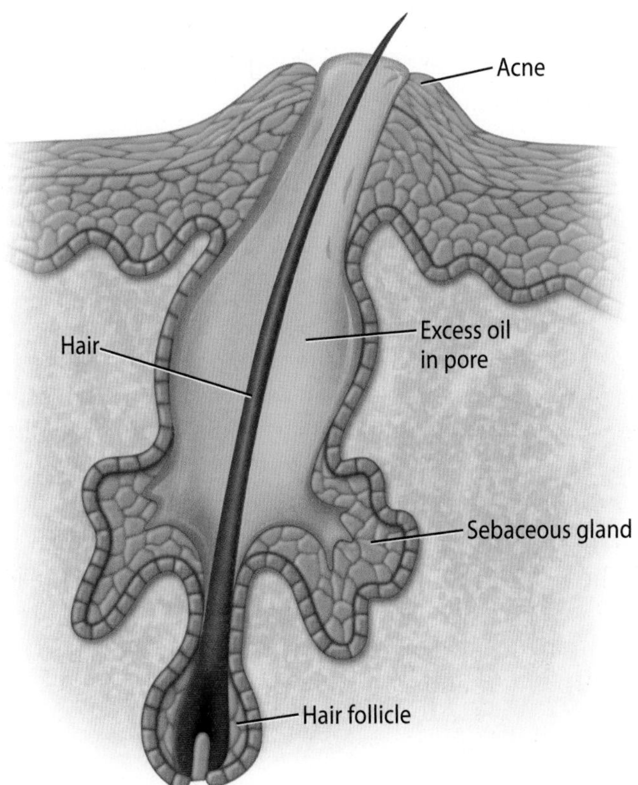

Figure 3 Oil, dirt, and bacteria can become trapped in follicles and erupt and spread to the surrounding area, causing localized inflammation.

■ **Figure 4** Muscles in the skin cause the hair of some mammals to stand on end, and cause "goose bumps" on human skin.
Relate ***what environmental changes produce "goose bumps."***

Fingernails and toenails grow from specialized epithelial cells at the base of each nail. As cells at the base of a nail divide, older dead cells are compacted and pushed out. Nails grow about 0.5 to 1.2 mm per day. You might have heard that nails and hair continue to grow for several days after death. This is a myth; cells surrounding the nail and hair cells dehydrate causing the cells to shrink and pull away from nails and hair. This makes both appear longer.

Functions of the Integumentary System

Skin serves several important functions including regulation of body temperature, production of vitamin D, protection, and perception of one's surroundings.

Temperature regulation What happens when a person is working outside on a hot summer day? In order to regulate body temperature, the person sweats. As sweat evaporates it absorbs body heat, thereby cooling the body. What happens to skin when a person gets cold or frightened? "Goose bumps" are caused by the contraction of muscle cells in the dermis. In other mammals, when these muscles contract, the hair (fur) stands on end.

Notice the frightened cat in **Figure 4.** The cat appears larger, perhaps as a way to scare off enemies. This also is a mechanism for trapping air, which insulates or warms the mammal. Humans do not have as much hair as most other mammals, but "goose bumps" are caused by the same type of muscles that make a cat's fur stand on end. Humans rely on fat in the subcutaneous layer instead of hair to keep warm.

MiniLAB 1

Examine Skin

How is chicken skin similar to human skin? The skin of chicken has characteristics similar to human skin. Using the chicken wing from the Launch Lab, you will further examine the characteristics of skin.

Procedure

1. Read and complete the lab safety form.
2. Wear disposable **lab gloves.** Remove the **chicken wing** from the **self-sealing bag** and place it in a **dissecting pan.**
3. Use a **dissecting kit** to remove the skin from the wing. Use **scissors** to carefully snip a hole in the skin that is loosely attached to the wing.
4. Make a cut about 6 cm in length. Pull the skin away from the wing. Use scissors and the **scalpel** to cut through the transparent membrane that attaches the skin to the muscles.
5. Try to remove the skin without making any more holes. Look for pockets of fat, blood vessels, and muscle fibers attached to the skin. Note the strength of the skin.
6. Dispose of the skin and used gloves as directed by your teacher. Clean your dissecting tools and dissecting pan with **warm, soapy water.** Save the skinned wing to use in the next MiniLab.

Analysis

1. **Think Critically** about follicles. Human skin contains hair follicles. What type of follicles might you find on chicken skin?
2. **Explain** why it is important for skin to be strong and elastic.

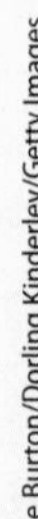
Jane Burton/Dorling Kinderley/Getty Images

Vitamin production Skin also responds to exposure to ultraviolet light rays from the Sun by producing vitamin D. Vitamin D increases absorption of calcium into the bloodstream and is essential for proper bone formation. Many food products are now fortified with vitamin D.

Protection and senses Intact skin prevents the entry of microorganisms and other foreign substances. Skin helps maintain body temperature by preventing excessive water loss. Melanin in the skin protects against ultraviolet rays. Information about changes in the environment, such as pain, pressure, and temperature changes, is relayed to the brain.

VOCABULARY

ACADEMIC VOCABULARY

Function
action, purpose
One function of the skin is to protect the body.

Damage to the Skin

Skin has the remarkable ability to repair itself. Without a repair mechanism, the body would be subject to invasion by microbes through breaks in the skin.

Cuts and scrapes Sometimes, as in the case of a minor scrape, only the epidermis is injured. Cells deep in the epidermis divide to replace the lost or injured cells. When the injury is deep, blood vessels might be injured, resulting in bleeding. Blood flows out of the wound and a clot is formed. Blood clots form a scab to close the wound, and cells beneath the scab multiply and fill in the wound. At the same time, infection-fighting white blood cells will help get rid of any bacteria that might have entered the wound.

Effects of the Sun and burns As people age, the elasticity of their skin decreases and they start to get wrinkles. Exposure to ultraviolet rays from the Sun accelerates this process and can result in burning of the skin and other damage.

Connection to Health Burns, whether caused by the Sun, heat, or chemicals, usually are classified according to their severity. The types of burns are summarized in **Table 1.** First-degree burns generally are mild and involve only cells in the epidermis. A burn that blisters or leaves a scar is a second-degree burn and involves damage to both the epidermis and dermis. Third-degree burns are the most severe. Muscle tissue and nerve cells in both the epidermis and dermis might be destroyed, and skin function is lost. Healthy skin might have to be transplanted from another place on the body in order to restore the protective layer of the body.

CAREERS IN BIOLOGY

Physical Therapist A physical therapist helps injured or disabled people to improve or regain physical functions using techniques such as exercise and massage.

Table 1 Classification of Burns — Interactive Table

Severity of burn	Damage	Effect
First-degree	Cells in the epidermis are injured and may die.	• Redness and swelling • Mild pain
Second-degree	Cells deeper in the epidermis die. Cells in the dermis are injured and may die.	• Blisters • Pain
Third-degree	Cells in the epidermis and dermis die. Nerve cells and muscles cells are injured.	• Skin function lost • Healthy skin needs to be transplanted • No pain because of nerve cell damage

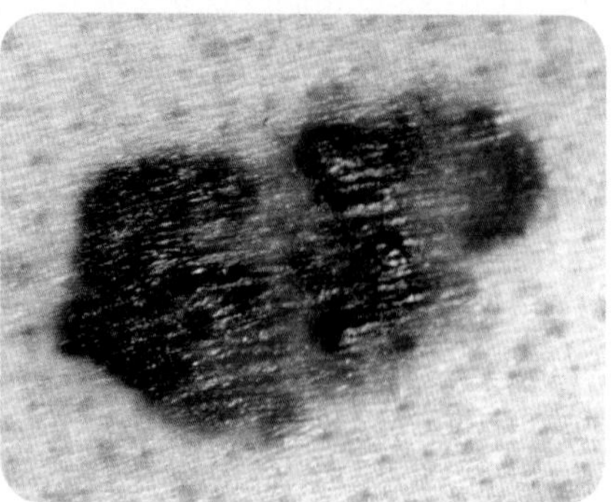

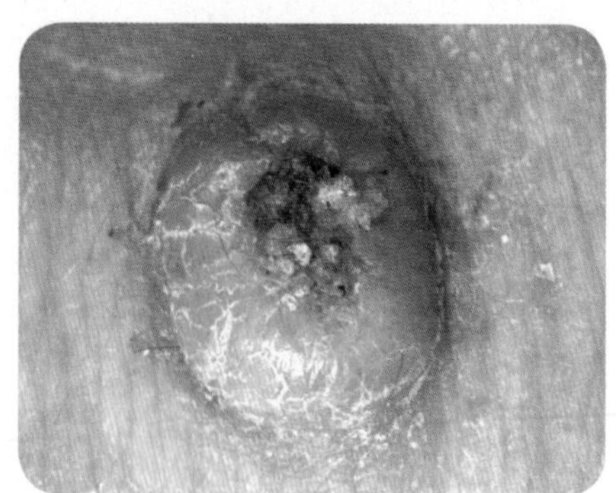

■ **Figure 5** Warning signs of skin cancer include any obvious change in a wart or mole, or moles that are irregularly shaped, varied in color, or are larger than the diameter of a pencil.

Skin cancer Exposure to ultraviolet radiation, whether it is from the Sun or from artificial sources such as tanning beds, is recognized as an important risk factor for the development of skin cancer. Ultraviolet radiation can damage the DNA in skin cells, causing those cells to grow and divide uncontrollably. When this happens, skin cancer results. Refer to **Figure 5** to see some warning signs of skin cancer.

Skin cancer is the most common cancer in the United States. There are two main categories of skin cancer: melanoma and nonmelanoma. Melanoma begins in melanocytes, the cells that produce the pigment melanin. Melanoma is the deadliest form of skin cancer. Melanoma can spread to internal organs and the lymphatic system. It is estimated that one person dies from melanoma every hour in the United States. Teens are at greater risk for melanoma because as they grow, their skin cells divide more rapidly than they will when they reach adulthood.

Anyone can get skin cancer. However, individuals with light skin, light-colored eyes, light hair color, and a tendency to burn or freckle are at the greatest risk. Everyone should try to avoid prolonged exposure to the Sun, especially between 10 a.m. and 4 p.m. when the Sun's rays are the strongest. Other preventative measures include wearing protective clothing or sunscreen with a Sun Protection Factor (SPF) of at least 15.

REVIEW IT! The Integumentary System

Section Summary

- The skin is the major organ of the integumentary system.
- Maintaining homeostasis is one function of the integumentary system.
- There are four types of tissues in the integumentary system.
- Hair, fingernails, and toenails develop from epithelial cells.
- Burns are classified according to the severity of the damage to skin tissues.

Self Check

Understand Main Ideas

1. MAINIDEA **Diagram** the two layers of the skin.
2. **Summarize** the types of tissues in the integumentary system and their functions.
3. **Generalize** different ways the integumentary system helps a human survive.
4. **Sequence** the process of skin repair in response to a cut.
5. **Compare** effects of first-degree, second-degree, and third-degree burns.

Think Critically

6. **Evaluate** the labels of two name-brand skin creams to compare how the two products claim to benefit the skin.

MATH IN ▶ Biology

7. To determine how long an SPF will protect a person from burning in the Sun, multiply the amount of time the person can spend in the Sun before starting to burn by the SPF rating. If an individual who usually burns in 10 min uses a product with an SPF of 15, how long will the protection last?

 USE IT! Science Notebook

2 The Skeletal System

1.1.1c, 4.1.2a, 4.1.2b, 4.1.2e

MAIN IDEA

The skeleton provides a structural framework for the body and protects internal organs such as the heart, lungs, and brain.

Essential Questions

- What are the differences between the bones of the axial and appendicular skeletons?
- How is new bone formed?
- What are the functions of the skeletal system?

BIOLOGY 4 U

Framing is an early stage of building a house. A person can walk through a house at that stage and know the plan of the house because of the framework. The skeletal system can be compared to the frame-work of a house. The framework provides structure and protection.

Review Vocabulary

cartilage: tough, flexible connective tissue that forms the skeletons of embryos and later covers the surface of bones that move against each other in joints

New Vocabulary

axial skeleton
appendicular skeleton
compact bone
osteocyte
spongy bone
red bone marrow
yellow bone marrow
osteoblast
ossification
osteoclast
ligament

Multilingual eGlossary

Structure of the Skeletal System

Notice all the bones in the adult skeleton pictured in **Figure 6.** If you counted them, you would find that there are 206 bones. The human skeleton consists of two divisions—the axial skeleton and the appendicular skeleton. The **axial skeleton** includes the skull, the vertebral column, the ribs, and the sternum. The **appendicular skeleton** includes the bones of the shoulders, arms, hands, hips, legs, and feet.

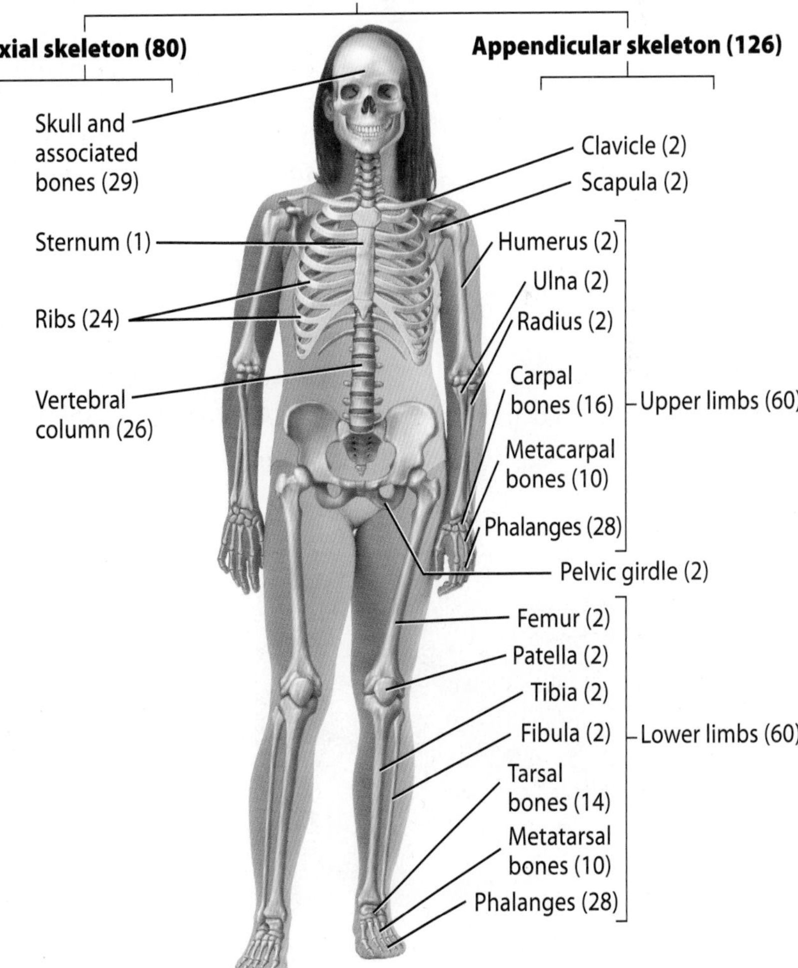

 **Personal Tutor**

■ **Figure 6** The axial skeleton includes the bones of the head, back, and chest. Bones in the appendicular skeleton are related to movement of the limbs.

Tim Fuller

CAREERS IN BIOLOGY

Medical Illustrator A medical illustrator combines a talent in art with an interest in biology to illustrate procedures or to create teaching models.

Compact and spongy bone Bone is a connective tissue that has many shapes and sizes. Bones are classified as long, short, flat, or irregular. Refer to **Figure 6.** Arm and leg bones are examples of long bones, and wrist bones are examples of short bones. Flat bones make up the skull. Facial bones and vertebrae are irregular bones.

The outer layers of all bones are composed of compact bone. **Compact bone** is dense and strong; it provides strength and protection. Running the length of compact bones are tubelike structures called osteons, or Haversian systems, which contain blood vessels and nerves. The blood vessels provide oxygen and nutrients to **osteocytes**—living bone cells.

The centers of bones can differ greatly, as illustrated in **Figure 7.** As the name suggests, **spongy bone** is less dense and has many cavities that contain bone marrow. Spongy bone is found in the center of short or flat bones and at the end of long bones. Spongy bone is surrounded by compact bone and does not contain Haversian systems.

There are two types of bone marrow—red and yellow. Red and white blood cells and platelets are produced in **red bone marrow.** Red bone marrow is found in the humerus bone of the arm, the femur bone of the leg, the sternum and ribs, the vertebrae, and the pelvis. The cavities of an infant's bones are composed of red marrow. Children's bones have more red marrow than adult bones. **Yellow bone marrow,** found in many other bones, consists of stored fat. The body can convert yellow bone marrow to red bone marrow in cases of extreme blood loss or anemia.

Formation of bone The skeletons of embryos are composed of cartilage. During fetal development, cells in fetal cartilage develop into bone-forming cells called **osteoblasts.** The formation of bone from osteoblasts is called **ossification.** Except for the tip of the nose, outer ears, discs between vertebrae, and the lining of movable joints, the human adult skeleton is all bone. Osteoblasts also are the cells responsible for the growth and repair of bones.

BrainPOP

■ **Figure 7** Bone is either compact bone or spongy bone.
***Classify** how spongy bone and compact bone differ in location and function.*

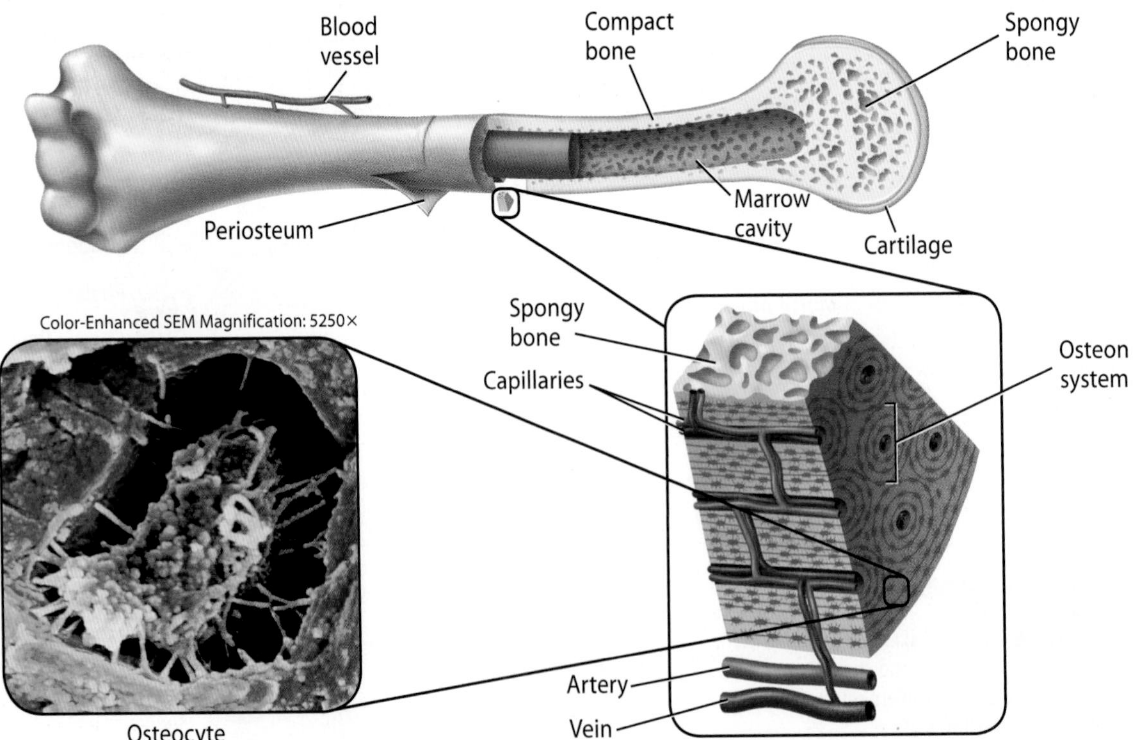

Remodeling of bone Bones constantly are being remodeled, which involves replacing old cells with new cells. This process is continual throughout life and is important in the growth of an individual. Cells called **osteoclasts** break down bone cells, which are then replaced by new bone tissue. Bone growth involves several factors, including nutrition and physical exercise. For example, a person with insufficient calcium can develop a condition known as osteoporosis that results in weak, fragile bones that break easily.

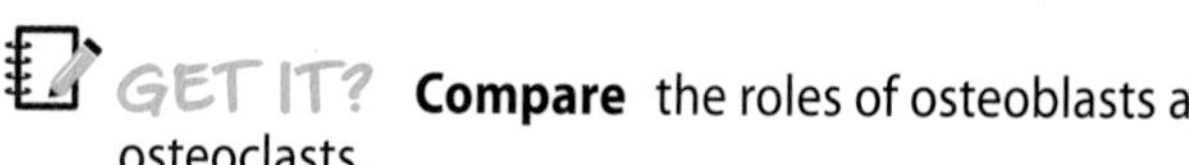

GET IT? **Compare** the roles of osteoblasts and osteoclasts.

Repair of bone Fractures are very common bone injuries. When a bone breaks but does not come through the skin, it is a simple fracture. A compound fracture is one in which the bone protrudes through the skin. A stress fracture is a thin crack in the bone. When a bone is fractured, repair begins immediately. Refer to **Figure 8,** which illustrates the steps in the repair of a broken bone.

Fracture Upon injury, endorphins, chemicals produced in the brain and sometimes called "the body's natural painkillers," flood the area of the injury to reduce the amount of pain temporarily. The injured area quickly becomes inflamed, or swollen. The swelling can last for two or three weeks.

Within about eight hours, a blood clot forms between the broken ends of the bone and new bone begins to form. First, a soft callus, or mass, of cartilage forms at the location of the break. This tissue is weak, so the broken bone must remain in place.

Callus formation About three weeks later, osteoblasts form a callus made of spongy bone that surrounds the fracture. The spongy bone is then replaced by compact bone. Osteoclasts remove the spongy bone while osteoblasts produce stronger, compact bone.

Splints, casts, and sometimes traction can ensure that the broken bone remains in place until new bone tissue has formed. Broken fingers often are kept in place by being taped to an adjacent finger.

Remodeling Bones require different amounts of time to heal. Age, nutrition, location, and severity of the break are all factors. A lack of calcium in a person's diet will slow down bone repair. Bones of younger people usually heal more quickly than bones of older people. For example, a fracture might take only four to six weeks to be repaired in a toddler, but it might take six months in an adult.

Video

Animation

■ **Figure 8** Bone repair requires several steps. First, a mass of clotted blood forms in the space between the broken bones. Then connective tissue fills the space of the broken bone. Eventually, osteoblasts produce new bone tissue.

Fracture

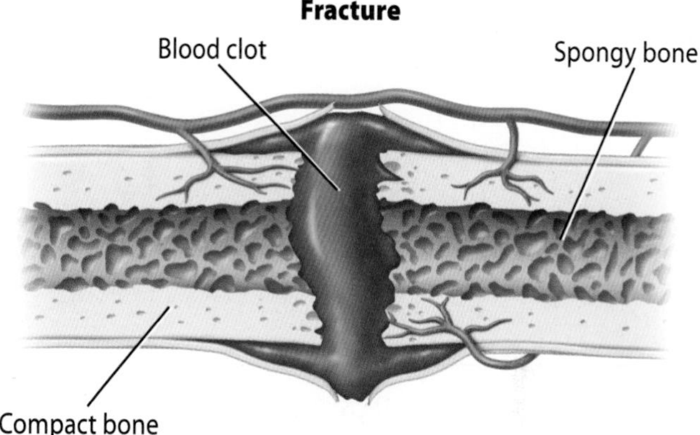

Callus Formation

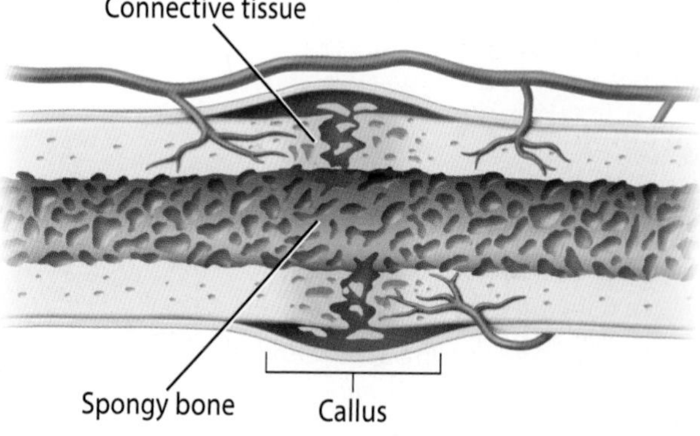

Remodeling

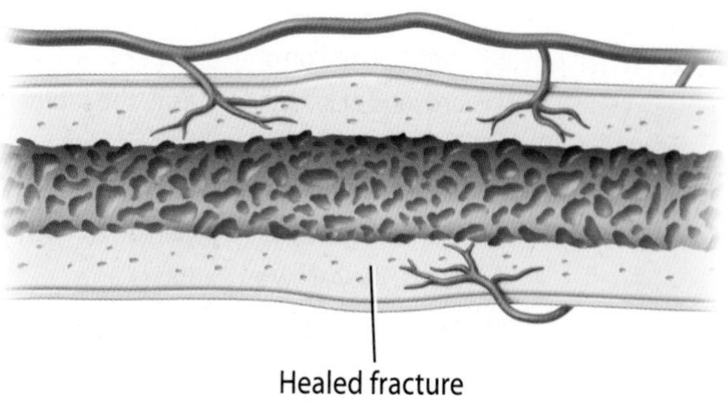

Joints

Joints occur where two or more bones meet. Except for the joints in the skull, they can be classified according to the movement they allow and the shapes of their parts. **Table 2** identifies five kinds of joints—ball-and-socket, pivot, hinge, gliding, and sutures. Study **Table 2** to identify the type of movement that each kind of joint allows and also the bones involved in each example.

Not all joints are movable. The joints between some skull bones are fixed. At birth, however, skull bones are not all fused together. They become fused by the time a baby is about three months old. Gliding joints, like those found in the hand, have limited movement. Other joints, such as the hinge joint of the elbow and the pivot joint in the lower arm, allow back-and-forth movement and twisting. The ball-and-socket joints of the hips and shoulders have the widest range of motion.

The bones of joints are held together by ligaments. **Ligaments** are tough bands of connective tissue that attach one bone to another. You will learn more about ligaments and tendons, which attach muscle to bone, in the following section.

Launch Lab

Review Based on what you have read about joints, how would you now answer the analysis questions?

BrainPOP 

GET IT? **Review** the types of joints and how joints are classified.

Table 2 Some Joints of the Skeletal System — Interactive Table

Name of Joint	Ball-and-Socket	Pivot	Hinge	Gliding	Sutures
Example					
Description	In a ball-and-socket joint, the ball-like surface of one bone fits into a cuplike depression of another bone and allows the widest range of motion of any kind of joint. The joints of the hips and shoulders are ball-and-socket joints. They allow a person to swing his or her arms and legs.	The primary movement at a pivot joint is rotation. One example of a pivot joint is the elbow joint where two bones of the lower arm, the radius, and the ulna meet. This joint allows a person to twist the lower arm.	In a hinge joint, the convex surface of one bone fits into the concave surface of another bone. Elbows and knees are hinge joints. They allow back-and-forth movement like that of a door hinge.	Gliding joints allow side-to-side and back-and-forth movement. The joints in wrists and ankles are gliding joints. The joints of vertebrae also are gliding joints.	Sutures are joints in the skull that are not movable. There are 22 bones in an adult skull. All skull bones except the lower jaw bone are joined at sutures.

Osteoarthritis (ahs tee oh ar THRI tus) The ends of bones in movable joints, such as the knee, are covered by cartilage, which serves as a cushion and allows smooth movement of the joint. Osteoarthritis is a painful condition that affects joints and results from the deterioration of the cartilage. It is a very common condition in knees and hips and also affects the neck and back. Osteoarthritis affects about ten percent of Americans and the frequency increases with age. A young person who has a joint injury is at risk to develop osteoarthritis later in life.

Rheumatoid arthritis Rheumatoid (roo MAH toyd) arthritis is another form of arthritis that affects joints. Rheumatoid arthritis is not the result of cartilage deterioration or of wear and tear on the joint. Affected joints lose strength and function and are inflamed, swollen, and painful. Fingers can look deformed, as illustrated in **Figure 9.**

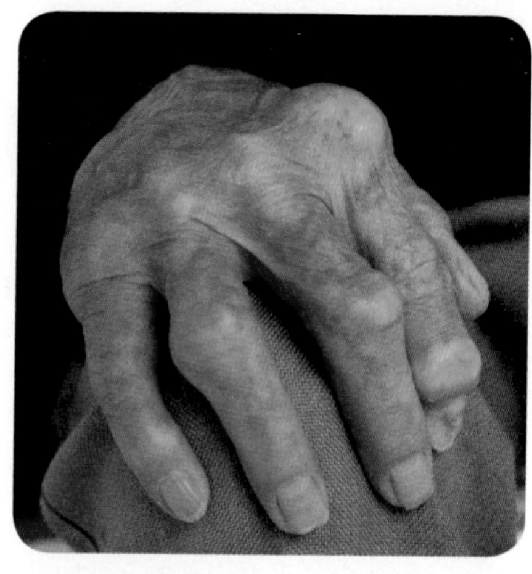

■ **Figure 9** Rheumatoid arthritis can cause loss of strength and function and involves severe pain.

Compare ***how rheumatoid arthritis differs from the more common osteoarthritis.***

Bursitis Shoulders and knees also have fluid-filled sacs called bursae that surround these joints. Bursae decrease friction and act as a cushion between bones and tendons. Bursitis is an inflammation of the bursae and can reduce joint movement and cause pain and swelling. Perhaps you have heard of "tennis elbow" which is a form of bursitis. Treatment usually involves resting the joint involved.

Sprains A sprain involves damage to the ligaments that hold joints together. It is caused when a joint is twisted or overstretched and usually causes the joint to swell and be tender and painful.

MiniLAB 2

Examine Bone Attachments

How are bones attached to muscles and other bones? Tendons attach muscle to bone, and ligaments attach bone to bone. You will examine these attachments using a skinned chicken wing.

Procedure

1. Read and complete the lab safety form.
2. Wear disposable **lab gloves.** Put the **skinned chicken wing** in a **dissection pan.**
3. Choose one muscle and use a pair of **dissection scissors** to cut the muscle away from the bone, leaving each end intact. Look for the long, white, tough tendons that connect the muscle to the bone.
4. Move the bones at the joint and notice how the tendon moves as the bones are pulled.
5. Carefully cut away all the muscles from the bones. The bones will still be attached to each other. Look for the white ligaments that hold them together. Examine the ends of each bone.
6. Draw a diagram of the wing without the muscles showing how the bones are attached to each other. Compare this drawing to the one you made in the Launch Lab.

Analysis

1. **Explain** how the drawing that you made in the Launch Lab is different from the drawing that you made of the wing in this lab.
2. **Observe and Infer** Did you notice how a muscle is attached at one end to a bone and then how the ligament at the other end runs across a joint to attach that end of the muscle to the next bone? Use a diagram to explain why this is important.
3. **Think critically** about the color of the ends of the bones at moveable joints. What do you think this material is?

Interactive Table

Table 3 Functions of the Skeletal System

Function	Description
Support	• Legs, pelvis, and vertebral column hold up the body • Mandible supports the teeth • Almost all bones support muscles
Protection	• Skull protects the brain • Vertebrae protect the spinal column • Rib cage protects the heart, lungs, and other organs
Formation of blood cells	• Red bone marrow produces red blood cells, white blood cells, and platelets
Reservoir	• Stores calcium and phosphorus
Movement	• Attached muscles pull on bones of arms and legs • Diaphragm allows normal breathing

Functions of the Skeletal System

You might think that the only purpose of a skeleton is to serve as a framework to support the body. The bones of the legs, pelvis, and the vertebral column hold up the body. The mandible supports the teeth, and almost all bones support muscles. Many soft organs are directly or indirectly supported by nearby bones.

The skeletal system serves other functions besides support, as shown in **Table 3.** The skull protects the brain, vertebrae protect the spinal cord, and the rib cage protects the heart, lungs, and other organs.

The outer layers of bone tissue also protect the bone marrow found inside bones. In addition to forming red blood cells and white blood cells, red bone marrow forms platelets, which are involved in blood clotting. Red blood cells are produced at the rate of more than two million per second.

Until a person reaches about seven years of age, all bone marrow is red bone marrow. Then, fat tissue replaces some red marrow and gives the marrow a yellowish appearance, which gives it its name. Fat is an important source of energy.

Bones are reservoirs for the storage of minerals such as calcium and phosphorus. When blood calcium levels are too low, calcium is released from bones. When blood calcium levels are high, excess calcium is stored in bone tissue. In this way, the skeletal system helps to maintain homeostasis.

Bones that have muscles attached to them allow movement of the body. For example, as muscles pull on the bones of the arms and legs, they cause movement. Muscles that are attached to your ribs allow you to breathe normally.

REVIEW IT! The Skeletal System

Section Summary

- The human skeleton consists of two divisions.
- Most bones are composed of two different types of tissue.
- Bones are being remodeled constantly.
- Bones work in conjunction with muscles.
- The skeleton has several important functions.

Self Check

Understand Main Ideas

1. MAINIDEA **Identify** and describe the functions of the axial skeleton and the appendicular skeleton.
2. **Compare** the compositions of red bone marrow and yellow bone marrow.
3. **Compare** the body's mechanism for repairing a fractured bone with the original development of bone.
4. **Construct** a classification scheme for all of the bones shown in **Figure 6.**

Think Critically

5. **Consider** what the result might be if osteoblast and osteoclast cells did not function properly both in a developing fetus and in an adult.
6. **Distinguish** between compact and spongy bone based on appearance, location, and function.

USE IT! **Science Notebook**

3 The Muscular System

1.3.5b, 4.1.2a, 4.1.2b, 4.1.2e

MAINIDEA

The three major types of muscle tissue differ in structure and function.

Essential Questions

- What are the three types of muscle tissue?
- What are the events involved in muscle contraction at the cellular and molecular levels?
- What are the differences between slow-twitch and fast-twitch muscle fibers?

BIOLOGY 4U

Leonardo da Vinci contributed a great amount of knowledge to the scientific community. He studied the human body by examining cadavers. Da Vinci replaced muscles with string and learned that muscles shorten and pull on bones to make them move.

Review Vocabulary

anaerobic: chemical reactions that do not require the presence of oxygen

New Vocabulary

smooth muscle
involuntary muscle
cardiac muscle
skeletal muscle
voluntary muscle
tendon
myofibril
myosin
actin
sarcomere

Multilingual eGlossary

Three Types of Muscle

A muscle consists of groups of fibers or muscle cells that are bound together. When the word muscle is used, many people immediately think of skeletal muscle. Examine **Figure 10** to see that there are three types of muscle: smooth muscle, cardiac muscle and skeletal muscle. Muscles are classified according to their structure and function.

Smooth muscle Many hollow internal organs such as the stomach, intestines, bladder, and uterus are lined with **smooth muscle.** Smooth muscle is called **involuntary muscle** because it cannot be controlled consciously. For example, food moves through the digestive tract because of the action of smooth muscles that line the esophagus, stomach, and small and large intestines. Under a microscope, smooth muscle does not appear striated, or striped, and each cell has one nucleus.

Cardiac muscle The involuntary muscle present only in the heart is called **cardiac muscle.** Cardiac muscle cells are arranged in a network, or web, that allows the heart muscle to contract efficiently and rhythmically. This arrangement gives strength to the heart. Cardiac muscle is striped, or striated, with light and dark bands of cells with many nuclei. Cells usually have one nucleus and are connected by gap junctions.

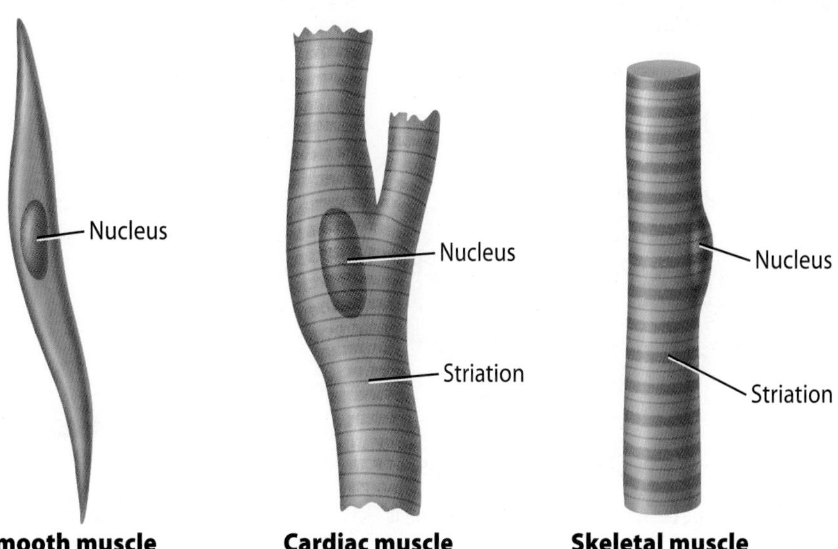

■ **Figure 10** When magnified, differences in muscle shape and appearance can be seen. Smooth muscle fibers appear spindle-shaped; cardiac muscle appears striated or striped; skeletal muscle also appears striated.
Explain ***how muscles are classified, in addition to their appearance.***

VOCABULARY

SCIENCE USAGE V. COMMON USAGE

Contract

Science usage: to tighten or to shorten

Muscles contract and cause movement.

Common usage: to become affected with

If you are exposed to the flu, you may contract the illness.

Skeletal muscle Most of the muscles in the body are skeletal muscles. **Skeletal muscles** are muscles attached to bones by tendons and when tightened, or contracted, cause movement. Skeletal muscles are **voluntary muscles** that are consciously controlled to move bones. **Tendons,** which are tough bands of connective tissue, connect muscles to bones. Under a microscope, skeletal muscles also appear striated.

GET IT? **Compare and contrast** the three types of muscles.

Skeletal Muscle Contraction

Most skeletal muscles are arranged in opposing, or antagonistic pairs. **Figure 11** illustrates muscles that you use to raise your arm and opposing muscles that you use to lower your arm. Skeletal muscle is arranged into fibers, which are fused muscle cells. Muscle fibers consist of many smaller units called **myofibrils.** Myofibrils consist of even smaller units, **myosin** and **actin,** which are protein filaments. Myofibrils are arranged in sections called sarcomeres. A **sarcomere** is the functional unit of a muscle and the part of the muscle that contracts as illustrated in **Figure 12.** The striations of skeletal muscles are a result of the sarcomeres, which run Z line to Z line. Z lines are where actin filaments attach within a myofibril. The overlap of actin and myosin filaments results in a dark band called the A band. The M line consists of only myosin filaments. The arrangement of the components of a sarcomere causes a muscle to shorten and then relax.

Virtual Lab 

Sliding filament theory The sliding filament theory is also illustrated in **Figure 12.** This theory states that once a nerve signal reaches a muscle, the actin filaments slide toward one another, causing the muscle to contract. Notice that the myosin filaments do not move. There are many skeletal muscles involved in a simple motion.

Connection to Chemistry When the nerve impulse reaches the muscle, calcium is released into the myofibrils causing the myosin and actin to attach to each other. The actin filaments are pulled toward the center of the sarcomere, resulting in muscle contraction. ATP is necessary for this step of muscle contraction. As the muscle relaxes, the filaments return into their original positions.

Figure 11 Skeletal muscles are arranged in antagonistic pairs.

 **Animation**

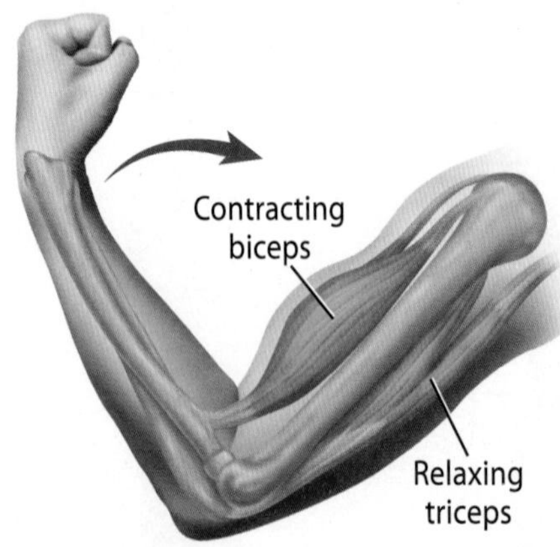

When the biceps muscle contracts, the lower arm is moved upward.

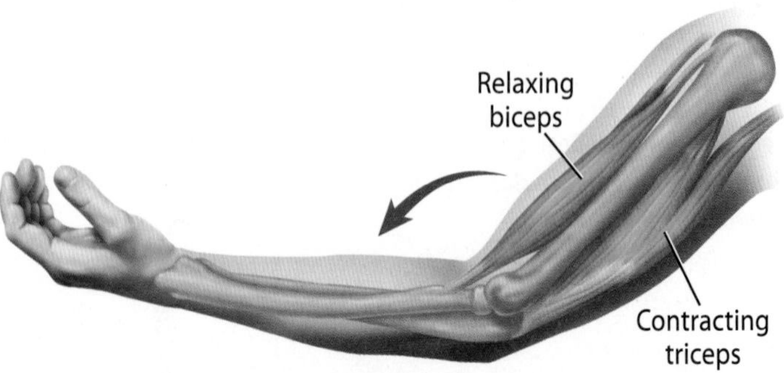

When the triceps muscle on the back of the upper arm contracts, the lower arm moves downward.

VISUALIZING Muscle Contraction

Figure 12 A muscle fiber is made of myofibrils. The protein filaments actin and myosin form myofibrils.

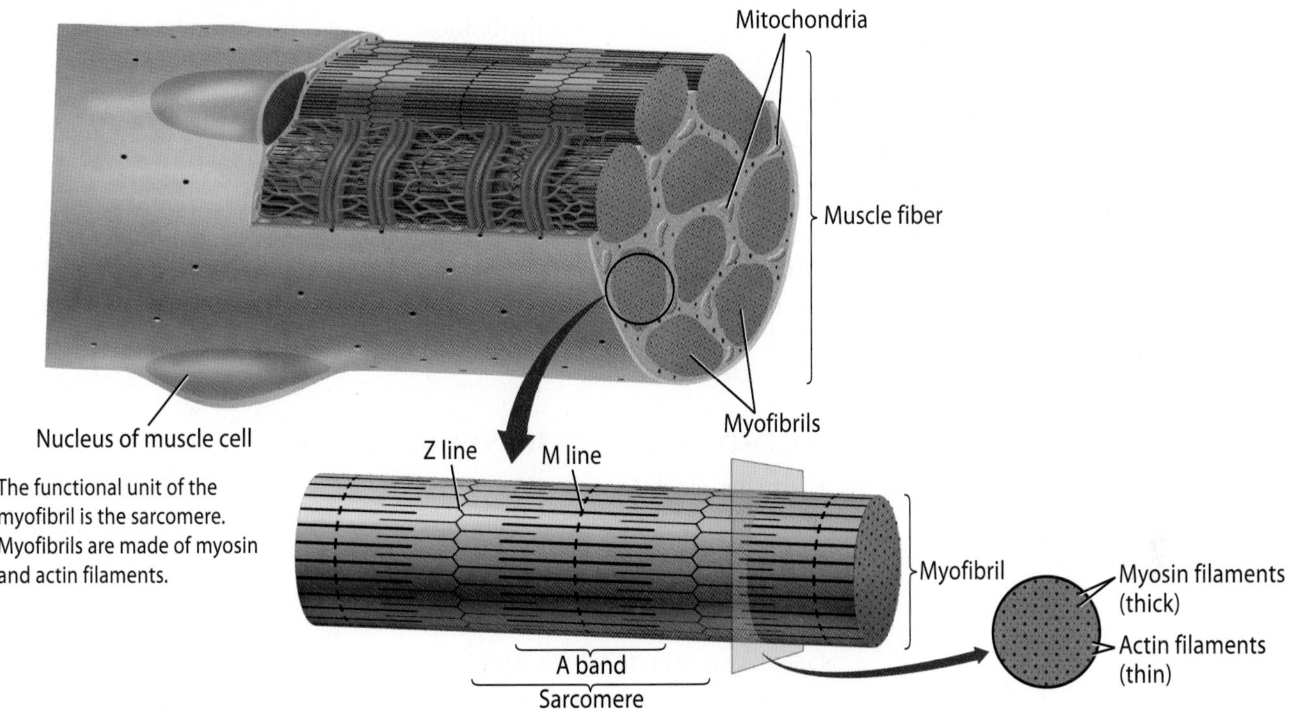

The functional unit of the myofibril is the sarcomere. Myofibrils are made of myosin and actin filaments.

Relaxed

Contracting In response to a nerve signal, cross bridges are formed between myosin and actin. ATP is used to change the position of the cross bridge, which causes the movement of actin filaments.

Fully contracted The sliding filament theory explains that muscles contract when actin filaments slide toward one another.

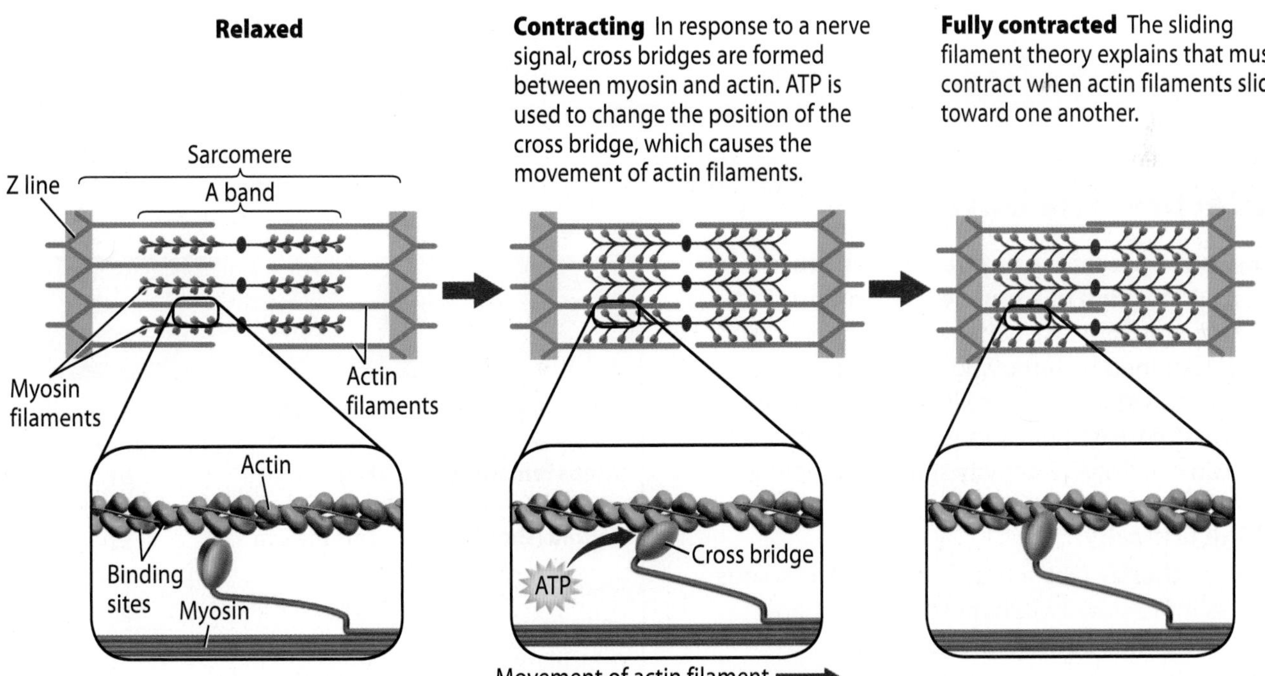

■ **Figure 13** Crossing the finish line is a moment of intense energy.

Explain ***why normal breathing is important after intense exercise.***

Energy for muscle contraction All muscle cells metabolize aerobically and anaerobically. When sufficient oxygen is available, aerobic cellular respiration occurs in muscle cells.

Recall that cellular respiration process provides ATP for energy. After a period of intense exercise, muscles might not get enough oxygen to sustain cellular respiration, limiting the amount of ATP that is available. Muscles, like those of the athlete in **Figure 13,** then must rely on the anaerobic process of lactic acid fermentation for energy.

During exercise, lactic acid builds up in muscle cells, causing fatigue. Excess lactic acid enters the bloodstream and this stimulates rapid breathing. After resting for a short time, adequate amounts of oxygen are restored and lactic acid is broken down.

You probably have seen a dead animal along the side of the road. When an animal dies, rigor mortis sets in. Rigor mortis is a state of prolonged muscular contraction. ATP is required to pump the calcium back out of the myofibrils, which causes the muscles to relax. In rigor mortis, the dead animal cannot produce ATP, so the calcium remains in the myofibrils and the muscle remains contracted. After 24 hours, cells and tissues begin degrading and the muscle fibers cannot remain contracted.

Skeletal Muscle Strength

Many people do not develop the physiques of champion bodybuilders, no matter how often they work out in the weight room. A person might be the fastest sprinter on the track team, but quickly becomes fatigued in a long-distance race. What might be the reason for these differences? The reason in both cases is the ratio of slow-twitch muscle fibers to fast-twitch muscle fibers. Both slow-twitch and fast-twitch fibers are present in every person's muscles.

Data Analysis LAB 1

Based on Real Data*

Interpret the Data

How is the percentage of slow-twitch muscle related to action of a muscle? The proportion of slow-twitch to fast-twitch muscle fibers can be determined by removing a small piece of a muscle and staining the cells with a dye called *ATPase stain.* Fast-twitch muscle fibers with a high amount of ATP activity stain dark brown.

Think Critically

1. **Hypothesize** why a muscle such as the soleus has more slow-twitch muscle fibers than a muscle such as the orbicularis oculi.
2. **Classify** muscles by giving examples of muscles that have a high proportion of fast-twitch muscle fibers.

Data and Observations

Muscle	Action	Percent Slow Twitch
Soleus (leg)	Elevates the foot	87
Biceps femoris (leg)	Flexes the leg	67
Deltoid (shoulder)	Lifts the arm	52
Sternocleidomastoideus (neck)	Moves the head	35
Orbicularis oculi (face)	Closes the eyelid	15

*Data adapted from: Lamb, D.R. 1984. *Physiology of Exercise* New York: Macmillan Co.

Slow-twitch muscles Muscles vary in the speeds at which they contract. Slow-twitch muscles contract more slowly than fast-twitch muscle fibers. Slow-twitch muscle fibers have more endurance than fast-twitch muscle fibers. The body of the triathlete in **Figure 14** has many slow-twitch fibers. These kinds of muscle fibers function well in long-distance running or swimming because they resist fatigue more than fast-twitch muscle fibers.

Slow-twitch muscle fibers have many mitochondria needed for cellular respiration. They also contain myoglobin, a respiratory molecule that stores oxygen and serves as an oxygen reserve. Myoglobin causes the muscles to have a dark appearance. Exercise increases the number of mitochondria in these fibers, but the overall increase in the size of the muscle is minimal.

Fast-twitch muscles Fast-twitch muscle fibers fatigue easily but provide great strength for rapid, short movements. Fast-twitch muscle fibers are adapted for strength. They function well in exercises requiring short bursts of energy such as sprinting or weightlifting, as illustrated in **Figure 14.**

Fast-twitch fibers are lighter in color because they lack myoglobin. Because they have fewer mitochondria, they rely on anaerobic metabolism, which causes a buildup of lactic acid. This causes these muscles to fatigue easily. Exercise increases the number of myofibrils in a muscle, thereby increasing the diameter of the entire muscle.

Most skeletal muscles contain a mixture of slow-twitch and fast-twitch muscle fibers. The ratio of these fibers is determined genetically. If there is a very high ratio of slow-twitch to fast-twitch, a person might be a champion cross-country runner. Champion sprinters have a high proportion of fast-twitch muscle fibers. Most people are somewhere in between.

■ **Figure 14** Triathletes have a high proportion of slow-twitch muscle fibers. Weight lifters have a high proportion of fast-twitch muscle fibers.

REVIEW IT! The Muscular System

Section Summary

- There are three types of muscle tissue.
- Skeletal muscles are arranged in antagonistic pairs that work opposite to each other.
- Smooth muscles line many internal organs.
- Cardiac muscle is present only in the heart.
- All muscle cells metabolize both aerobically and anaerobically.

Self Check

Understand Main Ideas

1. MAINIDEA **Construct** a chart that lists similarities and differences among the three types of muscles.
2. **Identify** which type of muscles are voluntary and which are involuntary.
3. **Explain** why aerobic respiration occurs before lactic acid fermentation in most muscles.
4. **Compare** the role of mitochondria in slow-twitch and fast-twitch muscle fibers.

Think Critically

5. **Infer** Wild turkeys have a higher ratio of dark meat (muscle) to white meat than farm-raised turkeys. Why does this allow wild turkeys to fly longer distances than domesticated turkeys?

WRITING IN ▶ Biology

6. Write a short story that describes the sequence of events involved in skeletal muscle contraction. Tell your story from the point of view of a calcium ion.

BIOLOGY & society

1.1.3b

SPFs and Sunscreens

When you are outside playing sports or hanging out with your friends, the Sun is a welcome companion. Its warm rays are a staple of summertime fun. But are you adequately protecting yourself from the potentially harmful effects of the Sun? Retailers display many shelves of sun-protection products, but how much protection do these products provide?

Damaged skin It is important to understand that tanned skin is damaged skin. Skin cells that have been exposed to and injured by the Sun's ultraviolet (UV) rays produce melanin in order to absorb the rays. The melanin causes the "tanned" look. There are two kinds of UV rays that can reach Earth. UVB rays cause sunburns. UVA rays, which penetrate skin more deeply than UVB rays, cause other kinds of skin damage, such as wrinkles and sunspots. The same problems can result from using tanning beds or sunlamps, both of which emit UV rays. Even if you do not become sunburned, exposure to both kinds of UV rays can increase your risk of skin cancers—especially melanoma, the most serious kind of skin cancer.

To protect skin from the Sun's rays, people can wear sunscreen. Many sunscreens are labeled with a number marked "SPF," which stands for "Sun Protection Factor." However, SPF only measures protection from UVB rays. Sunscreens that are labeled "broad-spectrum" offer some protection from UVA rays, but scientists have not yet developed a system of measuring how well a sunscreen protects from UVA rays.

Understanding SPF Using the best product may be difficult because SPF numbers can be misleading. For example, one might think that a sunscreen with an SPF of 30 would have twice the protection against UVB rays than a sunscreen with an SPF of 15.

These students should all be wearing sunscreen with at least SPF 15 on all skin surfaces exposed to the Sun's rays.

However, that is not the case. A sunscreen with an SPF of 15 protects against 93 percent of UVB rays, while a sunscreen with an SPF of 30 protects against 97 percent of UVB rays.

The American Cancer Society recommends that when outdoors, people of all ethnicities should wear a water-resistant sunscreen with an SPF of at least 15. About one ounce of sunscreen should be applied 15 to 30 minutes before going outside, even on cloudy days. Sunscreen should be reapplied every two hours. This simple habit goes a long way to protect skin from the Sun's rays. And for people who miss having that golden glow, there are always self-tanning products.

WRITING IN ▶ Biology

Create a skit Write a skit that explains SPF ratings and why wearing sunscreen is important to one's health. Research promotional materials for products and services related to tanning while you are planning your skit. Use data from the promotional materials about why people might think tanning is or isn't healthful in your skit. Research other steps that people can take to protect themselves from the Sun, and include those steps in the skit.

WebQuest

BioLAB 1.1.1c, 1.1.2a

Forensics: How can skeletons help you solve a "crime"?

Background: Imagine there is a National Museum of Domestic Chickens and it has been robbed. Several bones from the first chicken eaten in America are missing. Three dogs are suspects. Your job is to examine impressions of bones that were found in mud near the doghouse of each dog and to determine if any of the bones came from a chicken. You will be given a clue for each unknown bone.

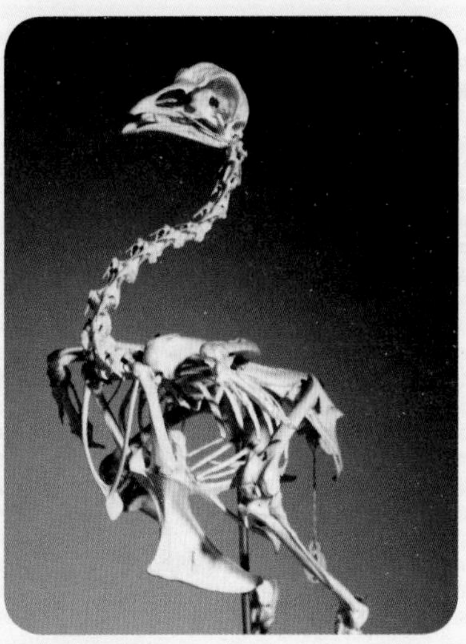

Question: *Can the structure and form of a bone tell you from which animal it came?*

Materials

impressions of three unknown bones
set of clues
various animal skeletons
hand lens
metric ruler
string

Safety Precautions

Procedure

1. Read and complete the lab safety form.
2. Collect materials you will use to measure and examine the skeletons. Determine what types of measurements you will make.
3. Obtain impressions of three bones and a set of clues from your teacher. Do not open the clues until you are told to do so.
4. Design a data table to record your measurements.
5. Examine the skeletons. Compare them to the impressions.
6. Make measurements and record the data.
7. Open the clues you were given and reexamine your data and answers.
8. **Cleanup and Disposal** Return any reusable materials to their proper storage areas.

Analyze and Conclude

1. **Analyze Data** Based on your observations and measurements, determine which one of the impressions came from a chicken.
2. **Interpret Data** How did you use information concerning the size and shape of each impression to help you determine from which animal it came?
3. **Evaluate** Did your conclusions change after you opened the clues? Explain your reasoning if your conclusions changed.
4. **Compare and Contrast** What similarities did you notice between each impression and bones in the human skeleton? What differences did you notice?
5. **Relate** Which skeletons seem to share the most characteristics with a human skeleton?
6. **Draw Conclusions** Which dog stole the chicken bones?

SHARE YOUR DATA

Poster Session Paleontologists are scientists who study fossils. Through their studies of fossil bones they have found evidence that birds had a dinosaur ancestor. Research the evidence that has been found and create a poster that shows what you learned.

CHAPTER 18 STUDY GUIDE

BIGIDEA **These systems work together to maintain homeostasis by protecting, supporting, and moving the body.**

SECTION 1 The Integumentary System

MAINIDEA Skin is a multilayered organ that covers and protects the body.

- The skin is the major organ of the integumentary system.
- Maintaining homeostasis is one function of the integumentary system.
- There are four types of tissues in the integumentary system.
- Hair, fingernails, and toenails develop from epithelial cells.
- Burns are classified according to the severity of the damage to skin tissues.

VOCABULARY

- **epidermis**
- **keratin**
- **melanin**
- **dermis**
- **hair follicle**
- **sebaceous gland**

SECTION 2 The Skeletal System

MAINIDEA The skeleton provides a structural framework for the body and protects internal organs such as the heart, lungs, and brain.

- The human skeleton consists of two divisions.
- Most bones are composed of two different types of tissue.
- Bones are being remodeled constantly.
- Bones work in conjunction with muscles.
- The skeleton has several important functions.

VOCABULARY

- **axial skeleton**
- **appendicular skeleton**
- **compact bone**
- **osteocyte**
- **spongy bone**
- **red bone marrow**
- **yellow bone marrow**
- **osteoblast**
- **ossification**
- **osteoclast**
- **ligament**

SECTION 3 The Muscular System

MAINIDEA The three major types of muscle tissue differ in structure and function.

- There are three types of muscle tissue.
- Skeletal muscles are arranged in antagonistic pairs that work opposite to each other.
- Smooth muscles line many internal organs.
- Cardiac muscle is present only in the heart.
- All muscle cells metabolize both aerobically and anaerobically.

VOCABULARY

- **smooth muscle**
- **involuntary muscle**
- **cardiac muscle**
- **skeletal muscle**
- **voluntary muscle**
- **tendon**
- **myofibril**
- **myosin**
- **actin**
- **sarcomere**

CHAPTER 18 ASSESSMENT

SECTION 1

Vocabulary Review

Explain the difference between the terms in each set.

1. epidermis, dermis
2. melanin, keratin
3. sebaceous glands, hair follicles

Understand Main Ideas

Use the diagram below to answer question 4.

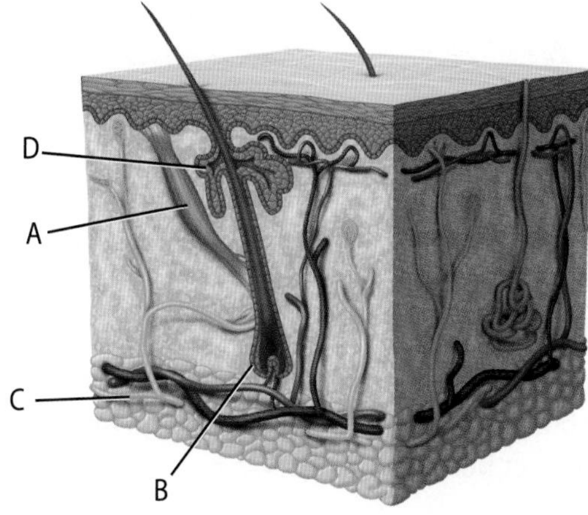

4. Which tissue type is responsible for "goose bump" formation?
   A. A
   B. B
   C. C
   D. D

5. When are blackheads formed?
   A. when sebaceous glands become clogged
   B. when grooves in the epidermis gather dirt
   C. when hair follicles grow inward rather than outward
   D. when there is an excess of keratin produced

6. How does the skin regulate body temperature?
   A. by increasing sweat production
   B. by retaining water
   C. by producing vitamin D
   D. by regulating fat content in the epidermis

7. Which are not found in the dermis?
   A. muscles
   B. sweat and oil glands
   C. fat cells
   D. nerve cells

8. What could be inferred from suntans?
   A. Sunning for the purpose of tanning produces healthier skin.
   B. A tan might indicate sun damage to the skin.
   C. Tanning strengthens the elastic in the skin making the skin feel tight.
   D. Tanning promotes skin that has a more youthful appearance.

Constructed Response

9. **MAIN IDEA** What possible effects on the body might there be if the epidermis was absent?
10. **Open Ended** What possible effects on the body might there be if the dermis was absent?
11. **THEME FOCUS** Describe how the integumentary system contributes to homeostasis.

Think Critically

12. **Explain** why it does not hurt when you get a haircut.
13. **Assess** the reason why people with third degree burns do not feel pain at the site of the burn.

SECTION 2

Vocabulary Review

Explain the difference between the terms in each set.

14. spongy bone, compact bone
15. tendons, ligaments
16. osteoblasts, osteoclasts

Understand Main Ideas

Use the figure below to answer question 17.

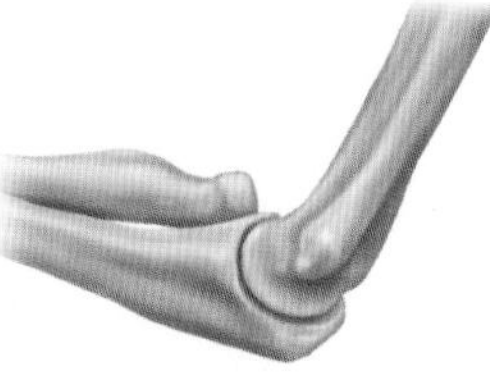

17. Where would you find the type of joint shown above?
    A. hip
    B. vertebrae
    C. elbow
    D. skull

18. Which is not a function of bone?
 A. production of vitamin D
 B. internal support
 C. protection of internal organs
 D. storage of calcium

Use the diagram below to answer question 19.

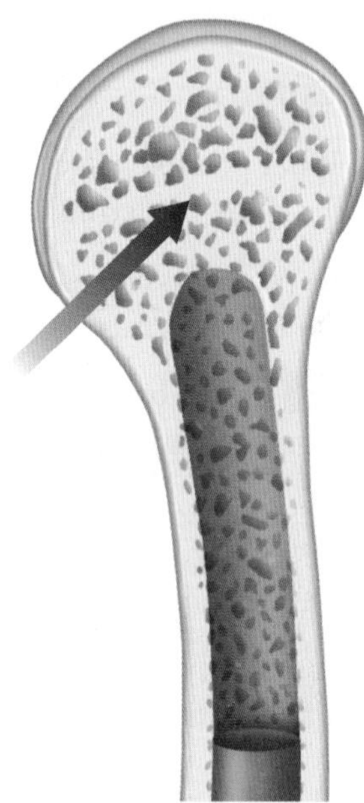

19. What is a characteristic of the portion of the bone indicated by the arrow?
 A. It contains no living cells.
 B. It contains bone marrow.
 C. It is the only type of bone tissue in long bones.
 D. It is made of overlapping osteon systems.

20. Which pair of terms is mismatched?
 A. cranium, sutures
 B. wrist, pivot joint
 C. shoulder, ball-and-socket joint
 D. knee, hinge joint

21. What are the cells that remove old bone tissue called?
 A. osteoblasts
 B. osteocytes
 C. osteoclasts
 D. osteozymes

22. Which is not part of the axial skeleton?
 A. skull
 B. ribs
 C. hip bone
 D. vertebral column

23. Which is part of the appendicular skeleton?

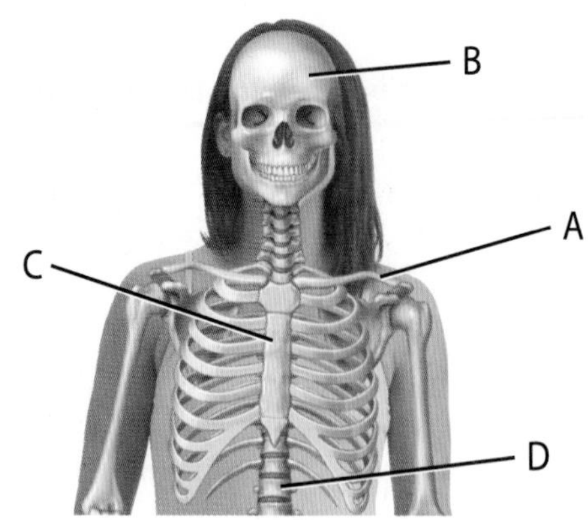

 A. A
 B. B
 C. C
 D. D

Constructed Response

24. **MAIN IDEA** Describe potential consequences if all bone tissue in humans was comprised of spongy bone and there was no compact bone.

25. **Open Ended** Describe potential consequences if all bone tissue in humans was comprised of compact bone and there was no spongy bone.

26. **Short Answer** Compare the function of osteoclasts and osteoblasts.

Think Critically

27. **Analyze** the following scenario. A person enters the emergency room with an ankle injury. What structures of the patient's ankle need to be examined to determine the proper treatment?

28. **Hypothesize** what might happen to a woman's bones if she did not increase her intake of calcium during pregnancy?

SECTION 3

Vocabulary Review

For each set of terms below, choose the one term that does not belong and explain why it does not belong.

29. actin, melanin, myosin

30. cardiac muscle, smooth muscle, fast-twitch muscle

31. sarcomere, myofibril, myoglobin

Understand Main Ideas

32. Which requires ATP?
    A. muscle contraction
    B. muscle relaxation
    C. both muscle contraction and relaxation
    D. neither muscle contraction nor relaxation

Use the diagram below to answer question 33.

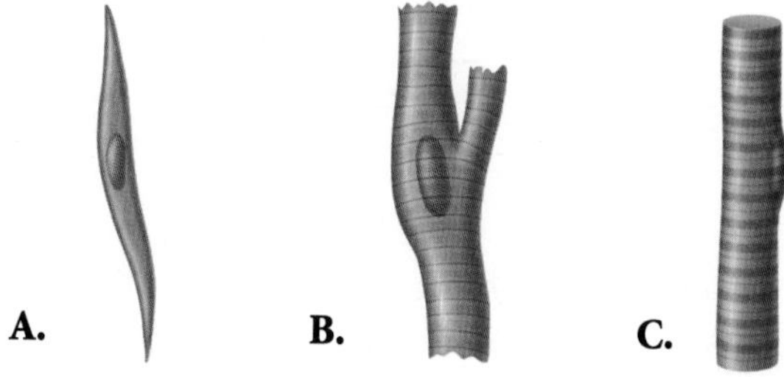

33. What muscles shown above are classified as voluntary muscles?
    A. the muscle type shown in A
    B. the muscle type shown in B
    C. the muscle type shown in C
    D. all muscles

34. Which is a characteristic of fast-twitch muscle fibers?
    A. They contain more myoglobin than slow-twitch fibers.
    B. They are resistant to fatigue.
    C. They have fewer mitochondria than slow-twitch fibers.
    D. They require high amounts of oxygen in order to function.

Constructed Response

35. **MAIN IDEA** Compare and contrast the structure of skeletal, smooth, and cardiac muscle.

36. **Short Answer** Explain, based on the structure of the muscle fibers, why skeletal muscles can contract but not lengthen.

Think Critically

37. **Predict** any possible consequences if cardiac and smooth muscle had the same structure as skeletal muscle.

38. **Infer** why it is important that no muscle contains solely slow-twitch or fast-twitch fibers.

Summative Assessment

39. **BIG IDEA** Explain how the loss of the integumentary body system would cause a breakdown of homeostasis.

40. **WRITING IN ▶ Biology** Imagine you are a writer for a health and fitness magazine. Write a brief article about the need for calcium in order for the skeletal and muscular systems to function correctly.

DBQ Document–Based Questions

Athletes burn fat at a maximum rate when they exercise at an intensity near the lactate threshold—the point at which lactic acid starts to build up in the muscles. In addition, athletes who consume the greatest amounts of oxygen during intense exercise [VO_{2peak}] burn the most fat. Researchers compared the lactate threshold and oxygen consumption of overweight subjects who did not exercise to those of highly-trained athletes.

Data obtained from: Bircher, S. and Knechtle, B. 2004. Relationship between fat oxidation and lactate threshold in athletes and obese women and men. Journal of Sports Science and Medicine 3:174–181.

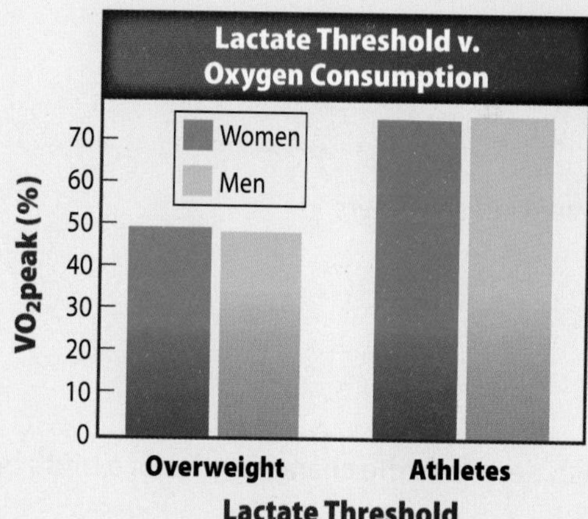

41. At what percent of VO_{2peak} was the lactate threshold reached in overweight subjects?

42. How might an overweight person who does not exercise increase his or her VO_{2peak} and, therefore, his or her lactate threshold?

CUMULATIVE
MULTIPLE CHOICE

1 Which characteristic makes bats unique among mammals?

A eyesight

B feathers

C flight

D teeth

Use the figure of the joint below to answer question 2.

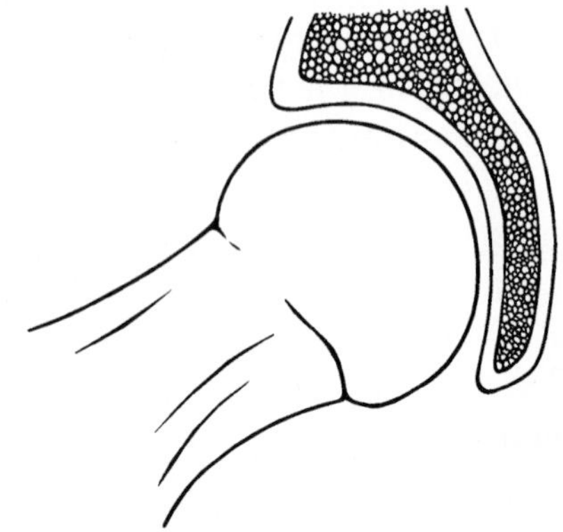

2 Where is the type of joint shown in the figure found?

A elbows and knees

B fingers and toes

C hips and shoulders

D wrists and ankles

3 Which describes the characteristics of a bird's brain?

A Birds have a large medulla to process their vision.

B Birds have a large cerebellum to control respiration and digestion.

C Birds have a large cerebrum to coordinate movement and balance.

D Birds have a large cerebral cortex to control flight.

SHORT ANSWER

Use the diagram below to answer questions 4 and 5.

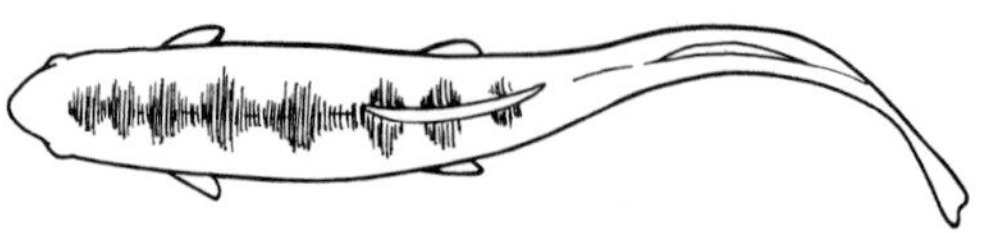

4 Describe the difference between how a fish with an S-shaped pattern swims and a fish that moves its tail only.

5 Decide where a fish with an S-shaped pattern would be likely found swimming.

6 Relate the key events in the life cycle of a butterfly to the key events in the life cycle of a grasshopper.

7 Howler monkeys are the loudest land animals. Their calls are heard for miles across the jungle. They use their calls to mark their territory. Assess this type of behavior.

8 Describe how fetal cartilage becomes bone.

9 A chimpanzee picks up a blade of grass and sticks it in an anthole. When it pulls the blade of grass out, it has ants on it. The chimpanzee eats the ants. The chimpanzee continues doing this because it is an easy way to get ants. Assess this activity as it relates to animal behaviors.

10 Describe two types of joint conditions.

EXTENDED RESPONSE

Use the diagram to answer questions 11 and 12.

Pigeon

Eagle

11 Evaluate what the location of the eyes on these two birds reveals about their behavior.

12 Explain how the beaks of these two birds give evidence of what they eat.

ESSAY QUESTION

Whooping cranes are an endangered species. One of the reasons for this is that they hatch in nesting areas and then migrate south for the winter. Humans can raise chicks, but teaching them to migrate is a different problem. Operation Migration solved this problem in 2001. Operation Migration used ultralight aircraft to lead a migration of human-raised whooping cranes on a 2000-km migration from Wisconsin to Florida. The whooping cranes followed the ultralight aircraft that used recorded calls to learn the migration route.

Using the information in the paragraph above, answer the following question in essay format.

13 Migratory behavior has been shown to be an innate behavior. Evaluate why it is necessary to use ultra-light aircraft to guide the birds so they can learn the migration route.

TEST PRACTICE

14 Which describes the circulatory system of most reptiles?

A double loop, four-chambered heart

B double loop, three-chambered heart

C single loop, three-chambered heart

D single loop, two-chambered heart

Use the figure below to answer question 15.

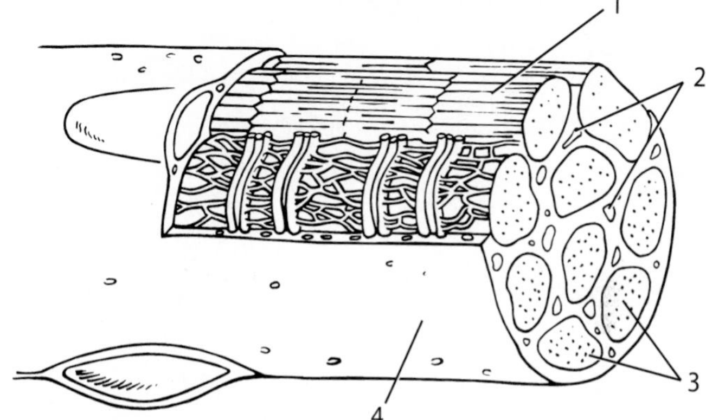

15 Which part of a muscle is used for cellular respiration?

A 1

B 2

C 3

D 4

16 What is the name of the muscle part used for cellular respiration?

A myofibril

B sarcomere

C actin

D mitochondria

NEED EXTRA HELP?																
If You Missed Question . . .	1	2	3	4	5	6	7	8	9	10	11	12	13	14	15	16
Review Section . . .	30.1	32.2	29.2	28.1	28.1	26.3	31.2	32.2	31.1	32.2	29.2	29.2	31.2	29.1	32.3	32.3

Transferring electrical messages to and from the brain and spinal cord quickly and accurately keeps us safe, keeps the body functioning properly, and allows us to survive in varying environments.

LaunchLAB

How does information travel in the nervous system?

Your body is bombarded by sounds, odors, sights, tastes, and physical contact almost constantly. The nervous system makes sense of these stimuli, and reacts in ways that promote your survival. In this lab, you will model that communication process.

CHAPTER 19

Nervous System

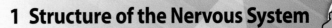

1 Structure of the Nervous System

4.1.2a, 4.1.2b, 4.1.2e, 4.1.2j, ¥a

2 Organization of the Nervous System

1.1.1b, 1.1.4a, 1.3.5b, 4.1.2a, 4.1.2b, 4.1.2e

3 The Senses

1.3.5b, 4.1.2a, 4.1.2b, 4.1.2e, ¥e, ¥i, ¥m, ¥n

4 Effects of Drugs

THEMEFOCUS

Cause and effect Changes in the body's internal or external environment can cause an action potential to be produced.

BIGIDEA

The nervous system is essential for communication among cells, tissues, and organs.

Nervous System

Make a three column chart using the labels shown. Use it to record how drugs affect the nervous system.

A. Increase	B. Block	C. Block

USE IT! **Science Notebook**

1 Structure of the Nervous System

4.1.2a, 4.1.2b, 4.1.2e, 4.1.2j, ¥a

MAINIDEA

Neurons conduct electrical impulses that allow cells, tissues, and organs to detect and respond to stimuli.

Essential Questions

- What are the major parts of a neuron and what is the function of each part?
- How is a nerve impulse similar to an electrical signal, and how does it move along a neuron?

BIOLOGY 4U

Imagine that you wake up in the middle of the night and get out of bed. On your way to the kitchen, you stub your toe. You know right away what happened. Was it one second before you said, "Ouch"? Or was it less than that? How did your brain get the message so quickly?

Review Vocabulary

diffusion: the random movement of particles from an area of higher concentration to an area of lower concentration resulting in even distribution

New Vocabulary

neuron
dendrite
cell body
axon
reflex arc
action potential
threshold
node
synapse
neurotransmitter

Multilingual eGlossary

Neurons

Electricity and chemistry were both involved as your brain received the message that you stubbed your toe. **Neurons** are specialized cells that help you gather information about your environment, interpret the information, and react to it. Neurons make up an enormous communication network in your body called the nervous system.

Figure 1 shows that a neuron consists of three main regions: the dendrites, a cell body, and an axon. **Dendrites** receive signals called impulses from other neurons and conduct the impulses to the cell body. Each neuron contains several dendrites. The nucleus of the neuron and many of the cell organelles are found in the **cell body.** Lastly, an **axon** carries the nerve impulse from the cell body to other neurons and muscles.

GET IT? **Relate** dendrites, axons, and cell bodies.

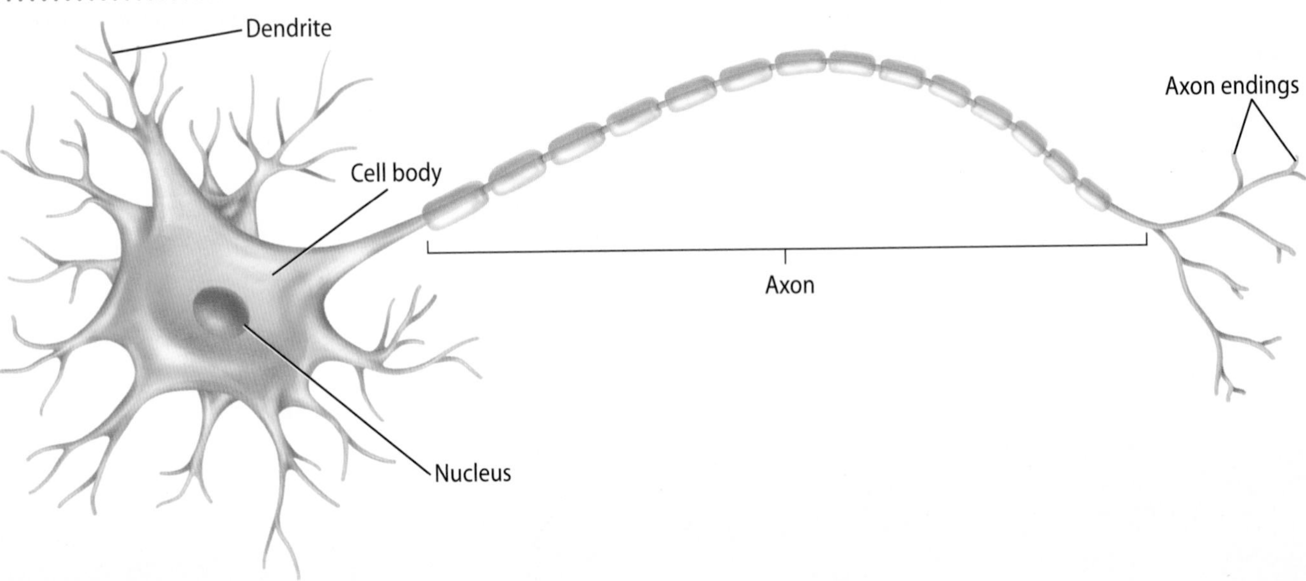

■ **Figure 1** There are three main parts of a neuron: the dendrites, a cell body, and an axon. Neurons are highly specialized cells that are organized to form complex networks.

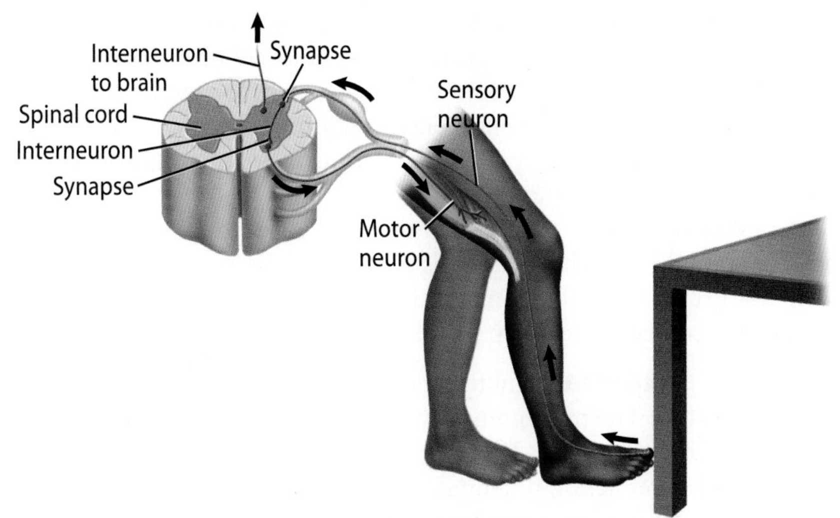

■ **Figure 2** A simple reflex involves a sensory neuron, an interneuron, and a motor neuron. Interneurons can also carry impulses to the brain.

Explain ***how a reflex might be completed before the brain interprets the event.***

 **Animation**

There are three kinds of neurons: sensory neurons, interneurons, and motor neurons. Sensory neurons send impulses from receptors in the skin and sense organs to the brain and spinal cord. Sensory neurons signal interneurons, which are found in the spinal cord and brain. Interneurons carry the impulse to motor neurons, which carry impulses away from the brain and spinal cord to a gland or muscle, which results in a response. Refer to **Figure 2** to follow the path of an impulse for a simple involuntary reflex. The nerve impulse completes what is called a reflex arc. A **reflex arc** is a nerve pathway that consists of a sensory neuron, an interneuron, and a motor neuron. Notice that the brain is not involved. A reflex arc is a basic structure of the nervous system.

A Nerve Impulse

Connection to Physics A nerve impulse is an electrical charge traveling the length of a neuron. An impulse results from a stimulus, such as a touch or perhaps a loud bang, which causes a person to jump.

A neuron at rest When a neuron is at rest, as shown in **Figure 3,** it is not conducting an impulse. Notice that there are more sodium ions (Na^+) outside the cell than inside the cell. The reverse is true for potassium ions (K^+)—there are more potassium ions inside the cell than outside the cell.

■ **Figure 3** The distribution of Na^+ and K^+ ions, and the presence of negatively charged protein molecules in the cytoplasm, keep the inside of the cell more negatively charged than the outside when a neuron is at rest.

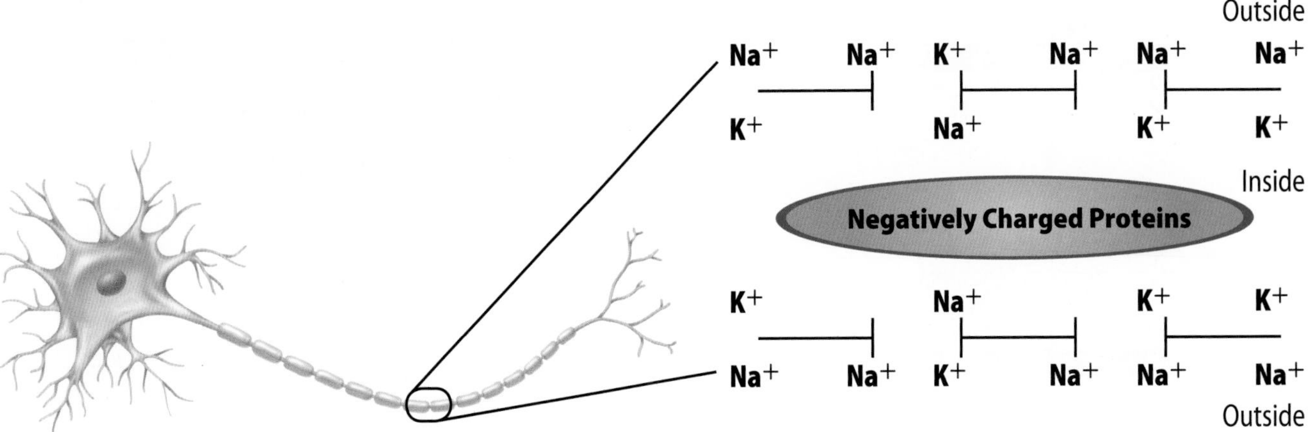

VOCABULARY

SCIENCE USAGE V. COMMON USAGE

Channel

Science usage: a path along which information in the form of ions or molecules passes

Nerve impulses move through neurons as channels open in the plasma membrane.

Common usage: the deeper part of a river, harbor, or strait

Large ships move through a harbor channel.

Recall that ions tend to diffuse across the plasma membrane from an area of high concentration of ions to an area of low concentration of ions. Proteins found in the plasma membrane work to counteract the diffusion of the sodium ions and potassium ions. These proteins, called the sodium-potassium pump, actively transport sodium ions out of the cell and potassium ions into the cell.

For every two potassium ions pumped into a neuron, three sodium ions are pumped out. This maintains an unequal distribution of positively charged ions, resulting in a positive charge outside the neuron and a negatively charged cytoplasm inside the neuron.

An action potential Another name for a nerve impulse is an **action potential.** The minimum stimulus to cause an action potential to be produced is a **threshold.** However, a stronger stimulus does not generate a stronger action potential. Action potentials are described as being "all or nothing," meaning that a nerve impulse is either strong enough to travel along the neuron or it is not strong enough.

When a stimulus reaches the threshold, channels in the plasma membrane open. Sodium ions rapidly move into the cytoplasm of the neuron through these channels, causing a temporary reversal in electrical charges. The inside of the cell then has a positive charge, which causes other channels to open. Potassium ions leave the cell through these channels, restoring a positive charge outside the cell. **Figure 4** shows that this change in charge moves like a wave along the length of the axon.

Figure 4 Follow as an action potential moves along an axon from left to right. Notice what happens to the Na^+ and K^+ and how this changes the relative electrical charges inside and outside the neuron.

Animation

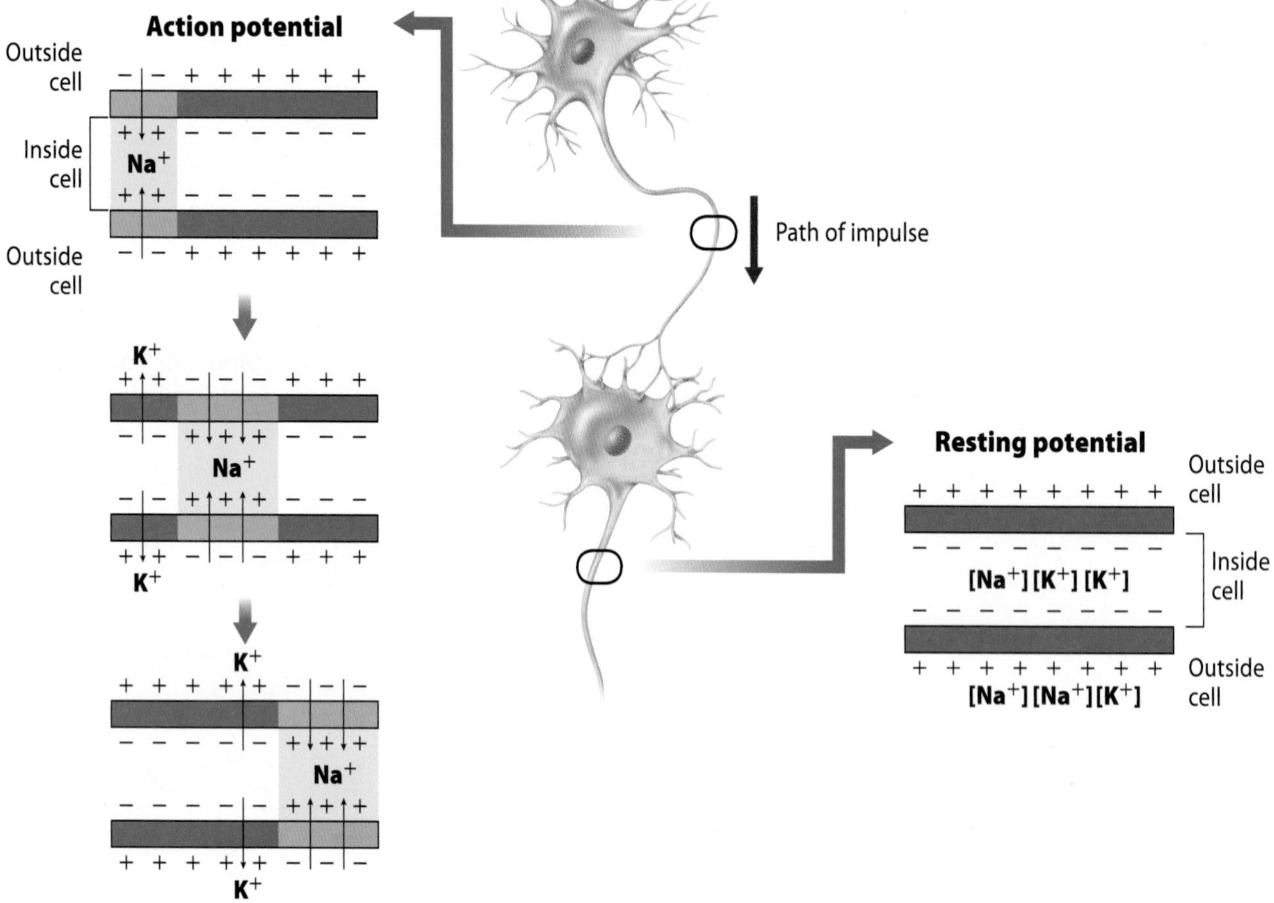

Action potential

Outside cell

Inside cell

Na^+

Outside cell

K^+

Na^+

K^+

K^+

Na^+

K^+

Path of impulse

Resting potential

Outside cell

Inside cell

$[Na^+][K^+][K^+]$

Outside cell

$[Na^+][Na^+][K^+]$

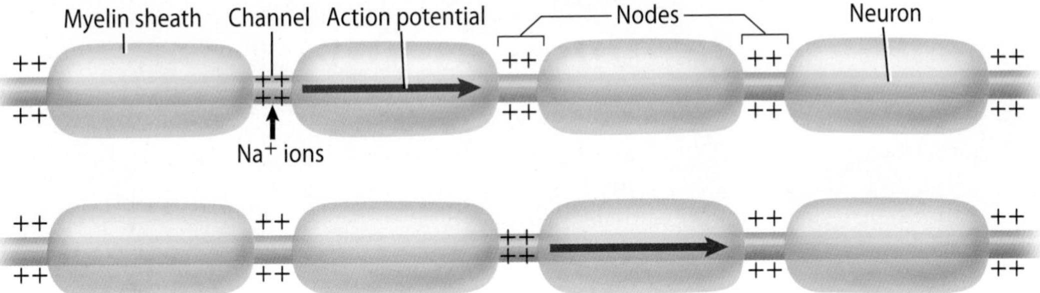

■ **Figure 5** A nerve impulse moves from node to node along myelinated axons.

Explain ***what happens at a node when an impulse moves along a myelinated axon.***

Speed of an action potential The speed of an action potential varies. Many axons have a covering of a lipid called myelin, which forms an insulating layer, called a sheath, around the axon. The myelin sheath has many gaps, called **nodes,** along the length of the axon, as shown in **Figure 5.** Sodium ions and potassium ions cannot diffuse through myelin, but they can reach the plasma membrane at these nodes. This allows the action potential to jump from node to node, greatly increasing the speed of the impulse as it travels the length of the axon.

In the human body, there are neurons that have myelin, and neurons that do not have myelin. Neurons with myelin carry impulses that are associated with sharp pain; neurons that lack myelin carry impulses associated with dull, throbbing pain. The action potentials in these neurons travel much more slowly than they do in neurons with myelin. When you stub your toe, which kind of neurons are involved?

Launch Lab

Review Based on what you've read about action potentials, how would you now answer the analysis questions?

GET IT? **Explain** the relationship of a threshold to an action potential.

MiniLAB 1

Investigate the Blink Reflex

What factors affect the blink reflex? Have you ever been in a car when an object hit the windshield? You probably blinked. The blink reflex, in which the eye closes and opens again rapidly, is an involuntary response to stimuli that the brain interprets as harmful. Nerve impulses associated with the blink reflex travel short, simple pathways in milliseconds, allowing for rapid reaction time that can prevent eye damage.

Procedure

1. Read and complete the lab safety form.
2. Form a group of three. One person, the subject, should sit behind a 1 m^2 piece of **acrylic.** A second person will monitor and record the subject's responses.
3. The third person should stand 1 m from the barrier and gently toss a **table-tennis ball** so that it hits the barrier.
4. Repeat Step 3 and record the subject's response after each trial.
5. Brainstorm variables that might affect the subject's response. Predict the effect of each on the blink reflex.

Analysis

Interpret Data Did the subject perceive the stimuli in each trial the same way? Explain.

VISUALIZING
VISUALIZING

VISUALIZING Action Potential

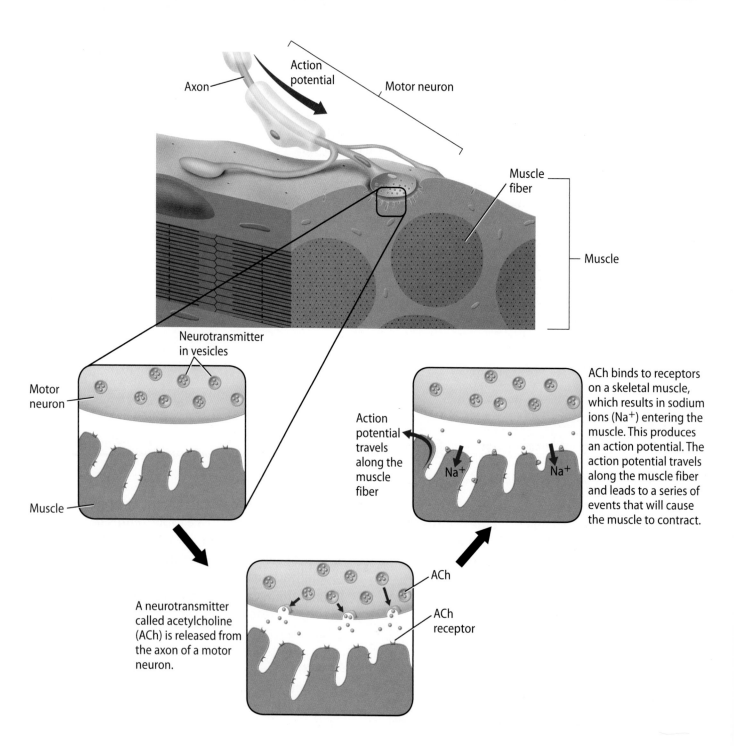

Figure 6 To cause the voluntary contraction of a muscle, a signal from the brain creates an action potential in a motor neuron. This action potential travels along the motor neuron, which leads to the release of a neurotransmitter that signals the fibers of the muscle to contract.

ACh binds to receptors on a skeletal muscle, which results in sodium ions (Na^+) entering the muscle. This produces an action potential. The action potential travels along the muscle fiber and leads to a series of events that will cause the muscle to contract.

A neurotransmitter called acetylcholine (ACh) is released from the axon of a motor neuron.

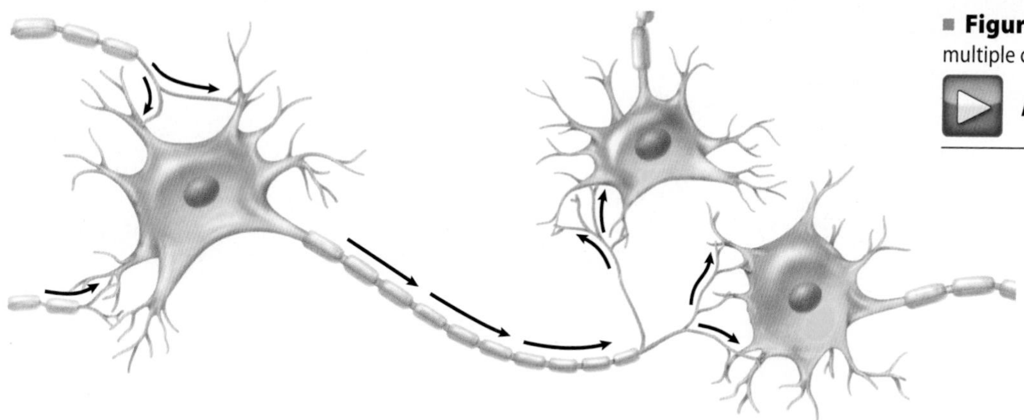

■ **Figure 7** A single neuron can have multiple connections with other neurons.

Animation

The synapse A small gap exists between the axon of one neuron and the dendrite of another neuron. This gap is called a **synapse** (SIH naps). When an action potential reaches the end of an axon, small sacs called vesicles carrying neurotransmitters fuse with the plasma membrane and release a neurotransmitter by exocytosis. When a motor neuron synapses with a muscle cell, as illustrated in **Figure 6,** the released neurotransmitter crosses the synapse and causes a muscle to contract.

Connection to Chemistry A **neurotransmitter** is a chemical that diffuses across a synapse and binds to receptors on the dendrite of a neighboring neuron. This causes channels to open on the neighboring cell and creates a new action potential.

There are more than 25 known neurotransmitters. Once a neurotransmitter has been released into a synapse, it does not remain there for long. Depending on the neurotransmitter, it might simply diffuse away from the synapse, or enzymes might break it down. Some neurotransmitters are recycled and used again. **Figure 7** shows that a single neuron can communicate with many other neurons.

REVIEW IT! Structure of the Nervous System

Section Summary

- There are three major parts of a neuron.
- There are three basic types of neurons.
- A nerve impulse is an electric charge and is called an action potential.
- Neurons use chemicals and electricity to relay impulses.

Self Check

Understand Main Ideas

1. MAINIDEA **Compare** How is the nervous system similar to the Internet as a communication network?
2. **Infer** why energy is necessary to counteract the diffusion of Na^+ and K^+ ions across the plasma membrane of a neuron.
3. **Predict** If the sensory nerves in a person's foot are nonfunctional, would the person feel pain if the foot was severely burned?

Think Critically

4. **Plan an experiment** that neurobiologists could use to show that an action potential travels faster along a myelinated axon than along a nonmyelinated axon.

MATH IN Biology

5. The sciatic nerve extends from the lower spinal cord to the foot. If a person's sciatic nerve is 0.914 m in length and the speed of an action potential is 107 m/s, how long will it take for a nerve impulse to travel the full distance of this nerve?

USE IT! **Science Notebook**

2 Organization of the Nervous System

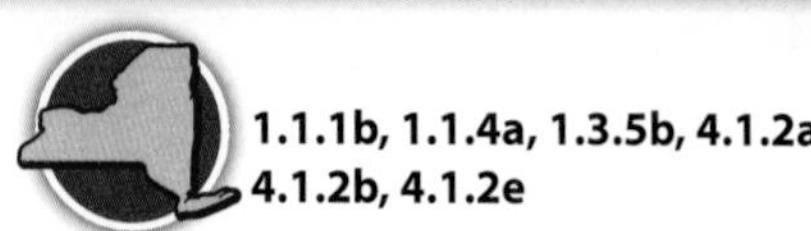

MAIN IDEA

The central nervous system and the peripheral nervous system are the two major divisions of the nervous system.

Essential Questions

- How can the major divisions of the nervous system be illustrated?
- What are the similarities and differences between the somatic nervous system and the autonomic nervous system?

BIOLOGY 4 U

Imagine that you are taking a test. When you look at the first question, you are not sure how to answer it. You picture your notes. Your memory clicks and you answer the question. How does this happen?

REVIEW VOCABULARY

sensory: conveying nerve impulses from the sense organs to the nerve centers

NEW VOCABULARY

central nervous system
peripheral nervous system
cerebrum
medulla oblongata
pons
hypothalamus
somatic nervous system
autonomic nervous system
sympathetic nervous system
parasympathetic nervous system

Multilingual eGlossary

The Central Nervous System

The nervous system consists of two major divisions. The interneurons of the brain and the spinal cord make up the **central nervous system** (CNS). The **peripheral nervous system** (PNS) consists of the sensory neurons and motor neurons that carry information to and from the CNS.

The function of the CNS is the coordination of all the body's activities. It relays messages, processes information, and analyzes responses. When sensory neurons carry information about the environment to the spinal cord, interneurons might respond via a reflex arc, or they might relay this information to the brain. Some brain interneurons send a message by way of the spinal cord to motor neurons, and the body responds. Other neurons in the brain might store the information.

GET IT? **Describe** the function of the central nervous system.

■ **Figure 8** Brainstorm
For thousands of years, scientists have studied the brain and investigated ways to treat neurological diseases.

2000 B.C. Ancient surgeons use bronze tools to drill holes in the skull.

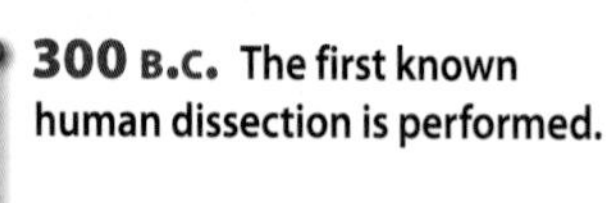

300 B.C. The first known human dissection is performed.

750 B.C. — 1800 — 1850

1818 Mary Wollstonecraft Shelley publishes *Frankenstein* as scientists begin to explore the connection between electricity and the nervous system.

1848 An iron rod pierces railroad worker Phineas Gage's frontal lobe. He survives, but his personality changes from quiet and hard-working to restless and aggressive.

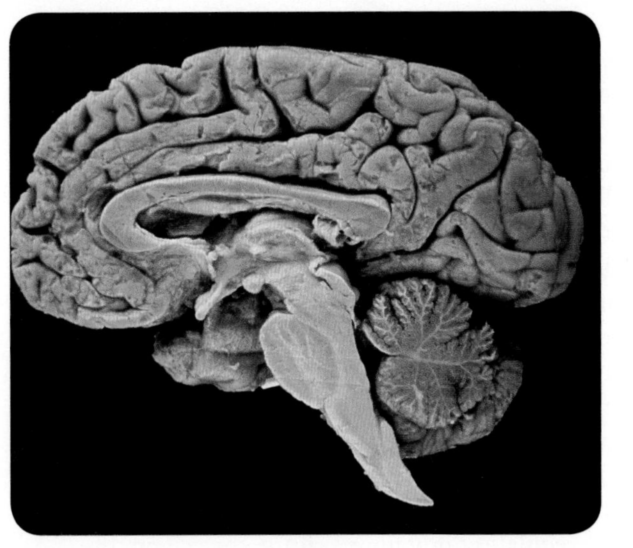

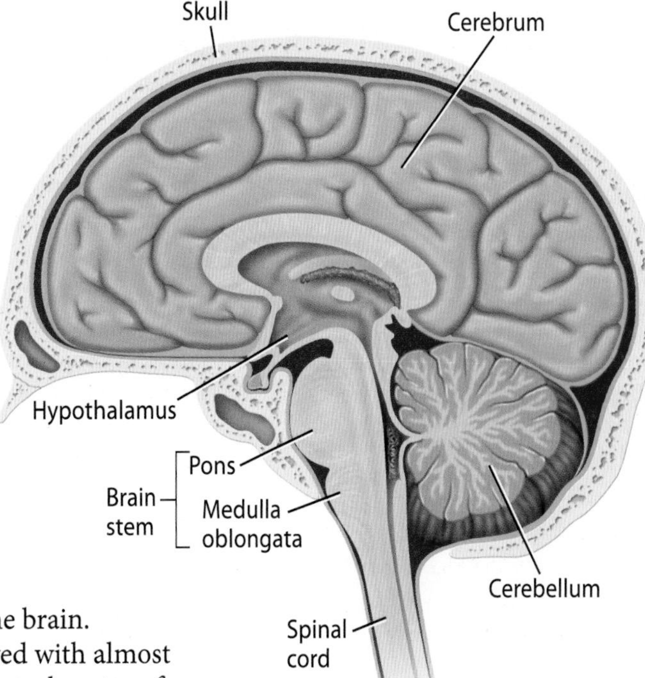

Figure 9
Left: A photograph of a human brain shows distinct sections.
Right: The major sections of the brain are the cerebrum, the cerebellum, and the brain stem.

The brain Over 100 billion neurons are found in the brain. Because the brain maintains homeostasis and is involved with almost all of the body's activities, it is sometimes called the control center of the body. Refer to **Figure 8** to learn about important events that have led to understanding of the functions of the brain.

Refer to **Figure 9.** The **cerebrum** (suh REE brum) is the largest part of the brain and is divided into two halves called hemispheres. The two hemispheres are not independent of each other; they are connected by a bundle of nerves. The cerebrum carries out thought processes involved with learning, memory, language, speech, voluntary body movements, and sensory perception. Most of these higher thought processes occur near the surface of the brain. The folds and grooves on the surface of the cerebrum, as shown in **Figure 9,** increase the surface area and allow more complicated thought processes.

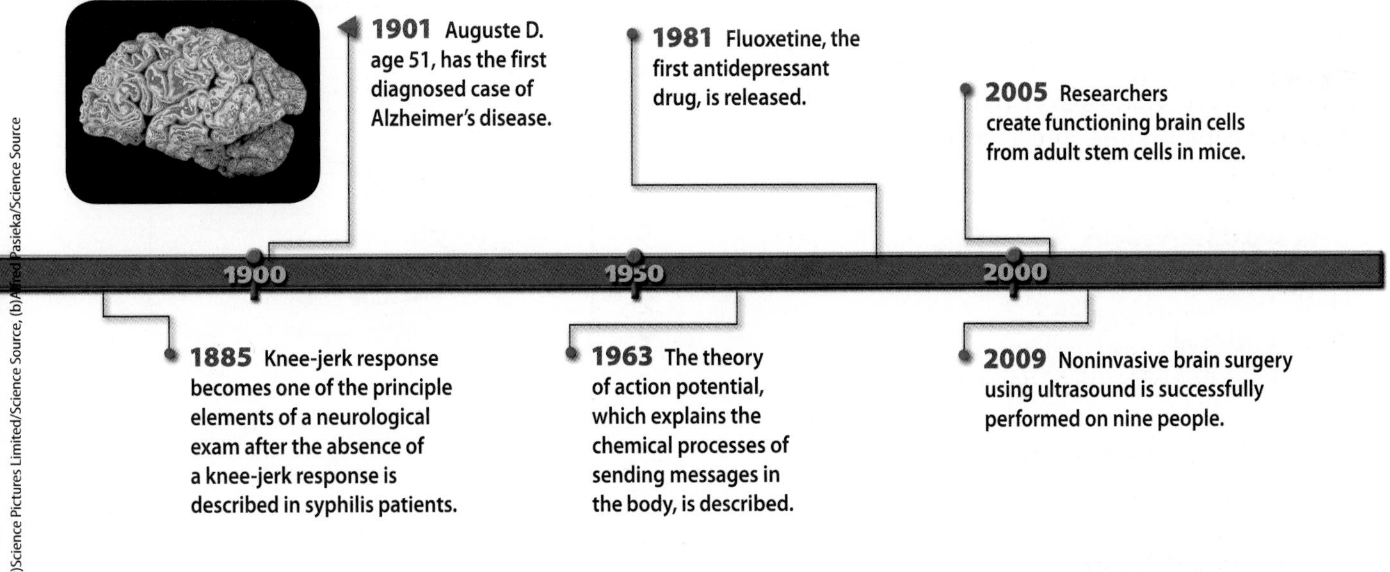

1901 Auguste D. age 51, has the first diagnosed case of Alzheimer's disease.
1981 Fluoxetine, the first antidepressant drug, is released.
2005 Researchers create functioning brain cells from adult stem cells in mice.
1900
1950
2000
1885 Knee-jerk response becomes one of the principle elements of a neurological exam after the absence of a knee-jerk response is described in syphilis patients.
1963 The theory of action potential, which explains the chemical processes of sending messages in the body, is described.
2009 Noninvasive brain surgery using ultrasound is successfully performed on nine people.

CAREERS IN BIOLOGY

EEG Technologist EEG technologists operate electroencephalographs, instruments that record the brain's activity (brain waves). Hospitals and community colleges offer training for people who want to be eligible to work in hospitals and clinics.

The cerebellum controls balance, posture, and coordination, and is located at the back of the brain. The cerebellum is responsible for the smooth and coordinated movement of skeletal muscles and is also involved with motor skills, such as playing the piano or riding a bike.

The brain stem connects the brain to the spinal cord and is made up of two regions called the medulla oblongata and the pons. The **medulla oblongata** relays signals between the brain and the spinal cord. It also helps control breathing rate, heart rate, and blood pressure. The **pons** relays signals between the cerebrum and the cerebellum. The pons also helps control the rate of breathing. Have you ever felt a gagging sensation when your doctor put a tongue depressor in your mouth? The medulla oblongata contains the interneurons responsible for the swallowing, gagging, vomiting, coughing, and sneezing reflexes.

Located between the brain stem and the cerebrum, the hypothalamus is essential for maintaining homeostasis. The **hypothalamus** (hi poh THA luh mus) regulates body temperature, thirst, appetite, and water balance. It also partially regulates blood pressure, sleep, aggression, fear, and sexual behavior. It is about the size of a fingernail and performs more functions than any other brain region of comparable size.

The spinal cord The spinal cord is a nerve column that extends from the brain to the lower back. It is protected by the vertebrae. Spinal nerves extend from the spinal cord to parts of the body and connect them to the central nervous system. Reflexes are processed in the spinal cord.

Review the functions of the CNS.

Data Analysis LAB 1

Based on Real Data*

Interpret the Data

Is there a correlation between head size, level of education, and the risk of developing dementia? In a ten-year study, 294 Catholic nuns were assessed annually for severe loss of mental function, or dementia. Data were recorded for each participant regarding head circumference—a measure of brain size—and level of education completed.

Data and Observations

The graph shows the overall results of the study.

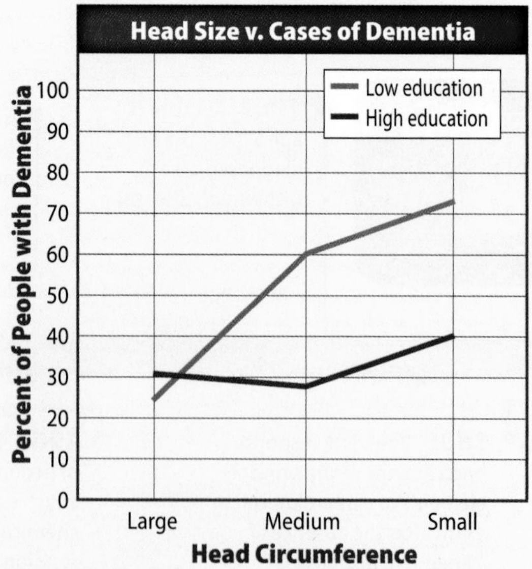

Data obtained from: Mortimer, James A., et al. 2003. Head circumference, education and risk of dementia: findings from the nun study. *Journal of Clinical & Experimental Neuropsychology* 25: 671–679.

Think Critically

1. **Analyze** how the risk of dementia is correlated with brain size and level of education.
2. **Explain** how the difference in education level and risk of dementia can be explained.
3. **Infer** why the researchers chose a group of nuns as their study group.

The Peripheral Nervous System

When you hear the word *nerve,* you might initially think of a neuron. However, a nerve is a bundle of axons. Many nerves contain both sensory and motor neurons. For example, there are 12 cranial nerves that lead to and from the brain and 31 spinal nerves (and their branches) that lead to and from the spinal cord, as shown in **Figure 10.** You could think of nerves as two-way streets. Information travels to and from the brain through these sensory and motor neurons.

Refer to **Figure 11** as you read about the peripheral nervous system. This system includes all neurons that are not part of the central nervous system, including sensory neurons and motor neurons. Neurons in the peripheral nervous system can be classified further as being either part of the somatic nervous system or part of the autonomic nervous system.

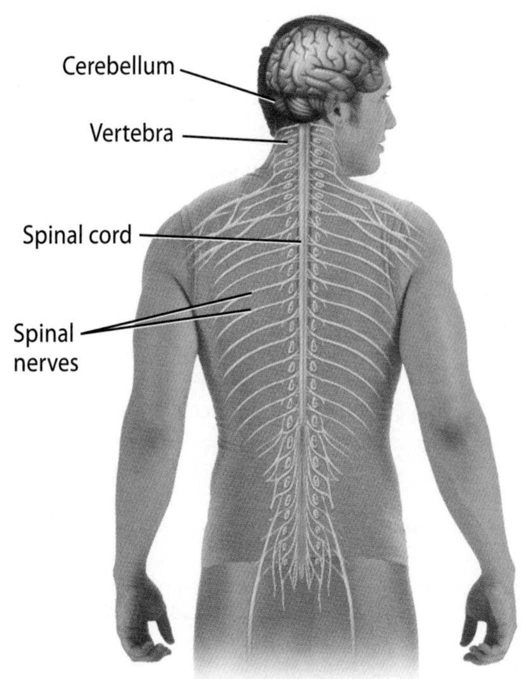

■ **Figure 10** Thirty-one pairs of spinal nerves extend from the spinal cord.

Differentiate ***how a neuron is related to a nerve.***

The somatic nervous system Nerves in the **somatic nervous system** relay information from external sensory receptors to the central nervous system. Somatic motor nerves relay information from the central nervous system to skeletal muscles. Usually, this is voluntary. However, not all reactions of the central nervous system are voluntary. Some responses are the result of a reflex, which is a fast response to a change in the environment. Reflexes do not require conscious thought and are involuntary. Most signals in reflexes go only to the spinal cord and not to the brain. Remember the example of stubbing your toe? Refer to **Figure 2** and note that the illustrated reflex is part of the somatic nervous system.

The autonomic nervous system Remember the last time you had a scary dream? You might have awakened and realized that your heart was pounding. This type of reaction is the result of the action of the autonomic nervous system. The **autonomic nervous system** carries impulses from the central nervous system to the heart and other internal organs. The body responds involuntarily, not under conscious control. The autonomic nervous system is important in two different kinds of situations. When you have a nightmare or find yourself in a scary situation, your body responds with what is known as a fight-or-flight response. When everything is calm, your body rests and digests.

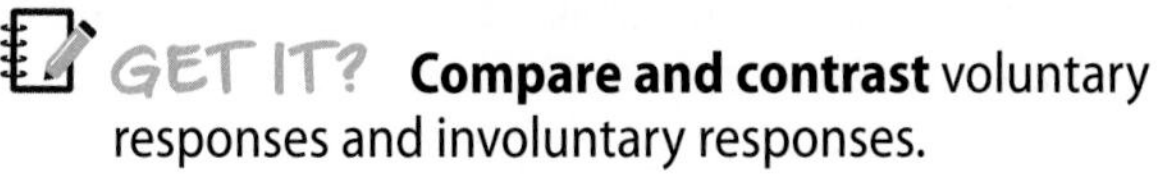
GET IT? **Compare and contrast** voluntary responses and involuntary responses.

Personal Tutor

■ **Figure 11** Each division of the nervous system functions in the control of the body and the communication within the body.

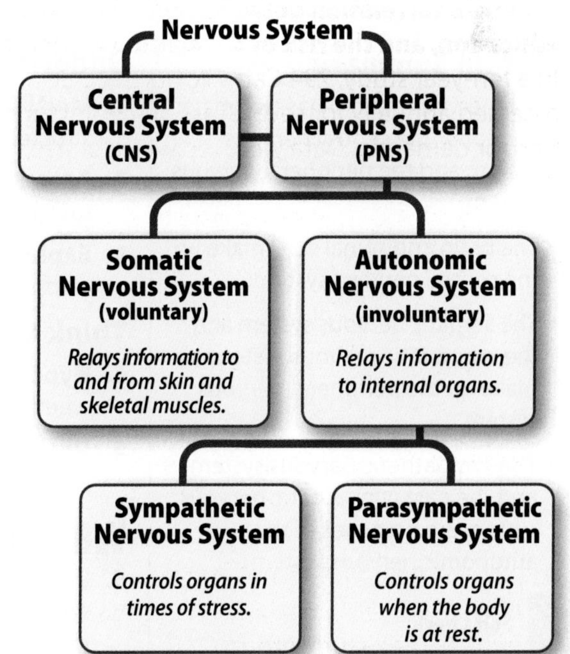

Table 1 The Autonomic Nervous System		Interactive Table
Structure	**Sympathetic Stimulation**	**Parasympathetic Stimulation**
Iris (eye muscle)	Pupil dilation	Pupil constriction
Salivary Glands	Saliva production reduced	Saliva production increased
Oral/Nasal Mucosa	Mucous production reduced	Mucous production increased
Heart	Heart rate and force increased	Heart rate and force decreased
Lung	Bronchial muscle relaxed	Bronchial muscle contracted
Stomach	Muscle contractions reduced	Gastric juice secreted; motility increased
Small Intestine	Muscle contractions reduced	Digestion increased
Large Intestine	Muscle contractions reduced	Secretions and motility increased

Connection to Health There are two branches of the autonomic nervous system, and they act together. The **sympathetic nervous system** is most active in times of emergency or stress, when the heart rate and breathing rate increase. The **parasympathetic nervous system** is most active when the body is relaxed. It counterbalances the effects of the sympathetic system and restores the body to a resting state after a stressful experience. **Table 1** compares and contrasts the two systems. Both the sympathetic and parasympathetic systems relay impulses to the same organs, but the overall response depends on the intensities of the opposing signals.

REVIEW IT! Organization of the Nervous System

Section Summary

- The nervous system has two major divisions: the central nervous system and the peripheral nervous system.
- The brain and spinal cord make up the central nervous system.
- The somatic nervous system and the autonomic nervous system make up the peripheral nervous system.
- The sympathetic nervous system and the parasympathetic nervous system are branches of the autonomic nervous system.

Self Check

Understand Main Ideas

1. MAINIDEA **Compare** the structures of the central nervous system with the structures of the peripheral nervous system and explain their relationships.
2. **Assess** the similarities and differences between the somatic nervous system and the autonomic nervous system.
3. **Explain** Which part of the nervous system is involved in a fight-or-flight response? Why is such a response important?

Think Critically

4. **Hypothesize** what types of tests a researcher could perform to check whether different sections of the brain were functioning.
5. **Design an experiment** to demonstrate the actions of the sympathetic and parasympathetic nervous systems on the iris of the eye.

WRITING IN Biology

6. Write a short story that describes a situation involving the heart when the sympathetic and parasympathetic nervous systems work together to maintain homeostasis.

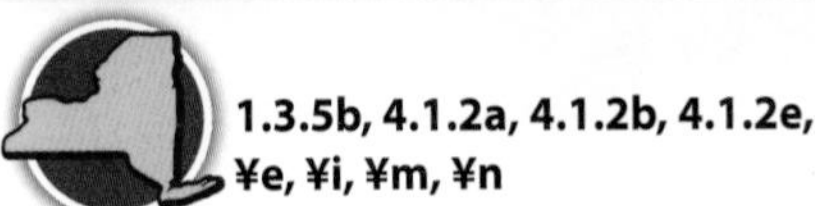

USE IT! Science Notebook

3 The Senses

1.3.5b, 4.1.2a, 4.1.2b, 4.1.2e, ¥e, ¥i, ¥m, ¥n

MAINIDEA

Sensory receptors allow you to detect the world around you.

Essential Questions

- What are the different sensory structures and what are each of them able to detect?
- How is each sense organ able to transmit a nerve impulse?
- What is the relationship between smell and taste?

BIOLOGY 4U

Who can resist the smell of chocolate-chip cookies baking in the oven? When the aroma travels from the kitchen, you are responding to chemicals in the air. Your senses allow you to be aware of changes in your environment. You are interpreting the environment around you every second. You even were reacting to environmental stimuli before you were born.

Review Vocabulary

stimulus: anything in the internal or external environment that causes an organism to react

New Vocabulary

taste bud
lens
retina
rods
cones
cochlea
semicircular canal

Multilingual eGlossary

Taste and Smell

Specialized neurons in your body called sensory receptors enable you to taste, smell, hear, see, and touch, and to detect motion and temperature.

The senses of taste and smell are stimulated by chemicals and often function together. Specialized receptors located high in the nose respond to chemicals in the air and send the information to the olfactory bulb in the brain. **Taste buds** are areas of specialized chemical receptors on the tongue that detect the tastes of sweet, sour, salty, and bitter. These receptors detect the different combinations of chemicals in food and send this information to another part of the brain.

The receptors associated with taste and smell are shown in **Figure 12.** Signals from these receptors work together to create a combined effect in the brain. Try eating while holding your nose. You will find that your food loses much of its flavor.

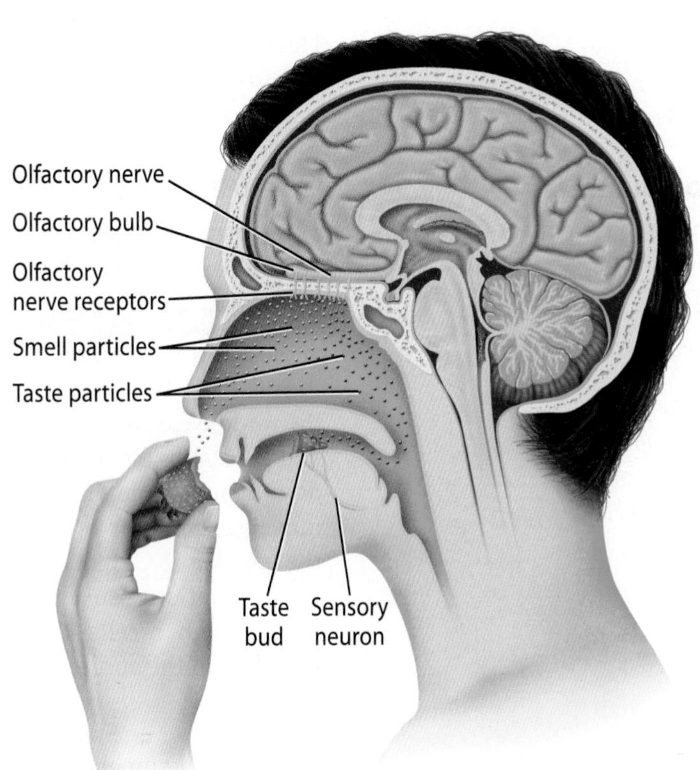

■ **Figure 12** The receptors of taste and smell function together and are stimulated in similar ways. Food is often smelled as it is tasted.

■ **Figure 13** Light travels through the cornea and the pupil to the lens, which focuses the image on the retina. Rods and cones in the retina send information to the brain through the optic nerve.

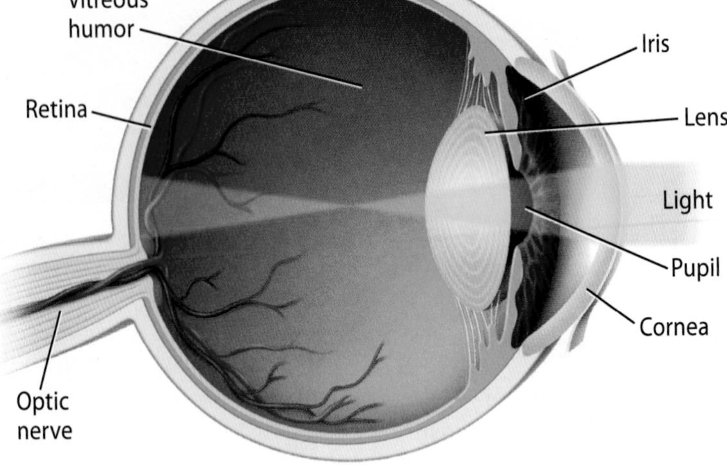

BrainPOP 

Sight

Figure 13 shows the path of light as it travels through the eye. Light first enters the eye through a transparent, yet durable, layer of cells called the cornea. The cornea helps to focus the light through an opening called the pupil. The size of the pupil is regulated by muscles in the iris—the colored part of the eye. Behind the iris is the **lens,** which inverts the image and projects it onto the retina. The image travels through the vitreous humor, which is a colorless, gelatinlike liquid between the lens and the retina. The **retina** contains numerous receptor cells called rods and cones. **Rods** are light-sensitive cells that are excited by low levels of light. **Cones** function in bright light and provide information about color to the brain. These receptors send action potentials to the brain via the neurons in the optic nerve. The brain then interprets the specific combination of signals received from the retina and forms a visual image.

CAREERS IN BIOLOGY

Ophthalmologist An ophthalmologist is a medical specialist who deals with the structure, functions, and diseases of the eye. Four years of specialized training after medical school are required to become an opthalmologist.

Hearing and Balance

Hearing and balance are the two major functions of the ear. From a soft sound, such as whispering, to a loud sound, such as a crowd cheering at a sporting event, specialized receptors in the ear can detect both the volume and the highness and lowness of sounds. Canals in the inner ear are responsible for your sense of balance, or equilibrium.

Hearing Vibrations called sound waves cause particles in the air to vibrate. **Figure 14** illustrates the path of sound waves as they travel through the ear.

Connection to Physics Sound waves enter the auditory, or ear, canal and cause a membrane, called the eardrum or tympanum, at the end of the ear canal to vibrate. These vibrations travel through three bones in the middle ear: the malleus (also called the hammer), the incus (anvil), and the stapes (stirrup). As the stapes vibrates, it causes the oval window, a membrane that separates the middle ear from the inner ear, to move back and forth. In the inner ear, a snail-shaped structure called the **cochlea** (KOH klee uh) is filled with fluid and lined with tiny hair cells. Vibrations cause the fluid inside the cochlea to move like a wave against the hair cells. The hairs cells respond by generating nerve impulses in the auditory nerve and transmitting them to the brain.

VOCABULARY

ACADEMIC VOCABULARY

Interpret
to explain or tell the meaning of
Our senses help us interpret our environment.

GET IT? **Summarize** how each sense organ detects changes in the environment.

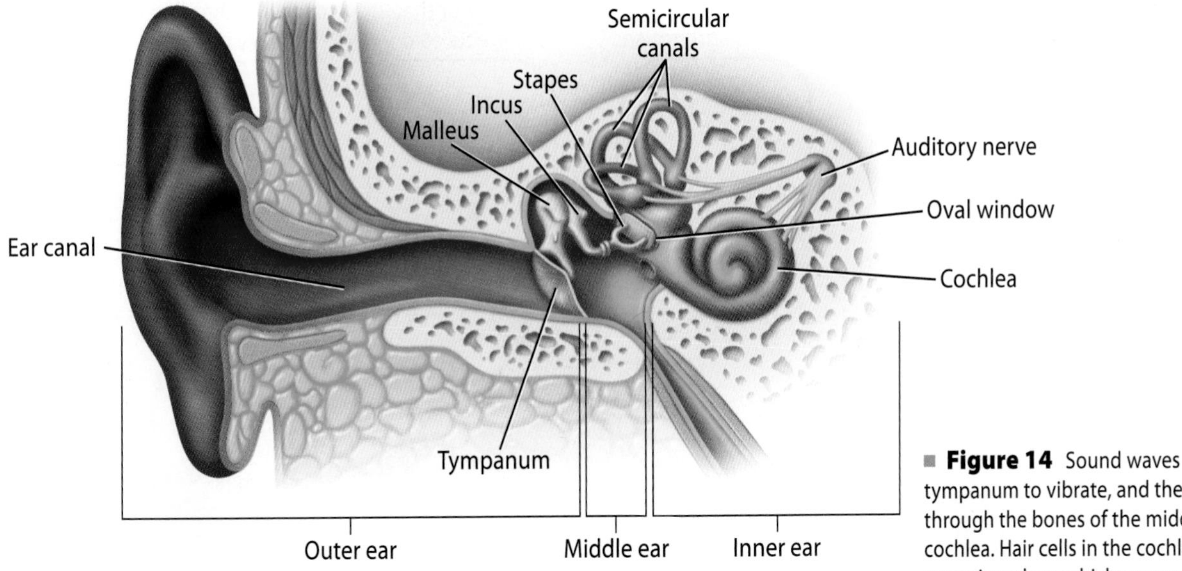

■ **Figure 14** Sound waves cause the tympanum to vibrate, and the vibrations travel through the bones of the middle ear to the cochlea. Hair cells in the cochlea generate nerve impulses, which are sent to the brain through the auditory nerve.

Balance The inner ear also contains organs for balance, including three semicircular canals. **Semicircular canals** transmit information about body position and balance to the brain. The three canals are positioned at right angles to one another, and they are fluid-filled and lined with hair cells. When the position of your head changes, fluid within the semicircular canals moves. This causes the hair cells to bend, which in turn sends nerve impulses to the brain. The brain then is able to determine your position and whether your body is still or in motion.

MiniLAB 2

Investigate Adaptations to Darkness

How fast do light receptors in the retina adapt to low-light conditions? The retina contains two types of receptor cells. Cones, adapted for vision in bright light, allow you to perceive color. Rods, adapted for vision in dim light, help you detect shape and movement. The brain combines and interprets nerve impulses received from these cells, making it possible for you to see in various light conditions.

1. Work with a partner. Using a **stopwatch,** time how long it takes to separate 30 **plastic bottle caps** into groups based on color.
2. Record the time, the number of caps in each group, and the percent accuracy of the grouping.
3. Predict changes in the data if the experiment is repeated in dim light.
4. Mix the caps into one group. Dim the lights. Immediately repeat Step 1.
5. Restore light conditions and record the data.
6. Discuss the data with your group. Predict changes in the data if the experiment is repeated after five minutes in dim light. Dim the lights.
7. Wait five minutes and repeat Step 1. Restore the light and record data.

Analysis

1. **Analyze** Graph the time required and the percent accuracy in each trial. How do these variables compare across trials?
2. **Think Critically** Based on the data, compare the action of the blink reflex **(MiniLab 1)** to the action of the eyes in adjusting to low-light conditions.

■ **Figure 15** Many types of receptors are found in the skin. A person can tell if an object is hot or cold, sharp or smooth.

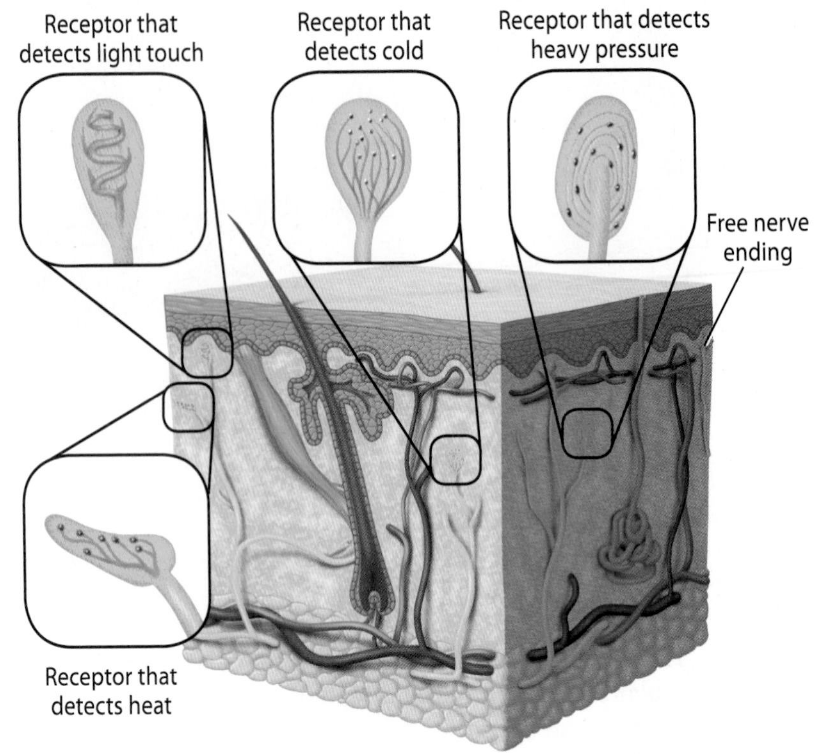

Touch

Many types of sensory receptors that respond to temperature, pressure, and pain are found in the epidermis and dermis layers of the skin. **Figure 15** illustrates the different types of receptors—some that respond to light touches and others that respond to heavy pressure.

Distribution of receptors is not uniform in all areas of the body. The tips of the fingers have many receptors that detect light touch. The soles of the feet have many receptors that respond to heavy pressure. Pain receptors are simple, consisting of free nerve endings that are found in all tissues of the body except the brain. The brain constantly receives signals from these receptors and responds appropriately.

REVIEW IT! The Senses

Section Summary

- The senses of taste and smell work together.
- The eye has two types of receptors.
- The ear is involved in both hearing and balance.
- The skin has many types of sensory receptors.

Self Check

Understand Main Ideas

1. MAINIDEA **Diagram** the route of a sound wave from the auditory canal until it causes a nerve impulse to be generated.
2. **Predict** what might be the result if the cornea was damaged.
3. **Analyze** the importance of the kind of receptors found in the fingers.
4. **Explain** why it might be difficult to taste when you have a cold and your nasal passages are clogged.

Think Critically

5. **Construct** an experiment to test the idea that certain areas of the tongue are taste-specific.
6. **Develop a hypothesis** as to why people who have lost their sense of sight still experience sight occasionally. People who once could hear occasionally experience sound. Why might these phenomena occur?

4 Effects of Drugs

MAINIDEA

Some drugs alter the function of the nervous system.

Essential Questions

- What are the four ways that drugs can affect the nervous system?
- What are different ways that drugs can harm the body or cause death?
- How, at the cellular level, can a person become addicted to a drug?

BIOLOGY 4U

What is a drug? Some people think of illegal substances such as heroin or cocaine when they hear the term *drug*. However, some drugs are common, everyday substances. When you have a headache and take aspirin, you are taking a drug.

Review Vocabulary

threshold: the minimum strength of a stimulus that causes an action potential to be generated

New Vocabulary

drug
dopamine
stimulant
depressant
tolerance
addiction

Multilingual eGlossary

How Drugs Work

A **drug** is a substance, natural or artificial, that alters the function of the body. There are many types of drugs, some of which are illustrated in **Table 2.** Drugs range from prescriptions such as antibiotics, which fight bacterial infections, to over-the-counter pain relievers. There are also illegal drugs, such as cocaine and heroin, which can cause addiction and death. Common substances such as caffeine, nicotine, and alcohol are also drugs.

Drugs affect a person's body in many different ways. Drugs that affect the nervous system work in one or more of the following ways:

- A drug can cause an increase in the amount of a neurotransmitter that is released into a synapse.
- A drug can block a receptor site on a dendrite, preventing a neurotransmitter from binding.
- A drug can prevent a neurotransmitter from leaving a synapse.
- A drug can imitate a neurotransmitter.

Table 2 Some Common Drugs — Interactive Table

Alcohol	Caffeine	Prescription Drugs	Over-the-Counter Drugs	Tobacco
beer, wine	coffee, tea, soda, chocolate	antibiotics, pain medications	aspirin, cold medications	cigarettes, cigars

(1)LADA/Science Source, (2)Don Farrall/Photodisc/Getty Images, (3)Michael P. Gadomski/Science Source, (4)Rosal/Science Source, (5)Michael P. Gadomski/Science Source

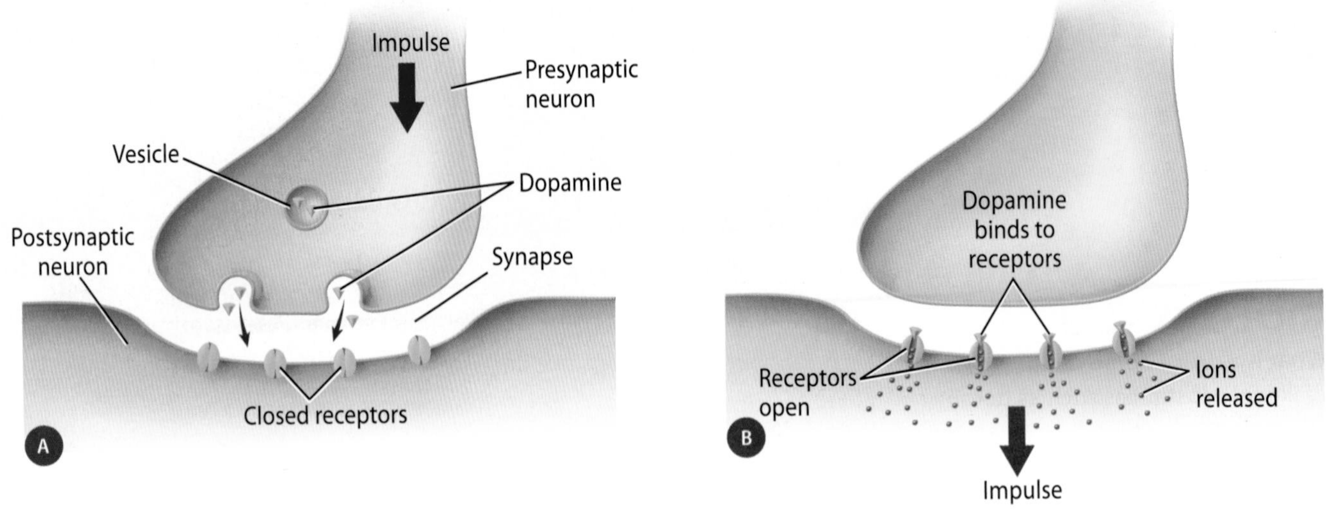

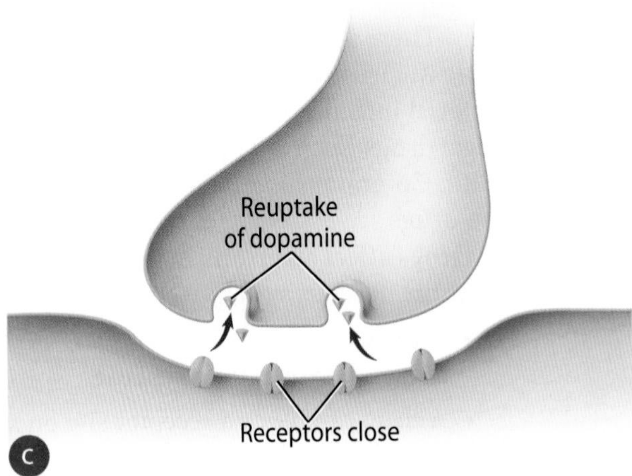

■ **Figure 16** Dopamine crosses the gap from one neuron and binds to receiver sites, or receptors, on the membrane of another neuron. This occurs at a synapse.

Many drugs that affect the nervous system influence the level of a neurotransmitter called dopamine. **Dopamine** (DOH puh meen) is a neurotransmitter found in the brain that is involved with the control of body movements and other functions. Dopamine also is strongly involved with feelings of pleasure or reward. Dopamine normally is removed from a synapse by being reabsorbed by the neuron that released it, as illustrated in **Figure 16.**

VOCABULARY

WORD ORIGIN

dopamine

dopa– refers to an amino acid

–***amine*** refers to a derivative of ammonia

Classes of Commonly Abused Drugs

Drug abuse does not necessarily involve the use of illegal drugs. Any use of a drug for reasons other than legitimate medical purposes, whether deliberate or unintentional, can be considered abuse of that drug.

Stimulants Drugs that increase alertness and physical activity are **stimulants. Figure 17** indicates some common stimulants.

Nicotine Nicotine in cigarette and cigar smoke increases the amount of dopamine released into a synapse. Nicotine also constricts blood vessels, raising blood pressure and causing the heart to work harder than normal. Cigarette smoking has been linked to about 90 percent of all lung cancer cases.

Caffeine The most commonly used, and often abused, stimulant is caffeine. Caffeine is found in coffee, tea, some soft drinks, and even some foods such as chocolate. Caffeine works by binding to adenosine receptors on neurons in the brain. Adenosine slows down neural activity, causing drowsiness. When caffeine binds to these receptors, it has the opposite effect. It makes users feel awake and alert. Caffeine also temporarily raises epinephrine (adrenaline) levels in the body, giving a quick burst of energy that soon wears off.

Depressants

Depressants Drugs that tend to slow down the central nervous system are **depressants.** These drugs can lower blood pressure, interrupt breathing, and slow the heart rate. Depressants can relieve anxiety, but they also can cause the noticeable effect of sedation.

Alcohol Alcohol is a depressant. It affects the central nervous system and is one of the most widely abused drugs in the world today. It is produced by the fermentation of grains and fruits. Alcohol is known to affect at least four different neurotransmitters, resulting in a feeling of relaxation and sluggishness. Short-term alcohol use impairs judgment, coordination, and reaction time. Long-term effects of alcohol abuse include a reduction in brain mass, liver damage, stomach and intestinal ulcers, and high blood pressure. Consumption of alcohol during pregnancy is the cause of fetal alcohol syndrome, which can result in damage to a baby's brain and nervous system.

Inhalants Inhalants are chemical fumes that have an influence on the nervous system. Exposure to inhalants might be accidental as a result of poor ventilation. Inhalants generally work by acting as a depressant on the central nervous system. Inhalants might produce a short-term effect of intoxication, as well as nausea and vomiting. Death can occur. Long-term exposure to inhalants can cause memory loss, hearing loss, vision problems, peripheral nerve damage, and brain damage.

STUDY TIP

CHART Create a three-column chart titled *The Effects of Drugs.* Before reading this section, check the section heads, the boldfaced terms, and figures. Identify what you know about drugs in the first column. In the second column, list what you would like to know. In the third column, write what you have learned after studying this section.

Laura Sifferlin

■ **Figure 17** There are many common stimulant drugs, such as coffee, tea, cocoa, and chocolate.

Illegal drugs Amphetamines and cocaine both increase dopamine levels, and both prevent dopamine from being reabsorbed, so it remains in the synapses. This ultimately increases the levels of dopamine in the brain, which results in a feeling of pleasure and well-being.

The use of cocaine and amphetamines has short-term and long-term effects. Cocaine abuse might result in disturbances in heart rhythm, heart attacks, chest pain, respiratory failure, strokes, seizures, headaches, abdominal pain, and nausea. Abuse of amphetamines might result in rapid heart rate, irregular heartbeat, increased blood pressure, and irreversible, stroke-producing damage to small blood vessels in the brain. Elevated body temperature, called hyperthermia, and convulsions can result from an amphetamine or cocaine overdose, and if not treated immediately, this can result in death. Abusers also can experience episodes of violent behavior, paranoia, anxiety, confusion, and insomnia. It can take a year or longer for users of methamphetamine—the strongest type of amphetamine—to recover after quitting the drug.

Marijuana is the most-used illegal drug in the United States. The active chemical in marijuana is tetrahydrocannabinol, or THC. Smoking marijuana quickly gets THC into the bloodstream, where it is carried to the brain. THC binds to receptors on neurons in the brain, which produces the effect of intense pleasure. These receptors are found on neurons associated with many body activities. Short-term effects of marijuana use include problems with memory and learning, loss of coordination, increased heart rate, anxiety, paranoia, and panic attacks. Long-term smoking of marijuana might also cause lung cancer.

GET IT? **Explain** the function of a neurotransmitter.

Data Analysis LAB 2

Based on Real Data*

Interpret the Data

Can the effects of alcohol use be observed?
Two groups of students, ages 15–16, were given memory tasks to perform. Group 1 included individuals dependent on alcohol. Group 2 were nondrinkers, the control. The images indicate typical results of comparing stu-dents from each group. The graph shows the difference in retention rate between the two groups when processing verbal information and nonverbal information.

Think Critically

1. **Describe** the difference in retention rate in both testing categories between people who are dependent on alcohol and nondrinkers.
2. **Analyze** what long-term consequences might result from drin king as a teen. Base your answer on these results.

Data and Observations

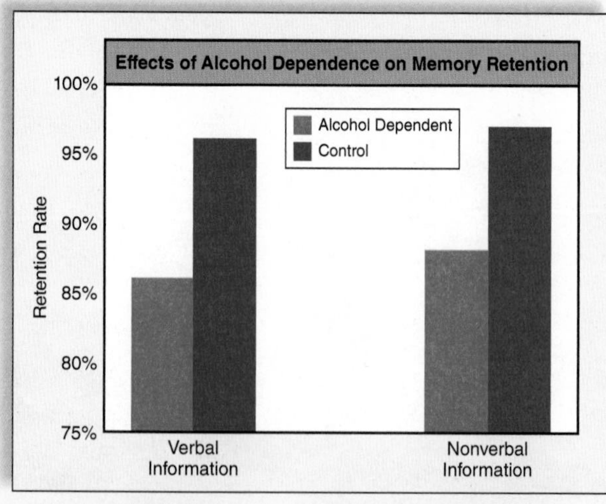

*Data obtained from: Brown, S.A., et al. 2000. Neurocognitive functioning of adolescents: effects of protracted alcohol use. *Alcoholism: Clinical and Experimental Research.* 24:164–171.

Tolerance and Addiction

Tolerance occurs when a person needs more and more of the same drug to get the same effect. The dosage needs to increase because the body becomes less responsive to the drug. Drug tolerance can lead to addiction.

Addiction The psychological and physiological dependence on a drug is **addiction.** Current research suggests that the neurotransmitter dopamine is involved with most types of physiological addiction. Recall that dopamine normally is removed from a synapse as it is reabsorbed by the neuron that released it. However, certain drugs prevent that reabsorption, which results in an increase of dopamine in the brain. A person addicted to drugs derives pleasure from increased levels of dopamine and builds up a tolerance to the drug. As a result, the person takes more of the drug. When people who are addicted try to quit, the levels of dopamine decrease, making it difficult to resist going back to the drug.

Addictions can also be psychological. An individual with a psychological dependence on a drug such as marijuana has a strong desire to use the drug for emotional reasons. Both physiological and psychological dependence can affect emotional and physical health. Both types are strong, making it difficult to quit a drug.

Treatment People who are either psychologically or physiologically dependent on a drug experience serious withdrawal symptoms without it. It is very difficult for dependent users to quit on their own. They might be able to quit for short periods of time, but they are likely to use the drug again. Medical supervision is necessary when people who are psychologically and physiologically dependent on a drug try to quit.

The best way to avoid an addiction is never to use drugs in the first place, even when pressured to use them. Encourage people who abuse drugs to seek treatment for drug dependency. Physicians, nurses, counselors, clergy, and social workers are trained to direct people to the resources they need to get help, as illustrated in **Figure 18.**

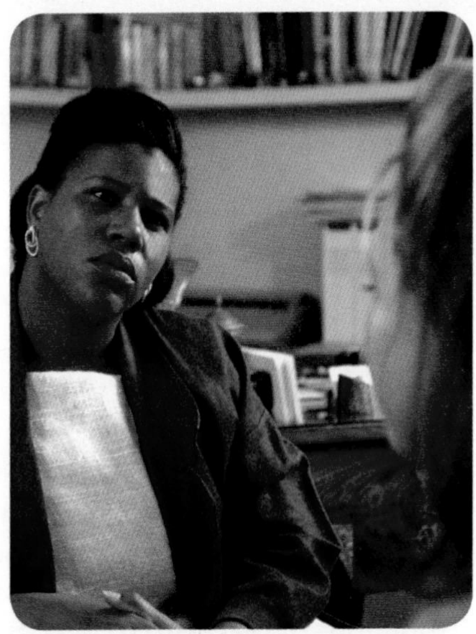

■ **Figure 18** Counseling often is necessary to break an addiction.

REVIEW IT! Effects of Drugs

Section Summary

- Drugs can affect the nervous system in four ways.
- Common substances such as caffeine and alcohol are considered drugs.
- Many addictive drugs increase levels of dopamine.
- Drug abuse has many negative consequences.
- A person can become psychologically and physiologically addicted to drugs.

Self Check

Understand Main Ideas

1. MAINIDEA **Describe** four ways that drugs can influence the nervous system.
2. **Compare** the actions of cocaine, amphetamines, and nicotine.
3. **Explain** why the effects of stimulants and depressants do not necessarily counteract each other.
4. **Infer** why students who abuse amphetamines are likely to experience failing grades.
5. **Discuss** how, on a cellular level, a person can become addicted to a drug.

Think Critically

6. **Design an experiment** Drugs affect people in different ways and at different rates. How would you design an experiment to determine the rate at which a drug is delivered to different body tissues?

Mary Kate Denny/PhotoEdit

Brain-Controlled Limbs: No Longer Science Fiction

For centuries, the only recourse for a person who loses an arm or leg to accident or disease has been a prosthetic, or artificial, limb. These limbs help people regain some of the functions of real arms or legs. However, their effectiveness is limited because the limbs are not controlled by the brain. Scientific research is changing such limits.

What are brain-controlled prostheses?
Scientists are developing thought-controlled robotic arms with fully mobile shoulders and elbows. Each hand is in the shape of a gripper that functions much like a real hand. Used primarily with monkeys and now with humans in research, these arms are connected to the brain using implants.

The implants are collections of hundreds of electrodes that are as thin as a human hair. The electrodes are placed in the motor cortex of the brain 3 mm beneath the skull to pick up nerve signals in the brain. The implant transmits these signals to a computer. A mathematical procedure translates them into instructions for the arm. For example, within 30 milliseconds of the command, the arm is able to pick up food and bring it to the mouth. The arm is equipped with several motors and moves in three dimensions, just like a real arm. The arm responds and brings food to the patient when the patient thinks about the food.

How were the arms tested? While testing the robotic arms, patients used his or her arms to experiment with a joystick and to get used to working with the robotic arm. Once a patient had practiced with the joystick, the scientists removed it and gently restrained the patient's own arm. To the scientists' amazement, the robotic arm began to move as a result of the patient's thoughts.

Scientists want to refine the technology so the system is completely wireless. One concern is that the current electrodes last only about six months.

How might these brain-controlled devices help society? Scientists plan to continue researching and using these devices with humans in the next few years. The hope is that these brain-computer interfaces (BCI) will help people who are parapalegic regain some movement or ability to communicate with others. Brain implants could also allow hand-free control of small robots that could perform everyday tasks. BCIs also might benefit people who are not paralyzed or who have not lost a limb. BCIs could also be used to perform tasks in dangerous environments or war zones.

MAKE A MODEL

Create a model of a device similar to that described in this feature. Use materials provided by your teacher or from your home. Write a 200-word description of your invention, how it works, and some benefits of this invention.

WebQuest

BioLAB ¥e, ¥i

How do neural pathways develop and become more efficient?

Background: Imagine forging a narrow path through a wooded area. As the path is traveled over time, it becomes more defined and easier to follow. In a similar manner, neural pathways are developed in the brain when you learn something new. As you practice what you have learned, connections between neurons strengthen, causing nerve impulses to pass more quickly and efficiently along the circuit.

Question: *What effect do learning strategies have on the efficiency of a neural circuit?*

Materials

graph paper
paper
pencil
calculator

Procedure

1. Read and complete the lab safety form.
2. Work with one student in your group to write a list of 20 concrete words that describe specific physical objects. Assign a number, 1 to 20, to each word.
3. Read the list aloud to three other members of your group who are the test subjects. Immediately, and without discussion, have them write down as many words as they can remember from the list.
4. Calculate and record the percent recall for each word: divide the number of subjects who recalled each word by the total number of subjects. Multiply by 100.
5. Graph the percent recall for each word. Note patterns in the data.
6. Calculate the average percent recall: add the percent recall for each word, divide by 20, and multiply by 100.
7. Brainstorm techniques to increase the average percent recall. Choose one technique. Predict how it will affect the average percent recall. Design an experiment to test the prediction.
8. Once your teacher approves the plan, implement it with the same test subjects, using another list of 20 concrete words that describe specific physical objects.
9. Repeat Steps 4–6 to evaluate changes in the average percent recall.

Analyze and Conclude

1. **Identify** patterns in the percent recall data after the list was read the first time. Which words were most likely to be remembered?
2. **Interpret Data** by describing the technique used to increase the average percent recall and by comparing the average percent recall before and after the technique was used.
3. **Analyze** whether the technique strengthened the neural circuits responsible for remembering the list of words as well as you had predicted. Explain.
4. **Error Analysis** Identify factors, other than the technique that you used, that might have affected the average percent recall.

APPLY YOUR SKILL

Design an experiment to determine whether a specific learning strategy is equally effective with different test subjects. Consider how sample size would impact your results.

CHAPTER 19 STUDY GUIDE

BIGIDEA **The nervous system is essential for communication among cells, tissues, and organs.**

SECTION 1 Structure of the Nervous System

MAINIDEA Neurons conduct electrical impulses that allow cells, tissues, and organs to detect and respond to stimuli.

- There are three major parts of a neuron.
- There are three basic types of neurons.
- A nerve impulse is an electric charge and is called an action potential.
- Neurons use chemicals and electricity to relay impulses.

VOCABULARY

- **neuron**
- **dendrite**
- **cell body**
- **axon**
- **reflex arc**
- **action potential**
- **threshold**
- **node**
- **synapse**
- **neurotransmitter**

SECTION 2 Organization of the Nervous System

MAINIDEA The central nervous system and the peripheral nervous system are the two major divisions of the nervous system.

- The nervous system has two major divisions: the central nervous system and the peripheral nervous system.
- The brain and spinal cord make up the central nervous system.
- The somatic nervous system and the autonomic nervous system make up the peripheral nervous system.
- The sympathetic nervous system and the parasympathetic nervous system are branches of the autonomic nervous system.

VOCABULARY

- **central nervous system**
- **peripheral nervous system**
- **cerebrum**
- **medulla oblongata**
- **pons**
- **hypothalamus**
- **somatic nervous system**
- **autonomic nervous system**
- **sympathetic nervous system**
- **parasympathetic nervous system**

SECTION 3 The Senses

MAINIDEA Sensory receptors allow you to detect the world around you.

- The senses of taste and smell work together.
- The eye has two types of receptors.
- The ear is involved in both hearing and balance.
- The skin has many types of sensory receptors.

VOCABULARY

- **taste bud**
- **lens**
- **retina**
- **rod**
- **cone**
- **cochlea**
- **semicircular canal**

SECTION 4 Effects of Drugs

MAINIDEA Some drugs alter the function of the nervous system.

- Drugs can affect the nervous system in four ways.
- Common substances such as caffeine and alcohol are considered drugs.
- Many addictive drugs increase levels of dopamine.
- Drug abuse has many negative consequences.
- A person can become psychologically and physiologically addicted to drugs.

VOCABULARY

- **drug**
- **dopamine**
- **stimulant**
- **depressant**
- **tolerance**
- **addiction**

SECTION 1

Vocabulary Review

For each set of terms below, choose the one term that does not belong and explain why it does not belong.

1. axon, dendrite, reflex arc

2. cell body, synapse, neurotransmitter

3. myelin, node, threshold

Understand Main Ideas

Use the diagram below to answer question 4.

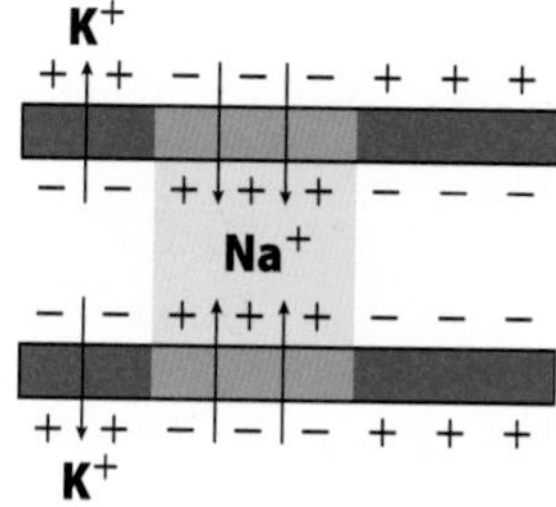

4. What is occurring in the diagram above?
- **A.** K^+ ions are entering the neuron.
- **B.** Negatively charged proteins are leaving the neuron.
- **C.** Na^+ ions are entering the neuron.
- **D.** The myelin coat has broken down, allowing ions to freely cross the plasma membrane.

5. Which is the correct path that a nerve impulse will follow in a reflex arc?
- **A.** motor neuron → interneuron → sensory neuron
- **B.** interneuron → motor neuron → sensory neuron
- **C.** motor neuron → sensory neuron → interneuron
- **D.** sensory neuron → interneuron → motor neuron

Constructed Response

6. **THEME FOCUS** Hypothesize why it takes more energy for a nerve impulse to travel along an axon that lacks myelin as opposed to an axon that has myelin.

7. **MAINIDEA** Explain the following analogy: A neuron is like a one-way street, while a nerve is like a two-way street.

Think Critically

8. **Infer** In most animals, an action potential will travel only in one direction along a neuron. Infer what the result might be in humans if nerve impulses could travel in both directions on a single neuron.

SECTION 2

Vocabulary Review

For each set of terms below, choose the one term that does not belong and explain why it does not belong.

9. somatic system, parasympathetic system, sympathetic system

10. cerebrum, pons, medulla oblongata

11. autonomic nervous system, somatic nervous system, central nervous system

Understand Main Ideas

12. Which is characteristic of the sympathetic division of the autonomic system?
- **A.** stimulates digestion
- **B.** dilates the bronchi
- **C.** slows the heart rate
- **D.** converts glucose to glycogen

Use the diagram below to answer question 13.

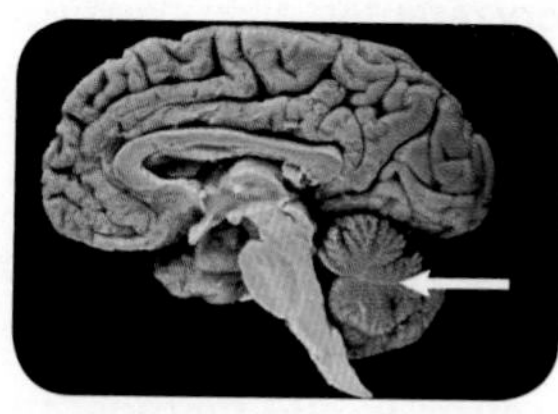

13. If the portion indicated by the arrow was damaged as a result of trauma, what effect would this person most likely experience?
- **A.** partial or complete memory loss
- **B.** body temperature fluctuations
- **C.** trouble maintaining balance
- **D.** rapid breathing

14. Which nervous system is the hypothalamus most involved in regulating?
- **A.** voluntary
- **B.** peripheral
- **C.** sensory
- **D.** autonomic

Science Pictures Limited/Science Source

Constructed Response

15. MAINIDEA Suppose you are on the debate team at school. You must support the following statement: The autonomic nervous system is more involved with homeostasis than the somatic nervous system. Build your case.

Think Critically

16. **Critique** You might have heard the statement, "Humans use only ten percent of their brains." Use the Internet or other sources to compile evidence that either supports or refutes this idea.

17. **Analyze** The human cerebrum is disproportionately large compared to the cerebrum of other animals. What advantage does this give to humans?

SECTION 3

Vocabulary Review

Distinguish between the terms in each of the following sets.

18. rods, cones

19. cochlea, semicircular canals

20. retina, taste buds

Understand Main Ideas

21. If there was a power outage in a movie theater and only a few dim emergency lights were lit, which cells of the retina would be most important for seeing your way to the exit?
    A. rods
    B. cones
    C. Rods and cones are equally important.

22. Which represents the correct sequence as sound waves travel in the ear to trigger an impulse?
    A. cochlea, incus, stapes, eardrum
    B. tympanum, bones in the middle ear, cochlea, hair cells
    C. auditory canal, tympanum, hair cells, cochlea
    D. hair cells, auditory canal, cochlea, malleus

23. With which sense are free nerve endings associated?
    A. taste **C.** touch
    B. hearing **D.** sight

Use the diagram below to answer question 24.

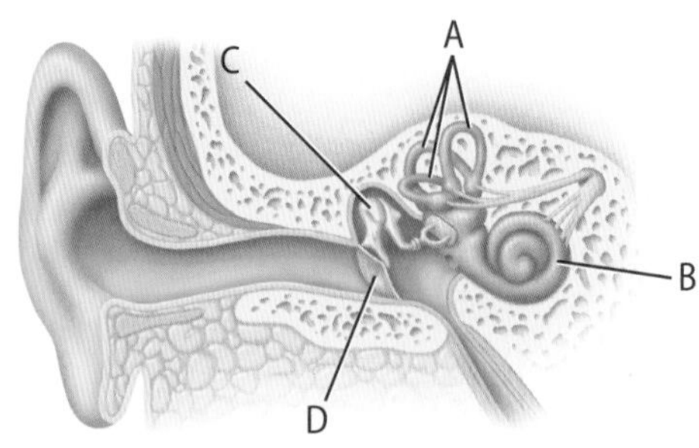

24. Some rides at amusement parks cause a person to become dizzy when the ride stops. Which structure in the diagram is most likely involved with the dizzy feeling?
    A. A **C.** C
    B. B **D.** D

Constructed Response

25. **Open Ended** A rare condition exists in which a person cannot feel pain. Is this desirable or undesirable? Explain your response.

Think Critically

26. **Explain** You have receptors for light (soft) touch all over your body. In terms of what you know about the nervous system, why are you not always conscious of things such as wearing clothes or a wristwatch?

27. MAINIDEA Rate the senses from 1 to 5 in order of importance (with 1 representing the most important.) Be prepared to debate this issue with other students in the class.

SECTION 4

Vocabulary Review

Explain the difference between the terms in each set. Then explain how the terms are related.

28. stimulants, depressants

29. tolerance, addiction

30. dopamine, drug

Understand Main Ideas

31. Which decreases brain activity?
    A. nicotine C. cocaine
    B. amphetamines D. alcohol

32. MAINIDEA What is the most likely function of amphetamines?
    A. to stimulate the sympathetic nervous system
    B. to stimulate the parasympathetic nervous system
    C. to stimulate the sympathetic and parasympathetic systems equally
    D. not to affect either the sympathetic or parasympathetic nervous system

Use the diagram below to answer question 33.

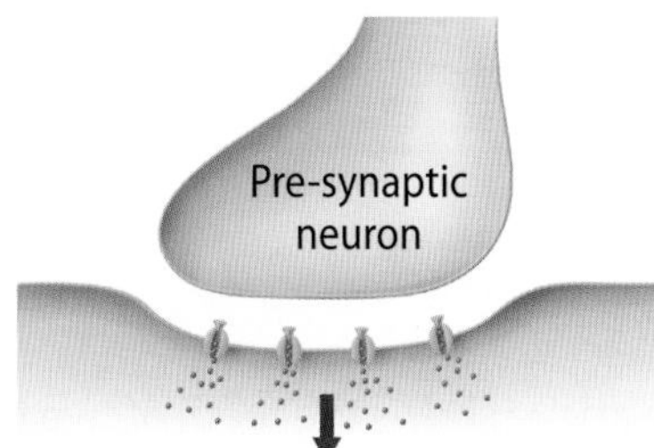

33. If a person is suffering from depression, which drug is one recommended treatment of the presynaptic neuron?
    A. one that increases the reuptake of dopamine
    B. one that increases the production of dopamine
    C. one that decreases the receptors for dopamine
    D. one that decreases the reuptake of dopamine

Constructed Response

34. **Short Answer** What does it mean when someone is addicted to a drug?

35. **Open Ended** Discuss what consequences might arise if a person's gene for the production of dopamine is defective.

Think Critically

36. **Defend** Form a conclusion about the following statement: "It is more difficult for someone to get addicted to drugs than it is to stop using drugs." Defend your position.

Summative Assessment

37. **BIGIDEA** The nervous system is essential for communication among cells, tissues, and organs. Predict the results if nerve impulses are interrupted due to injury or destruction of nerve fibers and the myelin sheath.

38. **WRITING IN ▶ Biology** Write a short story about a person who heard a loud noise and became afraid. Make sure to include in your story all of the events that might occur in each division of the nervous system during such an experience.

39. Imagine that you are a scientist who is developing a new drug. Explain how your drug works on the nervous system and what disease the drug treats. How could you determine what side effects the drug might have?

DBQ Document–Based Questions

Data obtained from: Blinkov, S.M., and Glezer, I.I. 1968. *The human brain in figures and tables: a quantitative handbook.* New York: Plenum Press.

Nieuwenhuys, R., Ten Donkelaar, H.J., and Nicholson, C. 1998. *The central nervous system of vertebrates.* Vol. 3. Berlin: Springer.

Berta, A., et al. 1999. *Marine mammals: evolutionary biology.* San Diego: Academic Press.

Average Brain Mass (in grams)

Species	Brain Mass (g)	Species	Brain Mass (g)
Fin whale	6930	Dog (beagle)	72
Elephant	6000	Cat	30
Cow	425–458	Turtle	0.3–0.7
Adult human	1300–1400	Rat	2

40. Does there appear to be a correlation between body size and brain mass?

41. Discuss possible explanations (in terms of adaptations) that would account for your response to question 40.

CUMULATIVE
MULTIPLE CHOICE

1 Which characteristic is unique to mammals?

A hair

B endothermy

C four-chambered heart

D internal fertilization

Use the diagram below to answer questions 2 and 3.

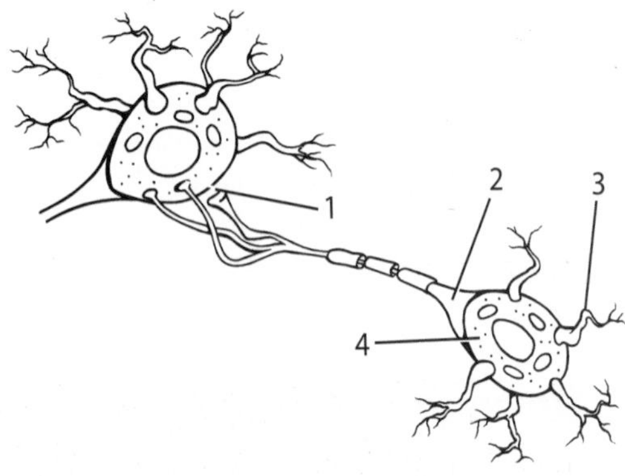

2 In which part of the diagram above would you expect to find myelin?

A 1

B 2

C 3

D 4

3 In which part of the diagram above would you expect to find neurotransmitters when an action potential reaches the end of the neuron?

A 1

B 2

C 3

D 4

SHORT ANSWER

Use the diagram below to answer questions 4 and 5.

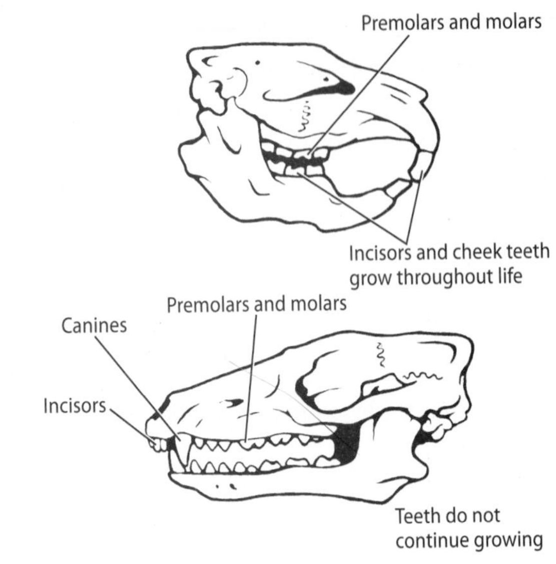

4 The figure above shows the teeth of two different types of mammals. From these teeth, what can you infer about the diets of these mammals?

5 Which animal's teeth most closely resemble those of humans? Explain your answer.

6 Explain how spiders predigest their food. Compare this process to the digestion process of another animal with which you are familiar.

7 Suppose that a person who used to drink one cup of coffee to stay awake at night finds that she needs to drink two cups. What is the name of this phenomenon and what causes it?

8 What is the role of the gametophyte generation in seed plants?

EXTENDED RESPONSE

9 Two abandoned whooping crane chicks are found several days after they hatched. A scientist wants to raise the chicks. To make the chicks feel comfortable, the scientist uses a hand puppet that looks like a whooping crane. The scientist offers the chicks mealworms, but they will not take them. Formulate a hypothesis that gives a possible explanation of the actions of the chicks.

10 How are the actions of myosin and actin fibers related to the contraction of a muscle?

11 What is the main difference between segmented worms and other worms? What is the importance of this difference?

ESSAY QUESTION

Each year, doctors perform more than 450,000 joint repair and replacement surgeries. These surgeries reduce pain and increase movement in the joints. Joint repair surgery involves removing any debris or excess bone growth from around the joint. This restores the functioning of the joint. Joint replacement surgery involves replacing the joint with a synthetic joint. The synthetic joint is made of polyethylene, ceramic, or metal. Joint replacement enables the joint to function in the same way as a natural joint. Joint replacements usually are performed on the knee, hip, or shoulder.

Using the information in the paragraph above, answer the following question in essay format.

12 Doctors usually replace only knee or hip joints on older patients who are less active than younger patients. Suggest why doctors recommend this.

TEST PRACTICE

13 What is the purpose of the epithelial tissue in the integumentary system?

- **A** cover the body surface and protect its tissues
- **B** move joints and bones
- **C** provide a structural framework for the body
- **D** transmit nerve signals

14 Which animal is a placental mammal?

- **A** hummingbird
- **B** kangaroo
- **C** duck-billed platypus
- **D** whale

Use the graph below to answer question 15.

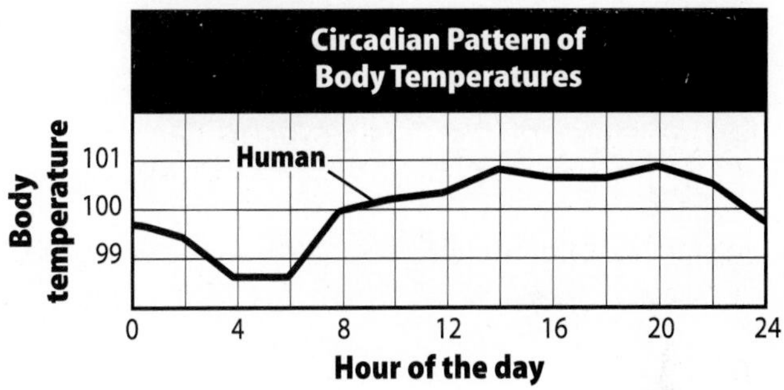

15 The graph above shows the circadian pattern of body temperature in humans. When does the body temperature of humans seem to be the lowest?

- **A** after eating
- **B** in the afternoon
- **C** just before dawn
- **D** late at night

NEED EXTRA HELP?															
If You Missed Question . . .	1	2	3	4	5	6	7	8	9	10	11	12	13	14	15
Review Section . . .	30.1	33.1	33.1	30.2	30.2	26.1	33.2	21.4	31.1	32.3	25.1	32.2	32.1	30.2	30.1

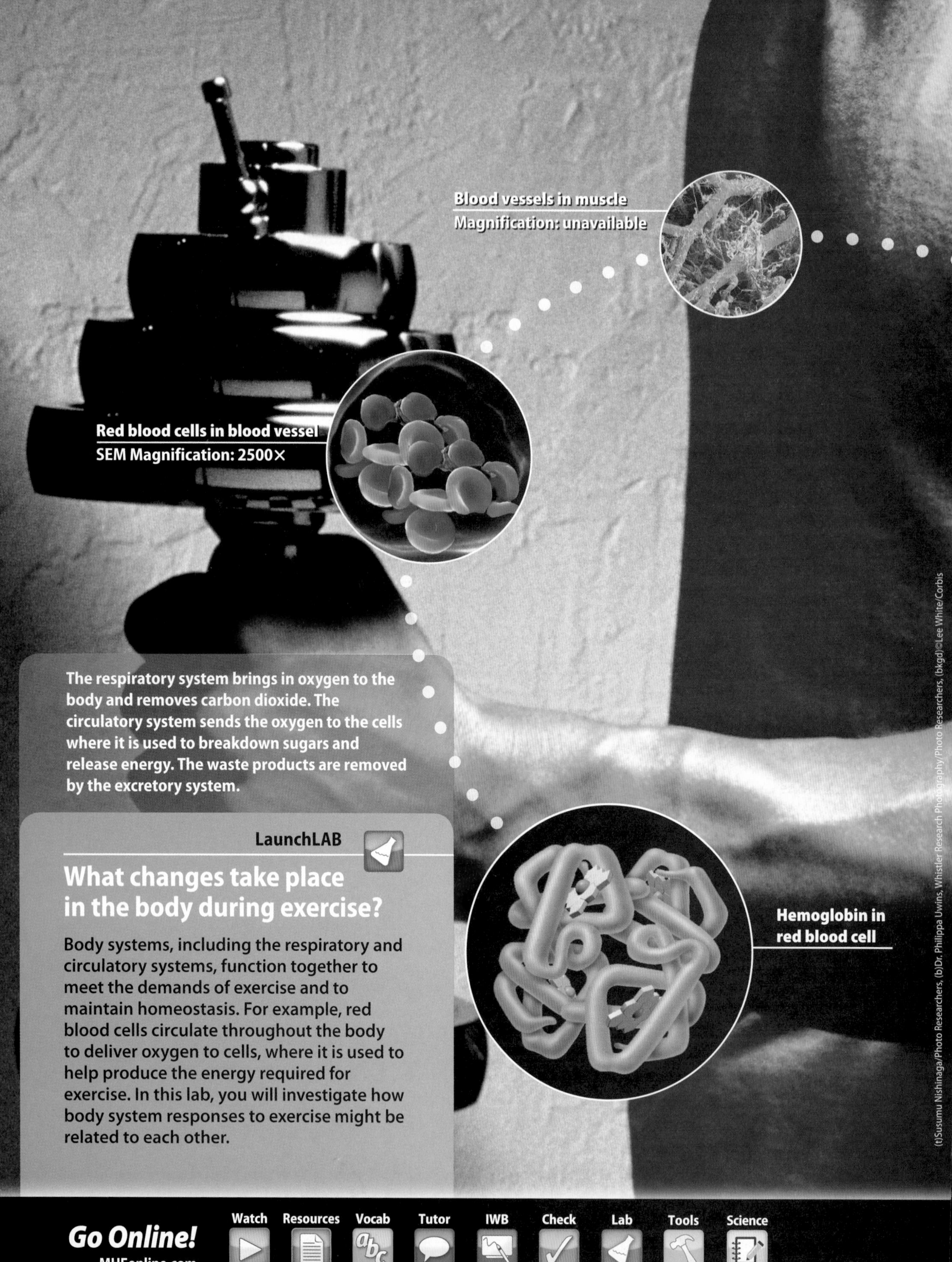

The respiratory system brings in oxygen to the body and removes carbon dioxide. The circulatory system sends the oxygen to the cells where it is used to breakdown sugars and release energy. The waste products are removed by the excretory system.

LaunchLAB

What changes take place in the body during exercise?

Body systems, including the respiratory and circulatory systems, function together to meet the demands of exercise and to maintain homeostasis. For example, red blood cells circulate throughout the body to deliver oxygen to cells, where it is used to help produce the energy required for exercise. In this lab, you will investigate how body system responses to exercise might be related to each other.

(t)Susumu Nishinaga/Photo Researchers, (b)Dr. Philippa Uwins, Whistler Research Photography/Photo Researchers, (bkgd)©Lee White/Corbis

Go Online! MHEonline.com

Watch | Resources | Vocab | Tutor | IWB | Check | Lab | Tools | Science Notebook

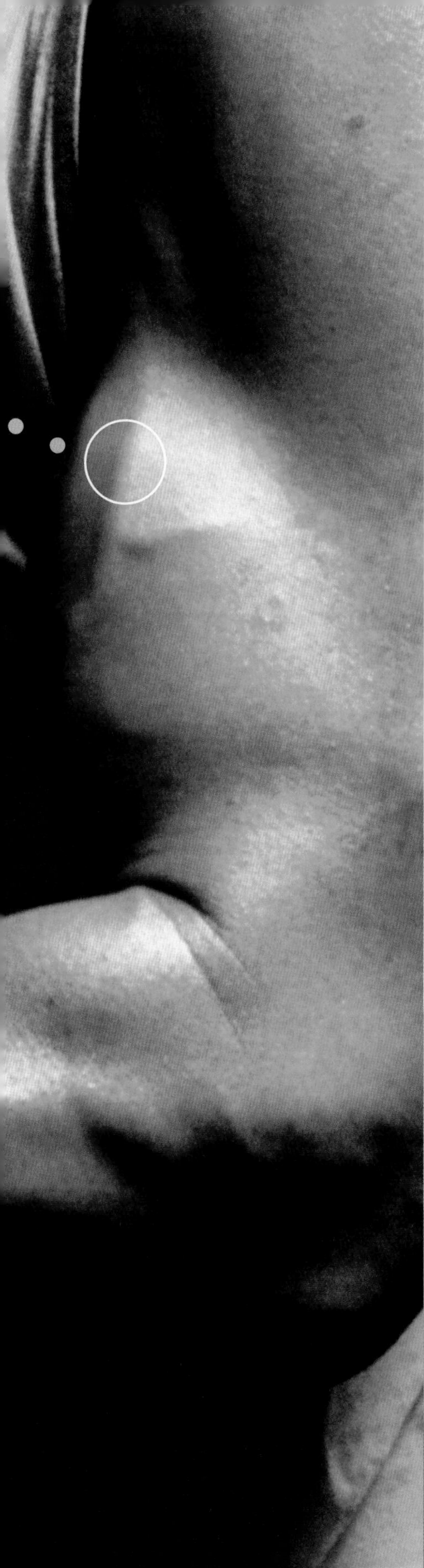

CHAPTER 20

Circulatory, Respiratory, and Excretory Systems

1 Circulatory System

1.1.1b, 1.1.4a, 4.1.2a, 4.1.2b, 4.1.2e, 4.5.2d

2 Respiratory System

4.1.2a, 4.1.2b, 4.1.2e, 4.5.2g, ¥e, ¥i, ¥n

3 Excretory System

4.1.2a, 4.1.2b, 4.1.2e, 4.5.1c

THEMEFOCUS

Energy and matter **Energy is used by the body for life processes such as respiration and circulation.**

BIGIDEA

These systems function together to maintain homeostasis by delivering important substances to the body's cells while removing wastes.

ABO Blood Group

Make a four-door book and label it as shown. Use it to organize your notes about the ABO blood group.

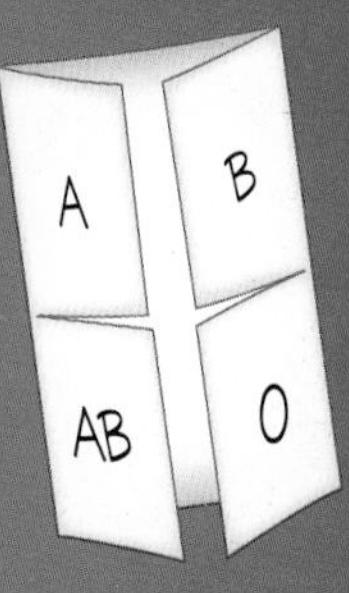

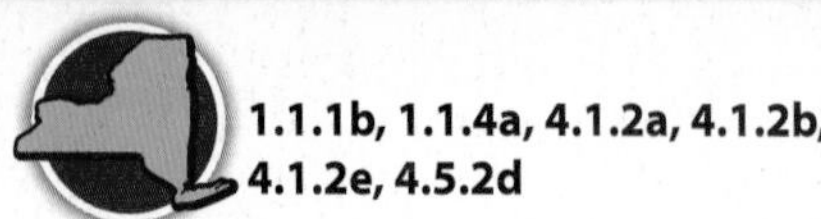

USE IT! Science Notebook

1 Circulatory System

1.1.1b, 1.1.4a, 4.1.2a, 4.1.2b, 4.1.2e, 4.5.2d

MAIN IDEA

The circulatory system transports blood to deliver important substances, such as oxygen, to cells and to remove wastes, such as carbon dioxide.

Essential Questions

- What are the main functions of the circulatory system?
- How does the blood flow through the heart and body?
- What are the similarities and differences between the major components of the blood?

BIOLOGY 4 U

Fast-moving highway traffic gets people to and from work quickly. Similarly, blood flowing in your body supplies nutrients and removes waste products quickly. When either traffic or blood flow is blocked, normal functions slow down or stop.

Review Vocabulary

muscle contraction: muscle cells or fibers shorten in response to stimuli

New Vocabulary

artery
capillary
vein
valve
heart
pacemaker
plasma
red blood cell
platelet
white blood cell
atherosclerosis

Multilingual eGlossary

Functions of the Circulatory System

Cells must have oxygen and nutrients and must also get rid of waste products. This exchange is accomplished by the circulatory system—the body's transport system. The circulatory system consists of blood, the heart, blood vessels, and the lymphatic system. Blood carries important substances to all parts of the body. The heart pumps blood through a vast network of tubes inside your body called blood vessels. The lymphatic system is considered part of the circulatory and immune systems. All of these components work together to maintain homeostasis in the body.

The circulatory system transports many important substances, such as oxygen and nutrients. The blood also carries disease-fighting materials produced by the immune system. The blood contains cell fragments and proteins for blood clotting. Finally, the circulatory system distributes heat throughout the body to help regulate body temperature.

■ **Figure 1 From Cadavers to Artificial Hearts** The human circulatory system has been studied for thousands of years, leading to great advances in medical technology.

350 B.C. Greek physician Praxagoras recognizes that veins and arteries are two different kinds of vessels.

1628 The first accurate description is made of the human heart—a pump that circulates blood in a one-way system.

1500 1600 1900

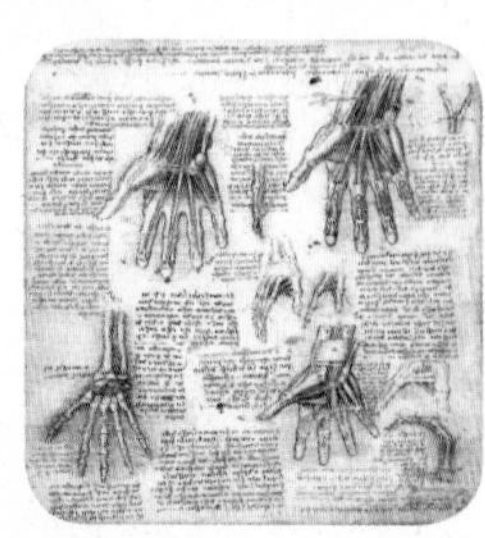

1452–1519 Leonardo da Vinci conducts extensive research on human cadavers. It is believed that he dissected about 30 corpses in his lifetime.

1903 The first electrocardiograph records the electrical activity of the heart.

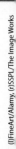

Blood Vessels

Highways have lanes that separate traffic. They also have access ramps that take vehicles to and from roads. Similarly, the body has a network of channels—the blood vessels. Blood vessels circulate blood throughout the body and help keep the blood flowing to and from the heart. The fact that there are different kinds of blood vessels was first observed by the Greek physician Praxagoras, as noted in **Figure 1.** The three major blood vessels are arteries, capillaries, and veins, as illustrated in **Figure 2.**

Arteries Oxygen-rich blood, or oxygenated blood, is carried away from the heart in large blood vessels called **arteries.** These strong, thick-walled vessels are elastic and durable. They are capable of withstanding high pressures exerted by blood as it is pumped by the heart.

As shown in **Figure 2,** arteries are composed of three layers: an outer layer of connective tissue, a middle layer of smooth muscle, and an inner layer of endothelial tissue. The endothelial layer of the artery is thicker than that of the other blood vessels. The endothelial layer of arteries needs to be thicker because blood is under higher pressure when it is pumped from the heart into the arteries.

Capillaries Arteries branch into smaller vessels called arterioles, which become smaller in diameter as they grow farther away from the main vessel. The smallest branches are capillaries. **Capillaries** are microscopic blood vessels where the exchange of important substances and wastes occurs. Capillary walls are only one cell thick, as illustrated in **Figure 2.** This permits the easy exchange of materials between the blood and body cells through the process of diffusion. Capillaries are so small that red blood cells move single-file through these vessels.

The diameter of blood vessels changes in response to the needs of the body. For example, when you are exercising, muscle capillaries expand, or dilate. This increases blood flow to working muscles, which brings more oxygen to cells and removes extra wastes from cells.

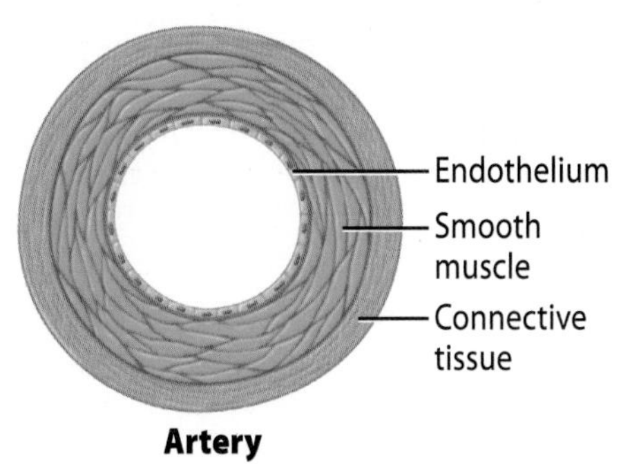

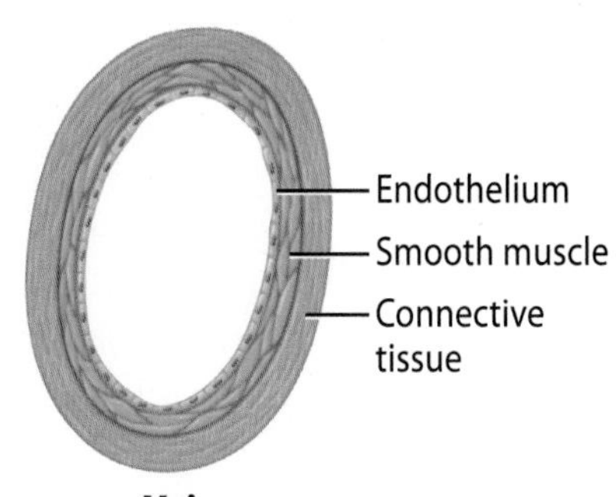

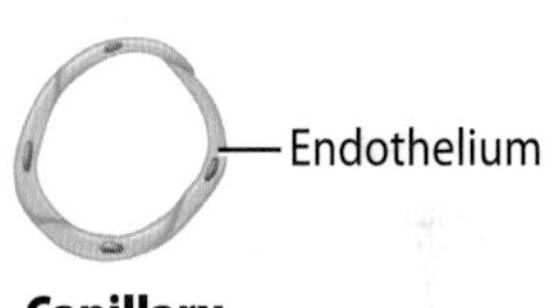

Figure 2 The three major blood vessels in the body are arteries, veins, and capillaries.

Predict ***By what process do you think materials cross the walls of capillaries?***

Animation

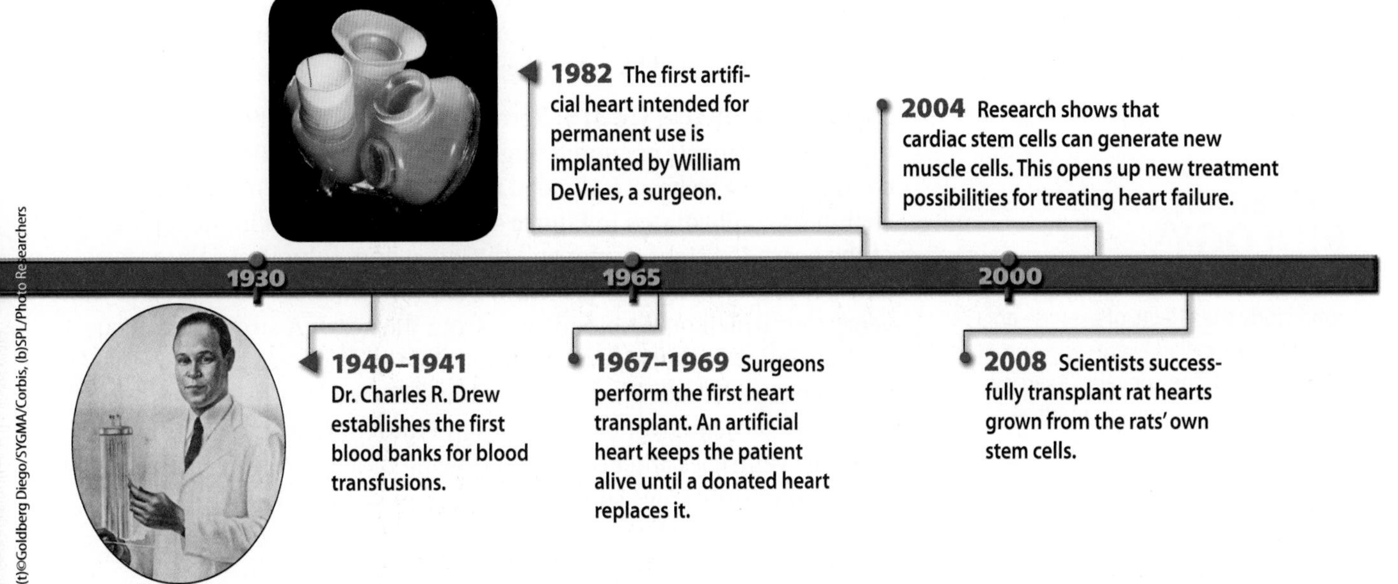

1930
1965
2000
1982 The first artificial heart intended for permanent use is implanted by William DeVries, a surgeon.
2004 Research shows that cardiac stem cells can generate new muscle cells. This opens up new treatment possibilities for treating heart failure.
1940–1941 Dr. Charles R. Drew establishes the first blood banks for blood transfusions.
1967–1969 Surgeons perform the first heart transplant. An artificial heart keeps the patient alive until a donated heart replaces it.
2008 Scientists successfully transplant rat hearts grown from the rats' own stem cells.

■ **Figure 3** Blood circulates throughout the body inside blood vessels.

***Hypothesize** how body temperature can be regulated by the diameter of blood vessels.*

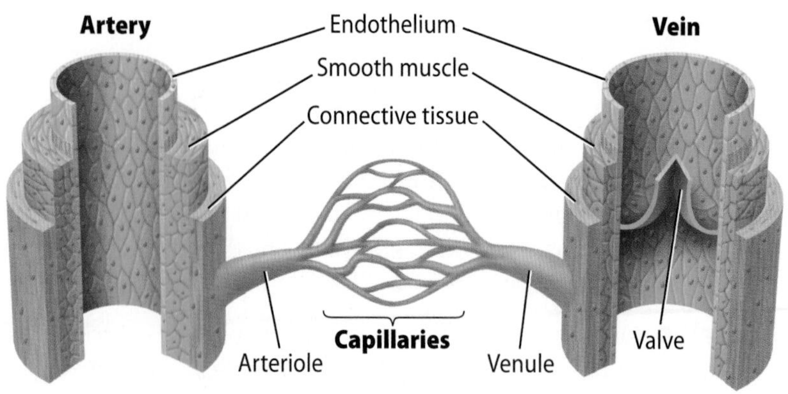

Veins After blood moves through the tiny capillaries, it enters the larger vessels called venules, and then enters the largest blood vessels, called veins. **Veins** carry oxygen-poor blood, or deoxygenated blood, back to the heart. The endothelial walls of veins are much thinner than the walls of arteries. The pressure of the blood decreases when the blood flows through capillaries before it enters the veins. By the time blood flows into the veins, the heart's original pushing force has less effect on making the blood move. So how does the blood keep moving? Many veins are located near skeletal muscles, and the contraction of these muscles helps keep the blood moving. Larger veins in the body also have flaps of tissue called **valves,** such as the one in **Figure 3,** which prevent blood from flowing backward. Lastly, breathing movements exert a squeezing pressure against veins in the chest, forcing blood back to the heart.

Virtual Lab 

BrainPOP 

 GET IT? **Describe** the differences in structure among arteries, capillaries, and veins.

The Heart

The **heart** is a muscular organ that is about as large as your fist and is located at the center of your chest. This hollow organ pumps blood throughout the body. The heart performs two pumping functions at the same time. The heart pumps oxygenated blood to the body, and it pumps deoxygenated blood to the lungs.

Structure of the heart Recall that the heart is made of cardiac muscle. It is capable of conducting electrical impulses for muscular contractions. The heart is divided into four compartments called chambers, as illustrated in **Figure 4.** The two chambers in the top half of the heart, the right atrium and the left atrium (plural, atria), receive blood that is returning to the heart. Below the atria are the right and left ventricles, which pump blood away from the heart. A strong muscular wall separates the left side of the heart from the right side of the heart. The right and left atria have thinner muscular walls and do less work than the ventricles. Notice the valves in **Figure 4** that separate the atria from the ventricles and keep blood flowing in one direction. Valves, such as the aortic valve shown in a closed position in **Figure 4,** are also located between each ventricle and the large blood vessels that carry blood away from the heart.

CAREERS IN BIOLOGY

Exercise Physiologist Scientists who study the effects of exercise on the body are called exercise physiologists. They develop exercise programs and administer medical tests, such as stress tests. Their responsibilities might include monitoring heart activity and monitoring blood pressure levels.

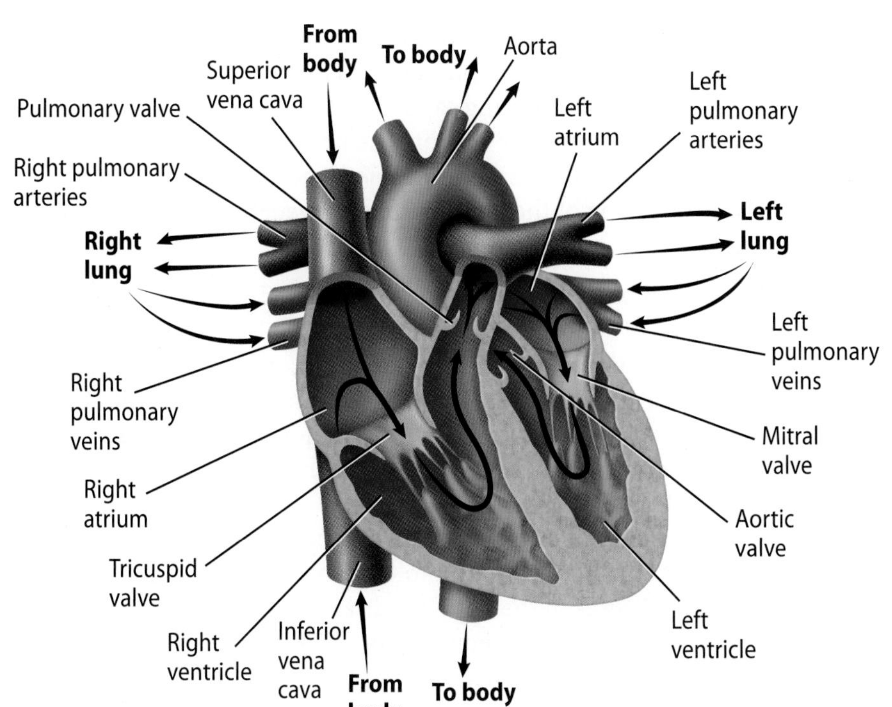

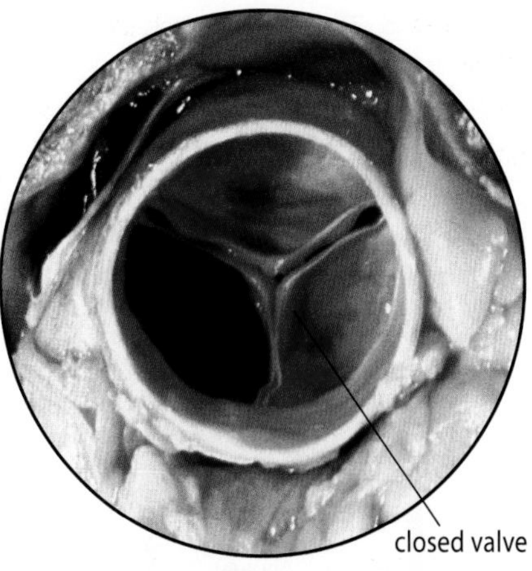

Aortic valve in a closed position

■ **Figure 4** The arrows map the path of blood as it circulates through the heart.
Diagram ***the path of blood through the heart.***

How the heart beats The heart acts in two main phases. In the first phase, the atria fill with blood. The atria contract, filling the ventricles with blood. In the second phase, the ventricles contract to pump blood out of the heart, into the lungs, and forward into the body.

The heart works in a regular rhythm. A group of cells located in the right atrium, called the **pacemaker** or sinoatrial (SA) node, send out signals that tell the heart muscle to contract. The SA node receives internal stimuli about the body's oxygen needs, and then it responds by adjusting the heart rate. The signal initiated by the SA node causes both atria to contract. Then the signal travels to another area in the heart called the atrioventricular (AV) node, as illustrated in **Figure 5.** The signal moves through fibers, causing both ventricles to contract. This two-step contraction makes up one complete heartbeat.

■ **Figure 5** The SA node initiates the contraction of the heart, which spreads through both atria to the AV node. The AV node transmits the signal through excitable fibers that stimulate both ventricles.

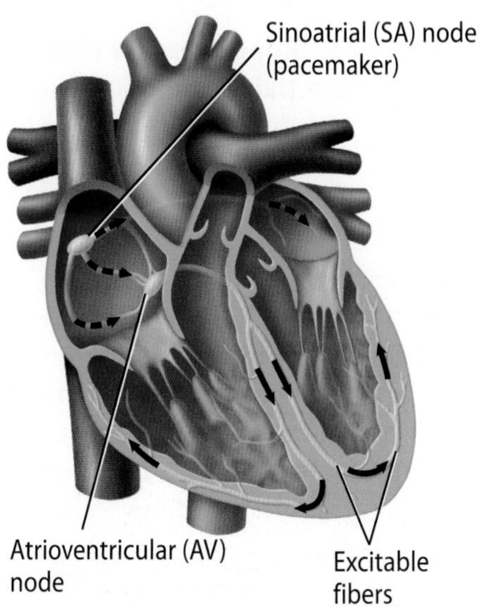

Pulse The heart pulses about 70 times each minute. If you touch the inside of your wrist just below your thumb, you can feel a pulse in the artery in your wrist rise and fall. This pulse is the alternating expansion and relaxation of the artery wall caused by the contraction of the left ventricle. The number of times the artery in your wrist pulses is the number of times your heart beats.

Blood pressure Blood pressure is a measure of how much pressure is exerted against the vessel walls by the blood. Blood-pressure readings can provide information about the condition of arteries. The contraction of the heart, or systole (SIS tuh lee), causes blood pressure to rise to its highest point, and the relaxation of the heart, or diastole (di AS tuh lee), brings blood pressure down to its lowest point. The ideal normal blood-pressure reading for a healthy adult is 120 (systolic pressure)/80 (diastolic pressure).

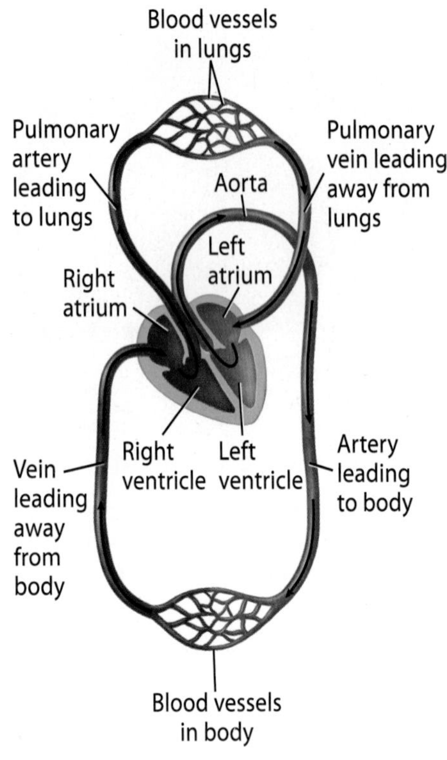

■ **Figure 6** Blood flow through the body consists of two different circulatory loops.

 **Animation**

Blood flow in the body If you follow the flow of blood shown in **Figure 6,** you will notice that it flows in two loops. First, the blood travels from the heart to the lungs and back to the heart. Then, the blood is pumped in another loop from the heart through the body and back. The right side of the heart pumps deoxygenated blood to the lungs, and the left side of the heart pumps oxygenated blood to the rest of the body.

To the lungs and back When blood from the body flows into the right atrium, it has a low concentration of oxygen but a high concentration of carbon dioxide. This deoxygenated blood is dark red. The blood flows from the right atrium into the right ventricle and is pumped into the pulmonary arteries that lead to the lungs, as shown in **Figure 6.**

Eventually, blood flows into capillaries in the lungs that are in close contact with the air that enters the lungs. The air in the lungs has a greater concentration of oxygen than the blood in the capillaries does, so oxygen diffuses from the lungs into the blood. At the same time, carbon dioxide diffuses in the opposite direction—from the blood into the airspace in the lungs. Oxygenated blood, which is now bright red, flows to the left atrium of the heart to be pumped out to the body.

To the body and back The left atrium fills with oxygenated blood from the lungs, beginning the second loop. As shown in **Figure 6,** the blood then moves from the left atrium into the left ventricle. The left ventricle pumps the blood into the largest artery in the body called the aorta. Eventually, blood flows into the capillaries that branch throughout the body. Importantly, the capillaries are in close contact with body cells. Oxygen is released from the blood into the body cells by diffusion, and carbon dioxide moves from the cells to the blood by diffusion. The deoxygenated blood then flows back to the right atrium through veins.

MiniLAB 1

Investigate Blood Pressure

How does blood pressure change in response to physical activity? Blood pressure changes from day to day and throughout the day. It is affected by physical, psychological, behavioral, and inherited factors.

Procedure

1. Read and complete the lab safety form.
2. Watch the instructor demonstrate how to safely measure blood pressure. Practice using a **blood-pressure cuff** to measure a partner's blood pressure. Refer to a **blood-pressure chart** to interpret the reading.
3. Predict how exercise will affect systolic and diastolic blood pressure.
4. Take the resting blood-pressure reading of one of your classmates.
5. Have the person whose blood pressure you took do a rhythmic exercise for one minute.
6. Take a second blood-pressure reading and compare it to the resting blood-pressure reading.

Analysis

1. **Identify** the experimental constants, the independent and dependent variables, and the control in your experiment.
2. **Conclude** whether your prediction was supported. Explain.

Blood Components

Blood is the fluid of life because it transports important substances throughout the body. Blood is made up of a liquid medium called plasma, red blood cells, platelets, and white blood cells.

Plasma The clear, yellowish fluid portion of blood is the **plasma.** More than 50 percent of blood is plasma. Ninety percent of plasma is water, and nearly 10 percent is dissolved materials. Plasma carries the broken-down products of digested food, such as glucose and fats. Plasma also transports vitamins, minerals, and chemical messengers including hormones that signal body activities, such as the uptake of glucose by the cells. In addition, waste products from the cells are carried away by plasma.

There are three groups of plasma proteins that give plasma its yellow color. One group helps to regulate the amount of water in blood. The second group, produced by white blood cells, helps fight disease. The third group helps to form blood clots.

GET IT? **Explain** the functions of plasma.

Color-Enhanced SEM Magnification: 3200×

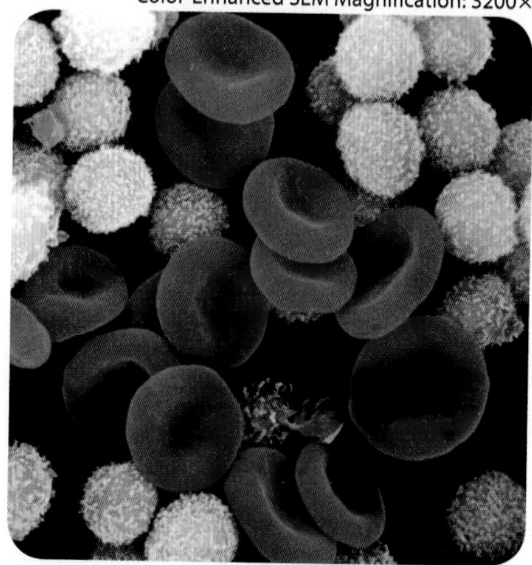

Figure 7 Blood is composed of liquid plasma, red blood cells (dimpled discs), white blood cells (irregularly shaped cells), and platelets (flat fragments).

Infer ***What might be occurring if there are too many white blood cells?***

Red blood cells The **red blood cells** carry oxygen to all of the body's cells. Red blood cells resemble discs with pinched-in centers, as shown in **Figure 7.** Recall that red blood cells develop in the marrow—the center portion of large bones. Red blood cells have no nuclei and live for only about 120 days.

Red blood cells mostly consist of an iron-containing protein called hemoglobin. Hemoglobin chemically binds with oxygen molecules and carries oxygen to the body's cells.

Platelets Have you ever cut your finger? If so, you probably noticed that in a short while, the blood flowing from the cut slowed down and then stopped as a blood clot formed a scab. **Platelets** are cell fragments, shown in **Figure 7,** that are important in forming blood clots.

When a blood vessel is cut, platelets collect and stick to the vessel at the site of the wound. The platelets then release chemicals that produce a protein called fibrin. Fibrin weaves a network of fibers across the cut that traps blood platelets and red blood cells, as shown in **Figure 8.** As more and more platelets and blood cells are trapped, a blood clot forms.

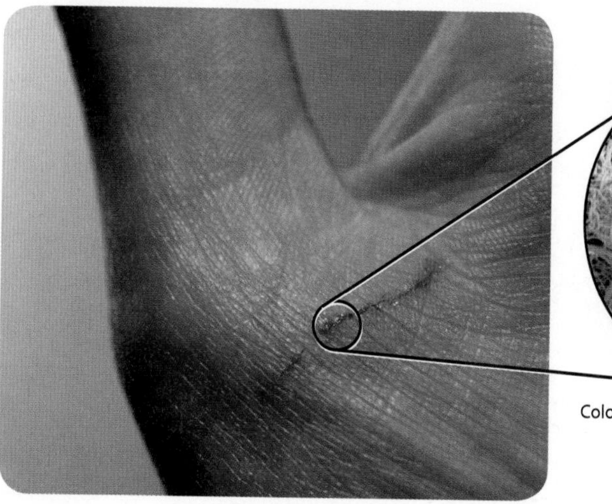

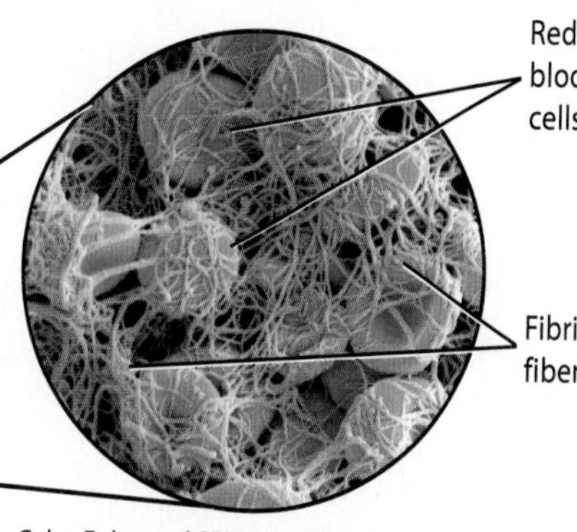

Color-Enhanced SEM Magnification: 5000×

Figure 8 A scab forms as fibrin threads trap blood cells and platelets.

STUDY TIP

GRAPHIC ORGANIZER Make a word map with the word *blood* in a large circle in the middle. Place the words *components, blood groups, circulation,* and *heart* in smaller circles around the large circle. Find information you learned in the chapter and add it to the appropriate smaller circles.

White blood cells The body's disease fighters are the **white blood cells.** Like red blood cells, white blood cells are produced in bone marrow. Some white blood cells recognize disease-causing organisms, such as bacteria, and alert the body that it has been invaded. Other white blood cells produce chemicals to fight the invaders. Still, other white blood cells surround and kill the invaders.

White blood cells are different from red blood cells in important ways. Many white blood cells move from the marrow to other sites in the body to mature. Unlike red blood cells, there are fewer white blood cells—only about one white blood cell for every 500 to 1000 red blood cells. Also, white blood cells have nuclei. Finally, most white blood cells live for months or years.

Personal Tutor 

Blood Groups

How do you know what type of blood you have? There are marker molecules attached to red blood cells. These markers are called blood groups, which determine blood type.

FOLDABLES®
Incorporate information from this section into your Foldable.

ABO blood group There are four types of blood: A, B, AB, and O. If your blood type is A, you have A markers on your blood cells. If your blood type is B, you have B markers on your blood cells. If your blood type is AB, you have both A and B markers. If your blood type is O, you do not have A or B markers.

Importance of blood type If you ever need a blood transfusion, you will be able to receive only certain blood types, as shown in **Table 1.** This is because plasma contains proteins called antibodies that recognize red blood cells with foreign markers and cause those cells to clump together. For example, if you have blood type B, your blood contains antibodies that cause cells with A markers to clump. If you received a transfusion of type-A blood, your clumping proteins would make the type-A cells clump together. Clumping of blood cells can be dangerous because it can block blood flow.

Table 1 Blood Types

Interactive Table

Blood type	A	B	AB	O
Marker molecule and antibody	Marker molecule: A Antibody: anti-B	Marker molecules: B Antibody: anti-A	Marker molecules: AB Antibody: none	Marker molecules: none Antibodies: anti-A, anti-B
Example	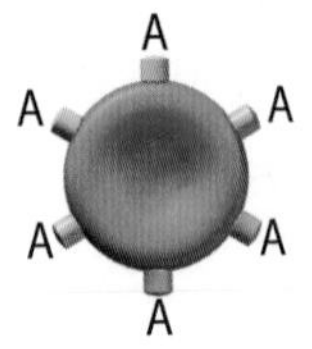 A A A A A A	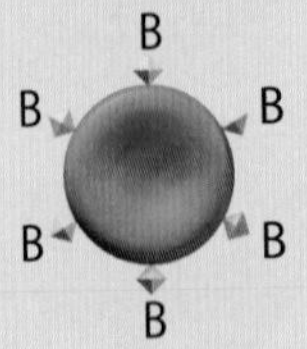 B B B B B B	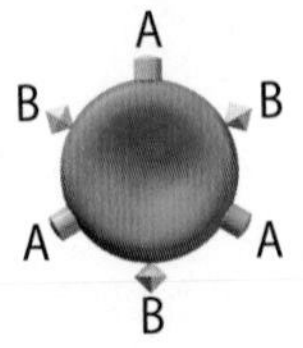 A B B A A B	
Can donate blood to:	A or AB	B or AB	AB	A, B, AB, or O
Can receive blood from:	A or O	B or O	A, B, AB, or O	O

Rh blood group Another marker found on the surface of red blood cells is called the Rh factor. A person with A positive blood has A markers and Rh markers on their blood cells. The Rh marker can cause a problem when an Rh-negative person, someone without the Rh factor, receives a transfusion of Rh-positive blood that has the Rh marker. This can result in clumping of red blood cells, because Rh negative blood contains Rh antibodies against Rh-positive cells.

The Rh factor can cause complications during some pregnancies. If the Rh-positive blood of a fetus mixes with the mother's Rh-negative blood, the mother will make anti-Rh antibodies. If the mother becomes pregnant again, these antibodies can cross the placenta and can destroy red blood cells if the fetus has Rh-positive blood. Rh-negative mothers are given a substance that prevents the production of Rh antibodies in the blood so that these problems can be avoided.

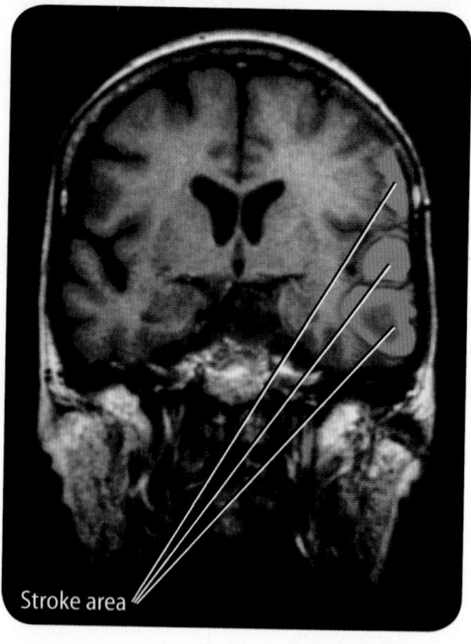

■ **Figure 9** A stroke is associated with ruptured blood vessels in the brain, as shown in red.

Circulatory System Disorders

Several disorders of the blood vessels, heart, and brain are associated with the circulatory system. Blood clots and other matter, such as fat deposits, can reduce the flow of oxygen-rich and nutrient-rich blood traveling through arteries. Physicians refer to the condition of blocked arteries as **atherosclerosis** (a thuh roh skluh ROH sus). When blood flow is reduced or blocked, the heart must work even harder to pump blood, and vessels can burst.

Atherosclerosis can lead to a heart attack or stroke. A heart attack occurs when blood does not reach the heart muscle. This can result in damage to the heart, and can even result in death if not treated. A stroke occurs when clots form in the blood vessels that supply oxygen to the brain. This can lead to ruptured blood vessels and internal bleeding, as shown in **Figure 9.** Parts of the brain die because brain cells are deprived of oxygen.

REVIEW IT! Circulatory System

Section Summary

- Blood vessels transport important substances throughout the body.
- The top half of the heart is made up of two atria, and the bottom half is made up of two ventricles.
- The heart pumps deoxygenated blood to the lungs, and it pumps oxygenated blood to the body.
- Blood is made up of plasma, red blood cells, white blood cells, and platelets.
- Blood is classified by the following four blood types: A, B, AB, and O.

Self Check

Understand Main Ideas

1. MAINIDEA **Explain** the main functions of the circulatory system.
2. **Diagram** the path of blood through the heart and body.
3. **Compare and contrast** the structure of arteries and the structure of veins.
4. **Calculate** the average number of red blood cells for every 100 white blood cells in the human body.
5. **Summarize** the functions of the four components of blood.

Think Critically

6. **Cause and Effect** If a pacemaker received faulty signals from the brain, what would happen?
7. **Hypothesize** why exercise helps to maintain a healthy heart.

MATH IN ▶ Biology

8. Count the number of times your heart beats during 15 seconds. What is your heart rate per minute?

Scott Camazine/Photo Researchers

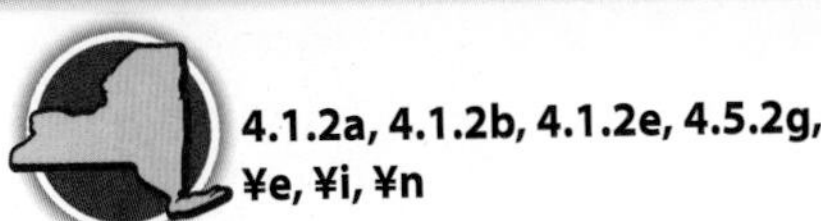

2 Respiratory System

4.1.2a, 4.1.2b, 4.1.2e, 4.5.2g, ¥e, ¥i, ¥n

BIOLOGY 4 U

Air filters separate dust and other particles from the air before they enter a car's engine. This prevents engine problems and helps ensure good air flow. Similarly, your respiratory system has features that ensure that enough clean air gets into your lungs.

REVIEW VOCABULARY

ATP: biological molecule that provides the body's cells with chemical energy

NEW VOCABULARY

breathing
external respiration
internal respiration
trachea
bronchus
lung
alveolus

Multilingual eGlossary

BrainPOP

MAINIDEA

The function of the respiratory system is the exchange of oxygen and carbon dioxide between the atmosphere and the blood and between the blood and the body's cells.

Essential Questions

- What is the difference between internal and external respiration?
- What is the path of the air through the respiratory system?
- What changes occur in the body during breathing?

The Importance of Respiration

Your body's cells require oxygen. Recall that oxygen and glucose are used by cells to produce energy-rich ATP molecules needed to maintain cellular metabolism. This process is called cellular respiration. In addition to releasing energy, cellular respiration releases carbon dioxide and water.

Breathing and respiration The respiratory system sustains cellular respiration by supplying oxygen to body cells and removing carbon dioxide waste from cells. The respiratory system can be divided into two processes: breathing and respiration. First, air must enter the body through breathing. **Breathing** is the mechanical movement of air into and out of your lungs. **Figure 10** illustrates air being released from the lungs into the air. Second, gases are exchanged in the body. **External respiration** is the exchange of gases between the atmosphere and the blood, which occurs in the lungs. **Internal respiration** is the exchange of gases between the blood and the body's cells.

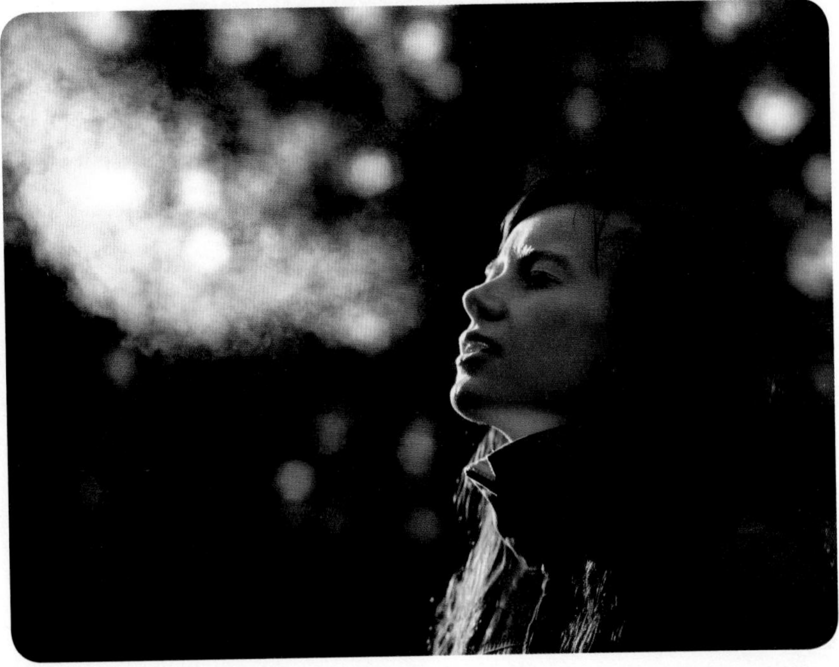

Lauri Rotko/Folio Images/Getty Images

■ **Figure 10** Exhaled air from a person's lungs can be seen on a chilly evening.
Infer ***how the air that you inhale is different from the air that you exhale.***

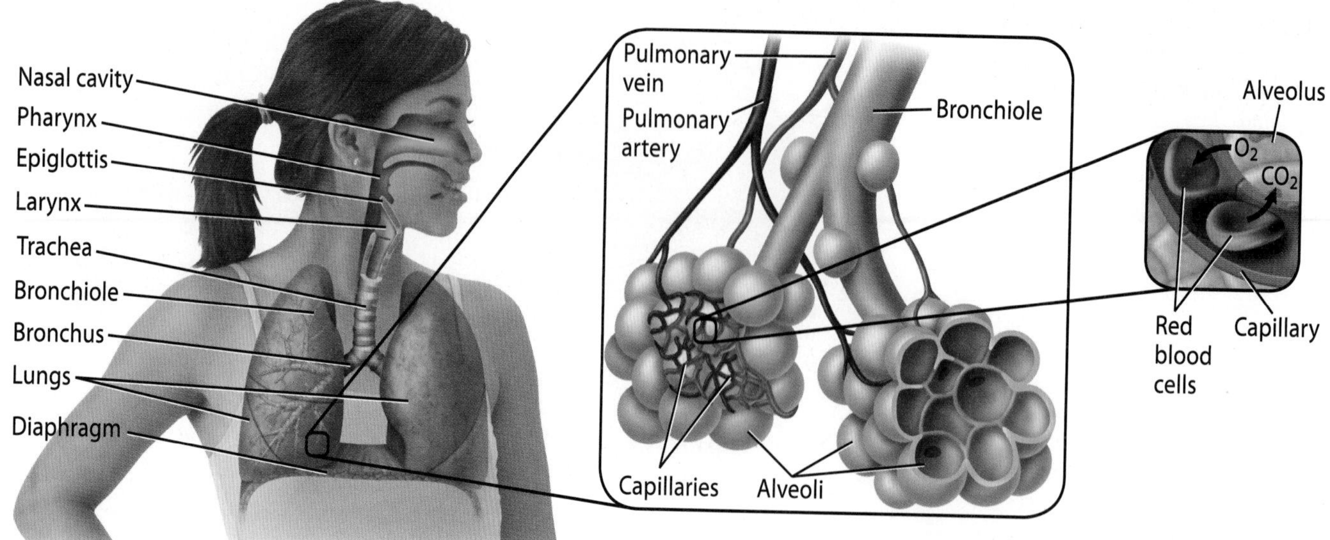

■ **Figure 11** Air travels into the alveoli of the lungs, where gases are exchanged across thin capillary walls.

Diagram ***Trace the path of oxygen from the atmosphere to the alveoli in the lungs.***

The Path of Air

The respiratory system is made up of the nasal passages, pharynx (FER ingks), larynx (LER ingks) or voice box, epiglottis, trachea, lungs, bronchi, bronchioles, alveoli (al VEE uh li), and diaphragm. Air travels from the outside environment to the lungs, where it passes through the alveoli, as shown in **Figure 11.**

First, air enters the mouth or nose. Hairs in the nose filter out dust and other large particles in the air. Hairlike structures called cilia, shown in **Figure 12,** also line the nasal passages, as well as other respiratory tubes. Cilia trap foreign particles from the air and sweep them toward the throat so that they do not enter the lungs. Mucous membranes beneath the cilia in the nasal passages, also shown in **Figure 12,** warm and moisten the air while trapping foreign materials.

Filtered air then passes through the upper throat, called the pharynx. A flap of tissue called the epiglottis, which covers the opening to the larynx, prevents food particles from entering the respiratory tubes. The epiglottis allows air to pass from the larynx to a long tube in the chest cavity called the **trachea,** or windpipe. The trachea branches into two large tubes, called **bronchi** (BRAHN ki) (singular, bronchus), which lead to the lungs. The **lungs** are the largest organs in the respiratory system, and gas exchange takes place in the lungs. Each bronchus branches into smaller tubes called bronchioles (Brahn kee ohlz), which continue to branch into even smaller passageways. Each of these ends in an individual air sac called an **alveolus** (plural, alveoli). Each alveolus has a thin wall—only one cell thick—and is surrounded by very thin capillaries.

Gas exchange in the lungs Air travels to individual alveoli, where oxygen diffuses across the moist, thin walls into capillaries and then into red blood cells. The oxygen is then transported to be released to tissue cells in the body during internal respiration. Meanwhile, carbon dioxide in the blood crosses capillary walls and diffuses into the alveoli to be returned to the atmosphere during external respiration. Carbon dioxide in the blood is found as carbonic acid in the red blood cells, dissolved in plasma, and bound to hemoglobin in plasma.

VOCABULARY

WORD ORIGIN

Alveolus
comes from the Latin word *alveus,* meaning *belly* or *hollow space*

■ **Figure 12** Hairlike cilia line the mucous membranes of the nasal cavity.

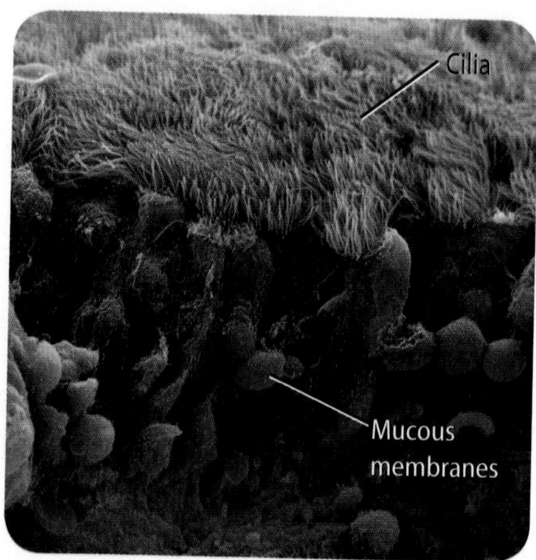

Color-Enhanced SEM Magnification: 2000×

■ **Figure 13** Rib and diaphragm muscles contract and relax during breathing.

***Analyze** how air pressure is involved in breathing.*

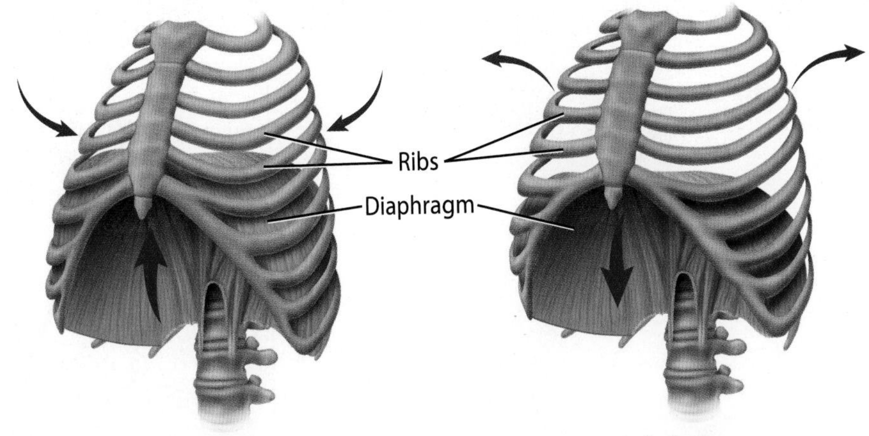

Breathing

The brain directs the rate of breathing by responding to internal stimuli that indicate how much oxygen the body needs. When the concentration of carbon dioxide in the blood is high, the breathing rate increases because cells need more oxygen.

Inhalation is the act of taking air into the lungs. During inhalation, as shown in **Figure 13,** the diaphragm contracts. This causes the chest cavity to expand as the diaphragm moves down, allowing air to move into the lungs. During exhalation, the diaphragm relaxes and returns to its normal resting position. This reduces the size of the chest cavity as the diaphragm moves up. Air naturally flows out from the greater pressure of the lungs. Follow **Figure 14** to learn how circulation and respiration work together to supply the needed oxygen and to get rid of carbon dioxide.

Launch Lab

Review Based on what you've read about respiration, how would you now answer the analysis questions?

MiniLAB 2

Recognize Cause and Effect

Does exercise affect metabolism? Most of the chemical reactions that occur in your cells make up your metabolism. In this lab, you will explore how exercise affects the circulatory and respiratory systems and infer how this affects metabolism.

Procedure

1. Read and complete the lab safety form.
2. Record the number of heartbeats and number of breaths per minute for ten classmates.
3. Instruct the same students to walk in place for five minutes. At the end of that time, record each person's heartbeat per minute and the number of breaths per minute.
4. After students have rested for five minutes, instruct them to jog or walk briskly in place for five minutes. Then record each person's heartbeat per minute and the number of breaths per minute.
5. Plot your results on **graph paper.** Each coordinate point should indicate breaths per minute on the horizontal axis and heartbeats per minute on the vertical axis.

Analysis

1. **Interpret** the relationship between the two dependent variables of your experiment—heart rate and breathing rate.
2. **Conclude** whether exercise affects metabolism. Why?
3. **Hypothesize** why students might have different numbers of heartbeats per minute and breaths per minute even though they all walked or jogged for the same amount of time.

VISUALIZING Gas Exchange

Figure 14 Gases are exchanged in the lungs and in the tissue cells of the body.

In the lungs, oxygen (O_2) that is inhaled moves into capillaries and is transported to body cells. Carbon dioxide (CO_2) leaves the capillaries and is exhaled from the lungs.

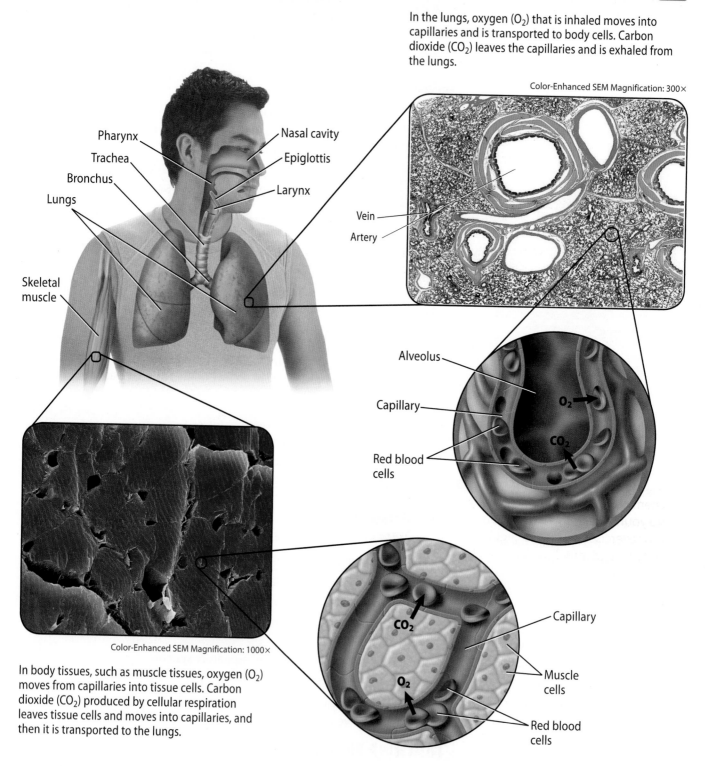

Color-Enhanced SEM Magnification: 300×

Color-Enhanced SEM Magnification: 1000×

In body tissues, such as muscle tissues, oxygen (O_2) moves from capillaries into tissue cells. Carbon dioxide (CO_2) produced by cellular respiration leaves tissue cells and moves into capillaries, and then it is transported to the lungs.

(l)Steve Gschmeissner/Science Source, (r)Dr. Keith Wheeler/Science Source

Table 2 Common Respiratory Disorders

Interactive Table

Lung Disorder	Brief Description
Asthma	Respiratory pathways become irritated, and bronchioles constrict.
Bronchitis	Respiratory pathways become infected, resulting in coughing and production of mucus.
Emphysema	Alveoli break down, resulting in reduced surface area needed for gas exchange with the alveoli's blood capillaries.
Pneumonia	Infection of the lungs causes the alveoli to collect mucous material.
Pulmonary tuberculosis	A specific bacterium infects the lungs, resulting in less elasticity of the blood capillaries surrounding the alveoli, thus decreasing effective gas exchange between the air and blood.
Lung cancer	Uncontrolled cell growth in lung tissue can lead to a persistent cough, shortness of breath, bronchitis, or pneumonia, and can lead to death.

Respiratory Disorders

Some diseases and disorders irritate, inflame, or infect the respiratory system, as described in **Table 2.** These disorders can produce tissue damage that reduces the effectiveness of the bronchi and alveoli. When these tissues become damaged, respiration becomes difficult. Smoking also causes chronic irritation to respiratory tissues and inhibits cellular metabolism. Finally, exposure to airborne materials, such as pollen, can produce respiratory problems in some people who have allergic reactions.

REVIEW IT! Respiratory System

Section Summary

- Alveoli in the lungs are the sites of gas exchange between the respiratory and circulatory systems.
- The pathway of air starts with the mouth or nose and ends at the alveoli located in the lungs.
- Inhalation and exhalation are the processes of taking in and expelling air.
- Respiratory disorders can inhibit respiration.

Self Check

Understand Main Ideas

1. MAINIDEA **Identify** the main function of the respiratory system.
2. **Distinguish** between internal and external respiration.
3. **Sequence** the path of air from the nasal passages to the bloodstream.
4. **Describe** the mechanics of inhalation and exhalation.
5. **Infer** how the respiratory system would compensate for a circulatory disorder.
6. **Describe** three disorders of the respiratory system.

Think Critically

7. **Hypothesize** an advantage of heating and moisturizing air before it reaches the alveoli.

MATH IN ▶ Biology

8. The total surface area of the alveoli tissue in your lungs is approximately 70 m^2. This is more than 40 times the surface area of the skin. What is the surface area of your skin?

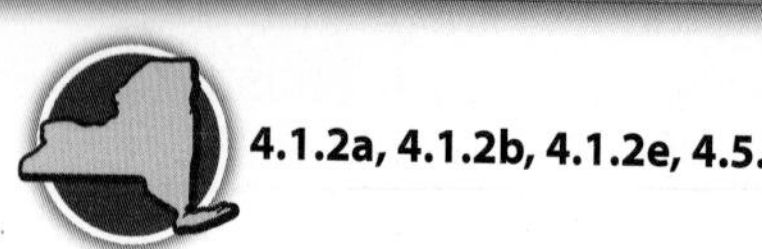

USE IT! Science Notebook

3 Excretory System

4.1.2a, 4.1.2b, 4.1.2e, 4.5.1c

MAINIDEA

The kidneys maintain homeostasis by removing wastes and excess water from the body and by maintaining the pH of blood.

Essential Questions

- What is the function of the kidney in the body?
- What are the steps of the excretion of wastes from the Bowman's capsule to the urethra?
- What is the difference between filtration and reabsorption in the kidneys?

BIOLOGY 4 U

Suppose that you cleaned your bedroom by first moving everything except large items into the hallway. You then return only the items that you will keep in your bedroom and leave the items that you do not want any longer in the hallway for later disposal. This is similar to how your kidneys filter materials in your blood.

REVIEW VOCABULARY

pH: the measure of acidity or alkalinity of a solution

NEW VOCABULARY — Multilingual eGlossary

kidney
urea

Parts of the Excretory System

The body collects wastes, such as toxins, waste products, and carbon dioxide, that result from metabolic functions of the body. The excretory system removes these toxins and wastes from the body. In addition, the excretory system regulates the amount of fluid and salts in the body, and it maintains the pH of the blood. All of these functions help to maintain homeostasis.

The components that make up the excretory system include the lungs, skin, and kidneys, as illustrated in **Figure 15.** The lungs primarily excrete carbon dioxide. The skin primarily excretes water and salts contained in sweat. The kidneys, however, are the major excretory organs in the body.

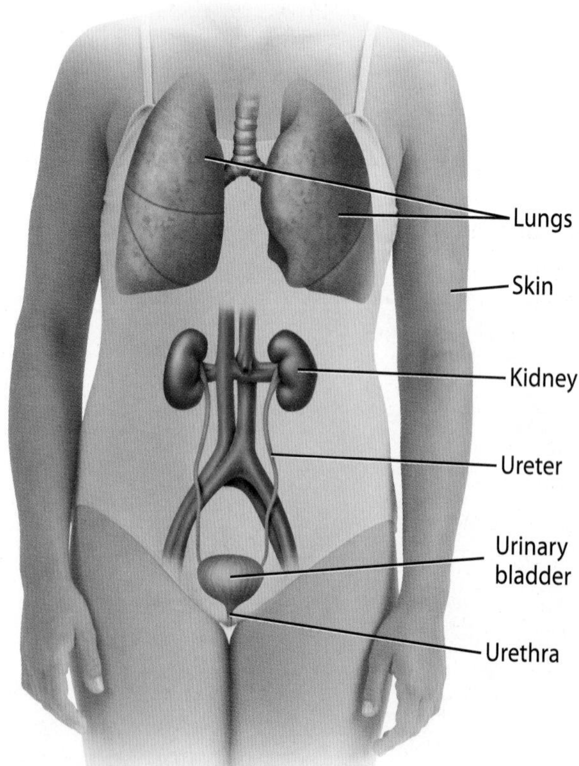

■ **Figure 15** The organs of excretion work together to eliminate wastes from the body. These organs include the lungs, skin, and kidneys.

Tim Fuller

The Kidneys

As shown in **Figure 16,** the **kidneys** are bean-shaped organs that filter out wastes, water, and salts from the blood. The kidneys are divided into two distinct regions, also illustrated in **Figure 16.** The outer portion is called the renal cortex and the inner region is called the renal medulla. Each of these regions contains microscopic tubes and blood vessels. In the center of each kidney is a region called the renal pelvis, where urine collection occurs. Follow **Figure 16** as you read about how the kidneys function.

Nephron filtration Each kidney contains approximately one million filtering units called nephrons. Blood enters each nephron through a long tube that is surrounded by a ball of capillaries called the glomerulus (gluh MER uh lus) (plural, glomeruli). The glomerulus is surrounded by a structure called the Bowman's capsule.

The renal artery transports nutrients and wastes to the kidney and branches into smaller and smaller blood vessels, eventually reaching the tiny capillaries in the glomerulus. The walls of the capillaries are very thin, and the blood is under great pressure. As a result, water and substances dissolved in the water, such as the nitrogenous waste product called **urea,** are pushed through the capillary walls into the Bowman's capsule. Larger molecules, such as red blood cells and proteins, remain in the bloodstream.

■ **Figure 16** Nephrons are the functional units of the kidneys.
Summarize *the path of urine as it is excreted from the body.*

Animation

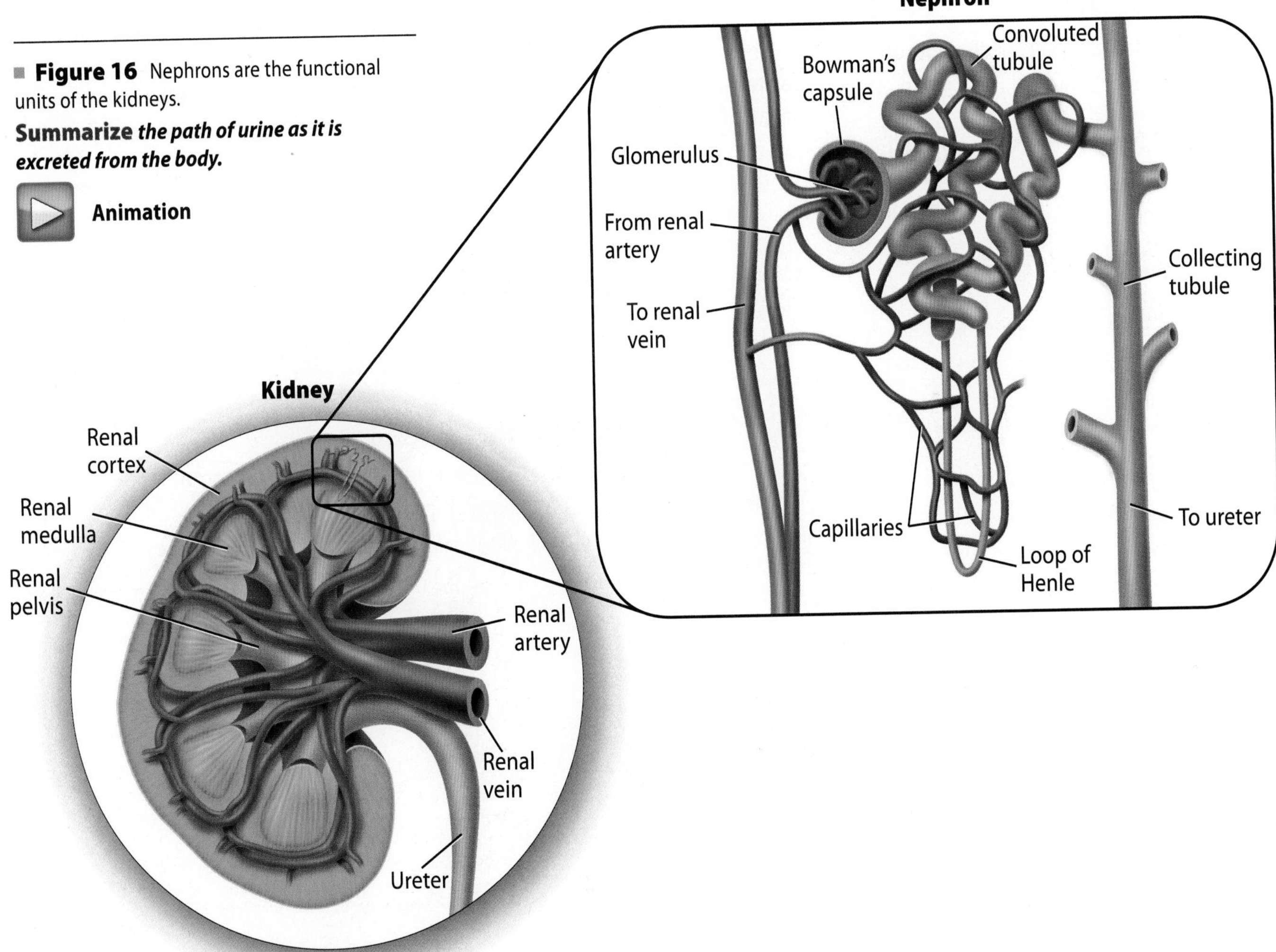

Reabsorption and the formation of urine The filtrate collected in the Bowman's capsule flows through the renal tubule, which consists of the convoluted tubule, the loop of Henle, and the collecting tubule, as illustrated in **Figure 16.** Much of the lost water and useful substances, such as glucose and minerals, are reabsorbed into the capillaries surrounding the renal tubule. This process is called reabsorption. At the same time, excess fluids and toxic substances in the capillaries are passed to the collecting tubules. This waste product is called urine. Urine leaves the kidney through ducts called the ureters (YOO ruh turz), as shown in **Figure 16.** Urine is then stored in the urinary bladder and exits the body through the urethra.

The kidneys filter about 180 L of blood each day in adults but produce only about 1.5 L of urine. The processes of filtration and reabsorption from the blood require large amounts of energy. Although kidneys account for only one percent of body weight, they use 20 to 25 percent of the body's oxygen intake for their internal energy requirements.

Connection to Chemistry The kidneys can help maintain a normal pH in the blood by adjusting the acid-base balance. Recall that low pH results when there is an abundance of H^+. When the blood pH is too low, the kidneys can increase pH levels in the body by excreting hydrogen (H^+) ions and ammonia into the renal tubules. The kidneys can decrease pH levels by reabsorbing buffers such as bicarbonate (HCO_3^+) and sodium (Na^+) ions. Because biological processes normally require pH between 6.5 and 7.5, the kidneys help to maintain homeostasis by keeping pH levels within the normal range.

CAREERS IN BIOLOGY

Urologist A urologist is a medical doctor who has specialized knowledge about problems of the male and female urinary systems. Responsibilities can include examining patients, performing laboratory tests, interpreting test results and examination findings, and treating injuries and disorders.

Data Analysis LAB 1

Based on Real Data*

Interpret the Data

How do extreme conditions affect the average daily loss of water in the human body? The body obtains water by absorbing it through the digestive tract. The body loses water primarily by excreting it in urine from the kidneys, through sweat, and through the lungs.

Think Critically

1. **Identify** what the major source of water loss is during normal temperatures.
2. **Hypothesize** why more water is lost in sweat during rigorous exercise than in urine.
3. **Calculate** the percent of water loss for each of the three conditions.

*Data obtained from: Beers, M. 2003. *The Merck Manual of Medical Information, Second Edition* West Point, PA.: Merck & Co. Inc.

Data and Observations

The table shows data collected for normal temperatures, for high temperatures, and during rigorous exercise.

Average Daily Water Loss in Humans (in mL)

Source	Normal Temperatures	High Temperatures	Rigorous Exercise
Kidneys	1500	1400	750
Skin	450	1800	5000
Lungs	450	350	650

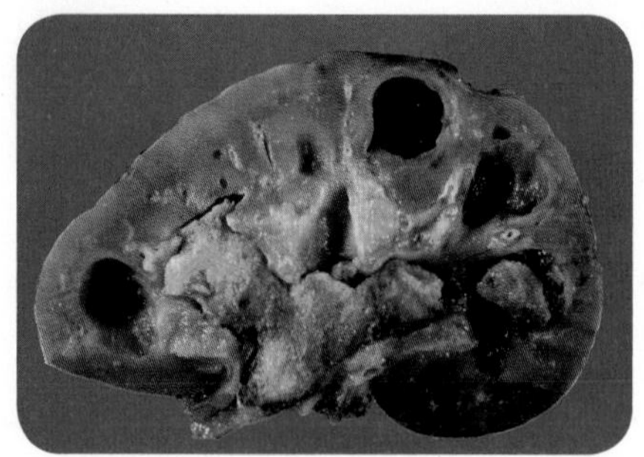

■ **Figure 17** Kidney stones form as minerals, such as calcium, become solid masses.

Kidney Disorders

Sometimes kidney function can be inhibited or impaired by infections or disorders. When kidney function is impaired, the body cannot rid itself of wastes and homeostasis might be disrupted.

Infections Symptoms of a kidney infection include fever, chills, and mid- to low-back pain. Kidney infections often start as urinary bladder infections that spread to the kidneys. Obstructions in the kidneys also can cause an infection. If the infection is not treated, the kidneys can become scarred and their function might be permanently impaired. Antibiotics usually are effective in treating bacterial infections.

Nephritis Another common kidney problem is nephritis (nih FRIH tus), which often is caused by inflammation or painful swelling of some of the glomeruli, as listed in **Table 3.** This occurs for many reasons, such as when large particles in the bloodstream become lodged in some of the glomeruli. Symptoms of this condition include blood in the urine, swelling of body tissues, and protein in the urine. If this condition does not improve on its own, the patient may need a special diet or prescription drugs to treat the infection.

Kidney stones Kidney stones are another type of kidney disorder, as listed in **Table 3** and shown in **Figure 17.** A kidney stone is a crystallized solid, such as calcium compounds, that forms in the kidney. Small stones can pass out of the body in urine; this can be quite painful. Larger stones often are broken into small pieces by ultrasonic sound waves. The smaller stones then can pass out of the body. In some cases, surgery might be required to remove large stones.

Kidneys also can be damaged by other diseases present in the body. Diabetes and high blood pressure are the two most common reasons for reduced kidney function and kidney failure. In addition, kidneys can be damaged by prescription and illegal drug use.

VOCABULARY

ACADEMIC VOCABULARY

Inhibit
to hold back, restrain, or block the action or function of something
The concentration of the protein in the blood inhibited the organ from producing more of the same protein.

Table 3 Common Excretory Disorders Interactive Table

Excretory Disorder	Brief Description
Nephritis	Inflammation of the glomeruli can lead to inflammation of the entire kidneys. This disorder can lead to kidney failure if it is left untreated.
Kidney stones	Hard deposits form in the kidneys that might pass out of the body in urine. Larger kidney stones can block urine flow or irritate the lining of the urinary tract, leading to possible infection.
Urinary tract blockage	Malformations present at birth can lead to blockage of the normal flow of urine. If it is untreated, this blockage can lead to permanent damage of the kidneys.
Polycystic (pah lee SIHS tihk) kidney disease	This is a genetic disorder distinguished by the growth of many fluid-filled cysts in the kidneys. This disorder can reduce kidney function and lead to kidney failure.
Kidney cancer	Uncontrolled cell growth often begins in the cells that line the tubules within the kidneys. This can lead to blood in the urine or a mass in the kidneys, or it can affect other organs as the cancer spreads, which can lead to death.

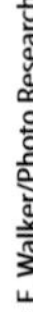

Kidney Treatments

A large percentage of kidney function can be lost before kidney failure becomes apparent. If kidney problems are left untreated, the buildup of waste products in the body can lead to seizures, a comatose state, or death. However, modern medicine offers two possible treatments for reduced kidney function or complete kidney failure.

Dialysis Dialysis (di AH luh sus) is a procedure in which an artificial kidney machine filters out wastes and toxins from a patient's blood. There are two different types of dialysis, one is illustrated in **Figure 18.** Blood is passed through a machine that temporarily filters and cleanses the blood. The filtered blood is then returned to the patient's body. The procedure lasts about three to four hours and requires three sessions per week.

In the second type of dialysis, the membrane lining the abdomen acts as an artificial kidney. The abdominal cavity is injected with a special fluid through a small tube attached to the body. The patient's fluid, which contains wastes from the blood, is drained. This procedure is performed on a daily schedule for 30 to 40 minutes.

Kidney transplant A kidney transplant is the surgical placement of a healthy kidney from another person, called a donor, into the patient's body. Kidney transplants have shown increasing success in recent years. However, there is a limited supply of donated kidneys. The number of patients waiting for kidney transplants far exceeds the organs available for transplant.

The major complication of a transplant is possible rejection of the donated organ. Rejection is prevented with medications such as steroids and cyclosporine. Cyclosporine is a drug given to transplant recipients to help prevent organ rejection. Many transplant patients also need blood-pressure medication and other drugs to prevent infections.

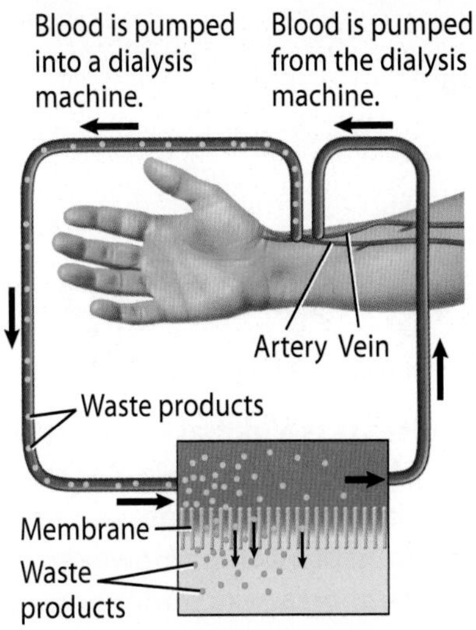

In the dialysis machine, waste products are filtered from the blood through an artificial membrane.

Figure 18 Dialysis is used to filter wastes and toxins from a patient's blood.

Personal Tutor

REVIEW IT! Excretory System

Section Summary

- The kidneys are the main excretory organs in the body.
- Nephrons are independent filtration units in the kidneys.
- Water and important substances are reabsorbed into the blood after filtration.
- The kidneys produce a waste product called urine.

Self Check

Understand Main Ideas

1. **MAIN**IDEA Explain how the kidneys help maintain homeostasis.
2. **Diagram** the excretion of waste from the Bowman's capsule to the urethra.
3. **Compare and contrast** filtration and reabsorption in a nephron.
4. **Identify** three types of kidney disorders.

Think Critically

5. **Hypothesize** why kidney failure without dialysis can result in death.

WRITING IN ▶ Biology

6. Research the effects of a high-protein diet on the excretory system. Summarize your findings in a public service announcement.

MATH IN ▶ Biology

7. Calculate the average amount of urine that the body produces in a week.

cutting-edgeBIOLOGY

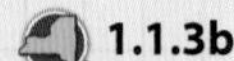 1.1.3b

Engineering Hearts

By Thomas Matthiesen, Tissue Engineer, Chicago, IL

Heart disease is a global killer—with over 22 million people affected worldwide. For many people with heart failure the only treatment option is to seek cardiac transplantation. However, because a there is a severe shortage of donor organs, most patients die waiting for a new heart.

Can science build organs? In the relatively new field of *Tissue Engineering* scientists are studying methods to generate new tissues in the lab by combining scaffolds and stem cells. Underlying nearly any biological tissue is a scaffold of proteins that forms the basis of its shape, structure, and support. This support scaffold is a major component of the *extracellular matrix* and allows for proper cell alignment and function. To-date, scientists have successfully engineered small vessels, hollow organs, and two-dimensional cardiac patches by stacking together plastics or polymer sheets to form a scaffold and coating them with cells.

In 2008, **Dr. Harald Ott** and colleagues published an article on how the extracellular matrix of a rat heart could be isolated by a process called *detergent perfusion decellularization*. This technique removes all cellular components from a cadaver organ, but keeps intact its natural vessel system and three-dimensional architecture. This vital network of vasculature (arteries and veins) can then be used to deliver nutrients to cells placed back into the matrix in a process called *recellularization*.

An important milestone On April 10, 2006, Ott and Matthiesen first observed that when they placed immature cardiac cells back into the extracellular matrix, and then delivered nutrients and a small electric charge, the recellularized heart began to beat! Using these biocompatible scaffolds gives the potential to use a patient's own stem cells and bioengineer a custom organ.

Bioreactors allow scientists to study organisms in a controlled environment. The bioreactor maintains all aspects of an organism's environment, including pH, temperature, and light levels.

Andrew Brookes, National Physical Laboratory/Science Source

This means that a patient's immune system would not recognize the bioengineered organ as a foreign object and reject it.

Looking forward, tissue engineering offers hope, yet holds many mysteries. Cells, scaffolds, and special machines called *bioreactors* must be optimized to allow scientists to develop this technology in years to come.

WRITING IN ▶ Biology

Research Investigate donor organ shortages in the United States—especially heart. What is a donor organ wait list? Which organs can be harvested and transplanted? How could tissue engineering help solve some of the donor shortages?

 **WebQuest**

BioLAB 

Internet: Make Positive Health Choices

Background: Both heredity and lifestyle choices affect overall health. Achieving optimal health involves making wise choices regarding exercise, nutrition, drugs and alcohol, stress management, and smoking. Because body systems function together to maintain homeostasis, changes in one system can impact overall health. In this lab, you will design a presentation that focuses on how specific health choices influence the functionality of body systems.

Question: *How do lifestyle choices affect the function of the circulatory, respiratory, and excretory systems?*

Materials

Choose materials that would be appropriate for creating the type of presentation that you create.

Possible materials include:

resource materials about health choices from the school library or classroom

Procedure

1. Read and complete the lab safety form.
2. Develop an outline of information that you would like to include in your presentation. Include information about how specific health choices affect the respiratory, circulatory, and excretory systems.
3. Use resources and data that you collected in this chapter's labs to determine the effects of specific health choices on your body.
4. Choose a presentation medium. Ideas include a multimedia presentation, video, poster, or pamphlet. The medium you choose should appeal to a specific audience.
5. Share your presentation with your target audience. If this is not possible, share your presentation with your class or another group of people from your school.
6. Use the evaluation information provided by your teacher to evaluate the effectiveness of the presentation.

Analyze and Conclude

1. **Describe** What is the intended audience for your presentation? How did you modify the information included to target this audience?
2. **Summarize** Identify the key points of your presentation.
3. **Explain** How do the health choices you described affect multiple body systems?
4. **Evaluate** Do you think your presentation will influence the health choices of your target audience? Explain.
5. **Critique your presentation** How could you increase the effectiveness of your presentation?

COMMUNITY INVOLVEMENT

Create Choose one or more health-promoting behaviors from your presentation. Design a survey to gather data about the choices that members of your target audience make regarding this health-promoting behavior. If possible, use the Internet to distribute your survey to members of your community and gather data.

Spencer Grant/PhotoEdit

CHAPTER 20 STUDY GUIDE

BIGIDEA **These systems function together to maintain homeostasis by delivering important substances to the body's cells while removing wastes.**

SECTION 1 Circulatory System

MAINIDEA The circulatory system transports blood to deliver important substances, such as oxygen, to cells and to remove wastes, such as carbon dioxide.

- Blood vessels transport important substances throughout the body.
- The top half of the heart is made up of two atria, and the bottom half is made up of two ventricles.
- The heart pumps deoxygenated blood to the lungs, and it pumps oxygenated blood to the body.
- Blood is made up of plasma, red blood cells, white blood cells, and platelets.
- Blood is classified by the following four blood types: A, B, AB, and O.

VOCABULARY

- **artery**
- **capillary**
- **vein**
- **valve**
- **heart**
- **pacemaker**
- **plasma**
- **red blood cell**
- **platelet**
- **white blood cell**
- **atherosclerosis**

SECTION 2 Respiratory System

MAINIDEA The function of the respiratory system is the exchange of oxygen and carbon dioxide between the atmosphere and the blood and between the blood and the body's cells.

- Alveoli in the lungs are the sites of gas exchange between the respiratory and circulatory systems.
- The pathway of air starts with the mouth or nose and ends at the alveoli located in the lungs.
- Inhalation and exhalation are the processes of taking in and expelling air.
- Respiratory disorders can inhibit respiration.

VOCABULARY

- **breathing**
- **external respiration**
- **internal respiration**
- **trachea**
- **bronchus**
- **lung**
- **alveolus**

SECTION 3 Excretory System

MAINIDEA The kidneys maintain homeostasis by removing wastes and excess water from the body and by maintaining the pH of blood.

- The kidneys are the main excretory organs in the body.
- Nephrons are independent filtration units in the kidneys.
- Water and important substances are reabsorbed into the blood after filtration.
- The kidneys produce a waste product called urine.

VOCABULARY

- **kidney**
- **urea**

SECTION 1

Vocabulary Review

Match each of the following definitions with the correct vocabulary term from the Study Guide page.

1. a vessel carrying oxygen-rich blood
2. involved in blood vessel repair
3. stimulates the heart to contract

Understand Main Ideas

4. When blood leaves the heart, where does it exit?
   A. the aorta
   B. the capillaries
   C. the lungs
   D. the pulmonary vein

Use the diagram below to answer questions 5 and 6.

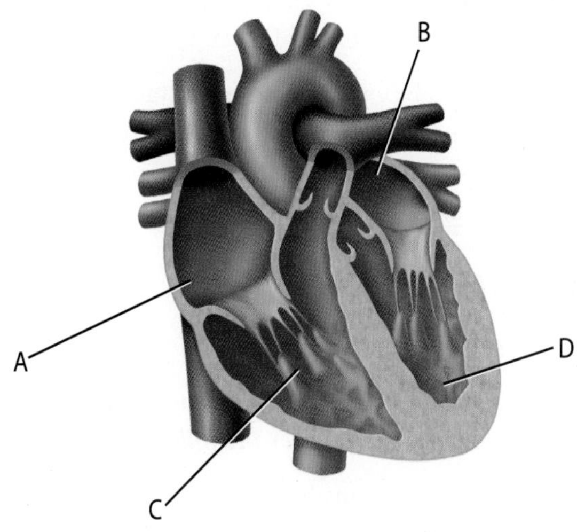

5. Which represents the right ventricle?
   A. A
   B. B
   C. C
   D. D

6. Into what part of the heart does oxygen-rich blood enter?
   A. A
   B. B
   C. C
   D. D

7. If a teenager with type A blood is injured in an auto accident and needs a blood transfusion, what type of blood will he or she receive?
   A. only type A
   B. type A or type O
   C. only type AB
   D. only type O

8. Where are one-way valves in the circulatory system located?
   A. arteries
   B. capillaries
   C. veins
   D. white blood cells

9. When a small blood vessel in your hand is cut open, which plays an active defensive role against possible disease?
   A. plasma
   B. platelets
   C. red blood cells
   D. white blood cells

Constructed Response

10. MAINIDEA Differentiate between the function of the atria and the function of the ventricles.

Use the diagram to answer question 11.

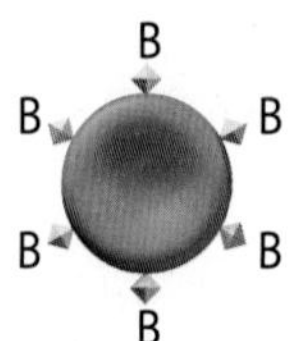

11. **Short Answer** A person has the blood type represented above. What type of blood can the person receive in a transfusion? Explain.

Think Critically

12. **Hypothesize** an advantage of your heart containing two pumping systems within the same organ, rather than two separate pumping organs.

13. **Deduce** which ABO blood type—A, B, AB or O—is the most valuable to medical personnel in an extreme emergency situation and explain why.

SECTION 2

Vocabulary Review

Use the vocabulary terms from the Study Guide page to answer the following questions.

14. In what structure does external respiration take place?

15. Which term defines the exchange of gases between the blood and the body's cells?

16. Which part of the air pathway branches off the trachea?

Understand Main Ideas

Use the diagram below to answer questions 17 and 18.

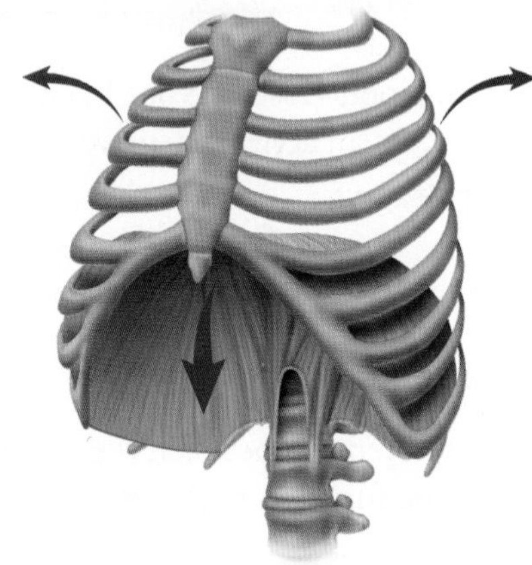

17. Which process is shown above?
    A. inhalation
    B. exhalation
    C. cellular respiration
    D. filtration

18. Which structure moves down as its muscles contract?
    A. trachea
    B. diaphragm
    C. pharynx
    D. ribs

19. Which process occurs inside the tissue cells in your legs?
    A. filtration
    B. breathing
    C. external respiration
    D. internal respiration

20. Which process causes the diaphragm to move back up?
    A. cellular respiration
    B. exhalation
    C. inspiration
    D. internal respiration

21. Which gas is needed by all cells?
    A. sulfur **C.** carbon dioxide
    B. hydrogen **D.** oxygen

22. How many breaths will a person take in one day if he or she takes 12 breaths per minute?
    A. about 1000 **C.** about 17,000
    B. about 10,000 **D.** about 1,000,000

Constructed Response

23. **Short Answer** Differentiate between asthma, bronchitis, and emphysema.

Use the photo below to answer question 24.

24. **Short Answer** Describe the function of the structures above. Where would these structures be found?

Think Critically

25. **MAIN**IDEA Hypothesize an advantage in breathing more deeply during exercise compared to another person engaged in similar exercise breathing at a normal rate.

SECTION 3

Vocabulary Review

Review the vocabulary terms found on the Study Guide page. Use the terms to answer the following questions.

26. Where are nephrons located?

27. Which waste product is found in urine?

Understand Main Ideas

28. Where is the loop of Henle?
    A. renal tubule
    B. glomerulus
    C. Bowman's capsule
    D. urethra

29. **THEME FOCUS** Which one of the kidney functions conserves water in the body?
    A. absorption **C.** reabsorption
    B. filtration **D.** breathing

30. Which process returns glucose to the blood?
    A. excretion **C.** reabsorption
    B. filtration **D.** exhalation

Eye of Science/Photo Researchers

Use the table below to answer questions 31, 32, and 33.

Reabsorption of Some Substances in the Kidneys			
Chemical Substance	Amount Filtered by Kidneys (g/day)	Amount Excreted by Kidneys (g/day)	Percent of Filtered Chemical Reabsorbed (per day)
Glucose	180	0	100
Urea	46.8	23.4	50
Protein	1.8	1.8	0

31. Based on the data from the table above, how much urea is reabsorbed by the kidneys?
A. 0.50 g/day
B. 23.4 g/day
C. 46.8 g/day
D. 50.0 g/day

32. Based on the table data above, what happens to glucose in the kidneys?
A. It is reabsorbed into the blood.
B. It is permanently filtered out of the blood.
C. It is treated in the kidney like creatinine.
D. It is treated in the kidney like urea.

33. Infer why proteins are not removed by nephrons.
A. The collecting ducts are too small.
B. Proteins cannot be filtered.
C. Proteins never enter the nephron.
D. Proteins are reabsorbed by nephrons.

Constructed Response

34. Short Answer How many liters of blood flow through your kidneys in one hour?

35. MAINIDEA Explain the differences between filtration and reabsorption in the kidneys.

36. Open Ended Infer why kidneys require so much energy to function.

Think Critically

37. CAREERSIN▸Biology Formulate a list of questions one might ask a urologist regarding urinary problems.

Summative Assessment

38. BIGIDEA What are the important substances that the circulatory and respiratory systems deliver to body cells? Why are these substances important? Give two examples of wastes that the excretory system removes from the body.

39. WRITINGIN▸Biology Construct an analogy about the circulatory system that is based on your local highway system in your town, city, or rural area.

DBQ Document–Based Questions

The following data compare the state of five subjects whose circulation was monitored. (The weight, age, and sex of all five subjects were the same.) All of Subject A's data were within normal limits; the other four were not.

Data obtained from: Macey, R. 1968. *Human Physiology.* Englewood Cliffs, NJ: Prentice Hall.

Subject	Hemoglobin (Hb) content of blood (Hb/100 mL blood)	Oxygen contents of blood in arteries (mL O_2/100 mL blood)	Oxygen content of blood in veins (mL O_2/100 mL blood)
A	15	19	15
B	15	15	12
C	8	9.5	6.5
D	16	20	13
E	15	19	18

40. Which subject might be suffering from a dietary iron deficiency? Explain your choice.

41. Which subject might have lived at a high altitude where the atmospheric oxygen is low? Explain your choice.

42. Which subject might have been poisoned by carbon monoxide that prevents tissue cells from using oxygen? Explain your choice.

CUMULATIVE MULTIPLE CHOICE

1 Which is an example of nurturing behavior?

A An animal in a colony spots a predator and warns the whole colony.

B A female chimpanzee takes care of her infant for three years.

C A male peacock displays its feathers in front of a female.

D A squirrel chatters at another squirrel to drive it away.

Use the table below to answer question 2.

Muscle Type	Function
Skeletal muscles	attached to bones and tighten when contracted causing movement
Smooth muscles	line the hollow internal organs such as stomach, intestines, bladder, and uterus
Cardiac muscles	

2 Where is the muscle type that is missing a description in the table located?

A in the heart

B in the kidneys

C lining the blood vessels

D lining the lymph vessels

3 Which answer choice is a result of parasympathetic stimulation?

A decreased heart rate

B decreased mucous production

C increased digestive activity

D increased pupil size

SHORT ANSWER

Use the diagram below to answer questions 4 and 5.

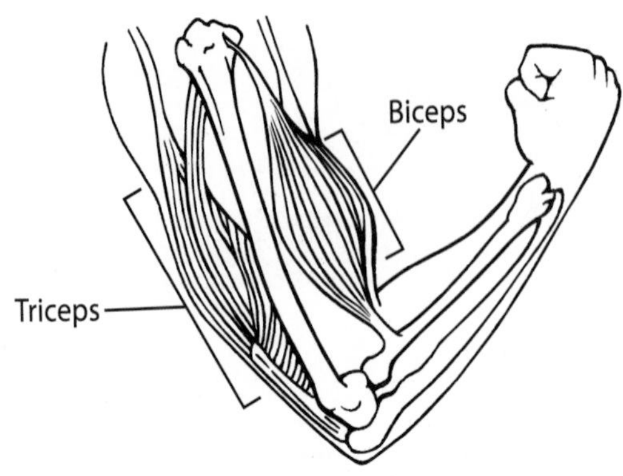

4 Describe how the biceps and triceps allow movement in the arm.

5 Explain why muscles are always in antagonistic pairs.

6 Some drugs cause an increased level of dopamine in nerve synapses. Name one of these drugs and relate the increased dopamine level to other effects that result from using the drug.

7 Use a table to organize information about the autonomic and somatic nervous systems. List the types of responses, systems affected, and include an example.

8 Monotremes are mammals that are similar to reptiles in some ways. Classify monotreme characteristics as similar to reptiles or similar to mammals.

9 A rare disease called amyotrophic lateral sclerosis (ALS) causes motor neurons in the body to lose myelin. What do you think would be the initial symptoms a person with ALS would have?

10 Explain how nephrons filter blood.

EXTENDED RESPONSE

Use the illustration below to answer question 11.

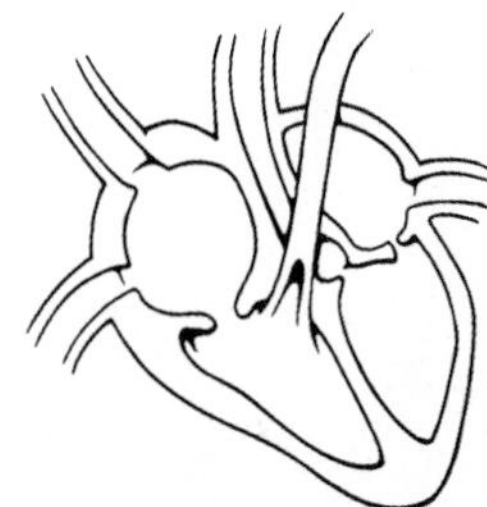

11 The illustration above shows a four-chambered mammalian heart. Write an explanation of the role of the four-chambered heart in circulating oxygenated blood throughout the body.

12 Compare and contrast apical meristems and lateral meristems in plants.

13 The invention of the microscope allowed scientists to discover hundreds of tiny living organisms that were never seen before. Distinguish, in a written statement, between an advance in technology and an advance in science using this historical example.

ESSAY QUESTION

The human nervous system consists of a complex arrangement of voluntary and involuntary responses and activities. The presence of these different types of responses has evolved in humans to help with survival.

Using the information in the paragraph above, answer the following question in essay format.

14 From what you know about different nervous system responses, write a well-organized essay explaining how different types of involuntary response systems in humans are helpful for survival.

TEST PRACTICE

Use the diagram to answer questions 15 and 16.

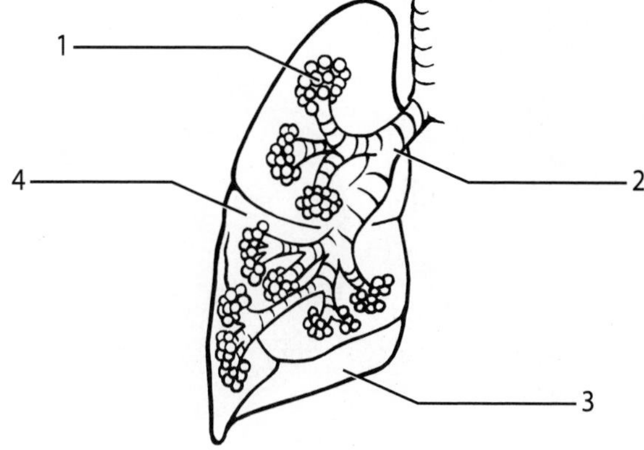

15 Which part of the respiratory system has hairs to filter particles from the air?

A 1

B 2

C 3

D 4

16 In which location does gas exchange occur?

A 1

B 2

C 3

D 4

17 Which characteristic directly affects homeostatic temperature control in mammals?

A four-chambered heart

B high metabolic rate

C milk production

D signaling devices in fur

NEED EXTRA HELP?																	
If You Missed Question . . .	1	2	3	4	5	6	7	8	9	10	11	12	13	14	15	16	17
Review Section . . .	31.2	32.3	33.2	32.3	32.3	33.4	33.2	22.1	33.1	34.3	30.2	22.1	1.2	33.2	34.2	34.2	30.1

Diet and exercise are key components to maintaining homeostasis in the digestive and endocrine systems. Maintaining a healthy lifestyle is important for the body.

LaunchLAB

How does the enzyme pepsin aid digestion?

The acidic digestive juices in the stomach contain the enzyme pepsin. In this lab, you will investigate the role of pepsin in digestion.

CHAPTER 21

Digestive and Endocrine Systems

1 The Digestive System

1.1.1c, 1.3.5b, 4.1.2a, 4.1.2b, 4.1.2e, 4.5.2h, 4.5.2j, 4.6.1a, 4.6.3b, ¥a, ¥e, ¥m, ¥n, ¥o

2 Nutrition

4.1.2h, 4.6.1c

3 The Endocrine System

4.1.2a, 4.1.2b, 4.1.2c, 4.1.2e, 4.1.2j, 4.5.1c, 4.5.3b, ¥q

THEMEFOCUS

Stability and change Negative feedback in the endocrine system maintains homeostasis.

BIGIDEA

The digestive system breaks down food to provide energy and nutrients for the body. The endocrine system produces hormones that regulate body functions.

FOLDABLES® Study Organizer

Hormone

Make a folded chart using the titles shown. Use it to organize your notes on hormones.

Parathyroid hormone
Antidiuretic hormone
Human growth hormone
Hormone

1 The Digestive System

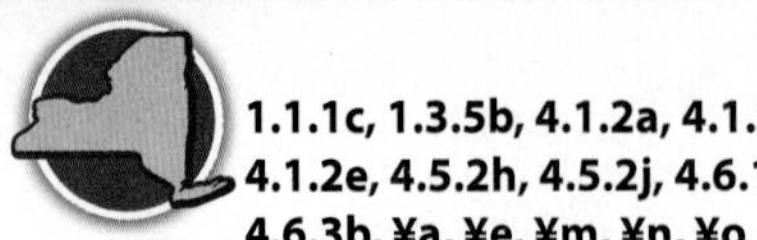
1.1.1c, 1.3.5b, 4.1.2a, 4.1.2b, 4.1.2e, 4.5.2h, 4.5.2j, 4.6.1a, 4.6.3b, ¥a, ¥e, ¥m, ¥n, ¥o

MAIN IDEA

The digestive system breaks down food so nutrients can be absorbed by the body.

Essential Questions

- What are the three main functions of the digestive system?
- What are the structures of the digestive system and what are their functions?
- What is the process of chemical digestion?

BIOLOGY 4 U

During an average lifespan, as much as 45 tons of food can pass through a person's digestive system. The food will travel almost 9 m through the digestive tract. What happens as food passes through this long tube?

Review Vocabulary

nutrient: vital component of foods that provides energy and materials for growth and body functions

New Vocabulary

mechanical digestion
chemical digestion
amylase
esophagus
peristalsis
pepsin
small intestine
liver
villus
large intestine

Multilingual eGlossary

Video Lab

Functions of the Digestive System

There are three main functions of the digestive system. The digestive system ingests food, breaks it down so nutrients can be absorbed, and eliminates what cannot be digested. Refer to **Figure 1** and **Figure 2** as you learn about the structure and function of the digestive system.

Digestion Suppose on Friday night, you and your friends meet to have pizza. You bite into a slice and begin to chew. How does your body digest that pizza?

Mechanical digestion involves chewing food to break it down into smaller pieces. It also includes the action of smooth muscles in the stomach and small intestine that churn the food. **Chemical digestion** involves the breakdown of large molecules in food into smaller substances by enzymes. The smaller substances can be absorbed into the body's cells. Enzymes are proteins that speed up biological reactions. When you chew the bites of pizza, **amylase,** an enzyme found in saliva, begins the process of chemical digestion by breaking down starches into sugars.

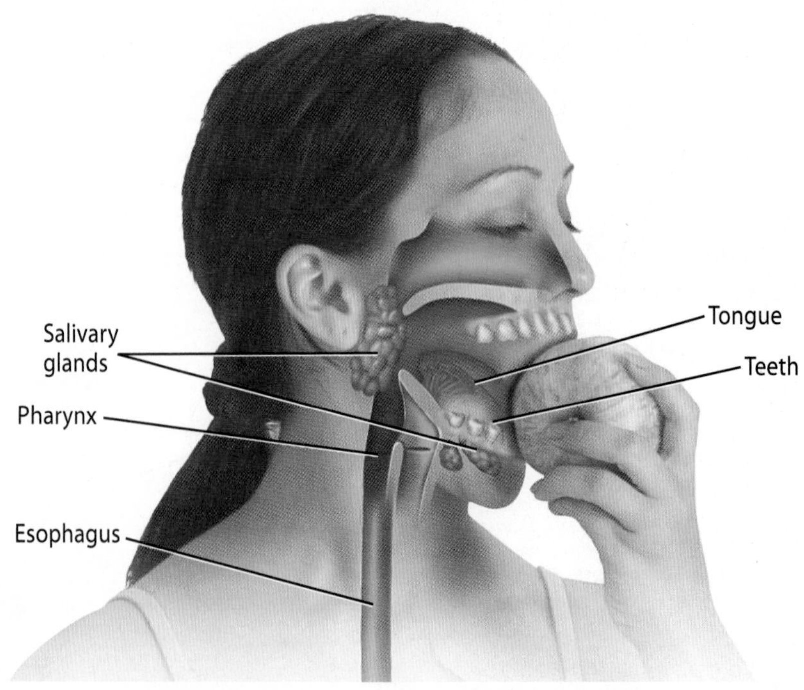

■ **Figure 1** Mechanical digestion starts in the mouth. Secretions from the salivary glands keep food moist and begin the process of chemical digestion. Food moves through the pharynx into the esophagus.

Animation

Esophagus When the tongue pushes chewed food to the back of the mouth, the swallowing reflex is stimulated. The food is forced by the action of the tongue into the upper portion of the esophagus. The **esophagus** (ih SAH fuh gus) is a muscular tube that connects the pharynx, or throat, to the stomach, as illustrated in **Figure 2.** The wall of the esophagus is lined with smooth muscles that contract rhythmically to move the food through the digestive system in a process called **peristalsis** (per uh STAHL sus). Peristalsis continues throughout the digestive tract. Even if a person were upside down, food would still move toward the stomach.

When a person swallows, the small plate of cartilage called the epiglottis covers the trachea. If this opening is not closed, food can enter the trachea and cause a person to choke. The body responds to this by initiating the coughing reflex in an attempt to expel the food to keep the food from entering the lungs.

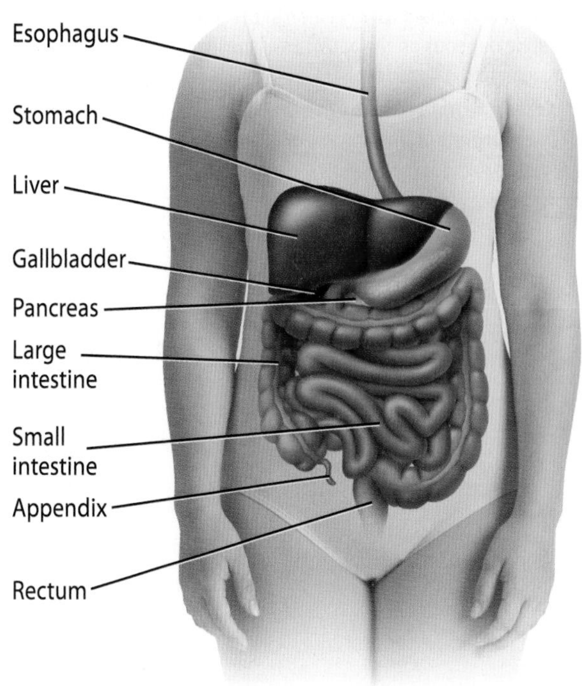

■ **Figure 2** The esophagus extends from the pharynx to the stomach and is approximately 25 cm long.

Describe *why humans are classified as coelomates.*

Stomach When food leaves the esophagus, it passes through a circular muscle called a sphincter, and into the stomach. The sphincter between the esophagus and stomach is the cardiac sphincter. The walls of the stomach are composed of three overlapping layers of smooth muscle that are involved with mechanical digestion. As the muscles contract, they further break down the food and mix it with the secretions of glands that line the inner wall of the stomach.

Connection to Chemistry Recall that pH is a measure of a solution's acidity. The environment inside the stomach is very acidic. Stomach glands, called gastric glands, secrete an acidic solution, which lowers the pH in the stomach to about 2. This is about the same level of acidity as lemon juice. If the sphincter in the upper portion of the stomach allows any leakage, some of this acid might move back into the esophagus, causing what is commonly known as heartburn.

The acidic environment in the stomach is favorable to the action of **pepsin,** an enzyme involved in the process of the chemical digestion of proteins. Cells in the lining of the stomach secrete mucus to help prevent damage from pepsin and the acidic environment. Although most absorption occurs in the small intestine, some substances, such as alcohol and aspirin, are absorbed by cells that line the stomach. While empty, the capacity of the stomach is about 50 mL. When full, it can expand to 2–4 L.

The muscular walls of the stomach contract and push food farther along the digestive tract. The consistency of the food resembles tomato soup as it passes through the pyloric sphincter at the lower end of the stomach into the small intestine. **Figure 3** illustrates peristalsis in the small intestine.

GET IT? **Compare** digestion in the mouth with digestion in the stomach.

■ **Figure 3** The smooth muscles in the walls of the digestive tract contract in the process of peristalsis.

Animation

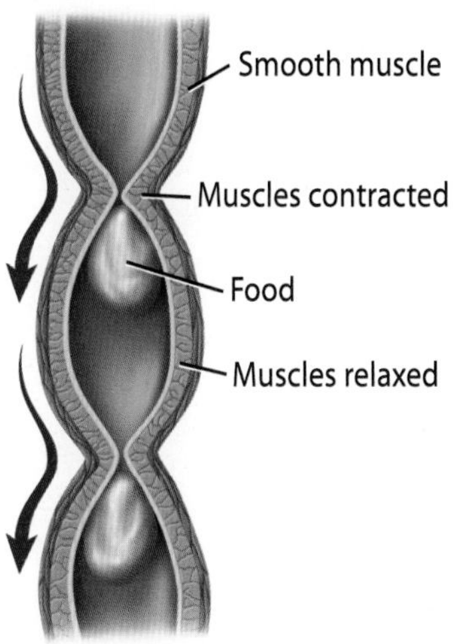

Tim Fuller

■ **Figure 4** Chemical digestion in the small intestine depends on the activities of the liver, pancreas, and gallbladder.

Discuss ***the importance of each of these organs in the process of chemical digestion.***

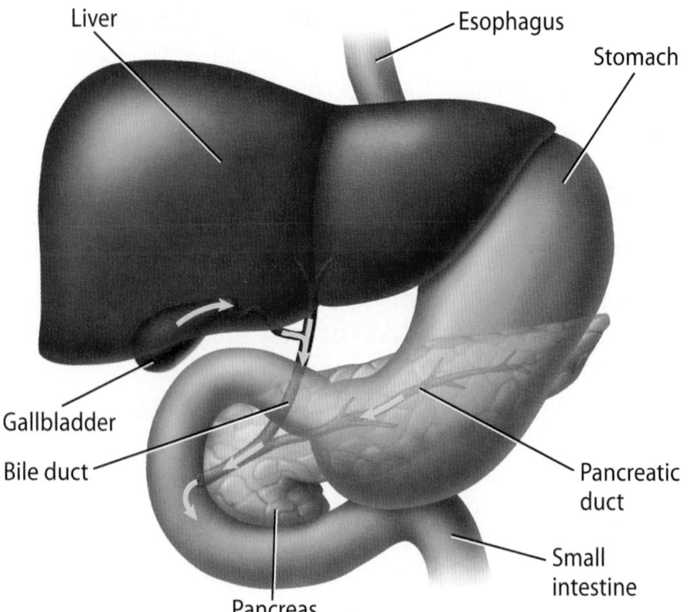

BrainPOP 

Small intestine The **small intestine** is approximately 7 m in length and is the longest part of the digestive tract. It is called *small* because its diameter is 2.5 cm compared to the 6.5 cm diameter of the large intestine. The smooth muscles in the wall of the small intestine continue the process of mechanical digestion and push the food farther through the digestive tract by peristalsis.

The completion of chemical digestion in the small intestine depends on three accessory organs—the pancreas, liver, and gallbladder, as illustrated in **Figure 4.** The pancreas serves two main functions. One is to produce enzymes that digest carbohydrates, proteins, and fats. The other is to produce hormones, which will be discussed later in this chapter. The pancreas secretes an alkaline fluid to raise the pH in the small intestine to slightly above 7, which creates a favorable environment for the action of intestinal enzymes.

The **liver** is the largest internal organ of the body and produces bile, which helps to break down fats. About 1 L of bile is produced every day, and excess bile is stored in the gallbladder to be released into the small intestine when needed. **Figure 5** shows gallstones, which are cholesterol crystals that can form in the gallbladder.

STUDY TIP

SEQUENCE AND ORDER Using your notes, work with a partner to review the sequence of the organs in the digestive system. Then, practice retelling the sequence without your notes. Ask questions of one another for deeper learning.

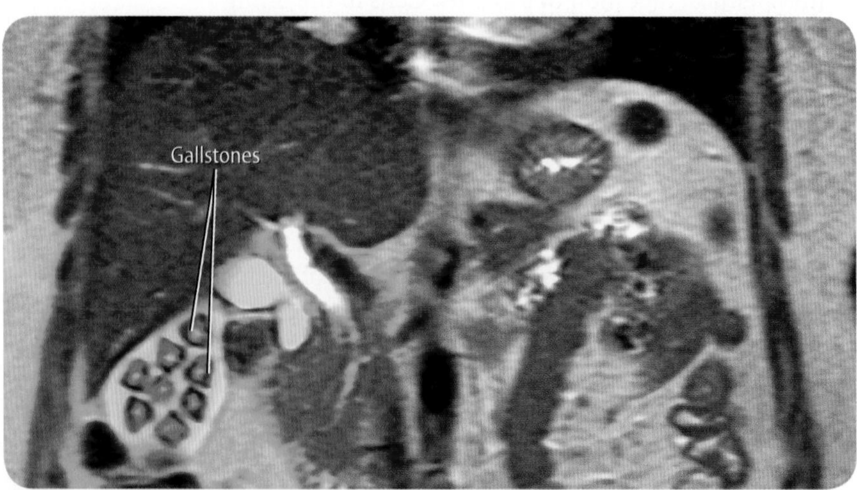

Simon Fraser/Science Source

■ **Figure 5** Gallstones can obstruct the flow of bile from the gallbladder. Note the gallstones on this MRI film of a gallbladder.

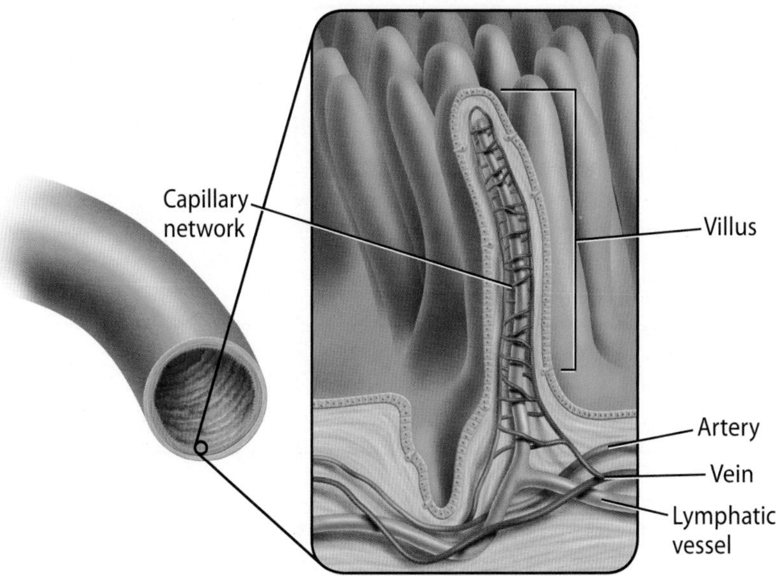

Figure 6 A villus is a fingerlike extension of the lining of the small intestine. Nutrients diffuse into capillaries in the villi and reach body cells by means of circulating blood.

Chemical digestion is completed and most of the nutrients from food are absorbed from the small intestine into the bloodstream through fingerlike structures called **villi** (VIH li) (singular, villus). Villi, illustrated in **Figure 6,** increase the surface area of the small intestine, giving the small intestine approximately the same surface area as a tennis court.

Refer again to **Figure 1** and **Figure 2** to follow the movement of digested food through the digestive system. Once digestion is complete, the remaining food, now in a semiliquid form called chyme (KIME), moves into the large intestine. Chyme is made up of materials that cannot be digested or absorbed by villi in the small intestine.

MiniLAB 1

Investigate Digestion of Lipids

How do bile salts and pancreatic solution affect digestion? Lipids, or fats, are not water soluble. The body compensates by producing bile, a chemical that breaks apart fat and helps the molecules mix with the watery solution in the small intestine. In this lab, you will investigate the breakdown of lipids.

Procedure

1. Read and complete the lab safety form.
2. Study the lab procedure and construct a data chart.
3. Label **three test tubes.** Add 5 mL **vegetable oil** and 8-10 drops **phenolphthalein** to each. Shake well. If the color is not pink, add **NaOH solution** one drop at a time until the solution turns pink.
4. Add 125 mL **water** to a **250-mL beaker.** Warm to about 40°C.
5. Prepare the test tubes as follows, then seal each with a **stopper.**
   Test Tube A: 5 mL **distilled water,** pinch of **bile salt**
   Test Tube B: 5 mL **pancreatic solution,** pinch of bile salt
   Test Tube C: 5 mL pancreatic solution
6. Shake each tube to mix the contents and gently place in the beaker. Record your observations.
7. Dispose of test tube contents in the designated container.

Analysis

1. **Analyze** What did a color change inside a test tube indicate? What caused the change?
2. **Draw conclusions** based on your results. Describe the roles of bile and pancreatic solution in digestion.

Table 1 Time for Digestion		Interactive Table
Digestive Structure	**Primary Function**	**Time Food in Structure**
Mouth	Mechanical and chemical digestion	5–30 s
Esophagus	Transport (swallowing)	10 s
Stomach	Mechanical and chemical digestion	2–24 h
Small intestine	Mechanical and chemical digestion	3–4 h
Large intestine	Water absorption	18 h–2 days

Large intestine The **large intestine** is the end portion of the digestive tract. It is about 1.5 m long and includes the colon, the rectum, and a small saclike appendage called the appendix. Although the appendix has no known function, it can become inflamed and swollen, resulting in appendicitis. If inflamed, the appendix will likely have to be removed surgically.

Some kinds of beneficial bacteria are normal in the colon. These bacteria produce vitamin K and some B vitamins available to the body.

A primary function of the colon is to absorb water from the chyme. The indigestible material then becomes more solid and is called feces. Peristalsis continues to move feces toward the rectum, causing the walls of the rectum to stretch. This initiates a reflex that causes the final sphincter muscle to relax, and the feces are eliminated from the body through the anus. Refer to **Table 1** to review the primary function of each structure of the digestive system and how long food usually remains in each structure as it is being digested.

REVIEW IT! The Digestive System

Section Summary

- The digestive system has three main functions.
- Digestion can be categorized as mechanical or chemical.
- Most nutrients are absorbed in the small intestine.
- Accessory organs provide enzymes and bile to aid digestion.
- Water is absorbed from chyme in the colon.

Understand Main Ideas

1. MAINIDEA **Describe** the process that breaks down food so that nutrients can be absorbed by the body.
2. **Analyze** the difference between mechanical digestion and chemical digestion. Explain why chemical digestion is necessary for the body.
3. **Summarize** the three main functions of the digestive system.
4. **Analyze** what the consequence might be if the lining of the small intestine were completely smooth instead of having villi.

Think Critically

5. **Design** an experiment to gather data about the effect of pH on the digestion of different types of food.

MATH IN Biology

6. A can of carbonated beverage typically holds about 354 mL of fluid. Compare this amount with the volume of an empty stomach. Give a ratio.
7. **Explain** why the pH in the digestive system changes. Give examples and explain the importance of these changes.

2 Nutrition

4.1.2h, 4.6.1c

MAINIDEA

Certain nutrients are essential for the proper function of the body.

Essential Questions

- Depending on activity level, what caloric intake is needed to maintain proper body weight?
- How are proteins, carbohydrates, and fats used by the body?
- What are the roles of vitamins and minerals in maintaining homeostasis?
- How can you apply the information in MyPyramid and on food labels to establishing healthy eating habits?

BIOLOGY 4U

There is a saying, "You are what you eat." What do you think that means? Much of the time, you have freedom to choose what you eat. However, your choices have consequences. What you eat can affect your health now and in the future.

Review Vocabulary

amino acid: the basic building block of proteins

New Vocabulary

nutrition
Calorie
vitamin
mineral

Multilingual eGlossary

Calories

Nutrition is the process by which a person takes in and uses food. Foods supply the building blocks and energy to maintain body mass. The daily input of energy from food should equal the amount of energy a person uses daily. A **Calorie** (with an uppercase C) is the unit used to measure the energy content of foods. A Calorie is equal to 1 kilocalorie, or 1000 calories (with a lowercase c). A calorie is the amount of heat needed to raise the temperature of 1 mL of water by 1°C.

The energy content of a food can be measured by burning the food and converting the stored energy to heat. Not all foods have the same energy content. The same mass of different foods does not always equal the same number of Calories. For example, one gram of carbohydrate or protein contains four Calories. One gram of fat contains nine Calories. To lose weight, more Calories must be used than consumed. The opposite is true to gain weight. In 2005, the United States Department of Agriculture released new guidelines for nutrition and suggested that people should become more active and use more Calories. **Table 2** compares average Calorie usage with different activities. The exact number of calories burned will vary depending on weight and gender.

Table 2 Activities and Average Calorie Usage — Interactive Table

Activity	Calories Used Per Hour	Activity	Calories Used Per Hour
Baseball	282	Hiking and backpacking	564
Basketball	564	Hockey (field and ice)	546
Bicycling	240–410	Jogging	740–920
Cross-country skiing	700	Skating	300
Football	540	Soccer	540

■ **Figure 7** Your body needs carbohydrate-rich foods like these every day.

VOCABULARY

SCIENCE USAGE V. COMMON USAGE

Consume

Science usage: to eat or drink
We consume Calories when we eat food.

Common usage: to destroy
The fire consumed several buildings.

Carbohydrates

Cereal, pasta, potatoes, strawberries, and rice all contain a high proportion of carbohydrates. Recall that sugars, such as glucose, fructose, and sucrose, are simple carbohydrates that are found in fruits, soda pop, and candy. Complex carbohydrates are macromolecules such as starches, which are long chains of sugars. Foods such as those shown in **Figure 7** have a high starch content, as do some vegetables.

Complex carbohydrates are broken down into simple sugars in the digestive tract. Simple sugars are absorbed through villi in the small intestine into blood capillaries and circulated throughout the body to provide energy for cells. Excess glucose is stored in the liver in the form of glycogen. Cellulose, sometimes called dietary fiber, is another complex carbohydrate found in plant foods. Although humans cannot digest fiber, it is important because fiber helps keep food moving through the digestive tract and helps with the elimination of wastes. Bran, whole-grain breads, and beans are good sources of fiber.

GET IT? **Compare** simple and complex carbohydrates.

■ **Figure 8** The way in which naturally low-fat foods are cooked and served can increase saturated fat content. Olive oil may be a better cooking option than butter for this reason.

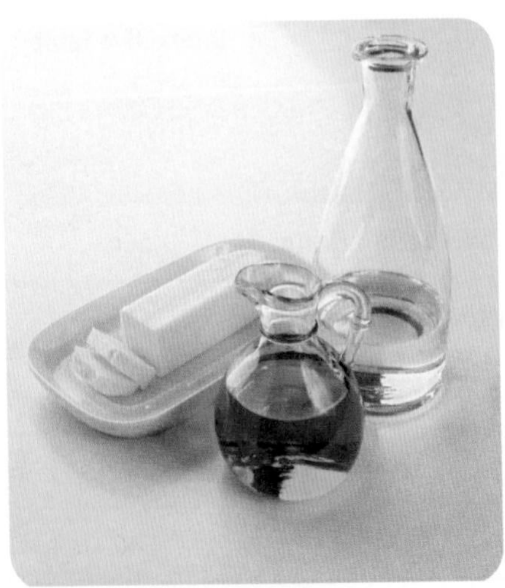

Fats

In proper amounts, fats are an essential part of a healthful diet. Fats are the most concentrated energy source available to the body, and they are building blocks for the body. Fats also protect some internal organs and help maintain homeostasis by providing energy and by storing and transporting certain vitamins. However, not all fats are beneficial.

Connection to Health Recall that fats are classified according to their chemical structure as saturated or unsaturated. Meats, cheeses, and other dairy products are sources of saturated fats. A diet high in saturated fats might result in high blood levels of cholesterol, which can lead to heart problems. Plants are the main source of unsaturated fats. They are not associated with heart disease, although excessive consumption of any type of fat can lead to weight gain.

A general rule is that saturated fats are solid and unsaturated fats are liquid at room temperature. The olive oil in **Figure 8** contains less saturated fat than the butter, which is why the olive oil is liquid at room temperature. Fats are digested in the small intestine and broken down into fatty acids and glycerol. Fatty acids can be absorbed through the villi and circulated in the blood throughout the body.

Proteins

You have learned that proteins are basic structural components of all cells, and that amino acids are the building blocks of proteins. Enzymes, hormones, neurotransmitters, and membrane receptors are just a few important proteins in the body.

During the process of digestion, proteins in foods are broken down to their subunit amino acids. The amino acids are absorbed into the bloodstream and carried to various body cells. These body cells, through the process of protein synthesis, assemble the amino acids into proteins needed for body structures and functions.

Humans require 20 different amino acids for protein synthesis. The human body can produce 12 of the 20 amino acids needed for cellular function. Essential amino acids are the eight amino acids that must be included in a person's diet. Animal products, such as meats, fish, poultry, eggs, and dairy products, are sources of all eight essential amino acids. Vegetables, fruits, and grains contain amino acids, but no single plant food source contains all eight essential amino acids. However, certain combinations, such as the beans and rice shown in **Figure 9,** provide all of the essential amino acids.

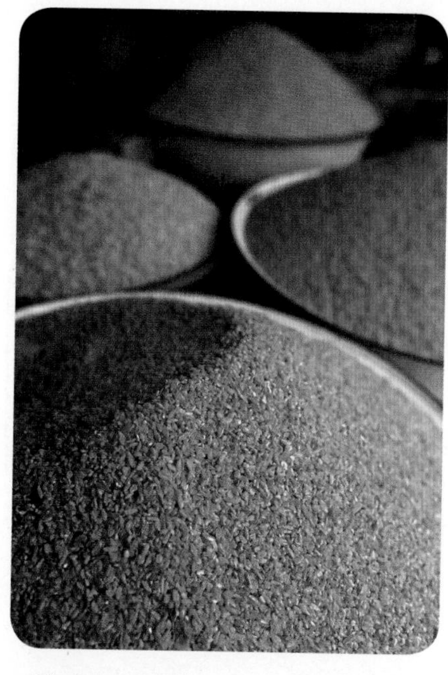

Figure 9 Beans and rice can be combined to provide all the essential amino acids.
Explain ***why it is important to eat foods that contain the essential amino acids.***

MyPlate

In 2011, the United States Department of Agriculture published a new nutrition guide, MyPlate, shown in **Figure 10**. MyPlate replaces the food pyramid, which had been a symbol of good nutrition since 1992. MyPlate emphasizes the ratios of food groups rather than exact serving sizes. It recommends that a person eat about 30 percent grains, 30 percent vegetables, 20 percent fruits, 20 percent protein, with a small side of dairy such as a yogurt cup or glass of skim milk.

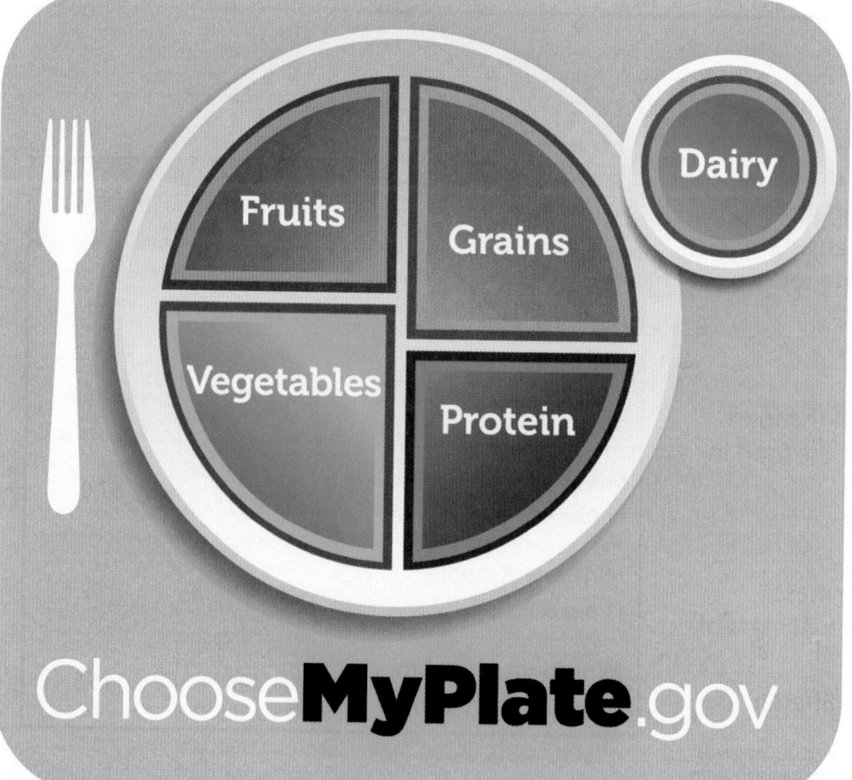

Figure 10 MyPlate can help you choose the foods and the amounts of those foods that are right for you.

(t)Jodi Cobb/National Geographic Stock, (b)USDA

Vitamins and Minerals

In addition to carbohydrates, fats, and proteins, your body needs vitamins and minerals to function properly. **Vitamins** are organic compounds that are needed in small amounts for metabolic activities. Many vitamins help enzymes function properly. Some vitamins are produced within the body. Vitamin D is made by cells in your skin. Some B vitamins and vitamin K are produced by bacteria living in the large intestine. However, sufficient quantities of most vitamins cannot be made by the body, but a well-balanced diet can provide the vitamins that are needed. Some vitamins that are fat-soluble can be stored in small quantities in the liver and fatty tissues of the body. Other vitamins are water-soluble and cannot be stored in the body. Foods providing an adequate level of these vitamins should be included in a person's diet on a regular basis.

CAREERS IN BIOLOGY

Registered Dietician A registered dietician addresses a variety of health issues by showing patients how to make healthful decisions about their diets.

Minerals are inorganic compounds used by the body as building materials, and they are involved with metabolic functions. For example, the mineral iron is needed to make hemoglobin. Recall that oxygen binds to hemoglobin in red blood cells and is delivered to body cells as blood circulates in the body. Calcium, another mineral, is an important component of bones.

Virtual Lab 

Vitamins and minerals are essential parts of a healthy diet. **Table 3** on the next page lists some important vitamins and minerals, their benefits, and some food sources that can provide these necessary nutrients. Over-the-counter vitamins are also available. Taking more than the recommended daily allowance, however, can be dangerous and should not be done without consulting a doctor.

Data Analysis LAB 1

Based on Real Data*

Compare Data

How reliable are food labels? In a study conducted at the U.S. Department of Agriculture Human Nutrition Research Center, scientists measured the mass of 99 single-serving food products.

Data and Observations

The table compares the mass listed on the food package label with the actual mass of the food in five single-serving packages.

Food (1 serving)	Label Mass (g)	Actual Mass (g)
Cereal, bran flakes with raisins (1 box)	39	54.2
Cereal, toasted grains with supplement (1 box)	23	39.6
Cookie, chocolate sandwich (1 pkg)	57	67.0
Mini danish, apple (1 per serving)	35	44.8
Mini donut, chocolate covered (4 per serving)	100	116.5

Think Critically

1. **Calculate** the percent difference in mass between the label mass and the actual mass of the cookies.
2. **Compare** the trend in the percent differences.

*Data obtained from: Conway, J.M., D.G. Rhodes, and W.V. Rumpler. 2004. Commercial portion-controlled foods in research studies: how accurate are label weights? *Journal of the American Dietetic Association* 104: 1420–1424.

Table 3 Major Roles of Some Vitamins and Minerals — Interactive Table

Vitamin	Major Role in the Body	Possible Sources	Mineral	Major Role in the Body
A	• Vision • Health of skin and bones		**Ca**	• Strengthening of teeth and bone • Nerve conduction • Contraction of muscle
D	• Health of bones and teeth		**P**	• Strengthening of teeth and bone
E	• Strengthening of red blood cell membrane		**Mg**	• Synthesis of proteins
Riboflavin (B_2)	• Metabolism		**Fe**	• Synthesis of hemoglobin
Folic Acid	• Formation of red blood cells • Formation of DNA and RNA		**Cu**	• Synthesis of hemoglobin
Thiamine	• Metabolism of carbohydrates		**Zn**	• Healing of wounds
Niacin (B_3)	• Metabolism		**Cl**	• Balance of water
Pyridoxine (B_6)	• Metabolism of amino acids		**I**	• Synthesis of thyroid hormone
B_{12}	• Formation of red blood cells		**Na**	• Nerve conduction • Balance of pH
C	• Formation of collagen		**K**	• Nerve conduction • Contraction of muscle

■ **Figure 11** Notice how many servings are in each food container. The percent daily values are based on an individual serving, not the entire package.

C. Sherburne/PhotoLink/Getty Images

Nutrition Labels

Nutrition labels are provided on commercially packaged foods like those shown in **Figure 11.** These labels are based on a 2000-Calorie-per-day diet. Labels can be especially useful for monitoring fat and sodium intake, which are two nutrients that need to be consumed in moderation. The FDA requires that food labels list the following information.

- name of the food
- net weight or volume
- name and address of manufacturer, distributor, or packager
- ingredients
- nutrient content

REVIEW IT! Nutrition

Section Summary

- The energy content of food is measured in Calories.
- Carbohydrates, fats, and proteins are three major groups of nutrients.
- Carbohydrates are a major source of energy for the body.
- Fats and proteins provide energy and are important building blocks for the body.
- Vitamins and minerals are essential for proper metabolic functioning.
- The *MyPyramid Plan* and food labels are tools that you can use to eat healthfully.

Self Check

Understand Main Ideas

1. MAINIDEA **Explain** the roles of vitamins and minerals in the process of maintaining homeostasis.
2. **Describe** what proteins, carbohydrates, and fats are used for in the process of digestion.
3. **Recommend** what nutrients a vegetarian should add to his or her diet.
4. **Explain** why keeping a count of Calories consumed and Calories used is important in maintaining proper functioning of the body.

Think Critically

5. **Summarize** how many Calories you consume during one day by recording everything you eat or drink. Compare this to how many Calories you burn in an average day.

WRITING IN ▶ Biology

6. Write a short article for your school newspaper describing what is needed for a well-balanced diet.

3 The Endocrine System

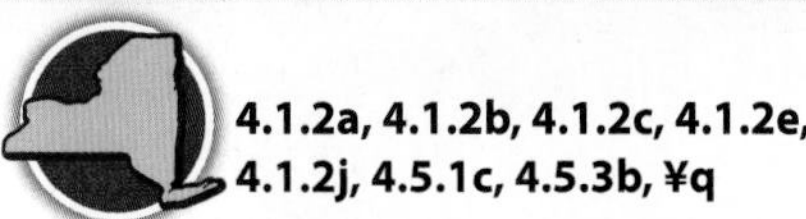

4.1.2a, 4.1.2b, 4.1.2c, 4.1.2e, 4.1.2j, 4.5.1c, 4.5.3b, ¥q

MAIN IDEA
Systems of the human body are regulated by hormonal feedback mechanisms.

Essential Questions

- What are the functions of the glands that make up the endocrine system?
- What is the role of the endocrine system in maintaining homeostasis?
- What are the feedback mechanisms that regulate hormone levels in the body?

BIOLOGY 4U
When driving a car, everyone usually maintains a similar speed. When cars go faster or slower than the accepted speed, the chance of an accident increases. Similarly, hormones must stay in the proper balance to maintain homeostasis in the body.

Review Vocabulary

homeostasis: the regulation of an organism's internal environment to maintain life

New Vocabulary

endocrine gland
hormone
pituitary gland
thyroxine
calcitonin
parathyroid hormone
insulin
glucagon
aldosterone
cortisol
antidiuretic hormone

Multilingual eGlossary

Action of Hormones

The endocrine system is composed of glands and functions as a communication system. **Endocrine glands** produce hormones, which are released into the bloodstream and distributed to body cells. A **hormone** is a substance that acts on certain target cells and tissues to produce a specific response. Hormones are classified as steroid hormones and nonsteroid or amino acid hormones, based on their structure and mechanism of action.

Steroid hormones Estrogen and testosterone are two examples of steroid hormones. Both of these hormones affect the human reproductive system. All steroid hormones work by causing the target cells to initiate protein synthesis, as illustrated in **Figure 12.**

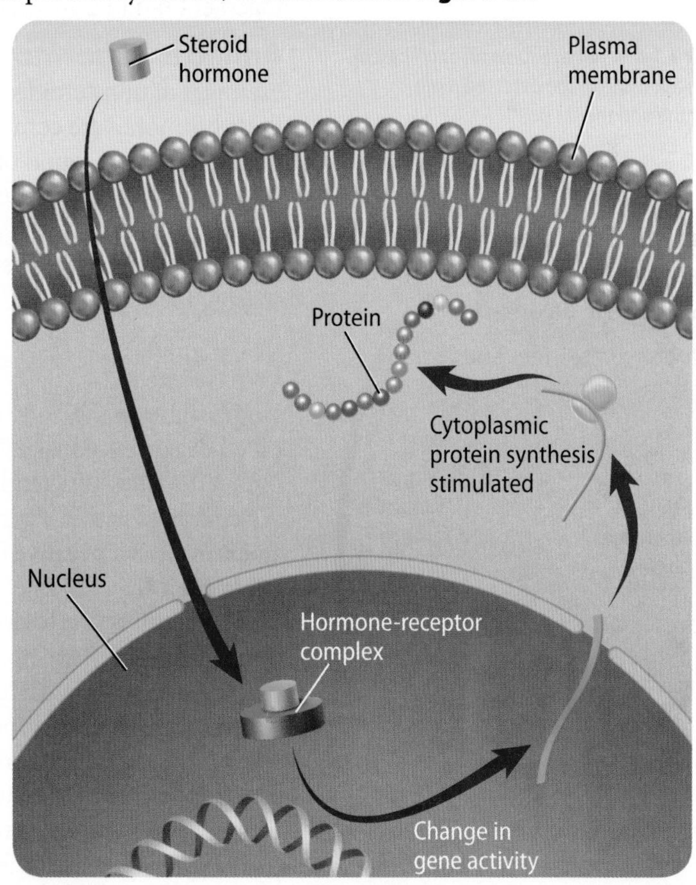

Figure 12 A steroid hormone passes through a cell membrane, binds to a receptor within the cell, and stimulates protein synthesis.

Animation

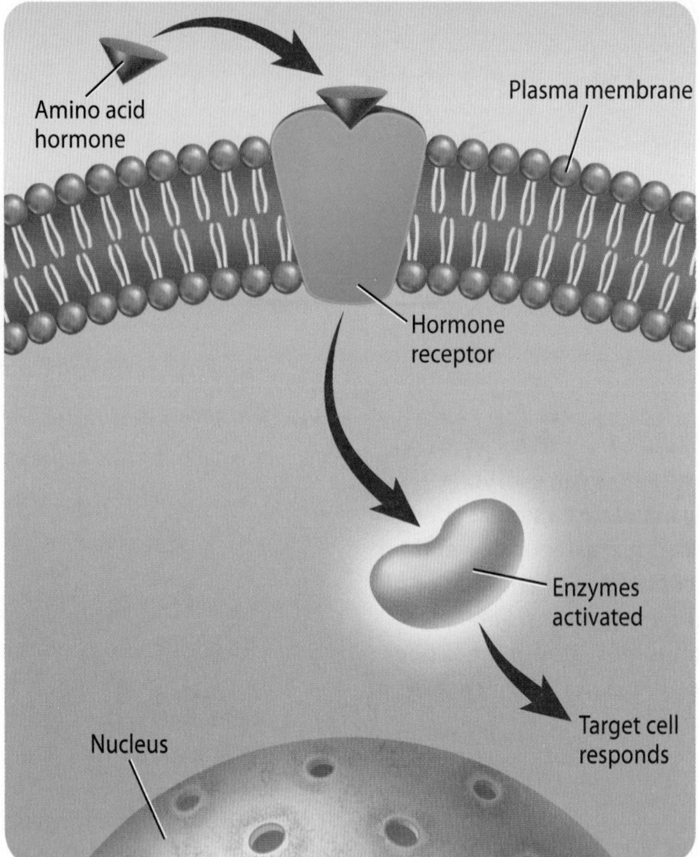

■ **Figure 13** An amino acid hormone binds to a receptor on the plasma membrane before entering the cell.

Explain ***the difference between amino acid hormones and steroid hormones.***

Animation

Steroid hormones are soluble in lipids and therefore can diffuse through the plasma membrane of a target cell. Once inside a target cell, they bind to a receptor in the cell. The hormone and the receptor that are bound together bind to DNA in the nucleus, which activates specific genes.

Amino acid hormones Insulin and growth hormones are two examples of nonsteroid, or amino acid, hormones. As the name implies, these hormones are composed of amino acids. Amino acid hormones must bind to receptors found on the plasma membrane of a target cell because they cannot diffuse through the plasma membrane. Once the hormone binds to the receptor, the receptor activates an enzyme found on the inside of the membrane. This usually initiates a biochemical pathway, eventually causing the cell to produce the desired response, as illustrated in **Figure 13.**

Negative Feedback

Homeostasis in the body is maintained by internal feedback mechanisms called negative feedback. Negative feedback returns a system to a set point once it deviates sufficiently from that set point. As a consequence, the system varies within a particular range. You already might be familiar with an example of a negative feedback system in your own home, as illustrated in **Figure 14.**

For example, the temperature in a house might be maintained at 21°C. The thermostat in the house detects the temperature, and when the temperature drops below 21°C, the thermostat sends a signal to the heat source, which turns it on and produces more heat. Soon the temperature rises above 21°C, and the thermostat sends a signal to the heat source to shut off. The heat source will not turn on again until the room temperature drops below 21°C and is detected by the thermostat. Because this process can go on indefinitely, negative feedback often is described as a loop.

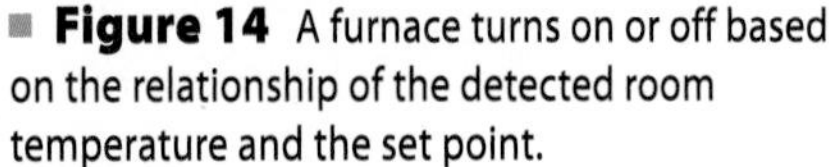
■ **Figure 14** A furnace turns on or off based on the relationship of the detected room temperature and the set point.

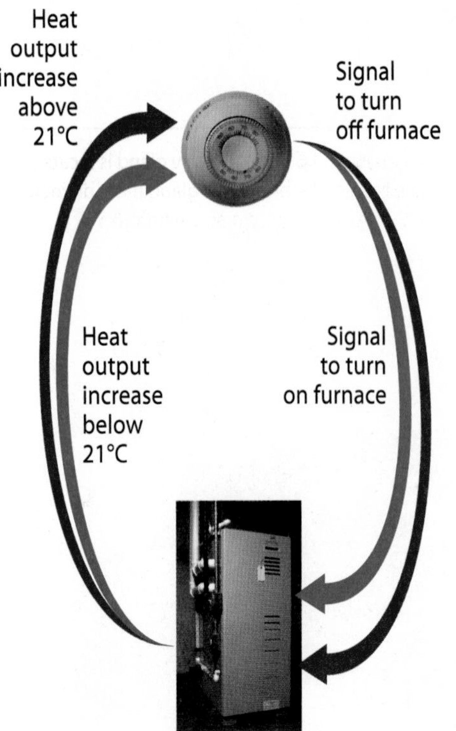

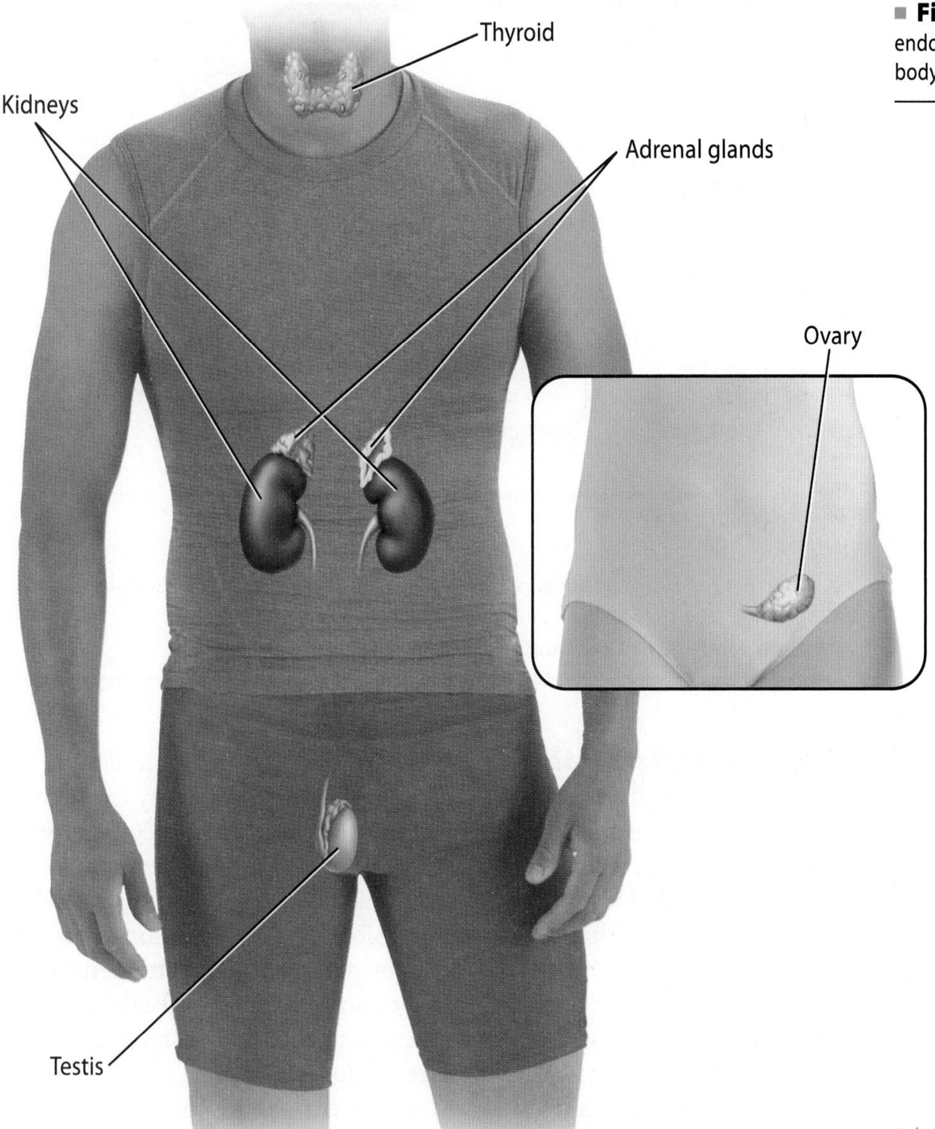

■ **Figure 15** The principal glands of the endocrine system are located throughout the body.

Endocrine Glands and Their Hormones

The endocrine system, shown in **Figure 15,** includes all the glands that secrete hormones—pituitary, thyroid, parathyroid, and adrenal glands, the pancreas, ovaries, testes, pineal gland, and the thymus gland.

Pituitary gland The pituitary gland is situated at the base of the brain, as illustrated in **Figure 16.** This gland is sometimes called the "master gland" because it regulates so many body functions. Despite its small size, it is the most important endocrine gland. The **pituitary gland** secretes hormones that not only regulate many body functions but also regulates other endocrine glands, such as the thyroid gland, the adrenal glands, the testes, and the ovaries.

A few pituitary hormones act on tissues rather than on specific organs. Human growth hormone (hGH) regulates the body's physical growth by stimulating cell division in muscle and bone tissue. This hormone is especially active during childhood and adolescence.

■ **Figure 16** The pituitary gland is located at the base of the brain. This gland has a diameter of approximately 1 cm and weighs 0.5–1 g.

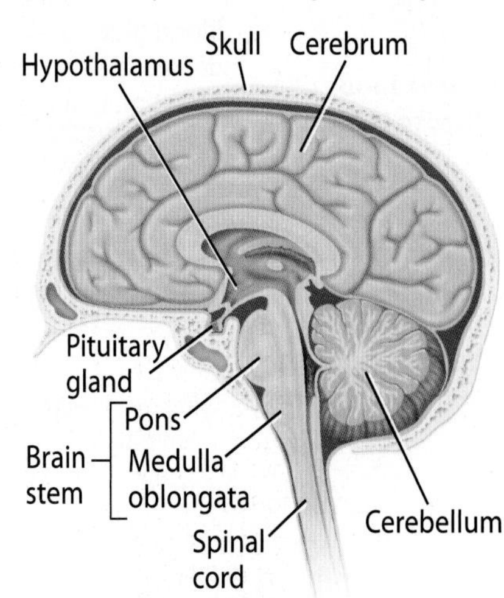

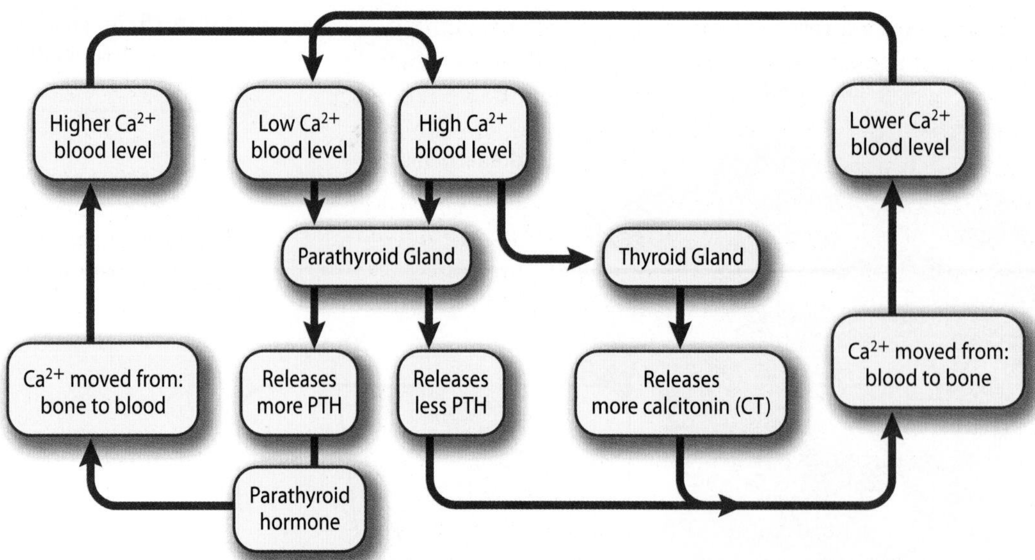

Figure 17 Parathyroid hormone (PTH) and calcitonin (CT) regulate the level of calcium in the blood.
Explain ***how PTH and CT illustrate negative feedback.***

Thyroid and parathyroid glands Identify the thyroid and parathyroid glands in **Figure 17.** One hormone produced by the thyroid gland is thyroxine. Like hGH, **thyroxine** does not act on specific organs; rather, it causes cells of the body to have a higher rate of metabolism. The thyroid gland also produces calcitonin. **Calcitonin** (kal suh TOH nun) is a hormone that is partly responsible for the regulation of calcium, an important mineral for bone formation, blood clotting, nerve function, and muscle contraction. Calcitonin lowers blood calcium levels by signaling bones to increase calcium absorption and also signaling the kidneys to excrete more calcium.

Personal Tutor

When blood calcium levels are too low, the parathyroid glands increase production of parathyroid hormone. **Parathyroid hormone** increases blood calcium levels by stimulating the bones to release calcium. The action of this hormone also causes the kidneys to reabsorb more calcium and the intestines to absorb more calcium from food. The thyroid and parathyroid glands have opposite effects on blood calcium levels. However, as they work together, they maintain homeostasis.

GET IT? **Explain** how negative feedback is important in maintaining homeostasis.

Figure 18 Glucagon and insulin work together to maintain the level of sugar in the blood.

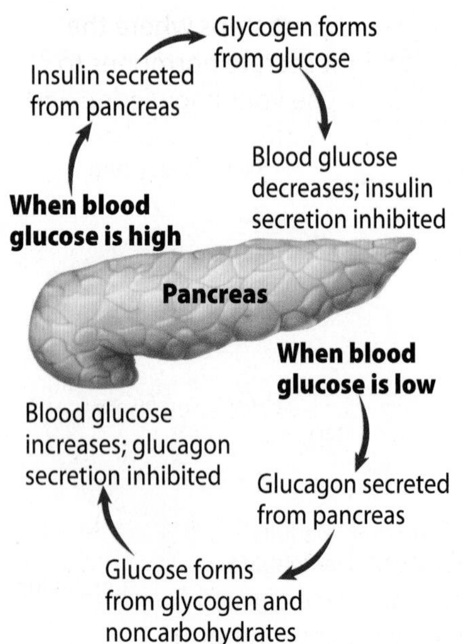

Pancreas As discussed in Section 1, the pancreas has a crucial role in the production of enzymes that digest carbohydrates, proteins, and fats. The pancreas also secretes the hormones insulin and glucagon, which work together to maintain homeostasis, as illustrated in **Figure 18.** When blood glucose levels are high, the pancreas releases insulin. **Insulin** signals body cells, especially liver and muscle cells, to accelerate the conversion of glucose to glycogen, which is stored in the liver. When blood glucose levels are low, glucagon is released from the pancreas. **Glucagon** (GLEW kuh gahn) binds to liver cells, signaling them to convert glycogen to glucose and release the glucose into the blood.

Diabetes is a disease that results from the body not producing enough insulin or not properly using insulin. Type 1 diabetes, which usually appears in people by the age of 20, occurs when the body cannot produce insulin. Type 2 diabetes occurs in 70–80 percent of people diagnosed with diabetes, and usually occurs after the age of 40. It results from the cells of the body becoming insensitive to insulin. Complications from diabetes include coronary heart disease, retinal and nerve damage, and acidosis, or low blood pH. In both types of diabetes, the blood glucose levels must be monitored and maintained to prevent complications from the disease.

Adrenal glands Refer again to **Figure 15.** The adrenal glands are located just above the kidneys. The outer part of the adrenals is called the cortex, which manufactures the steroid hormone aldosterone and a group of hormones called glucocorticoids. **Aldosterone** (al DAWS tuh rohn) primarily affects the kidneys and is important for reabsorbing sodium. **Cortisol,** another glucocorticoid, raises blood glucose levels and also reduces inflammation.

The body has different mechanisms for responding to stress, such as those concerning the role of the nervous system and the "fight or flight response." The endocrine system also is involved with these types of responses. An "adrenaline rush" occurs when there seems to be a sudden burst of energy during a stressful situation. The inner portions of the adrenal glands secrete epinephrine (eh puh NEH frun), also called adrenaline, and norepinephrine. Together, these hormones increase heart rate, blood pressure, breathing rate, and blood sugar levels, all of which are important in increasing the activity of body cells.

CAREERS IN BIOLOGY

Endocrinologist An endocrinologist studies glands that secrete hormones and the diseases involving those glands.

FOLDABLES®
Incorporate information from this section into your Foldable.

MiniLAB 2

Model the Endocrine System

How do hormones help the body maintain homeostasis? Activities such as taking a test or running a race place demands on your body. Your body's responses to these demands cause changes in your body. Your endocrine and nervous systems work together to ensure a stable internal environment.

Procedure

1. Read and complete the lab safety form.
2. Identify a sport or activity. Brainstorm what body actions occur as you prepare for, take part in, and recover from the activity.
3. Imagine that you are writing a computer program that your body will follow to complete the activity. Sequence the steps that you brainstormed in Step 2.
4. Review your program. Insert steps where the endocrine system might secrete hormones to maintain homeostasis. Use your knowledge and available resources to identify the specific hormones involved. Include body responses to these hormones as separate steps.
5. Compare your program with those developed by other students.

Analysis

1. **Think Critically** Did some of the same hormones appear in most of the other programs that you studied in Step 5? Why or why not?
2. **Draw conclusions** by describing the major body systems represented in your program. What does this show about the range of body functions controlled by the endocrine system?

VISUALIZING the Endocrine System

Figure 19 The hypothalamus maintains homeostasis by serving as a link between the nervous system and the endocrine system. The pituitary releases growth hormone, ADH, and oxytocin as needed by the body. The pituitary gland also manufactures and secretes hormones that regulate the testes, the ovaries, and the thyroid and adrenal glands.

Hypothalamus

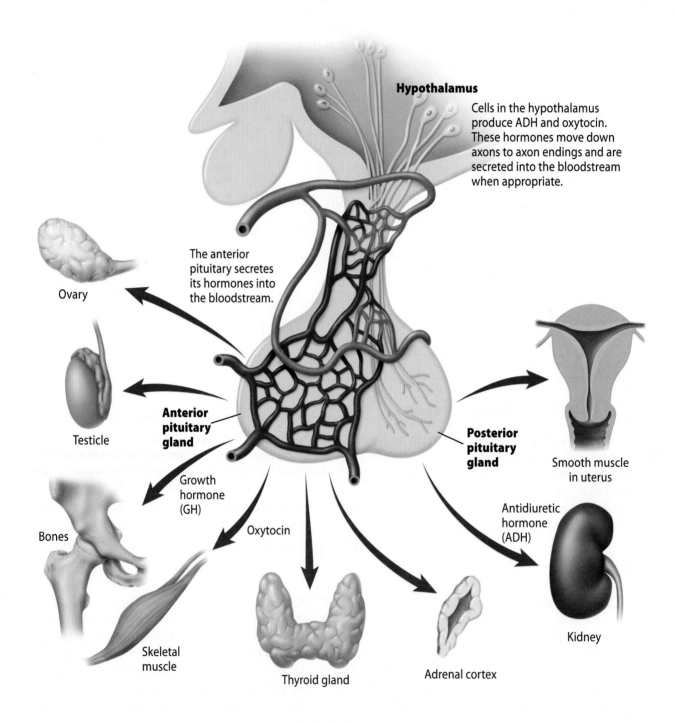

Cells in the hypothalamus produce ADH and oxytocin. These hormones move down axons to axon endings and are secreted into the bloodstream when appropriate.

The anterior pituitary secretes its hormones into the bloodstream.

Ovary

Testicle

Anterior pituitary gland

Posterior pituitary gland

Smooth muscle in uterus

Growth hormone (GH)

Bones

Oxytocin

Antidiuretic hormone (ADH)

Skeletal muscle

Thyroid gland

Adrenal cortex

Kidney

Link to the Nervous System

The nervous and endocrine systems are similar in that they both are involved in regulating the activities of the body and maintaining homeostasis. Refer to **Figure 19** to study the role of the hypothalamus in homeostasis. Recall that this part of the brain is involved with many aspects of homeostasis. The hypothalamus produces two hormones, oxytocin (ahk sih TOH sun) and antidiuretic hormone (ADH). These hormones are transported through axons and stored in axon endings located in the pituitary gland.

The **antidiuretic** (AN ti DY yuh REH tic) **hormone** (ADH) functions in homeostasis by regulating water balance. ADH affects portions of the kidneys called the collecting tubules. Think back to the last time you were working outside on a hot summer day. You produced a lot of sweat to help keep you cool, and you might have become dehydrated. When this happens, cells in your hypothalamus detect that you are dehydrated—that the level of water in the blood is low—and respond by releasing ADH from axons in the pituitary gland that have been storing the hormone.

As illustrated in **Figure 20,** ADH travels in the blood to the kidneys, where it binds to receptors on certain kidney cells. This causes the kidneys to reabsorb more water and decrease the amount of water in the urine, increasing the water level in the blood. If there is too much water in a person's blood, the hypothalamus decreases the release of ADH, and the urine tends to be more dilute. ADH production is stimulated by nausea and vomiting, both of which cause dehydration. Blood loss of 15 or 20 percent by hemorrhage results in the release of ADH.

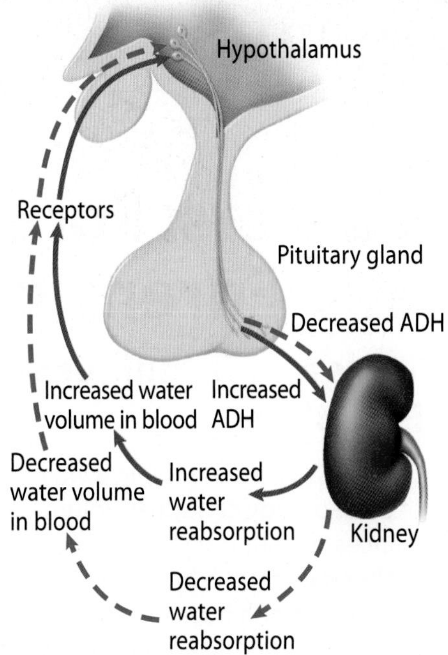

Figure 20 Antidiuretic hormone (ADH) helps to control the concentration of water in the blood.

REVIEW IT! The Endocrine System

Section Summary

- Endocrine glands produce substances called hormones.
- Hormones travel throughout the body in the bloodstream.
- Hormones are classified as steroid hormones or amino acid hormones.
- Hormone levels are influenced by feedback systems.
- The endocrine system helps to maintain homeostasis with signals from internal mechanisms called negative feedback.

Self Check

Understand Main Ideas

1. MAINIDEA **Assess** the reasons why hormone feedback systems are referred to as "negative feedback."
2. **Predict** when you would expect to find high levels of insulin in a person's blood and when you would expect to find high levels of glucagon in a person's blood.
3. **Explain** how the endocrine and nervous systems work together to maintain homeostasis.
4. **Identify** and describe the functions of pituitary, thyroid, parathyroid, pancreas, and adrenal glands.

Think Critically

5. **Research** Iodine is essential for thyroid gland function. Fetal and childhood iodine deficiency is a major cause of mental retardation in the world, yet the deficiency is preventable. Predict how iodine deficiency might lead to mental retardation or other health issues. Research what has been and what is being done to alleviate this concern. Include information about sources of iodine in your response.
6. **Analyze** how a malfunction in a negative feedback mechanism can lead to the death of an organism.

IN THE FIELD

Careers: Forensic Pathologist and Forensic Toxicologist

Tools and Techniques of Forensic Pathology

Can a dead person talk? In a way, yes. The condition of a dead body can speak volumes about the circumstances surrounding the death. Forensic pathologists gather data from a body, then analyze it to determine when and how a person died. The tools, techniques, and scientific methods that forensic pathologists use help investigators plot the last hours of a person's life, as well as the events that led to death.

Clues from an autopsy The purpose of an autopsy is to make a permanent legal record of a body's characteristics. A forensic pathologist is trained to examine victims of sudden, unexpected, or violent deaths. During an autopsy, the pathologist examines and weighs the lungs, brain, heart, liver, and stomach. He or she uses a scalpel to slice thin sections of the organs, such as the brain slice shown at the right. The slices are chemically preserved to prevent further decay.

Digestion and time of death During the autopsy, the pathologist examines the victim's stomach contents. Why is this important? At the moment of death, digestion stops. The pathologist can use the condition of the stomach to estimate a time line. If the stomach is entirely empty, the victim probably died at least three hours after he or she last ate. If the small intestine also is empty, death likely occurred at least ten hours after the last meal.

Is it possible to identify the type of food in the stomach? In some cases, yes. A scanning electron microscope can be used to identify food particles. A stomach sample that matches the last known meal also can help investigators establish a time period.

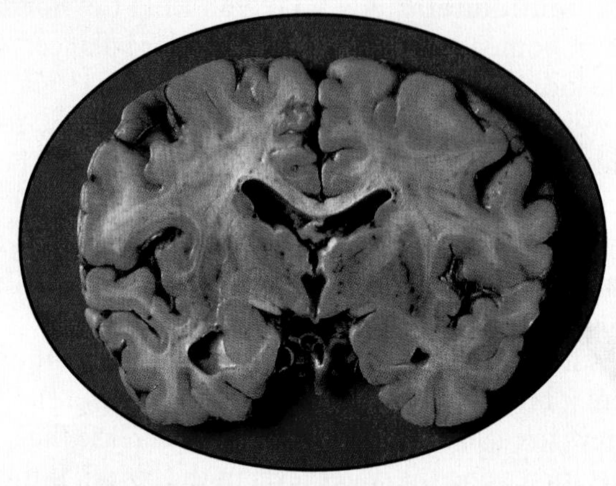

A brain slice might be used to determine a cause of death.

Stomach contents can reveal poisoning Toxic substances such as household products, poisons, and drugs can be involved in a death. A forensic toxicologist, a specialist who can identify foreign chemicals that can lead to death, might be called.

While one piece of evidence rarely serves as conclusive proof, forensic pathologists are trained to note specific details. These details can add up and sometimes help tell the story of the final hours of a person's life.

WRITING IN ▶ Biology

Classifieds Your city has an opening for a forensic pathologist. Write an advertisement for the job. Be sure to include specific techniques and procedures with which applicants should be familiar, as well as general skills and characteristics applicants should have.

WebQuest

BioLAB DESIGN YOUR OWN

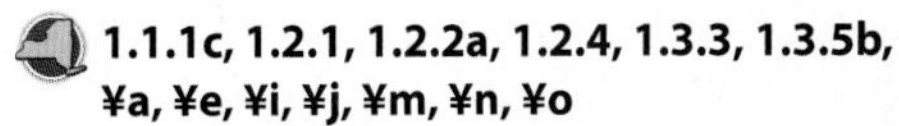

How does the rate of starch digestion compare among crackers?

Background: Starch digestion begins in the mouth. The enzyme amylase, present in saliva, catalyzes the breakdown of starch into sugar molecules, the smallest of which is glucose, an important energy source. Foods, including crackers, vary in starch content. In this lab, you will compare how quickly starch is digested in several types of crackers to determine the relative amount in each.

Question: *How does the amount of time required for starch digestion by amylase compare among various types of crackers?*

Possible Materials

variety of crackers	Bunsen burner or hot plate
mortar and pestle	graduated cylinder
test tubes and test tube rack	iodine solution
filter paper	droppers
funnels	watch glasses
balance	amylase solution
beaker	glass markers or wax pencil

Safety Precautions

WARNING: ***Iodine can irritate and will stain skin.***

Plan and Perform the Experiment

1. Read and complete the lab safety form.
2. Examine three types of crackers. Design an experiment to compare the amount of time required to digest the starch in each. You will use the enzyme amylase to stimulate the digestion of starch. Iodine, a chemical indicator that turns blue-black when starch is present, will indicate when starch digestion is complete.
3. Write a hypothesis about the rate of digestion in crackers.
4. Develop questions that compare the rate(s) of digestion among crackers.
5. Construct a data chart to record your observations.
6. Consider these points with your group and modify the plan as necessary.
   - What factors will be held constant?
   - Have you established a control sample?
   - How will you know when starch digestion is complete in each sample?
   - How will you keep constant the amount of each type of cracker tested?
   - Will the chart accommodate your data?
7. Make sure your teacher approves your plan before you proceed.
8. Carry out your experiment once appropriate equipment and technology is selected.
9. **Cleanup and Disposal** Dispose of test tube contents as directed. Clean and return glassware and equipment. Wash your hands thoroughly after handling chemicals and glassware.

Analyze and Conclude

1. **Analyze** how the amylase affected the starch in the crackers.
2. **Observe and Infer** In which cracker was starch digested most quickly? What does this indicate about the amount of starch in this cracker compared to the others?
3. **Think Critically** What variations among human mouths might affect the action of amylase on starch? Explain.
4. **Error Analysis** Did any steps in your procedure introduce uncontrolled variables into the experiment? Explain how the procedure could be redesigned to make these factors constant.

APPLY YOUR SKILL

Design an experiment to determine how varying a condition such as temperature or pH would affect the digestion of starch by amylase in one of the crackers.

CHAPTER 21 STUDY GUIDE

BIGIDEA **The digestive system breaks down food to provide energy and nutrients for the body. The endocrine system produces hormones that regulate body functions.**

SECTION 1 The Digestive System

MAINIDEA The digestive system breaks down food so nutrients can be absorbed by the body.

- The digestive system has three main functions.
- Digestion can be categorized as mechanical or chemical.
- Most nutrients are absorbed in the small intestine.
- Accessory organs provide enzymes and bile to aid digestion.
- Water is absorbed from chyme in the colon.

VOCABULARY

- **mechanical digestion**
- **chemical digestion**
- **amylase**
- **esophagus**
- **peristalsis**
- **pepsin**
- **small intestine**
- **liver**
- **villus**
- **large intestine**

SECTION 2 Nutrition

MAINIDEA Certain nutrients are essential for the proper function of the body.

- The energy content of food is measured in Calories.
- Carbohydrates, fats, and proteins are three major groups of nutrients.
- Carbohydrates are a major source of energy for the body.
- Fats and proteins provide energy and are important building blocks for the body.
- Vitamins and minerals are essential for proper metabolic functioning.
- The *MyPyramid Plan* and food labels are tools you can use to eat healthfully.

VOCABULARY

- **nutrition**
- **Calorie**
- **vitamin**
- **mineral**

SECTION 3 The Endocrine System

MAINIDEA Systems of the human body are regulated by hormonal feedback mechanisms.

- Endocrine glands produce substances called hormones.
- Hormones travel throughout the body in the bloodstream.
- Hormones are classified as steroid hormones or amino acid hormones.
- Hormone levels are influenced by feedback systems.
- The endocrine system helps to maintain homeostasis with signals from internal mechanisms called negative feedback.

VOCABULARY

- **endocrine gland**
- **hormone**
- **pituitary gland**
- **thyroxine**
- **calcitonin**
- **parathyroid hormone**
- **insulin**
- **glucagon**
- **aldosterone**
- **cortisol**
- **antidiuretic hormone**

SECTION 1

Vocabulary Review

For each set of terms, choose the one term that does not belong and explain why it does not belong.

1. esophagus, pancreas, large intestine
2. pepsin, glycogen, glucose
3. bile, amylase, peristalsis

Understand Main Ideas

4. Which action takes place in the stomach?
   A. Large fat molecules are digested into smaller molecules.
   B. Proteins are broken down.
   C. Amylase breaks down starches into smaller sugar molecules.
   D. Insulin is secreted for use in the small intestine.

5. Which row in the chart contains the words that best complete this statement? The (1) produces (2), which is secreted into the (3).

Row	1	2	3
A	liver	bile	small intestine
B	gallbladder	pepsin	stomach
C	pancreas	acid	large intestine
D	villi	amylase	mouth

   A. Row A
   B. Row B
   C. Row C
   D. Row D

6. A person complaining of digestion problems is not digesting fats well. Which is a reasonable explanation for this condition?
   A. The pyloric sphincter is blocked.
   B. The bile duct is blocked.
   C. The person is secreting excess bile.
   D. The stomach is secreting too much acid.

Use the graph to answer question 7.

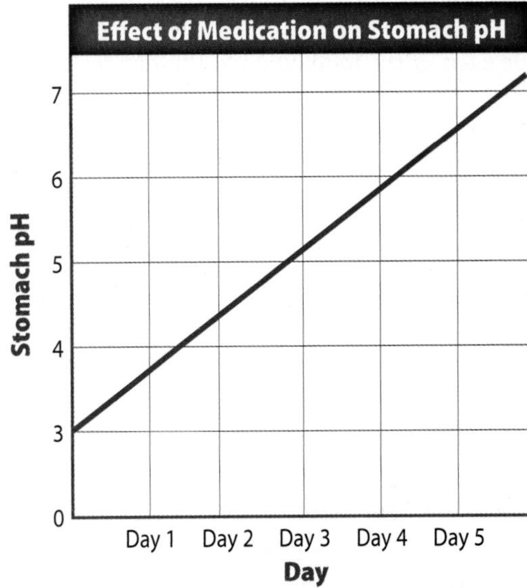

7. A person has been taking a medication for 5 days. Which of the following is likely to be a consequence of this medication?
   A. Pepsin would not be able to break down proteins.
   B. Amylase would not be able to break down starch.
   C. Bile would not be able to be produced.
   D. Enzymes secreted by the pancreas would not function well.

Constructed Response

8. **Short Answer** Explain why the term *heartburn* is an inaccurate description of this condition.

9. MAINIDEA Refer to **Table 1** to summarize the digestive processes that occur in the following structures: mouth, large intestine, stomach, small intestine, and esophagus.

10. **Open Ended** Why can a person live without a gall bladder? Assess the effects, if any, that this would have on the person's ability to digest food.

Think Critically

11. **Explain** why a drug manufacturer might add vitamin K to some antibiotics in tablet or pill form.

12. **Hypothesize** why the human body has an appendix if the appendage has no known useful function.

SECTION 2

Vocabulary Review

Describe each of the following vocabulary terms.

13. nutrition

14. vitamin

15. Calorie

Understand Main Ideas

16. Which are characteristics of saturated fats?
- **A.** liquid at room temperature and found in vegetable oils
- **B.** mostly absorbed in the large intestine
- **C.** derived from animal sources and are solid at room temperature
- **D.** tend to lower blood cholesterol

17. Which carbohydrate is not digestible and provides fiber in your diet?
- **A.** sucrose
- **B.** starch
- **C.** glycogen
- **D.** cellulose

18. Which combinations in the stomach break down high-protein foods?
- **A.** a low pH and pepsin
- **B.** a high pH and bile
- **C.** a high pH and pepsin
- **D.** a low pH and bile

Use the image below to answer question 19.

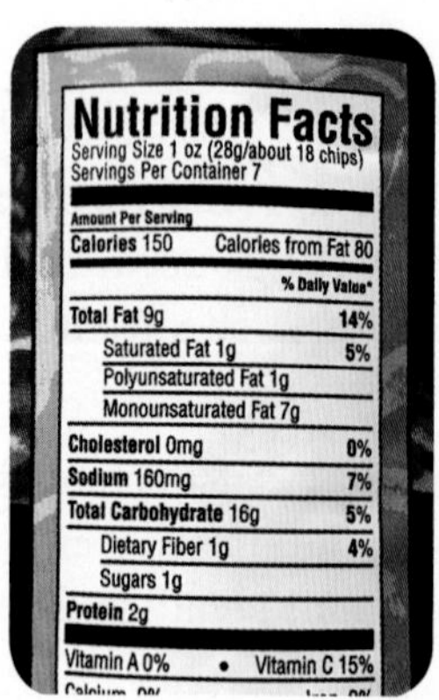

19. If you ate the entire bag of chips, what percent of the recommended daily value of saturated fat would you consume?
- **A.** 14 percent
- **B.** 28 percent
- **C.** 5 percent
- **D.** 35 percent

Constructed Response

20. **CAREERS IN ▶ Biology** According to dieticians, low-carbohydrate diets are usually high in fat and protein. Evaluate what health risks might be associated with a long-term intake of foods high in fats and proteins.

21. **MAIN IDEA** Describe what factors, besides not having enough food, might cause a person to be malnourished.

Think Critically

22. **Explain** why a diet high in fiber might reduce the chance of colon cancer.

23. **Infer** the reasons why obesity rates in the United States have continued to rise steadily for at least the past 30 years.

SECTION 3

Vocabulary Review

Explain the difference between the terms in each pair. Then explain how the terms are related.

24. insulin, glucagon

25. estrogen, growth hormone

26. cortisol, epinephrine

Understand Main Ideas

Use the graph below to answer question 27.

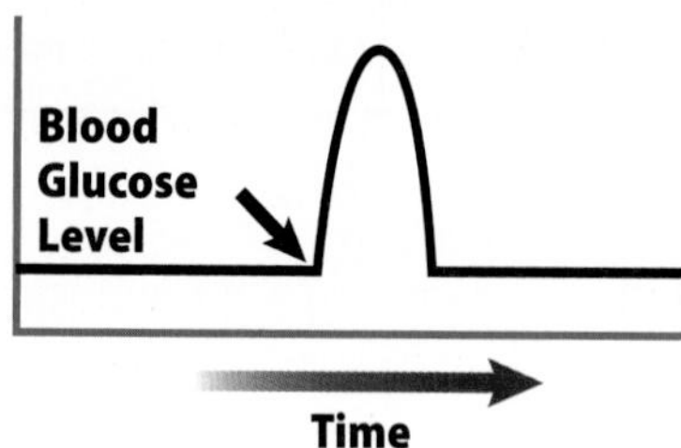

27. The graph shows blood glucose levels over a period of time. Which hormone might have caused a sudden surge as indicated by the arrow?
- **A.** antidiuretic hormone
- **B.** growth hormone
- **C.** glucagon
- **D.** insulin

28. Which hormones are released from nerve cells rather than from endocrine glands?
   A. antidiuretic hormone and oxytocin
   B. growth hormone and thyroxine
   C. insulin and glucagon
   D. norepinephrine and epinephrine

29. Which pairs of hormones have opposite effects?
   A. calcitonin and parathyroid hormone
   B. epinephrine and norepinephrine
   C. growth hormone and thyroxine
   D. aldosterone and cortisol

Use the photos below to answer question 30.

A.

B.

30. Which person is likely to have high levels of epinephrine?
   A. person A
   B. person B
   C. both persons
   D. neither person

Constructed Response

31. **THEME FOCUS** What would be the direct effect of overproduction of calcitonin? Analyze how this might disrupt homeostasis in systems other than the endocrine system.

32. **Short Answer** Assess how the long-term use of cortisol would impact a person's ability to fight infection.

Think Critically

33. **MAIN**IDEA Create an analogy using a balance describing the relationship between calcitonin and parathyroid hormone.

34. **Hypothesize** Why is insulin usually injected instead of taken orally?

Summative Assessment

35. **BIG**IDEA Breakfast is considered the most important meal of the day. Based on MyPlate, plan a balanced breakfast and explain why the nutrients are important. Then describe the processes that will take place in your digestive and endocrine systems after you have eaten. Why is breakfast so important?

36. **WRITING IN ▶ Biology** This chapter began with a situation where you were eating a pizza. Write a short story describing the events that occur as the food moves through your digestive tract. *Hint: Be sure to include all major groups of nutrients.*

DBQ Document-Based Questions

Source: *Dietary Guidelines for America* 2005

Estimated Calorie Requirements in Gender and Age Groups

Gender	Age	Moderately Active	Active
Female	9–13	1600–2000	1800–2200
	14–18	2000	2400
	19–30	2000–2200	2400
	31–50	2000	2200
	51+	1800	2000–2200
Male	9–13	1800–2200	2000–2600
	14–18	2400–2800	2800–3200
	19–30	2600–2800	3000
	31–50	2400–2600	2800–3000
	51+	2400	2400–2800

37. According to the chart, which gender needs more Calories?

38. Describe the general trend regarding the number of Calories needed to maintain energy balance in relation to age.

39. Why do individuals in the 19–30-year-old group need the most Calories?

CUMULATIVE

MULTIPLE CHOICE

1 What is the function of melanin in the epidermis?

A to protect tissue from ultraviolet radiation

B to provide support for blood vessels

C to stimulate the growth of hair in the follicles

D to waterproof and protect the skin surface

2 Which process happens first in a nerve cell when a stimulus reaches its threshold?

A Potassium channels in the cell membrane open.

B Neurotransmitters are released into the synapse.

C Sodium ions move into the nerve cell.

D The cell becomes negatively charged.

Use the diagram below to answer question 3.

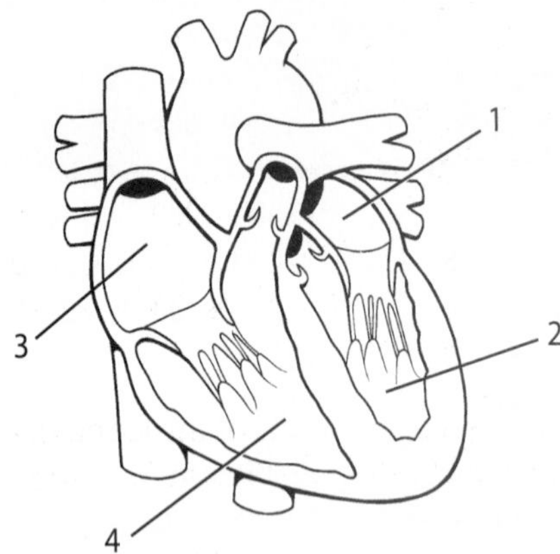

3 Which is the path that blood follows as it flows through the heart immediately after returning from the head and body?

A 1 → 2

B 2 → 1

C 3 → 4

D 4 → 3

SHORT ANSWER

Use the graph below to answer questions 4 and 5.

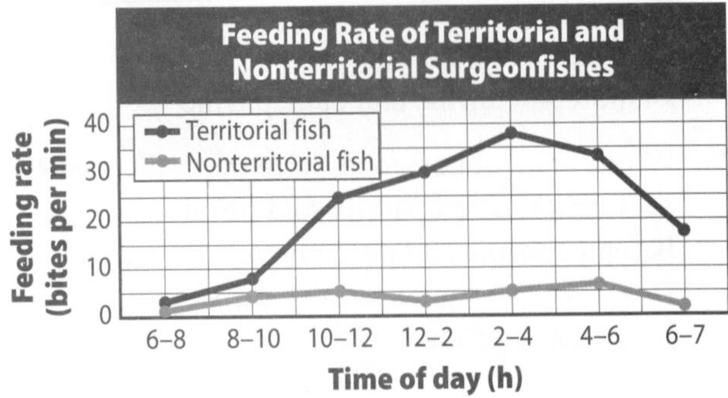

4 Compare and contrast the feeding behavior of the fishes shown in the graph.

5 Predict how the graph might appear if the territorial fish showed territorial behavior only during one season of the year.

6 Assess why a diet with no protein would be unhealthy.

7 What are two benefits to the young of mammals in receiving milk from their mothers?

8 Explain how the different body structures in roundworms and annelids enable them to move.

9 A person who exercises in extreme heat can lose salts that contain potassium and sodium through his or her sweat. What can you infer about the effect of overexertion on the nervous system?

10 Differentiate the three main vessels through which blood flows as it goes from the heart through the body and returns to the heart.

EXTENDED RESPONSE

11 Evaluate how a swim bladder helps a fish maintain its depth.

12 Evaluate how high blood pressure and kidney damage could be related.

13 Name three components of sympathetic stimulation, and assess how they could be helpful to a human's survival.

ESSAY QUESTION

Humans need vitamin C in their diets because it strengthens the function of the immune system and prevents a disease called scurvy. Vitamin C is water-soluble, so it is not stored in the body. Vitamin C is often suggested for someone who is just getting sick or is already sick. Some people recommend taking very high doses of vitamin C, sometimes even thousands of times higher than the recommended dose. Medical researchers disagree about the effectiveness of taking large doses of vitamin C. Some think that it does nothing, while others think that it is helpful. However, almost all medical researchers agree that taking large doses of vitamin C for short periods of time is probably not harmful.

Using the information in the paragraph above, answer the following question in essay format.

14 Formulate a hypothesis about whether taking large doses of vitamin C for a cold is helpful. Explain one way this hypothesis could be tested.

TEST PRACTICE

Use the diagram below to answer questions 15 and 16.

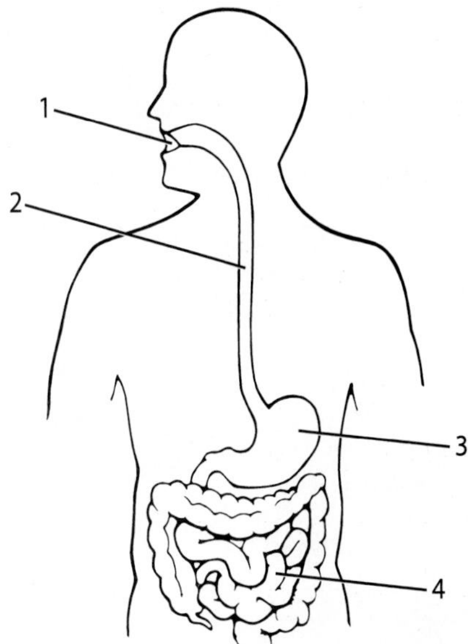

15 In which part of the digestive system do chemical and mechanical digestion first occur?

A 1

B 2

C 3

D 4

16 Which describes how filtering occurs in the excretory system?

A Blood enters nephrons of the kidneys, and excess water and wastes are filtered from the blood.

B Urine leaves the kidneys through ureters.

C Water and nutrients are absorbed back into the blood.

D Water is added to excess nitrogenous wastes from the digestive system to form urine.

NEED EXTRA HELP?																
If You Missed Question . . .	1	2	3	4	5	6	7	8	9	10	11	12	13	14	15	16
Review Section . . .	32.1	33.1	34.1	31.1	31.1	35.2	30.1	25.3	33.1	34.1	28.2	34.3	33.2	35.2	35.1	34.3

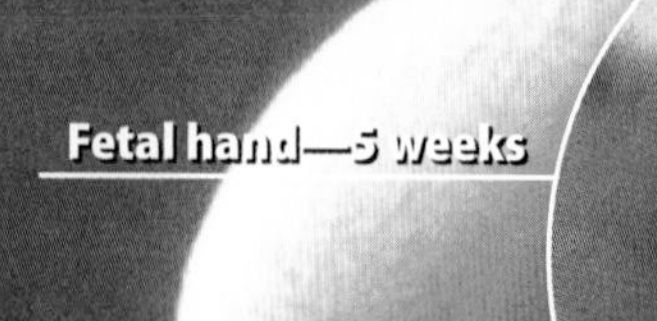

The result of the human reproductive process is the union of an egg cell and a sperm cell, development of the fetus, and the birth of an infant. The infant will go through many stages of growth throughout its life.

LaunchLAB 

Sex Cell Characteristics

How are sex cells specialized for the formation of a zygote? Reproduction is a process that follows a predictable pattern. The production of sex cells is a crucial step in reproduction. Sperm and egg cells have specific characteristics that support their roles in reproduction. In this lab, you will investigate how the design of sex cells supports their function.

CHAPTER 22

Human Reproduction and Development

1 Reproductive Systems

4.1.2a, 4.1.2b, 4.1.2e, 4.1.2j, 4.3.1c, 4.4.1c, 4.4.1e, 4.4.1f, 4.4.1g, ¥a, ¥q

2 Human Development Before Birth

4.1.2j, 4.2.1k, 4.4.1d, 4.4.1f, 4.4.1g, 4.4.1h

3 Birth, Growth, and Aging

1.3.5b, ¥o

THEMEFOCUS

Structure and function Prior to birth, cells differentiate to perform highly specialized functions.

BIGIDEA

Human reproduction involves the joining together of sperm and egg.

Egg Production

Make a two door book and label it as shown. Use it to organize your notes about sperm and egg production.

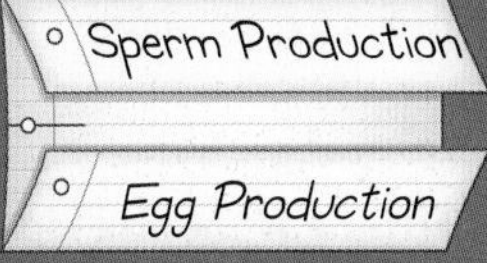

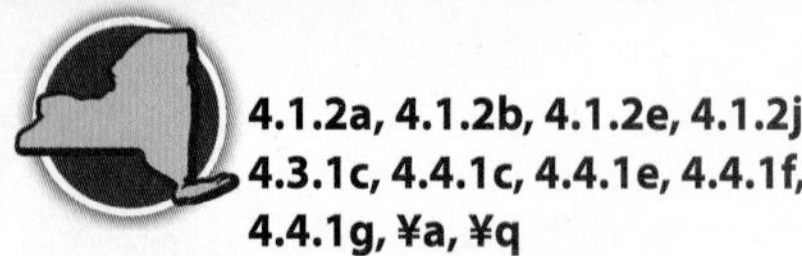

USE IT! Science Notebook

1 Reproductive Systems

4.1.2a, 4.1.2b, 4.1.2e, 4.1.2j, 4.3.1c, 4.4.1c, 4.4.1e, 4.4.1f, 4.4.1g, ¥a, ¥q

MAINIDEA

Hormones regulate human reproductive systems, including the production of gametes.

BIOLOGY 4 U

You might have noticed how the temperature of a room affects the thermostat that controls furnace activity. If the room is warm, the thermostat will not allow the furnace to run. Similarly, male and female hormones in the human body have effects on body structures and influence human reproduction.

Essential Questions

- What are the structures of the male and female reproductive systems and what are the functions of each?
- How do hormones regulate the male and female reproductive systems?
- What are the events that take place during a menstrual cycle?

Review Vocabulary

hypothalamus: portion of the brain that connects the endocrine and nervous systems, and controls the pituitary gland

New Vocabulary

seminiferous tubule
epididymis
vas deferens
urethra
semen
puberty
oocyte
oviduct
menstrual cycle
polar body

Human Male Reproductive System

Reproduction is necessary to ensure continuation of a species. The result of the human reproductive process is the union of an egg cell and a sperm cell, development of the fetus, and the birth of an infant. The organs, glands, and hormones of the male and female reproductive systems are instrumental in meeting this goal.

Figure 1 illustrates the male reproductive structures. The male reproductive glands are called the testes (tes TEEZ) (singular, testis) and are located outside of the body cavity in a pouch called the scrotum (SKROH tum). A temperature lower than 37°C—the average body temperature—is required for the development of sperm. Because the scrotum is located outside of the body cavity, it is several degrees cooler. This makes the environment suitable for the normal development of sperm.

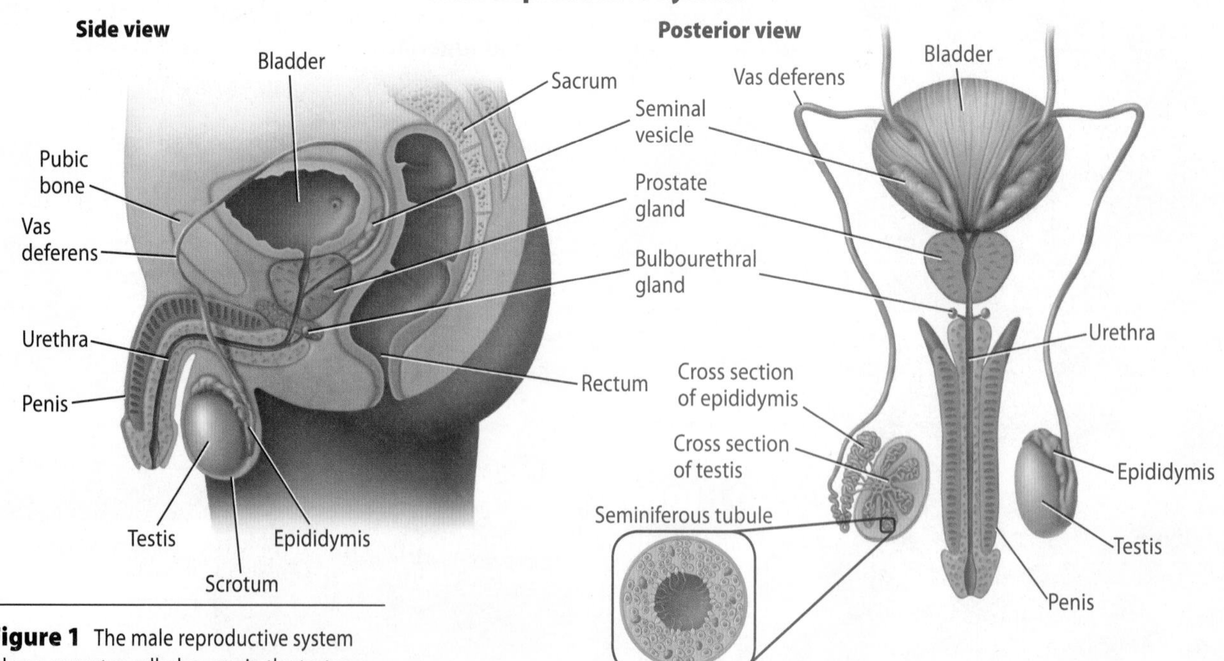

■ **Figure 1** The male reproductive system produces gametes called sperm in the testes.

Sperm cells The male reproductive cells, called sperm cells, are produced in the testes. Follow the path that sperm travel in **Figure 1** as you read about the structures in the male reproductive system. Sperm, like the one shown in **Figure 2,** develop in the testes in the **seminiferous tubules** (se muh NIHF rus • TEW byulz). These tubules produce 100–200 million sperm each day. Next, sperm travel to the **epididymis** (eh puh DIH duh mus), a structure located on top of each testis where sperm mature and are stored. When the sperm are released from the body, they travel through the **vas deferens** (VAS • DEF uh runz), a duct leading away from the testis. There are two vas deferens, one leading away from each testis. The two vas deferens join together and enter the **urethra** (yoo REE thruh), the tube that carries both semen and urine outside of the body through the penis.

Sperm require a nourishing fluid to survive long enough to fertilize an egg. **Semen** (SEE mun) refers to the fluid that contains sperm, the nourishment, and other fluids from the male reproductive glands. The seminal vesicles contribute over half of the semen and secrete sugar into the fluid, which provides energy, other nutrients, proteins, and enzymes for the sperm. The prostate gland and bulbourethral glands contribute an alkaline solution to the fluid to neutralize acidic conditions that sperm might encounter in the urethra and the female reproductive tract.

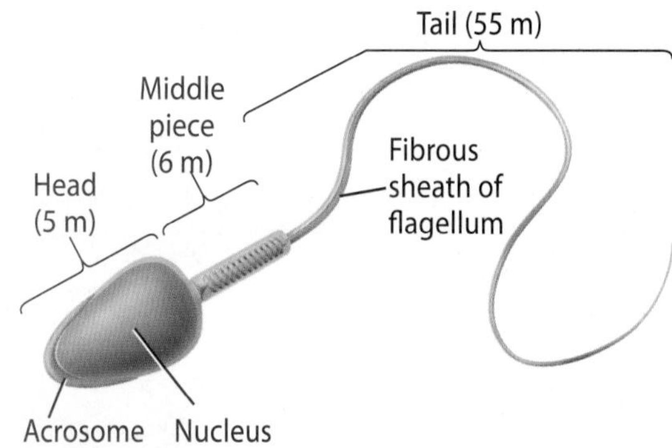

Figure 2 A sperm is a flagellated cell composed of a head, midpiece, and tail.

***Identify,** in correct sequence, the structures that a sperm cell passes through or encounters as it makes its way out of the body.*

Figure 3 The hypothalamus produces gonadotropin, the releasing hormone, which travels to the pituitary gland. GnRH influences the rate of LH and FSH production. The levels of LH and FSH are regulated by a negative feedback pathway.

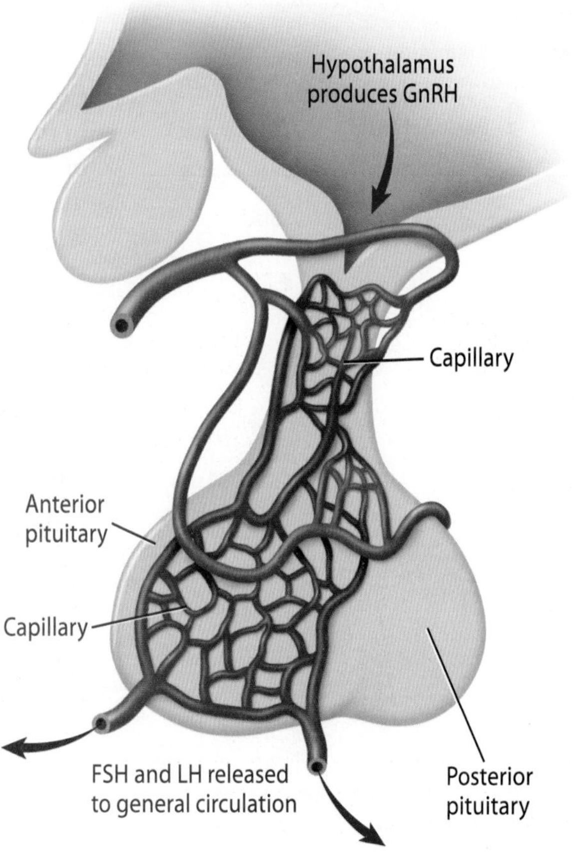

Male hormones Testosterone (tes TAHS tuh rohn), which is made in the testes, is a steroid hormone that is necessary for the production of sperm. It also influences the development of male secondary sex characteristics that begin to appear at **puberty,** the period of growth when sexual maturity is reached. These characteristics include hair on the face and chest, broader shoulders, increased muscle development, and a deeper voice. Recall that the larynx contains the vocal cords. Because the vocal cords are longer in males than in females, the male voice is deeper. Later in life, testosterone might lead to a receding hairline or baldness.

Three hormones influence testosterone production. **Figure 3** indicates that the hypothalamus produces gonadotropin-releasing hormone (GnRH), which acts on the anterior pituitary gland. GnRH increases the production of follicle-stimulating hormone (FSH) and luteinizing (LEW tee uh ni zing) hormone (LH). Both FSH and LH travel from the anterior pituitary gland through the bloodstream and to the testes. In the testes, FSH promotes the production of sperm and LH stimulates the production and secretion of testosterone.

Levels of the male hormones are regulated by a negative feedback system that starts with the hypothalamus. Increased levels of testosterone in the blood are detected by cells in the hypothalamus and anterior pituitary, and the production of LH and FSH is decreased. When testosterone levels in the blood drop, the body responds by making more LH and FSH, as shown in **Figure 3.**

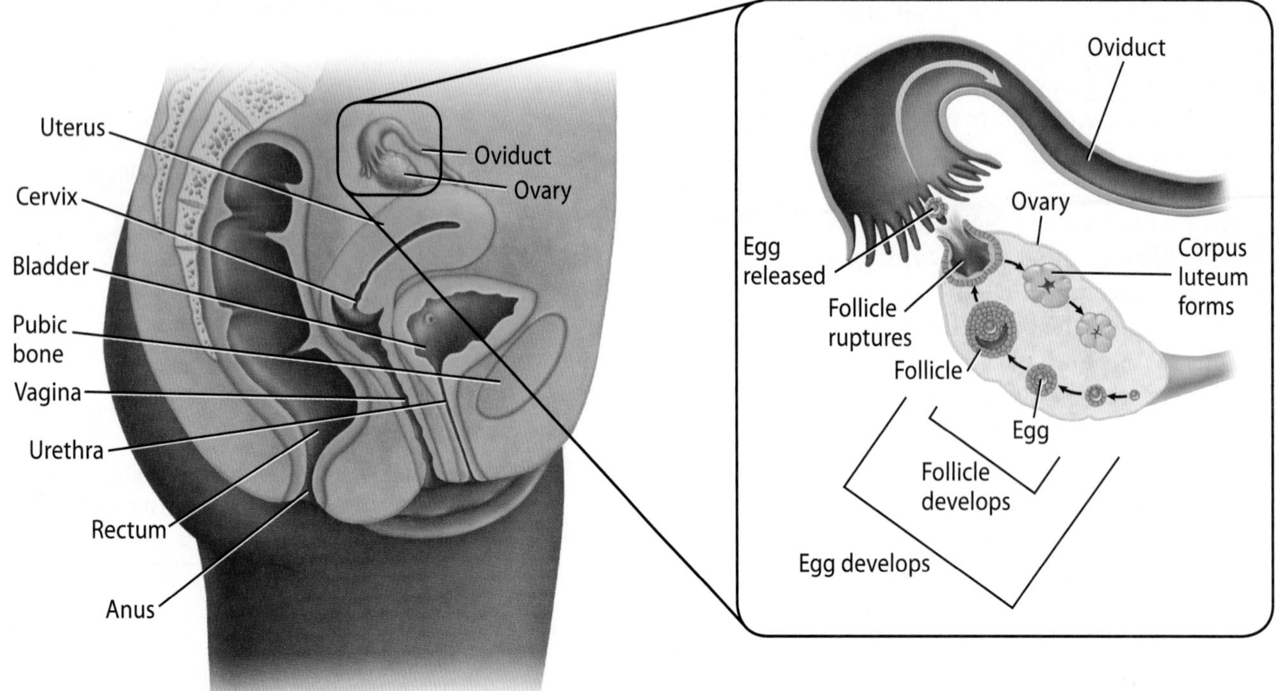

Figure 4
Left: The main structures of the female reproductive system are the vagina, uterus, and ovaries.
Right: During every menstrual cycle, one follicle fully matures and releases an egg. The follicle is then called the corpus luteum.

Predict ***what the result might be if more than one follicle fully develops during a cycle.***

 **Animation**

 **Personal Tutor**

Human Female Reproductive System

A female's reproductive system is specialized to produce egg cells, receive sperm, and provide an environment that is right for fertilization of an egg and the development of an embryo. Refer to **Figure 4** as you read about the structures of the female reproductive system.

Egg cells The female reproductive cells, called egg cells, are produced in the ovaries, also illustrated in **Figure 4.** Each ovary is about the size of an almond. Inside each ovary are **oocytes** (OH uh sites), which are immature eggs. Approximately once every 28 days, oocyte development is stimulated and an egg, called an ovum, is formed. The ovum is surrounded by follicle cells that provide protection and nourishment.

After the egg is released from the ovary, it travels through an **oviduct** (OH vuh duct), a tube that connects to the uterus. The uterus, or womb, is about the size of an average human fist and is where a baby develops before birth. The cervix, at the lower end of the uterus, has a narrow opening into the vagina, which leads to the outside of the female's body.

Female hormones Estrogen and progesterone (proh JES tuh rohn) are steroid hormones made by cells in the ovaries. A female's anterior pituitary gland also produces LH and FSH, which influence estrogen and progesterone levels in a negative feedback loop. Effects of LH and FSH are different in males and females. During puberty, an increase in estrogen levels causes a female's breasts to develop, her hips to widen, and her amount of fat tissue to increase. During puberty, a female also will experience her first **menstrual** (MEN stroo ul) **cycle,** the events that take place each month in the human female to help prepare the female body for pregnancy.

Sex Cell Production

Through meiosis one cell in the male or female gonads—called testes and ovaries in humans—gives rise to four sex cells called gametes. In the human male, sperm are produced daily from primary spermatocytes, beginning at puberty and continuing throughout a male's lifetime.

The production of eggs in the human female differs, as illustrated in **Figure 5.** A female is born with all of her eggs already beginning to develop. The genetic material has replicated in primary oocytes before birth, and the process of meiosis stops before the first meiotic division is completed. Then, once each menstrual cycle during the reproductive years, meiosis continues for a single developing oocyte. The resulting structures at the end of the first meiotic division of the oocyte are of unequal size. The smaller of the two structures is called a **polar body.** The chromosomes have segregated, but there is an unequal division of the cytoplasm. Most of the cytoplasm from the original cell goes to the cell that eventually will become the egg, and the polar body disintegrates.

During the second meiotic division, a similar process takes place. During metaphase of the second meiotic division, an egg ruptures through the ovary wall in a process called ovulation. The second meiotic division is completed only if fertilization takes place. Then, the zygote and the second polar body are formed, as shown in **Figure 5.** The second polar body also disintegrates.

Thus, the two meiotic divisions have yielded only one egg instead of four. If four eggs were formed and released midway through a female's menstrual cycle, more multiple births would be expected.

The Menstrual Cycle

The length of the menstrual cycle can vary from 23 to 35 days, but it typically lasts around 28 days. The entire menstrual cycle can be divided into three phases: the flow phase, the follicular phase, and the luteal phase.

Flow phase Day one of the menstrual cycle is when menstrual flow begins. Menstrual flow is the shedding of blood, tissue fluid, mucus, and epithelial cells from the endometrium—the tissue that lines the uterus. The endometrium is where the embryo will implant if fertilization of the egg occurs. Because an embryo will need oxygen and nutrients, the endometrium has a good supply of blood. During menstruation, bleeding occurs because the outer layers of the endometrium tear away, and blood vessels that supply the endometrium are ruptured. Around day five, repair of the endometrial lining begins, and it becomes thicker as the cycle continues.

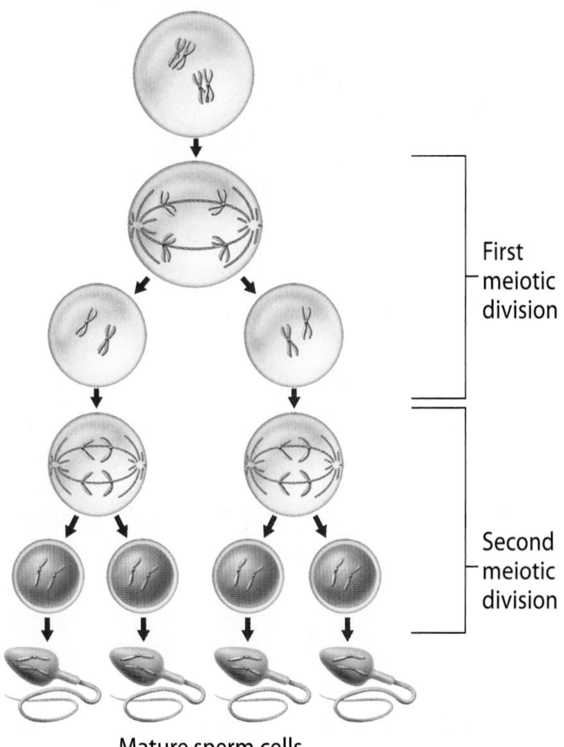

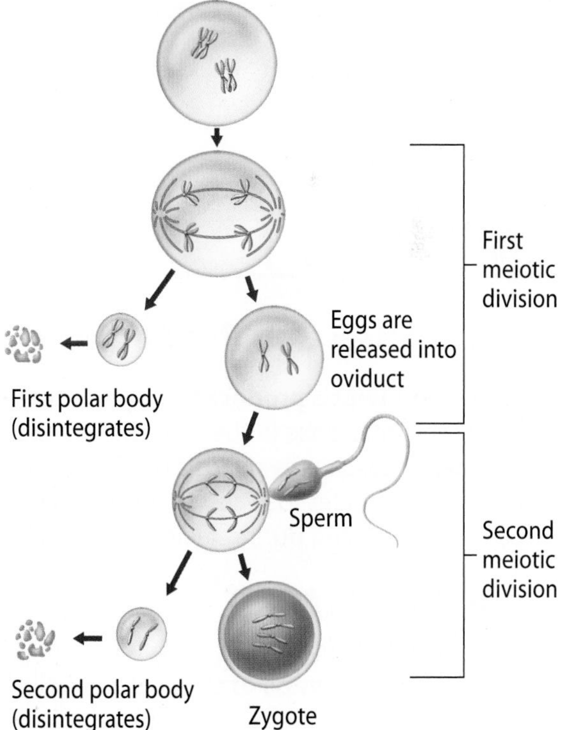

Figure 5
Top: The human male sex cell production follows the general pattern of meiosis and results in many sperm.
Bottom: Meiosis in the human female results in one egg. The second division in meiosis will not be completed in a human female unless the egg is fertilized.

LM Magnification: 10×

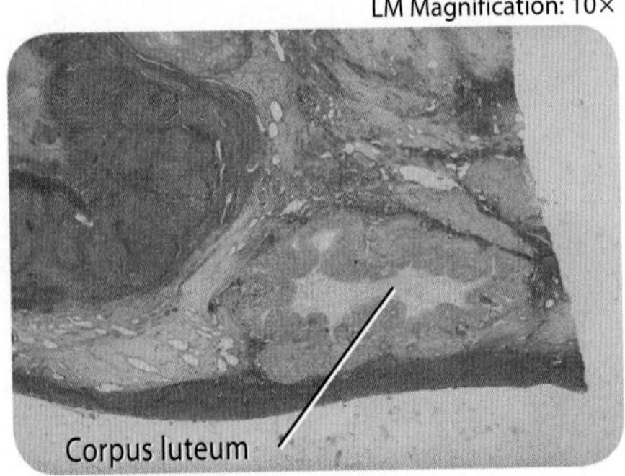

■ **Figure 6** The corpus luteum produces progesterone and some estrogen.

Follicular phase During the menstrual cycle, changes also occur in the ovaries as a result of changing hormone levels, as illustrated in **Table 1.** At the beginning of a menstrual cycle, when estrogen levels are low, the anterior pituitary begins to increase production of LH and FSH. This stimulates a few follicles to begin to mature in the ovary. Cells in the follicles then begin to produce estrogen and a small amount of progesterone. Inside each follicle is an immature egg, the oocyte. After about a week, usually only one of the growing follicles remains. This remaining follicle continues to grow and secrete estrogen, which keeps levels of LH and FSH low. This is an example of negative feedback.

On about day 12, the high level of estrogen causes the anterior pituitary gland to release a surge of LH. This rapid release of a large quantity of LH causes the follicle to rupture, and ovulation occurs.

Luteal phase After ovulation, the cells of the follicle change, and the follicle is transformed into a structure called the corpus luteum (KOR pus • LEW tee um), as illustrated in **Figure 6.** The corpus luteum slowly degenerates as the menstrual cycle continues. The corpus luteum produces high amounts of progesterone and some estrogen, which keep levels of LH and FSH low through negative feedback. Recall that FSH and LH stimulate new follicles to develop, but when these hormones are kept at low levels, new follicles are temporarily prevented from maturing. Toward the end of the cycle, the corpus luteum breaks down, and it no longer produces progesterone and estrogen. This results in a rapid decrease in progesterone and estrogen levels. A rapid decrease in hormones triggers detachment of the endometrium, and the flow phase of a new menstrual cycle will begin.

VOCABULARY

WORD ORIGIN

Corpus luteum
corpus from Latin, meaning *body*
luteum from Latin, meaning *yellow*

MiniLAB 1

Model Sex Cell Production

Why does meiosis produce four sperm but only one egg? The difference in the division of cytoplasm is the major reason why meiosis is different in human males and females. Use clay to model how the sex cells are produced during meiosis.

Procedure

1. Read and complete the lab safety form.
2. Choose **two lumps of clay,** each of a different color. Choose one to represent a primary spermatocyte and the other a primary oocyte.
3. Use the primary spermatocyte to simulate the meiotic divisions as they occur in males.
4. Simulate maturation of the sperm by removing about half of the clay from each sperm and using a small part of it to add a flagellum to each cell.
5. Next, simulate the first meiotic division in females.
6. Use one of the sperm and mold it to one side of the large cell. Now simulate the second meiotic division.

Analysis

1. **Model** Make drawings of each step above. Label the following: primary spermatocyte and oocyte, egg, sperm, first polar body, second polar body, fertilized egg, and zygote.
2. **Explain** the benefit of meiosis concentrating most of the cytoplasm into one egg.

Table 1 Menstrual Cycle Phases Interactive Table

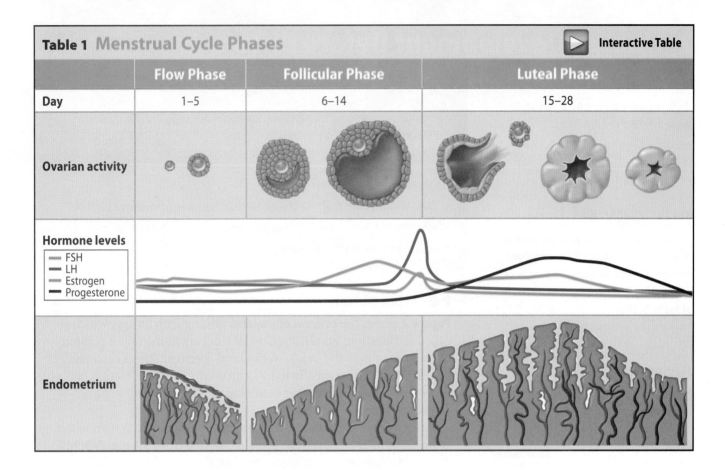

	Flow Phase	Follicular Phase	Luteal Phase
Day	1–5	6–14	15–28
Ovarian activity			
Hormone levels (FSH, LH, Estrogen, Progesterone)			
Endometrium			

If the egg is fertilized, a different chain of events occurs, and a new menstrual cycle does not begin. The progesterone levels remain high and increase the blood supply to the endometrium. The corpus luteum does not degenerate and hormone levels do not drop. The endometrium accumulates lipids and begins secreting a fluid rich in nutrients for the developing embryo.

REVIEW IT! Reproductive Systems

Section Summary

- Levels of male and female hormones are regulated by negative feedback systems.
- The human male produces millions of sperm cells every day.
- The number of sex cells resulting from meiosis differs in males and females.
- The human female has a reproductive cycle called the menstrual cycle.
- The menstrual cycle has three phases: the flow phase, the follicular phase, and the luteal phase.

Understand Main Ideas

1. MAINIDEA **Describe** how hormones regulate sperm and egg cells.
2. **Summarize** the structures of the reproductive systems and their functions.
3. **Describe** the origin and importance of substances found in semen.
4. **Explain** the major events that take place in the endometrium and in the ovary during the menstrual cycle.

Think Critically

5. **Infer** On about day 12, estrogen levels cause a sharp increase in the amount of LH that is released. According to a negative feedback model, what would you expect to happen?

MATH IN Biology

6. Suppose a female began menstruating at age 12 and stopped menstruating at age 55. If she never became pregnant and her menstrual cycles averaged 28 days, how many eggs did she ovulate during her reproductive years?

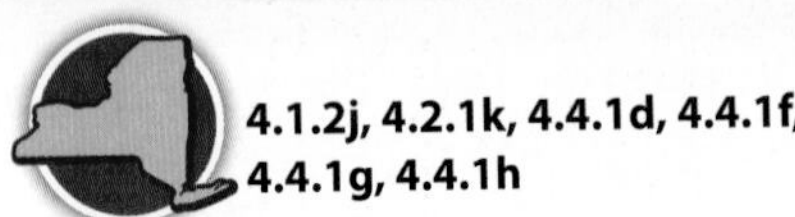

2 Human Development Before Birth

4.1.2j, 4.2.1k, 4.4.1d, 4.4.1f, 4.4.1g, 4.4.1h

MAIN IDEA

A human develops from a single fertilized cell into trillions of cells with specialized functions.

Essential Questions

- What are the events that take place during the first week following fertilization?
- What are the major changes that occur during each trimester of development?
- How are female hormone levels altered during pregnancy?

BIOLOGY 4U

Just as a single seed can grow into a plant with a beautiful flower, your complex body began as a single cell at the union of an egg and a sperm at fertilization.

Review Vocabulary

lysosome: organelle that contains digestive enzymes

New Vocabulary

morula
blastocyst
amniotic fluid

Multilingual eGlossary

BrainPOP

Fertilization

Figure 7 shows the process of a sperm joining with an egg, which is called fertilization. Fertilization usually occurs in the upper portion of an oviduct near the ovary. In humans, sperm and eggs each are haploid, and each normally has 23 chromosomes. Fertilization brings these chromosomes together, restoring the diploid number of 46 chromosomes.

Sperm enter the vagina of the female's reproductive system when strong muscular contractions ejaculate semen from the male's penis during intercourse. Some sperm can exit through the penis before ejaculation without the male's knowledge. As a result, sexual activity that does not result in ejaculation can lead to the release of sperm, fertilization, and pregnancy.

Sperm can survive for 48 hours in the female reproductive tract, but an unfertilized egg can survive for only 24 hours. Fertilization can happen if intercourse occurs anytime from a few days before ovulation to a day after ovulation. Overall, there is a relatively short time when fertilization can occur successfully. However, it is important to remember that the length of the menstrual cycle can vary and ovulation can occur at any time.

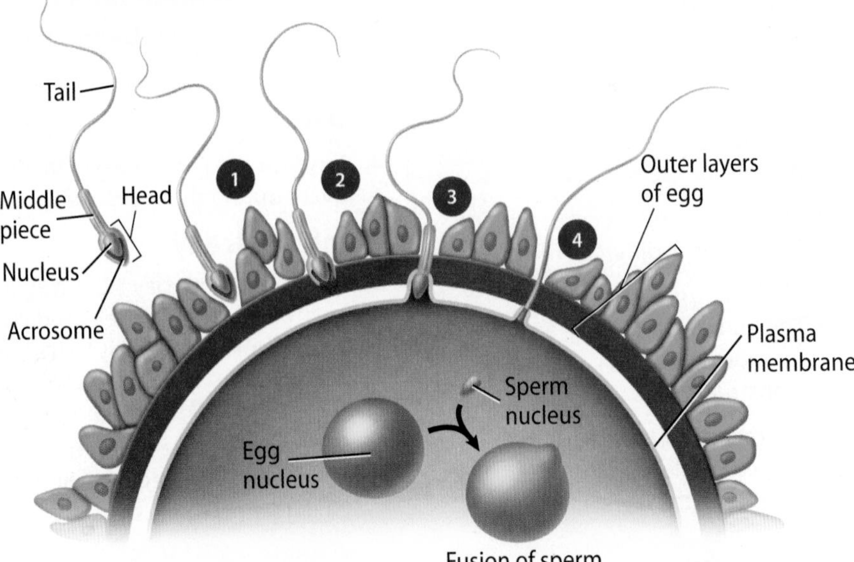

■ **Figure 7** Although many sperm are needed to weaken the barrier that surrounds the egg, only one sperm fertilizes an egg (steps 1–4). Fertilization is complete when the sperm nucleus fuses with the egg nucleus.

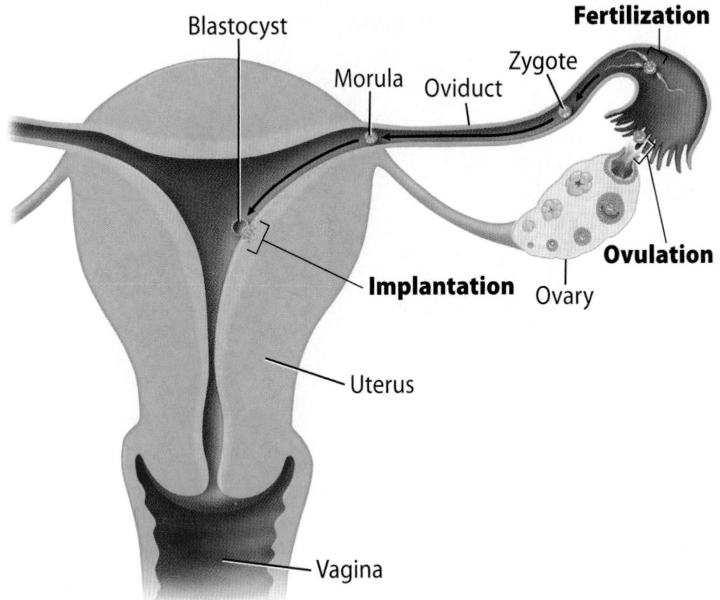

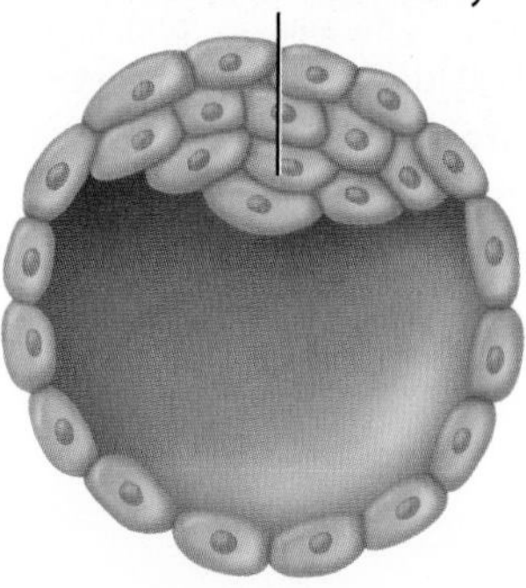

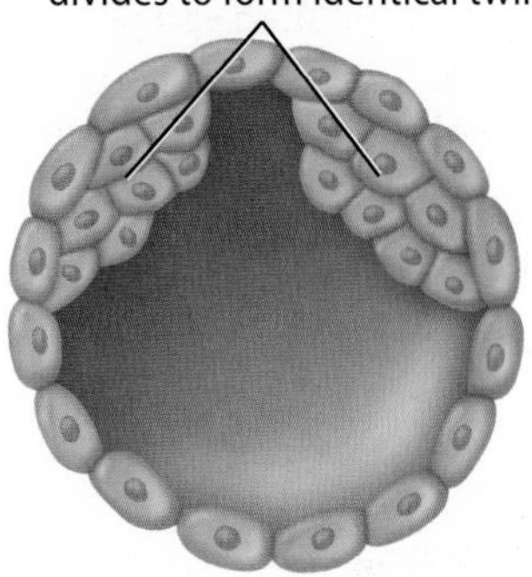

Figure 8
Left: During the first week of development, many changes occur as the zygote travels through the oviduct.
Right: The inner cell mass of the blastocyst will develop into a fetus (top). If the inner cell mass divides, identical twins might form (bottom).

About 300 million sperm are released into the vagina during intercourse. Only several hundred of them will successfully complete the journey to the egg. Many never make it through the vagina, some are attacked by white blood cells, and many simply die along the way. Only one sperm can fertilize an egg, but it takes several hundred to participate in the process.

Connection to Chemistry A single sperm cannot penetrate the plasma membrane that surrounds the human egg. Recall that lysosomes are organelles that contain digestive enzymes. Notice in **Figure 7** that the tip of each sperm is a specialized lysosome called an acrosome. As each of several hundred sperm bombard the egg, the enzymes inside of the acrosome weaken the plasma membrane surrounding the egg. Eventually the plasma membrane becomes weak enough that one sperm can penetrate the egg. Immediately following this penetration, the egg forms a barrier to prevent other sperm from entering the now-fertilized egg.

GET IT? **Explain** why hundreds of sperm are necessary for fertilization to take place.

Early Development

Figure 8 illustrates the first week of human development. The fertilized egg, which is called a zygote (ZI goht), moves through the oviduct propelled by involuntary smooth muscle contractions and by the cilia lining the oviduct. Around 30 hours after fertilization, the zygote undergoes its first mitosis and cell division. Cell division continues, and by the third day, the embryo leaves the oviduct and enters the uterus. At this point, the embryo is described as a **morula,** a solid ball of cells.

By the fifth day, the morula has developed into a **blastocyst,** which can be described as a hollow ball of cells. The blastocyst attaches to the endometrium around the sixth day and is fully implanted by day 10. **Figure 8** shows that the blastocyst is not completely hollow. Inside the blastocyst is a group of cells called the inner cell mass. The inner cell mass eventually will become the embryo. Sometimes, the inner cell mass splits, and identical twins might form.

CAREERS IN BIOLOGY

Reproductive Endocrinologist
Physicians who have advanced training in the treatment of infertility and disorders involving the reproductive hormones are called reproductive endocrinologists. A reproductive endocrinologist also might conduct research or train medical students.

■ **Figure 9** Four extraembryonic membranes—the amnion, chorion, yolk sac, and allantois—are important in development.
***Identify** the role of the yolk sac in humans.*

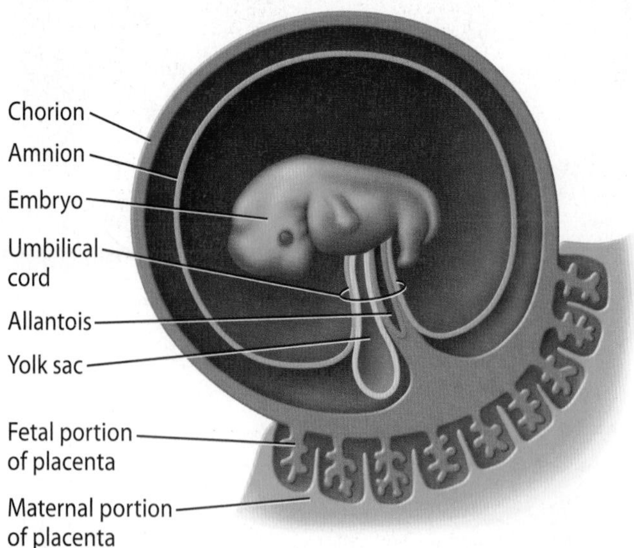

Extraembryonic membranes The membranes that extend beyond an embryo are called the extraembryonic membranes. You also might have learned about the development of the amniotic egg, and how this enabled animals to reproduce on land. Developing humans have these membranes, as shown in **Figure 9.** But because humans and most other mammals develop inside the mother's body, these membranes have somewhat different functions.

Early in human development, four extraembryonic membranes form. These membranes are the amnion, the chorion (KOR ee ahn), the yolk sac, and the allantois (uh LAN tuh wus), as illustrated in **Figure 9.** The amnion is a thin layer that forms a sac around the embryo. Inside this sac is the **amniotic fluid** (am nee AH tihk • FLU id), which protects, cushions, and insulates the embryo. Outside of the amnion is the chorion, which, together with the allantois, contributes to the formation of the placenta. The yolk sac in humans does not contain any yolk but serves as the first site of red blood cell formation for the embryo.

VOCABULARY

ACADEMIC VOCABULARY
Enable
to make able or feasible
Amniotic eggs enable reproduction on land.

The placenta About two weeks after fertilization, tiny fingerlike projections of the chorion, called chorionic villi (VIH li), begin to grow into the wall of the uterus. The placenta (pluh SEN tuh), the organ that provides food and oxygen and also removes waste, begins to form and is fully formed by the tenth week. The placenta has two surfaces—a fetal side that forms from the chorion and faces the fetus and a maternal side that forms from uterine tissue. When completely formed, the placenta is 15–20 cm in diameter, 2.5 cm thick, and has a mass of about 0.45 kg. The umbilical cord, a tube containing blood vessels, serves as the connection between the fetus and the mother. **Figure 10** illustrates the connection between the mother and fetus.

The placenta regulates what passes from the mother to the fetus and from the fetus to the mother. Oxygen and nutrients can travel from the mother to the fetus. Alcohol, drugs, various other substances, and the human immunodeficiency virus (HIV) also can pass through the placenta to the developing fetus.

Metabolic waste products and carbon dioxide travel from the fetus to the mother. Because the mother and the fetus have their own separate circulatory systems, blood cells do not pass through the placenta. However, the mother's antibodies pass to the fetus and help protect the newborn until its immune system is functioning.

STUDY TIP

TIME LINE Create a time line showing the development of a human being from fertilization to adulthood. Use average ages for various stages of development. Include major characteristics of each stage of development.

VISUALIZING a Placenta

Figure 10 A growing fetus exchanges nutrients, oxygen, and wastes with the mother through the placenta. The placenta contains tissue from both mother and fetus.

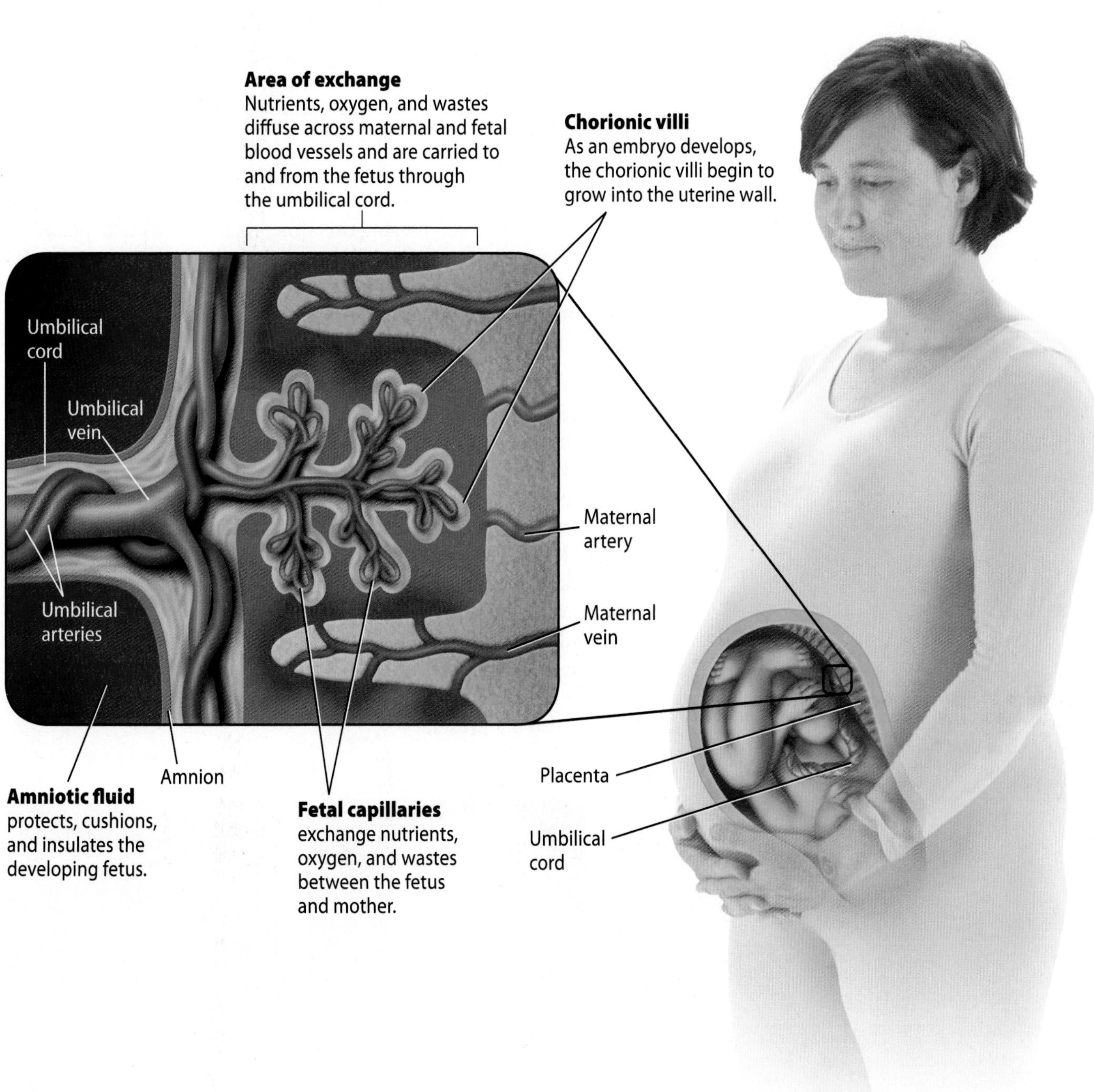

Area of exchange
Nutrients, oxygen, and wastes diffuse across maternal and fetal blood vessels and are carried to and from the fetus through the umbilical cord.
Chorionic villi
As an embryo develops, the chorionic villi begin to grow into the uterine wall.
Umbilical cord
Umbilical vein
Umbilical arteries
Maternal artery
Maternal vein
Amnion
Amniotic fluid protects, cushions, and insulates the developing fetus.
Fetal capillaries exchange nutrients, oxygen, and wastes between the fetus and mother.
Placenta
Umbilical cord

Tim Fuller

Hormonal regulation during pregnancy During the first week of development, the embryo begins to secrete a hormone, called human chorionic gonadotropin (hCG) (kor ee AH nihk • go na duh TROH pen), which keeps the corpus luteum from degenerating. If the corpus luteum remains active, progesterone levels, and to a lesser extent estrogen levels, remain high. Remember from the previous section that the decline of progesterone triggers a new menstrual cycle. If levels of these hormones remain high, a new menstrual cycle will not begin. Two to three months into development, the placenta secretes enough progesterone and estrogen to maintain the proper conditions for pregnancy.

GET IT? **Compare** two functions of the placenta.

Three Trimesters of Development

On average, human development takes around 266 days from fertilization to birth. This time span is divided into three trimesters, each around three months long. During this time, many events take place. The zygote grows from a single cell into a baby that has trillions of cells. These cells develop into tissues and organs with specialized functions. Follow **Figure 11,** which shows different stages of human development during the first trimester.

The first trimester In the first trimester, all tissues, organs, and organ systems begin to develop. During this time of development, the embryo is especially vulnerable to the effects of alcohol, tobacco, drugs, and other environmental influences, such as environmental pollutants. During the first two weeks of development, the mother might not realize that she is pregnant because she has not yet missed a menstrual period. A lack of certain essential nutrients during this time might cause irreversible damage to the developing embryo. A few of the major causes of preventable birth defects are listed in **Table 2.**

At the end of eight weeks, the embryo is called a fetus. All of the organ systems have begun to form. By the end of the first trimester, the fetus can move its arms, fingers, and toes and make facial expressions. Fingerprints also are present.

■ **Figure 11** The embryo develops into a fetus during the first trimester of pregnancy. By the end of the third month, the fetus can make small movements.

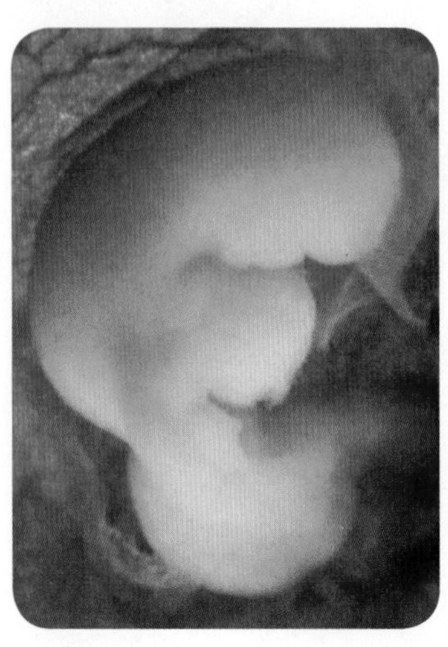
4 weeks

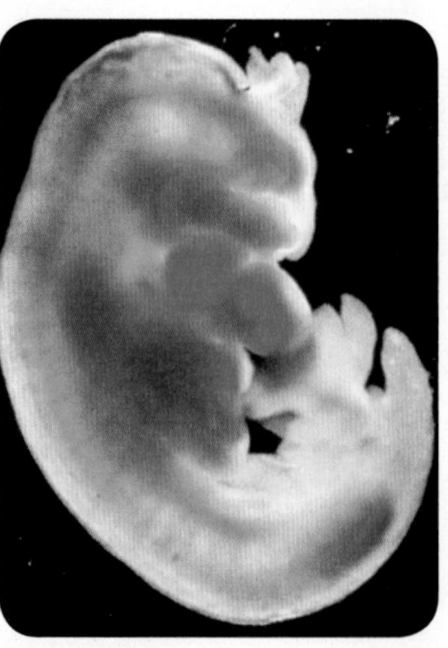
5–6 weeks

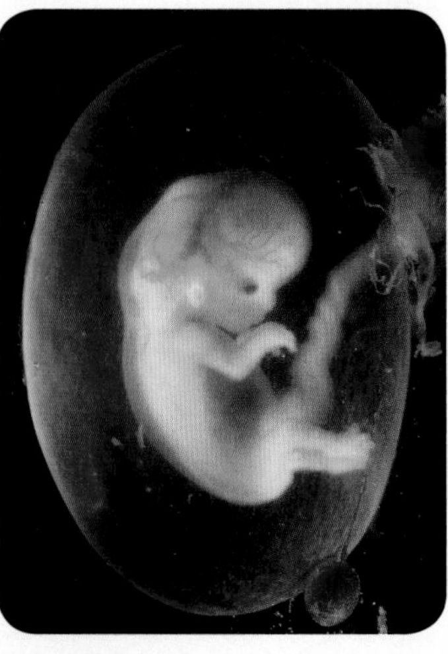
7–8 weeks

Table 2 Preventable Causes of Birth Defects	Interactive Table
Cause	**Defect**
Alcohol consumption	• Mental retardation
Cigarette smoking	• Health problems related to premature births and underweight babies
Lack of folic acid in diet	• Anencephaly (head and brain do not completely form) • Spina bifida (nerve cells from the spinal cord are exposed, leading to paralysis)
Cocaine	• Low birth weight • Premature birth • Possible permanent brain damage and behavioral disorders
Methamphetamine	• Premature birth • Extreme irritability

The second trimester The second trimester primarily is a period of growth. Around 18 to 20 weeks, the fetal heartbeat might be heard using a stethoscope. The developing fetus is capable of sucking its thumb and can develop the hiccups. The mother might feel a fluttering sensation or might even feel light kicks. Hair usually forms, and the fetal eyes will open during this period. At the end of this trimester, the fetus might be able to survive outside the mother's uterus with the aid of medical intervention, but the chances for survival are not very high. If born this early, the baby cannot maintain a constant body temperature. The baby's lungs have not developed fully, so respiratory failure is a great risk. Also, the baby is very likely to become seriously ill because its immune system is not fully functional.

The third trimester During the third trimester, the fetus continues to grow at a rapid rate. Fat accumulates under the skin to provide insulation for the fetus once it is born. Adequate protein intake by the mother is important during this time. Protein is essential for the rapid amount of brain growth that occurs. New nerve cells in the brain are forming at a rate of 250,000 cells per minute. The fetus now might respond to sounds in the environment, such as music or the sound of its mother's voice.

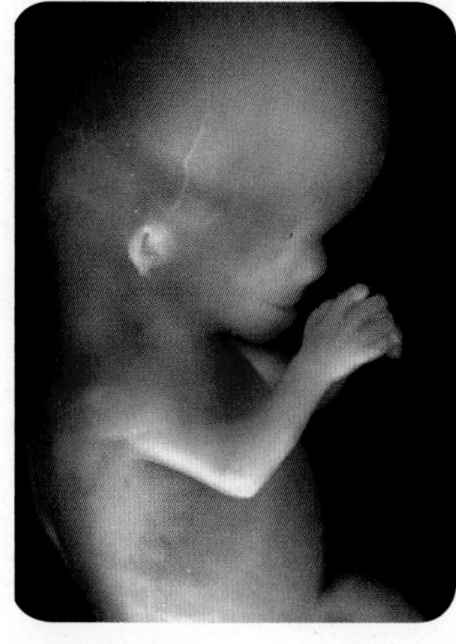

9–10 weeks

12 weeks

■ **Figure 12** In amniocentesis, fluid and cells lost from the fetus are removed from the amniotic fluid and analyzed.

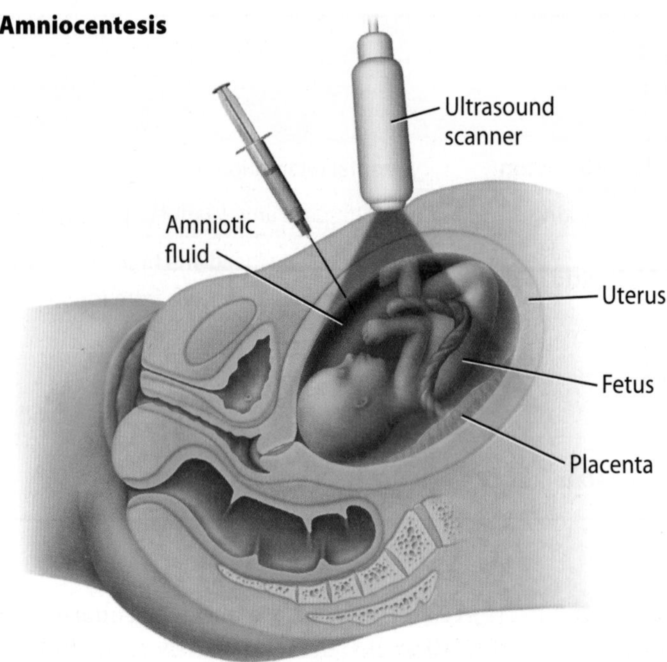

CAREERS IN **BIOLOGY**

Ultrasound Technician
Technical skills are needed in biology. An ultrasound technician obtains ultrasound images that are interpreted by a physician.

Diagnosis in the Fetus

Many conditions can be diagnosed before a baby is born. Identifying certain conditions as early as possible increases the chance for proper medical treatment to help a newborn baby have the highest quality of life possible.

Ultrasound One way to identify conditions in the fetus is by using ultrasound, a procedure in which sound waves are bounced off the fetus. These sound waves are converted into light images that can be seen on a video monitor. Ultrasound can be used to determine if the fetus is growing properly, the position of the fetus in the uterus, and the gender of the fetus.

MiniLAB 2

Sequence Early Human Development

What developmental changes occur during the first eight weeks of life? Fertilization begins when a sperm penetrates the egg. The zygote undergoes predictable developmental changes. Cell division produces increasing numbers of cells. Cells move and arrange themselves to form specific organs, making it possible for cells to perform specific functions.

Procedure

1. Refer to **Figure 11** to see **images of embryos.**
2. Study the images for the first trimester of pregnancy. Choose one factor to track through this developmental period. Factors might include embryonic size, overall structural changes, specific organ or organ system development, or others.
3. Chart the development of this factor along a time line through the first trimester of pregnancy.

Analysis

1. **Analyze** the time line you created. Identify developmental milestones related to this factor during the ten-week period.
2. **Summarize** the level of development of the factor you examined by the end of the first twelve weeks.

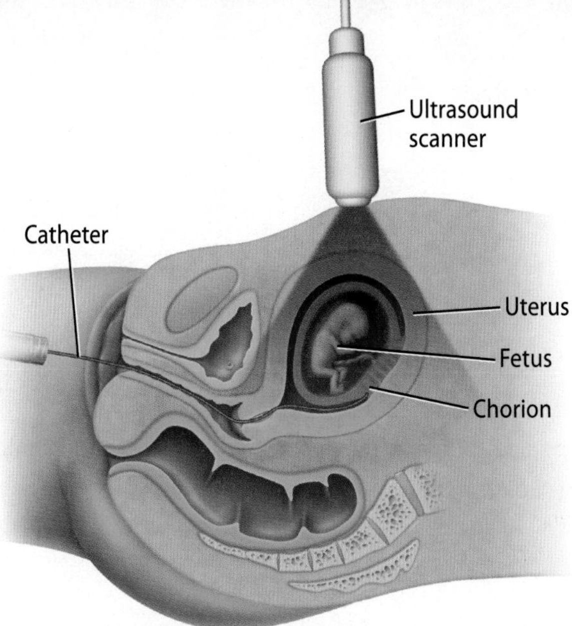

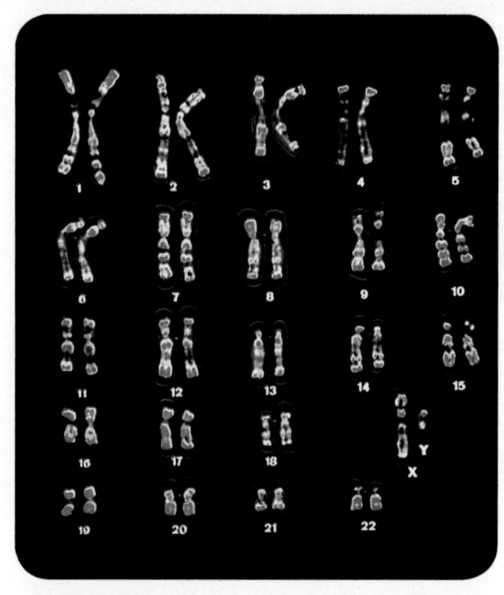

Karyotype

■ **Figure 13**
Left: Chorionic villus sampling involves removing cells from the chorion and analyzing them. This procedure carries a small risk of a miscarriage.
Right: Karyotypes can be analyzed to help with diagnosis.

Amniocentesis and chorionic villus sampling Amniocentesis (am nee oh sen TEE sus) and chorionic villus sampling are prenatal tests. During amniocentesis—usually performed in the second trimester—a needle is inserted through the abdomen of the pregnant female, illustrated in **Figure 12.** Fluid from the amniotic sac is removed and analyzed. Tests that measure enzyme levels associated with certain conditions can be performed. Fetal cells can be examined by a karyotype or even by DNA analysis. Remember a karyotype is a chart of chromosome pairs, shown in **Figure 13,** that is valuable in identifying unusual chromosome numbers or the sex of the fetus.

In chorionic villus sampling—usually performed during the first trimester—a small tube, called a catheter, is inserted through the vagina and cervix of the mother, as illustrated in **Figure 13.** Cells from the chorion are removed and analyzed by karyotyping. The chromosomes in the cells of the chorion are identical to those of the cells in the fetus.

REVIEW IT! Human Development Before Birth

Section Summary

- Fertilization is the joining of egg and sperm.
- Four extraembryonic membranes are associated with a human embryo.
- The placenta regulates what substances can be exchanged between a fetus and its mother.
- Hormone regulation during pregnancy is different from hormone regulation during the menstrual cycle.
- Pregnancies are divided into three trimesters.
- Some medical conditions of a baby can be detected before it is born.

Self Check

Understand Main Ideas

1. MAINIDEA Describe the changes that the zygote undergoes during the first week following fertilization.
2. **Describe** how defective acrosomes would affect the process of fertilization.
3. **Summarize** the development that occurs during each trimester in a concept map.
4. **Compare and contrast** hormonal regulation during pregnancy with hormonal regulation during the menstrual cycle.

Think Critically

WRITING IN ▶ Biology

5. Write a paragraph explaining the functions of the extraembryonic membrane in humans, and contrast those functions with the functions in other animals.

MATH IN ▶ Biology

6. Determine the due date (predicted birth date) of a baby if the egg was fertilized on January 1.

CNRI/Science Source

 Science Notebook

3 Birth, Growth, and Aging

1.3.5b, ¥o

MAINIDEA
Developmental changes continue throughout the stages of life.

Essential Questions

- What are the events that occur during the three stages of birth?
- What are the stages of human development from infancy to adulthood?
- What are the hormones necessary for growth?

BIOLOGY 4U
You know from looking at your family photo album that you have grown and changed since you were born. Your bones, teeth, eyes, and muscles have changed. You can look forward to continued changes in your face and body structure throughout your life.

Review Vocabulary

growth: increase in the amount of living material and formation of new structures in an organism

New Vocabulary

labor
dilation
expulsion stage
placental stage
adolescence
infancy
adulthood

Multilingual eGlossary

Birth

Birth occurs in three stages: dilation, expulsion, and the placental stage, as shown in **Figure 14.** Just before giving birth, the posterior pituitary gland releases the hormone oxytocin (ahk sih TOH sun), which stimulates involuntary muscles in the wall of the uterus to contract. This is the beginning of the birthing process called **labor.**

Another sign that the baby is going to be born is the **dilation** (di LAY shun), or opening, of the cervix. The cervix must open to allow the baby to leave the uterus. Contractions of the uterus become stronger and more frequent, and at some point the amniotic sac tears. The amniotic fluid flows out of the vagina, which is sometimes described as the "water breaking."

After a period of time that could be as short as a few hours or as long as a couple of days, the cervix fully dilates to around 10 cm. The uterine contractions are now very strong. The mother consciously will contract her abdominal muscles to help push the baby, usually head first, through the vagina in the **expulsion stage.** When the baby is out of the mother's body, the umbilical cord is clamped and cut. A small piece of the cord still attached to the baby soon will dry up and fall off, forming the navel, or belly button.

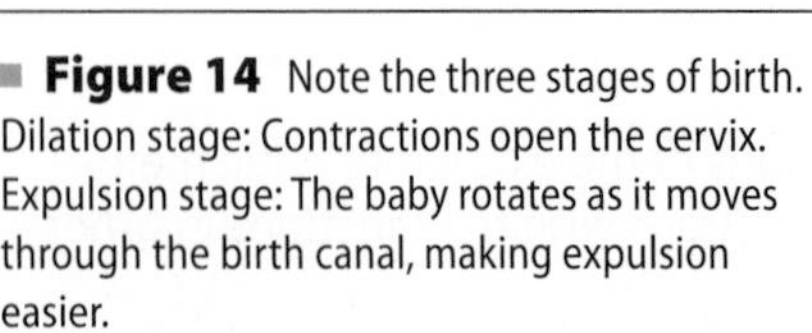

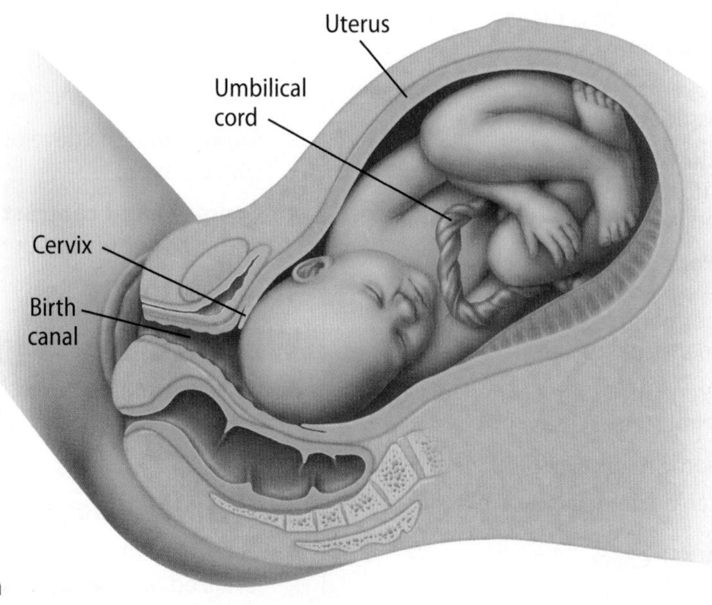

Dilation

■ **Figure 14** Note the three stages of birth.
Dilation stage: Contractions open the cervix.
Expulsion stage: The baby rotates as it moves through the birth canal, making expulsion easier.
Placental stage: The placenta and umbilical cord are expelled.
Hypothesize ***what might happen if the placenta was not expelled quickly.***

Shortly after the baby is delivered, the placenta detaches from the uterus and leaves the mother's body along with extraembryonic membranes. This is the **placental stage** of the birthing process.

Sometimes, complications prevent the baby from being born through the vagina. In these cases, an incision is made through the mother's abdomen and uterus, and the baby is removed from the mother's body. This process is called a cesarean section.

During the first four weeks of life, the baby is called a newborn. Human newborns vary in size. However, on average, a newborn human baby has a mass of 3300 g and is 51 cm long.

GET IT? **Describe** major events that occur during each stage of labor.

VOCABULARY

SCIENCE USAGE V. COMMON USAGE

Labor

Science usage: the process of giving birth

There are three stages of labor: dilation, expulsion, and the placental stage.

Common usage: the use of physical or mental effort

Lifting the heavy bags of soil requires labor.

Growth and Aging

Humans go through many stages of growth during their lives. After you were born, you were in your infancy, but soon you will enter adulthood. You now are in a major development phase called **adolescence** (a dul ES unts), which began with puberty and ends at adulthood.

Hormones, such as human growth hormone, thyroxine, and steroids, influence growth. Human growth hormone stimulates most areas of the body to grow as cells replicate by the process of mitosis. This hormone works by increasing the rates of protein synthesis and the breakdown of fats. Thyroxine from the thyroid increases the overall metabolic rate and is essential for growth to occur. Steroid hormones, such as estrogen and testosterone, are also important for growth. Recall that testosterone and estrogen pass through the plasma membrane and into the nucleus of a target cell. The hormones activate certain genes that promote the formation of proteins. In this way, testosterone, and to a lesser extent, estrogen, cause an increase in the size of cells.

GET IT? **Summarize** the roles of human growth hormone and thyroxine.

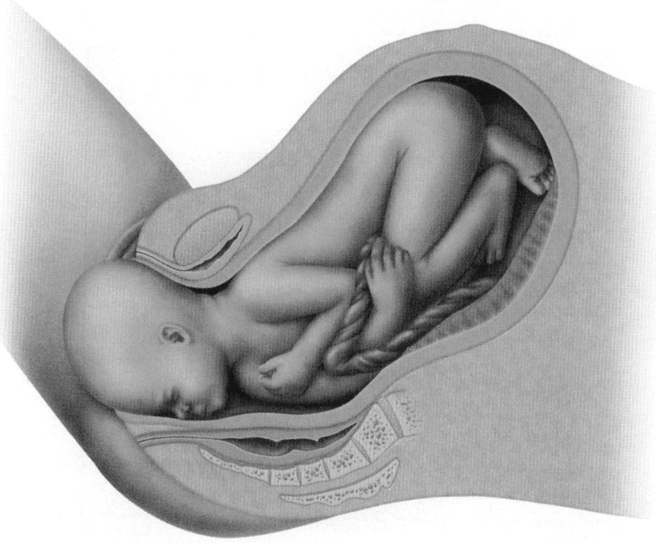

Expulsion stage

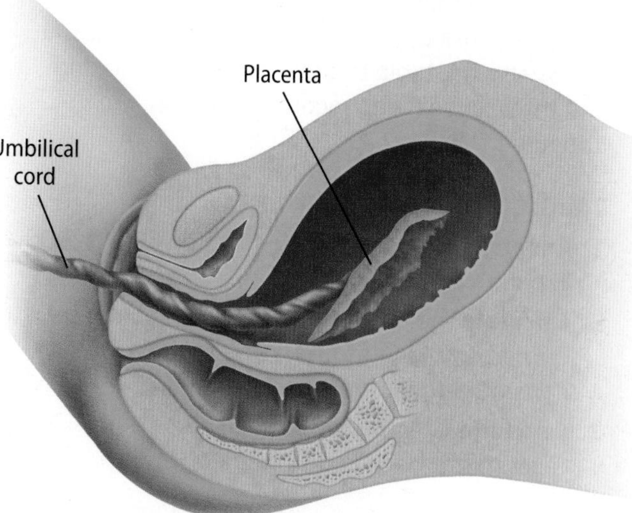

Placental stage

Infancy The first two years of life are known as **infancy.** Many changes take place during these years. An infant learns how to roll and crawl, grasp objects, and perform simple tasks. By the end of the first year, the infant likely is walking and might be uttering a few words. An enormous amount of mental development also occurs during these first two years.

In the first year, a baby typically grows about 25 cm in length and weighs three times more than when the baby was born. The child's growth slows during the second year; children grow at a rate of around 6 cm per year until the beginning of puberty.

Childhood and adolescence Childhood is the period of growth and development that extends from infancy to adolescence. The child's ability to reason and solve problems develops progressively during childhood. Puberty marks the beginning of adolescence, the period of growth between childhood and adulthood. Puberty usually begins between ages 8 to 13 in girls and ages 10 to 15 in boys.

In addition to the hormonal and sexual development that occur during this time, other physical changes also take place. An adolescent experiences a growth spurt—girls grow approximately 6–11 cm and boys grow approximately 7–13 cm—in one year. In girls, the hips become wider and the waist might become narrower. In boys, the shoulders usually become broader. At the end of adolescence, physical growth is complete, marking the beginning of **adulthood.** The transition between adolescence and adulthood can be hard to define because of physical, emotional, and behavioral changes.

Data Analysis LAB 1

Based on Real Data*

Form a Conclusion

Is SIDS linked to smoking? Researchers studied the annual SIDS rate per 1000 infants for mothers who smoked and mothers who did not smoke during pregnancy. In 1994, doctors began to recommend that infants sleep on their backs to reduce the risk of Sudden Infant Death Syndrome (SIDS). Use the table to determine how smoking and the Back to Sleep recommendation impacted SIDS.

SIDS Deaths

Year	Smoke Exposed	Unexposed
1989	3.21	1.33
1990	2.96	1.34
1991	3.32	1.72
1992	2.93	1.41
1993	3.28	1.17
1994	1.65	0.79
1995	2.19	0.65
1996	1.61	0.82
1997	3.21	0.64
1998	1.80	0.37

Think Critically

1. **Analyze** whether sleeping position affects SIDS. Explain.
2. **Calculate** the percentage of SIDS for babies born to smoking mothers and to those of nonsmoking mothers each year.
3. **Conclude** how this data shows that some SIDS cases might be linked to smoking.

*Data obtained from: Anderson, M.E., et al. 2005. Sudden Infant Death Syndrome and prenatal maternal smoking: rising attributed risk in the Back to Sleep era. *BMC Medicine* 3: 4.

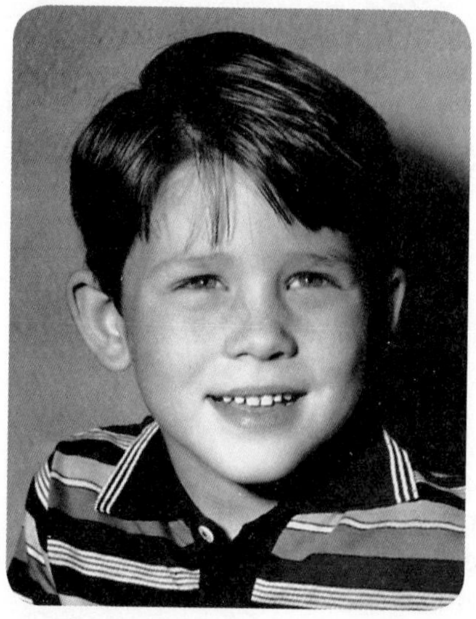

■ **Figure 15** These photos show actor and director Ron Howard in various stages of life.
Summarize ***changes that occur in adulthood.***

Adulthood There are a number of theories on why people age. However, scientists do agree that the body goes through many changes as it ages, as shown in **Figure 15.** Physical changes perhaps are the most noticeable signs of aging, such as hair turning gray or white as pigment production declines. An individual might lose as much as two centimeters of height during the aging process because the discs between the vertebrae in the spine become flattened. Other changes include a decrease in muscle mass, a slowing of overall metabolism, and a decreased pumping ability of the heart. The skin loses its elasticity, and sensory perceptions might diminish somewhat. In women, the ability to have children ends with menopause (MEN uh pawz). Sperm production decreases in men.

Despite all of the potential challenges of aging, many people continue to be physically and mentally active as they grow older. Some older adults even begin new careers. Anna Mary Robertson Moses, known as Grandma Moses, became a famous artist when she was in her late 70s.

REVIEW IT! Birth, Growth, and Aging

Section Summary

- Humans go through many changes throughout the stages of life.
- There are three stages of the birthing process.
- Levels of several hormones influence human growth.
- The first year of life is a time of learning motor skills and of rapid growth.
- Puberty causes many changes in the body, and changes continue to occur as an adult grows older.

Self Check

Understand Main Ideas

1. MAINIDEA **Construct** a chart that illustrates major changes that occur during the stages of human growth and aging.
2. **Identify** two signs that tell a pregnant woman she is almost ready to give birth.
3. **Name** the events that occur during the three stages of birth.
4. **Describe** how the human growth hormone causes a person to grow.

Think Critically

5. **Hypothesize** Robert Wadlow, the tallest human being on record, was 272 cm tall and weighed 220 kg when he died at age 22. He was an average-sized newborn but developed a tumor in his anterior pituitary gland. Develop a hypothesis to explain how this tumor led to his great height.
6. **Infer** How do you think scientists determine which specific substances cause birth defects?

BIOLOGY & society

1.1.2a, 1.1.2b, 1.1.3b

hGH: The Tall and Short of It

Terry is a 157.5-cm tall high school senior. He has not grown in the last two years. His dad is 190.5 cm, and his other three brothers are 177.8 cm or taller. He doesn't seem to mind his height—or lack of it. His mom, though, wonders if he might have a disadvantage in sports because he is short. She suggests that he take growth hormones to become taller. She thinks that they might help him be more successful in sports—and in life. What should he do?

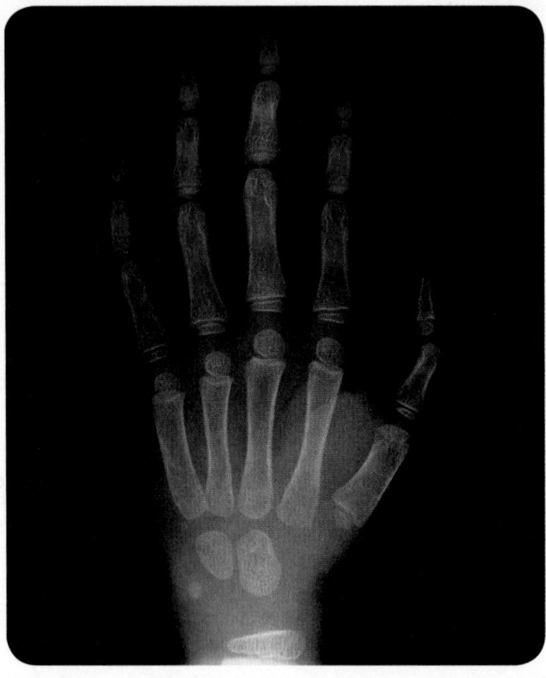

The oval bones are the growth plates, where bone growth occurs. If the growth plate is no longer visible, no more growth can occur.

What is human growth hormone? Human growth hormone (hGH) is a protein produced in the pituitary gland found in the brain. It is plentiful during the growth period of youth. Children with a lack of hGH are known as pituitary dwarfs and generally do not reach a height of over 135 cm.

What is hGH therapy? During adolescence, pituitary dwarfs can receive injections of synthetic hGH to increase their growth 10–12 cm during the first year. Less growth occurs during subsequent years. In 2003, the Food and Drug Administration approved hGH therapy for children who are otherwise healthy, but are predicted to reach adult heights of 160.0 cm or shorter for males and 149.9 cm or shorter for females. For these children, hGH therapy adds an average of 4–7 cm of height by adulthood. Using X-rays, a child's bone age—and therefore their growth potential—can be determined.

Therapy v. enhancement Sometimes hGH therapy can be used by physicians for individuals who are short and want to be taller or stronger athletes; however, this type of treatment is rare. There have been instances in which hGH drugs have been sold illegally and obtained by professional athletes to enhance their performance. These athletes were fined heavily or suspended because the drugs were in their systems.

hGH supplements sold in health food stores have less than one percent of hGH in them. Based on numerous scientific studies, they show no significant impact on human performance. Only hGH injections can improve growth and increase one's metabolism.

DEBATE IN ▶ Biology

Debate Should hGH therapy be permissible when a teen is dissatisfied with his or her height for primarily cosmetic or athletic reasons? Consider Terry's situation, where he is feeling pressured to use hGH to become taller simply because the option exists. Conduct additional research about hGH and hGH therapy.

WebQuest

Jim Wehtje/Getty Images

BioLAB ¥o

Internet: How are ultrasound images used to track fetal development?

Background: Ultrasound is a medical imaging technique that uses high-frequency sound waves and their echoes to produce an image of something inside the body. While two-dimensional images are the current standard, technology capable of producing three-dimensional fetal images and four-dimensional, or moving images, is now available.

Question: *How are ultrasound images used to assess fetal characteristics and development?*

Materials

computer with Internet access
labeled ultrasound images showing embryos and fetuses at various developmental stages
ultrasound images showing embryos and fetuses at unknown stages of development

Procedure

1. Read and complete the lab safety form.
2. Visit the Internet to examine fetal development from the second trimester through week 40. Use this information to complete the development time line you started in **MiniLab 2.**

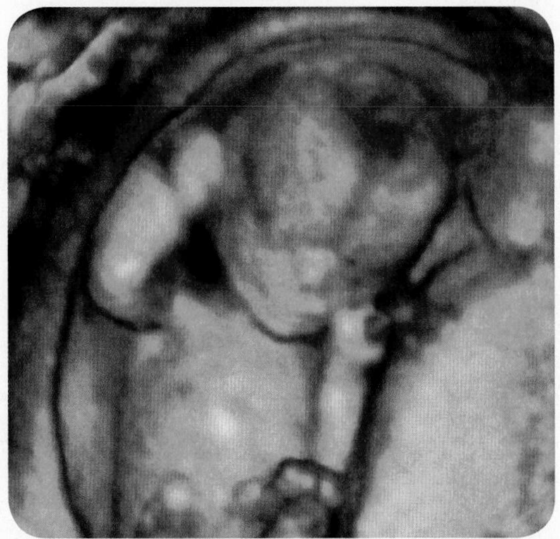

Zephyr/Science Source

3. Study the ultrasound images of fetuses during identified stages of development provided by your teacher. Compare these to your time line, and identify as many features as possible. As you study the images, choose a body structure that you would like to examine further.
4. Study the ultrasound images provided by your teacher of fetuses at unknown stages of development. Use your time line and what you have learned to determine the approximate stage of fetal development. Look for clues based on the development of the system you choose.

Analyze and Conclude

1. **Interpret Data** During which time period does the developing embryo or fetus change the most? Justify your answer.
2. **Analyze** What physical characteristics were most helpful in identifying the level of fetal development? Explain.
3. **Compare** two- and three-dimensional ultrasound images. Which are easiest to interpret?
4. **Think Critically** What advantages are provided by four-dimensional imaging?
5. **Error Analysis** How accurate were your estimates of fetal development? Explain how your estimates could have been improved.

WRITING IN ▶ Biology

Poster Session Create a flowchart that illustrates the reproductive process. Begin with the creation of sex cells and end with a fetus at full term.

CHAPTER 22 STUDY GUIDE

BIGIDEA **Human reproduction involves the joining together of sperm and egg.**

SECTION 1 Reproductive Systems

MAINIDEA Hormones regulate human reproductive systems, including the production of gametes.

- Levels of male and female hormones are regulated by negative feedback systems.
- The human male produces millions of sperm cells every day.
- The number of sex cells resulting from meiosis differs in males and females.
- The human female has a reproductive cycle called the menstrual cycle.
- The menstrual cycle has three phases: the flow phase, the follicular phase, and the luteal phase.

VOCABULARY
- **seminiferous tubule**
- **epididymis**
- **vas deferens**
- **urethra**
- **semen**
- **puberty**
- **oocyte**
- **oviduct**
- **menstrual cycle**
- **polar body**

SECTION 2 Human Development Before Birth

MAINIDEA A human develops from a single fertilized cell into trillions of cells with specialized functions.

- Fertilization is the joining of egg and sperm.
- Four extraembryonic membranes are associated with a human embryo.
- The placenta regulates what substances can be exchanged between a fetus and its mother.
- Hormone regulation during pregnancy is different from hormone regulation during the menstrual cycle.
- Pregnancies are divided into three trimesters.
- Some medical conditions of a baby can be detected before it is born.

VOCABULARY
- **morula**
- **blastocyst**
- **amniotic fluid**

SECTION 3 Birth, Growth, and Aging

MAINIDEA Developmental changes continue throughout the stages of life.

- Humans go through many changes throughout the stages of life.
- There are three stages of the birthing process.
- Levels of several hormones influence human growth.
- The first year of life is a time of learning motor skills and of rapid growth.
- Puberty causes many changes in the body, and changes continue to occur as an adult grows older.

VOCABULARY
- **labor**
- **dilation**
- **expulsion stage**
- **placental stage**
- **adolescence**
- **infancy**
- **adulthood**

ASSESSMENT

SECTION 1

Vocabulary Review

Explain the difference between the terms in each pair below, and then explain how the terms are related.

1. urethra, semen
2. oocyte, oviduct
3. menstrual cycle, polar body

Understand Main Ideas

4. What would happen if the testes were located inside the body cavity?
   A. Sperm would not be produced because it is too warm.
   B. Testosterone levels would increase because of the warm temperature.
   C. The seminal vesicles would no longer be needed.
   D. Hormones from the testes would have difficulty entering the bloodstream.

Use the diagram below to answer questions 5 and 6.

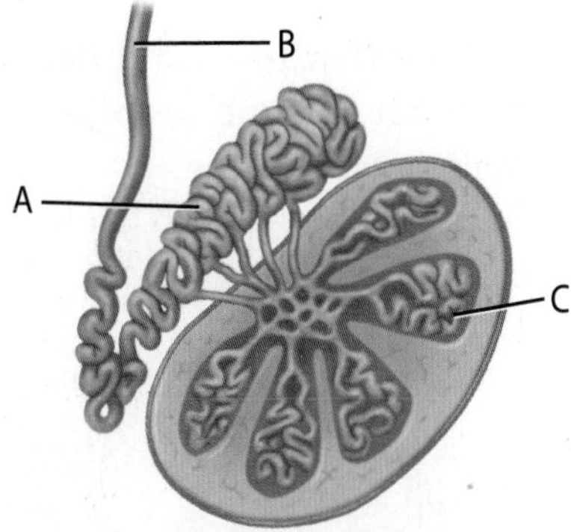

5. What occurs in the structure labeled C in the illustration?
   A. sperm cell storage and maturation
   B. sperm cell production
   C. secretion of sugar
   D. production of FSH
6. What is the function of the structure labeled A in the illustration?
   A. sperm cell storage and maturation
   B. sperm cell production
   C. secretion of sugar
   D. production of FSH

Constructed Response

7. **Short Answer** Why are the secretions of the male reproductive glands so important to sperm?
8. MAINIDEA Compare the actions of FSH and LH in the ovaries and testes.
9. **Short Answer** What advantages are there for the formation of one egg and polar bodies as compared to four eggs?

Think Critically

Use the diagram below to answer question 10.

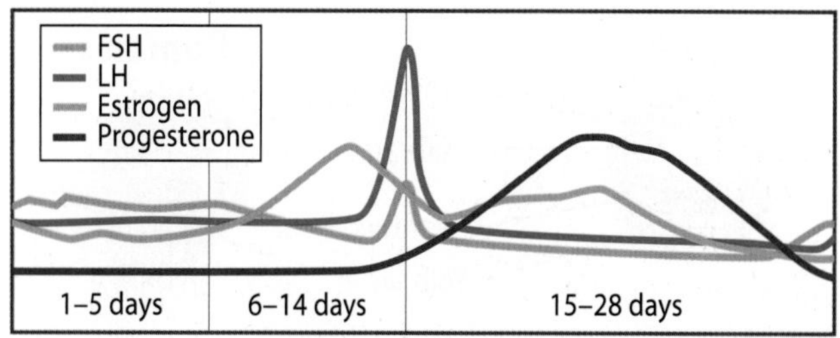

10. **Cause and Effect** Based on what you know about the hormonal control of a woman's reproductive cycle shown above, explain the hormonal basis of why a woman cannot get pregnant again while she is pregnant.
11. **Hypothesize** All of the reproductive hormones in a human male are present at birth. Develop a hypothesis to explain why the hormones have a greater influence on the body once puberty begins.

SECTION 2

Vocabulary Review

For questions 12–14, describe each of the following vocabulary terms.

12. morula
13. blastocyst
14. amniotic fluid

Understand Main Ideas

15. Where in the human female reproductive tract does fertilization usually occur?
    A. in the uterus
    B. in the vagina
    C. in the corpus luteum
    D. in an oviduct

16. Which of the following describes the proper sequence of development?
    A. zygote, blastocyst, morula
    B. morula, zygote, blastocyst
    C. zygote, morula, blastocyst
    D. morula, blastocyst, zygote

17. Which is produced by the placenta?
    A. human chorionic gonadotropin
    B. estrogen and progesterone
    C. oxytocin
    D. endometrial birth hormone

Use the diagram below to answer question 18.

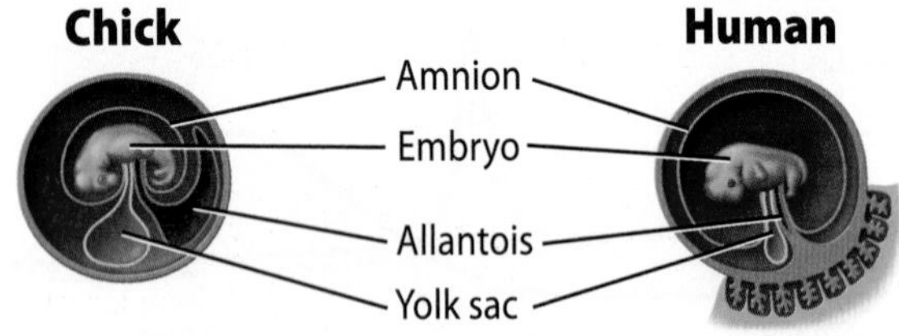

18. Why is the human yolk sac shown in the illustration smaller than that of the chick?
    A. The yolk in humans is converted into muscle.
    B. The yolk sac in chicks keeps the embryo warm.
    C. Developing humans get their nourishment from the placenta.
    D. The yolk sac serves no purpose for a developing human.

19. When can a pregnant woman first feel the movements of her fetus?
    A. in the first trimester
    B. in the second trimester
    C. in the third trimester
    D. in the last month only

Constructed Response

20. **Short Answer** Why is it important that the endometrium is refreshed each cycle?

21. **CAREERS IN Biology** Some couples consult with a reproductive endocrinologist because they are having difficulty conceiving a child. What are some possible biological reasons that could contribute to this difficulty?

22. **MAIN IDEA** What do you think are the reasons that the greatest amount of harm to an embryo or fetus caused by alcohol or drugs occurs in the first trimester?

Think Critically

23. **Compare and contrast** the division of the inner cell mass during normal development and during the development of identical twins.

24. **Formulate a Model** A woman is carrying an embryo, but not enough hCG is getting into her system. Propose a possible treatment that might allow the embryo to be saved.

SECTION 3

Vocabulary Review

Explain the difference between the terms in each pair below. Then explain how the terms are related.

25. labor, placental stage
26. dilation, expulsion
27. adolescence, adulthood

Understand Main Ideas

28. At which measurement is the cervix fully dilated?
    A. 10 mm
    B. 2 cm
    C. 10 cm
    D. 20 cm

29. When a pregnant woman tells her doctor that "her water broke," what does she mean?
    A. The amniotic sac has torn.
    B. There is a lot of pressure on her bladder.
    C. The yolk sac has torn.
    D. The placenta is leaking.

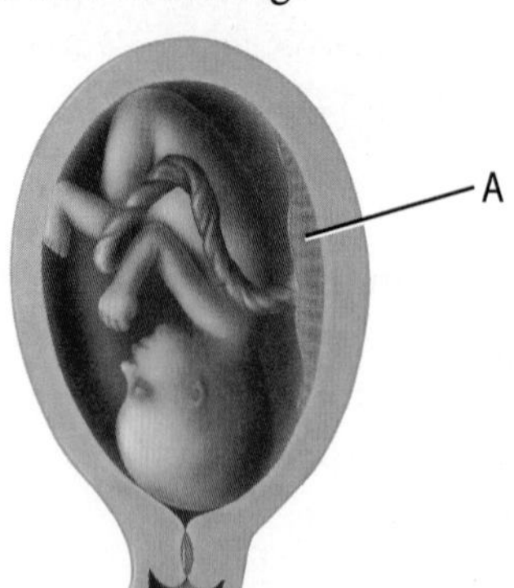

Use the diagram below to answer questions 30 and 31.

30. What is the name of the structure labeled A in the illustration?
    A. uterus
    B. placenta
    C. fetus
    D. cervix

31. During which stage of birth does structure A leave the female's body?
A. first
B. second
C. third
D. fourth

32. During which year of a person's life does the most rapid rate of growth occur?
A. the first year of infancy
B. the first year of puberty
C. the second year of puberty
D. the first year of adulthood

Constructed Response

33. **Open Ended** What biological reasons can you think of to explain why women go through menopause and stop producing eggs, while men can produce sperm all their lives?

34. **MAIN**IDEA Compare puberty in females with puberty in males.

35. **CAREERS**IN ▶ **Biology** During rare occasions, a pediatrician examines a newborn baby who does not produce enough thyroxin. What are some possible results of this? Suggest a treatment for this condition.

Think Critically

Use the graph below to answer question 36.

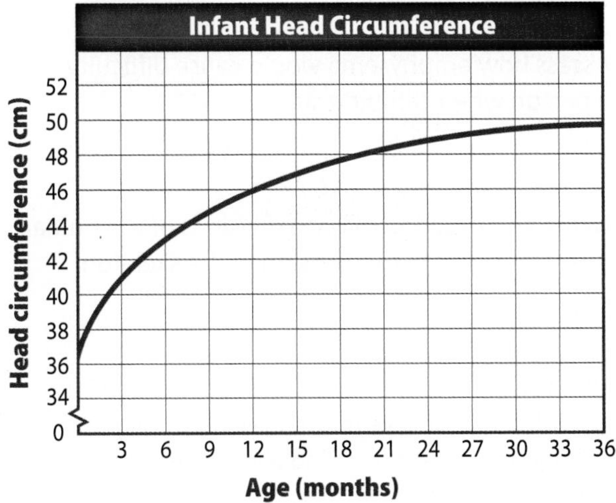

36. **Change** During which period shown on the graph is the rate of change in head circumference greatest?

Summative Assessment

37. **BIG**IDEA Human reproduction involves the joining together of sperm and egg. What is the result of human reproduction? What is the ultimate goal of human reproduction? Construct your answer from a scientific point of view.

38. **WRITING**IN ▶ **Biology** Prepare a pamphlet for pregnant women on health and lifestyle issues during pregnancy. Include a chart about the major events of fetal development.

DBQ Document–Based Questions

To reduce the chances of brain and spine birth defects, the U.S. Public Health Service recommended in 1992 that women of childbearing age increase folic acid in their diets. The U.S. Food and Drug Administration required all cereal products be enriched with folic acid beginning in January 1998 (an optional period began in March 1996).

Below is a table showing the rate per 100,000 births of anencephaly—incomplete head and brain development—from 1991–2002.

Year	Rate	Year	Rate
1991	18.38	**1997**	12.51
1992	12.79	**1998**	9.92
1993	13.50	**1999**	10.81
1994	10.97	**2000**	10.33
1995	11.71	**2001**	9.42
1996	11.96	**2002**	9.55

Data obtained from: Mathews, T.J. Trends in Spina Bifida and Anencephalus in the United States, 1991–2002. National Center for Health Statistics/Centers for Disease Control and Prevention/ Department of Health and Human Services.

39. Construct a graph to represent these data and describe the relationship between the variables that you observe.

40. Explain the overall trend in the number of cases of anencephaly during this time period.

CUMULATIVE
MULTIPLE CHOICE

1 Which is the role of arteries in the circulatory system?

A to carry blood away from the heart

B to carry blood back to the heart

C to provide individual cells with nutrients

D to prevent blood from flowing backward

2 What is the role of hormones in the body?

A They act as reaction catalysts.

B They control the breathing process.

C They help synthesize proteins.

D They regulate many body functions.

3 Which is the sequence of human development during the first week?

A egg → morula → blastocyst → zygote

B egg → zygote → morula → blastocyst

C morula → blastocyst → egg → zygote

D morula → egg → zygote → blastocyst

4 Which function of the kidneys help maintain homeostasis?

A Kidneys deplete carbon dioxide from the blood.

B Kidneys eliminate undigested foods from the body.

C Kidneys remove excess water and wastes from the blood.

D Kidneys rid excess proteins from the blood.

SHORT ANSWER

Use the diagram below to answer questions 5 and 6.

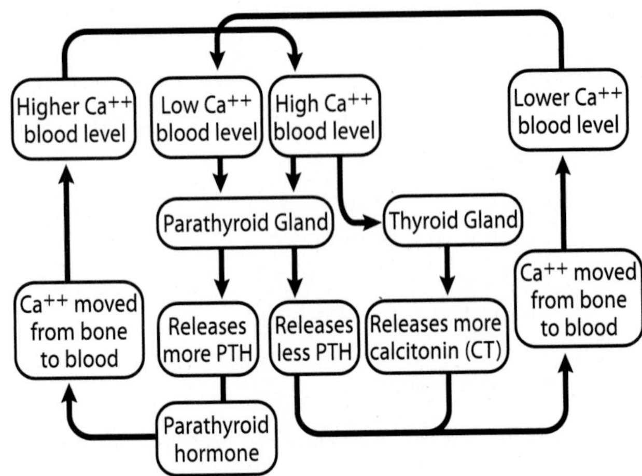

5 Assess how the parathyroid hormone affects bone tissue.

6 Evaluate how a person's blood calcium levels would be affected if his or her thyroid gland stopped working.

7 Analyze how Ivan Pavlov conditioned dogs to salivate when they heard a bell.

8 Assess how emphysema would cause difficulty for a person when climbing stairs.

9 Name and describe the two divisions of the human skeleton. Critique this division of the skeleton.

10 Think about the structure of the middle and inner ear. Infer why people might experience a temporary hearing loss after attending a loud concert.

11 Explain how the villi in the small intestine affect the rate of absorption.

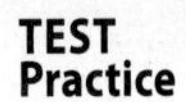

EXTENDED RESPONSE

12 A student did an experiment in a sunny room using unripe bananas. He found that bananas ripened faster in a paper bag than on top of a plate. Based on these results, what conclusion could the student make about the ripening of the bananas? Give one example of a way to improve the experiment.

13 Muscles in the legs tend to store large amounts of glycogen and fat. Muscles in the arms do not. When the muscles are used repeatedly, why do the muscles in the arm fatigue more quickly?

14 Different kinds of mammals have different digestive systems. Explain how the digestive systems of ruminant herbivores differ from other herbivores.

ESSAY QUESTION

As elevation increases, air pressure decreases. At sea level, air pressure is about 760 mmHg. The percentage of oxygen in the atmosphere is about 21 percent. At 3200 m in elevation, the air pressure is 30 percent less than that at sea level; however, the percentage of oxygen is the same. The difference in pressure occurs because the molecules of gas are spread farther apart. As altitude continues to increase, the pressure continues to decrease. Mountain climbers face the problems of decreased pressure when they climb a mountain. When climbers go to the summit of the highest mountains, they carry oxygen tanks with them to help them breathe.

Using the information in the paragraph above, answer the following question in essay format.

15 Evaluate why breathing oxygen would enable a mountain climber to reach a higher altitude.

TEST PRACTICE

Use the diagram below to answer question 16.

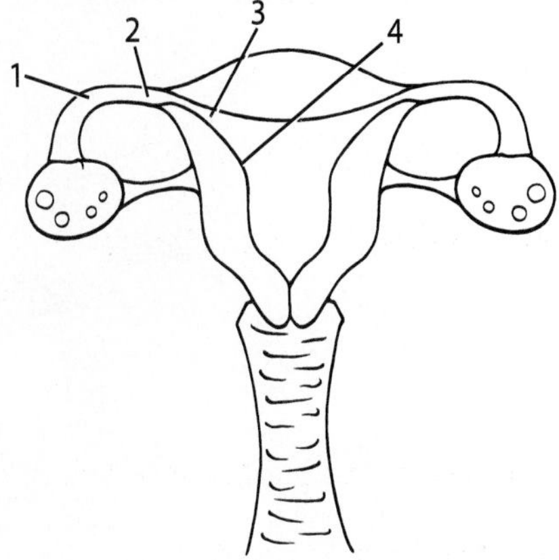

16 Where does fertilization take place?

A 1

B 2

C 3

D 4

17 When blood glucose levels are very high, how does the pancreas restore homeostasis?

A It secretes glycogen.

B It secretes insulin.

C It secretes insulin and glycogen.

D It secretes hCG.

NEED EXTRA HELP?																	
If You Missed Question . . .	1	2	3	4	5	6	7	8	9	10	11	12	13	14	15	16	17
Review Section . . .	34.1	35.1	36.2	34.3	35.3	35.3	31.1	34.2	32.2	33.3	35.1	1.3	32.3	30.2	34.2	36.2	35.3

Your body has non-specific immunities to pathogens, such as the skin and saliva, but when pathogens get past these your body has specific immune responses, such as the tonsils.

LaunchLAB

How do you track a cold?

Colds and many other illnesses are caused by pathogens that can pass from person to person. In this lab, you will trace the path of a cold.

CHAPTER 23

The Immune System

1 Infectious Diseases

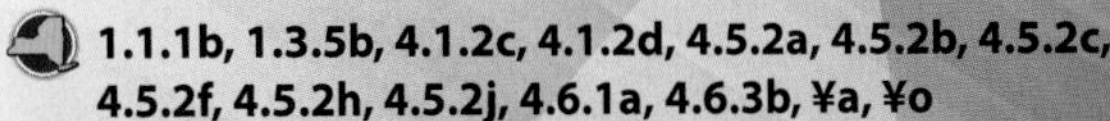
1.1.1b, 1.3.5b, 4.1.2c, 4.1.2d, 4.5.2a, 4.5.2b, 4.5.2c, 4.5.2f, 4.5.2h, 4.5.2j, 4.6.1a, 4.6.3b, ¥a, ¥o

2 The Immune System

4.5.2c, 4.5.2d, 4.5.2e, 4.5.2f

3 Noninfectious Disorders

4.2.2e, 4.5.2g, 4.5.2h, 4.5.2j, ¥a

THEMEFOCUS

Cause and effect **The variety of pathogens has caused the necessity of many different treatments.**

BIGIDEA

The immune system attempts to protect the body from contracting an infection through pathogens.

Immunity

Make a layered-look book using the titles shown. Use it to organize your notes on immunity.

Acquired Immunity
Passive Immunity
Cellular Immunity
Antibody Immunity
Innate Immunity
Immunity from Disease

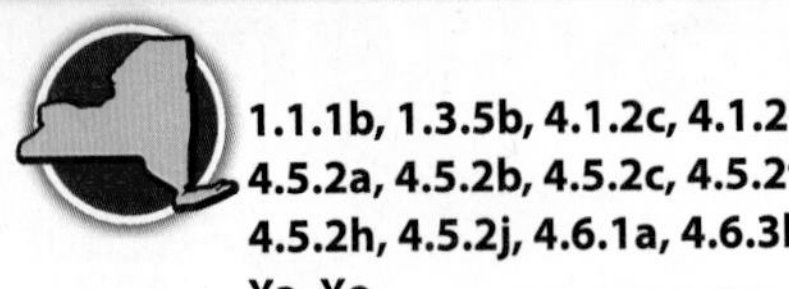

1 Infectious Diseases

1.1.1b, 1.3.5b, 4.1.2c, 4.1.2d, 4.5.2a, 4.5.2b, 4.5.2c, 4.5.2f, 4.5.2h, 4.5.2j, 4.6.1a, 4.6.3b, ¥a, ¥o

BIOLOGY 4 U

Have you ever gotten something sticky on your hands? As you touched other objects, they too became sticky. In a similar manner, viruses transfer to objects that you touch. When these objects are touched by someone else, the virus can be picked up by another person.

Review Vocabulary

protozoan: unicellular, heterotrophic, animal-like protist

New Vocabulary

infectious disease
pathogen
Koch's postulates
reservoir
endemic disease
epidemic
pandemic
antibiotic

Multilingual eGlossary

Figure 1 These rodlike bacteria cause the disease anthrax.

Color-Enhanced SEM Magnification: 50×

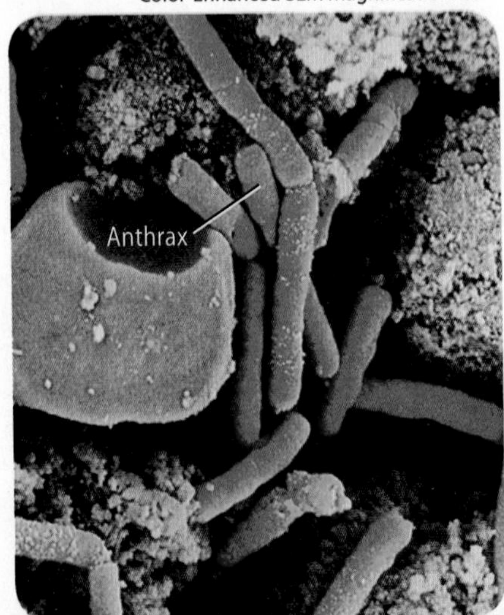

MAIN IDEA

Pathogens are dispersed by people, other animals, and objects.

Essential Questions

- What are Koch's postulates?
- How are diseases transmitted and how do reservoirs play a role in disease dispersal?
- What are the symptoms and treatment of infectious diseases?
- What are disease patterns?

Pathogens Cause Infectious Disease

What do a cold and athlete's foot have in common? They are both examples of an infectious disease. An **infectious disease** is a disease that is caused by a pathogen passed from one organism to another, disrupting homeostasis in the organism's body. Agents called **pathogens** are the cause of infectious diseases. Some but not all types of bacteria, viruses, protozoans, fungi, and parasites are pathogens.

Many types of these organisms are present in the world around us without causing infectious diseases. Your body benefits from organisms, such as certain types of bacteria and protozoans, that normally live in your intestinal and reproductive tracts. Other bacteria live on your skin, especially in the shafts of your hair follicles. These organisms keep pathogens from thriving and multiplying on your body.

Germ Theory and Koch's Experiments

Before the invention of the microscope, people thought "something" passed from a sick person to a well person to cause an illness. Then, scientists discovered microorganisms and Louis Pasteur demonstrated that microorganisms from the air are able to grow in nutrient solutions. With the knowledge gained from these and other discoveries, doctors and scientists began to develop the germ theory. The germ theory states that some microorganisms are pathogens. However, scientists were not able to clearly demonstrate this theory until Robert Koch developed his postulates.

Identification of the first disease pathogen In the late 1800s, Robert Koch, a German physician, was studying anthrax (AN thraks)—a deadly disease that affects cattle and sheep and can also affect people. Koch isolated bacteria, like those in **Figure 1,** from the blood of cattle that had died from anthrax. After growing the bacteria in the laboratory, Koch injected the bacteria into healthy cattle. These animals developed the disease anthrax. He then isolated bacteria from the blood of newly infected cattle and grew the bacteria in the laboratory. The characteristics of the two sets of cultures were identical, indicating that the same type of bacteria caused the illness in both sets of cattle. Thus, Koch demonstrated that the bacteria he originally isolated were the cause of anthrax.

Explain how Koch proved the germ theory correct.

Scott Camazine/Science Source

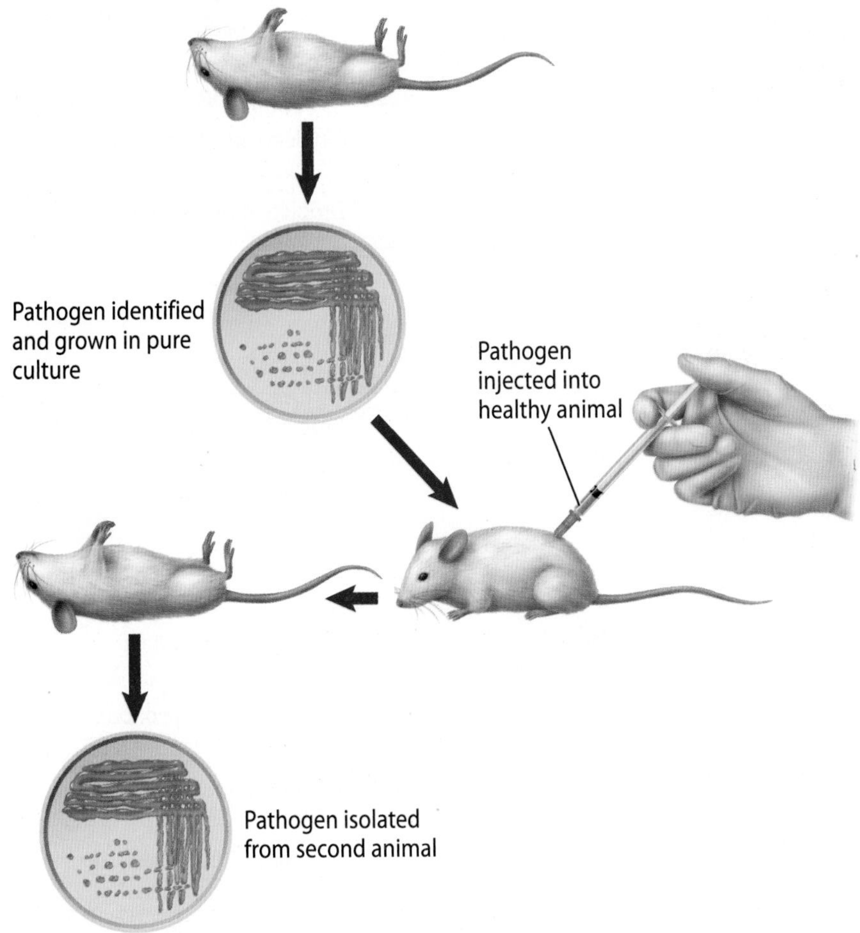

Postulate 1

The suspected pathogen must be isolated from the diseased host in every case of the disease.

Postulate 2

The suspected pathogen must be grown in pure culture on artificial media in the laboratory.

Postulate 3

The suspected pathogen from the pure culture must cause the same disease when placed in a healthy new host.

Postulate 4

The suspected pathogen must be isolated from the new host, grown again in pure culture, and shown to have the same characteristics as the original pathogen.

■ **Figure 2** Koch's postulates demonstrate that a specific pathogen causes a specific disease.

Infer ***what Koch demonstrated when he isolated the same bacteria from the cattle the second time.***

Koch's postulates Koch established and published experimental steps known as **Koch's postulates,** which are rules for demonstrating that an organism causes a disease. These steps are followed today to identify a specific pathogen as the agent of a specific disease. Follow the steps in **Figure 2** as you read each of the four postulates.

Postulate 1: The suspected pathogen must be isolated from the diseased host in every case of the disease.

Postulate 2: The suspected pathogen must be grown in pure culture on artificial media in the laboratory. A pure culture is a culture that contains no other types of microorganisms—only the suspected pathogen.

Postulate 3: The suspected pathogen from the pure culture must cause the disease when placed in a healthy new host.

Postulate 4: The suspected pathogen must be isolated from the new host, grown again in pure culture, and shown to have the same characteristics as the original pathogen.

Some exceptions to Koch's postulates do exist. Some pathogens, such as the pathogen that is thought to cause syphilis (SIH fuh lus), cannot be grown in pure culture on artificial media. Artificial media are the nutrients that the bacteria need to survive and reproduce. Pathogens are grown on this media in the laboratory. Also, in the case of viruses, cultured cells are needed because viruses cannot be grown on artificial media.

STUDY TIP

PURPOSEFUL READING Before reading, predict how the information you learn about diseases can be applied to your daily life. Scan the chapter and focus on the boldfaced headings to get an idea about what you will study. Record your ideas. Refer to the list as you study the chapter.

Table 1 Human Infectious Diseases

Interactive Table

Disease	Cause	Affected Organ System	How Disease is Spread
Tetanus	Bacterium	Nervous system	Soil in deep puncture wound
Strep throat	Bacterium	Respiratory system	Droplets/direct contact
Tuberculosis	Bacterium	Respiratory system	Droplets
Lyme disease	Bacterium	Skeletal and nervous system	Vector (tick)
Chicken pox	Virus	Skin	Droplets/direct contact
Rabies	Virus	Nervous system	Animal bite
Common cold	Virus	Respiratory system	Droplets/direct contact
Influenza	Virus	Respiratory system	Droplets/direct contact
Hepatitis B	Virus	Liver	Direct contact with exchange of body fluids
West Nile	Virus	Nervous system	Vector (mosquito)
Giardia	Protozoan	Digestive tract	Contaminated water
Malaria	Protozoan	Blood and liver	Vector (mosquito)
Athlete's foot	Fungus	Skin	Direct contact or contaminated objects

Spread of Disease

Of the large number of microorganisms that coexist with humans, only a few cause disease. The pathogens vary as much as the diseases themselves. Some might cause mild diseases, such as the common cold. Others cause serious diseases, such as meningitis (men in JI tus), an infection of the coverings of the brain and spinal cord. **Table 1** lists some of the human infectious diseases you might know.

For a pathogen to spread, it must have both a reservoir and a way to spread. A disease **reservoir** is a source of the pathogen in the environment. Reservoirs might be animals, people, or inanimate objects, such as soil.

Human reservoirs Humans are the main reservoir for pathogens that affect humans. They might pass the pathogen directly or indirectly to other humans. Many pathogens might be passed on to other hosts before the person even knows he or she has the disease. An individual that is symptom-free but capable of passing the pathogen is called a carrier. Pathogens that cause colds, influenza (commonly referred to as the flu), and sexually transmitted diseases, such as human immunodeficiency (ih MYEWN noh dih fih shun see) virus (HIV), can be passed on without the person knowing he or she is infected.

VOCABULARY

SCIENCE USAGE V. COMMON USAGE

Carrier

Science usage: person who spreads germs while remaining well
Typhoid fever was spread by a carrier known as "Typhoid Mary."

Common usage: a person or corporation in the transportation business
Freight is shipped by carriers.

Animal reservoirs Other animals also are reservoirs of pathogens that can be passed to humans. Influenza and rabies are examples of human diseases listed in **Table 1** that are caused by pathogens passed to humans from other animals. Influenza can infect pigs and various types of birds. Rabies is found in domestic dogs and many wild animals, such as bats, foxes, skunks, and raccoons.

Other reservoirs Some bacteria normally found in the soil, such as tetanus bacteria, can cause disease in humans. The tetanus bacteria can cause a serious infection if it contaminates a deep wound in the body. Contamination of wounds by bacteria was a major cause of death during wars before the development of antibiotics and vaccinations.

Contaminated water or food is another reservoir of pathogens for human disease. One of the main purposes of sewage treatment plants is the safe disposal of human feces, which prevents contamination of the water supply by pathogens. Contaminated water used in growing or preparing food can transfer pathogens. Food also can become contaminated through contact with humans or insects such as flies.

Transmission of pathogens Pathogens mainly are transmitted to humans in four ways: direct contact, indirectly through the air, indirectly through touching contaminated objects, or by organisms called vectors that carry pathogens. **Figure 3** illustrates some of the ways pathogens can be transmitted to humans.

Direct Contact Direct contact with other humans is one of the major modes of transmission of pathogens. Diseases such as colds, infectious mononucleosis (mah noh new klee OH sus)(commonly referred to as mono, or the "kissing disease"), herpes (HUR peez), and sexually transmitted diseases are caused by pathogens passed through direct contact.

CAREERS IN BIOLOGY

Epidemiologist An epidemiologist studies disease patterns to help prevent and control the spread of diseases. An epidemiologist might track the spread of a new strain of influenza and advise the public on safety concerns.

Figure 3 Diseases can be transmitted to humans in various ways.

Identify ***ways to prevent contracting diseases if contact cannot be avoided.***

Direct contact

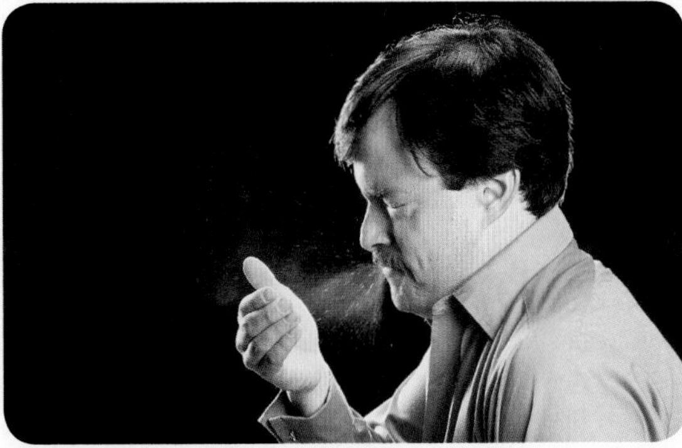

Indirect contact through air

Indirect contact by objects

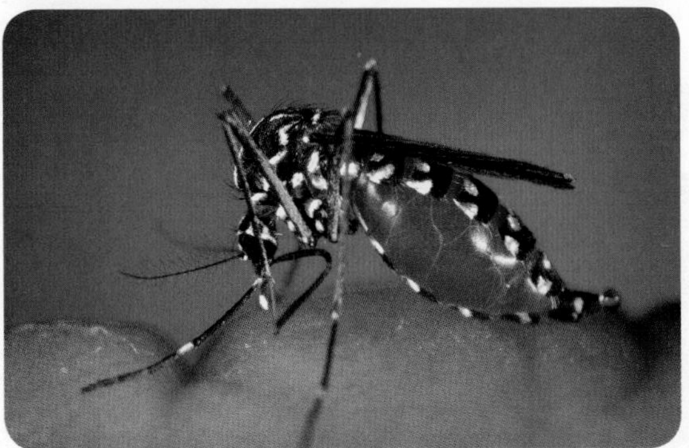

Vectors

(tl)SuperStock, (tr)Grapes-Michaud/Science Source, (bl)Bonnie Kamin/PhotoEdit, (br)CDC/James Gathany

Indirect contact Some pathogens can be passed through the air. When a person with an infectious disease sneezes or coughs, pathogens can be passed along with the tiny mucous droplets. These droplets then can spread pathogens to another person or to an object.

Many organisms can survive on objects handled by humans. Cleansing of dishes, utensils, and countertops with detergents as well as careful hand-washing help prevent the spread of diseases that are passed in this manner. As a result, there are various food rules that restaurants must abide by that are based on preventing the spread of disease.

Vectors Certain diseases can be transmitted by vectors. The most common vectors are arthropods, which include biting insects such as mosquitoes and ticks. Recall from **Table 1** that Lyme disease, malaria, and West Nile virus are diseases that are passed to humans by vectors. The West Nile virus, which is currently spreading across the United States, is transmitted from horses and other mammals to humans by mosquitoes. Flies can transmit pathogens by landing on infected materials, such as feces, and then landing on materials handled or eaten by humans.

Launch Lab

Review Based on what you have read about the spread of disease, how would you now answer the analysis questions?

Describe how diseases are spread to humans.

Symptoms of Disease

When you become ill with a disease such as the flu, why do you feel aches and pains, and why do you cough and sneeze? The pathogen, such as an influenza virus or bacteria, has invaded some of the cells of your body. The virus multiplies in the cells and leaves the cells either by exocytosis or by causing the cell to burst. Thus, the virus damages tissues and even kills some cells. When pathogenic bacteria invade the body, harmful chemicals or toxins might be produced. The toxins can be carried throughout the body via the bloodstream and damage various parts of the body.

■ **Figure 4 Immunology Through Time**
For centuries, scientists have struggled to learn about the human immune system. Today, scientists are working to stop HIV, a virus that has attacked the immune system of over 40 million people worldwide.

1800 — 1900 — 1970

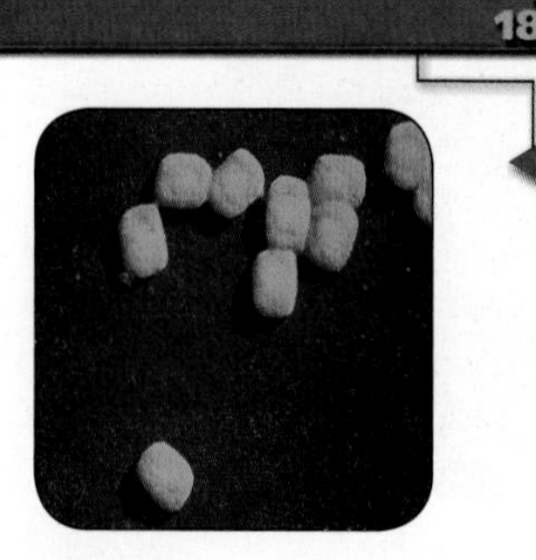

1796 Edward Jenner discovers that a patient vaccinated with the cowpox virus is immune to smallpox.

1908 Elie Metchnikoff observes phagocytosis, and Paul Ehrlich describes antibodies. They share a Nobel Prize for their discoveries.

1975 César Milstein and his research team develop a technique to clone a specific antibody.

1981 The first clinical description of acquired immunodeficiency syndrome (AIDS) is established.

Toxins produced by pathogens can affect specific organ systems. The tetanus bacteria produce a potent toxin that causes spasms in the voluntary muscles. The disease botulism (BAH chuh lih zum) usually is caused when a person consumes food in which the botulism bacteria have grown and produced a toxin. This toxin paralyzes nerves. The toxin from the botulism bacteria can cause disease in humans even when no bacteria are present.

Some types of bacteria, some protozoans, and all viruses invade and live inside cells, causing damage. Because the cells are damaged, they might die, causing symptoms in the host. Some disease symptoms, such as coughing and sneezing, are triggered by the immune system, as discussed later in this chapter. For a closer look at research on the immune system, examine **Figure 4.**

Disease Patterns

As outbreaks of diseases spread, certain patterns are observed. Agencies such as community health departments, the Centers for Disease Control and Prevention (CDC), and the World Health Organization (WHO) continually monitor disease patterns to help control the spread of diseases. The CDC, with headquarters in Atlanta, Georgia, receives information from doctors and medical clinics and publishes a weekly report about the incidence of specific diseases, as shown in **Figure 5.** The WHO similarly watches disease incidence throughout the world.

Some diseases, such as the common cold, are known as **endemic diseases** because they continually are found in small amounts within the population. Sometimes, a particular disease will have a large outbreak in an area and afflict many people, causing an **epidemic.** If an epidemic is widespread throughout a large region, such as a country, continent, or the entire globe, it is described as **pandemic.**

TABLE 2. Reported cases of notifiable diseases,* by geographic division and area — United States, 2003

Area	Total resident population (in thousands)	AIDS†
UNITED STATES	287,974	44,232**
NEW ENGLAND	14,134	1,697
Maine	1,295	52
N.H.	1,274	37
Vt.	616	16
Mass.	6,422	757
R.I.	1,068	102
Conn.	3,459	733
MID. ATLANTIC	40,038	10,142
Upstate N.Y.	11,385	1,589
N.Y. City	7,749	5,133
N.J.	8,575	1,514
Pa.	12,329	1,906
E.N. CENTRAL	45,635	3,875
Ohio	11,409	775
Ind.	6,157	506
Ill.	12,586	1,734
Mich.	10,043	676
Wis.	5,440	184
W.N. CENTRAL	19,464	844
Minn.	5,025	179
Iowa	2,936	75
Mo.	5,670	404
N. Dak.	634	2
S. Dak.	760	13
Nebr.	1,728	60
Kans.	2,712	111
S. ATLANTIC	53,564	12,191
Del.	806	216
Md.	5,451	1,572
D.C.	569	961

Figure 5 The Centers for Disease Control and Prevention publish reports on the incidence of certain diseases.

***Infer** how these reports are helpful in understanding disease patterns.*

1985 Flossie Wong-Staal and her team clone HIV, enabling scientists to create a test to determine whether or not a person has HIV.

2004 HIV infection is pandemic in sub-Saharan Africa, where 10 percent of the world's population has 60 percent of the world's HIV infections.

1980 1990 2000

1984 Luc Montagnier and Robert Gallo independently announce the discovery of the virus that causes AIDS.

1999 Dr. Beatrice Hahn hypothesizes that humans most likely were exposed to HIV from a chimp species found in west equatorial Africa.

2009 Treatments for HIV/AIDS that use a combination of targeted chemotherapy and highly active retroviral treatments seek out and destroy HIV/AIDS-infected cells.

(t)James Gathany/Centers for Disease Control, (c)Bill Branson/National Cancer Institute, (b)Steve Wood/UAB Creative and Marketing

■ **Figure 6** Penicillin, a widely used antibiotic, is secreted by the mold called *Penicillium,* shown growing on these oranges.
Determine ***why many strengths and varieties of penicillin and other antibiotics are needed.***

Treating and Fighting Diseases

A medical professional may prescribe a drug to help the body fight a disease. One type of prescription drug is an **antibiotic** (an ti bi AH tihk), which is a substance that can kill or inhibit the growth of microorganisms. Penicillin is secreted by the fungus *Penicillium,* which is shown in **Figure 6.** This fungus secretes the chemical penicillin to kill competing bacteria that grow on the fungal food source. Penicillin was isolated, purified, and first used in humans during World War II. Many other fungal secretions are used as antibiotics, such as erythromycin, neomycin, and gentamicin. Synthetic antibiotics also have been developed by pharmaceutical companies.

Chemical agents also are used in the treatment of protozoan and fungal diseases. Some antiviral drugs are used to treat herpes infections, influenza in the elderly, and HIV infections. Most viral diseases are handled by the body's built-in defense system—the immune system.

Connection to Health Over the last 60 years, the widespread use of antibiotics has caused many bacteria to become resistant to particular antibiotics. Natural selection occurs when organisms with favorable variations survive, reproduce, and pass their variations to the next generation. Bacteria in a population might have a trait that enables them to survive when a particular antibiotic is present. These bacteria can reproduce quickly and pass on the variation. Because reproduction can occur so rapidly in bacteria, the number of antibiotic-resistant bacteria in a population can increase quickly, too.

MiniLAB 1

Evaluate the Spread of Pathogens

How can you evaluate the spread of disease?
Investigate what possible diseases might be transmitted by common items.

Procedure

1. Read and complete the lab safety form.
2. Observe all the items given to you by your teacher.
3. Infer the types of diseases each item could pass on to a human (if any).
4. Evaluate the likelihood of each item transmitting a disease to a human and devise a scale for assessing each item's probability for transmitting an infectious disease.

Analysis

1. **Identify** the types of pathogens that might be transmitted by the items you were given and the methods of transmission of each pathogen.
2. **Infer** the items most likely to be disease reservoirs.
3. **Describe** possible disease patterns of each pathogen.
4. **Infer** how you could prevent getting diseases from these possible pathogens.

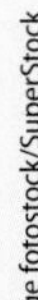

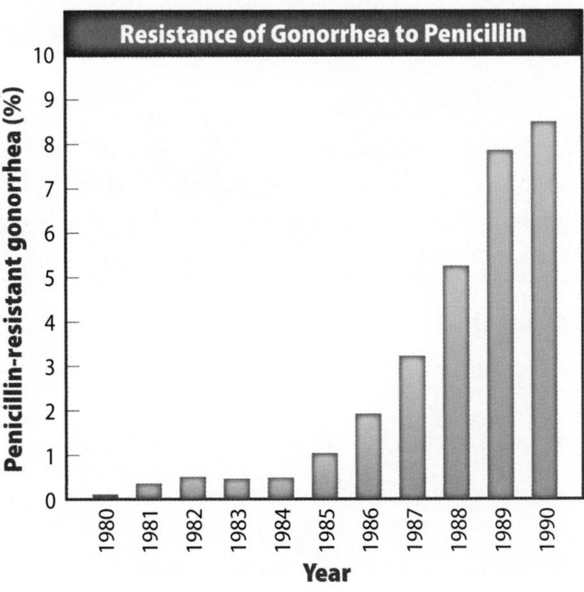

■ **Figure 7** The graph shows the reported incidence of penicillin-resistant gonorrhea in the United States from 1980–1990.

Analyze ***What is the percentage increase from 1980 to 1990?***

Antibiotic resistance of bacteria has presented the medical community with some problems with treating certain diseases. For example, penicillin was used effectively for many years to treat gonorrhea (gah nuh REE uh), a sexually transmitted disease, but now most strains of gonorrhea bacteria are resistant to penicillin. As a result, new drug therapies are needed to treat gonorrhea. **Figure 7** shows the increase in gonorrhea resistance as the bacteria have gained resistance to treatment with antibiotics.

Another treatment problem is with staphylococcal disease—it is acquired in high-density living conditions, which can result in skin infections, pneumonia (noo MOH nyuh), or meningitis. These staphylococci are often strains of bacteria that are resistant to many current antibiotics and can be difficult to treat.

REVIEW IT! Infectious Diseases

Section Summary

- Pathogens, such as bacteria, viruses, protozoans, and fungi, cause infectious diseases.
- Koch's postulates demonstrate how a particular pathogen causes a certain disease.
- Pathogens are found in disease reservoirs and are transmitted to humans directly and indirectly.
- The symptoms of disease are caused by invasion of the pathogen and the response of the host immune system.
- Treatment of infectious disease includes the use of antibiotics and antiviral drugs.

Self Check

Understand Main Ideas

1. MAINIDEA **Compare** the mode of transmission of the common cold with that of malaria.
2. **Summarize** some symptoms of bacterial infectious disease.
3. **Define** *infectious disease* and give three examples of infectious diseases.
4. **Illustrate** Koch's postulates for a bacterial infectious disease in a rabbit by drawing a graphic organizer or a concept map.
5. **Describe** how viruses can cause infectious diseases.
6. **Infer** why a person might be exposed to tetanus bacteria after stepping on a dirty nail.

Think Critically

7. **Evaluate** how the practice of medicating animal feed with a low level of antibiotics might play a role in the development of antibiotic-resistant bacteria.

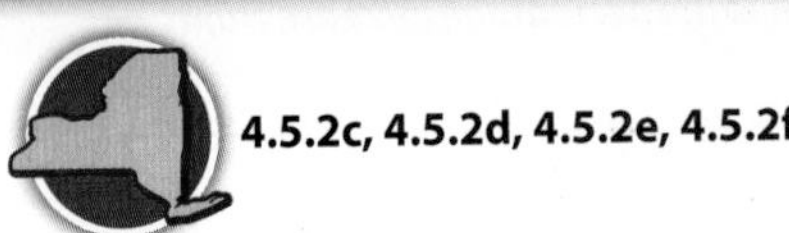 Science Notebook

2 The Immune System

4.5.2c, 4.5.2d, 4.5.2e, 4.5.2f

BIOLOGY 4U

We live with a number of potential pathogens such as bacteria and viruses that can cause disease. Like a fort protecting a city from attack, the immune system protects the body against these and other disease-causing organisms.

REVIEW VOCABULARY

white blood cells: large, nucleated blood cells that play a major role in protecting the body from foreign substances and microorganisms

NEW VOCABULARY

complement protein
interferon
lymphocyte
antibody
B cell
helper T cell
cytotoxic T cell
memory cell
immunization

Multilingual eGlossary

Figure 8 These bacteria normally are found on human skin and provide protection from pathogens.

Color-Enhanced SEM Magnification: 14,000×

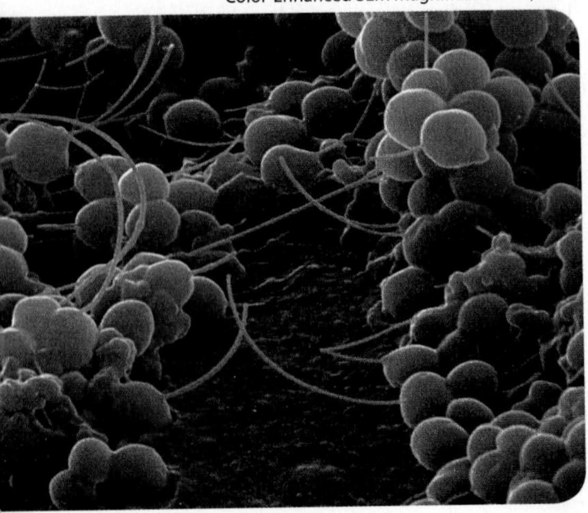

MAIN IDEA

The immune system has two main components: nonspecific immunity and specific immunity.

Essential Questions

- What are the similarities and differences between nonspecific and specific immunity?
- What is the structure and function of the lymphatic system?
- What is the importance of B cells and T cells?
- What are the differences between passive and active immunity?

Nonspecific Immunity

At the time of birth, the body has a number of defenses in the immune system that fight off pathogens. These defenses are nonspecific because they are not aimed at a specific pathogen. They protect the body from any pathogen that the body encounters.

The nonspecific immunity provided by the body helps to prevent disease. Nonspecific immunity also helps to slow the progression of the disease while the specific immunity begins to develop its defenses. Specific immunity is the most effective immune response, but non-specific immunity is the first line of defense.

Barriers Like the strong walls of a fort, barriers are used by the body to protect against pathogens. These barriers are found in areas of the body where pathogens might enter.

Skin barrier The first major line of defense is the unbroken skin and its secretions. Skin contains layers of living cells covered by many layers of dead skin cells. By forming a barrier, the layers of dead skin cells help protect against invasion by microorganisms. Many of the bacteria that live symbiotically on the skin digest skin oils to produce acids that inhibit many pathogens. **Figure 8** shows some normal bacteria found on the skin that protect the skin from attack.

Chemical barriers Saliva, tears, and nasal secretions contain the enzyme lysozyme. Lysozyme breaks down bacterial cell walls, which kills pathogens.

Another chemical defense is mucus, which is secreted by many inner surfaces of the body. It acts as a protective barrier, blocking bacteria from sticking to the inner epithelial cells. Cilia also line the airway. Their beating motion sends any bacteria caught in the mucus away from the lungs. When the airway becomes infected, extra mucus is secreted, which triggers coughing and sneezing to help move the infected mucus out of the body.

A third chemical defense is the hydrochloric acid secreted in your stomach. In addition to digestion, stomach acid kills many microorganisms found in food that could cause disease.

GET IT? **Compare and contrast** the different types of barriers of the immune system.

David Scharf/Science Source

Nonspecific responses to invasion Even if an enemy gets through the walls of a town's fort, defense doesn't end. Similarly, the body has nonspecific immune responses to pathogens that get beyond its barriers.

Cellular defense If foreign microorganisms enter the body, the cells of the immune system, shown in **Table 2,** defend the body. One method of defense is phagocytosis. White blood cells, especially neutrophils and macrophages, are phagocytic. Recall that phagocytosis is the process by which phagocytic cells surround and internalize the foreign microorganisms. The phagocytes then release digestive enzymes and other harmful chemicals from their lysosomes, destroying the microorganism.

A series of about 20 proteins that are found in the blood plasma are called complement proteins. **Complement proteins** enhance phagocytosis by helping the phagocytic cells bind better to pathogens and activating the phagocytes. Some complement proteins can form a complex in the plasma membrane of a pathogen. This complex forms a pore, which aids in the destruction of the pathogen, as shown in **Figure 9.**

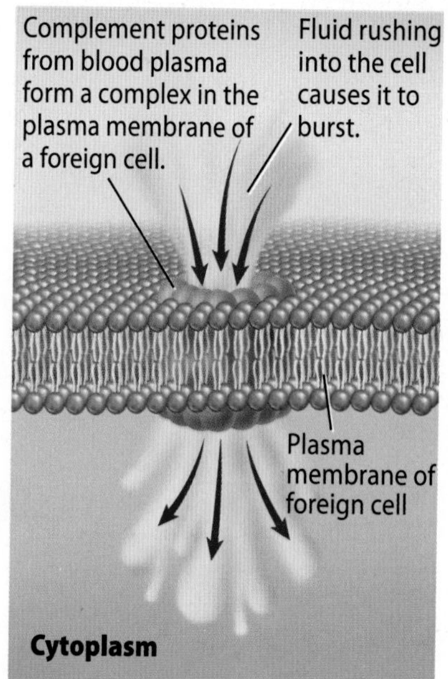

Complement proteins from blood plasma form a complex in the plasma membrane of a foreign cell.
Fluid rushing into the cell causes it to burst.
Plasma membrane of foreign cell
Cytoplasm

Figure 9 For some pathogens, complement proteins can form a pore in the plasma membrane of the invading cell.

Animation

Interferon When a virus enters the body, another cellular defense helps prevent the virus from spreading. Virus-infected cells secrete a protein called **interferon.** Interferon binds to neighboring cells and stimulates these cells to produce antiviral proteins which can prevent viral replication in these cells.

Inflammatory response Another nonspecific response, the inflammatory response, is a complex series of events that involves many chemicals and immune cells that help enhance the overall immune response. When pathogens damage tissue, chemicals are released by both the invader and cells of the body. These chemicals attract phagocytes to the area, increase blood flow to the infected area, and make blood vessels more permeable to allow white blood cells to escape into the infected area. This response aids in the accumulation of white blood cells in the area. Some of the pain, heat, and redness experienced during an infectious disease are the result of the inflammatory response.

Table 2 Cells of the Immune System

Interactive Table

Type of Cell	Example	Function
Neutrophils	Stained LM Magnification: 2150×	Phagocytosis: blood cells that ingest bacteria
Macrophages	Stained LM Magnification: 380×	Phagocytosis: blood cells that ingest bacteria and remove dead neutrophils and other debris
Lymphocytes	Stained LM Magnification: 1800×	Specific immunity (antibodies and killing of pathogens): blood cells that produce antibodies and other chemicals

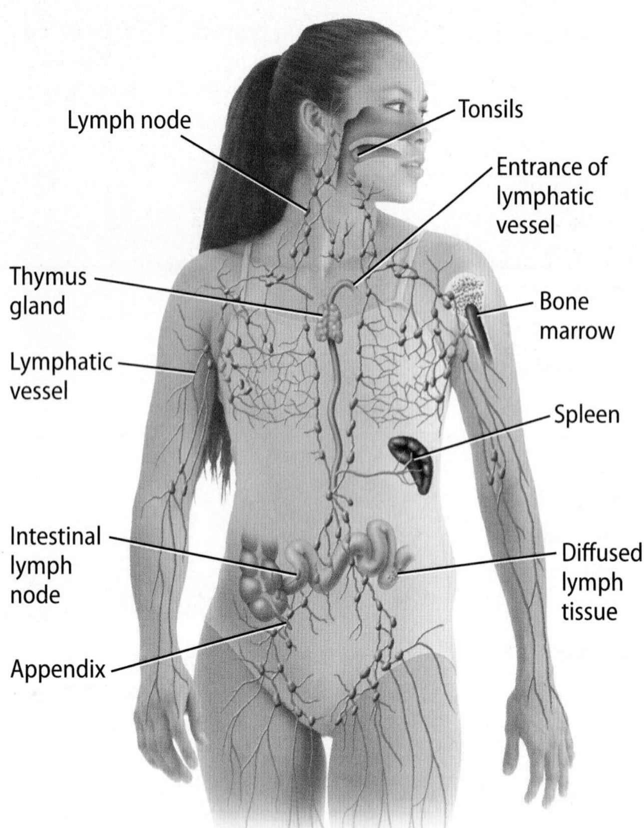

■ **Figure 10** The lymphatic system contains the organs involved in the specific immune response.
***Identify** the lymphatic organ where T cells mature.*

BrainPOP 

VOCABULARY
WORD ORIGIN
Thymus
comes from the Greek word *thymos,* meaning *warty excrescence*

Specific Immunity

Pathogens sometimes get past the nonspecific defense mechanisms. The body has a second line of defense that attacks these pathogens. Specific immunity is more effective, but takes time to develop. This specific response involves the tissues and organs found in the lymphatic system.

Lymphatic system The lymphatic (lim FA tihk) system, illustrated in **Figure 10,** includes organs and cells that filter lymph and blood, destroy foreign microorganisms, and absorb fat. Lymph is the fluid that leaks out of capillaries to bathe body cells. This fluid circulates among the tissue cells, is collected by lymphatic vessels, and is returned to the veins near the heart.

Lymphatic organs The organs of the lymphatic system contain lymphatic tissue, lymphocytes, a few other cell types, and connective tissue. **Lymphocytes** are a type of white blood cell that is produced in red bone marrow. These lymphatic organs include the lymph nodes, tonsils, spleen, thymus (THI mus) gland, and diffused lymphatic tissue found in mucous membranes of the intestinal, respiratory, urinary, and genital tracts.

The lymph nodes filter the lymph and remove foreign materials from the lymph. The tonsils form a protective ring of lymphatic tissue between the nasal and oral cavities. This helps protect against bacteria and other harmful materials in the nose and mouth. The spleen stores blood and destroys damaged red blood cells. It also contains lymphatic tissue that responds to foreign substances in the blood. The thymus gland, which is located above the heart, plays a role in activating a special kind of lymphocyte called T cells. T cells are produced in the bone marrow, but they mature in the thymus gland.

B Cell Response

Antibodies are proteins produced by B lymphocytes that specifically react with a foreign antigen. An antigen is a substance foreign to the body that causes an immune response; it can bind to an antibody or T cell. B lymphocytes, often called **B cells,** are located in all lymphatic tissues and can be thought of as antibody factories. When a portion of a pathogen is presented by a macrophage, B cells produce antibodies. Follow along in **Figure 11,** as you learn about how B cells are activated to produce antibodies.

VISUALIZING Specific Immune Responses

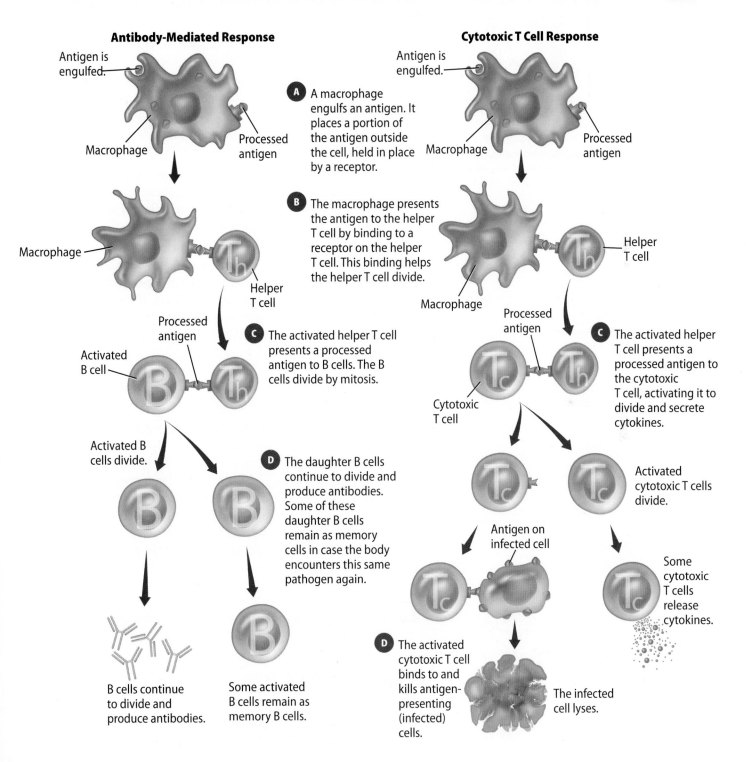

Figure 11 Specific immune responses involve antigens, phagocytes, B cells, helper T cells, and cytotoxic T cells. The antibody-mediated response involves antibodies produced by B cells and memory B cells. The cytotoxic T cell response results in cytotoxic T cell activation.

Antigen is engulfed.

A A macrophage engulfs an antigen. It places a portion of the antigen outside the cell, held in place by a receptor.

Activated B cells divide.

Antigen is engulfed.

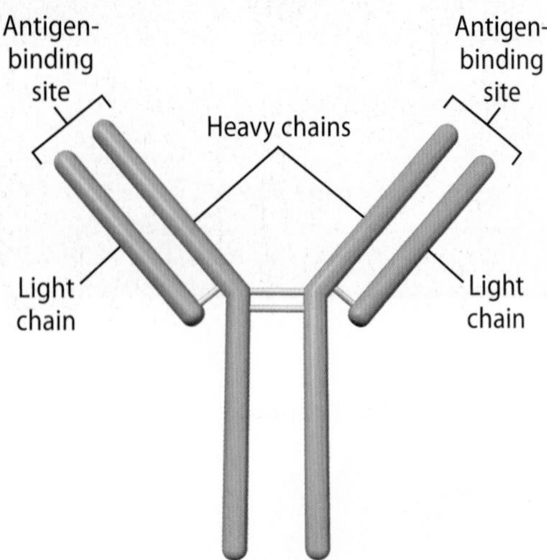

■ **Figure 12** Antibodies are made up of two types of protein chains—heavy and light chains.
Summarize ***which cells produce antibodies.***

When a macrophage surrounds, internalizes, and digests a pathogen, it takes a piece of the pathogen, which is called a processed antigen, and displays it on its membrane, as illustrated in **Figure 11.** In the lymphatic tissues, such as the lymph nodes, the macrophage, with the processed antigen on its surface, binds to a type of lymphocyte called a **helper T cell.** This process activates the helper T cell. This lymphocyte is called a "helper" because it activates antibody secretion in B cells and another type of T cell, which will be discussed later, that aids in killing microorganisms:

- The activated helper T cell reproduces, binds processed antigens, and attaches to a B cell.
- The new helper T cells continue the process of binding antigens, attaching to B cells, and reproducing.
- Once an activated helper T cell binds to a B cell holding an antigen, the B cell begins to manufacture antibodies that specifically bind to the antigen.
- The antibodies can enhance the immune response by binding to microorganisms, making them more susceptible to phagocytosis and by initiating the inflammatory response, helping promote the nonspecific response.

B cells make many combinations of antibodies by using DNA that codes for the production of various heavy and light protein chains that make up antibodies as shown in **Figure 12.** Any heavy chain can combine with any light chain. If a B cell can make 16,000 different kinds of heavy chains and 1200 kinds of light chains, it can make 19,200,000 different types of antibodies (1200 × 16,000).

T Cell Response

Once helper T cells are activated by the presentation of an antigen by macrophages, helper T cells can also bind to and activate a group of lymphocytes called cytotoxic T cells. Activated **cytotoxic T cells** destroy pathogens and release chemicals called cytokines. Cytokines stimulate the cells of the immune system to divide and recruit immune cells to an area of infection. Cytotoxic T cells bind to pathogens, release a chemical attack, and destroy the pathogens. Multiple target cells can be destroyed by a single cytotoxic T cell. **Figure 11** summarizes the activation of cytotoxic T cells.

GET IT? **Summarize** the role that lymphocytes play in immunity.

Passive and Active Immunity

The body's first response to an invasion by a pathogen is called the primary response. For example, if the viral pathogen that causes chicken pox enters the body, nonspecific and specific immune responses eventually defeat the foreign virus and the body is cleared of the pathogen.

One result of the specific immune response is the production of memory B and T cells. **Memory cells** are long-living cells that are exposed to the antigen during the primary immune response. These cells are ready to respond rapidly if the body encounters the same pathogen later. Memory cells protect the body by reducing the likelihood of developing the disease if exposed again to the same pathogen.

Passive immunity Sometimes temporary protection against an infectious disease is needed. This type of temporary protection occurs when antibodies are made by other people or animals and are transferred or injected into the body. For example, passive immunity occurs between a mother and her child. Antibodies produced by the mother are passed through the placenta to the developing fetus and through breast milk to the infant child. These antibodies can protect the child until the infant's immune system matures.

Antibodies developed in humans and animals that are already immune to a specific infectious disease are used to treat some infectious diseases in others. These antibodies are injected into people who have been exposed to that particular infectious disease. Passive immune therapy is available for people who have been exposed to hepatitis A and B, tetanus, and rabies. Antibodies also are available to inactivate snake and scorpion venoms.

Vocabulary

Academic vocabulary

Passive
not active; acted upon
The passive monkey stared lazily at the zoo visitors.

Active immunity Active immunity occurs after the immune system is exposed to disease antigens and memory cells are produced. Active immunity can result from having an infectious disease or immunization. **Immunization,** also called vaccination, is the deliberate exposure of the body to an antigen so that a primary response and immune memory cells will develop. **Table 3** lists some of the common immunizations offered in the United States. Immunizations contain killed or weakened pathogens, which are incapable of causing the disease.

Most immunizations include more than one stimulus to the immune system, given after the first immunization. These booster shots increase the immune response, providing further protection from the disease-causing organism.

Table 3 Common Immunizations — Interactive Table

Immunization	Disease	Contents
DPT	Diphtheria (D), tetanus (T), pertussis (P) (whooping cough)	D: inactivated toxin, T: inactivated toxin, P: inactivated bacteria
Inactivated polio	Poliomyelitis	Inactivated virus
MMR	Measles, mumps, rubella	All three inactivated viruses
Varicella	Chicken pox	Inactivated virus
HIB	Haemophilus influenzae (flu) type b	Portions of bacteria cell wall covering
HBV	Hepatitis B	Subunit of virus

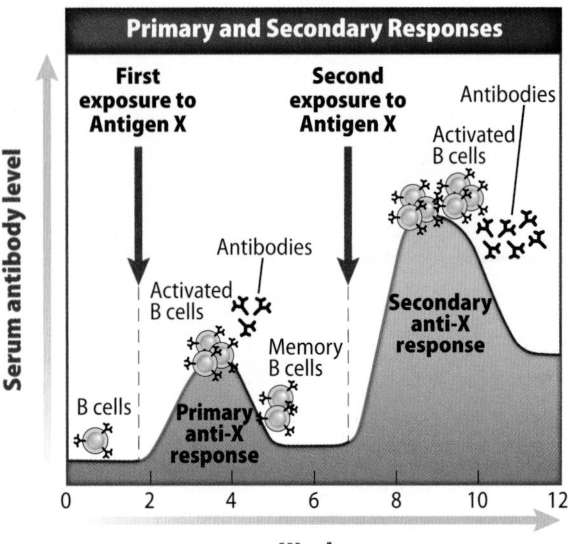

■ **Figure 13** This graph shows the difference between the primary and secondary immune responses to exposure to an antigen.

Analyze ***the differences between the primary and secondary immune responses.***

Personal Tutor

Why are immunizations effective in preventing disease? The characteristics of the secondary immune response, which is the response to a second exposure to an antigen, enable immunizations to be effective in preventing disease. Study the graph in **Figure 13.** Note that the secondary response to the antigen has a number of different characteristics. First, the response is more rapid than the primary response, as shown by the greater steepness in the portion of the curves plotted in red. Second, the overall response, both B and T cell response, is greater during the second exposure. Lastly, the overall memory lasts longer after the second exposure.

Immune System Failure

Defects in the immune system can result in an increased likelihood of developing infectious diseases as well as certain types of cancers. Some diseases can affect the immune system's effectiveness. One such disease called acquired immunodeficiency syndrome (AIDS) results from an infection by human immunodeficiency virus (HIV). AIDS is a serious health problem worldwide.

In 2006, approximately 36,828 AIDS cases were diagnosed in the U.S. In 2006, 14,016 people died of AIDS in the U.S. In 2007, an estimated 33 million people globally were living with HIV infection.

Virtual Lab

Data Analysis LAB 1

Based on Real Data*

Draw a Conclusion

Is passive immune therapy effective for HIV infection? The standard treatment for a patient with an HIV infection is antiviral drug therapy. Unfortunately, the side effects and increasing prevalence of drug-resistant viruses create a need for additional therapies. One area being studied is passive immune therapy.

Data and Observations

The graph shows HIV patient responses to passive immune therapy. The number of viral copies/mL is a measure of the amount of virus in the patient's blood.

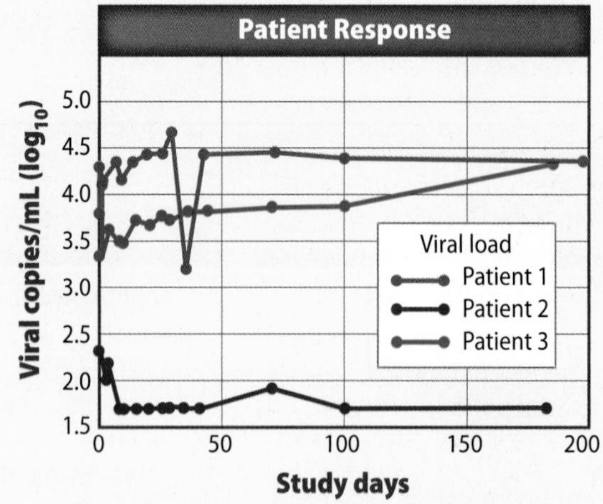

*Data obtained from: Stiegler G., et al. 2002. Antiviral activity of the neutralizing antibodies 2FS and 2F12 in asymptomatic HIV-1-infected humans: a phase I evaluation. *AIDS* 16: 2019–2025.

Think Critically

1. **Compare** the patient responses to passive immune therapy.
2. **Explain** whether the researchers can conclude if passive immune therapy is effective.

Recall the important role that helper T cells play in specific immunity. HIV infects mainly helper T cells, also called $CD4^+$ cells because these cells have a receptor on the outside of their plasma membrane. This $CD4^+$ receptor is used by medical professionals to identify these cells, as illustrated in **Figure 14.**

HIV is an RNA virus that infects helper T cells. The helper T cells become HIV factories, producing new viruses that are released and infect other helper T cells. Over time, the number of helper T cells in an infected person decreases, making the person less able to fight disease. HIV infection usually has an early phase during the first six to twelve weeks while viruses are replicating in helper T cells.

The patient suffers symptoms such as night sweats and fever, but these symptoms are reduced after about eight to ten weeks. Then, the patient exhibits few symptoms for a period of time as long as ten years but is capable of passing the infection through sexual intercourse or blood products. HIV is a secondary immunodeficiency disease, which means that the immune system of a previously healthy person fails. Without antiviral drug therapy, the patient usually dies from a secondary infection from another pathogen after about ten years of being infected with HIV. Current antiviral drug therapy is aimed at controlling the replication of HIV in the body. Resistant strains, expensive drugs, and side effects are all issues that patients face. Researchers and health care providers are working to meet these needs and continue the search for a cure.

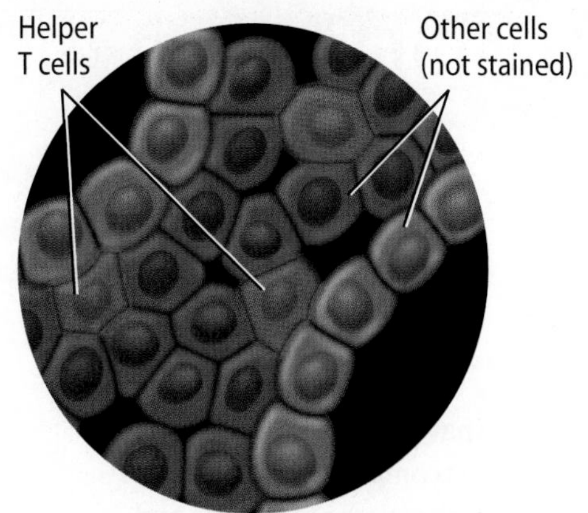

■ **Figure 14** Helper T cells have receptors on the surface that are used to identify them in the laboratory.

REVIEW IT! The Immune System

Section Summary

- The nonspecific immune response includes the skin barrier, secreted chemicals, and cellular pathways that activate phagocytosis.
- The specific immune response involves the activation of B cells, which produce antibodies, and T cells, which include helper T cells and cytotoxic T cells.
- Passive immunity involves receiving antibodies against a disease.
- Active immunity results in immune memory against a disease.
- HIV attacks helper T cells, causing an immune system failure.

Self Check

Understand Main Ideas

1. MAINIDEA **Compare** specific and nonspecific immune responses.
2. **Describe** the steps involved in activating an antibody response to an antigen.
3. **Identify** ways passive and active immunity can be acquired.
4. **Describe** the structure and function of the lymphatic system.
5. **Infer** why the destruction of helper T cells in HIV infection is so devastating to specific immunity.

Think Critically

6. **Hypothesize** what happens when an HIV strain mutates such that viral-replication drugs are no longer effective.
7. **Evaluate** the effects of severe combined immune deficiency on a child born without T cell immunity.

MATH IN ▶ Biology

8. Antibodies are made of two light protein chains and two heavy protein chains. If the molecular weight of a light chain is 25,000 and the molecular weight of a heavy chain is 50,000, what is the molecular weight of an antibody?

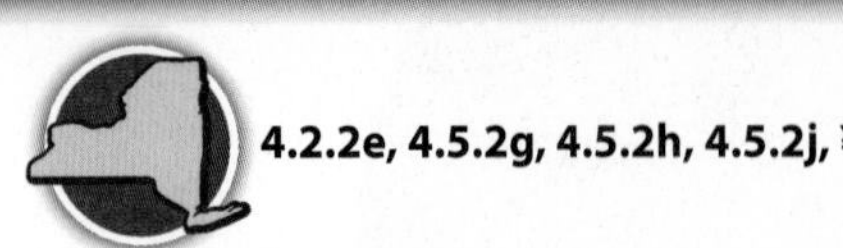

USE IT! Science Notebook

3 Noninfectious Disorders

4.2.2e, 4.5.2g, 4.5.2h, 4.5.2j, ¥a

MAIN IDEA

Noninfectious disorders include genetic disorders, degenerative diseases, metabolic diseases, cancer, and inflammatory diseases.

Essential Questions

- What are the five categories of noninfectious diseases?
- What is the role of allergens in allergies?
- What is the difference between allergies and anaphylactic shock?

BIOLOGY 4 U

Maybe you have heard your parents or grandparents complain about their arthritis, which causes achy bones and joints. Perhaps some of your relatives have diabetes or have survived cancer. You or a friend might have an allergy to dust, plant pollens, or other environmental substances. These disorders are different from infectious diseases caused by pathogens.

Review Vocabulary

cancer: uncontrolled cell division that can be caused by environmental factors or changes in enzyme production in the cell cycle

New Vocabulary

degenerative disease
metabolic disease
allergy
anaphylactic shock

Multilingual eGlossary

Genetic Disorders

Not all diseases or body disorders are caused by pathogens. Some diseases are caused by the inheritance of genes that do not function properly in the body, such as albinism, sickle cell anemia, Huntington's disease, and hemophilia. There are also chromosomal disorders that result from abnormal chromosome numbers, such as Down syndrome. Many diseases are complex and have both an environmental and a genetic cause.

Coronary artery disease (CAD) is an example of a condition with environmental and genetic origins. This cardiovascular disease can result in blockage of arteries, shown in **Figure 15,** that deliver oxygenated blood to the heart muscle. There is a genetic component that increases a person's risk of developing CAD. Environmental factors such as diet contribute to the development of this complex disease. Families with a history of CAD have a two to seven times greater risk of having CAD than families without a history of CAD. The exact genetic factors, however, are not known.

GET IT? **Summarize** the factors that cause coronary artery disease.

■ **Figure 15** When blood cannot flow through a coronary artery, such as the diseased artery shown here, a heart attack or sudden death can result.

Stained LM Magnification: 25×

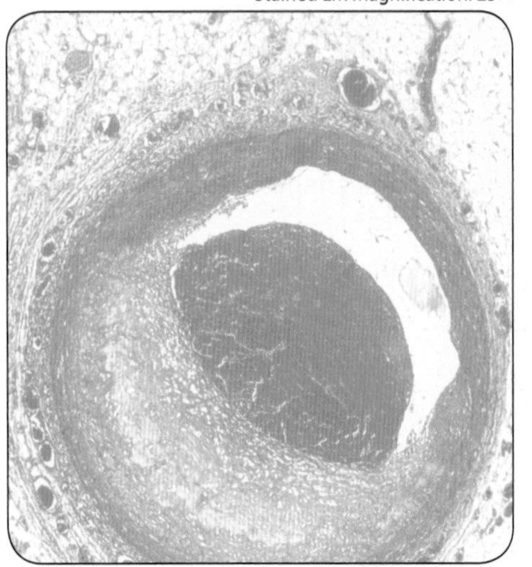

Degenerative Diseases

Some diseases called **degenerative** (dih JEH nuh ruh tihv) **diseases** are the result of a part of the body wearing out. This can be due to the natural aging process. However, a degenerative condition, such as degenerative arthritis, could occur sooner than would be expected if the person is genetically predisposed to the disease or if the person's joints have experienced an increased amount of wear and tear. Degenerative arthritis is common; most people have it by age 70. It is found in almost all vertebrate animals. Arteriosclerosis (ar tir ee oh skluh ROH sus), which is a hardening of the arteries, is another example of a degenerative disease. Because degenerative diseases also have a genetic component, some individuals might be more likely to develop a degenerative disease because of their genetic makeup.

Metabolic Diseases

Metabolic disease results from an error in a biochemical pathway. Some metabolic diseases result in the inability to digest specific amino acids or to regulate body processes. When the pancreas does not make the proper amount of insulin and glucose does not enter body cells normally, the condition is known as Type 2 diabetes. This results in high glucose levels in the bloodstream, which causes damage to many organs including the kidneys and the retinas of the eyes. Metabolic diseases can have a genetic component but also can involve environmental factors such as diet.

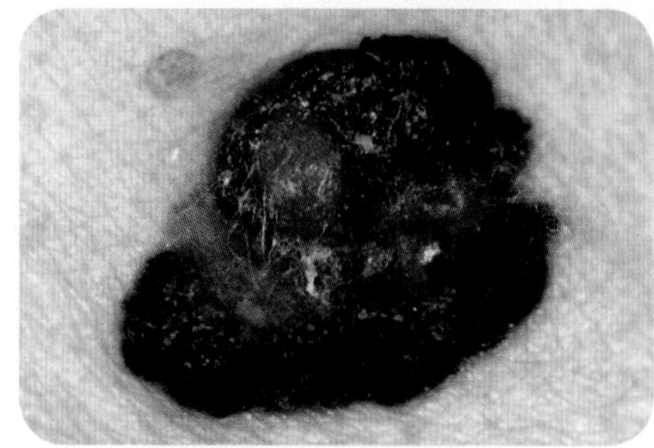

■ **Figure 16** Cancer is due to an abnormal increase in cell division in the body, resulting in a tumor such as this skin tumor.

Infer *why this large growth is so life-threatening.*

Cancer

Cancer is characterized by abnormal cell growth. Normally, certain regulatory molecules in the body control the beginning and end of the cell cycle. If this control is lost, abnormal cell growth results that could lead to various types of tumors, as shown in **Figure 16.** The abnormal cells can interfere with normal body functions and can travel throughout the body. Cancer can develop in any body tissue or organ, including the blood cells. Cancer in the blood cells is called leukemia. Both genetic and environmental factors have been shown to cause cancer.

Connection to History Cancer has been a disease that affects humans since ancient times. Egyptian mummies show evidence of bone cancer, and ancient Greek scientists described different kinds of cancer. Medieval manuscripts have reported details about cancer.

MiniLAB 2

Compare Cancerous and Healthy Cells

How do cancerous cells and healthy cells differ in appearance? Observe and compare liver cells afflicted with this common noninfectious disease to healthy liver cells.

Procedure

1. Read and complete the lab safety form.
2. Place a prepared **slide of healthy human liver cells** on a **microscope.**

WARNING: ***Never touch broken microscope slides or other broken glass materials.***

3. Observe the healthy liver cells under several different magnifications.
4. Sketch a diagram of several healthy liver cells.
5. Repeat steps 2–4 with a prepared **slide of cancerous human liver cells.**

Analysis

1. **Compare and contrast** the features of healthy liver cells with those of cancerous liver cells.
2. **Infer** why it would not be dangerous to handle an object that was handled by a patient with liver cancer.
3. **Describe** how cancer disrupts the body's homeostasis.

LM Magnification: 50×

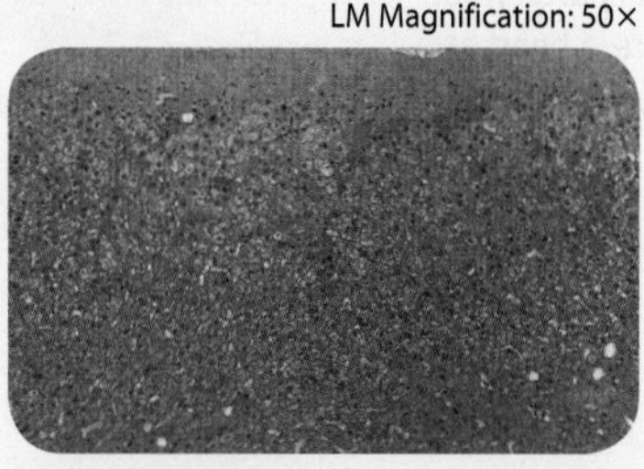

Healthy cells

LM Magnification: 50×

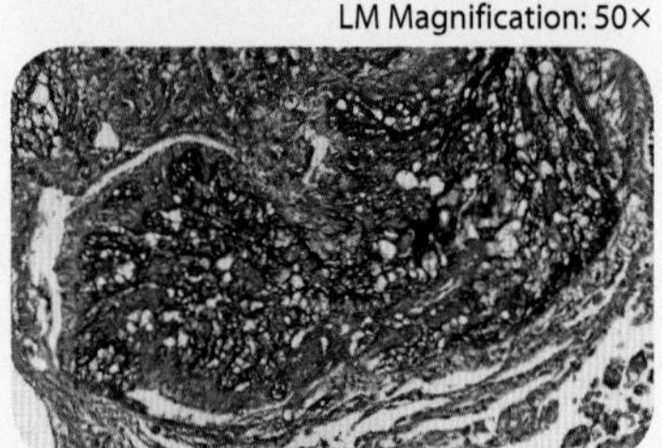

Cancerous cells

Inflammatory Diseases

Inflammatory diseases, such as allergies and autoimmunity, are diseases in which the body produces an inflammatory response to a common substance. Recall from Section 2 that infectious diseases also result in an inflammatory response. However, the inflammatory response in an infectious disease enhances the overall immune response. This inflammatory response is a result of the immune system removing bacteria or other microorganisms from the body. In inflammatory disease, the inflammatory response is not helpful to the body.

Allergies Certain individuals might have an abnormal reaction to environmental antigens. A response to environmental antigens is called an **allergy.** These antigens are called allergens and include things such as plant pollens, dust, dust mites, and various foods, as illustrated in **Table 4.** An individual becomes sensitized to the allergen and has localized inflammatory response with swollen itchy eyes, stuffy nose, sneezing, and sometimes a skin rash. These symptoms are the result of a chemical called histamine that is released by certain white blood cells. Antihistamine medications can help alleviate some of these symptoms.

GET IT? **Explain** how allergies are related to the immune system.

Table 4 Common Allergens — Interactive Table

Allergen	Example	Description
Dust mite	Color-Enhanced SEM Magnification: 170×	Dust mites are found in mattresses, pillows, and carpets. Mites and mite feces are allergens.
Plant pollen	Color-Enhanced SEM Magnification: 2300×	Different parts of the country have very different pollen seasons; people can react to one or more pollens, and a person's pollen allergy season might be from early spring to late fall.
Animal dander	Color-Enhanced SEM Magnification: 1175×	Dander is skin flakes; cat and dog allergies are the most common, but people also are allergic to pets such as birds, hamsters, rabbits, mice, and gerbils.
Peanut		Allergic reaction to peanuts can result in anaphylaxis. Peanut allergy is responsible for more fatalities than any other type of allergy.
Latex		Latex comes from the milky sap of the rubber tree, found in Africa and Southeast Asia; the exact cause of latex allergy is unknown.

(1)Andrew Syred/Science Source, (2)Eye of Science/Science Source, (3)Biophoto Associates/Science Source, (4)C Squared Studios/Getty Images, (5)Brian G. Green/Getty Images

Severe allergic reactions to particular allergens can result in **anaphylactic** (an uh fuh LAK tik) **shock,** which causes a massive release of histamine. In anaphylactic shock, the smooth muscles in the bronchioles contract, which restricts air flow into and out of the lungs.

Common allergens that cause severe allergic reactions are bee stings, penicillin, peanuts, and latex, which is used to make balloons and surgical gloves. People who are extremely sensitive to these allergens require prompt medical treatment if exposed to these agents because anaphylactic reactions are life-threatening. Allergies and anaphylactic reactions are known to have an inherited component.

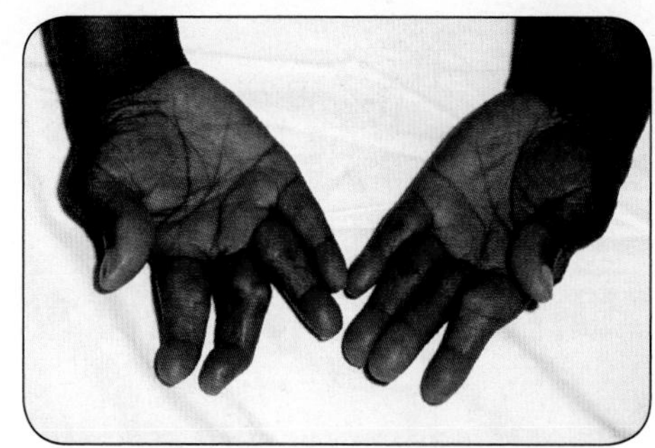

Figure 17 The large knobs and deformaties of these fingers are due to rheumatoid arthritis, an autoimmune disease.

Sue Ford/Science Source

Autoimmunity During the development of the immune system, the immune system learns not to attack proteins produced by the body. However, some people develop autoimmunity (aw toh ih MYOON ih tee) and do form antibodies to their own proteins, which injures their cells.

Figure 17 shows the hands of a person with rheumatoid arthritis—a form of arthritis in which antibodies attack the joints. Degenerative arthritis, the form of arthritis that you read about earlier in the section on degenerative diseases, is not caused by autoimmunity.

Rheumatic fever and lupus (LEW pus) are other examples of autoimmune disorders. Rheumatic fever is an inflammation in which antibodies attack the valves of the heart. This can lead to damage to the heart valves and cause the valves to leak or not close properly as blood moves through the heart. Lupus is a disorder in which autoantibodies are formed and attack healthy tissue. As a result, many organs are vulnerable to attack by the body's own immune system.

REVIEW IT! Noninfectious Disorders

Section Summary

- Noninfectious disorders often have both a genetic and an environmental component.
- The inflammatory response to an infectious disease enhances the immune response, but the inflammatory response to an inflammatory disease is not helpful to the body.
- Allergies are due to an overactive immune response to allergens found in the environment.
- Anaphylactic shock is a severe hypersensitivity to particular allergens.
- Autoimmunity results in an immune attack on body cells.

Self Check

Understand Main Ideas

1. MAINIDEA **Identify** the type of noninfectious disease shown in **Figure 15.**
2. **Explain** the role of allergens in allergies.
3. **Create** a diagram demonstrating the process of anaphylactic shock.
4. **Categorize** the following diseases into the categories used in this section: sickle cell disease, diabetes, vertebral degeneration, autoimmunity, and leukemia.

Think Critically

5. **Hypothesize** several causes of chronic bronchitis (inflammation of the bronchioles) found in coal miners.
6. **Create** a plan that limits a child's exposure to cat dander when the child is found to be allergic to that allergen.

WRITING IN ▶ Biology

7. Create a pamphlet explaining the symptoms of allergies and listing common allergens.

cutting-edge BIOLOGY

1.1.1b, 1.1.2a, 1.1.3b, 4.5.2e

Uncovering New Medical Treatments

Scientific advances such as the buckyball and the human genome project are being used to develop treatments for common ailments and life-threatening diseases.

An Allergy Treatment A recent study gives hope to allergy sufferers in the form of a tiny, carbon ball. Buckminsterfullerenes (nicknamed buckyballs) are spherical cages about 1–10 nanometers in size made up of 60 carbon atoms. They were discovered in 1985 by scientists at Rice University in Houston who vaporized graphite with a laser. Their discovery has started a new field of research in chemistry. Buckyballs have many possible uses because they are so stable and can be easily combined with other types of atoms.

In 2007, a study revealed that buckyballs prevent allergic responses in tissue cultures and in mice. Your immune system reacts to allergens by releasing histamines and other chemicals. It is thought that buckyballs can prevent allergens from activating the histamine response.

Mapping Diseases Since the completion of the Human Genome Project in 2003, scientists at the Baylor College of Medicine Human Genome Sequencing Center (BCM-HGSC) have been using what they know about the human genome to research the causes of diseases and develop more customized treatments. Researchers at BCM-HGSC can now sequence whole genomes, testing for every known genetic disorder.

They are currently looking at variation in human DNA associated with diseases such as autism, Parkinson's disease, heart disease, bipolar disorder and many types of cancer. Genome sequencing can improve diagnosis and early detection of disease and can help researchers develop vaccines and antibiotics.

The buckyball is a soccer ball-shaped molecule of carbon atoms.

Sequencing DNA from cancer cells is very promising. It is known that cancer is caused by genetic mutations. However, the tumors in each cancer patient can be unique as a result of the specific mutations in that tumor. By understanding the mutations, doctors can develop personalized treatments.

Investigate

Communicate Research other new medical advances and treatments discovered in New York. Work with a partner to develop a creative way to share your findings with the class. Ideas include a public service announcement, news article, poster, or presentation.

WebQuest

BioLAB

1.1.1c, 1.1.2a, 1.1.3b, 1.3.5b, ¥a, ¥m, ¥o

Forensics: How do you find patient zero?

Background: Imagine that a new disease—"cellphonitis"—has invaded your school. One of the symptoms of this disease is the urge to use a cell phone during class. Cellphonitis is easily transferred from person to person by direct contact and there is no natural immunity to the disease. A student in your class has the disease, and is Patient Zero. The disease is spreading in your class and you need to track the disease to prevent the spread of an epidemic.

Question: *Is it possible to track a disease and determine the identity of Patient Zero?*

Materials

Pasteur pipets (1 per group)
numbered test tubes of water, one infected with simulated "cellphonitis" (1 per group)
test tube racks (1 per group)
small paper cups (1 per group)
pencil and paper
testing indicator

Safety Precautions

Procedure

1. Read and complete the lab safety form.
2. Prepare a table to keep track of the contacts you make. Select a test tube and record the number of the test tube.
3. Use a Pasteur pipet and move a small amount of the fluid from the test tube to a paper cup.
4. Your teacher will divide your class into groups. When your group is called, you will simulate the sharing of saliva during drinking water by using your pipets to exchange the fluid in your test tubes with another member of your group.
5. Record who you exchanged with in your tables.
6. Roll the test tube gently between your hands to mix and repeat Step 4 every time your group is told to exchange. Be sure to pick someone different to exchange with each time.
7. When the exchanges are complete, your teacher will act as the epidemiologist and use the testing indicator to see who has the disease.
8. Share the information and work together as groups to see if you can determine the identity of Patient Zero.
9. Once each group has made their hypothesis, test the original fluid in each cup to see who really was Patient Zero.
10. Return the test tubes. Dispose of the other materials you used as instructed by your teacher.

Analyze and Conclude

1. **Analyze** Use your data and draw a diagram for each possible Patient Zero. Use arrows to show who should be infected with each possible Patient Zero.
2. **Compare and Contrast** How was the spread of "cellphonitis" in this simulation similar to the spread of disease in real life? How was it different?
3. **Think Critically** If this simulation were run in a large class, why might the disease not be passed in later exchanges?
4. **Error Analysis** What problems did you run into as you tried to determine the identity of Patient Zero?

COMMUNICATE

Newscast Research a current disease epidemic. Prepare a newscast about how epidemiologists are searching for the source of disease and present it to your class.

CHAPTER 23 STUDY GUIDE

BIGIDEA **The immune system attempts to protect the body from contracting an infection through pathogens.**

SECTION 1 Infectious Diseases

MAINIDEA Pathogens are dispersed by people, other animals, and objects.

- Pathogens, such as bacteria, viruses, protozoans, and fungi, cause infectious diseases.
- Koch's postulates demonstrate how a particular pathogen causes a certain disease.
- Pathogens are found in disease reservoirs and are transmitted to humans directly and indirectly.
- The symptoms of disease are caused by invasion of the pathogen and the response of the host immune system.
- Treatment of infectious disease includes the use of antibiotics and antiviral drugs.

VOCABULARY

- **infectious disease**
- **pathogen**
- **Koch's postulates**
- **reservoir**
- **endemic disease**
- **epidemic**
- **pandemic**
- **antibiotic**

SECTION 2 The Immune System

MAINIDEA The immune system has two main components: nonspecific immunity and specific immunity.

- The nonspecific immune response includes the skin barrier, secreted chemicals, and cellular pathways that activate phagocytosis.
- The specific immune response involves the activation of B cells, which produce antibodies, and T cells, which include helper T cells and cytotoxic T cells.
- Passive immunity involves receiving antibodies against a disease.
- Active immunity results in immune memory against a disease.
- HIV attacks helper T cells, causing an immune system failure.

VOCABULARY

- **complement protein**
- **interferon**
- **lymphocyte**
- **antibody**
- **B cell**
- **helper T cell**
- **cytotoxic T cell**
- **memory cell**
- **immunization**

SECTION 3 Noninfectious Disorders

MAINIDEA Noninfectious disorders include genetic disorders, degenerative diseases, metabolic diseases, cancer, and inflammatory diseases.

- Noninfectious disorders often have both a genetic and an environmental component.
- The inflammatory response to an infectious disease enhances the immune response, but the inflammatory response to an inflammatory disease is not helpful to the body.
- Allergies are due to an overactive immune response to allergens found in the environment.
- Anaphylactic shock is a severe hypersensitivity to particular allergens.
- Autoimmunity results in an immune attack on body cells.

VOCABULARY

- **degenerative disease**
- **metabolic disease**
- **allergy**
- **anaphylactic shock**

SECTION 1

Vocabulary Review

Match the definitions below with a vocabulary term from the Study Guide page.

1. A(n) __________ is an agent that causes an infectious disease.
2. When a disease becomes widespread in a particular area, it is called a/an __________.
3. A source of disease organisms is called a __________.

Understand Main Ideas

4. Which national organization tracks disease patterns in the United States?
   A. The Centers for Disease Control and Prevention
   B. National Disease Center
   C. World Health Organization
   D. United Nations
5. Which scientist established a method for determining whether a microorganism caused a specific disease?
   A. Koch C. Sagan
   B. Hooke D. Mendel
6. Which is the most common way that humans acquire an infectious disease?
   A. contaminated water
   B. mosquito bites
   C. sick animals
   D. infected humans

Use the photo below to answer question 7.

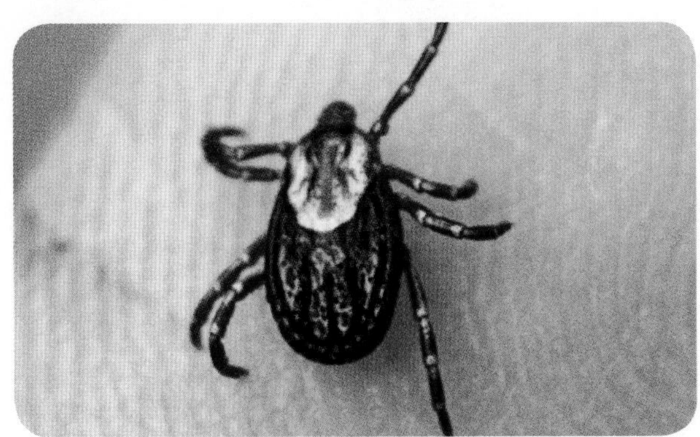

7. Which type of disease transmission is shown above?
   A. direct contact C. object transmission
   B. air transmission D. vector transmission

Use the photo below to answer question 8.

8. Which substance is secreted by the organism shown above?
   A. anthrax C. gentamicin
   B. influenza D. penicillin

Constructed Response

9. **THEME FOCUS** Explain how you could prove that a particular bacteria was causing an infectious disease in a mouse population.
10. **Open Ended** Explain how the Centers for Disease Control and Prevention would be able to determine if an epidemic was occurring in your city.
11. **CAREERS IN ▸ Biology** Imagine you are the school nurse. Describe to students more than one way the cold virus could be transmitted from one person to another.

Think Critically

12. **MAIN IDEA** Design a feasible plan that could decrease the spread of infectious disease within your school.
13. **Evaluate** why growing viruses in cell cultures would be an exception to Koch's postulates.

SECTION 2

Vocabulary Review

For questions 14–16, match each definition with a vocabulary term from the Study Guide page.

14. a chemical produced by B cells in response to antigen stimulation
15. a cell that activates B cells and cytotoxic T cells
16. a type of white blood cell produced in the bone marrow that includes B and T cells

Understand Main Ideas

Use the diagram below to answer questions 17 and 18.

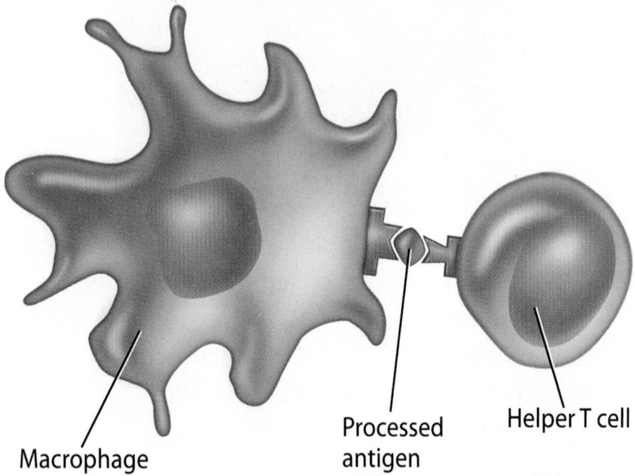

17. What kind of immune response is demonstrated in the diagram above?
- **A.** genetic
- **B.** nonspecific
- **C.** specific
- **D.** hormonal

18. To which does the activated helper T cell present its antigen?
- **A.** a pathogen
- **B.** bone marrow
- **C.** a B cell
- **D.** the thymus gland

19. Which is the first defense your body has against infectious disease?
- **A.** the helper T cell
- **B.** an antibody
- **C.** your skin
- **D.** phagocytosis

20. What is the role of complement proteins, found in the plasma, in the immune response?
- **A.** enhance phagocytosis
- **B.** activate phagocytes
- **C.** enhance destruction of a pathogen
- **D.** all of the above

21. Where are lymphocytes produced?
- **A.** bone marrow
- **B.** thymus gland
- **C.** spleen
- **D.** lymph nodes

Constructed Response

22. Short Answer Describe how the thymus gland is involved in the development of immunity.

23. MAINIDEA Evaluate why the body needs both a nonspecific and a specific immune response.

24. Open Ended Form a hypothesis as to why the proportion of unvaccinated Americans is increasing.

Think Critically

25. Organize the sequence of events that occurs to activate an antibody response to tetanus bacteria.

26. Compare the role of helper T cells and cytotoxic T cells in the specific immune response.

SECTION 3

Vocabulary Review

Use a vocabulary term from the Study Guide page to answer questions 27–29.

27. What type of reaction is a hypersensitivity to an allergen such as a bee sting?

28. Which type of disease occurs when people abnormally respond to environmental antigens?

29. Which type of disease is caused by a body part wearing out?

Understand Main Ideas

Use the photo below to answer question 30.

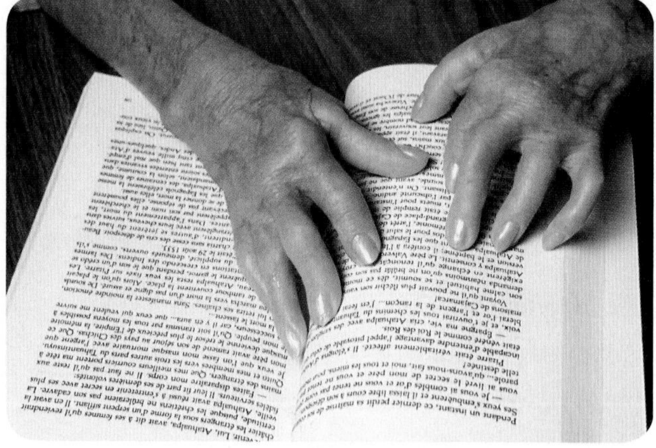

30. The above photo demonstrates which disease?
- **A.** tetanus
- **B.** sickle-cell disease
- **C.** rheumatoid arthritis
- **D.** allergy

31. Which type of noninfectious disease is defined as a problem in a biochemical pathway in the body?
- **A.** inflammatory disease
- **B.** metabolic disease
- **C.** degenerative disease
- **D.** cancer

Publiphoto/Science Source

32. Which of the following substances is released in the body to cause most of the symptoms of allergies?
A. insulin
B. allergens
C. histamine
D. acetylcholine

33. Individuals can have a dangerous response to particular allergens, such as latex, and go into anaphylactic shock. What will be the result?
A. breathing problems
B. epileptic seizures
C. atherosclerosis
D. arthritis

34. In autoimmunity, which attacks the body's own proteins?
A. antigens
B. allergens
C. antibodies
D. antihistamines

Constructed Response

35. **Short Answer** Describe how an allergy differs from a common cold, considering that the symptoms are similar.

36. **Short Answer** Discuss the effects on the organs of the body when the smooth muscles in the bronchioles constrict, causing breathing to be difficult.

37. **Short Answer** Evaluate why lupus causes systemic problems in the body.

Think Critically

38. **MAINIDEA** Construct a table listing each of the types of non-infectious disease and give an example of each type.

Use the graph below to answer question 39.

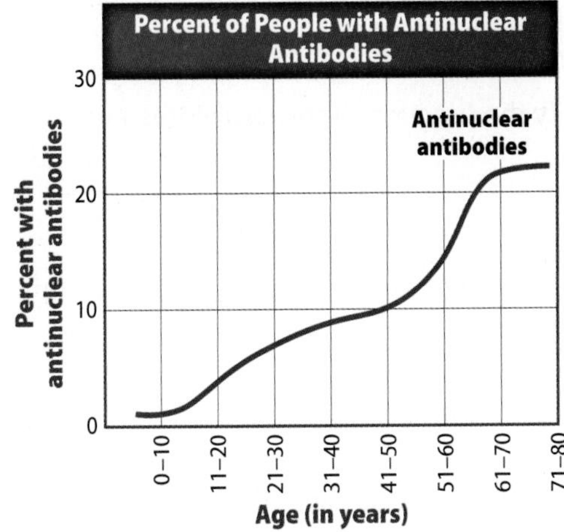

39. **Summarize** the relationship between antinuclear antibodies and age.

Summative Assessment

40. **BIGIDEA** A friend of yours has been diagnosed with chicken pox. Describe how your body protects itself from infection and what you can do to lessen your chances of contracting the disease.

41. Choose a pathogen and make a sequence diagram showing the steps of how each type of immunity is involved in preventing or fighting infection.

42. **WRITING IN ▶ Biology** Construct an analogy comparing the immune system to a castle being attacked by invaders from a neighboring territory.

DBQ Document-Based Questions

The table below illustrates the effectiveness of using vaccinations to prevent the contraction of disease. There was a large decrease in cases of the diseases listed after the use of vaccinations.

Data obtained from: Mandell, G. L., et al. 1995. *Principles and Practice of Infectious Diseases,* 4th ed. Churchill Livingstone, and Centers for Disease Control and Prevention. 2000. *Morbidity and Mortality Weekly Report* 48: 1162–1192.

Disease	Maximum Number of Cases in a Year	Number of Cases in 1999 in U.S.	Percent Change
Measles	894,134	60	−99.99
Mumps	152,209	352	−99.77
Polio (paralytic)	21,269	0	−100.0
Tetanus	1560	33	−97.88
Hepatitis B	26,611	6495	−75.59

43. Which disease has shown the greatest change in occurrence since the year of its maximum number of cases?

44. Tetanus has shown a large decline since the United States started vaccinating. Explain why this disease will not be completely eradicated.

45. Create a bar graph showing the percent change in number of cases as a result of vaccination for each disease.

CUMULATIVE

MULTIPLE CHOICE

Use the diagram below to answer questions 1 and 2.

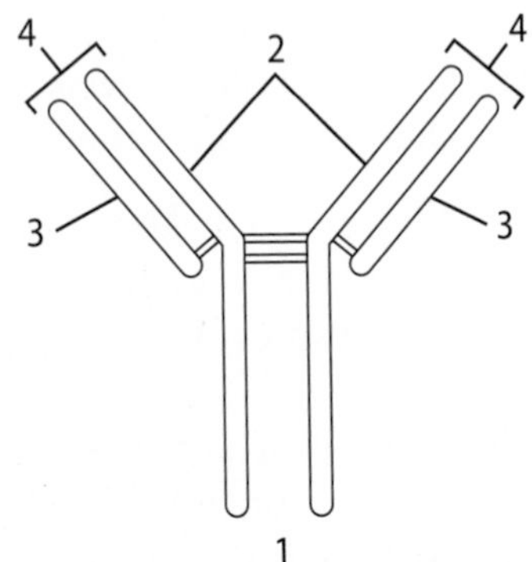

1 The diagram above shows the basic structure of an antibody. Which part of the diagram corresponds to the antigen binding site?

A 1

B 2

C 3

D 4

2 Why are parts 2 and 3 of the diagram above important for the formation of antibodies?

A They allow for an enormous number of possible antibodies to form.

B They are created by the T cells in the immune system.

C They help reduce the number of antibodies that form.

D They help stimulate the inflammatory response.

SHORT ANSWER

Use the graph below to answer questions 3 and 4.

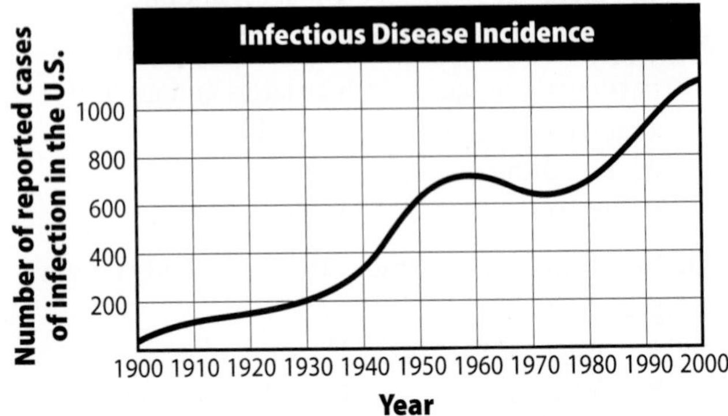

3 What is the overall trend shown in the above graph?

4 What are two possible explanations for the pattern in the above graph?

5 What characteristics are used to classify protists into three groups?

6 Describe the process of dilation during birthing. Assess why it is important.

7 Identify the function of the large intestine.

8 Assess how the respiratory system of most reptiles is adapted for life on land.

9 Free-living flatworms have some unique body structures: eyespots, a ganglion, and auricles that detect chemical stimuli. How are these body structures related to each other?

EXTENDED RESPONSE

10 Arthropods first moved onto land about 400 million years ago and have survived several mass extinctions. Propose a hypothesis about why arthropods have been so successful.

11 Compare the production of sperm cells and egg cells during meiosis.

ESSAY QUESTION

Scientist Marc Lappé wrote the following in 1981 in a book called *Germs That Won't Die.*

"Unfortunately, we played a trick on the natural world by seizing control of these [natural] chemicals, making them more perfect in a way that has changed the whole microbial constitution of the developing countries. We have organisms now proliferating that never existed before in nature. We have selected them. We have organisms that probably caused a tenth of a percent of human disease in the past that now cause twenty, thirty percent of the diseases that we're seeing. We have changed the whole face of the earth by the use of antibiotics."

Using the information in the paragraph above, answer the following question in essay format.

12 As Lappé predicted in 1981, many diseases have emerged in forms that are resistant to treatment by antibiotics and other powerful drugs. Have antibiotics "changed the whole face of the earth" for the better or for the worse? In an organized essay, discuss the advantages and disadvantages of antibiotics as they are used today.

TEST PRACTICE

Use the diagram below to answer question 13.

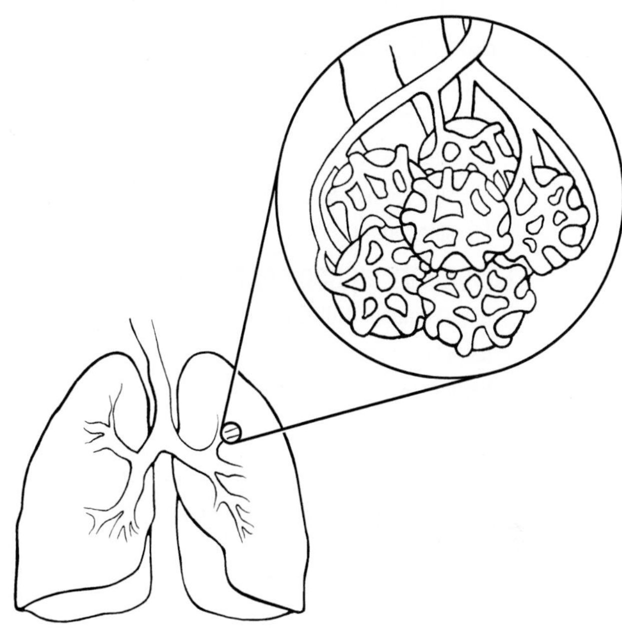

13 Which happens in the blood in these structures?

A Carbon dioxide and oxygen are exchanged.

B Carbon dioxide and oxygen remain constant.

C Nitrogen and carbon dioxide are exchanged.

D Nitrogen and carbon dioxide remain constant.

14 What is the role of hormones in the body?

A to act as reaction catalysts

B to control breathing process

C to help synthesize proteins

D to regulate many body functions

NEED EXTRA HELP?														
If You Missed Question . . .	1	2	3	4	5	6	7	8	9	10	11	12	13	14
Review Section . . .	37.2	37.2	37.1	37.1	19.1	36.2	35.1	29.1	25.1	26.1	36.1	37.1	34.2	35.2

STUDENT RESOURCES

Investigation and Experimentation

Laboratory Guidelines

Data Collection

Laboratory Equipment and Techniques

Skillbuilder Handbook

Problem-Solving Skills

Math Skills

Reference Handbook

Rubberball/Getty Images

INVESTIGATION AND EXPERIMENTATION

1.1.1c, ¥a, ¥b1, ¥b2, ¥b3, ¥b4, ¥b5, ¥c1, ¥c2, ¥c3, ¥c4, ¥e, ¥h, ¥n

The foundation of scientific knowledge is Investigation and Experimentation. In this section, you will read about lab safety, the proper way to take measurements, and some laboratory techniques. While not every situation you might encounter in the laboratory is covered here, you will gain practical and useful knowledge to make your investigation and experimentation successful experiences.

Laboratory Safety

Follow these safety guidelines and rules to help protect you and others during laboratory investigations.

Complete the Lab Safety Form

- Prior to each investigation, your teacher will have you complete a lab safety form. This contract will inform your teacher that you have read the procedure and are prepared to perform the investigation.
- After your teacher reviews your comments, make any necessary corrections, and sign or initial the form.
- Use the lab safety form to help you prepare for each procedure and take responsibility for your own safety.

Teacher Approval Initials

Date of Approval

Lab Safety Form

Name: __________

Date: __________

Lab type (circle one) : Launch Lab MiniLab ChemLab

Lab Title: __________

Read carefully the entire lab and then answer the following questions. Your teacher must initial this form before you begin the lab.

1. What is the purpose of the investigation?
2. Will you be working with a partner or on a team? __________
3. Is this a design-your-own procedure? Circle: Yes No
4. Describe the safety procedures and additional warnings that you must follow as you perform this investigation.
5. Are there any steps in the procedure or lab safety symbols that you do not understand? Explain.

Prevent Accidents

- Always wear chemical-splash safety goggles (not glasses) in the laboratory. Goggles should fit snugly against your face to prevent any liquid from entering the eyes. Put on your goggles before beginning the lab and wear them throughout the entire activity, cleanup, and hand washing.
- Wear protective aprons and the proper type of gloves as your teacher instructs.
- Keep your hands away from your face and mouth while working in the laboratory.
- Do not wear sandals or other open-toed shoes in the lab.
- Remove jewelry on hands and wrists before doing lab work. Remove loose jewelry, such as chains and long necklaces, to prevent them from getting caught in equipment.
- Do not wear clothing loose enough to catch on anything. If clothing is loose, tape or tie it down.
- Tie back long hair to keep it away from flames and equipment.
- Do not use hair spray or other flammable hair products just before or during laboratory work when an open flame is used. These products ignite easily.
- Eating, drinking, chewing gum, applying makeup, and smoking are prohibited in the laboratory.
- You are expected to behave properly in the laboratory. Practical jokes and fooling around can lead to accidents or injury.
- Notify your teacher about allergies or other health conditions that can affect your participation in a lab.

Follow Lab Procedures

- Study all procedures before you begin a laboratory investigation. Ask questions if you do not understand any part of the procedures.
- Review and understand all safety symbols associated with the investigation. A table of the safety symbols is found on page 1108 for your reference.
- Do not begin any activity until directed to do so by your teacher.
- Use all lab equipment for its intended purpose only.
- Collect and carry all equipment and materials to your work area before beginning the lab.
- When obtaining laboratory materials, dispense only the amount you will use.
- If you have materials left over after completing the investigation, check with your teacher to determine the best choice for recycling or disposing of the materials.
- Keep your work area uncluttered.
- Learn and follow procedures for using specific laboratory equipment, such as balances, microscopes, hot plates, and burners.
- When heating or rinsing a container such as a test tube or flask, point it away from yourself and others.
- Do not taste, touch, or smell any chemical or substance in the lab.
- If your teacher instructs you to smell a substance in a container, hold the container a short distance away and fan vapors toward your nose.
- Do not substitute other chemicals or substances for those in the materials list unless instructed to do so by your teacher.
- Do not take any chemical or material outside of the laboratory.

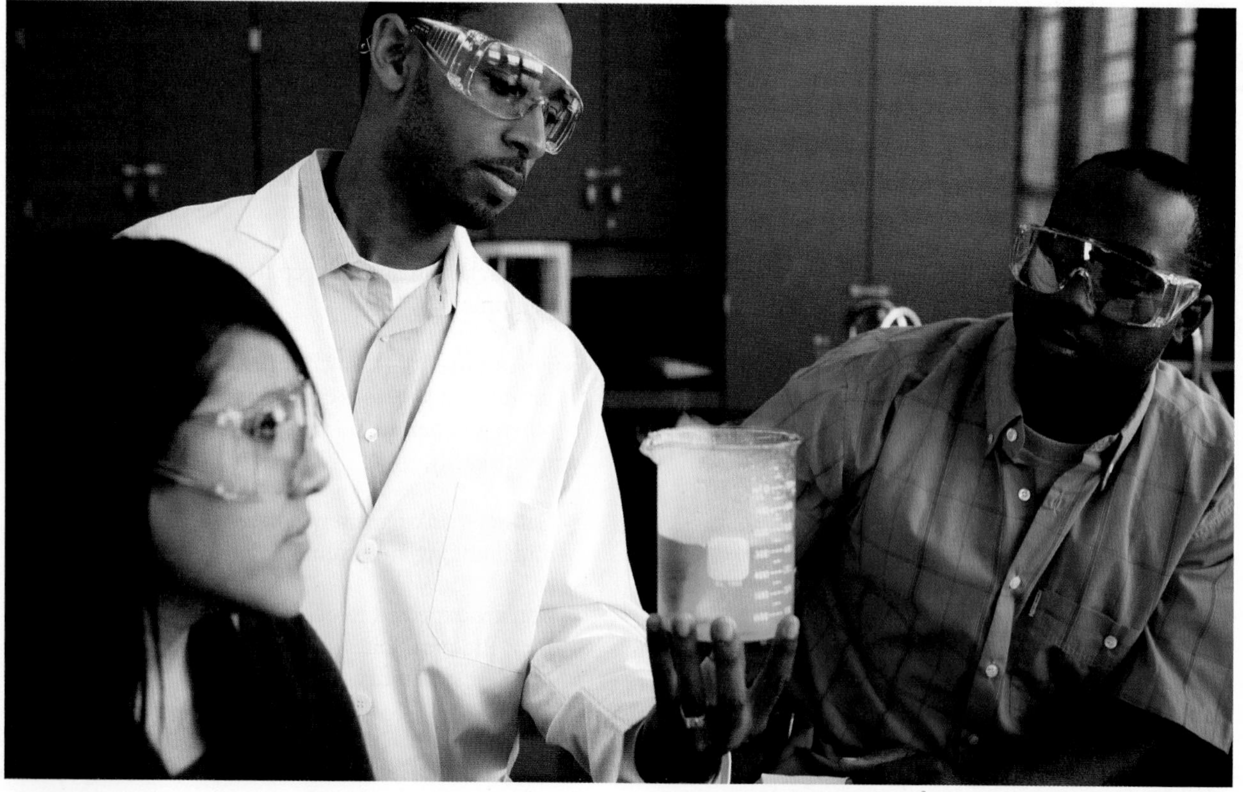

Clean up the Lab

- Turn off all burners, gas valves, and water faucets before leaving the laboratory. Disconnect all electrical devices.
- Clean all equipment as instructed by your teacher. Return everything to the proper storage place.
- Dispose of all materials properly. Place disposable items in containers specifically marked for those types of items. Do not pour liquids down the drain unless instructed to do so by your teacher.
- **Wash your hands thoroughly with soap and warm water after each activity and before removing your goggles.**

Know How to Handle Emergencies

- **Inform your teacher immediately of any mishap, such as fire, bodily injuries, burns, electrical shock, glassware breakage, and chemical or other spills.**
- Do not attempt to clean up spills unless you are given permission and instructions on how to do so. In most instances, your teacher will clean up spills.
- Know the location of the fire extinguisher, safety shower, eyewash, fire blanket, and first-aid kit. After receiving instructions, you can use the safety shower, eyewash, and fire blanket in an emergency without your teacher's permission. However, the fire extinguisher and first-aid kit should be used only by your teacher or, in an extreme emergency, with your teacher's permission.
- If chemicals come into contact with your eyes or skin, notify your teacher immediately and flush your skin or eyes with water.
- If someone is injured or becomes ill, only a professional medical provider or someone certified in first aid should perform first-aid procedures.

Be Responsible

Because your teacher cannot anticipate every safety hazard that might occur and he or she cannot be everywhere in the room at the same time, you need to take some responsibility for your own safety. The general information below should apply to nearly every science lab.

You must:

- review any safety symbols in the labs and be certain you know what they mean;
- follow all teacher instructions for safety and make certain you understand all the hazards related to the lab you are about to perform;
- be able to explain the purpose of the lab;
- be able to explain, or demonstrate, all reasonable emergency procedures, such as:
    - how to evacuate the room during emergencies;
    - how to react to any chemical emergencies;
    - how to deal with fire emergencies;
    - how to perform a scientific investigation safely;
    - how to anticipate some safety concerns and be prepared to address them; and
    - how to use equipment properly and safely.
- be able to locate and use all safety equipment as directed by your teacher, such as:
    - fire extinguishers;
    - fire blankets;
    - eye protective equipment (goggles, safety glasses, face shield);
    - eyewash; and
    - a drench shower.
- be sure to ask questions about any safety concerns that you might have BEFORE starting any investigation.

Safety Symbols

These safety symbols are used in laboratory and field investigations in this book to indicate possible hazards. Learn the meaning of each symbol and refer to this page often. *Remember to wash your hands thoroughly after completing lab procedures.*

SAFETY SYMBOLS	HAZARD	EXAMPLES	PRECAUTION	REMEDY
DISPOSAL	Special disposal procedures need to be followed.	certain chemicals, living organisms	Do not dispose of these materials in the sink or trash can.	Dispose of wastes as directed by your teacher.
BIOLOGICAL	Organisms or other biological materials that might be harmful to humans	bacteria, fungi, blood, unpreserved tissues, plant materials	Avoid skin contact with these materials. Wear mask or gloves.	Notify your teacher if you suspect contact with material. Wash hands thoroughly.
EXTREME TEMPERATURE	Objects that can burn skin by being too cold or too hot	boiling liquids, hot plates, dry ice, liquid nitrogen	Use proper protection when handling.	Go to your teacher for first aid.
SHARP OBJECT	Use of tools or glassware that can easily puncture or slice skin	razor blades, pins, scalpels, pointed tools, dissecting probes, broken glass	Practice common-sense behavior and follow guidelines for use of the tool.	Go to your teacher for first aid.
FUME	Possible danger to respiratory tract from fumes	ammonia, acetone, nail polish remover, heated sulfur, moth balls	Make sure there is good ventilation. Never smell fumes directly. Wear a mask.	Leave foul area and notify your teacher immediately.
ELECTRICAL	Possible danger from electrical shock or burn	improper grounding, liquid spills, short circuits, exposed wires	Double-check setup with teacher. Check condition of wires and apparatus. Use GFI-protected outlets.	Do not attempt to fix electrical problems. Notify your teacher immediately.
IRRITANT	Substances that can irritate the skin or mucous membranes of the respiratory tract	pollen, moth balls, steel wool, fiberglass, potassium permanganate	Wear dust mask and gloves. Practice extra care when handling these materials.	Go to your teacher for first aid.
CHEMICAL	Chemicals that can react with and destroy tissue and other materials	bleaches such as hydrogen peroxide; acids such as sulfuric acid, hydrochloric acid; bases such as ammonia, sodium hydroxide	Wear goggles, gloves, and an apron.	Immediately flush the affected area with water and notify your teacher.
TOXIC	Substance may be poisonous if touched, inhaled, or swallowed.	mercury, many metal compounds, iodine, poinsettia plant parts	Follow your teacher's instructions.	Always wash hands thoroughly after use. Go to your teacher for first aid.
FLAMMABLE	Open flame may ignite flammable chemicals, loose clothing, or hair.	alcohol, kerosene, potassium permanganate, hair, clothing	Avoid open flames and heat when using flammable chemicals.	Notify your teacher immediately. Use fire safety equipment if applicable.
OPEN FLAME	Open flame in use, may cause fire.	hair, clothing, paper, synthetic materials	Tie back hair and loose clothing. Follow teacher's instructions on lighting and extinguishing flames.	Always wash hands thoroughly after use. Go to your teacher for first aid.

Eye Safety Proper eye protection must be worn at all times by anyone performing or observing science activities.

Clothing Protection This symbol appears when substances could stain or burn clothing.

Animal Safety This symbol appears when safety of animals and students must be ensured.

Radioactivity This symbol appears when radioactive materials are used.

Handwashing After the lab, wash hands with soap and water before removing goggles.

Field Investigation Safety

On occasion, your teacher might conduct a field investigation—an investigation on school grounds or off-campus. While many of the laboratory safety guidelines apply, the field has unique safety considerations.

Work Together

- Work with at least one other person.
- Never stray from the main group either alone or with a small group.
- Make sure that each person in your group understands his or her task and how to perform it. Ask your teacher for clarification if necessary.
- Determine how members of your group will communicate in case of a loud environment or an emergency.
- Your teacher or chaperones should be equipped with either cell phones or walkie-talkies. They should be able to communicate with one another, the school, and emergency personnel, if needed, so be sure to let your teacher know if you need help.

Dress Appropriately

- Wear your safety goggles, apron, and gloves as indicated by the procedure.
- Protect yourself from the Sun with sunblock and a hat.
- Long pants and shirts with long sleeves will protect you from the Sun, insects, and plants such as poison ivy and poison oak.

Poison ivy

Poison oak

- Insect-repellent sprays or creams may be necessary for you to use.
- Be sure to wear shoes that have closed toes and heels as well as textured soles.
- If your investigation requires that you wade into a stream, river, lake, or other body of water, wear water-resistant clothing. Do not enter the water if you have any open sores.

Consider Your Environment

- Never approach animals.
- Never drink water from a stream, river, lake, or other body of water.
- Do not remove anything from the habitat. Create a sketch of organisms you are studying.
- Stay away from power lines.
- Stay away from the edges of cliffs and ledges.
- Stay on marked trails.

Follow General Guidelines

- Treat your field investigation like a laboratory investigation. There should be no horseplay.
- A first-aid kit should be brought to the investigation site.
- Always wash your hands when you are finished. If soap and water are unavailable, use an alcohol-based hand sanitizer.

Data Collection

Biologists take measurements in many types of investigations.
- **A population biologist might count tree frogs in a rain-forest survey.**
- **A physical therapist might observe the range of motion of an injured knee.**
- **A microbiologist might measure the diameters of bacteria.**

In this section, you will learn how biologists take careful measurements. When you plan and perform your biology labs, use this section as a guide.

Accuracy, Precision, and Error

In any measurement, there always will be some error—the difference between the measured value and the real or accepted value. Error comes from several sources, including the experimenter, the equipment, and even changes in experimental conditions. Errors can affect both the accuracy and the precision of measurements.

- **Accuracy** refers to how close a measurement is to the real value or the accepted value.
- **Precision** refers to how close a series of measurements are to one another.

Examine the targets in **Figure 1** below while you consider a food scientist who measures the mass of a sample three times.

- Proper equipment setup and good technique: accurate and precise data
- Incorrect equipment setup but good technique: precise but inaccurate data
- Incorrect equipment setup and careless technique: inaccurate and imprecise data

The arrows clustered in the center represent measurements that are both accurate and precise.

The arrows clustered together far from the center represent three measurements that are precise but inaccurate.

These arrows are both far apart and far from the center. They represent three measurements that are inaccurate and imprecise.

Error Analysis

Imagine that an epidemiologist (eh puh dee mee AHL uh just), a biologist who studies epidemics, tested a hypothesis about the way in which avian flu might spread from chickens to humans. All data have been gathered. The epidemiologist must now perform an error analysis, which is a process to identify and describe possible sources of error in measurements.

In your biology investigations, you will need to think of possible sources of measurement errors. Ask yourself questions such as:
- Did I take more than one reading of each measurement?
- Did I use the equipment properly?
- Was I objective, or did I make the results turn out as I expected they might?

Measure Mass

Triple-Beam Balance

A triple-beam balance has a pan and three beams with sliding masses called riders. At one end of the beams is a pointer that indicates whether the mass on the pan is equal to the masses shown on the beams.

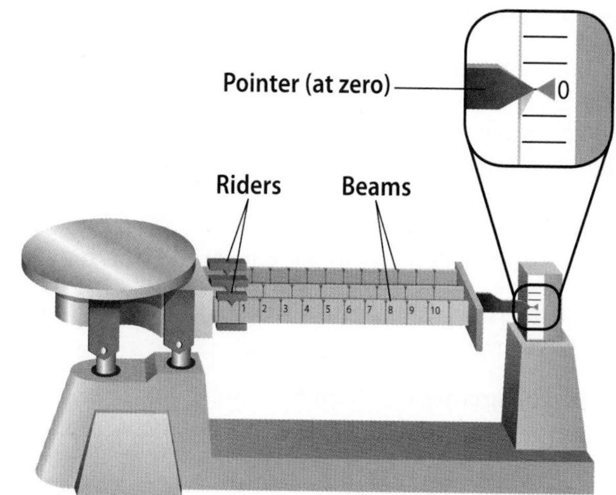

Figure 2

To use:

1. Make sure the balance is zeroed before measuring the mass of an object. The balance is zeroed if the pointer is at zero when nothing is on the pan and riders are at their zero points.
2. Place the object to be measured on the pan.
3. Move the riders one notch at a time away from the pan. Begin with the largest rider. If moving the largest rider one notch brings the pointer below zero, begin measuring the mass with the next, smaller rider.
4. Change the positions of the riders until they balance the mass on the pan and the pointer is at zero. Then add the readings from the three beams to determine the mass of the object.

TIP

When using a weighing boat or weighing paper, be sure to zero the balance after you've placed the boat or paper on the pan and before you add a substance to the boat or paper.

Measure Volume

Graduated Cylinder

Use a graduated cylinder to measure the volume of a liquid.

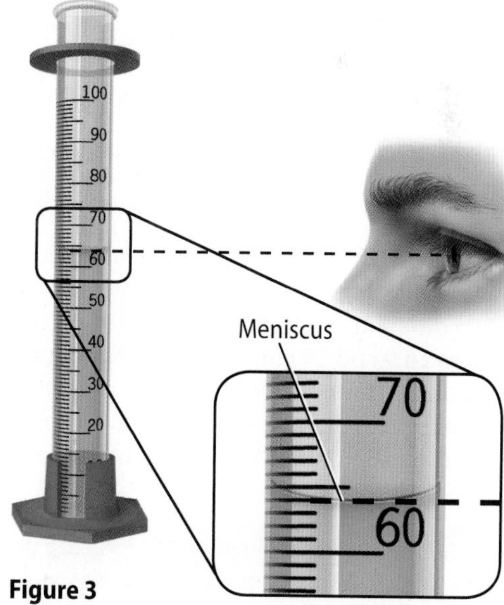

Figure 3

To use:

1. Be sure to have your eyes at the level of the surface of the liquid when reading the scale on a graduated cylinder.
2. The surface of a liquid usually will be curved slightly downward when it is held in a graduated cylinder. This curve is called the meniscus. Read the volume of the liquid at the bottom of the meniscus, as shown in **Figure 3.**
3. The volume will often be between two lines on the graduated cylinder. You should estimate the final digit in your measurement. For example, if the bottom of the meniscus appears to be exactly halfway between the marks for 96 mL and 97 mL, you would read the volume as 96.5 mL.
4. To find the volume of a small solid object, record the volume of some water in a graduated cylinder. Then, measure the volume of the water after you add the object to the cylinder. The volume of the object is the difference between the first and second measurements.

TIP

Do not use a beaker to measure the volume of a liquid. Beakers are used for holding and pouring liquids. To avoid overflow, be sure to use a beaker that holds roughly twice as much liquid as you need.

Measure Temperature

Thermometer

The thermometer that you will be using measures temperature in degrees Celsius (°C). Each division on the scale represents 1°C. The average human body temperature is 37°C. A typical room temperature is between 20°C and 25°C. The freezing point of water is 0°C, and the boiling point of water is 100°C, as shown in **Figure 4.**

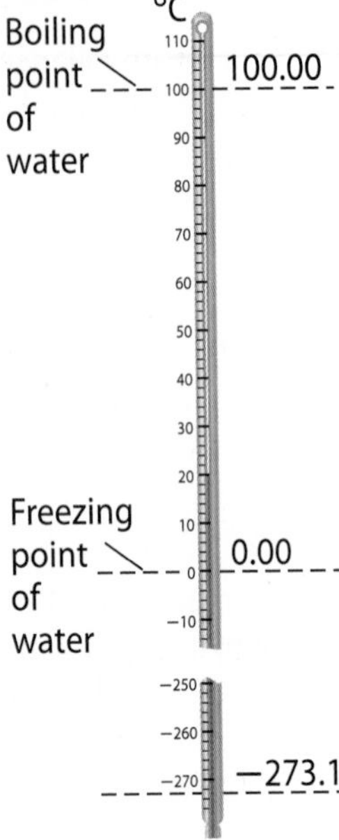

Figure 4

To use:

1. Place the thermometer in the sample and wait for 30 s before taking the reading.
2. Be sure to have your eyes at the level of the surface of the liquid when reading the scale on a thermometer.
3. The temperature will often be between two lines on the thermometer. You should estimate the final digit in your measurement. For example, if the liquid appears to be about halfway between the marks for 50°C and 51°C, you would read the temperature as 50.5°C.
4. Do not touch the sides or bottom of the container that is holding the sample with the thermometer. This can yield a false temperature.

Electronic thermometers, often called temperature probes, are used to record temperatures over a range of time or to give more accurate and precise readings.

Measure Length

Metric Ruler

Use a metric ruler or meterstick to measure the length of an object. On the ruler, each marked number represents one centimeter (cm). The smaller lines between each centimeter represent millimeters (mm). There are 10 mm in one centimeter and 100 cm in one meter (m).

To use:

1. Place the metric ruler so that the 0-cm mark lines up with the end of the object.
2. Be sure to have your eyes at the level of the object when reading the scale on the ruler.
3. The accuracy of your measurement reflects the measuring tool that you use and your technique. **Figure 5** shows the estimation of the length of the same object using two different measuring tools. Based on the bottom measuring tool, the length is between 9 and 10 cm. The measurement would be estimated to the nearest tenth of a centimeter. You would estimate the length to be 9.5 cm. Based on the top measuring tool, the length is between 9.4 and 9.5 cm. The measurement would be estimated to the nearest hundredth of a centimeter. You would estimate the length to be 9.45 cm.

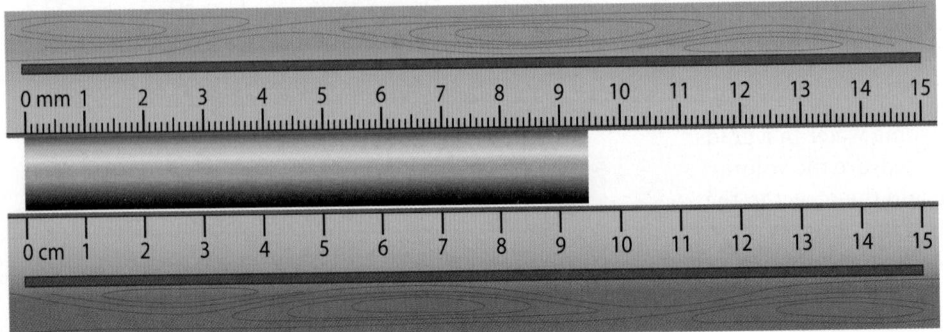

Figure 5

Laboratory Equipment and Techniques

This page and the following five pages discuss common lab equipment and techniques that you might use in a biology lab. Refer to these pages prior to performing labs that require the use of microscopes, chromatography, gel electrophoresis, or indicators.

Use a Compound Microscope

The parts of a compound microscope are listed and diagrammed in the table below.

1. Always carry the microscope by holding the arm of the microscope with one hand and supporting the base with the other hand.
2. Place the microscope on a flat surface. The arm should be positioned toward you.
3. Look through the eyepieces. Adjust the diaphragm so that the light comes through the opening in the stage.
4. Place a slide on the stage so that the specimen is in the field of view. Hold the slide firmly in place by using the stage clips.
5. Always focus first with the coarse adjustment and the low-power objective lens. Once the object is in focus on low power, the high-power objective can be used. Use only the fine adjustment to focus the high-power objective lenses.
6. Store the microscope covered.

Parts of the Compound Light Microscope

Part	Function
Base	Supports the microscope
Arm	Used to carry the microscope
Stage	Platform where the slide with specimen is placed
Stage clips	Holds the slide in place on the stage
Eyepiece	Magnifies image for the viewer
Objective lens	Low-power and high-power lenses that magnify the specimen
Coarse adjustment	Large knob used for focusing the image under low-power
Fine adjustment	Smaller knob used for focusing the image with the high-power objective
Diaphragm	Controls the amount of light that passes through the specimen
Light source	Provides light for viewing the specimen

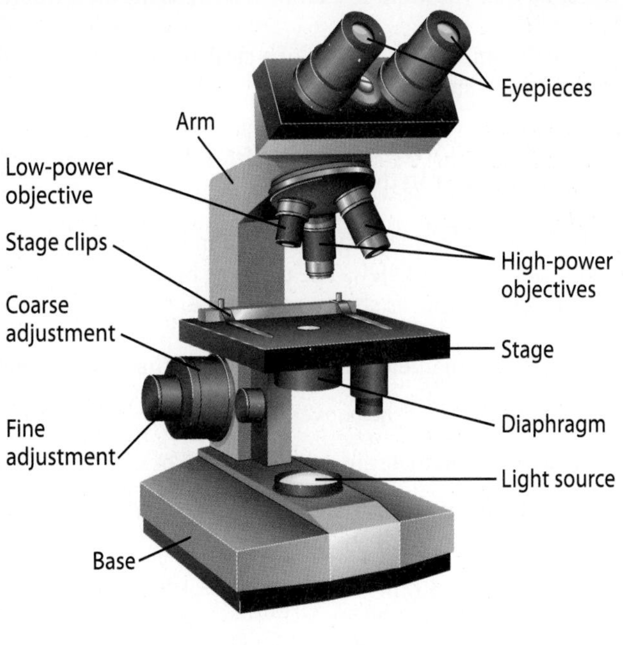

Calculate Magnification

Magnification describes how much larger an object appears when it is viewed through a microscope compared to the unaided eye. The numbers on the eyepiece and the objectives that are marked with the multiplication symbol (×) tell you how many times the lens of each microscope part magnifies an object.

- To calculate the total magnification of any object viewed under a microscope, multiply the number on the eyepiece by the number on the objective through which you are viewing the object.

- For example, if the eyepiece magnification is 4× and the low-power magnification is 10×, the total magnification under the low-power objective is 40×. With the same eyepiece and a high-power magnification of 40×, the total magnification under the high-power objective would be 160×.

Practice Problem 1 Calculate the low-power and the high-power magnifications of a microscope with an eyepiece magnification of 10×, a low-power objective of 40×, and a high-power objective of 60×.

Calculate the Field of View

The area you see when you look into a microscope is called the field of view. To measure the field of view of a microscope, you must use a unit called a micrometer (μm). There are 1000 micrometers in a millimeter. Use the following steps to calculate field of view and then to determine the diameters of the microscopic specimens that you are viewing.

Diameter of Low-Power Field of View Use a low-power objective to select the section of a slide that you want to examine, such as the area where pollen grains are located.

- Place the millimeter section of a clear plastic ruler over the central opening of the microscope stage.

- Use the low-power objective to locate the lines of the ruler. Center the ruler in the field of view.

- Place one of the lines representing a millimeter at the very edge of the field of view. The distance between two lines on the ruler is 1 mm, as shown in **Figure 6.**

- Estimate the diameter, in millimeters, of the field of view on low power. Use the conversion factor $\frac{1000\ \mu\text{m}}{1\ \text{mm}}$ to calculate the diameter in micrometers. For example, if you estimate the diameter to be 1.5 mm, the field of view is 1500 μm.

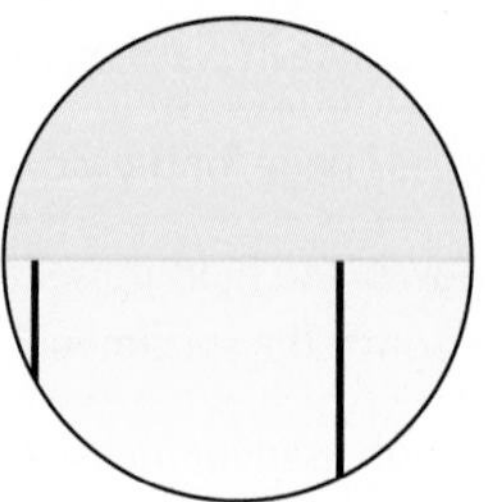
Figure 6

$$1.5\ \text{mm} \times \frac{1000\ \mu\text{m}}{1\ \text{mm}} = 1500\ \mu\text{m}$$

Diameter of High-Power Field of View After selecting a slide section on low power, use the high-power field of view to see the details on the slide, such as individual pollen grains.

- To calculate the diameter of the high-power field of view, divide the magnification of the high-power objective by the magnification of the low-power objective. For example, changing from a low power of 10× to a high power of 40×, you would write:

$$\frac{40\times}{10\times} = 4$$

- Then, divide the diameter of the low-power field of view in micrometers by this quotient. The result is the diameter of the high-power field of view in micrometers. For the low-power field of view calculated on the previous page, the diameter of the high-power field of view is

$$\frac{1500\ \mu m}{4} = 375\ \mu m$$

- To determine the diameter of a specimen in your field of view, first estimate how many of the specimens would fit end-to-end across your field of view. Then divide the diameter of the field of view by the estimated number of specimens. In the example, five specimens could fit in the field of view. The diameter of the specimen is

$$\frac{375\ \mu m}{5} = 75\ \mu m.$$

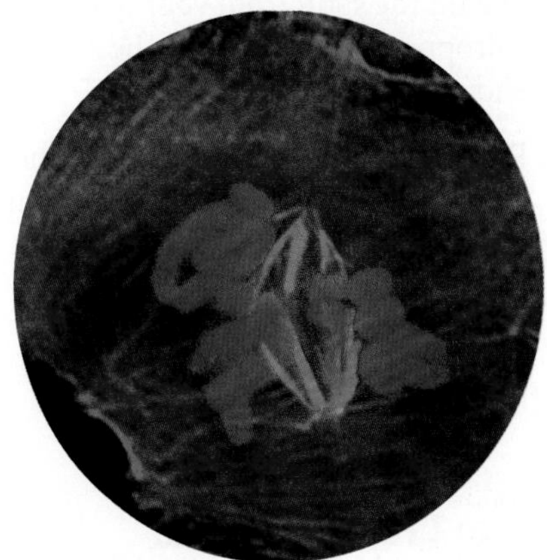

Figure 7 Dividing cell

Practice Problem 2 Calculate the width of the dividing cell shown in **Figure 7** if the diameter of the low-power field of view is 720 μm, the low power is 10×, the high power is 60×, and the number of cells that fit in the field of view is 1.

Make a Wet Mount

Many of the slides that you will prepare for observation under the microscope will be wet mounts. Wet mounts are named as such because the object to be viewed is prepared, or mounted, in water. Follow these steps to make a wet mount.

1. Obtain a clean microscope slide and a coverslip. Add a drop or two of water to the center of the microscope slide.
2. Place the specimen in the drop of water, as shown in **Figure 8.**
3. Pick up the coverslip by its edges. Do not touch the surface of the coverslip. Stand the coverslip on its edge next to the drop of water.
4. Slowly lower the coverslip over the drop of water, and the specimen, as shown in **Figure 9.**
5. Make sure that the object is totally covered with water. If it is not, remove the coverslip, add a little more water, and replace the coverslip.

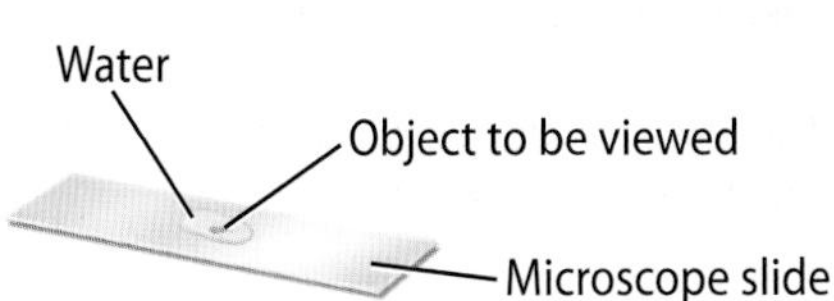

Figure 8

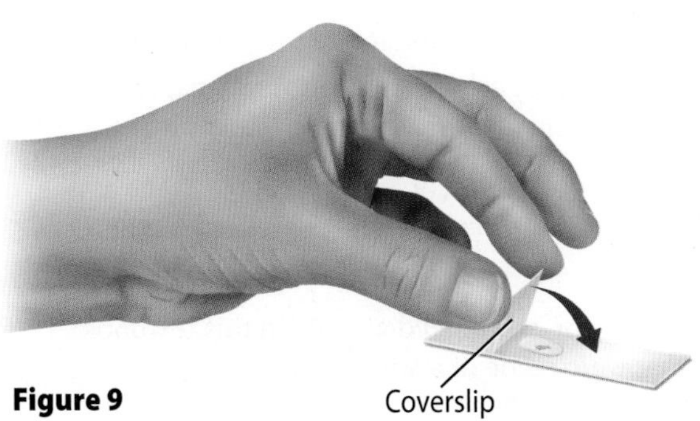

Figure 9

Stain a Slide

Staining a slide can make it easier to view a specimen. Stains enhance contrast and can emphasize certain features. For example, using iodine as a stain will cause carbohydrates in the specimen to become bluish-black in color. The following steps and **Figure 10** indicate one way to stain a microscope slide.

1. Prepare a wet mount, as indicated in the steps on the previous page.
2. Obtain the stain from your teacher. Using a dropper, place a drop of the stain at one end of the coverslip.
3. Place a paper towel at the end of the coverslip opposite the stain. The towel will draw the stain under the coverslip, staining the specimen.

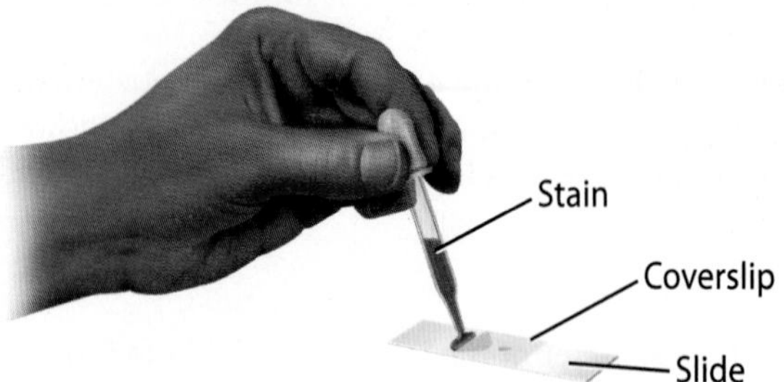

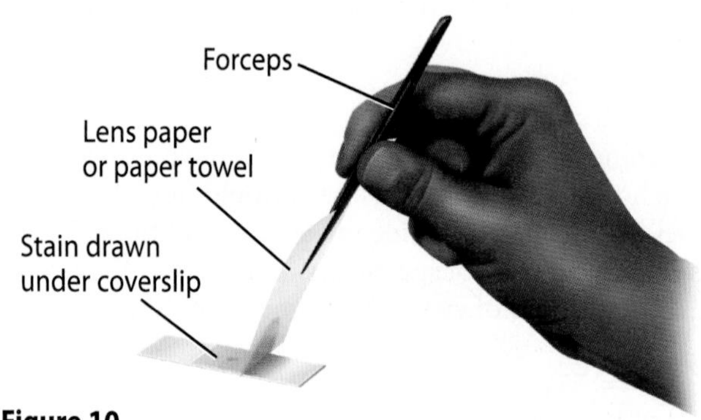

Figure 10

Make Cross Sections

When a biologist decides to study the inner structure of a biological specimen, a basic way to expose or cut a specimen to reveal its inner structure is called a cross section. A cross-sectional exposure, or cut, is made at right angles to the axis of the specimen. For example, the tree trunk in **Figure 11** has been cut at right angles to the height of the trunk. Note that microscopic cross sections reveal microscopic structures, such as the bacterium's cell wall in **Figure 11.**

Think Critically Investigate cross sections by performing the following procedure using everyday materials. Then apply what you have learned to recognize more cross sections in the textbook.

1. Obtain log-shaped, rolled snack cakes that have contrasting color filling. The axis of this specimen runs through the center of one end to the center of the other end.
2. Place a snack cake on a sheet of wax paper and predict what a crosswise cut would look like.
3. Make a crosswise cut at a right angle to the axis and look at the cut ends. This view of the snack cake is a cross section.
4. Find cross-sectional diagrams in this textbook that were made in a similar way.

Figure 11

Tree trunk

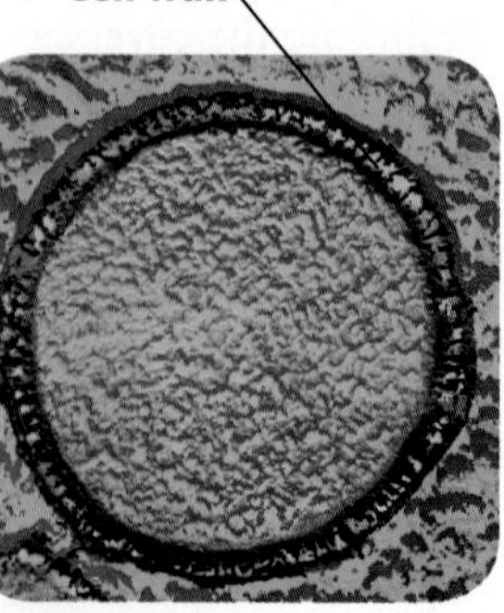

Bacterium

Use a Stereomicroscope

A stereomicroscope, also called a dissecting microscope, is used to observe a larger, thicker, often opaque object. A light source illuminates the object from above and a second source illuminates the object from below. The magnifying power of a stereomicroscope is much less than for a compound microscope; objects are magnified only by 10–50 diameters.

- Turn on the light source, and place the specimen on the stage so that it is in the field of view.
- Use the focus knob to adjust the focus.

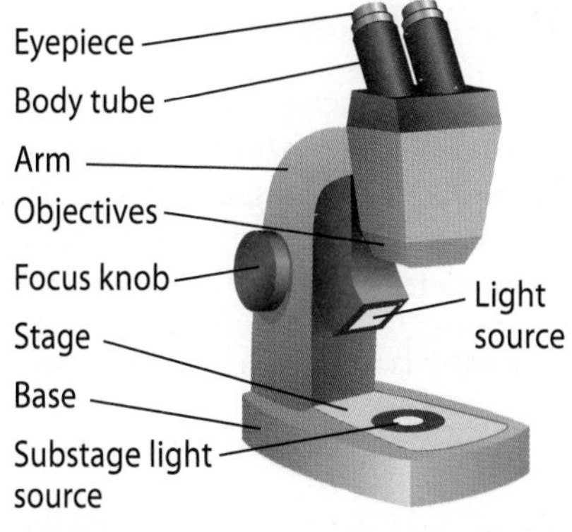

Figure 12

Perform Gel Electrophoresis

A technique called gel electrophoresis is used by scientists to separate mixtures of molecules based on their size, charge, and shape. This technique is most often used in separating DNA, RNA, and protein molecules.

Below are general guidelines for gel electrophoresis. Refer to your specific instrument's user's manual for complete instructions.

1. In the process of gel electrophoresis, scientists analyze DNA by first using special enzymes to cut a DNA sample at specific nucleotide sequences.
2. Small samples of cut DNA are prepared and placed in wells located on one end of a semisolid, gelatinlike gel, as shown in **Figure 13.**
3. The gel is placed in a buffer solution between two electrodes in a gel electrophoresis chamber. The electrodes are connected to a power supply (chamber and electrode not shown). When an electric current is applied, the buffer solution conducts the current. The current also moves through the gel. One end of the gel electrophoresis chamber becomes positively charged, and the other end becomes negatively charged.

   Negatively charged DNA fragments move toward the positive end of the gel. The shorter the fragment, the farther it moves through the gel. This allows the DNA fragments to form distinct and unique patterns for study, like those shown in **Figure 13.**

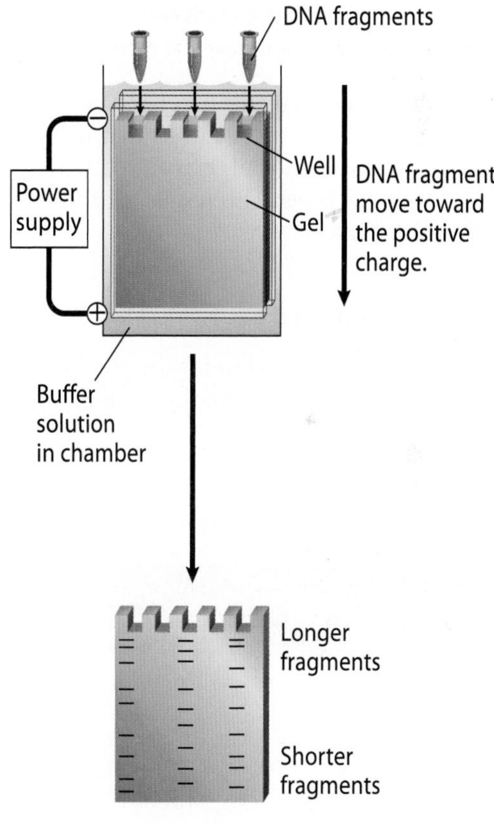

Figure 13

This process is also used to examine protein patterns. Proteins are extracted from cells and treated with chemicals to give them a negative charge. The prepared protein samples are placed in the wells of a gel. When an electric current is applied, the protein molecules move through the gel. The separation of protein molecules is based on the size, shape, and charge of the proteins.

Perform Chromatography

Paper chromatography is a commonly used technique in the biology laboratory for separating mixtures of substances. You will perform chromatography with a special chromatography paper or with filter paper and a liquid solvent. Separation occurs based on the ability of substances in the mixture to dissolve in the solvent. The general steps for this type of chromatography follow.

1. A mixture is dissolved in a liquid and placed on the paper.

2. One end of the paper is placed in a solvent.

3. The substances separate based on their tendencies to move along the surface of the paper while in the solvent.

For example, chlorophyll from leaves can be separated by paper chromatography, as shown in **Figure 14.** A dot of the chlorophyll extract is placed near one end of the strip of paper. The end of the paper nearest the dot is placed in alcohol, which acts as the solvent. The alcohol should not touch the extract to be separated, but should be just below it.

Figure 14

The alcohol moves up the paper and picks up substances in the chlorophyll extract. Substances in the extract that are tightly held to the paper will move slowly up the paper, while extract substances that are not as tightly held move quickly up the paper. This results in bands of different substances on the chromatography paper.

Use Indicators

Indicators are used to test for the presence of specific types of chemicals or substances. The table below lists commonly used indicators, what they test for, and how they react.

Indicators

Indicator	What it indicates in a solution	Reaction
Litmus paper	acid or base	• red litmus turns blue if the solution is a base • blue litmus turns red if the solution is an acid
pH paper	pH	• a color change compared to a color chart to estimate the pH
Bromothymol blue	presence of carbon dioxide	• turns yellow if carbon dioxide is present • changes to blue from yellow when carbon dioxide is removed
Phenolphthalein solution	presence of carbon dioxide or a basic solution	• turns from clear to a bright pink in the presence of either substance
Benedict's solution	presence of simple sugars when heated	• high sugar concentration, changes from blue to red • low sugar concentration, changes from blue to yellow
Biuret solution	presence of protein	• turns from light blue to purple
Lugol's solution	presence of starch	• turns from deep brown to bluish-black

4.1.1e, ¥e, ¥g, ¥h, ¥n

Make Comparisons

Why learn this skill?

Suppose you want to buy a portable MP3 music player, and you must choose between three models. You would probably compare the characteristics of the three models, such as price, amount of memory, sound quality, and size to determine which model is best for you. In the study of biology, you often make comparisons between the structures and functions of organisms. You will also compare scientific discoveries or events from one time period with those from another period.

Learn the Skill

When making comparisons, you examine two or more items, groups, situations, events, or theories. You must first decide what will be compared and which characteristics you will use to compare them. Then identify any similarities and differences.

For example, comparisons can be made between the two illustrations on this page. The different structures of the animal cell can be compared to the different structures of the plant cell. By reading the labels, you can see that both types of cells have a nucleus.

Practice the Skill

Create a table with the heading *Animal and Plant Cells.* Make three columns. Label the first column *Cell Structures.* Label the second column *Animal Cells.* Label the third column *Plant Cells.* List all the cell structures in the first column. Place a check mark under either *Animal Cell* or *Plant Cell* or both if that structure is shown in the illustration. When you have finished the table, answer these questions.

1. What items are being compared? How are they being compared?
2. What structures do animal and plant cells have in common?
3. What structures are unique to animal cells? What structures are unique to plant cells?

Apply the Skill

Make Comparisons In **Figure 10** of Chapter 9, you will find two images of cell division within plant and animal cells. Compare the two illustrations carefully. Then, identify the similarities and the differences between the two cells.

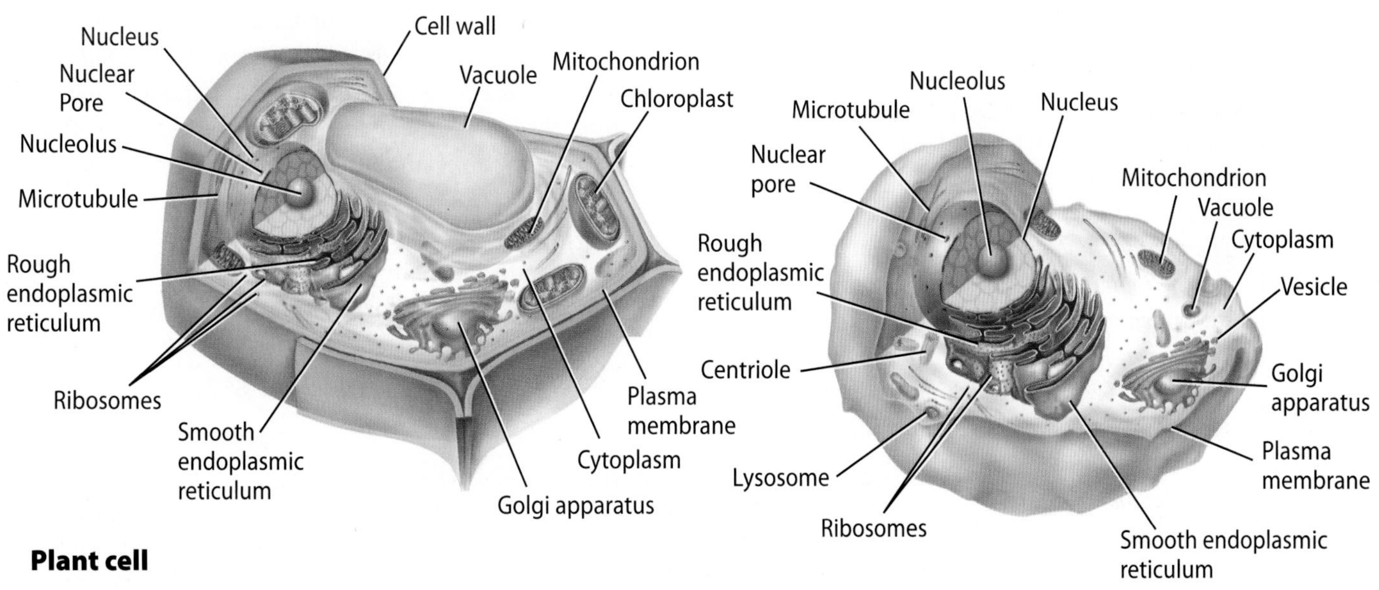

Plant cell

Animal cell

Analyze Information

Why learn this skill?

Analyzing, or looking at separate parts of something to understand the entire piece, is a way to think critically about written work. The ability to analyze information is important when determining which ideas are the most important.

Learn the Skill

To analyze information, use the following steps:

- identify the topic being discussed
- examine how the information is organized—identify the main points
- summarize the information in your own words, and then make a statement based on your understanding of the topic and what you already know

Practice the Skill

Read the following excerpt from *National Geographic.* Use the steps listed above to analyze the information and answer the questions that follow.

Like something straight out of a Jules Verne novel, an enormous tentacled creature looms out of the inky blackness of the deep Pacific waters. But this isn't science fiction. A set of extraordinary images captured by Japanese scientists marks the first-ever record of a live giant squid (Architeuthis) in the wild.

The animal—which measures roughly 8 meters long—was photographed 900 meters beneath the North Pacific Ocean. Japanese scientists attracted the squid toward cameras attached to a baited fishing line. The scientists say they snapped more than 500 images of the massive cephalopod before it broke free after snagging itself on a hook. They also recovered one of the giant squid's two longest tentacles, which severed during its struggle.

The photo sequence, taken off Japan's Ogasawara Islands in September 2004, shows the squid homing in on the baited line and enveloping it in "a ball of tentacles." Tsunemi Kubodera of the National Science Museum in Tokyo and Kyoichi Mori of the Ogasawara Whale Watching Association report their observations in the journal Proceedings of the Royal Society B.

"Architeuthis appears to be a much more active predator than previously suspected, using its elongated feeding tentacles to strike and tangle prey," the researchers write. They add that the squid was found feeding at depths where no light penetrates even during the day.

Giant squid on a fishing line

Koji Sashara/AP Images

Squid expert Martin Collins of the British Antarctic Survey based in Cambridge, England is especially interested in clues the images might provide to the way giant squid swim and hunt in the deep ocean.

Collins says there were two competing schools of thought among giant squid experts. "One was the idea that [giant squid] were fairly inactive and just drifted around, dangling their tentacles below them like fishing lures to catch what came by," he said.

"The other theory was that they were actually quite active. This new evidence supports this, suggesting they are active predators which can move reasonably quickly. The efforts the squid went to untangle itself [from the baited fishing line] also shows they are capable of quite strong and rapid movement," he added.

1. What topic is being discussed?
2. What are the main points of the article?
3. Summarize the information in this article, and then provide your analysis based on this information and your own knowledge.

Apply the Skill

Analyze Information Analyze a short, informative article on a scientific discovery or technology, such as the hybrid car. Summarize the information and make a statement of your own.

Synthesize Information

Why learn this skill?

The skill of synthesizing involves combining and analyzing information gathered from separate sources or at different times to make logical connections. Being able to synthesize information can be a useful skill for you as a student when you need to gather data from several sources for a report or a presentation.

Learn the Skill

Follow these steps to synthesize information:

- select important and relevant information
- analyze the information and build connections
- reinforce or modify the connections as you acquire new information

Suppose you need to write a research paper on endangered species. You would need to synthesize what you learn to inform others. You could begin by detailing the ideas and information you already have about endangered species. A table such as the one below could help you categorize the facts.

Table 1 Endangered Species Statistics

Group	October 2000		October 2005	
	U.S.	Foreign	U.S.	Foreign
Mammals	63	251	68	251
Birds	78	175	77	175
Reptiles	14	64	14	64
Amphibians	10	8	12	8
Fishes	69	11	71	11
Clams	61	2	62	2
Snails	20	1	24	1
Insects	30	4	35	4
Arachnids	6	0	12	0
Crustaceans	18	0	19	0

Source: U.S. Fish and Wildlife Service

Then you could select a passage about endangered species like the sample below.

Stable ecosystems can be changed by the activity of other organisms, climate, or natural disasters. This natural process of extinctions is not what scientists are worried about. Many worry about a recent increase in the rate of extinction.

One of the factors that is increasing the current rate of extinction is the overexploitation, or excessive use, of species that have economic values. Historically, overexploitation was the primary cause of species extinction. However, the number one cause of species extinction today is the loss or destruction of habitat.

There are several ways that species can lose their habitats. If a habitat is destroyed or disrupted, the native species might have to relocate or die. For example, humans are clearing areas of tropical rain forests and are replacing the native plants with agricultural crops or grazing lands.

Practice the Skill

Use the table and the passage on this page to answer these questions.

1. What information is presented in the table?
2. What is the main idea of the passage? What information does the passage add to your knowledge about the topic?
3. By synthesizing the two sources and using your own knowledge, what conclusions can you draw about habitat conservation practices for endangered species?
4. Using what you learned in your studies and from this activity, contrast two types of habitat changes and their effects on the ecosystem.

Apply the Skill

Synthesize Information Find two sources of information on the same topic and write a short report. In your report, answer the following questions: What are the main ideas of each source? How does each source add to your understanding of the topic? Do the sources support or contradict each other? What conclusions can you draw from the sources?

Take Notes and Outline

Why learn this skill?

One of the best ways to remember something is to write it down. Taking notes—writing down information in a brief and orderly format—not only helps you remember, but also makes studying easier.

Learn the Skill

There are several styles of note taking, but all explain and put information in a logical order. As you read, identify and summarize the main ideas and details that support them and write them in your notes. Paraphrase, that is, state in your own words, the information rather than copying it directly from the text. Using note cards or developing a personal "shorthand," using symbols to represent words, can help.

You might also find it helpful to create an outline when taking notes. When outlining material, first read the material to identify the main ideas. In textbooks, section headings provide clues to main topics. Identify the subheadings. Place supporting details under the appropriate heading. The basic pattern for outlines is as follows:

MAIN TOPIC
- I. FIRST IDEA OR ITEM
  - A. FIRST DETAIL
    - 1. SUBDETAIL
    - 2. SUBDETAIL
  - B. SECOND DETAIL
- II. SECOND IDEA OR ITEM
  - A. FIRST DETAIL
  - B. SECOND DETAIL
    - 1. SUBDETAIL
    - 2. SUBDETAIL
- III. THIRD IDEA OR ITEM

Practice the Skill

Read the following excerpt from *National Geographic.* Use the steps you just read about to take notes or create an outline. Then answer the questions that follow.

Mapping the three billion letters of the human genome has helped researchers better understand the 99.9 percent of DNA that is identical in all humans. Now a new project aims to map the 0.1 percent of DNA where differences occur. The International HapMap Project will look at variations that dictate susceptibility to genetic influences, such as environmental toxins and inherited diseases.

Researchers "read" DNA code by its structural units called nucleotides. These chemical building blocks are designated by the letters A (adenine), C (cytosine), G (guanine), and T (thymine). Single-letter variations in genes—called single nucleotide polymorphisms, or SNPs (pronounced "snips")—are often the culprits behind a wide range of genetic diseases. For example, changing an A to a T in the gene for the blood molecule hemoglobin causes sickle cell anemia.

But most diseases and disorders are not caused by a single gene. Instead they are caused by a complex combination of linked genetic variations at multiple sites on different chromosomes.

Haplotypes are sets of adjacent SNPs that are closely associated and are inherited as a group. Certain haplotypes are known to have a role in diseases, including Alzheimer's, deep vein thrombosis, type 2 diabetes, and age-related macular degeneration, a leading cause of blindness.

1. What is the main topic of the article?
2. What are the first, second, and third ideas?
3. Name one detail for each of the ideas.
4. Name one subdetail for each of the details.

Apply the Skill

Take Notes and Outline Go to Chapter 2, Section 1 and take notes by paraphrasing and using shorthand or by creating an outline. Use the section title and headings to help you create your outline. Summarize the section using only your notes.

Understand Cause and Effect

Why learn this skill?

In order to understand an event, you should look for how that event or chain of events came about. When scientists are unsure of the cause for an event, they often design experiments. Although there might be an explanation, an experiment should be performed to be certain the cause created the event you observed. This process examines the causes and effects of events.

Learn the Skill

Every human body regulates its own temperature to maintain conditions suitable for survival. Exercise *causes* a body to heat up. The stimulated nerves in the skin are the *effect,* or result, of exercise. The figure below shows how one event—the **cause**—led to another—the **effect.**

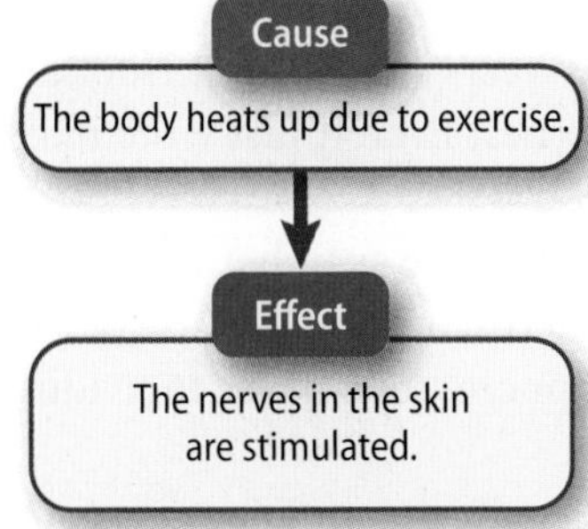

You can also identify cause-and-effect relationships in sentences from clue words such as:

because	**thus**
that is why	**due to**
led to	**for this reason**
so that	**produced**
consequently	**therefore**
as a result	**in order to**

Read the sample sentences below.

"A message is sent to sweat glands. As a result, perspiration occurs."

In the example above, the cause is a message being sent. The cause-and-effect clue words "as a result" tell you that the perspiration is the effect of the message.

In a chain of events, an effect often becomes the cause of other events. The next chart shows the complete chain of events that occur when exercise raises body temperature and the body returns to homeostasis.

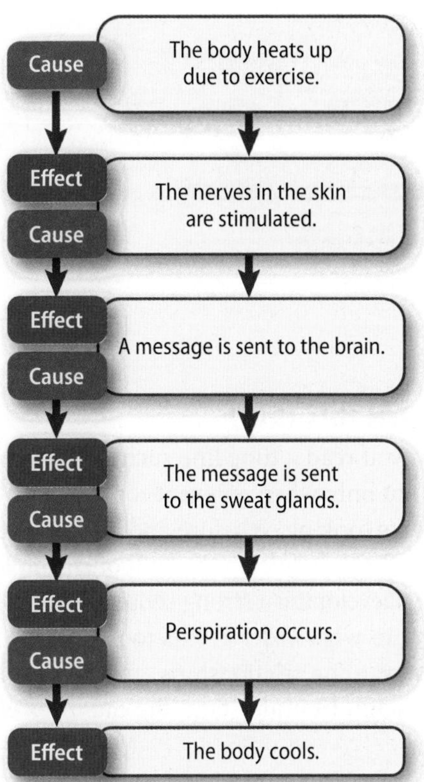

Practice the Skill

Make a chart, like the one above, showing which events are causes and which are effects using these sentences.

1. The hair cells respond by generating nerve impulses in the auditory nerve and transmitting them to the brain.
2. As the stapes vibrates, it causes the oval window to move back and forth.
3. Sound waves enter the auditory canal and cause the eardrum to vibrate.
4. Vibrations cause the fluid inside the cochlea to move like a wave against the hair cells.
5. Vibrations travel through the malleus, the incus, and the stapes.

Apply the Skill

Understand Cause and Effect Read an account of a recent scientific event or discovery in a science article. Determine the causes and effects that lead to the event or discovery. Show the chain of events in a chart.

Skillbuilder Handbook

Read a Time Line

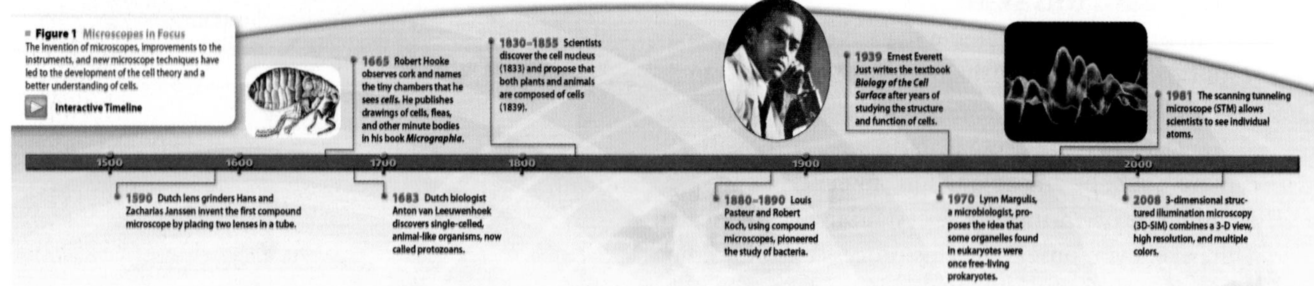

1590 Dutch lens grinders Hans and Zacharias Janssen invent the first compound microscope by placing two lenses in a tube.
1665 Robert Hooke observes cork and names the tiny chambers that he sees *cells*. He publishes drawings of cells, fleas, and other minute bodies in his book *Micrographia*.
1683 Dutch biologist Anton van Leeuwenhoek discovers single-celled, animal-like organisms, now called protozoans.
1830–1855 Scientists discover the cell nucleus (1833) and propose that both plants and animals are composed of cells (1839).
1880–1890 Louis Pasteur and Robert Koch, using compound microscopes, pioneered the study of bacteria.
1939 Ernest Everett Just writes the textbook *Biology of the Cell Surface* after years of studying the structure and function of cells.
1970 Lynn Margulis, a microbiologist, proposes the idea that some organelles found in eukaryotes were once free-living prokaryotes.
1981 The scanning tunneling microscope (STM) allows scientists to see individual atoms.
2008 3-dimensional structured illumination microscopy (3D-SIM) combines a 3-D view, high resolution, and multiple colors.
1500
1600
1700
1800
1900
2000
Interactive Timeline

■ **Figure 1** Microscopes in Focus
The invention of microscopes, improvements to the instruments, and new microscope techniques have led to the development of the cell theory and a better understanding of cells.

Why learn this skill?

When you read a time line such as the one above, you see not only when an event took place, but also what events took place before and after it. A time line can help you develop the skill of chronological thinking. Developing a strong sense of chronology—when and in what order events took place—will help you examine relationships among the events. It will also help you understand the causes or effects of events.

Learn the Skill

A time line is a linear chart that list events that occurred on specific dates. The number of years between dates at the begining and end of the time line is the time span. A time line that begins in 1910 and ends in 1920 has a ten-year time span. Some time lines span centuries. Examine the time lines below. What time spans do they cover?

Time lines are usually divided into smaller parts called time intervals. On the two time lines below, the first time line has a 300-year time span divided into 100-year time intervals. The second time line has a six-year time span divided into two-year time intervals.

Practice the Skill

Study the time line above and then answer these questions.

1. What time span and intervals appear on this time line?
2. Which scientist was the first to observe cells with a microscope?
3. How many years after Robert Hooke observed cork did Ernest Everett Just write *Biology of the Cell Surface?*
4. What was the time span between the creation of the first microscope and the use of the scanning tunneling microscope to see individual atoms?

Apply the Skill

Read a Time Line Sometimes a time line shows events that occurred during the same period, but related to two different subjects. The time line above shows events related to cells between 1500 and 2008. Copy the time line and events onto a piece of paper. Then use a different color to add events related to genetics during this same time span. Use the chapters in Unit 3 to help you.

Analyze Media Sources

Why learn this skill?

To stay informed, people use a variety of media sources, including print media, broadcast media, and electronic media. The Internet has become an especially valuable research tool. It is convenient to use, and the information contained on the Internet is plentiful. Whichever media source you use to gather information, it is important to analyze the source to determine its accuracy and reliability.

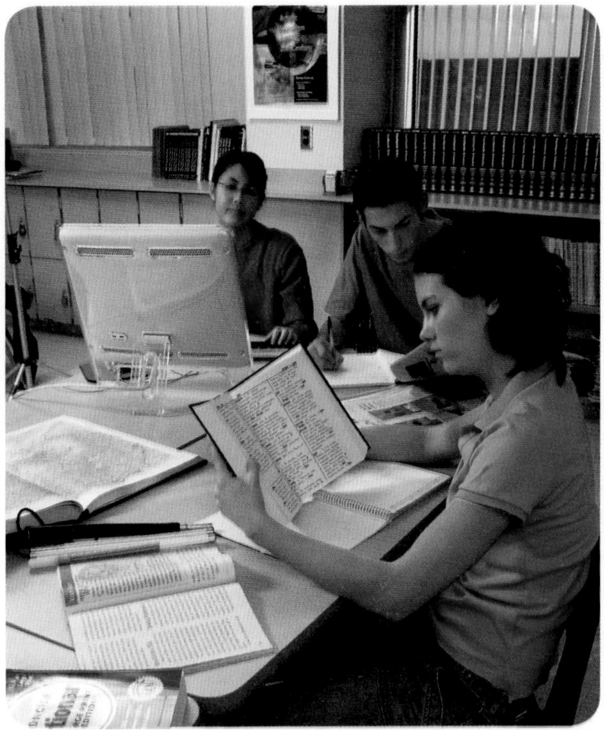

Learn the Skill

There are a number of issues to consider when analyzing a media source. Most important is to check the accuracy of the source and content. The author and publisher or sponsors should be credible and clearly indicated. To analyze print media or broadcast media, ask yourself the following questions:

- Is the information current?
- Are the resources revealed?
- Is more than one resource used?
- Is the information biased?
- Does the information represent both sides of an issue?
- Is the information reported firsthand or secondhand?

For electronic media, ask yourself these questions in addition to the ones above.

- Is the author credible and clearly identified? Web site addresses that end in .edu, .gov, and .org tend to be credible and contain reliable information.
- Are the facts on the Web site documented?
- Are the links within the Web site appropriate and current?
- Does the Web site contain links to other useful resources?

Practice the Skill

To analyze print media, choose two articles, one from a newspaper and the other from a newsmagazine, on an issue on which public opinion is divided. Then, answer these questions.

1. What points are the articles trying to make? Were the articles successful? Can the facts be verified?
2. Did either article reflect a bias toward one viewpoint or another? List any unsupported statements.
3. Was the information reported firsthand or secondhand? Do the articles seem to represent both sides fairly?
4. How many resources can you identify in the articles? List them.

To analyze electronic media, read through the list of links provided by your teacher. Choose one link from the list, read the information on that Web site, and then answer these questions.

1. Who is the author or sponsor of the Web site?
2. What links does the Web site contain? How are they appropriate to the topic?
3. What resources were used for the information on the Web site?

Apply the Skill

Analyze Sources of Information Think of an issue in the nation on which public opinion is divided. Use a variety of media resources to read about this issue. Which news source more fairly represents the issue? Which news source has the most reliable information? Can you identify any biases? Can you verify the credibility of the news source?

Use Graphic Organizers

Why learn this skill?

While you read this textbook, you will be looking for important ideas or concepts. One way to arrange these ideas is to create a graphic organizer. In addition to Foldables®, you will find various other graphic organizers throughout your book. Some organizers show a sequence, or flow, of events. Other organizers emphasize the relationship between concepts. Develop your own organizers to help you better understand and remember what you read.

Learn the Skill

An **events chain concept map** describes a sequence of events, such as stages of a process or procedure. When making an events-chain map, first identify the event that starts the sequence and add events in chronological order until you reach an outcome.

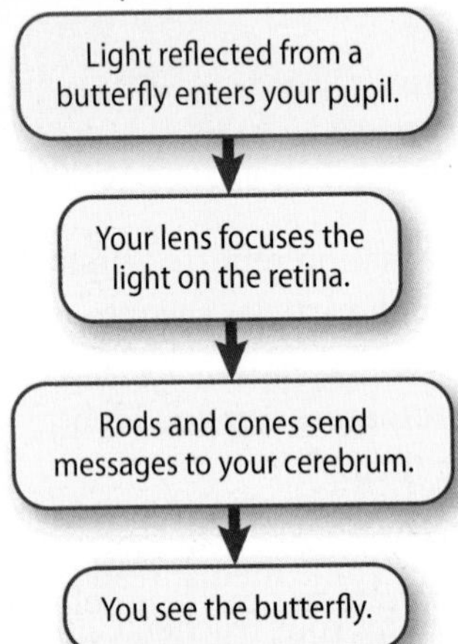

In a **cycle concept map,** the series of events do not produce a final outcome. The event that appears to be the final event relates back to the event that appears to be the initiating event. Therefore, the cycle repeats itself.

Blood Flow in the Body

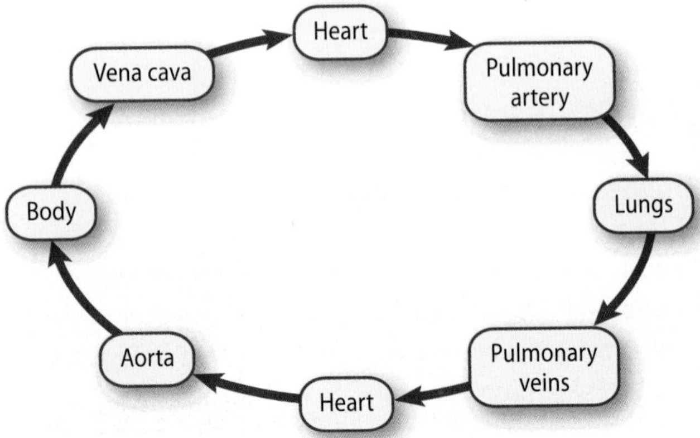

A **network tree concept map** shows the relationship among concepts, which are written in order from general to specific. The words written on the lines between the circles, called linking words, describe the relationships among the concepts; the concepts and the linking words can form a sentence.

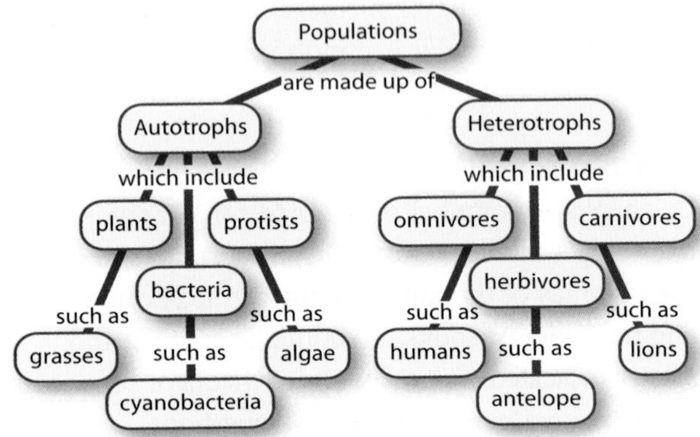

Practice the Skill

1. Create an events chain concept map that describes the process of hearing the ring of a bell. Begin with sound waves entering the outer ear. End with hearing the bell ring.
2. Create a cycle concept map of human respiration. Make sure that the cycle is complete with the event that appears to be the final event relating back to the event that appears to be the starting event.
3. Create a network tree concept map with these words: *Biomes, aquatic biomes, terrestrial biomes, marine biomes, estuary biomes, freshwater biomes, desert, grasslands, temperate forest, salt water, mixed waters, freshwater, sparse plant life, grasses,* and *broad-leaved trees.* Add linking words to describe the relationships between concepts. Refer to Chapter 3 for help.

Apply the Skill

Use Graphic Organizers Create an events chain concept map of succession using information from Chapter 3. Create a cycle concept map of the water cycle using information from Chapter 2. Create a network tree concept map of animals that includes invertebrates and vertebrates, characteristics of each type, and examples. Work with a partner.

Debate Skills

New research leads to new scientific information. There are often opposing points of view on how this research is conducted, how it is interpreted, and how it is communicated. The *Biology and Society* features in your book offer a chance to debate a current controversial topic. Here is an overview on how to conduct a debate.

Choose a Position and Research

First, choose a scientific issue that has at least two opposing viewpoints. The issue can come from current events, your textbook, or your teacher. These topics could include human cloning or environmental issues. Topics are stated as affirmative declarations, such as "Cloning human beings is beneficial to society."

One speaker will argue the viewpoint that agrees with the statement, called the positive position, and another speaker will argue the viewpoint that disagrees with the statement, called the negative position. Either individually or with a group, choose the position for which you will argue. The viewpoint that you choose does not have to reflect your personal belief. The purpose of debate is to create a strong argument supported by scientific evidence.

After choosing your position, conduct research to support your viewpoint. Use resources in your media center or library to find articles, or use your textbook to gather evidence to support your argument. A strong argument is supported by scientific evidence, expert opinions, and your own analysis of the issue. Research the opposing position also. Becoming aware of what points the other side might argue will help you to strengthen the evidence for your position.

Hold the Debate

You will have a specific amount of time, determined by your teacher, in which to present your argument. Organize your speech to fit within the time limit: explain the viewpoint that you will be arguing, present an analysis of your evidence, and conclude by summing up your most important points. Try to vary the elements of your argument. Your speech should not be a list of facts, a reading of a newspaper article, or a statement of your personal opinion, but an analysis of your evidence in an organized manner. It is also important to remember that you must never make personal attacks against your opponent. Argue the issue. You will be evaluated on your overall presentation, organization and development of ideas, and strength of support for your argument.

Additional Roles There are other roles that you or your classmates can play in a debate. You can act as the timekeeper. The timekeeper times the length of the debaters' speeches and gives quiet signals to the speaker when time is almost up (usually a hand signal).

You can also act as a judge. There are important elements to look for when judging a speech: an introduction that tells the audience what position the speaker will be arguing, strong evidence that supports the speaker's position, and organization. The speaker also must speak clearly and loudly enough for everyone to hear. It is helpful to take notes during the debate to summarize the main points of each side's argument. Then, decide which debater presented the strongest argument for his or her position. You can have a class discussion about the strengths and weaknesses of the debate and other viewpoints on this issue that could be argued.

Tim Fuller

Experimental data is often quantitative and is expressed using numbers and units. The following sections provide an overview of the common system of units and some calculations involving units.

Measure in SI

The International System of Measurement, abbreviated SI, is accepted as the standard for measurement throughout most of the world. The SI system contains seven base units. All other units of measurement can be derived from these base units.

Table 2 SI Base Units

Measurement	Unit	Symbol
Length	Meter	m
Mass	Kilogram	kg
Time	Second	s
Electric current	Ampere	A
Temperature	Kelvin	K
Amount of substance	Mole	mol
Intensity of light	Candela	cd

Some units are derived by combining base units. For example, units for volume are derived from units of length. A liter (L) is a cubic decimeter ($dm^3 = dm \times dm \times dm$). Units of density (g/L) are derived from units of mass (g) and units of volume (L).

When units are multiplied by factors of ten, new units are created. For example, if a base unit is multiplied by 1000, the new unit has the prefix *kilo-*. Prefixes for some units are shown in **Table 3.**

To convert a given unit to a unit with a different factor of ten, multiply the unit by a conversion factor. A conversion factor is a ratio equal to one. The equivalents in **Table 3** can be used to make such a ratio. For example, 1 km = 1000 m. Two conversion factors can be made from this equivalent.

$$\frac{1000 \text{ m}}{1 \text{ km}} = 1 \quad \text{and} \quad \frac{1 \text{ km}}{1000 \text{ m}} = 1$$

To convert one unit to another factor of ten, choose the conversion factor that has the unit you are converting from in the denominator. For example, to convert one kilometer to meters, use the following equation.

$$1 \cancel{\text{km}} \times \frac{1000 \text{ m}}{1 \cancel{\text{km}}} = 1000 \text{ m}$$

A unit can be multiplied by several conversion factors to obtain the desired unit.

Table 3 Common SI Prefixes

Prefix	Symbol	Equivalents
mega	M	1×10^6 base units
kilo	k	1×10^3 base units
hecto	h	1×10^2 base units
deka	da	1×10^1 base units
deci	d	1×10^{-1} base units
centi	c	1×10^{-2} base units
milli	m	1×10^{-3} base units
micro	μ	1×10^{-6} base units
nano	n	1×10^{-9} base units
pico	p	1×10^{-12} base units

Practice Problem 1 How would you change 1000 micrometers to kilometers?

Convert Temperature

The following formulas can be used to convert between Fahrenheit and Celsius temperatures. Notice that each equation can be obtained by algebraically rearranging the other. Therefore, you only need to remember one of the equations.

Conversion of Fahrenheit to Celsius

$$°C = \frac{(°F) - 32}{1.8}$$

Conversion of Celsius to Fahrenheit

$$°F = 1.8(°C) + 32$$

Make and Use Tables

Tables help organize data so that it can be interpreted more easily. Tables are composed of several components—a title describing the contents of the table, columns and rows that separate and organize information, and headings that describe the information in each column or row.

Table 4 Effects of Exercise on Heart Rate

Pulse taken	Individual heart rate (Beats per min)	Class average (Beats per min)
At rest	73	72
After exercise	110	112
1 minute after exercise	94	90
5 minutes after exercise	76	75

Looking at this table, you should not only be able to pick out specific information, such as the class average heart rate after five minutes of exercise, but you should also notice trends.

Practice Problem 2 Did the exercise have an effect on the heart rate one minute after exercise? How can you tell? What can you conclude about the effects of exercise on heart rate during and after exercise?

Make and Use Graphs

After scientists organize data in tables, they often display the data in graphs. A graph is a diagram that shows relationships among variables. Graphs make interpretation and analysis of data easier. The three basic types of graphs used in science are the line graph, the bar graph, and the circle graph.

Line Graphs A line graph is used to show the relationship between two variables. The independent variable is plotted on the horizontal axis, called the *x*-axis. The dependent variable is plotted on the vertical axis, called the *y*-axis. The dependent variable *(y)* changes as a result of a change in the independent variable *(x)*.

Suppose a school started a bird-watching group to observe the number of birds in the school courtyard. The number of birds in the courtyard was recorded each day for four months. The average number of birds per month was calculated. A table of the birds' visitations is shown below.

Table 5 Average Number of Birds Viewed

Time (days)	Average Number of Birds per Day
30	24
60	27
90	30
120	32

To make a graph of the average number of birds over a period of time, start by determining the dependent and independent variables. The average number of birds after each period of time is the dependent variable and is plotted on the *y*-axis. The independent variable, or the number of days, is plotted on the *x*-axis.

Plain or graph paper can be used to construct graphs. Draw a grid on your paper or a box around the squares that you intend to use on your graph paper. Give your graph a title and label each axis with a title and units. In this example, label the number of days on the *x*-axis. Because the lowest average of birds viewed was 24 and the highest was 32, you know that you will have to start numbers on the *y*-axis of at least 24 and number to at least 32. You could decide to number 20–40 by intervals of two spaced at equal distances.

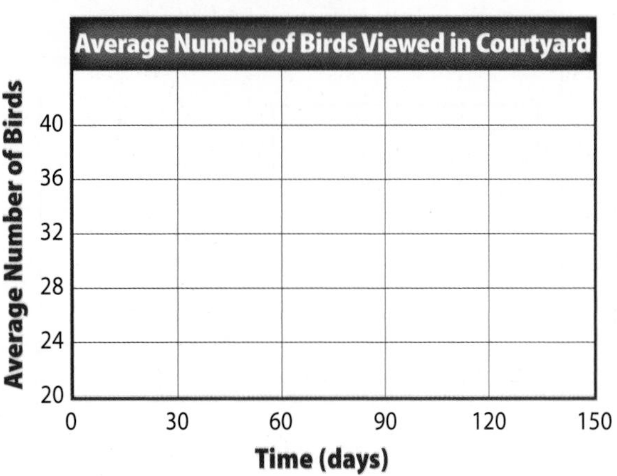

Begin plotting points by locating 30 days on the x-axis and 24 on the y-axis. Where an imaginary vertical line from the x-axis and an imaginary horizontal line from the y-axis meet, place the first data point. Place other data points using the same process. After all the points are plotted, draw a "best fit" straight line through all the points.

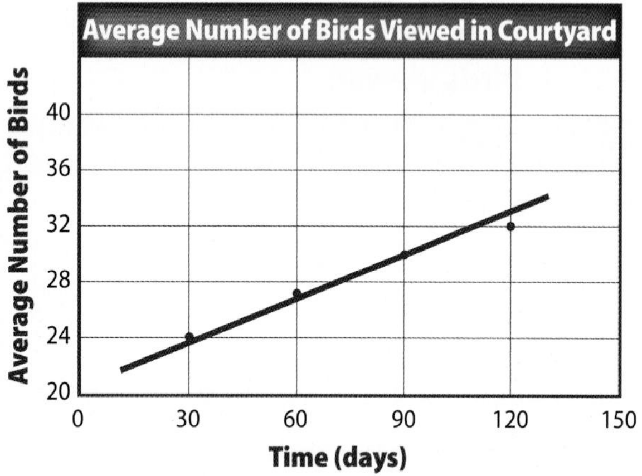

The bird-watching group also recorded the average number of brown-feathered birds they observed in the school courtyard. In the first month they averaged 21 brown-feathered birds per day. In the second month they averaged 24 brown-feathered birds. An average of 28 brown-feathered birds per day was observed in the third month. In the final month an average of 30 brown-feathered birds was observed.

What if you want to compare the average number of birds viewed with the average number of brown-feathered birds? The average brown-feathered bird data can be plotted on the same graph. Include a key with different lines indicating different sets of data.

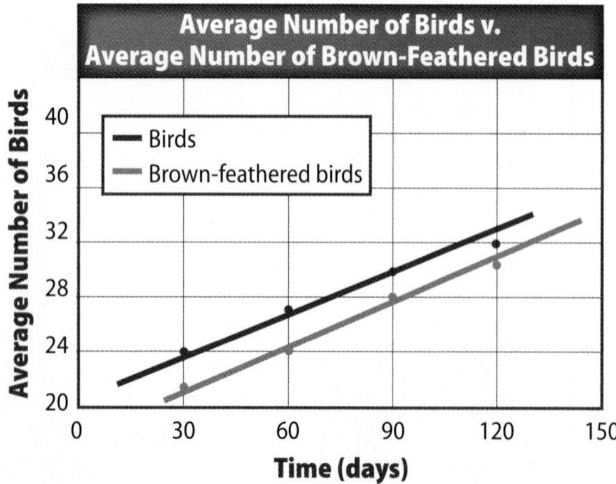

Practice Problem 3 Between 30 days and 120 days, what is the change in the average number of birds viewed?

Practice Problem 4 For the 120 days how did the average number of brown-feathered birds change as the average number of birds changed?

Slope of a Linear Graph The slope of a line is a number determined by any two points on the line. This number describes how steep the line is. The greater the absolute value of the slope, the steeper the line. Slope is the ratio of the change in the y-coordinates (rise) to the change in the x-coordinates (run) as you move from one point to the other.

The graph below shows a line that passes through (5, 4) and (9, 6).

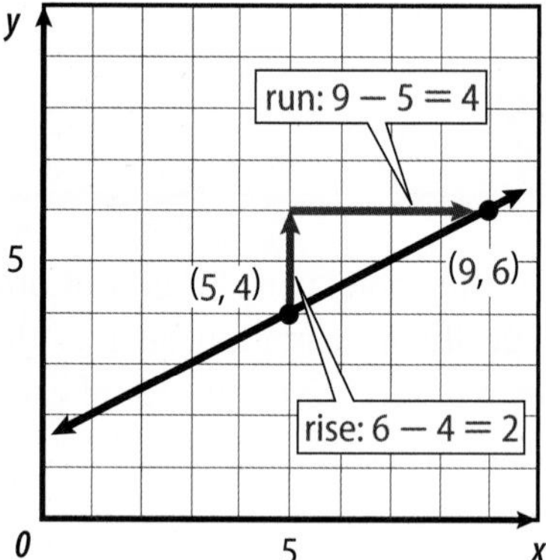

$$\text{Slope} = \frac{\text{rise}}{\text{run}}$$

$$= \frac{\text{change in } y\text{-coordinates}}{\text{change in } x\text{-coordinates}}$$

$$= \frac{6-4}{9-5}$$

$$= \frac{2}{4} \text{ or } \frac{1}{2}$$

So, the slope of the line is $\frac{1}{2}$.

A linear relationship can be translated into equation form. The equation for a straight line is

$$y = mx + b$$

where y represents the dependent variable, m is the slope of the line, x represents the independent variable, and b is the y-intercept, which is the point where the line crosses the y-axis.

Linear and Exponential Trends Two types of trends you are likely to see when you graph data in biology are linear trends and exponential trends. A linear trend has a constant increase or decrease in data values. In an exponential trend the values are increasing or decreasing more and more rapidly. The graphs below are examples of these two common trends.

In the graph below, there are two lines describing two frog species. Both lines show an increasing linear trend. As the temperature increases, so does the call pulse rates of the frogs. The rate of increase is constant.

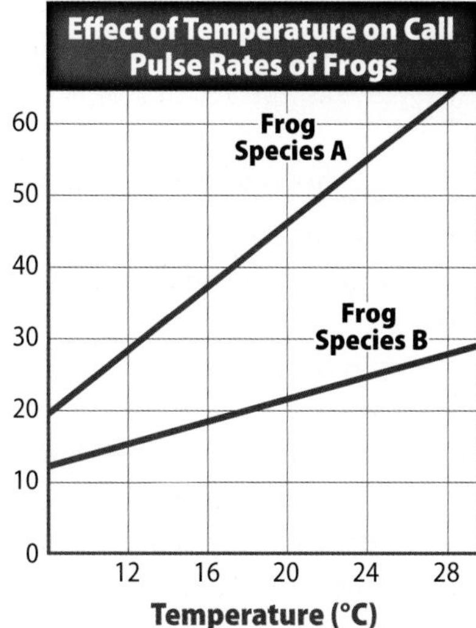

The example below shows how a mouse population would grow if the mice were allowed to reproduce unhindered. At first the population would grow slowly. The population growth rate soon accelerates because the total number of mice that are able to reproduce has increased. Notice that the portion of the graph where the population is increasing more and more rapidly is J-shaped. A J-shaped curve generally indicates exponential growth.

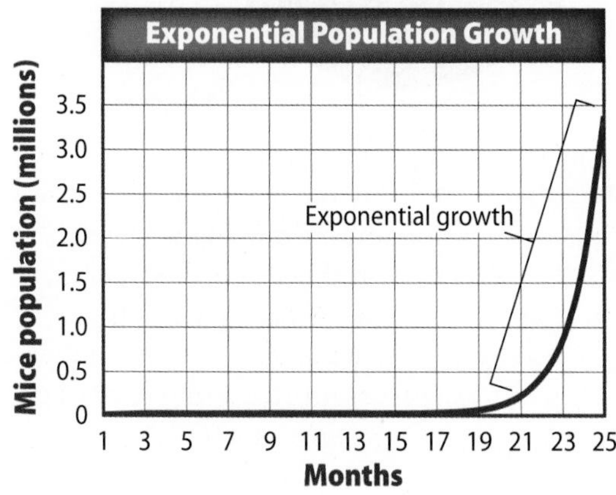

Bar Graphs A bar graph displays a comparison of different categories of data by representing each category with a bar. The length of the bar is related to the category's frequency. To make a bar graph, set up the x-axis and y-axis as you did for the line graph. Plot the data by drawing thick bars from the x-axis up to the y-axis point.

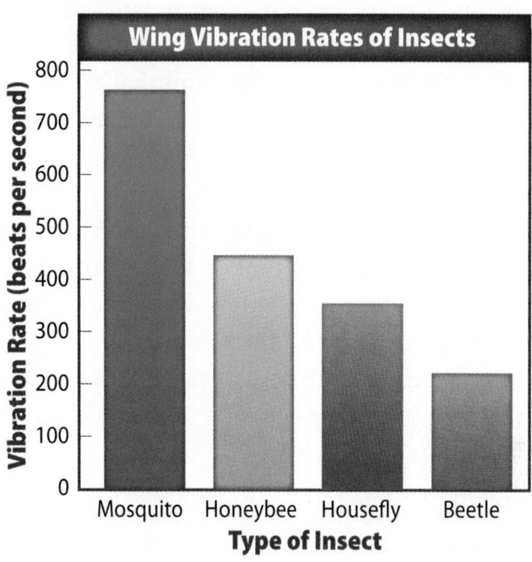

Look at the graph above. The independent variable is the type of insect. The dependent variable is the number of wing vibrations per second.

Bar graphs can also be used to display multiple sets of data in different categories at the same time. A bar graph that displays two sets of data is called a double bar graph. Double bar graphs have a legend to denote which bars represent each set of data. The graph below is an example of a double bar graph.

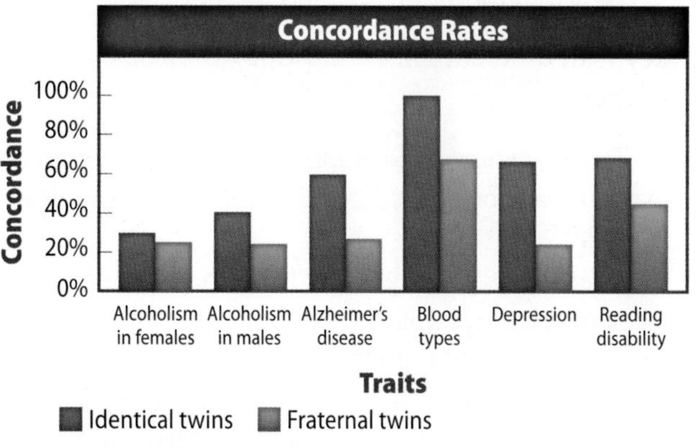

Practice Problem 5 Which type of insect has the highest number of wing vibrations per second? Is this more than twice as fast as the housefly? Explain.

Skillbuilder Handbook

Circle Graphs A circle graph consists of a circle divided into sections that represent parts of a whole. When all the sections are placed together, they equal 100 percent of the whole.

Suppose you want to make a circle graph to show the number of seeds that germinate in a package. You would first determine the total number of seeds and the numbers of seeds that germinate out of the total. You plant 143 seeds. Therefore, the whole circle represents this amount. You find that 129 seeds germinate. The seeds that germinate make up one section of the circle graph and the seeds that do not germinate make up another section.

To find out how much of the circle each section should cover, divide the number of seeds that germinate by the total number of seeds. Then multiply the answer by 360, the number of degrees in a circle. Round your answer to the nearest whole number. The sum of all the segments of the circle graph should add up to 360°.

$$\text{Segment of circle for seeds that germinated} = \frac{\text{Seeds that germinated}}{\text{Total number of seeds}}$$

Divide $= \frac{129}{143}$

Multiply by number of degrees in a circle $= 0.902 \times 360°$

$= 324.72°$

Round to nearest whole number $= 325°$

Segment of circle for seeds that did not germinate $= 360° - 325°$

$= 35°$

To draw your circle graph, you will need a compass and a protractor. First, use the compass to draw a circle.

Then, draw a straight line from the center to the edge of the circle. Place your protractor on this line, and mark the point on the circle where the 35° angle will intersect the circle. Draw a straight line from the center of the circle to the intersection point. This is the section for the seeds that did not germinate. The other section represents the group of seeds that did germinate.

Next, determine the percentages for each part of the whole. Calculate percentages by dividing the part by the total and multiplying by 100. Repeat this calculation for each part.

$$\text{Percent of seeds that germinate} = \frac{\text{Seeds that germinated}}{\text{Total number of seeds}}$$

$= \frac{129}{143}$

Multiply by 100 and add the % $= 0.902 \times 100$

$= 0.902$

$= 90.2\%$

Percent of seeds that did not germinate $= 100\% - 90.2\%$ $= 9.8\%$

Complete the graph by labeling the sections of the graph with percentages and giving the graph a title. Your completed graph should look similar to the one below.

If your circle graph has more than two sections, you will need to construct a segment for each entry. Place your protractor on the last line segment that you have drawn and mark off the appropriate angle. Draw a line segment from the center of the circle to the new mark on the circle. Continue this process until all of the segments have been drawn.

Percentage of Germinating and Non-Germinating Seeds

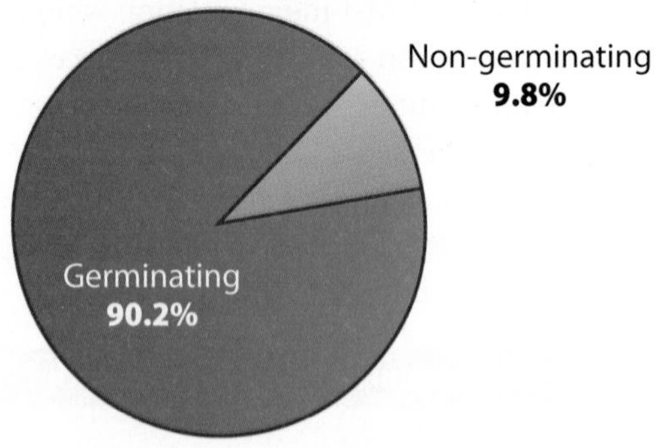

Practice Problem 6 There are 25 varieties of flowering plants growing around the high school. Construct a circle graph showing the percentage of each flower's color. Two varieties have yellow blooms, five varieties have blue-purple blooms, eight varieties have white blooms, and ten varieties have red blooms.

4.1.3a, 4.5.2f

Domains

As you learned in Chapter 17, most scientists organize living things into three domains: Archaea, Bacteria, and Eukarya. Within those domains are six kingdoms. The Domain Archaea has only one kingdom, Kingdom Archaeabacteria. In Domain Bacteria, the organisms are classified into Kingdom Bacteria. Organisms in Domain Eukarya are classified into four kingdoms: Protista, Fungi, Plantae, and Animalia.

Domain Archaea, Kingdom Archeabacteria

In extreme environments that are too hostile for most forms of life, archaeabacteria dominate. These organisms are often called extremophiles because they inhabit extreme environments. Thermoacidophiles live in hot, acidic environments including sulfur hot springs and ocean thermal vents, and around volcanoes. Halophiles live in very salty environments, such as the Great Salt Lake and the Dead Sea, where the salt concentration is near 15 percent. Methanogens are the third group of archaeabacteria. They are obligate anaerobes that use carbon dioxide during respiration and produce methane as a by-product. Methanogens are found in sewage treatment plants, swamps, bogs, and near volcanic vents. They even thrive in the gastrointestinal tract of humans and other animals.

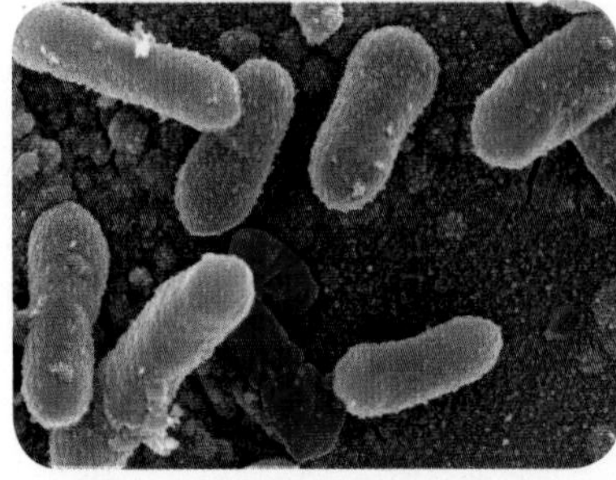

Figure 1 *Salmonella typhimurium* are rod-shaped bacteria.

Domain Bacteria, Kingdom Bacteria

A bacterium is a unicellular prokaryote. Most of its genes are part of a circular chromosome in the cytoplasm. A cell wall surrounds its plasma membrane. Bacteria are heterotrophs, photosynthetic autotrophs, or chemosynthetic autotrophs. They reproduce asexually by binary fission and sexually by conjugation.

Many bacteria are obligate aerobes, needing oxygen for cellular respiration. Some bacteria are obligate anaerobes and cannot survive in the presence of oxygen. Still other bacteria can live either with or without oxygen. Some bacteria can produce endospores to help them survive unfavorable environmental conditions.

Some bacteria cause diseases. Other bacteria fix nitrogen, recycle nutrients, and help make food products and medicines.

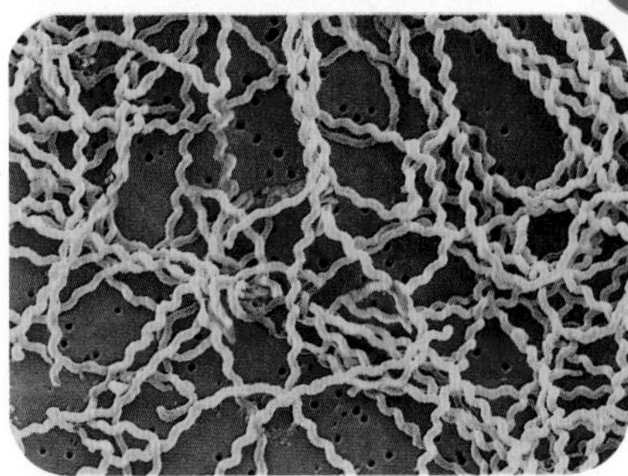

Figure 2 Spiral-shaped bacteria are called spirochetes. These are members of the genus, *Leptospira*.

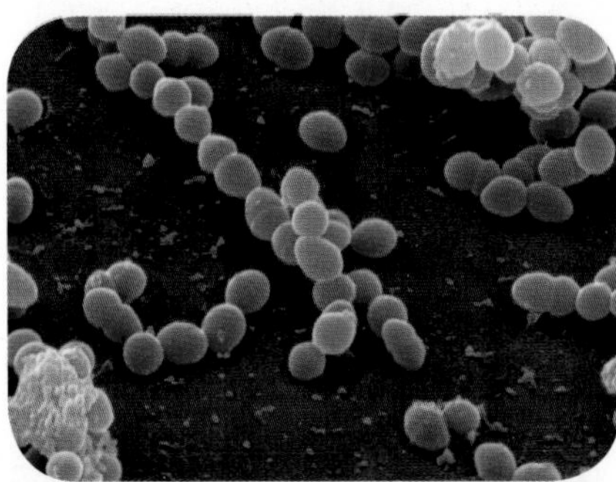

Figure 3 *Enterococcus faecalis* typically are in chains of cells.

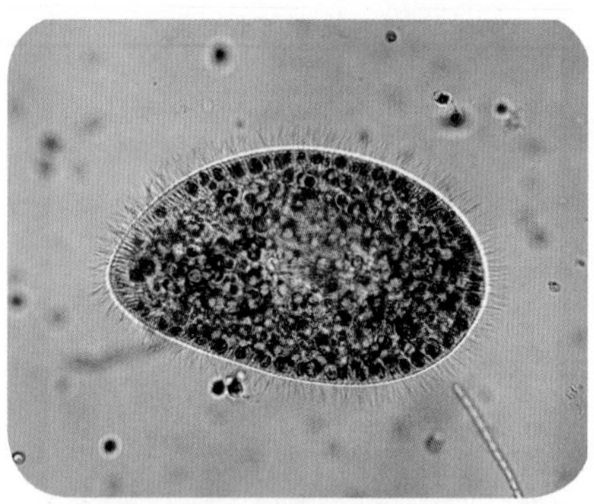

■ **Figure 4** The beating cilia of a paramecium produce water currents for collecting food.

BioFacts

Protists

Distribution: worldwide in aquatic and moist habitats

Niches: producers, herbivores, predators, parasites, and decomposers

Number of species: more than 60,000

Size range: less than 2 mm in length to greater than 100 m in length

Domain Eukarya, Kingdom Protista

Protists are heterotrophic, autotrophic, parasitic, or saprophytic eukaryotes. Although many protists are unicellular, some are multicellular. They all live in aquatic or moist environments.

Protozoans: Animal-like protists Protozoans are unicellular, heterotrophic organisms. Many protozoans are classified based on their adaptations for locomotion in an environment.

Phylum Sarcodina includes protozoans called amoebas that use pseudopods, extensions of their plasma membrane, to move and engulf prey. Phylum Zoomastigina is composed of protozoans that use flagella to move around. Some are parasitic and cause diseases such as sleeping sickness. Members of phylum Ciliophora move by beating hairlike projections called cilia. *Paramecium* species are widely studied ciliates.

Sporozoans belong to the phylum Apicomplexa. They are parasites and many produce spores. Most have very complex life cycles. *Plasmodium* is a protozoan that causes the disease malaria. It has a sexual stage in mosquitoes and an asexual stage in humans.

Algae: Plantlike Protists Autotrophic protists are called algae. They are grouped on the basis of the pigments they contain, their method of food storage, and the composition of their cell walls. Photosynthetic algae produce much of Earth's atmospheric oxygen. They are unicellular and multicellular.

Unicellular Algae Phylum Euglenophyta includes autotrophs and heterotrophs. Most species have chlorophyll for photosynthesis. When there is no light, some euglenas can ingest food.

Diatoms, which are part of phylum Bacillariophyta, contain chlorophyll and carotenoids, pigments with a golden-yellow color. Diatoms live in both saltwater and freshwater environments. Members of the phylum Pyrrophyta, dinoflagellates, are unicellular algae surrounded by hard, armorlike plates and propelled by flagella. They can contain a variety of pigments, including chlorophyll, caretenoids, and red pigments. Marine blooms of dinoflagellates can cause toxic red tides.

Yellow-brown algae and golden-brown algae, members of phylum Chrysophyta, are unicellular or colonial. A chrysophyte usually has two flagella attached at one end.

Multicellular Algae Members of the phylum Rhodophyta are marine algae. Because of their red pigments, some species can grow at depths of 100 meters.

Organisms in phylum Phaeophyta contain a brown pigment. Brown algae, such as the giant kelps, grow along rocky coasts in cool areas.

The green algae in the phylum Chlorophyta are unicellular, colonial,or multicellular. The major pigment in their cells is chlorophyll.

Funguslike Protists Funguslike protists include the slime molds, water molds, and downy mildews. They are saprophytes, decomposing organic material to obtain its nutrients.

■ **Figure 5** The cell walls of diatoms contain silica. These hard walls form many shapes and sizes.

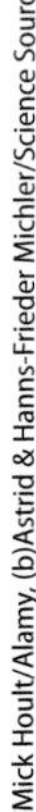

Domain Eukarya, Kingdom Fungi

Fungi are mostly multicellular, eukaryotic organisms that have cell walls made of chitin. The structural units of a fungus are hyphae. Fungi secrete enzymes into a food source to digest the food and then absorb the digested nutrients. They are saprophytes, parasites, or mutualists, and they play a major role in decomposing organic material and recycling Earth's nutrients.

Members of phylum Chytridiomycota are aquatic fungi that produce flagellated spores. Originally grouped with protists, recent molecular evidence suggests chytrids, which have chitin-containing cell walls, are related more closely to fungi.

Mushrooms are members of phylum Basidiomycota, the club fungi. The fruiting body of a mushroom is called the basidiocarp. Club fungi have club-shaped structures called basidia in which their sexual spores are produced.

Members of phylum Zygomycota, the common molds, produce thick-walled, sexual spores called zygospores. Zygomycotes also form many asexual spores in sporangia.

Fungi that produce sexual spores called ascospores in saclike structures called asci are classified in phylum Ascomycota. Also called sac fungi, they produce asexual spores, called conidia, which develop in chains or clusters from the tips of elongated hyphae called conidiophores.

A lichen is a symbiotic association of a mutualistic fungus and a photosynthetic alga or cyanobacterium. Lichens live in many inhospitable areas but are sensitive to pollution and do not grow well in polluted areas.

Figure 6 This club fungi, *Cricibulum vulgare*, has basidiocarps that resemble eggs in a bird's nest.

Survey of Domains

Adaptations

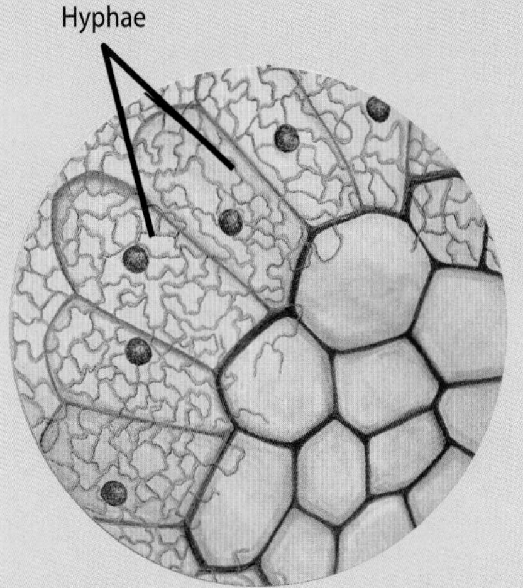

Figure 7 Fungal hyphae can grow among a plant's root cells.

Mycorrhizae

Some plants live in association with mutualistic fungi. These relationships, called mycorrhizae (my kuh RHY zuh), benefit both the fungi and the plants. The hyphae of the fungus are entwined with the roots of the plant, and absorb sugars and other nutrients from the plant's root cells. In turn, the fungus increases the surface area of the plant's roots, allowing the roots to absorb more water and minerals. The relationship enables the fungus to obtain food and the plant to grow larger. Some plants cannot grow without mychorrhizal relationships.

Domain Eukarya, Kingdom Plantae

Plants provide food and shelter for most of Earth's organisms. Through the process of photosynthesis, they transform the radiant energy in light into chemical energy in food and release oxygen. All plants are multicellular eukaryotes whose cells are surrounded by a cell wall made of cellulose.

NonSeed Plants Nonseed plants reproduce by forming spores. A spore is a haploid (n) reproductive cell, produced by meiosis, which can withstand harsh environmental conditions. When conditions become favorable, a spore can develop into the haploid, gametophyte generation of a plant.

Divisions Bryophyta (mosses), Hepaticophyta (liverworts), and Anthocerophyta (hornworts) are nonseed nonvascular plants that live in cool, moist habitats. These plant groups have no vascular tissues to move water and nutrients from one part of the plant to another. They usually grow no more than several centimeters tall.

Club mosses are nonseed vascular plants in division Lycophyta. They are found primarily in moist environments and are usually less than 30 cm high. Fossil lycophytes grew as high as 30 m and formed a large part of the vegetation of Paleozoic forests.

Horsetails and ferns are nonseed vascular plants in division Pterophyta. Horsetails are common in areas with damp soil, such as stream banks and sometimes along roadsides. Present-day horsetails are small, but their ancestors were treelike.

Ferns have leaves called fronds that grow up from an underground stem called the rhizome. Ferns are found in many different habitats, including shady forests, stream banks, roadsides, and abandoned pastures.

■ **Figure 8** Fern fronds are sometimes divided into leaflets.

■ **Figure 9** Mosses often grow in masses that form thick carpets.

Nonflowering Seed Plants A seed is a reproductive structure that contains a sporophyte embryo and a food supply (called the endosperm) that are enclosed in a protective coating. The food supply nourishes the young plant during the first stages of growth. Like spores, seeds can survive harsh conditions. The seed develops into the sporophyte generation of the plant.

Plants in divisions Cycadophyta (cycads), Ginkgophyta (ginkgoes), and Gnetophyta (gnetophytes), along with those in Coniferophyta, are sometimes called gymnosperms. Seeds of these plants are not part of a fruit. Their male and female reproductive organs are in separate structures. Seeds develop in the female reproductive structure. These plants have different forms and grow in diverse environments.

Conifers, which are part of division Coniferophyta, produce seeds, usually in woody strobili called cones, and have needle-shaped or scalelike leaves. Most conifers are evergreen plants, which means they bear leaves all year round. Conifers are common in cold or dry habitats. Their needles have a compact shape and a thick, waxy covering that helps reduce water loss. Conifer stems are covered with a thick layer of bark that insulates the tissues inside. These structural adaptations enable conifers to survive below freezing temperatures.

BioFacts

Protists

Distribution: worldwide in aquatic and moist habitats

Niches: producers, herbivores, predators, parasites, and decomposers

Number of species: more than 60,000

Size range: less than 2 mm in length to greater than 100 m in length

Survey of Domains

Adaptations

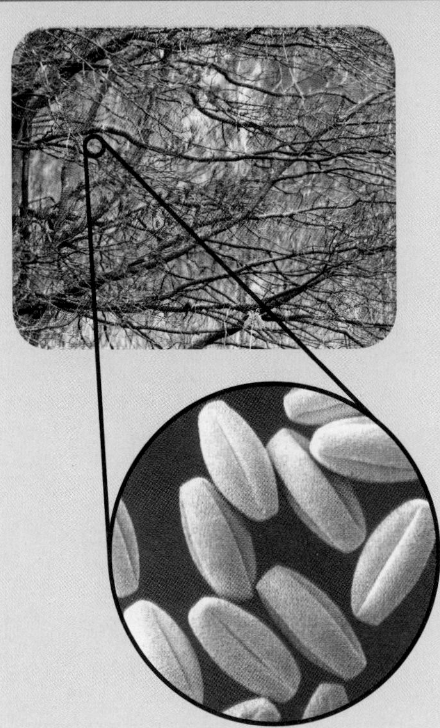

Alternation of Generations

The life cycles of plants have two stages, called generations. The diploid (2*n*) stage is called the sporophyte generation. It produces haploid (*n*) spores that develop into the gametophyte generation. The gametophyte generation produces male and female gametes that can unite and begin a new sporophyte generation.

In nonvascular plants, the sporophyte is smaller than the gametophyte, and usually remains attached to the gametophyte. The nonvascular sporophyte is dependent on the nonvascular gametophyte for water and its nutrition. In vascular plants, the sporophyte is dominant and independent of the gametophyte. Vascular gametophytes are minute and usually are buried in soil or are enclosed within the vascular sporophyte.

■ **Figure 10** Maple pollen, the gametophyte generation, is haploid. The maple tree, the sporophyte generation, is diploid

(t)blickwinkel/Alamy, (c)Johann Schumacher/Oxford Scientific/Getty Images, (b)SCIMAT/Science Source

■ **Figure 11** Seeds of monocots differ from those of eudicots. For example, cotyledons of eudicot seeds provide much of the nourishment for the embryo. Endosperm nourishes the monocot embryo.

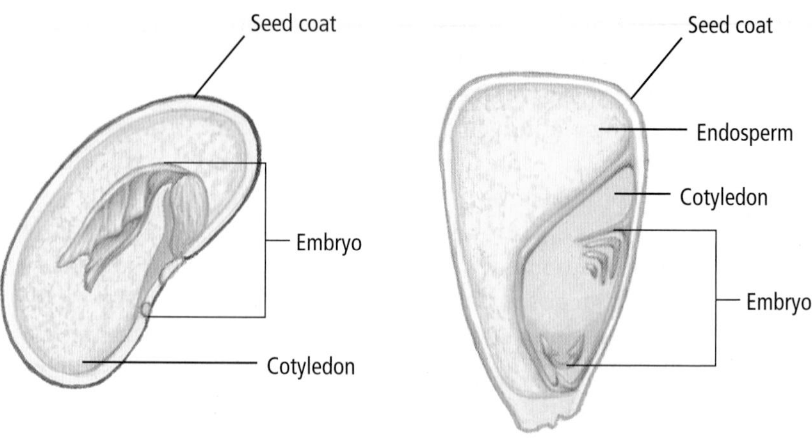

Flowering Seed Plants The flowering plants, division Anthophyta, form the largest and most diverse group of plants on Earth today. They provide much of the food eaten by humans. Anthophytes, also known as angiosperms, produce flowers and develop seeds that are part of a fruit.

Cotyledons, or "seed leaves," are part of the seed along with the plant embryo. Monocots have one seed leaf. Dicots and eudicots have two seed leaves and are further classified based on the structure of their pollen. About 75 percent of anthophytes are eudicots and include many trees, shrubs, and garden plants. There are few dicots and examples include maples, oaks, and sycamores. Monocots are the second largest group and include palms, lilies, onions, and grasses.

Adaptations

Moving from Water to Land

All plants probably evolved from filamentous green algae that lived in nutrient-rich waters of Earth's ancient oceans. As land plants evolved, new structures developed that allowed water and dissolved minerals to be taken in from the environment and transported to all parts of the plant.

Nonvascular plants In nonvascular plants, water and nutrients travel from one cell to another by the processes of osmosis and diffusion. As a result, nonvascular plants are limited to moist environments.

Vascular plants Vascular tissues are made up of tubelike, elongated cells through which water, food, and other materials move from one part of the plant to another. One structure that allows vascular plants to grow larger than nonvascular plants is vascular tissue: it allows a more efficient method of internal transport than osmosis and diffusion and includes thickened fibers that can support upright growth.

■ **Figure 12** Plants probably evolved from filamentous green algae.

Andrew Syred/Science Source

■ **Figure 13** Honeybees or other insects must transfer pollen from a male squash flower to a female squash flower for the fruit—a squash—to form.

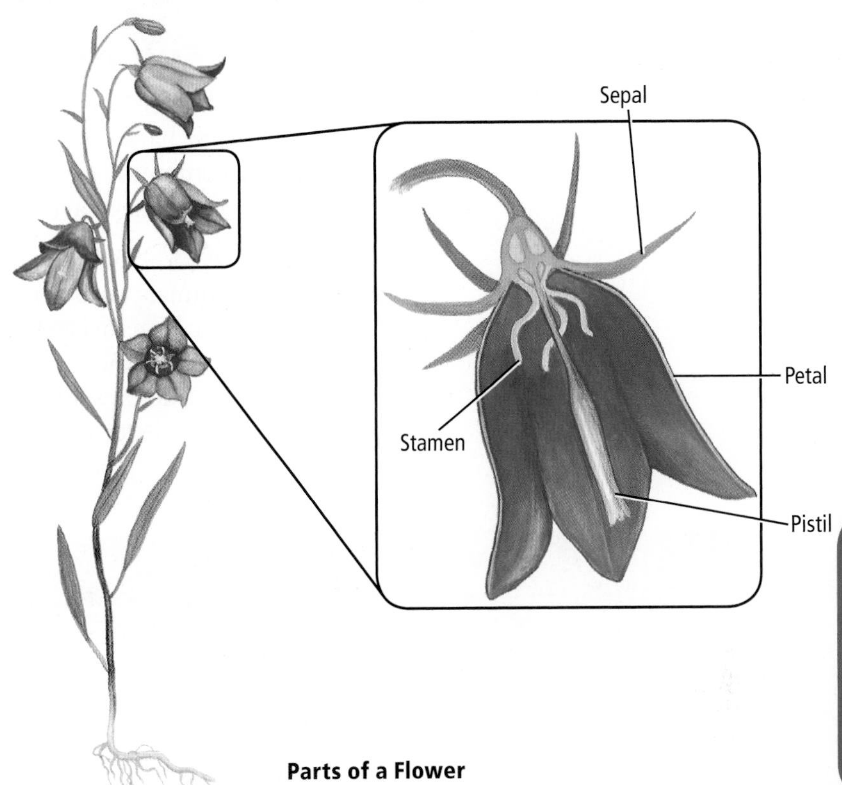

Parts of a Flower

Flowers are the organs of reproduction in anthophytes. The pistil is the female reproductive organ. At the base of the pistil is the ovary. Inside the ovary are the ovules. Ovules contain the female gametophyte. A female gamete—an egg cell—forms in each ovule. The stamen is the male reproductive organ of a flower. Pollen grains that form inside the anther eventually contain male gametes called sperm. In seed plants, the sperm develop inside of the thick-coated pollen grains. Pollen is an important structural adaptation that has enabled seed plants to live in diverse land habitats.

Pollination is the transfer of pollen grains from the anther to the stigma of the pistil. It can be transferred by wind, insects, birds, and even bats. Some flowers have colorful or perfumed petals that attract pollinators. Flowers also can contain sweet nectar, as well as pollen, which provides pollinators with food.

Following fertilization, a fruit with seeds can develop. Fruits help protect seeds until they are mature. Some flowering plants develop fleshy fruits, such as apples, melons, tomatoes, or squash. Other flowering plants develop dry fruits, such as peanuts, walnuts, or sunflowers. Fruits also can help disperse seeds.

Plant Responses Plants respond to stimuli in their environment such as light, temperature, and water availability. Chemicals called hormones control some of these responses by increasing cell division and growth.

■ **Figure 14** The phototropic response shown here is the result of increased cell growth on the side of the stem away from the light.

Domain Eukarya, Kingdom Animalia

Recall from Chapter 17 that animals are heterotrophic, multicellular organisms. They have varied body plans and live in many habitats. Animals are commonly classified as invertebrates or vertebrates based on whether or not they have a backbone.

Invertebrates How are sponges, clams, sea urchins, and beetles alike? These animals are invertebrates—animals without backbones. Ancestors of modern invertebrates had simple body plans. They lived in water and obtained food, oxygen, and other materials from their surroundings, as do presentday sponges, jellyfishes, and worms. Some invertebrates have external structures that provide protection and support.

Adaptations

Body Cavities

The type of body cavity an animal has determines how large it can grow and how it takes in food and eliminates wastes. Acoelomate animals, such as planarians, have no body cavity. Water and digested food particles travel through a solid body by the process of diffusion.

Animals such as roundworms have a pseudocoelom (soo duh SEE lum), a fluid-filled body cavity that is partly lined with mesoderm. Mesoderm is a layer of cells between the ectoderm and endoderm that differentiates into muscles, circulatory vessels, and excretory organs. The pseudocoelom provides support for the attachment of muscles, making movement more efficient.

Earthworms have a coelom, a body cavity surrounded by mesoderm in which internal organs are suspended. The coelom acts as a watery skeleton against which muscles can work.

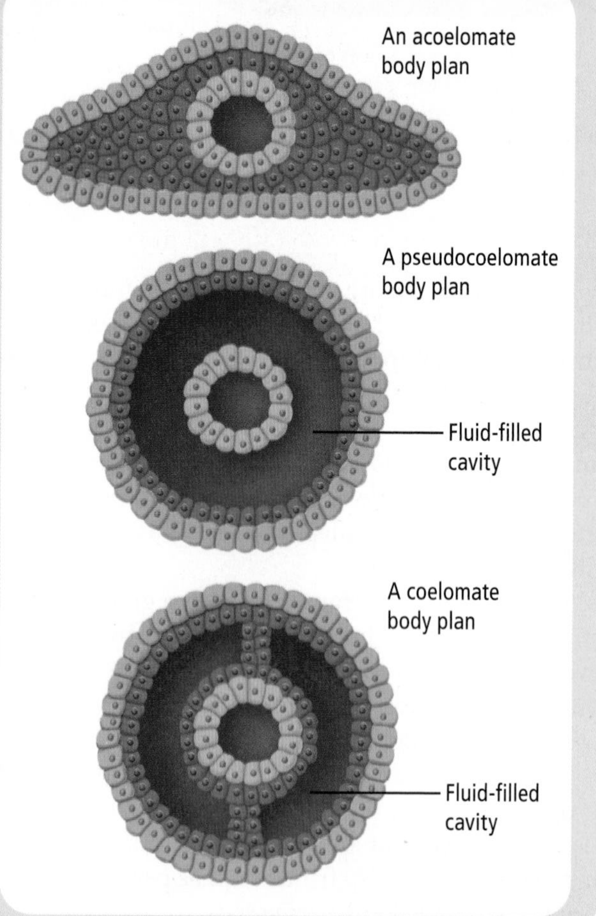

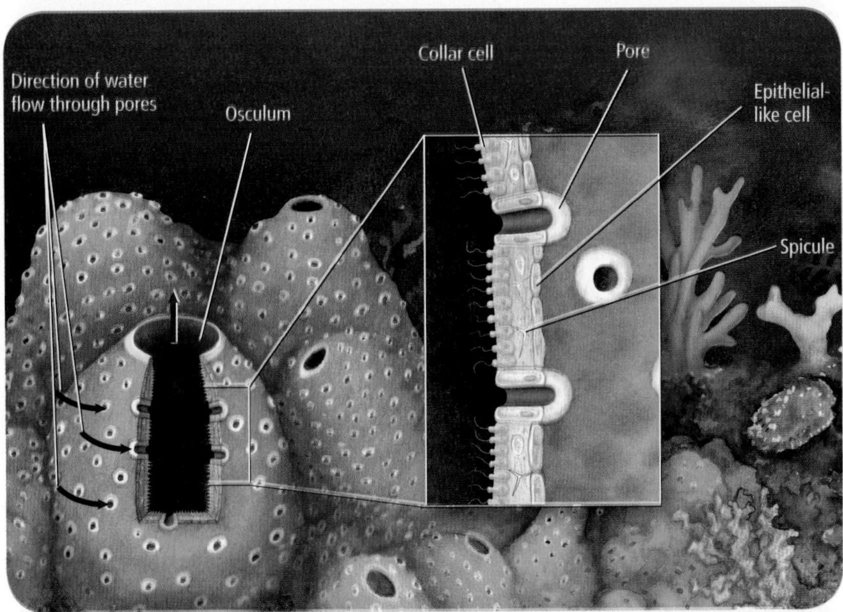

■ **Figure 15** Sponges are filter feeders. Epitheliallike cells protect the sponge and spicules give it support. Collar-cell flagella draw water and food into the sponge through pores. Water and wastes exit through the osculum.

Sponges, Cnidarians, and Roundworms Sponges, which are part of phylum Porifera, are invertebrates made up of two cell layers. They have no tissues, organs, or organ systems. In general, sponges are asymmetrical. Most adult sponges are sessile—they do not move from place to place.

Cnidarians have radial symmetry and are made up of two cell layers organized into tissues with different functions. They have only one body opening. Cnidarians are named for stinging cells that contain nematocysts used to capture food. Jellyfishes, corals, sea anemones, and hydras belong to phylum Cnidaria.

Roundworms, phylum Nematoda, have a pseudocoelom and a tubelike digestive system with two body openings. Most roundworms are freeliing, but many plants and animals are affected by parasitic roundworms.

■ **Figure 16** Jellyfishes have nematocysts on their tentacles.

■ **Figure 17** A Portuguese man-of-war is a colony of jellyfishes. One jellyfish forms the float and others cluster below it.

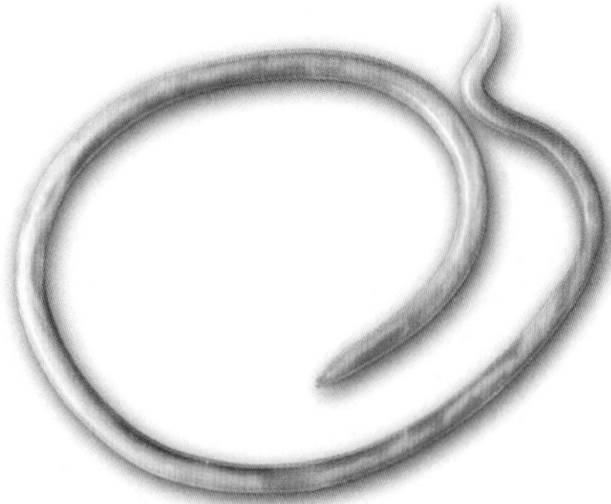

■ **Figure 18** Ascarid worms cause the most common roundworm infection in humans. Infection can result when unwashed vegetables from contaminated soil are eaten.

■ **Figure 19** Flatworms have a head end with organs that sense the environment. Flatworms can detect light, chemicals, food, and movements in their surroundings.

Flatworms Flatworms, phylum Platyhelminthes, include free-living planarians, parasitic tapeworms, and parasitic flukes. Flatworms are bilaterally symmetrical animals with flattened solid bodies and no body cavities. Flatworms have one body opening through which food enters and wastes leave.

Mollusks Slugs, snails, clams, squids, and octopuses are members of phylum Mollusca. All mollusks are bilaterally symmetrical and have a coelom, a digestive tract with two openings, a muscular foot for movement, and a mantle, which is a membrane that surrounds the internal organs. In mollusks with shells, the mantle secretes the shell.

There are three major classes of mollusks. Gastropods have one shell or no shell. Bivalves have two hinged shells called valves. Cephalopods have muscular tentacles and are capable of swimming by jet propulsion. All mollusks, except bivalves, have a rough, tonguelike organ called a radula used for obtaining food

■ **Figure 20** Cephalopods, such as cuttlefishes, capture prey using the suckers on their long tentacles.

■ **Figure 21** A gastropod, such as an abalone, uses its radula to scrape algae from surfaces.

■ **Figure 22** Bivalves, such as scallops, strain food from water by filtering it through their gills.

■ **Figure 23** Leeches have flattened bodies and usually no setae. Most species are parasites that suck blood and body fluids from turtles, fishes, and mammals

■ **Figure 24** Most bristleworms have a distinct head and a body with many setae.

Segmented Worms Members of phylum Annelida, the segmented worms, are bilaterally symmetrical, coelomate animals that have segmented, cylindrical bodies with two body openings. Most annelids have setae, bristlelike hairs that extend from body segments, that help them move.

Segmentation is an adaptation that provides these animals with great flexibility. Each segment has its own muscles. Groups of segments have different functions, such as digestion or reproduction.

Phylum Annelida includes three classes: Hirudinae, the leeches; Oligochaeta, the earthworms; and Polychaeta, the bristleworms.

Arthropods Two out of three animals on Earth today are arthropods. The success of arthropods can be attributed to adaptations that provide efficient gas exchange, acute senses, and varied types of mouthparts for feeding.

Arthropods are bilaterally symmetrical, segmented, coelomate invertebrates with tough outer coverings called exoskeletons. Exoskeletons protect and support their soft internal tissues and organs. They have jointed appendages that are used for walking, sensing, feeding, and mating. Jointed appendages allow for powerful and efficient movements.

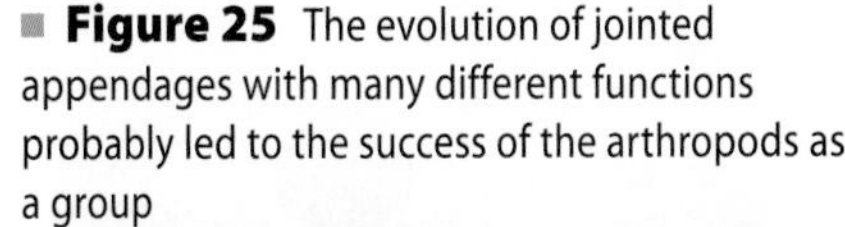

■ **Figure 25** The evolution of jointed appendages with many different functions probably led to the success of the arthropods as a group

■ **Figure 26** Centipedes, which are part of class Chilopoda, are carnivores. They have one pair of legs on each body segment.

■ **Figure 27** This dragonfly, an insect, has three pairs of jointed legs and two pairs of wings.

The major groups of phylum Arthropoda are the crustaceans, arachnids, centipedes and millipedes, and insects. Crustaceans, such as crabs, lobsters, shrimps, and barnacles, are aquatic animals. They have modified appendages for obtaining food, walking, and swimming. Spiders, scorpions, ticks, and mites are examples of arachnids. Four pair of legs and two body sections are identifying features of arachnids. Centipedes have one pair of legs per body segment and are carnivores. Millipedes are herbivores and have two pair of legs per body segment. Insects are the most familiar arthropods and include beetles, ants, bees, flies, grasshoppers, and many others. An insect has three body segments— a head with antennae, eyes, and mouthparts; a thorax with three pairs of legs and sometimes wings; and an abdomen.

Adaptations

Insect Mouthparts

If you have ever been bitten by a mosquito, you know that mosquitoes have piercing mouthparts that cut through your skin to suck up blood. In contrast, butterflies and moths have long, coiled tongues that they extend deep into tubular flowers to sip nectar. Grasshoppers, ants, and many beetles have hard, sharp mandibles they use to cut off and chew leaves. Flies have sponging and lapping mouthparts that take up liquids.

Insects have complex mouthparts that are well adapted for chewing, sucking, piercing, biting, or lapping for eating a variety of foods.

Different foods for different stages Because insects undergo metamorphosis, they often utilize different food sources at different times of the year. For example, monarch butterfly larvae feed on milkweed leaves, whereas the adults feed on milkweed flower nectar. Apple blossom weevil larvae feed on the stamens and pistils of unopened flower buds, but the adult weevils eat apple leaves. Some adult insects, such as mayflies, do not eat at all! Instead, they rely on food stored in the larval stage for energy to mate and lay eggs.

■ **Figure 28** A leafcutter ant uses mandibles to cut a leaf.

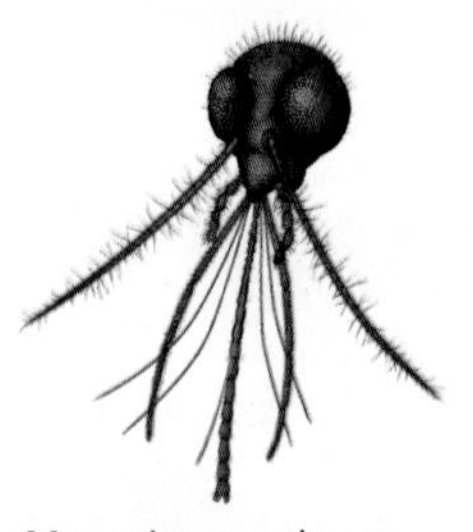

Mosquito mouthparts

Grasshopper mouthparts

Butterfly mouthparts

Fly mouthparts

■ **Figure 29** The long, thin arms of brittle stars are fragile and break easily, but they grow back. Brittle stars use their arms to move along the ocean bottom.

■ **Figure 30** Sea cucumbers have a leathery skin which gives them flexibility. Like most echinoderms, they move using tube feet.

Echinoderms Members of phylum Echinodermata are radially symmetrical coelomate animals with hard, bumpy, spiny endoskeletons covered by a thin epidermis. The endoskeleton is made primarily of calcium carbonate. They move using a unique water-vascular system with tiny, suction-cup-like tube feet. Echinoderms have bilaterally symmetrical larvae and are deuterostomes, which suggests a close relationship to the chordates.

There are six living classes of echinoderms. They include sea stars, brittle stars, sea urchins and sand dollars, sea cucumbers, sea lilies and feather stars, and sea daisies.

Invertebrate Chordates All chordates have, at some stage in their development cycles, a notochord, a dorsal hollow nerve cord, pharyngeal pouches, and a postanal tail. A notochord is a long, semi-rigid, rodlike structure along the dorsal side of these animals. The dorsal hollow nerve cord is a fluid-filled canal lying above the notochord. Pharyngeal pouches are paired openings in the pharynx that develop into gill slits in some invertebrate chordates, and are used to strain food from the water and for gas exchange. A muscular postanal tail is used primarily for locomotion. Recent evidence suggests that all chordates also might have some form of a thyroid gland.

The invertebrate chordates include the lancelets and the tunicates, also known as sea squirts. Lancelets are small, fishlike animals without scales. They have all the features of chordates throughout their lives. Tunicates have small, saclike bodies with a thick outer covering. Larval tunicates have all of the chordate features. The only chordate feature that remains in the adult tunicate is pharyngeal gill slits.

■ **Figure 31** The lancelet is an invertebrate chordate. The lancelet's body is shaped like that of a fish even though it is a burrowing filter feeder.

BioFacts

Fishes

Size ranges: largest: whale shark, length: 15 m; smallest: dwarf goby, length: 1 cm

Distribution: freshwater, salt water, and estuarine habitats worldwide

Unusual adaptations: electric eels can deliver an electrical charge of 650 volts, which stuns or kills their prey. Some deep-sea fishes have their own bioluminescent lures to help capture prey

Longest-lived: lake sturgeon, 80 years

Numbers of species:

- Class Myxini—hagfishes, 43 species
- Class Cephalaspidomorphi—lampreys, 17 species
- Class Chondrichthyes—cartilaginous fishes, 850 species
- Class Osteichthyes—bony fishes, 18,007 species

Vertebrates Like all chordates, a vertebrate has a notochord, pharyngeal pouches, a dorsal hollow nerve cord, and a postanal tail at some time during its life. However, in a vertebrate the notochord is replaced during development by a backbone. A vertebrate is a bilaterally symmetrical, coelomate animal that has an endoskeleton, a closed circulatory system, an efficient respiratory system, and a complex brain and nervous system

Fishes All fishes are ectotherms, animals with body temperatures dependent upon an external heat source. Fishes have two-chambered hearts and breathe through gills.

Fishes are grouped into four different classes. Lampreys and hagfishes make up the two classes of jawless fishes. Jawless fishes have endoskeletons made of cartilage, like sharks and rays, but they do not have jaws.

Sharks, skates, and rays are cartilaginous fishes. Cartilaginous fishes have endoskeletons made of cartilage, paired fins, and a lateralline system that enables them to detect movement and vibrations in water.

Most fish species belong to the bony fishes. All bony fishes have a bony skeleton, gills, paired fins, flattened bony scales, and a lateral-line system. When a bony fish draws water into its mouth and passes it over its gills, gas exchange occurs. Most bony fishes adjust their depth in the water by regulating the amount of gas that diffuses out of their blood into a swim bladder. Most bony fishes fertilize their eggs externally and leave the survival of the offspring to chance.

■ **Figure 32** Cartilaginous fishes, such as this great white shark, have internal fertilization. In some species of cartilaginous fishes, development of fertilized eggs is external; other species give live birth to well-developed young.

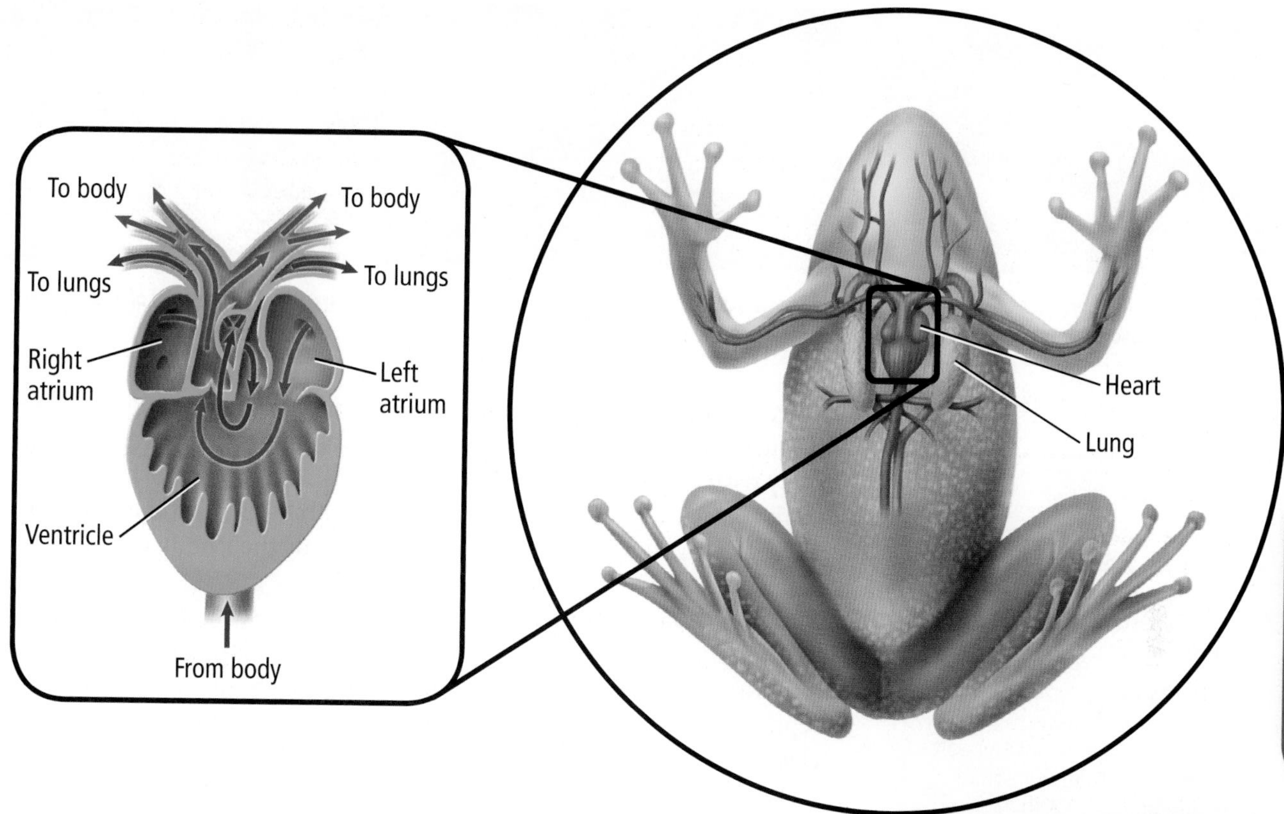

■ **Figure 33** The circulatory system of an amphibian consists of a double loop that moves blood throughout its body

Amphibians Amphibians are ectothermic vertebrates with three-chambered hearts, lungs, and thin, moist skin. Although they have lungs, most gas exchange in amphibians is carried out through the skin. As adults, the majority of amphibians live on land, however, many of these species rely on water for reproduction. Most amphibians go through metamorphosis, in which the young hatch into tadpoles that gradually lose their tails and gills as they develop legs, lungs, and other adult structures.

There are three orders of amphibians: Anura, frogs and toads; Caudata, salamanders and newts; and Gymnophiona, legless caecilians. Frogs and toads lack tails and have long legs enabling them to jump. Frogs have thin, smooth, moist skin and toads have thick, bumpy skin with poison glands. Salamanders have long, slender bodies with a neck and tail. Caecilians are amphibians with long, wormlike bodies and no legs

■ **Figure 34** Salamanders have smooth, moist skin. They are carnivorous, feeding on insects, worms, and other invertebrates

■ **Figure 35** Caecilians are long, limbless amphibians adapted for burrowing and living underground.

■ **Figure 36** Alligators such as this American alligator, have broad snouts.

■ **Figure 37** Tuaturas reach a length of about 2 m and can live up to 80 years in the wild.

■ **Figure 38** The shell of a turtle makes it different from other reptiles.

Survey of Domains

Reptiles The first group of vertebrates to live entirely on land were reptiles. They evolved a thick, scaly skin that prevented water loss from body tissues. They evolved strong skeletons, with limbs positioned somewhat underneath their bodies. These limbs enabled them to move quickly on land, avoiding or seeking the sun as their body temperatures demanded.

Present-day reptiles are ectotherms with dry, scaly skin and clawed toes. They include snakes, lizards, turtles, crocodiles, alligators, and tuataras. With the exception of snakes, all reptiles have four legs. Most reptiles have a three-chambered heart, but crocodilians have a four-chambered heart in which oxygenated blood is kept entirely separate from blood without oxygen. In addition to reducing the loss of body moisture on land, a reptile's scales also prevent the skin from absorbing or releasing gases to the air. Most reptiles are primarily dependent upon lungs for this essential gas exchange

BioFacts

Reptiles

Size ranges: largest: anaconda snake, length: 9 m; leatherback turtle, mass: 680 kg; smallest: thread snake, length: 1.3 cm

Distribution: temperate and tropical forests, deserts, and grasslands, and freshwater, salt water, and estuarine habitats worldwide

Reptile that causes most human death: king cobra, 7500 deaths per year

Numbers of species:
Class Reptilia

- Order Squamata—snakes and lizards, 6800 species
- Order Chelonia—turtles, 250 species
- Order Crocodilia—crocodiles and alligators, 25 species
- Order Rhynchocephalia—tuataras, 2 species

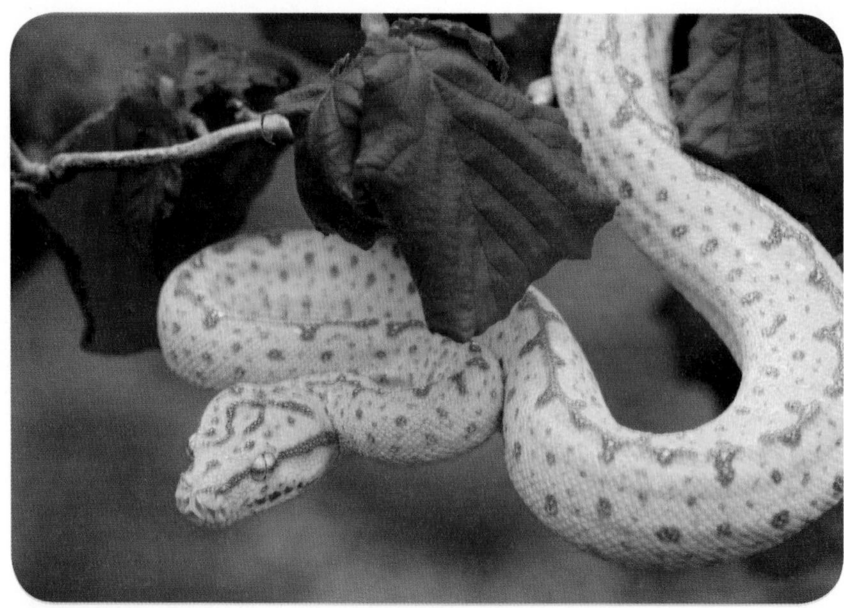

■ **Figure 39** Constrictors, such as this green tree python, hold prey with their mouths, then wrap coils around the prey's body. The snake tightens its coils, preventing inhalation, and the prey suffocates.

All reptiles have internal fertilization and most species lay eggs. However, some female snakes and lizards keep the fertilized eggs inside their bodies until the young hatch. Then, the fully developed young leave their mother's body.

The development of the amniotic egg enabled reptiles to decrease their dependence on water for reproduction. The amniotic egg provides nourishment to the embryo and protects it from drying out as it develops.

■ **Figure 40** Female San Francisco garter snakes give birth to live young.

Adaptations

The Amniotic Egg

Perhaps the most important adaptation to life on land for reptiles was the development of the amniotic egg.

Protecting the embryo An amniotic egg encloses the embryo in the amnion, which contains amniotic fluid; provides the yolk, a source of food for the embryo; and surrounds both the embryo and yolk with membranes and a tough, leathery shell. These structures in the egg help prevent dehydration and injury to the embryo as it develops on land. Most reptiles lay their eggs in holes in the ground or in plant debris.

Membranes inside the egg Membranes found inside the amniotic egg include the amnion, the chorion, and the allantois. The amnion is a membrane filled with fluid that surrounds the developing embryo. The embryo's wastes are excreted into a membranous sac called the allantois. The chorion, the outermost membrane, allows oxygen to enter and keeps the fluid inside the egg. With this egg, reptiles do not need water for reproduction. The evolution of the amniotic egg completed the move of tetrapods from water to land.

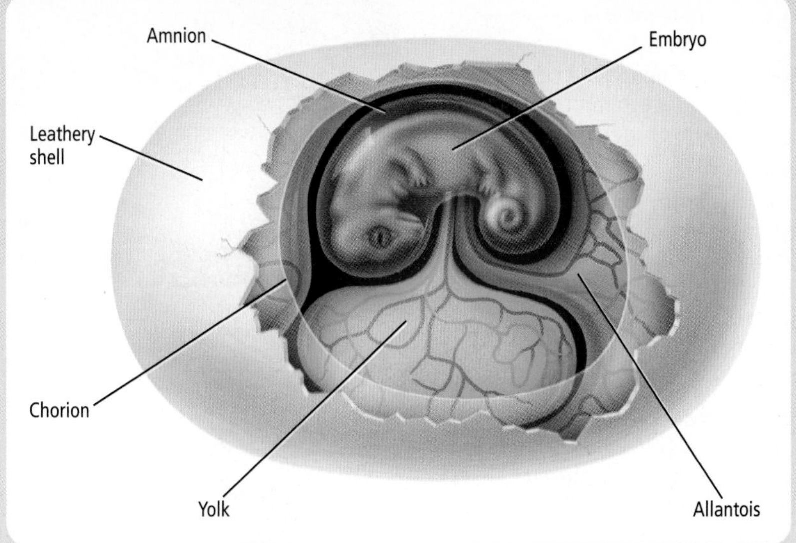

Survey of Domains

Suzanne L. and Joseph T. Collins/Science Source

■ **Figure 41** Penguins are flightless birds with wings and feet modified for swimming. A thick layer of insulating fat helps keep these penguins warm in the cold antarctic climate in which they live. This young emperor penguin might reach a height of 1 m and weigh nearly 34 kg.

Birds Birds are the only class of animals with feathers. Feathers, which are specialized outgrowths of the skin of birds, help insulate birds and enable them to fly. Birds have forelimbs that are modified into wings. Like reptiles, birds have scales on their feet and clawed toes; unlike reptiles, they are endotherms, animals that maintain a constant body temperature. Endotherms must eat frequently to provide the energy needed for producing body heat.

Adaptations

Bird Flight

What selection pressure might have resulted in bird flight? Maybe an early bird's need to escape from a predator caused it to run so fast its feet left the ground. Whatever caused birds to evolve an ability to fly, there must first have been adaptations that made flight possible. What are some of these adaptations? Birds are endotherms, meaning they are able to generate body heat internally. They have feathers and lightweight bones. The respiratory and circulatory systems of birds also are adapted to provide more oxygen to working muscles to support flight.

Efficient respiration Birds receive oxygenated air when they breathe in as well as when they breathe out. Air sacs enable birds to get more oxygen because the air inhaled by a bird passes directly into posterior air sacs rather than into its lungs. When a bird exhales, oxygenated air in the sacs passes into its lungs, then into anterior air sacs and out through the trachea. This one-way flow of air provides the oxygen that birds need to power flight muscles.

Lightweight bones The bones of birds are unique because they contain cavities of air; however, they are still strong. The fusion of bones in the skeleton of a bird makes the skeleton sturdier. Large breast muscles, which can make up 30 percent of a bird's total weight, provide the power for flight. These muscles connect the wing to the breastbone, called the sternum. The sternum is large and has an extension, called a keel, to which the muscles attach.

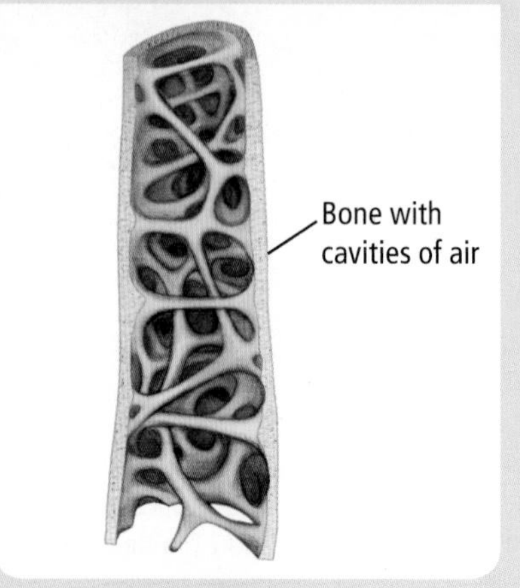

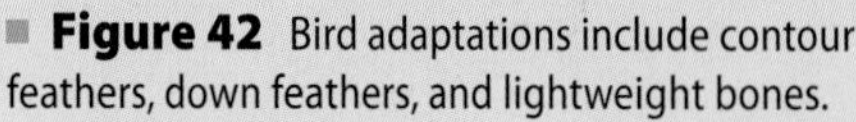

■ **Figure 42** Bird adaptations include contour feathers, down feathers, and lightweight bones.

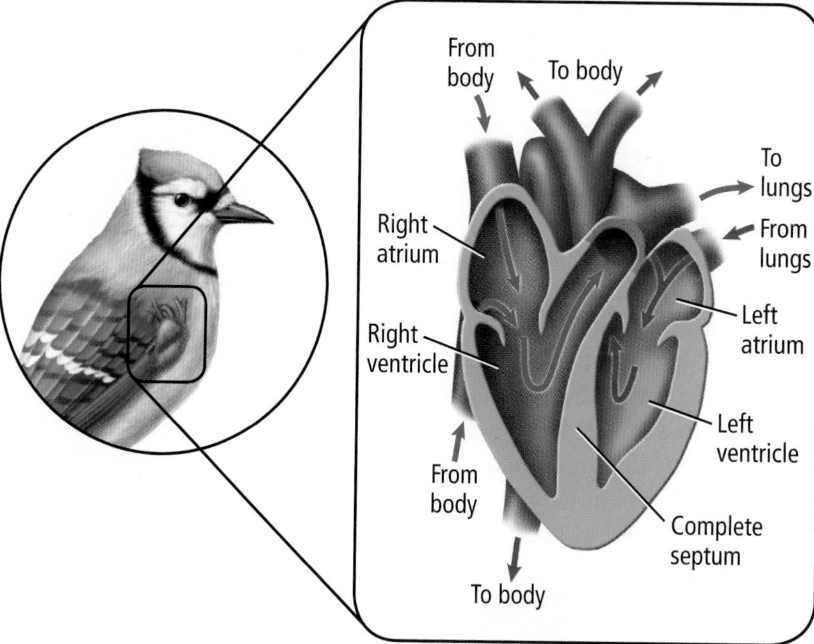

■ **Figure 43** A bird's four-chambered heart keeps oxygenrich blood and oxygen-poor blood separate.

Birds have strong, lightweight bones that provide support for strong flight muscles. Birds also have a four-chambered heart and a unique respiratory system in which air always flows in a single direction, and highly efficient gas exchange can be achieved.

Like reptiles, birds lay amniotic eggs. Unlike reptiles, birds incubate their eggs in nests, keeping eggs warm until the young birds hatch.

■ **Figure 44** Although some birds lay their eggs on the ground or rocks, most birds construct some type of nest into which eggs are laid. Bald eagles build the largest nests, some of which are 2 m across and 2 tons in mass.

BioFacts

Birds

Size ranges: largest: ostrich, height, 2.4 m, mass: 156 kg; smallest: bee hummingbird, length: 57 mm, mass: 1.5 g

Distribution: tworldwide in all habitats

Widest wingspan: wandering albatross, 3.7 m

Fastest flyer: white-throated spinetail swift, 171 km/h

Largest egg: ostrich, length: 13.5 cm, mass: 1.5 kg

Longest yearly migration: Arctic tern, 40,000 km

Numbers of species: Class Aves—8600 species in 27 present-day orders:

Order Passeriformes—perching songbirds, 5000 species

Order Ciconiiformes—herons, bitterns, ibises, 90 species

Order Anseriformes—swans, ducks, geese, 150 species

Order Strigiformes—owls, 135 species

BioFacts

Mammals

Size ranges: largest: blue whale, length: 30 m, mass: 190 metric tons; smallest: Etruscan shrew, length: 6 cm, mass: 1.5 g

Distribution: worldwide in all habitats

Fastest:: Cheetah, 110 km/h

Longest-lived: Asiatic elephant, 80 years; humans, up to 120 years

Numbers of species: Class Mammalia

- Subgroup Monotremata—egg-laying mammals, 3 species
- Subgroup Marsupialia—pouched mammals, 280 species
- Orders of Placental Mammals—4400 species

Mammals Mammals are endotherms that are named for their mammary glands, which produce milk to feed their young. Most mammals have hair that helps insulate their bodies and sweat glands that help keep them cool. Mammals need a high level of energy for maintaining body temperature and high levels of physical activity. An efficient four-chambered heart and the muscular diaphragm beneath the lungs help to deliver the necessary oxygen for these activities.

All mammals have internal fertilization, and the young begin development inside the mother's uterus. But from that point, developmental patterns in mammals diverge. Mammals are classified into three subgroups. Monotremes are mammals that lay eggs. Marsupials are mammals in which the young complete a second stage of development after birth in a pouch made of skin and hair on the outside of the mother's body. Placental mammals give birth to young that do not need further development within a pouch.

Adaptations

Hair

If an animal has feathers, it is a bird. In a similar way, if an animal has hair, it is a mammal. Mammals' hair has several functions.

Insulation One of the most important functions of hair is to insulate against the cold. Fur or hair traps body heat and prevents it from escaping.

Waterproofing Many aquatic animals, such as the sea otter, have hair that keeps water from reaching their skin. This helps them maintain their body temperature.

Camouflage The striped coat of a Bengal tiger allows it to blend into its natural habitat—the jungle.

Sensory devices In some cases, hair has been modified into sensitive whiskers. Seals use the whiskers on their snouts to track prey in murky water by sensing changes in water movements when a fish is near.

Signaling White-tailed deer raise their tails, the undersides of which are covered with white hair, when they run, signaling other deer to follow them.

Defense Hair can function as a defense against predators. A porcupine has sharp quills, which are modified hairs. The quills stick to and stab predators that touch the porcupine.

Sea otter

Porcupine

(t)©Kevin Schafer/Corbis, (b)Art Wolfe/Getty Images

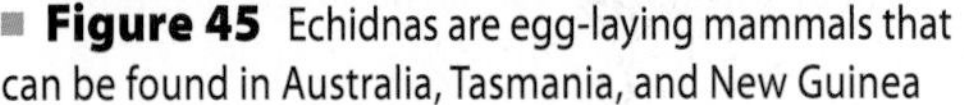

■ **Figure 45** Echidnas are egg-laying mammals that can be found in Australia, Tasmania, and New Guinea

■ **Figure 46** Opossums are the only marsupials in North America.

■ **Figure 47** Most mammals living today, such as this pygmy shrew, are placentals.

Mammals can be classified by the number and type of teeth they have. All mammals have diversified teeth used for different purposes. Incisors, top and bottom front teeth, are used to cut food. Canines—long, pointed teeth—are used to stab or pierce food. Molars and premolars have flat surfaces with ridges and are used to grind and chew food. By examining an animal's teeth, scientists can hypothesize what type of consumer it is. Carni vores, such as wolves, have canine teeth that pierce food. Herbivores, such as cattle and other grazing animals, rely on incisors to cut plants and molars to grind and crush their food. Humans, who are omnivores, have incisors, canines, premolars, and molars in order to process many different kinds of food.

■ **Figure 48** Humpback whales do not have teeth. Instead, they have a cartilaginous, comblike structure called a baleen that acts as a food filter.

■ **Figure 49** Carnivores, such as this lioness, use their canines to stab and pierce prey.

■ **Figure 50** Beavers are gnawing herbivores. Because a beaver's incisors grow throughout its life, gnawing does not wear away a beaver's incisors, it only sharpens them.

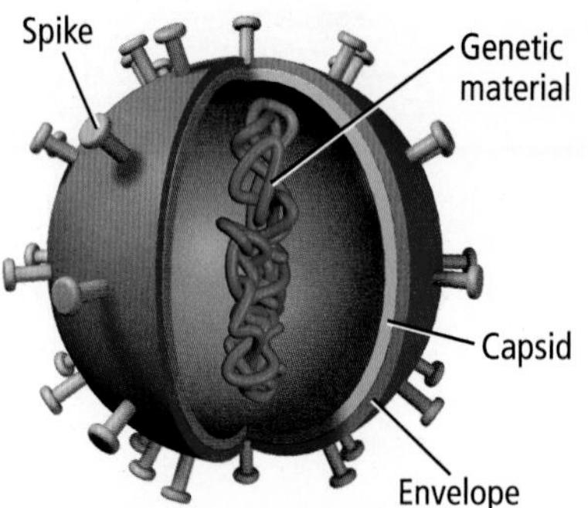

Influenza virus

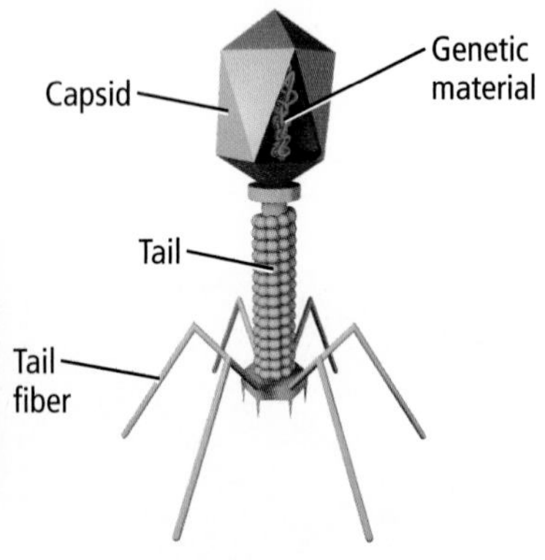

Bacteriophage

■ **Figure 52** All viruses have at least two parts—an outer capsid and genetic material.

Viruses

There are many kinds of viruses, nonliving particles, most of which can cause diseases in the organisms they infect. Most viruses are much smaller than the smallest bacterium, and none respire or grow. Because viruses are nonliving, they usually are not included in the biological classification system.

Viruses consist of a core of DNA or RNA surrounded by a protein coat, called a capsid. Depending on their nucleic acid content, viruses are classified as either DNA viruses or RNA viruses (retroviruses). HIV is a retrovirus.

Viruses replicate only inside living cells. First, a virus attaches to a specific molecule on a cell's plasma membrane. Different types of organisms have receptors for different types of viruses. Then, a virus enters the cell where it begins either a lytic or a lysogenic cycle. In the lytic cycle, the viral nucleic acid causes the host to produce new virus particles that are then released, killing the host cell. In the lysogenic cycle, the viral nucleic acid becomes part of the host's chromosome, and later the cell enters a lytic cycle.

■ **Figure 51** During HIV replication, viral DNA is made from the RNA template. It enters the human DNA and causes the producton of viral RNA.

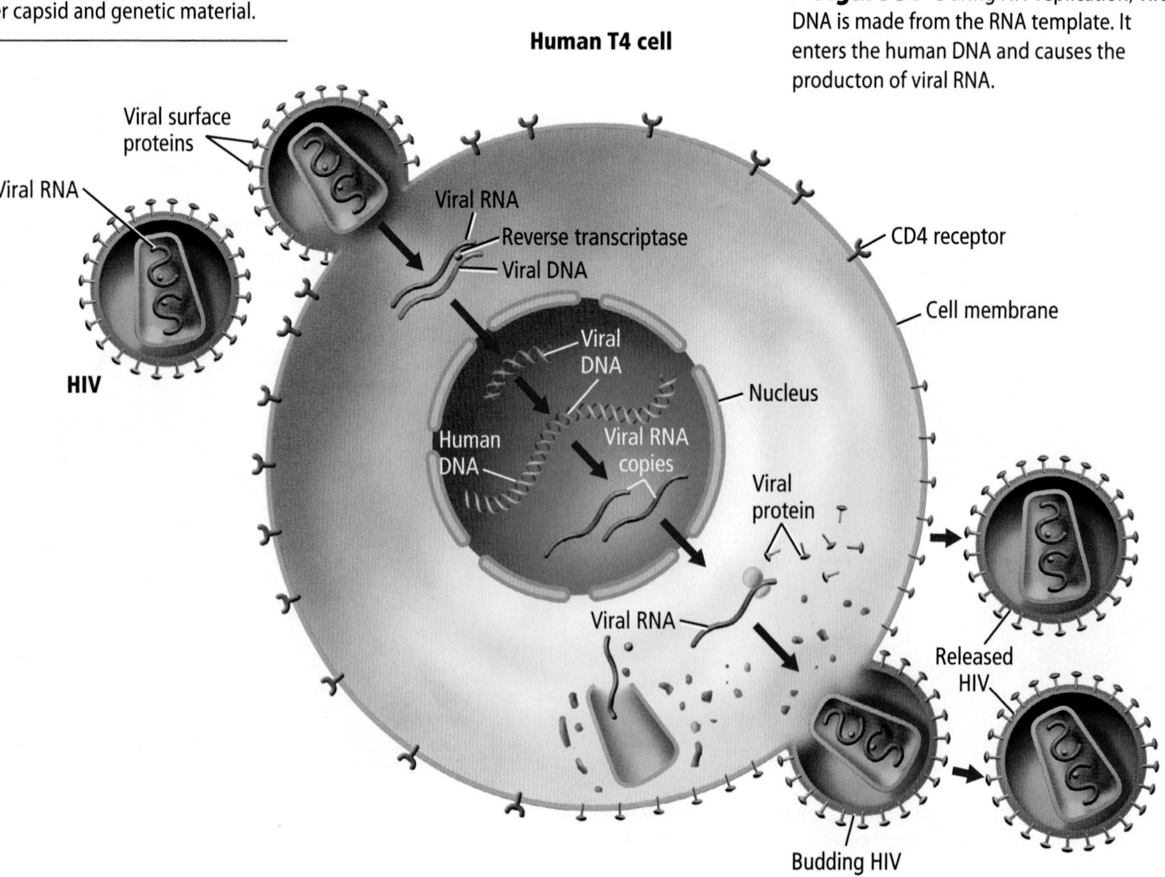

Scientific Word Origins

This list of prefixes, suffixes, and roots is provided to help you understand science terms used throughout this biology textbook. The list identifies whether the prefix, suffix, or root is of Greek *(G)* or Latin *(L)* origin. Also listed is the meaning of the prefix, suffix, or root and a science word in which it is used.

Origin	Meaning	Example
A		
ad *(L)*	to, toward	adaxial
aero *(G)*	air	aerobic
an *(G)*	without	anaerobic
ana *(G)*	up	anaphase
andro *(G)*	male	androceium
angio *(G)*	of seed	angiosperm
anth/o *(G)*	flower	anthophyte
anti *(G)*	against	antibody
aqu/a *(L)*	of water	aquatic
archae *(G)*	ancient	archaeologist
arthro, *artio (G)*	jointed	arthropod
askos *(G)*	bag	ascospore
aster *(G)*	star	Asteroidea
autos *(G)*	self	autoimmune
B		
bi *(L)*	two	bipedal
bio *(G)*	life	biosphere
C		
carn *(L)*	flesh	carnivore
ceph *(G)*	head	cephalopod
chloros *(G)*	light green	chlorophyll
chroma *(G)*	pigmented	chromosome
cide *(L)*	to kill	insecticide
circ *(L)*	circular	circadian
cocc/coccus *(G)*	small and round	streptococcus
con *(L)*	together	convergent
cyte *(G)*	cell	cytoplasm
D		
de *(L)*	remove	decompose
dendron *(G)*	tree	dendrite
dent *(L)*	tooth	edentate
derm *(G)*	skin	epidermis
di *(G)*	two	disaccharide
dia *(G)*	apart	diaphragm
dorm *(L)*	sleep	dormancy

Origin	Meaning	Example
E		
echino *(G)*	spiny	echinoderm
ec *(G)*	outer	ecosystem
ella(e) *(L)*	small	organelle
endo *(G)*	within	endosperm
epi *(G)*	upon	epidermis
eu *(G)*	true	eukaryote
exo *(G)*	outside	exoskeleton
F		
fer *(L)*	to carry	conifer
G		
gastro *(G)*	stomach	gastropod
genesis *(G)*	to originate	oogenesis
gen/(e)(o) *(G)*	kind	genotype
gon *(G)*	reproductive	archegonium
gravi *(L)*	heavy	gravitropism
gymn/o *(G)*	naked	gymnosperm
gyn/e *(G)*	female	gynecium
H		
hal(o) *(G)*	salt	halophyte
hapl(o) *(G)*	single	haploid
hemi *(G)*	half	hemisphere
hem(o) *(G)*	blood	hemoglobin
herb/a(i) *(L)*	vegetation	herbivore
heter/o *(G)*	different	heterotrophic
hom(e)/o *(G)*	same	homeostasis
hom *(L)*	human	hominid
hydr/o *(G)*	water	hydrolysis
I		
inter *(L)*	between	internode
intra *(L)*	within	intracellular
is/o *(G)*	equal	isotonic
J		
jug *(L)*	to join	jugular

Origin	Meaning	Example
K		
kary *(G)*	nucleus	eukaryote
kera *(G)*	hornlike	keratin
L		
leuc/o *(G)*	white	leukocyte
logy *(G)*	study of	biology
lymph/o *(L)*	water	lymphocyte
lysis *(G)*	break up	dialysis
M		
macr/o *(G)*	large	macromolecule
meg/a *(G)*	great	megaspore
meso *(L)*	in the middle	mesophyll
meta *(G)*	after	metaphase
micr/o *(G)*	small	microscope
mon/o *(G)*	only one	monocotyledon
morph/o *(G)*	form	morphology
N		
nema *(G)*	a thread	nematode
neuro *(G)*	nerve	neuron
nod *(L)*	knot	nodule
nomy(e) *(G)*	system of laws	taxonomy
O		
olig/o *(G)*	small, few	oligochaete
omn *(L)*	all	omnivore
orni(s) *(G)*	bird	ornithology
oste/o *(G)*	bone formation	osteocyte
ov *(L)*	an egg	oviduct
P		
pal(a)e/o *(G)*	ancient	paleontology
para *(G)*	beside	parathyroid
path/o *(G)*	suffering	pathogen
ped *(L)*	foot	centipede
per *(L)*	through	permeable
peri *(G)*	around, about	peristalsis
phag/o *(G)*	eating	phagocyte
phot/o *(G)*	light	photosynthesis
phyl *(G)*	race, class	phylogeny
phyll *(G)*	leaf	chlorophyll
phyte *(G)*	plant	epiphyte
pinna *(L)*	feather	pinnate

Origin	Meaning	Example
P (continued)		
plasm/o *(G)*	to form	plasmodium
pod *(G)*	foot	gastropod
poly *(G)*	many	polymer
post *(L)*	after	posterior
pro *(G) (L)*	before	prokaryote
prot/o *(G)*	first	protocells
pseud/o *(G)*	false	pseudopodium
R		
re *(L)*	back to original	reproduce
rhiz/o *(L)*	root	rhizoid
S		
scope *(G)*	to look	microscope
some *(G)*	body	lysome
sperm *(G)*	seed	gymnosperm
stasis *(G)*	remain constant	homeostasis
stom *(G)*	mouthlike opening	stomata
syn *(G)*	together	synapse
T		
tel/o *(G)*	end	telophase
terr *(L)*	of Earth	terrestrial
therm *(G)*	heat	endotherm
thylak *(G)*	sack	thylakoid
trans *(L)*	across	transpiration
trich *(G)*	hair	trichome
trop/o *(G)*	a change	gravitropism
trophic *(G)*	nourishment	heterotrophic
U		
uni *(L)*	one	unicellular
V		
vacc/a *(L)*	cow	vaccine
vore *(L)*	eat greedily	omnivore
X		
xer/o *(G)*	dry	xerophye
Z		
zo/o *(G)*	living being	zoology
zygous *(G)*	two joined	homozygous

PERIODIC TABLE OF THE ELEMENTS

Element — Hydrogen
Atomic number — 1
Symbol — H
Atomic mass — 1.008
State of matter

Gas
Liquid
Solid
Synthetic

Metal
Metalloid
Nonmetal
Recently observed

	1	2	3	4	5	6	7	8	9	10	11	12	13	14	15	16	17	18
1	Hydrogen 1 H 1.008																	Helium 2 He 4.003
2	Lithium 3 Li 6.941	Beryllium 4 Be 9.012											Boron 5 B 10.811	Carbon 6 C 12.011	Nitrogen 7 N 14.007	Oxygen 8 O 15.999	Fluorine 9 F 18.998	Neon 10 Ne 20.180
3	Sodium 11 Na 22.990	Magnesium 12 Mg 24.305											Aluminum 13 Al 26.982	Silicon 14 Si 28.086	Phosphorus 15 P 30.974	Sulfur 16 S 32.066	Chlorine 17 Cl 35.453	Argon 18 Ar 39.948
4	Potassium 19 K 39.098	Calcium 20 Ca 40.078	Scandium 21 Sc 44.956	Titanium 22 Ti 47.867	Vanadium 23 V 50.942	Chromium 24 Cr 51.996	Manganese 25 Mn 54.938	Iron 26 Fe 55.847	Cobalt 27 Co 58.933	Nickel 28 Ni 58.693	Copper 29 Cu 63.546	Zinc 30 Zn 65.39	Gallium 31 Ga 69.723	Germanium 32 Ge 72.61	Arsenic 33 As 74.922	Selenium 34 Se 78.96	Bromine 35 Br 79.904	Krypton 36 Kr 83.80
5	Rubidium 37 Rb 85.468	Strontium 38 Sr 87.62	Yttrium 39 Y 88.906	Zirconium 40 Zr 91.224	Niobium 41 Nb 92.906	Molybdenum 42 Mo 95.94	Technetium 43 Tc (98)	Ruthenium 44 Ru 101.07	Rhodium 45 Rh 102.906	Palladium 46 Pd 106.42	Silver 47 Ag 107.868	Cadmium 48 Cd 112.411	Indium 49 In 114.82	Tin 50 Sn 118.710	Antimony 51 Sb 121.757	Tellurium 52 Te 127.60	Iodine 53 I 126.904	Xenon 54 Xe 131.290
6	Cesium 55 Cs 132.905	Barium 56 Ba 137.327	Lanthanum 57 La 138.905	Hafnium 72 Hf 178.49	Tantalum 73 Ta 180.948	Tungsten 74 W 183.84	Rhenium 75 Re 186.207	Osmium 76 Os 190.23	Iridium 77 Ir 192.217	Platinum 78 Pt 195.08	Gold 79 Au 196.967	Mercury 80 Hg 200.59	Thallium 81 Tl 204.383	Lead 82 Pb 207.2	Bismuth 83 Bi 208.980	Polonium 84 Po 208.982	Astatine 85 At 209.987	Radon 86 Rn 222.018
7	Francium 87 Fr (223)	Radium 88 Ra (226)	Actinium 89 Ac (227)	Rutherfordium 104 Rf (261)	Dubnium 105 Db (262)	Seaborgium 106 Sg (266)	Bohrium 107 Bh (264)	Hassium 108 Hs (277)	Meitnerium 109 Mt (268)	Darmstadtium 110 Ds (281)	Roentgenium 111 Rg (272)	Copernicium 112 Cn (285)	Ununtrium * 113 Uut (284)	Flerovium 114 Fl (289)	Ununpentium * 115 Uup (288)	Livermorium 116 Lv (293)		Ununoctium * 118 Uuo (294)

The number in parentheses is the mass number of the longest lived isotope for that element.

* The names and symbols for elements 113, 115, and 118 are temporary. Final names will be selected when the elements' discoveries are verified.

Lanthanide series	Cerium 58 Ce 140.115	Praseodymium 59 Pr 140.908	Neodymium 60 Nd 144.242	Promethium 61 Pm (145)	Samarium 62 Sm 150.36	Europium 63 Eu 151.965	Gadolinium 64 Gd 157.25	Terbium 65 Tb 158.925	Dysprosium 66 Dy 162.50	Holmium 67 Ho 164.930	Erbium 68 Er 167.259	Thulium 69 Tm 168.934	Ytterbium 70 Yb 173.04	Lutetium 71 Lu 174.967
Actinide series	Thorium 90 Th 232.038	Protactinium 91 Pa 231.036	Uranium 92 U 238.029	Neptunium 93 Np (237)	Plutonium 94 Pu (244)	Americium 95 Am (243)	Curium 96 Cm (247)	Berkelium 97 Bk (247)	Californium 98 Cf (251)	Einsteinium 99 Es (252)	Fermium 100 Fm (257)	Mendelevium 101 Md (258)	Nobelium 102 No (259)	Lawrencium 103 Lr (262)

Multilingual eGlossary

The multilingual science glossary includes Arabic, Bengali, Chinese, English, Haitian Creole, Hmong, Korean, Portuguese, Russian, Spanish, Tagalog, Urdu, and Vietnamese.

Cómo usar el glorasio en español:

1. Busca el término en inglés que desees encontrar.
2. El término en español, junto con la definición, se encuentran en la columna de la derecha.

Pronunciation Key

Use the following key to help you sound out words in the glossary.

a	b**a**ck (BAK)	**ew**	f**oo**d (FEWD)
ay	d**ay** (DAY)	**yoo**	p**u**re (PYOOR)
ah	f**a**ther (FAH thur)	**yew**	f**ew** (FYEW)
ow	fl**ow**er (FLOW ur)	**uh**	comm**a** (CAHM uh)
ar	c**ar** (CAR)	**u** (+con)	r**u**b (RUB)
e	l**e**ss (LES)	**sh**	**sh**elf (SHELF)
ee	l**ea**f (LEEF)	**ch**	na**t**ure (NAY chur)
ih	tr**i**p (TRIHP)	**g**	**g**ift (GIHFT)
i (i+con+e)	**i**dea, l**i**fe (i DEE uh, life)	**j**	**g**em (JEM)
oh	g**o** (GOH)	**ing**	s**ing** (SING)
aw	s**o**ft (SAWFT)	**zh**	vi**s**ion (VIHZH un)
or	**or**bit (OR but)	**k**	ca**k**e (KAYK)
oy	c**oi**n (COYN)	**s**	**s**eed, **c**ent (SEED, SENT)
oo	f**oo**t (FOOT)	**z**	**z**one, rai**s**e (ZOHN, RAYZ)

Glossary • Glosario

ENGLISH — A — ESPAÑOL

abiotic (ay bi AH tihk) factor: **(p. 35)** any nonliving factor in an organism's environment, such as soil, water temperature, and light availability.

factor abiótico: **(pág. 35)** todo factor inanimado en el ambiente de un organismo, como el suelo, el agua, la temperatura del agua y la disponibilidad de luz.

abyssal zone: **(p. 81)** deepest, very cold region of the open ocean.

zona abisal: **(pág. 81)** la zona más profunda y más fría del océano.

acid: **(p. 164)** substance that releases hydrogen ions (H+) when dissolved in water; an acidic solution has a pH less than 7.

ácido: **(pág. 164)** sustancia que libera iones hidrógeno (H+) cuando se halla disuelta en agua; una solución ácida contiene un pH menor que 7.

actin: **(p. 538)** protein filament in muscle cells that functions with myosin in contraction.

actina: **(pág. 538)** filamento proteico de las células musculares que, junto con la miosina, participan en la contracción muscular.

action potential: **(p. 554)** nerve impulse.

potencial de acción: **(pág. 554)** un impulso nervioso.

activation energy: **(p. 158)** minimum amount of energy needed for reactants to form products in a chemical reaction.

energía de activación: **(pág. 158)** cantidad mínima de energía que requieren los reactivos para formar productos durante una reacción química.

active site: **(p. 160)** specific place where a substrate binds on an enzyme.

sitio activo: **(pág. 160)** lugar específico donde un sustrato se une a una enzima.

active transport: **(p. 205)** energy-requiring process by which substances move across the plasma membrane against a concentration gradient.

transporte activo: **(pág. 205)** proceso que requiere energía y que le permite a una sustancia atravesar la membrana plasmática contra un gradiente de concentración.

adaptation (a dap TAY shun): (p. 10) inherited characteristic of a species that develops over time in response to an environmental factor, enabling the species to survive.

adaptive radiation: (p. 439) diversification of a species into a number of different species, often over a relatively short time span.

addiction: (p. 571) psychological and/or physiological dependence on a drug.

adenosine triphosphate (uh DEN uh seen • tri FAHS fayt) (ATP): (p. 221) energy-carrying biological molecule, which, when broken down, drives cellular activities.

adolescence (a dul ES unts): (p. 653) developmental phase that begins with puberty and ends at adulthood.

adulthood: (p. 654) developmental phase that occurs at the end of adolescence, when physical growth is complete.

aerobic process: (p. 228) a metabolic process that requires oxygen.

aerobic respiration: (p. 228) metabolic process in which pyruvate is broken down and electron-carrier molecules are used to produce ATP through electron transport.

age structure: (p. 104) in any population, the number of individuals in their pre-reproductive, reproductive, and post-reproductive years.

aldosterone (al DAWS tuh rohn): (p. 625) steroid hormone produced by the adrenal cortex that acts on the kidneys and is important for sodium reabsorption.

allele: (p. 278) alternative form that a single gene may have for a particular trait.

allergy: (p. 684) overactive immune response to environmental antigens.

allopatric speciation: (p. 438) occurs when a population divided by a geographic barrier evolves into two or more populations unable to interbreed.

alveolus: (p. 591) in the lung, a thin-walled air sac surrounded by capillaries.

amino acid: (p. 170) carbon compound joined by peptide bonds; building block of proteins.

amniotic fluid (am nee AH tihk • FLU id): (p. 646) amniotic sac fluid that cushions, insulates, and protects the embryo.

amylase: (p. 610) digestive enzyme in saliva that begins the process of chemical digestion in the mouth by breaking down starches into sugars.

anaerobic process: (p. 228) metabolic process that does not require oxygen.

analogous structure: (p. 426) structure that has the same function but different construction and was not inherited from a common ancestor.

adaptación: (pág. 10) característica heredada de una especie; esta característica evoluciona a lo largo del tiempo en respuesta a un factor ambiental y le ayuda a la especie a sobrevivir.

radiación adaptativa: (pág. 439) diversificación de una especie en diferentes especies, a menudo en un período relativamente corto.

adicción: (pág. 571) dependencia psicológica o fisiológica a una droga.

trifosfato de adenosina (ATP): (pág. 221) molécula biológica que transporta energía, y que al desdoblarse, hace funcionar las actividades celulares.

adolescencia: (pág. 653) fase del desarrollo que se inicia en la pubertad y termina al comenzar la edad adulta.

edad adulta: (pág. 654) fase del desarrollo que empieza al terminar la adolescencia, cuando se completa el crecimiento físico.

proceso aeróbico: (pág. 228) proceso metabólico que requiere oxígeno.

respiración aeróbica: (pág. 228) proceso metabólico en que se desdobla el piruvato y las moléculas transportadoras de electrones ayudan a producir ATP mediante el transporte de electrones.

estructura etaria: (pág. 104) el número de individuos en edad prereproductora, reproductora y postreproductora en una población.

aldosterona: (pág. 625) hormona esteroide producida por la corteza adrenal, la cual actúa sobre los riñones y es importante para la reabsorción de sodio.

alelo: (pág. 278) forma alternativa de un gene determinado para un rasgo dado.

alergia: (pág. 684) acentuada respuesta inmune a un antígeno del ambiente.

especiación alopátrica: (pág. 438) sucede cuando una población separada en dos por una barrera geográfica, evoluciona y se convierte en dos poblaciones incapaces de entrecruzarse.

alvéolo: (pág. 591) saco aéreo de paredes delgadas, localizado dentro de los pulmones, y que está rodeado por capilares.

aminoácido: (pág. 170) compuestos de carbono con enlaces peptídicos; son la unidad básica de las proteínas.

fluido amniótico: (pág. 646) fluido del saco amniótico que acojina, aísla y protege al embrión.

amilasa: (pág. 610) enzima digestiva de la saliva que inicia el proceso de digestión química en la boca, al desdoblar almidones en azúcares.

aproceso anaeróbico: (pág. 228) proceso metabólico que no requiere oxígeno.

estructura análoga: (pág. 426) estructura que tiene la misma función, pero diferente construcción y que no se originó a partir de un antepasado común.

anaphase: (p. 251) third stage of mitosis in which sister chromatids are pulled apart and microtubules, along with motor proteins, move the chromosomes to opposite poles of the cell.

anaphylactic (an uh fuh LAK tik) shock: (p. 685) severe hypersensitivity to a specific antigen, causing a massive histamine release.

ancestral character: (p. 495) morphological or biochemical feature present in various groups within the line of descent.

ancestral trait: (p. 424) more-primitive characteristic that appeared in common ancestors.

anthropoid: (p. 455) part of haplorhines; humanlike primates that include New World monkeys, Old World monkeys, and hominoids.

antibiotic (an ti bi AH tihk): (p. 672) substance that is able to kill or inhibit the growth of some microorganisms.

antibody: (p. 676) protein produced by B lymphocytes that specifically reacts with a foreign antigen.

antidiuretic (an ti di yuh REH tic) hormone: (p. 627) functions in homeostasis by regulating water balance.

antigen: (p. 676) a substance foreign to the body that causes an immune response; it can bind to an antibody or T cell.

aphotic zone: (p. 80) open-ocean zone through which sunlight cannot penetrate.

apoptosis (a pup TOH sus): (p. 256) programmed cell death.

appendicular skeleton: (p. 531) one of the two divisions of the human skeleton; includes the bones of the arms, legs, feet, hands, hips, and shoulders.

arboreal: (p. 455) tree dwelling—it is a characteristic of many primates.

archaea: (p. 500) prokaryotes whose cell walls do not contain peptidoglycan.

artery: (p. 583) elastic, thick-walled blood vessel that carries oxygenated blood away from the heart.

artificial selection: (p. 419) Darwin's term for the selective breeding of organisms selected for certain traits in order to produce offspring having those traits.

atherosclerosis (a thuh roh skluh ROH sus): (p. 589) circulatory system disorder in which arteries are blocked, restricting blood flow.

atom: (p. 148) building block of matter; contains subatomic particles—neutrons, protons, and electrons.

australopithecine: (p. 465) genus that lived in the east-central and southern part of Africa between 4.2 and 1 mya.

anafase: (pág. 251) tercera fase de la mitosis. En ella, las cromátides hermanas se separan y los microtúbulos, junto con proteínas motoras, mueven los cromosomas hacia polos opuestos de la célula.

choque anafiláctico: (pág. 685) grave hipersensibilidad a un antígeno específico que causa una liberación masiva de histamina.

carácter ancestral: (pág. 495) característica morfológica o bioquímica presente en varios grupos dentro de un linaje.

rasgo ancestral: (pág. 424) característica más primitiva que aparecían en antepasados comunes.

antropoide: (pág. 455) parte de los haplorrinos; primates parecidos a humanos que incluyen los monos del Nuevo Mundo, monos del Viejo Mundo y los homínidos.

antibiótico: (pág. 672) sustancia que destruye algunos microorganismos o que inhibe su crecimiento.

anticuerpo: (pág. 676) proteína producida por los linfocitos B que reacciona específicamente con un antígeno extraño.

hormona antidiurética: (pág. 627) hormona que ayuda en la homeostasis al regular el equilibrio del agua.

antígeno: (pág. 676) sustancia foránea al cuerpo que causa una reacción inmunológica; se puede enlazar a un anticuerpo o a una célula T.

zona afótica: (pág. 80) zona del mar abierto a la que no llega la luz solar.

apoptosis: (pág. 256) muerte celular programada.

esqueleto apendicular: (pág. 531) una de las dos divisiones del esqueleto humano; incluye los huesos de brazos, piernas, manos, pies, caderas y hombros.

arborícola: (pág. 455) que vive en los árboles: es una característica de muchos primates.

archaea: (pág. 500) procariotas cuyas paredes celulares no contienen peptidoglucanos.

arteria: (pág. 583) vaso sanguíneo de paredes gruesas y elásticas que transporta sangre oxigenada desde el corazón hacia el resto del cuerpo.

selección artificial: (pág. 419) término empleado por Darwin para referirse a la cría de selección de organismos, la cual se efectúa para seleccionar y obtener una progenie con ciertos rasgos.

aterosclerosis: (pág. 589) trastorno del sistema circulatorio en que las arterias se bloquean y restringen el flujo de sangre.

átomo: (pág. 148) unidad básica de la materia; contiene las siguientes partículas subatómicas: neutrones, protones y electrones.

australopitecinos: (pág. 465) género que vivió en la parte centro oriental y meridional de África entre hace 4.2 y 1 millón de años.

autonomic nervous system: (**p. 561**) part of the peripheral nervous system that transmits impulses from the central nervous system to internal organs.

autosome: (**p. 305**) chromosome that is not a sex chromosome.

autotroph (AW tuh trohf): (**p. 41**) organism that captures energy from sunlight or inorganic substances to produce its own food; provides the foundation of the food supply for other organisms; also called a producer.

axial skeleton: (**p. 531**) one of the two divisions of the human skeleton; includes the bones of the vetebral column, ribs, skull, and sternum.

axon: (**p. 552**) neuron structure that transmits nerve impulses from the cell body to other neurons and muscles.

sistema nervioso autónomo: (**pág. 561**) parte del sistema nervioso periférico que transmite impulsos desde el sistema nervioso central hacia los órganos internos.

autosoma: (**pág. 305**) cromosoma que no es un cromosoma sexual.

autótrofo: (**pág. 41**) organismo que captura energía del sol o de sustancias inorgánicas para producir sus propios alimentos; es la base para la alimentación de otros organismos; también llamado productor.

esqueleto axial: (**pág. 531**) una de las dos divisiones del esqueleto humano e incluye los huesos de la columna vertebral, las costillas, el cráneo y el esternón.

axón: (**pág. 552**) estructura de la neurona que transmite impulsos nerviosos desde el cuerpo de la célula hacia los músculos y otras neuronas.

B

B cell: (**p. 676**) antibody-producing B lymphocyte.

background extinction: (**p. 122**) gradual process of a species becoming extinct.

base: (**p. 164**) substance that releases hydroxide ions (OH–) when dissolved in water; a basic solution has a pH greater than 7.

benthic zone: (**p. 80**) ocean-floor area consisting of sand, silt, and dead organisms.

binocular vision: (**p. 452**) overlapping fields of vision as a result of eyes located on the front of the face—a characteristic of primates.

binomial nomenclature (bi NOH mee ul • NOH mun klay chur): (**p. 485**) Linnaeus's system of naming organisms, which gives a scientific two-word Latin name to each species—the first part is the genus name and the second is the specific epithet.

biodiversity: (**p. 116**) number of different species living in a specific area.

biogeochemical cycle: (**p. 45**) exchange of matter through the biosphere involving living organisms, chemical processes, and geological processes.

biogeography: (**p. 428**) study of the distribution of plants and animals on Earth.

bioinformatics: (**p. 375**) field of study that creates and maintains databases of biological information, especially genomic data.

biological augmentation: (**p. 135**) technique of adding essential materials to a degraded ecosystem.

biological community: (**p. 36**) all the interacting populations of different species that live in the same geographic location at the same time.

célula B: (**pág. 676**) linfocito B productor de antígenos.

extinción tradicional o natural: (**pág. 122**) proceso paulatino de extinción de una especie.

base: (**pág. 164**) sustancia que libera iones hidróxido (OH–) al disolverse en agua; una solución básica tiene un pH mayor que 7.

zona béntica: (**pág. 80**) zona del fondo marino formada por arena, limo y organismos muertos.

visión binocular: (**pág. 452**) campos de visión sobrepuestos como resultado de ojos ubicados enfrente de la cara: una característica de los primates.

nomenclatura binaria: (**pág. 485**) sistema desarrollado por Linneo para nombrar los organismos, en que se otorga un nombre científico de dos palabras a cada especie, la primera palabra es el género y la segunda es la especie.

biodiversidad: (**pág. 116**) número de especies diferentes que viven en un área determinada.

ciclo biogeoquímico: (**pág. 45**) intercambio de material a través de la biosfera en que participan seres vivos, procesos químicos y proceso geológicos.

biogeografía: (**pág. 428**) estudio de la distribución de plantas y animales en la Tierra.

bioinformática: (**pág. 375**) campo de estudio en que se crean y mantienen bases de datos con información biológica, particularmente genética.

bioaumento: (**pág. 135**) técnica en que se agregan materiales esenciales a un ecosistema degradado.

comunidad biológica: (**pág. 36**) todas las poblaciones de diferentes especies que interactúan y viven en una misma zona geográfica, al mismo tiempo.

biological magnification: (**p. 126**) increasing concentration of toxic substances, such as DDT, in organisms as trophic levels increase in food chains or food webs.

amplificación biológica: (**pág. 126**) aumento en la concentración de sustancias tóxicas (como el DDT) en los organismos, a medida que aumenta el nivel trófico de cadenas y redes alimenticias.

biology: (**p. 4**) science of life; examines how living things interact, how systems function, and how they function at a molecular level.

biología: (**pág. 4**) ciencia que estudia la vida; examina las interacciones entre los seres vivos, el funcionamiento de sus sistemas y el funcionamiento a nivel molecular.

biomass: (**p. 44**) total mass of living matter at each trophic level.

biomasa: (**pág. 44**) masa total de materia viva en cada nivel trófico.

biome: (**p. 36**) large group of ecosystems that share the same climate and have similar types of communities.

bioma: (**pág. 36**) gran grupo de ecosistemas que comparte un mismo clima y que posee comunidades similares.

bioremediation: (**p. 134**) technique using living organisms to detoxify a polluted area.

biorremediación: (**pág. 134**) técnica en que se usan organismos vivos para descontaminar un área.

biosphere (BI uh sfihr): (**p. 34**) relatively thin layer of Earth and its atmosphere that supports life.

biosfera: (**pág. 34**) capa relativamente delgada de la Tierra y su atmósfera que mantiene la vida.

biotic (by AH tihk) factor: (**p. 35**) any living factor in an organism's environment.

factor biótico: (**pág. 35**) todo factor vivo en el ambiente de un organismo.

bipedal: (**p. 463**) walking upright on two legs.

bípedo: (**pág. 463**) que camina erguido sobre dos piernas.

blastocyst: (**p. 645**) a modified blastula whose inner cell mass will develop into a fetus.

blastocisto: (**pág. 645**) blástula modificada; sus células internas se convierten más tarde en el feto.

boreal forest: (**p. 68**) biome south of the tundra with dense evergreen forests and long, cold, dry winters.

bosque boreal: (**pág. 68**) bioma situado al sur de la tundra, tiene densos bosques de siempreverdes e inviernos largos, fríos y secos.

bottleneck: (**p. 433**) process in which a large population declines in number, then rebounds.

cuello de botella: (**pág. 433**) proceso en que el número de miembros de una población declina y luego aumenta.

breathing: (**p. 590**) mechanical movement of air into and out of the lungs.

respiración: (**pág. 590**) movimiento mecánico de entrada y salida de aire de los pulmones.

bronchus (BRAHN kuhs): (**p. 591**) one of the two large tubes that carries air from the trachea to the lungs.

bronquio: (**pág. 591**) uno de los dos grandes conductos por el que se introduce aire de la tráquea a los pulmones.

buffer: (**p. 165**) mixture that can react with an acid or a base to maintain the pH within a specific range.

amortiguador: (**pág. 165**) mezcla que puede reaccionar con un ácido o una base y mantener un pH dentro de cierto rango.

C

calcitonin (kal suh TOH nun): (**p. 624**) thyroid hormone involved in regulation of blood calcium levels.

calcitonina: (**pág. 624**) hormona tiroidea que participa en la regulación de los niveles de calcio en la sangre.

Calorie: (**p. 615**) unit used to measure the energy content of food; 1 Calorie equals 1 kilocalorie, or 1000 calories.

Caloría: (**pág. 615**) unidad de medida de la energía que contienen los alimentos; 1 Caloría equivale a 1 kilocaloría ó 1000 calorías.

Calvin cycle: (**p. 226**) light-independent reactions during phase two of photosynthesis in which energy is stored in organic molecules as glucose.

ciclo de Calvin: (**pág. 226**) reacciones independiente de la luz de la fase II de la fotosíntesis, en que la energía es almacenada como glucosa en moléculas orgánicas.

Cambrian explosion: (**p. 398**) rapid diversification of most major animal groups marking the start the Paleozoic era.

explosión del Cámbrico: (**pág. 398**) rápida diversificación de la mayoría de los grupos animales que marca el inicio de la era Paleozoica.

camouflage (KA muh flahj): (**p. 428**) morphological adaptations that allow organisms to blend into their surroundings.

camuflaje: (**pág. 428**) adaptaciones morfológicas que permiten a los organismos disimularse en su ambiente.

cancer: (**p. 254**) uncontrolled growth and division of cells that can be caused by changes in control of the cell cycle and also may be caused by environmental factors.	**cáncer:** (**pág. 254**) crecimiento y división descontrolados de células que puede ser producido por cambios en ciclo celular o también puede ser causado por factores ambientales.
capillary: (**p. 583**) microscopic, one-cell-wall thick blood vessel where exchange of materials occurs between blood and body cells.	**capilares:** (**pág. 583**) vaso sanguíneo microscópico con paredes de una célula de grosor, en que sucede el intercambio de materiales entre la sangre y las células corporales.
carbohydrate: (**p. 168**) organic compound containing carbon, hydrogen, and oxygen in a ratio of one oxygen and two hydrogen atoms for each carbon atom.	**carbohidrato:** (**pág. 168**) compuesto orgánico que contiene carbono, hidrógeno y oxígeno, en una razón de un átomo de oxígeno y dos átomos de hidrógeno, por cada átomo de carbono.
carcinogen (kar SIH nuh jun): (**p. 254**) cancer-causing substance.	**carcinógeno:** (**pág. 254**) sustancia que causa cáncer.
cardiac muscle: (**p. 537**) involuntary muscle found only in the heart.	**músculo cardíaco:** (**pág. 537**) músculo involuntario que sólo se halla en el corazón.
carnivore (KAR nuh vor): (**p. 41**) heterotroph that preys on other heterotrophs.	**carnívoro:** (**pág. 41**) heterótrofo que se alimenta de otros heterótrofos.
carrier: (**p. 296**) individual heterozygous for a recessive disorder such as cystic fibrosis or Tay-Sachs disease.	**portador:** (**pág. 296**) individuo heterocigoto para un trastorno recesivo como la fibrosis quística o la enfermedad de Tay-Sachs.
carrying capacity: (**p. 98**) largest number of individuals in a species that an environment can support long-term.	**capacidad de carga:** (**pág. 98**) el número mayor de individuos de una misma especie que un ambiente puede mantener a largo plazo.
catalyst: (**p. 159**) substance that speeds up a chemical reaction by reducing the activation energy.	**catalizador:** (**pág. 159**) sustancia que acelera una reacción química al reducir energía de activación.
cell body: (**p. 552**) neuron structure that contains the nucleus and many organelles.	**cuerpo celular:** (**pág. 552**) estructura de la neurona que contiene el núcleo y muchos organelos.
cell cycle: (**p. 246**) process of cellular reproduction, occurring in three main stages—interphase (growth), mitosis (nuclear division), and cytokinesis (cytoplasm division).	**ciclo celular:** (**pág. 246**) proceso de reproducción celular; consta de tres fases principales: interfase (crecimiento), mitosis (división nuclear) y citoquinesis (división del citoplasma).
cell theory: (**p. 183**) states that (1) organisms are made of one or more cells; (2) cells are the basic unit of life; and (3) all cells come only from other cells.	**teoría celular:** (**pág. 183**) establece que (1) los organismos están formados por una o más células; (2) las células son la unidad básica de la vida y (3) todas las células provienen de otras células.
cell wall: (**p. 198**) in plants, the rigid barrier that surrounds the outside of the plasma membrane, is made of cellulose, and provides support and protection to the cell.	**pared celular:** (**pág. 198**) barrera rígida que rodea el exterior de la membrana plasmática de las plantas; está formada por celulosa y brinda soporte y protección a la célula.
cell: (**p. 182**) basic unit of structure and organization of all living organisms.	**célula:** (**pág. 182**) unidad básica de estructura y organización de todos los seres vivos.
cellular respiration: (**p. 220**) catabolic pathway in which organic molecules are broken down to release energy for use by the cell.	**respiración celular:** (**pág. 220**) vía catabólica en que se desdoblan moléculas orgánicas a fin de obtener energía para la célula.
central nervous system: (**p. 558**) consists of the brain and spinal cord and coordinates all of the body's activities.	**sistema nervioso central:** (**pág. 558**) está formado por el encéfalo y la medula espinal y coordina todas las actividades del cuerpo.
centriole: (**p. 196**) organelle that plays a role in cell division and is made of microtubules.	**centríolo:** (**pág. 196**) organelo formado por microtúbulos y que participa en la división celular.
centromere: (**p. 248**) cell structure that joins two sister chromatids.	**centrómero:** (**pág. 248**) estructura celular que une a dos cromátides hermanas.
cerebrum (suh REE brum): (**p. 559**) largest part of the brain; is divided into two hemispheres and carries out higher thought processes involved with language, learning, memory, and voluntary body movements.	**cerebro:** (**pág. 559**) órgano más grande del encéfalo; se divide en dos hemisferios y realiza los procesos más complejos de pensamiento relacionados con el lenguaje, el aprendizaje, la memoria y los movimientos voluntarios del cuerpo.

character: (p. 492) inherited morphological or biochemical feature that varies among species and can be used to determine patterns of descent.

chemical digestion: (p. 610) chemical breakdown of food by digestive enzymes such as amylase into smaller molecules that cells can absorb.

chemical reaction: (p. 156) energy-requiring process by which atoms or groups of atoms in substances are changed into different substances.

chloroplast: (p. 197) double-membrane organelle that captures light energy and converts it to chemical energy through photosynthesis.

chromatin (KROH muh tun): (p. 247) relaxed form of DNA in the nucleus of a cell.

chromosome (KROH muh sohm): (p. 247) DNA-containing structure that carries genetic material from one generation to another.

cilium: (p. 198) short, hairlike projection that functions in cell movement.

cladistics (kla DIHS tiks): (p. 495) taxonomic method that models evolutionary relationships based on shared derived characters and phylogenetic trees.

cladogram (KLA duh gram): (p. 496) diagram with branches that represents the hypothesized phylogeny or evolution of a species or group; uses bioinformatics, morphological studies, and information from DNA studies.

class: (p. 488) taxonomic group that contains one or more related orders.

classification: (p. 484) grouping of organisms or objects based on a set of criteria that helps organize, communicate, and retain information.

climate: (p. 66) average weather conditions in a specific area, determined by latitude, elevation, ocean currents, and other factors.

climax community: (p. 63) stable, mature ecological community with little change in the composition of species.

cloning: (p. 367) process in which large numbers of identical recombinant DNA molecules are produced.

cochlea (KOH klee uh): (p. 564) snail-shaped, sound-sensitive, inner ear structure filled with fluid and lined with hair cells; generates nerve impulses sent to the brain through the auditory nerve.

codominance: (p. 302) complex inheritance pattern that occurs when neither allele is dominant and both alleles are expressed.

codon: (p. 338) three-base code in DNA or RNA.

commensalism (kuh MEN suh lih zum): (p. 40) symbiotic relationship in which one organism benefits and the other organism is neither helped nor harmed.

carácter: (pág. 492) característica morfológica o bioquímica heredada que varía entre especies y que sirve para determinar patrones de la herencia.

digestión química: (pág. 610) desdoblamiento químico de los alimentos por enzimas digestivas, como la amilasa, en moléculas más pequeñas que las células puedan absorber.

reacción química: (pág. 156) proceso que requiere energía, en que los átomos o grupos de átomos se convierten en diferentes sustancias.

cloroplasto: (pág. 197) organelo de doble membrana que captura la energía de la luz y la convierte en energía química mediante la fotosíntesis.

cromatina: (pág. 247) forma no condensada de DNA en el núcleo de una célula.

cromosoma: (pág. 247) estructura que contiene DNA y que lleva el material genético de una generación a la siguiente.

cilio: (pág. 198) extensión corta y filiforme que funciona en la locomoción celular.

cladística: (pág. 495) método taxonómico que modela las relaciones evolutivas basándose en caracteres derivados compartidos y árboles filogenéticos.

cladograma: (pág. 496) diagrama con ramas que representan la filogenia hipotética, o evolución, de una especie o grupo; utiliza la bioinformática, los estudios morfológicos y la información proveniente de estudios del DNA.

clase: (pág. 488) grupo taxonómico que contiene uno o más órdenes relacionados.

clasificación: (pág. 484) agrupamiento de organismos u objetos en base a una serie de criterios y que permite organizar, comunicar y retener información.

clima: (pág. 66) condiciones meteorológicas promedio en un área específica; son determinadas por la latitud, la elevación, las corrientes oceánicas y otros factores.

comunidad clímax: (pág. 63) comunidad ecológica madura y estable que presenta pocos cambios en el número de especies.

clonación: (pág. 367) proceso en que se producen grandes cantidades de moléculas idénticas de DNA recombinante.

cóclea: (pág. 564) estructura del oído interno, con forma de caracol y sensible al sonido, que está llena de un fluido y revestida con células ciliadas; genera impulsos nerviosos que envía al encéfalo a través del nervio auditivo.

codominancia: (pág. 302) patrón hereditario complejo que sucede cuando ninguno de los alelos es dominante y ambos se expresan.

codón: (pág. 338) código de tres bases del DNA o el RNA.

comensalismo: (pág. 40) relación simbiótica en que un organismo se beneficia, mientras que el otro no obtiene beneficios pero tampoco es perjudicado.

community: (**p. 60**) group of interacting populations that live in the same geographic area at the same time.

compact bone: (**p. 532**) strong, dense outer bone layer that contains Haversian systems.

complement protein: (**p. 675**) protein in blood plasma that enhances phagocytosis.

compound: (**p. 151**) pure substance with unique properties; formed when two or more different elements combine.

constant: (**p. 19**) a factor that remains fixed during an experiment while the independent and dependent variables change.

control group: (**p. 19**) in a controlled experiment, the group not receiving the factor being tested.

cortisol: (**p. 625**) a glucocorticoid that raises blood glucose levels, reduces inflammation, and is produced by the adrenal cortex.

covalent bond: (**p. 152**) type of chemical bond formed when atoms share electrons.

Cro-Magnon: (**p. 473**) a species also referred to as *Homo sapiens;* seem to have replaced Neanderthals.

crossing over: (**p. 272**) exchange of chromosomal segments between a pair of homologous chromosomes during prophase I of meisois.

cyclin-dependent kinase: (**p. 253**) enzyme to which cyclin binds during interphase and mitosis, triggering and controlling activities during the cell cycle.

cyclin: (**p. 253**) one of the specific proteins that regulate the cell cycle.

cytokinesis (si toh kih NEE sis): (**p. 246**) third main stage of the cell cycle, during which the cell's cytoplasm divides, creating a new cell.

cytoplasm: (**p. 191**) semifluid material inside the cell's plasma membrane.

cytoskeleton: (**p. 191**) supporting network of protein fibers that provide a framework for the cell within the cytoplasm.

cytotoxic T cell: (**p. 678**) lymphocyte that destroys pathogens and releases cytokines when activated.

comunidad: (**pág. 60**) grupo de poblaciones que interactúan y que viven en la misma región geográfica al mismo tiempo.

hueso compacto: (**pág. 532**) capa de hueso externa, más fuerte y más densa, que contiene los canales de Havers.

complemento: (**pág. 675**) proteínas del plasma de la sangre que estimulan la fagocitosis.

compuesto: (**pág. 151**) sustancia pura con propiedades particulares y que se forma cuando se combinan dos o más elementos.

constante: (**pág. 19**) factor que permanece fijo durante un experimento mientras que las variables independiente y dependiente cambian.

grupo control: (**pág. 19**) en un experimento controlado, el grupo al que no se aplica el factor que se está probando.

cortisol: (**pág. 625**) un glucocorticoide que eleva el nivel de glucosa en sangre, reduce la inflamación y que es producido por la corteza suprarrenal.

enlace covalente: (**pág. 152**) tipo de enlace químico que se forma cuando los átomos comparten electrones.

Cromañón: (**pág. 473**) especie también conocida como Homo sapiens sapiens; parece haber reemplazado a los Neandertales.

entrecruzamiento: (**pág. 272**) intercambio de segmentos de cromosomas entre un par de cromosomas homólogos, el cual ocurre durante la profase I de la meiosis.

quinasa dependiente de la ciclina: (**pág. 253**) enzima a la que se une la ciclina durante la interfase y la mitosis, iniciando y controlando, de este modo, las actividades del ciclo celular.

ciclina: (**pág. 253**) una de las proteínas específicas que regulan el ciclo celular.

citoquinesis: (**pág. 246**) tercera etapa del ciclo celular; en esta etapa el citoplasma de la célula se divide y se origina una nueva célula.

citoplasma: (**pág. 191**) material semifluido que está rodeado por la membrana plasmática de la célula.

citoesqueleto: (**pág. 191**) red de fibras proteicas de soporte que provee una estructura para la célula, dentro del citoplasma.

linfocito T citotóxico: (**pág. 678**) linfocito que al ser activado, destruye patógenos y libera citoquinas.

D

data: (**p. 19**) quantitative or qualitative information gained from scientific investigation.

degenerative (di JEH nuh ruh tihv) disease: (**p. 682**) noninfectious disease, such as arthritis, that results from part of the body wearing out.

datos: (**pág. 19**) información cualitativa o cuantitativa obtenida durante una investigación científica.

enfermedad degenerativa: (**pág. 682**) trastorno no infeccioso, como la artritis, que resulta del desgaste de una parte del cuerpo.

demographic transition: (p. 102) population change from high birth rates and death rates to low birth rates and death rates.

demography (de MAH gra fee): (p. 100) study of human populations based on size, density, movement, distribution, and birth and death rates.

dendrite: (p. 552) neuron structure that receives nerve impulses from other neurons and transmits them to the cell body.

denitrification: (p. 48) process in which fixed nitrogen compounds are converted back into nitrogen gas and returned to the atmosphere.

density-dependent factor: (p. 95) environmental factor, such as predation, disease, and competition, that depends on the number of members in a population per unit area.

density-independent factor: (p. 94) environmental factor, such as storms and extreme heat or cold, that affects populations regardless of their density.

dependent variable: (p. 19) factor being measured in a controlled experiment; its value changes because of changes to the independent variable.

depressant: (p. 569) substance/drug that slows down the central nervous system.

derived character: (p. 495) morphological or biochemical feature found in one group of a line but not in common ancestors.

derived trait: (p. 424) new feature that had not appeared in common ancestors.

dermis: (p. 527) skin layer beneath the epidermis; contains nerve cells, muscle fibers, sweat glands, oil glands, and hair follicles.

desert: (p. 70) area with low rainfall, whose annual rate of evaporation exceeds its annual rate of precipitation; can support cacti and some grasses and animal species such as snakes and lizards.

detritivore (duh TRYD tuh vor): (p. 42) heterotroph that decomposes organic material and returns the nutrients to soil, air, and water, making the nutrients available to other organisms.

development: (p. 8) changes an organism undergoes in its lifetime before reaching its adult form.

diffusion: (p. 201) net movement of particles from an area of higher concentration to an area of lower concentration.

dilation (di LAY shun): (p. 652) the opening of the cervix during labor.

diploid: (p. 271) having two copies of each chromosome (2n).

directional selection: (p. 435) shift of a population toward an extreme version of a beneficial trait.

transición demográfica: (pág. 102) cambio en una población que pasa de tener altas tasas de natalidad y de mortalidad, a tener bajas tasas de natalidad y de mortalidad.

demografía: (pág. 100) estudio de las poblaciones humanas en base al tamaño, la densidad, el movimiento, la distribución y las tasas de natalidad y mortalidad de dichas poblaciones.

dendrita: (pág. 552) estructura de la neurona que recibe impulsos nerviosos de otras neuronas y que luego los transmite hacia el cuerpo de la neurona.

desnitrificación: (pág. 48) proceso en que los compuestos de nitrógeno fijado son convertidos a gas nitrógeno y devueltos a la atmósfera.

factor dependiente de la densidad: (pág. 95) factor ambiental, como la depredación, las enfermedades y la competencia, que depende del número de miembros de la población por unidad de área.

factor independiente de la densidad: (pág. 94) factor ambiental, como las tormentas y el calor o el frío extremos, que afectan a las poblaciones independientemente de su densidad.

variable dependiente: (pág. 19) factor que se mide en un experimento controlado; su valor cambia de acuerdo con los cambios en la variable independiente.

depresor: (pág. 569) sustancia o droga que disminuye la actividad del sistema nervioso central.

carácter derivado: (pág. 495) característica morfológica o bioquímica presente en un grupo de un linaje, pero no en los antepasados comunes.

rasgo derivado: (pág. 424) nueva característica que no aparece en antepasados comunes.

dermis: (pág. 527) capa de la piel situada bajo la epidermis; contiene células nerviosas, fibras musculares, glándulas sudoríparas y folículos pilosos.

desierto: (pág. 70) área con lluvias escasas y en que la tasa anual de evaporación excede la tasa anual de precipitación; es la morada de cactos, pastos y especies animales como serpientes y lagartijas.

detritívoro: (pág. 42) heterótrofo que descompone material orgánico y devuelve los nutrientes al suelo, al aire y al agua, poniendo los nutrientes a disposición de otros organismos.

desarrollo: (pág. 8) cambios que sufre un organismo a lo largo de su vida, hasta alcanzar la vida adulta.

difusión: (pág. 201) movimiento neto de partículas de una región de mayor concentración hacia una región de menor concentración.

dilatación: (pág. 652) apertura del cuello uterino durante el parto.

diploide: (pág. 271) células con dos copias de cada cromosoma (2n).

selección direccional: (pág. 435) cambio en una población hacia una versión extrema de un rasgo benéfico.

dispersion: (p. 92) arrangement of a population in its environment.

disruptive selection: (p. 436) process in which individuals with average traits are removed, creating two populations with extreme traits.

diurnal: (p. 452) organisms that are active during the day.

division: (p. 488) taxonomic term used instead of phylum to group related classes of plants and bacteria.

DNA fingerprinting: (p. 373) separating an individual's unique sequence of DNA fragments to observe distinct banding patterns; can be used by forensic scientists to identify suspects and determine paternity.

DNA ligase: (p. 366) enzyme that chemically links DNA fragments together.

DNA microarray: (p. 375) silicon chips or microscope slides with DNA fragments that can allow many genes in a genome to be studied simultaneously.

DNA polymerase: (p. 334) enzyme that catalyzes synthesis of new DNA molecules.

domain: (p. 488) taxonomic group of one or more kingdoms.

dominant: (p. 278) Mendel's name for a specific trait that appeared in the F1 generation.

dopamine: (p. 568) neurotransmitter in the brain involved with feelings of pleasure, control of body movement, and other functions.

double helix: (p. 330) twisted-ladder shape of DNA, formed by two nucleotide strands twisted around each other.

drug: (p. 567) natural or artificial substance that alters the body's function.

dynamic equilibrium: (p. 202) condition of continuous, random movement of particles but no overall change in concentration of materials.

dispersión: (pág. 92) diseminación de una población en su ambiente.

selección disruptiva: (pág. 436) proceso en que los individuos con rasgos promedio son eliminados, creando dos poblaciones con rasgos extremos.

diurno: (pág. 452) organismos activos durante el día.

división: (pág. 488) término taxonómico que se usa en vez de *phylum* para agrupar clases relacionadas de plantas y bacterias.

huella genética: (pág. 373) separación de las secuencias de fragmentos de DNA propias de un individuo, para obtener su patrón único de bandas; se puede usar en estudios forenses para identificar a sospechosos o en estudios de paternidad.

DNA ligasa: (pág. 366) enzima que une químicamente entre sí, fragmentos de DNA.

micromatrices de DNA: (pág. 375) chips de silicio, o placas microscópicas con fragmentos de DNA que permiten el estudio simultáneo de todos los genes de un genoma.

DNA polimerasa: (pág. 334) enzima que cataliza la síntesis de nuevas moléculas de DNA.

dominio: (pág. 488) grupo taxonómico formado por uno o más reinos.

dominante: (pág. 278) nombre que dio Mendel a rasgos específicos que aparecían en la generación F1.

dopamina: (pág. 568) neurotransmisor cerebral presente en las sensaciones de placer, control de los movimientos del cuerpo y otras funciones.

doble hélice: (pág. 330) forma del DNA; semeja una escalera que se tuerce sobre sí misma y está constituida por dos cadenas enroscadas de nucleótidos.

droga: (pág. 567) sustancia natural o artificial que altera las funciones corporales.

equilibrio dinámico: (pág. 202) condición en que ocurre movimiento continuo y aleatorio de partículas, sin que haya un cambio general en la concentración de materiales.

E

ecological succession: (p. 62) process by which one community replaces another community because of changing abiotic and biotic factors.

ecology: (p. 32) scientific study of all the interrelationships between organisms and their environment.

ecosystem diversity: (p. 118) variety of ecosystems in the biosphere.

ecosystem: (p. 36) biological community and all the nonliving factors that affect it.

edge effect: (p. 126) any different environmental condition occurring along an ecosystem's boundaries.

sucesión ecológica: (pág. 62) proceso en que una comunidad reemplaza a otra, debido a cambios en los factores bióticos y abióticos.

ecología: (pág. 32) ciencia que estudia todas las interrelaciones entre los organismos y su ambiente.

diversidad de ecosistemas: (pág. 118) variedad de ecosistemas en la biosfera.

ecosistema: (pág. 36) comunidad biológica y todos los factores inanimados que la afectan.

efecto borde: (pág. 126) son todas las condiciones ambientales diferentes que suceden a lo largo de los límites de un ecosistema.

electron: (**p. 148**) negatively charged particle that occupies space around an atom's nucleus.

element: (**p. 149**) pure substance composed of only one type of atom; cannot be broken down into another substance by physical or chemical means.

embryo: (**p. 426**) organism's early prebirth stage of development.

emigration (em uh GRAY shun): (**p. 97**) movement of individuals away from a population.

endemic disease: (**p. 671**) a disease found in only a few individuals within a population.

endemic: (**p. 133**) found only in one specific geographic area.

endocrine gland: (**p. 621**) hormone-producing gland that releases its product into the bloodstream.

endocytosis: (**p. 207**) energy-requiring process by which large substances from the outside environment can enter a cell.

endoplasmic reticulum (en duh PLAZ mihk • rih TIHK yuh lum): (**p. 194**) highly folded membrane system in eukaryotic cells that is the site for protein and lipid synthesis.

endosymbiont theory: (**p. 406**) explains that eukaryotic cells may have evolved from prokaryotic cells.

energy: (**p. 218**) ability to do work; energy cannot be created or destroyed, only transformed.

enzyme: (**p. 159**) protein that speeds up a biological reaction by lowering the activation energy needed to start the reaction.

eon: (**p. 396**) longest unit of time in the geologic time scale and can include billions of years.

epidemic: (**p. 671**) large outbreak of a particular disease in a specific area.

epididymis (eh puh DIH duh mus): (**p. 639**) structure on top of each testis where sperm mature and are stored.

epistasis: (**p. 305**) interaction between alleles in which one allele hides the effects of another allele.

era: (**p. 396**) a large division of Earth's geologic time scale that is further divided into one or more periods.

esophagus (ih SAH fuh gus): (**p. 611**) muscular tube that connects the pharynx to the stomach and moves food to the stomach by the process of peristalsis.

estuary (ES chuh wer ee): (**p. 78**) unique, transitional ecosystem that supports diverse species and is formed where freshwater and ocean water merge.

ethics: (**p. 15**) a set of values.

eukaryotic cell: (**p. 186**) unicellular organism with membrane-bound nucleus and organelles; generally larger and more complex than a prokaryotic cell.

eutrophication (yoo troh fih KAY shun): (**p. 127**) water pollution from nitrogen-rich and phosphorus-rich substances flowing into waterways, causing algal overgrowth.

electrón: (**pág. 148**) partícula con carga negativa que gira alrededor del núcleo del átomo.

elemento: (**pág. 149**) sustancia pura compuesta por un solo tipo de átomo; no se puede descomponer en otra sustancia por medios físicos ni por medios químicos.

embrión: (**pág. 426**) etapa inicial del desarrollo de un organismo antes del nacimiento.

emigración: (**pág. 97**) salida de individuos de una población.

enfermedad endémica: (**pág. 671**) enfermedad que sólo contraen unos cuantos individuos dentro de una población.

endémico: (**pág. 133**) que sólo se halla en una región geográfica determinada.

glándula endocrina: (**pág. 621**) glándula productora de hormonas que libera su producto hacia el torrente sanguíneo.

endocitosis: (**pág. 207**) proceso que requiere energía y que permite la entrada de sustancias muy grandes a la célula.

retículo endoplásmico: (**pág. 194**) sistema de membranas de las células eucariotas; presenta numerosos pliegues y es el sitio donde ocurre la síntesis de proteínas y lípidos.

teoría endosimbiótica: (**pág. 406**) propone que las células eucarióticas evolucionaron a partir de células procariotas.

energía: (**pág. 218**) capacidad de realizar trabajo; la energía no se puede crear o destruir, sólo se puede transformar.

enzima: (**pág. 159**) proteína que acelera una reacción biológica, al disminuir energía de activación que se requiere para iniciar la reacción.

eon: (**pág. 396**) la unidad de tiempo más larga en escala del tiempo geológico, la cual puede incluir billones de años.

epidemia: (**pág. 671**) diseminación amplia de una enfermedad dada, en un área específica.

epidídimo: (**pág. 639**) estructura situada en la parte superior del testículo en que los espermatozoides maduran y se almacenan.

epistasis: (**pág. 305**) interacción entre alelos en que un alelo oculta el efecto de otro.

era: (**pág. 396**) gran división de la escala del tiempo geológico de la Tierra que incluye uno o más períodos.

esófago: (**pág. 611**) conducto muscular que conecta la faringe con el estómago; transporta los alimentos hacia el estómago mediante movimientos peristálticos.

estuario: (**pág. 78**) ecosistema único de transición que mantiene gran diversidad de especies y que se forma donde el agua dulce se mezcla con el agua de los mares.

ética: (**pág. 15**) conjunto de valores.

célula eucariota: (**pág. 186**) organismo unicelular con núcleo y organelos rodeados de membrana; generalmente son más grandes y complejas que las células procariotas.

eutroficación: (**pág. 127**) contaminación del agua causada por sustancias ricas en nitrógeno y fósforo que fluyen hacia masas de agua y que producen un crecimiento explosivo de algas.

evolution: (p. 422) hereditary changes in groups of living organisms over time.

evolución: (pág. 422) cambios hereditarios que sufren grupos de organismos a lo largo del tiempo.

exocytosis: (p. 207) energy-requiring process by which a cell expels wastes and secretes substances at the plasma membrane.

exocitosis: (pág. 207) proceso que requiere energía y que permite a una célula expulsar desechos y secretar sustancias, a través de la membrana plasmática.

exon: (p. 337) in RNA processing, the coding sequence that remains in the final mRNA.

exón: (pág. 337) durante el procesamiento de RNA, la secuencia codificadora que queda en el mRNA final.

experiment: (p. 18) procedure performed in a controlled setting to test a hypothesis and collect precise data.

experimento: (pág. 18) procedimiento realizado bajo condiciones controladas, para recopilar datos precisos y probar una hipótesis.

experimental group: (p. 19) in a controlled experiment, the group receiving the factor being tested.

grupo experimental: (pág. 19) grupo al que se aplica el factor que se está probando durante un experimento controlado.

expulsion stage: (p. 652) birthing stage during which a baby travels through the birth canal and exits the mother's body.

etapa de expulsión: (pág. 652) etapa del nacimiento durante la cual el bebé pasa a través del canal de parto y sale del cuerpo de la madre.

external respiration: (p. 590) gas exchange between the atmosphere and the blood, occurring in the lungs.

respiración externa: (pág. 590) intercambio de gases entre la atmósfera y la sangre, que ocurre en los pulmones.

extinction: (p. 116) the disappearance of a species when the last of its members dies.

extinción: (pág. 116) desaparición de una especie que ocurre cuando muere el último de sus miembros.

F

facilitated diffusion: (p. 202) passive transport of ions and small molecules across the plasma membrane by transport proteins.

difusión facilitada: (pág. 202) transporte pasivo de iones y moléculas pequeñas, a través de la membrana plasmática, por medio de proteínas transportadoras.

family: (p. 487) taxonomic group of similar, related genera that is smaller than an order and larger than a genus.

familia: (pág. 487) grupo taxonómico que contiene géneros similares relacionados, está por encima del orden y por debajo del género.

fermentation: (p. 231) process in which NAD+ is regenerated, allowing cells to maintain glycolysis in the absence of oxygen.

fermentación: (pág. 231) proceso de regeneración de NAD+ que permite a las células realizar la glucólisis en ausencia de oxígeno.

fertilization: (p. 271) process by which haploid gametes combine, forming a diploid cell with $2n$ chromosomes, with n chromosomes from the female parent and n chromosomes from the male parent.

fecundación: (pág. 271) proceso de combinación de gametos haploides que origina una célula diploide con $2n$ cromosomas; n cromosomas provienen de la madre y n cromosoma provienen del padre.

fitness: (p. 428) measure of a trait's relative contribution to the following generation.

aptitud: (pág. 428) medida de la contribución relativa de un rasgo a la siguiente generación.

flagellum: (p. 198) long, tail-like projection with whiplike or propellar motion that helps a cell move.

flagelo: (pág. 198) filamento largo y móvil que, al sacudirse como un látigo o un propellar, permite a una célula moverse.

fluid mosaic model: (p. 190) a plasma membrane with components constantly in motion, sliding past one another within the lipid bilayer.

modelo del mosaico fluido: (pág. 190) membrana plasmática cuyos componentes se encuentran en movimiento constante, deslizándose dentro de la capa doble de lípidos.

food chain: (p. 43) simplified model that shows a single path for energy flow through an ecosystem.

cadena alimenticia: (pág. 43) modelo simplificado que muestra una sola vía para el flujo de energía en un ecosistema.

food web: (p. 43) model that shows many interconnected food chains and pathways in which energy and matter flow through an ecosystem.

red alimenticia: (pág. 43) modelo que muestra muchas cadenas alimenticias y vías interconectadas a través de las cuales fluyen la materia y la energía en un ecosistema.

forensics: (p. 15) the field of study that applies science to matters of legal interest and other areas such as archaeology.

medicina forense: (pág. 15) campo de estudio que aplica la ciencia a asuntos de interés legal y otras áreas como la arqueología.

fossil: (p. 393) preserved evidence of an organism, often found in sedimentary rock, that provides evidence of past life.

fósil: (pág. 393) pruebas preservadas de un organismo que a menudo se hallan en rocas sedimentarias y que aportan datos y hechos sobre la vida en el pasado.

founder effect: (p. 433) random effect that can occur when a small population settles in an area separated from the rest of the population and interbreeds, producing unique allelic variations.

efecto fundador: (pág. 433) efecto aleatorio que sucede cuando una población pequeña se establece y se entrecruza en una región, separada del resto de la población, produciendo variaciones alélicas únicas.

fungus: (p. 501) unicellular or multicellular eukaryote that is stationary, absorbs nutrients from organic materials in the environment, and has cell walls that contain chitin.

hongo: (pág. 501) eucariota sésil, unicelular o multicelular, que absorbe nutrientes de la materia orgánica del ambiente y que tiene una pared celular de quitina.

G

gamete: (p. 271) a haploid sex cell, formed during meiosis, that can combine with another haploid sex cell and produce a diploid fertilized egg.

gameto: (pág. 271) célula sexual haploide, formada durante la meiosis, que se puede combinar con otra célula sexual haploide y producir un huevo diploide fecundado.

gel electrophoresis: (p. 365) process that involves using electric current to separate certain biological molecules by size.

electroforesis en gel: (pág. 365) proceso en que se usa corriente eléctrica para separar ciertas moléculas biológicas, según su tamaño.

gene regulation: (p. 342) ability of an organism to control which genes are transcribed in response to the environment.

regulación génica: (pág. 342) capacidad de un organismo para controlar los genes que se transcriben en respuesta a un ambiente.

gene therapy: (p. 378) technique to correct mutated disease-causing genes.

terapia génica: (pág. 378) técnica para corregir genes con mutaciones que causan enfermedades.

gene: (p. 270) functional unit that controls inherited trait expression that is passed on from one generation to another generation.

gene: (pág. 270) unidad funcional que controla la expresión de un rasgo heredado y que se transmite de una generación a otra.

genetic diversity: (p. 116) variety of inheritable characteristics or genes in an interbreeding population.

diversidad genética: (pág. 116) variedad de características o genes heredables en una población que se entrecruza.

genetic drift: (p. 433) random change in allelic frequencies in a population.

deriva genética: (pág. 433) cambio aleatorio de frecuencias alélicas en una población.

genetic engineering: (p. 363) technology used to manipulate an organism's DNA by inserting the DNA of another organism.

ingeniería genética: (pág. 363) tecnología que se aplica para manipular el DNA de un organismo, mediante la inserción del DNA de otro organismo.

genetic recombination: (p. 283) new combination of genes produced by crossing over and independent assortment.

recombinación genética: (pág. 283) nueva combinación de genes producida por el entrecruzamiento y la distribución independiente de genes.

genetics: (p. 277) science of heredity.

genética: (pág. 277) ciencia que estudia la herencia.

genome: (p. 364) total DNA in each cell nucleus of an organism.

genoma: (pág. 364) todo el DNA en el núcleo de cada célula de un organismo.

genomics: (p. 378) study of an organism's genome.

genómica: (pág. 378) estudio del genoma de un organismo.

genotype: (p. 279) an organism's allele pairs.

genotipo: (pág. 279) pares de alelos de un organismo.

genus: (p. 487) taxonomic group of closely related species with a common ancester.

género: (pág. 487) grupo taxonómico de especies estrechamente emparentadas que comparten un antepasado común.

geologic time scale: (p. 396) model showing major geological and biological events in Earth's history.

escala del tiempo geológico: (pág. 396) modelo que muestra los principales eventos geológicos y biológicos de la historia de la Tierra.

glucagon (GLEW kuh gahn): (p. 624) hormone produced by the pancreas that signals liver cells to convert glycogen to glucose and release glucose into the blood.

glucagón: (pág. 624) hormona producida por el páncreas; les indica a las células del hígado que conviertan glucógeno en glucosa y que liberen la glucosa hacia el torrente sanguíneo.

glycolysis: (p. 229) anaerobic process; first stage of cellular respiration in which glucose is broken down into two molecules of pyruvate.

Golgi apparatus: (p. 195) flattened stack of tubular membranes that modifies, sorts, and packages proteins into vesicles and transports them to other organelles or out of the cell.

gradualism: (p. 440) theory that evolution occurs in small, gradual steps over time.

granum: (p. 223) one of the stacks of pigment-containing thylakoids in a plant's chloroplasts.

grassland: (p. 70) biome characterized by fertile soils with a thick cover of grasses.

growth: (p. 9) process that results in mass being added to an organism; may include formation of new cells and new structures.

glucólisis: (pág. 229) proceso anaeróbico; primera etapa de la respiración celular, en la cual la glucosa se transforma en dos moléculas de piruvato.

aparato de Golgi: (pág. 195) conjunto de membranas tubulares aplanadas que modifica, acomoda y empaca proteínas en vesículas y luego las transporta hacia otros organelos o hacia afuera de la célula.

gradualismo: (pág. 440) teoría que señala que la evolución sucede gradualmente, en pasos pequeños, a lo largo del tiempo.

grana: (pág. 223) conjunto de tilacoides con pigmentos de los cloroplastos de una planta.

pradera: (pág. 70) bioma caracterizado por suelos fértiles con una espesa cubierta de pastos.

crecimiento: (pág. 9) proceso que provoca el aumento de masa en un organismo; puede incluir la formación de células y estructuras nuevas.

H

habitat fragmentation: (p. 127) habitat loss from separation of an ecosystem into small pieces of land.

habitat: (p. 38) physical area in which an organism lives.

hair follicle: (p. 527) narrow cavity in the dermis from which a hair grows.

half-life: (p. 395) amount of time required for half of a radioactive isotope to decay.

haploid: (p. 271) cell with half the number of chromosomes (n) as a diploid ($2n$) cell.

haplotype: (p. 378) area of linked genetic variations in the human genome.

Hardy-Weinberg principle: (p. 431) states that allelic frequencies in populations stay the same unless they are affected by a factor that causes change.

heart: (p. 584) hollow, muscular organ that pumps oxygenated blood to the body and deoxygenated blood to the lungs.

helper T cell: (p. 678) lymphocyte that activates antibody secretion in B cells and cytotoxic T cells.

herbivore (HUR buh vor): (p. 41) heterotroph that eats only plants.

heterotroph (HE tuh roh trohf): (p. 41) organism that cannot make its own food and gets its nutrients and energy requirements by feeding on other organisms; also called a consumer.

heterozygous (heh tuh roh ZI gus): (p. 279) organism with two different alleles for a specific trait.

fragmentación del hábitat: (pág. 127) pérdida de hábitat como resultado de la partición de un ecosistema en terrenos pequeños.

hábitat: (pág. 38) área física en que vive un organismo.

folículo piloso: (pág. 527) cavidad estrecha de la dermis de la cual crece un cabello.

media vida: (pág. 395) cantidad de tiempo que se requiere para que se desintegre la mitad de un isótopo radiactivo.

haploide: (pág. 271) célula con la mitad del número de cromosomas (n) que una célula diploide (2n).

haplotipo: (pág. 378) área del genoma humano con variaciones genéticas ligadas.

principio de Hardy-Weinberg: (pág. 431) establece que las frecuencias alélicas de una población permanecen inalterables, a menos que sean afectadas por un factor que produzca un cambio.

corazón: (pág. 584) órgano muscular y hueco que bombea sangre oxigenada hacia el cuerpo y sangre desoxigenada hacia los pulmones.

célula T ayudante: (pág. 678) linfocito que activa los linfocitos B y los linfocitos T citotóxicos para que secreten anticuerpos.

herbívoro: (pág. 41) heterótrofo que sólo se alimenta de plantas.

heterótrofo: (pág. 41) organismo que no puede producir su propio alimento y que obtiene los nutrientes y la energía que necesita, alimentándose de otros organismos; también se llaman consumidores.

heterocigoto: (pág. 279) organismo con dos diferentes alelos para un rasgo específico.

homeostasis (hoh mee oh STAY sus): (p. 10) regulation of an organism's internal environment to maintain conditions needed for life.

homeostasis: (pág. 10) regulación del ambiente interno de un organismo a fin de mantener las condiciones necesarias para la vida.

hominin: (p. 458) humanlike primate that appears to be more closely related to present-day humans than to present-day chimpanzees and bonobos.

hominiano: (pág. 458) primate tipo humano que parece estar más estrechamente emparentado con los humanos actuales que los chimpancés y bonobos actuales.

hominoid: (p. 461) group that includes all nonmonkey anthropoids—the living and extinct gibbons, orangutans, chimpanzees, gorillas, and humans.

hominoide: (pág. 461) grupo que incluye todos los antropoides que no son monos: los gibones, orangutanes, chimpancés, gorilas y humanos vivos y extintos.

Homo: (p. 467) genus that includes living and extinct humans.

Homo: (pág. 467) género que incluye a los humanos vivos y extintos.

homologous chromosome: (p. 270) one of two paired chromosomes, one from each parent, that carries genes for a specific trait at the same location.

cromosoma homólogo: (pág. 270) uno de los cromosomas, de un par de cromosomas, que contienen en un mismo sitio los genes para un rasgo específico. Cada progenitor contribuye un cromosoma de cada par.

homologous structure: (p. 424) anatomically similar structure inherited from a common ancestor.

estructura homóloga: (pág. 424) estructura anatómicamente similar heredada de un antepasado común.

homozygous (ho muh ZI gus): (p. 279) organism with two of the same alleles for a specific trait.

homocigoto: (pág. 279) organismo con dos alelos iguales para un rasgo específico.

hormone: (p. 621) substance, such as estrogen, that is produced by an endocrine gland and acts on target cells.

hormona: (pág. 621) sustancia, como el estrógeno, que es producida por una glándula endocrina y que actúa sobre células blanco.

hybrid: (p. 279) organism heterozygous for a specific trait.

híbrido: (pág. 279) organismo heterocigoto para un rasgo específico.

hydrogen bond: (p. 161) weak electrostatic bond formed by the attraction of opposite charges between a hydrogen atom and an oxygen, fluorine, or nitrogen atom.

enlace de hidrógeno: (pág. 161) enlace electrostático débil, formado por la atracción de cargas opuestas entre un átomo de hidrógeno y un átomo de oxígeno, flúor o nitrógeno.

hypertonic solution: (p. 205) a solution that has a higher concentration of solute outside than inside a cell, causing water to leave the cell by osmosis.

solución hipertónica: (pág. 205) solución que tiene una mayor concentración de soluto que el interior de la célula, la cual se encoge y arruga debido a que el agua sale de su interior por osmosis.

hypothalamus (hi poh THA luh mus): (p. 560) part of the brain that regulates body temperature, appetite, thirst, and water balance.

hipotálamo: (pág. 560) parte del encéfalo que regula la temperatura del cuerpo, el apetito, la sed y el equilibrio del agua.

hypothesis (hi PAH thuh sus): (p. 16) testable explanation of a situation.

hipótesis: (pág. 16) explicación comprobable de una situación.

hypotonic solution: (p. 204) a solution that has a lower concentration of solute outside than inside the cell, causing water to flow into the cell by osmosis.

solución hipotónica: (pág. 204) solución que tiene una menor concentración de soluto; hay más agua fuera que dentro de la célula.

I

immigration (ih muh GRAY shun): (p. 97) movement of individuals into a population.

inmigración: (pág. 97) entrada de individuos a una población.

immunization: (p. 679) vaccination; develops active immunity.

inmunización: (pág. 679) vacunación; desarrolla inmunidad activa.

inbreeding: (p. 361) selective breeding of closely related organisms to produce desired traits and eliminate undesired traits, resulting in pure lines—however, harmful recessive traits can also be passed on.

endogamia: (pág. 361) cruce selectivo de organismos emparentados para obtener rasgos deseados y eliminar rasgos indeseados; permite obtener linajes puros, aunque también puede transmitir rasgos recesivos dañinos.

incomplete dominance: (**p. 302**) complex inheritance pattern in which the heterozygous phenotype is intermediate between those of the two homozygous parent organisms.

dominancia incompleta: (**pág. 302**) patrón complejo de herencia en que el fenotipo heterocigoto es intermedio entre los dos fenotipos de los progenitores homocigotos.

independent variable: (**p. 19**) the one factor that can be changed in a controlled experiment; is the factor tested and affects the experiment outcome.

variable independiente: (**pág. 19**) el único factor que se puede cambiar en un experimento controlado; es el factor que se está probando y afecta los resultados del experimento.

infancy: (**p. 654**) first two years of human life.

lactancia: (**pág. 654**) los primeros dos años de vida en los humanos.

infectious disease: (**p. 666**) pathogen-caused disease passed from one organism to another organism.

enfermedad infecciosa: (**pág. 666**) enfermedad causada por un patógeno que se transmite de un organismo a otro.

inference: (**p. 16**) assumption based on prior experience.

inferencia: (**pág. 16**) supuesto basado en la experiencia previa.

insulin: (**p. 624**) hormone produced by the pancreas that works with glucagon to maintain the level of sugar in the blood.

insulina: (**pág. 624**) hormona producida por el páncreas que, junto con el glucagón, mantiene los niveles adecuados de azúcar en la sangre.

interferon: (**p. 675**) antiviral protein secreted by virus-infected cells.

interferón: (**pág. 675**) proteína secretada por células infectadas por virus.

internal respiration: (**p. 590**) gas exchange between the body's cells and the blood.

respiración interna: (**pág. 590**) intercambio de gases entre las células del cuerpo y la sangre.

interphase: (**p. 246**) first stage of the cell cycle, during which a cell grows, matures, and replicates its DNA.

interfase: (**pág. 246**) primera fase del ciclo celular; en esta fase, la célula crece, madura y replica su DNA.

intertidal zone: (**p. 79**) narrow band of shoreline where the ocean and land meet that is alternately submerged and exposed and is home to constantly changing communities.

zona intermareal: (**pág. 79**) franja estrecha de la costa donde se encuentran la tierra y el mar; es inundada periódicamente por las mareas y presenta un cambio constante en su comunidad.

introduced species: (**p. 128**) nonnative species deliberately or accidentally introduced into a new habitat.

especie introducida: (**pág. 128**) especie no nativa que es introducida deliberadamente o por accidente a un nuevo hábitat.

intron: (**p. 337**) in RNA processing, the intervening coding sequence missing from the final mRNA.

intrón: (**pág. 337**) en la transcripción del RNA, la secuencia de codones que se transcribe pero que no forma parte del mRNA final.

involuntary muscle: (**p. 537**) smooth muscle, which cannot be controlled consciously.

músculo involuntario: (**pág. 537**) músculo liso, no se puede controlar a voluntad.

ion: (**p. 153**) atom that is negatively or positively charged because it has lost or gained one or more electrons.

ion: (**pág. 153**) átomo con carga positiva o negativa porque ha perdido o ganado uno o más electrones.

ionic bond: (**p. 153**) electrical attraction between two oppositely charged atoms or groups of atoms.

enlace iónico: (**pág. 153**) atracción eléctrica entre dos átomos o grupos de átomos con carga opuesta.

isotonic solution: (**p. 204**) a solution with the same concentration of water and solutes as inside a cell, resulting in the cell retaining its normal shape because there is no net movement of water.

solución isotónica: (**pág. 204**) solución con la misma concentración de agua y solutos que el interior de la célula; permite a la célula mantener su forma original porque no hay movimiento neto de agua.

isotope: (**p. 150**) two or more atoms of the same element having different numbers of neutrons.

isótopo: (**pág. 150**) dos o más átomos de un mismo elemento que tienen diferente número de neutrones.

K

K-T boundary: (**p. 399**) layer of iridium-rich material betweeen rocks of the Cretaceous period and rocks of the Paleogene period that provides evidence of a meteorite impact.

límite KT: (**pág. 399**) capa de material rico en iridio, situada entre las rocas de los períodos Cretáceo y Paleoceno; provee pruebas del impacto de un meteorito.

karyotype (KER ee uh tipe): (p. 311) micrograph in which the pairs of homologous chromosomes are arranged in decreasing size.

keratin (KER uh tun): (p. 526) protein contained in the skin's outer epidermal cells that waterproofs and protects underlying cells and tissues.

kidney: (p. 596) bean-shaped, excretory system organ that filters out wastes, water, and salts from the blood and maintains blood pH.

kingdom: (p. 488) taxonomic group of related phyla or divisions.

Koch's postulates: (p. 667) rules for demonstrating that an organism causes a disease.

Krebs cycle: (p. 229) series of reactions in which pyruvate is broken down into carbon dioxide inside the mitochondria of cells; also called the tricarboxylic acid cycle and the citric acid cycle.

cariotipo: (pág. 311) micrografía en que los pares de cromosomas homólogos aparecen ordenados en tamaño decreciente.

queratina: (pág. 526) proteína que contienen las células más externas de la epidermis; es impermeable al agua y protege las células y tejidos subyacentes.

riñón: (pág. 596) órgano del sistema excretor con forma de frijol; mantiene el pH y elimina por filtración los desechos, el agua y las sales.

reino: (pág. 488) grupo taxonómico que incluye filos o divisiones relacionadas.

postulados de Koch: (pág. 667) reglas para demostrar que un organismo causa una enfermedad.

ciclo de Krebs: (pág. 229) serie de reacciones en que el piruvato se desdobla en dióxido de carbono dentro de las mitocondrias de las células; también se llama ciclo del ácido tricarboxílico y ciclo del ácido cítrico.

L

labor: (p. 652) three-stage birthing process that begins with uterine contractions and ends with expulsion of the placenta and umbilical cord.

large intestine: (p. 614) end portion of the digestive tract; involved primarily in water absorption.

latitude: (p. 65) distance of a point on Earth's surface north or south of the equator.

law of independent assortment: (p. 280) Mendelian law stating that a random distribution of alleles occurs during the formation of gametes.

law of segregation: (p. 279) Mendelian law stating that two alleles for each trait separate during meiosis.

law of superposition: (p. 394) states that the oldest layers of rock are found at the bottom and the youngest layers of rock are found at the top of a formation if the rock layers have not been disturbed.

lens: (p. 564) part of the eye behind the iris that inverts an image and focuses it on the retina.

ligament: (p. 534) tough connective tissue band that attaches bones to each other.

limiting factor: (p. 61) biotic or abiotic factor that restricts the number, distribution, or reproduction of a population within a community.

limnetic zone: (p. 77) well-lit, open-water area of a lake or pond.

lipid: (p. 169) hydrophobic biological molecule composed mostly of carbon and hydrogen; fats, oils, and waxes are lipids.

parto: (pág. 652) las tres etapas del proceso de alumbramiento; se inicia con las contracciones uterinas y termina con la expulsión de la placenta y el cordón umbilical.

intestino grueso: (pág. 614) porción final del tracto digestivo; su función principal es la absorción de agua.

latitud: (pág. 65) distancia de un punto sobre la superficie de la Tierra, hacia el norte o hacia el sur del ecuador.

ley de la distribución independiente: (pág. 280) ley de Mendel que establece que la distribución independiente de alelos sucede durante la formación de los gametos.

ley de la segregación: (pág. 279) ley de Mendel que establece que los dos alelos para cada rasgo se separan durante la meiosis.

ley de superposición: (pág. 394) establece que, en una formación rocosa inalterada, los estratos rocosos más antiguos se hallan a mayor profundidad y los estratos más recientes se hallan más cerca de la superficie.

cristalino: (pág. 564) parte del ojo situada detrás del iris; invierte la imagen y la enfoca sobre la retina.

ligamento: (pág. 534) bandas fuertes de tejido conectivo que unen los huesos entre sí.

factor limitante: (pág. 61) factor biótico o abiótico que restringe el número, la distribución o la reproducción de una población en una comunidad.

zona limnética: (pág. 77) área de agua abierta y bien iluminada de un lago o laguna.

lípido: (pág. 169) molécula biológica hidrofóbica compuesta principalmente por carbono e hidrógeno; las grasas, los aceites y las ceras son lípidos.

littoral zone: (p. 76) area of a lake or pond closest to the shore.

zona litoral: (pág. 76) en lagos y lagunas, comprende la zona de agua poco profunda de la orilla y parte del fondo hasta donde penetra la luz solar.

liver: (p. 612) largest internal organ of the body; produces bile.

hígado: (pág. 612) es el órgano interno más grande del cuerpo; produce bilis.

lung: (p. 591) largest respiratory system organ in which gas exchange takes place.

pulmón: (pág. 591) órgano más grande del sistema respiratorio en que se lleva a cabo el intercambio de gases.

lymphocyte: (p. 676) white blood cell involved in specific immunity; a B cell or a T cell.

linfocito: (pág. 676) glóbulo blanco que participa en la inmunidad específica; linfocitos B o linfocitos T.

lysosome: (p. 196) vesicle that uses enzymes to digest excess or worn-out cellular substances.

lisosoma: (pág. 196) vesícula que usa enzimas para digerir sustancias celulares gastadas o que se hallan en número excesivo.

M

macromolecule: (p. 167) large molecule formed by joining smaller organic molecules together.

macromolécula: (pág. 167) molécula de gran tamaño formada por la unión de moléculas orgánicas más pequeñas.

mass extinction: (p. 122) a large-scale dying out of a large percentage of all living organisms in an area within a short time.

extinción masiva: (pág. 122) desaparición a gran escala de un porcentaje grande de todos los organismos vivos de un área dada durante un corto tiempo.

matter: (p. 45) anything that takes up space and has mass.

materia: (pág. 45) cualquier cosa que ocupa lugar y tiene masa.

mechanical digestion: (p. 610) physical breakdown of food that occurs when food is chewed into smaller pieces and then churned by the stomach and small intestine.

digestión mecánica: (pág. 610) desintegración física del alimento que ocurre al masticarlo en trozos más pequeños y luego revolverlo en el estómago y el intestino delgado.

medulla oblongata: (p. 560) part of the brain stem that helps control blood pressure, heart rate, and breathing rate.

médula oblongada: (pág. 560) parte del bulbo raquídeo que ayuda a controlar la presión sanguínea y el ritmo cardíaco y el respiratorio.

meiosis: (p. 271) reduction division process, occurring only in reproductive cells, in which one diploid (2n) cell produces four haploid (n) cells that are not genetically identical.

meiosis: (pág. 271) proceso divisorio de reducción que sólo ocurre en las células reproductoras, mediante el cual una célula diploide (2n) produce cuatro células haploides (n) no idénticas genéticamente.

melanin: (p. 527) pigment in the inner layer of the epidermis that protects against harmful ultraviolet radiation and influences skin color.

melanina: (pág. 527) pigmento que se encuentra en la capa interna de la epidermis; protege a las células del daño causado por la radiación solar e influye en el color de la piel.

memory cell: (p. 679) long-lived lymphocyte produced during exposure to an antigen during the primary immune response; can function in future immune response to the same antigen.

célula de memoria: (pág. 679) linfocito de larga vida producido debido a la exposición a un antígeno durante la respuesta inmunológica primaria; capaz de funcionar en una futura respuesta inmunológica al mismo antígeno.

menstrual (MEN strew ul) cycle: (p. 640) monthly reproductive cycle that helps prepare the human female body for pregnancy; involves the shedding of blood, tissue fluid, mucus, and epithelial cells if an egg is not fertilized.

ciclo menstrual: (pág. 640) ciclo reproductor mensual que ayuda a preparar el cuerpo de la hembra humana para el embarazo; comprende derrame de sangre, tejido líquido, mucosidad y células epiteliales si el óvulo no ha sido fecundado.

messenger RNA: (p. 336) type of RNA that carries genetic information from DNA in the nucleus to direct protein synthesis in the cytoplasm.

RNA mensajero: (pág. 336) tipo de RNA que transporta información desde el DNA en el núcleo hasta la síntesis directa de proteína en el citoplasma.

metabolic disease: (p. 683) disease, such as type 1 diabetes, that results from an error in a biochemical pathway.

enfermedad metabólica: (pág. 683) enfermedad, como la diabetes tipo 1, que resulta de un error en un trayecto bioquímico.

metabolism: (p. 220) all of the chemical reactions that occur within an organism.

metabolismo: (pág. 220) todas las reacciones químicas que ocurren dentro de un organismo.

metaphase: (p. 250) second stage of mitosis in which motor proteins pull sister chromatids to the cell's equator.

metric system: (p. 19) measurement system whose divisions are powers of ten.

mimicry: (p. 429) morphological adaptation in which one species evolves to resemble another species for protection or other advantages.

mineral: (p. 618) inorganic compound, such as calcium, that is used as building material by the body and is involved with metabolic functions.

mitochondrion (mi tuh KAHN dree un): (p. 197) membrane-bound organelle that converts fuel into energy that is available to the rest of the cell.

mitosis (mi TOH sus): (p. 246) second main stage of the cell cycle during which the cell's replicated DNA divides and two genetically identical diploid daughter cells are produced.

mixture: (p. 163) combination of two or more different substances in which each substance keeps its individual characteristics; can have a uniform composition (homogeneous) or have distinct areas of substances (heterogeneous).

molecular clock: (p. 495) model that uses comparisons of DNA sequences to estimate phylogeny and rate of evolutionary change.

molecule: (p. 152) compound whose atoms are held together by covalent bonds.

morula: (p. 645) solid ball of embryonic cells that forms before the blastocyst.

multiple alleles: (p. 304) having more than two alleles for a specific trait.

mutagen (MYEW tuh jun): (p. 348) substance, such as a chemical, that causes mutations.

mutation: (p. 345) permanent change in a cell's DNA, ranging from changes in a single base pair to deletions of large sections of chromosomes.

mutualism (MYEW chuh wuh lih zum): (p. 39) symbiotic relationship in which both organisms benefit.

myofibril: (p. 538) small muscle fiber that functions in contraction and consists of myosin and actin protein filaments.

myosin: (p. 538) protein filament in muscle cells that functions with actin in contraction.

metafase: (pág. 250) segunda fase de la mitosis en la cual las proteínas motores atraen a las cromátides hermanas hacia el ecuador de la célula.

sistema métrico: (pág. 19) sistema de medida cuyas divisiones son potencias de diez.

mimetismo: (pág. 429) adaptación morfológica en la cual una especie evoluciona para parecerse a otra a modo de protección u otras ventajas.

mineral: (pág. 618) compuesto inorgánico, como el calcio, utilizado por el cuerpo como material de construcción, presente en las funciones metabólicas.

mitocondria: (pág. 197) organelo membranoso que transforman el combustible en energía disponible al resto de las célula.

mitosis: (pág. 246) segundo período principal del ciclo celular, durante el cual el DNA replicado de la célula se divide y se forman dos células hijas diploides idénticas.

mezcla: (pág. 163) combinación de dos o más sustancias diferentes en la cual cada una mantiene sus características individuales; pueden tener una composición uniforme (homogénea) o áreas distintivas de sustancias (heterogénea).

reloj molecular: (pág. 495) modelo que usa las comparaciones secuenciales de DNA para calcular la filogenia y la tasa de cambio evolutivo.

molécula: (pág. 152) compuesto cuyos átomos se mantienen unidos por medio de enlaces covalentes.

mórula: (pág. 645) bola sólida de células embrionarias que se forma antes del blastocito.

alelos múltiples: (pág. 304) presencia de más de dos alelos para un rasgo genético.

mutágeno: (pág. 348) sustancia, como un químico, que causa mutaciones.

mutación: (pág. 345) cambio permanente en el DNA de una célula, desde cambios en un par de base simple a eliminaciones de grandes secciones de cromosomas.

mutualismo: (pág. 39) relación simbiótica en la cual ambos organismos se benefician.

miofibrilla: (pág. 538) fibra muscular pequeña que funciona por contracción, compuesta por los filamentos proteicos miosina y actina.

miosina: (pág. 538) filamento proteico en las células musculares que funciona con la actina en la contracción muscular.

N

NADP+: (p. 224) in photosynthesis, the major electron carrier involved in electron transport.

natural resource: (p. 123) any material or organism in the biosphere, including water, soil, fuel, and plants and animals.

NADP+: (pág. 224) en la fotosíntesis, el principal portador de electrones presente en el transporte de electrones.

recurso natural: (pág. 123) cualquier material u organismo en la biosfera, incluidos agua, suelo, combustible, plantas y animales.

natural selection: (p. 420) theory of evolution developed by Darwin, based on four ideas: excess reproduction, variations, inheritance, and the advantages of specific traits in an environment.

Neanderthal: (p. 470) a species also referred to as *Homo neanderthalensis* that evolved exclusively in Europe and Asia about 200,000 years ago.

neuron: (p. 552) cell that carries nerve impulses throughout the body and is composed of a cell body, an axon, and dendrites.

neurotransmitter: (p. 557) chemical that diffuses across a synapse and binds to receptors on a neighboring neuron's dendrite, causing channels to open on the neighboring cell and the creation of a new action potential.

neutron: (p. 148) particle without a charge in an atom's nucleus.

niche (NIHCH): (p. 38) role, or position, of an organism in its environment.

nitrogen fixation: (p. 48) process in which nitrogen gas is captured and converted into a form plants can use.

nocturnal: (p. 452) organisms that are active at night.

node: (p. 555) gap in the myelin sheath along the length of an axon; nerve impulses move from node to node.

nondisjunction: (p. 313) cell division in which the sister chromatids do not separate correctly, resulting in gametes with an abnormal number of chromosomes.

nonrenewable resource: (p. 130) any natural resource available in limited amounts or replaced extremely slowly by natural processes.

nucleic acid: (p. 171) complex macromolecule that stores and communicates genetic information.

nucleolus: (p. 193) the site of ribosome production within the nucleus of eukaryotic cells.

nucleosome: (p. 332) repeating subunit of chromatin fibers, consisting of DNA coiled around histones.

nucleotide: (p. 171) a subunit of nucleic acid formed from a simple sugar, a phosphate group, and a nitrogenous base.

nucleus: (p. 148) center of an atom; contains neutrons and protons. **(p. 186)** in eukaryotic cells, the central membrane-bound organelle that manages cellular functions and contains DNA.

nutrient: (p. 45) chemical substance that living organisms obtain from the environment to carry out life processes and sustain life.

nutrition: (p. 615) process by which an individual takes in and uses food, which provides building blocks for growth and energy to maintain body mass.

selección natural: (pág. 420) teoría de la evolución desarrollada por Darwin, basada en cuatro ideas: reproducción excesiva, variaciones, herencia y las ventajas de cualidades específicas en un medioambiente.

Neanderthal: (pág. 470) especie también conocida como Homo neanderthalensis, la cual evolucionó exclusivamente en Europa y Asia hace unos 200,000 años.

neurona: (pág. 552) célula nerviosa que conduce los impulsos a través del cuerpo y se compone de un cuerpo celular, un axón y dendritas.

neurotransmisores: (pág. 557) químico que se difunde por la sinapsis y se enlaza a los receptores en la dendrita de una neurona vecina; causa la apertura de los canales en la célula vecina para crear un nuevo impulso.

neutrón: (pág. 148) partícula sin carga en el núcleo de un átomo.

nicho: (pág. 43) la función o posición de un organismo en su ambiente.

nitrificación: (pág. 48) proceso mediante el cual el gas nitrógeno se captura y se convierte en una forma utilizable por las plantas.

nocturno: (pág. 452) organismos activos durante la noche.

nódulo: (pág. 555) brecha en la vaina de mielina a lo largo de un axón; los impulsos nerviosos se desplazan de nodo a nodo.

no disyunción: (pág. 313) división celular en la cual las cromátides no se separan correctamente lo cual resulta en gametos con un número anormal de cromosomas.

recurso no renovable: (pág. 130) cualquier recurso natural disponible en cantidades limitadas o reemplazado en forma extremadamente lenta por los procesos naturales.

ácido nucleico: (pág. 171) macromolécula compleja que almacena y comunica información genética.

nucléolo: (pág. 193) el sitio de producción de ribosomas dentro del núcleo de las células eucariotas.

nucleosoma: (pág. 332) subunidad repetitiva de fibras de cromatina que consiste en DNA enroscado alrededor de histonas.

nucleótido: (pág. 171) subunidades de ácidos nucleicos formadas por un azúcar simple, un grupo fosfato y una base nitrogenada.

núcleo: (pág. 148) centro de un átomo; contiene neutrones y protones. **(pág. 186)** en las células eucariotas es el organelo membranoso central que se encarga de las funciones celulares y que contiene el DNA.

nutriente: (pág. 45) sustancia química que obtienen los organismos vivos del medioambiente para el desarrollo de los procesos vitales y el sustento de la vida.

nutrición: (pág. 615) proceso mediante el cual un individuo consume y usa alimento, lo cual provee las bases para el crecimiento y la energía para mantener la masa corporal.

O

observation: (**p. 16**) orderly, direct information gathering about a natural phenomenon.

Okazaki fragment: (**p. 334**) short segment of DNA synthesized discontinuously in small segments in the 3' to 5' direction by DNA polymerase.

omnivore (AHM nih vor): (**p. 42**) heterotroph that consumes both plants and animals.

oocyte (OH uh site): (**p. 640**) immature egg inside an ovary.

operon: (**p. 342**) section of DNA containing genes for proteins required for a specific metabolic pathway—consists of an operator, promoter, regulatory gene, and genes coding for proteins.

opposable first digit: (**p. 452**) a digit, either a thumb or a toe, that is set apart from the other digits and can be brought across the palm or foot so that it touches or nearly touches the other digits; this allows animals to grasp an object in a powerful grip.

order: (**p. 488**) taxonomic group that contains related families.

organelle: (**p. 186**) specialized internal cell structure that carries out specific cell functions such as protein synthesis and energy transformation.

organism: (**p. 6**) anything that has or once had all the characteristics of life.

organization: (**p. 8**) orderly structure shown by living things.

osmosis (ahs MOH sus): (**p. 203**) diffusion of water across a selectively permeable membrane.

ossification: (**p. 532**) formation of bone from osteoblasts.

osteoblast: (**p. 532**) bone-forming cell.

osteoclast: (**p. 533**) cell that breaks down bone cells.

osteocyte: (**p. 532**) living bone cell.

overexploitation: (**p. 124**) overuse of species with economic value—a factor in species extinction.

oviduct (OH vuh duct): (**p. 640**) tube that transports an egg released from an ovary to the uterus.

observación: (**pág. 16**) forma directa y ordenada de recopilar información sobre un fenómeno natural.

fragmento Okazaki: (**pág. 334**) segmento corto de DNA que la enzima polimerasa de DNA sintetiza discontinuamente en segmentos pequeños en la dirección de 3' a 5'.

omnívoro: (**pág. 42**) heterótrofo que consume tanto plantas como animales.

oocito: (**pág. 640**) óvulo inmaduro dentro de un ovario.

operón: (**pág. 342**) sección de DNA que contiene los genes para las proteínas requeridas para un trayecto metabólico específico; consiste en un operador, un promotor, un gene regulador y un código de genes para las proteínas.

primer dígito oponible: (**pág. 452**) dígito, ya sea un pulgar o un dígito del pie, que se diferencia del resto de los dígitos y el cual se puede cruzar a través de la palma de la mano o del pie y puede tocar o casi tocar los otros dígitos; esto les permite a los animales asir objetos fuertemente.

orden: (**pág. 488**) agrupación taxonómica de familias relacionadas.

organelo: (**pág. 186**) estructura celular especializada interna con funciones celulares específicas como la síntesis y la transformación de energía.

organismo: (**pág. 6**) cualquier cosa que tuvo o tiene todas las características de la vida.

organización: (**pág. 8**) estructura ordenada de todos los seres vivos.

osmosis: (**pág. 203**) difusión del agua a través de una membrana de permeabilidad selectiva.

osificación: (**pág. 532**) formación ósea a partir de los osteoblastos.

osteoblasto: (**pág. 532**) célula formadora de hueso.

osteoclasto: (**pág. 533**) célula que destruye las células óseas.

osteocito: (**pág. 532**) célula ósea viva.

sobre-explotación: (**pág. 124**) uso excesivo de las especies con un valor económico; es un factor en la extinción de especies.

oviducto: (**pág. 640**) conducto que transporta un óvulo desde el ovario hasta el útero.

P

pacemaker: (**p. 585**) heart's sinoatrial node, which initiates contraction of the heart.

paleontologist (pay lee ahn TAH luh just): (**p. 394**) scientist who studies fossils.

pandemic: (**p. 671**) widespread epidemic.

marcapaso: (**pág. 585**) nódulo atrioventricular del corazón que inicia la contracción cardíaca.

paleontólogo: (**pág. 394**) científico que estudia los fósiles.

pandemia: (**pág. 671**) epidemia que se extiende a muchos países.

parasitism (PER uh suh tih zum): (**p. 40**) symbiotic relationship in which one organism benefits at the expense of another organism.

parasitismo: (**pág. 40**) relación simbiótica en la cual un organismo se beneficia a expensas de otro.

parasympathetic nervous system: (**p. 562**) branch of the autonomic nervous system that controls organs and is most active when the body is at rest.

sistema nervioso parasimpático (SNP): (**pág. 562**) división del sistema nervioso autónomo que controla los órganos y es más activo cuando el cuerpo está en reposo.

parathyroid hormone: (**p. 624**) substance produced by the parathyroid gland that increases blood calcium levels by stimulating bones to release calcium.

hormona paratiroides: (**pág. 624**) sustancia producida por la glándula tiroides que aumenta los niveles de calcio en la sangre al estimular la liberación de calcio en los huesos.

pathogen: (**p. 666**) agent, such as a bacterium, virus, protozoan, or fungus, that causes infectious disease.

patógeno: (**pág. 666**) agente, como las bacterias, los virus, los protozoarios o los hongos, causante de enfermedades infecciosas.

pedigree: (**p. 299**) diagrammed family history that is used to study inheritance patterns of a trait through several generations and that can be used to predict disorders in future offspring.

pedigrí: (**pág. 299**) historia familiar diagramada que se emplea para el estudio de los patrones hereditarios de un rasgo a través de varias generaciones, capaz de predecir trastornos en la progenie futura.

peer review: (**p. 14**) a process in which the procedures used during an experiment may be repeated and the results are evaluated by scientists who are in the same field or are conducting similar research.

evaluación de compañeros: (**pág. 14**) proceso en que los procedimientos que se usan durante un experimento pueden repetirse y otros científicos en el mismo campo de estudio o que realizan investigaciones similares pueden evaluar los resultados.

pepsin: (**p. 611**) digestive enzyme involved in the stomach's chemical digestion of proteins.

pepsina: (**pág. 611**) enzima digestiva presente en la digestión química de las proteínas.

period: (**p. 396**) subdivision of an era on the geologic time scale.

período: (**pág. 396**) subdivisión de una era en la escala geológica.

peripheral nervous system: (**p. 558**) consists of sensory and motor neurons that transmit information to and from the central nervous system.

sistema nervioso periférico (SNP): (**pág. 558**) compuesto por neuronas sensoriales y motoras que transportan información desde y hacia el sistema nervioso central.

peristalsis (per uh STAHL sus): (**p. 611**) rhythmic, wavelike muscular contractions that move food throughout the digestive tract.

peristaltismo: (**pág. 611**) serie de contracciones musculares rítmicas ondulantes que mueven el alimento por el esófago.

pH: (**p. 165**) measure of the concentration of hydrogen ions (H+) in a solution.

pH: (**pág. 165**) medida de la concentración de iones de hidrógeno (H+) en una solución.

pharmacogenomics (far muh koh jeh NAH mihks): (**p. 378**) study of how genetic inheritance affects the body's response to drugs in order to produce safer and more specific drug dosing.

farmacogenética: (**pág. 378**) estudio de la influencia de la herencia genética en la respuesta corporal a los medicamentos a fin de producir posologías más seguras y específicas.

phenotype: (**p. 279**) observable characteristic that is expressed as a result of an allele pair.

fenotipo: (**pág. 279**) apariencia externa que se expresa como resultado de un par de alelos.

phospholipid bilayer: (**p. 188**) plasma membrane layers composed of phospholipid molecules arranged with polar heads facing the outside and nonpolar tails facing the inside.

bicapa fosfolípida: (**pág. 188**) capas membranosas del plasma compuestas por moléculas fosfolípidas cuyas cabezas polares miran hacia fuera y cuyas colas no polares miran hacia adentro.

photic zone: (**p. 80**) open-ocean zone shallow enough for sunlight to penetrate.

zona fótica: (**pág. 80**) zona a mar abierto lo suficientemente baja para que penetre la luz solar.

photosynthesis: (**p. 220**) two-phase anabolic pathway in which the Sun's light energy is converted to chemical energy for use by the cell.

fotosíntesis: (**pág. 220**) sendero anabólico bifásico por medio del cual la energía luminosa solar se transforma en energía química para uso de la célula.

phylogeny (fy LAH juh nee): (p. 491) evolutionary history of a species.

phylum (FI lum): (p. 488) taxonomic group of related classes.

pigment: (p. 223) light-absorbing colored molecule, such as chlorophyll and carotenoid, in the thylakoid membranes of chloroplasts.

pituitary gland: (p. 623) endocrine gland located at the base of the brain; called the "master gland" because it regulates many body functions.

placental stage: (p. 653) birthing stage in which the placenta and umbilical cord are expelled from the mother's body.

plankton: (p. 77) tiny marine or freshwater organisms that serve as a food source for many fish species; often autotrophic.

plasma membrane: (p. 185) flexible, selectively permeable boundary that helps control what enters and leaves the cell.

plasma: (p. 587) clear, yellowish fluid portion of the blood.

plasmid: (p. 366) any of the small, circular, double-stranded DNA molecules that can be used as a vector.

plate tectonics: (p. 400) geologic theory that Earth's surface is broken into several huge plates that move slowly on a partially molten rock layer.

platelet: (p. 587) flat cell fragment that functions in blood clotting.

polar body: (p. 641) tiny cell that is produced and eventually disintegrates in the development of an oocyte.

polar molecule: (p. 161) molecule with oppositely charged regions.

polygenic trait: (p. 309) characteristic, such as eye color or skin color, that results from the interaction of multiple gene pairs.

polymer: (p. 167) large molecule formed from smaller repeating units of identical, or nearly identical, compounds linked by covalent bonds.

polymerase chain reaction (PCR): (p. 368) genetic engineering technique that can make copies of specific regions of a DNA fragment.

polyploidy: (p. 285) having one or more extra sets of all chromosomes, which, in polyploid plants, can often result in greater size and better growth and survival.

pons: (p. 560) part of the brain stem that helps control breathing rate.

filogenia: (pág. 491) historia evolutiva de una especie.

filo: (pág. 488) agrupación taxonómica de clases que se relacionan.

pigmento: (pág. 223) molécula de color que absorbe la luz, como la clorofila y la carotenoide, en la membranas tilacoides de los cloroplastos.

glándula pituitaria: (pág. 623) glándula endocrina localizada en la base del cerebro, conocida como la "glándula maestra" puesto que regula muchas funciones corporales.

etapa placentaria: (pág. 653) etapa de alumbramiento en la cual la placenta y el cordón umbilical se expulsan del cuerpo de la madre.

plancton: (pág. 77) diminutos organismos marinos o de agua dulce, que flotan libremente y constituyen la fuente alimenticia de muchas especies de peces, a menudo autótrofos.

membrana plasmática: (pág. 185) frontera flexible, selectivamente permeable, que ayuda a controlar lo que entra y sale de la célula.

plasma: (pág. 587) porción fluida clara y amarillenta de la sangre.

plásmido: (pág. 366) cualquiera de las pequeñas moléculas de DNA circulares de filamento doble que pueden usarse como vector.

tectónica de placas: (pág. 400) teoría geológica que afirma que la corteza terrestre se divide en varias placas enormes que se mueven lentamente sobre una capa rocosa parcialmente fundida.

plaqueta: (pág. 587) fragmentos celulares planos que funcionan en la coagulación de la sangre.

cuerpo polar: (pág. 641) célula diminuta que se produce y posteriormente se desintegra en el desarrollo de un oocito.

molécula polar: (pág. 161) molécula con regiones cargadas opuestamente.

rasgo poligénico: (pág. 309) característica, como el color de los ojos o de la piel, que resulta de la interacción de múltiples pares de genes.

polímero: (pág. 167) molécula gigante formada por unidades pequeñas, repetitivas, idénticas, o casi idénticas, de compuestos unidos por enlaces covalentes.

reacción en cadena de polimerasa (RCP): (pág. 368) técnica de ingeniería genética capaz de hacer copias de regiones específicas de un fragmento de DNA.

poliploide: (pág. 285) que tiene uno o más grupos de todos los cromosomas que, en plantas poliploides, puede resultar en un mayor tamaño y mejor crecimiento y supervivencia.

pons: (pág. 560) parte del bulbo raquídeo que ayuda a controlar el ritmo de la respiración.

population density: (p. 92) number of organisms per unit of living area.

densidad demográfica: (pág. 92) número de organismos por unidad de área o superficie habitable.

population growth rate: (p. 97) how fast a specific population grows.

tasa de crecimiento demográfico: (pág. 97) el grado de rapidez con que crece una población específica.

population: (p. 36) group of organisms of the same species that occupy the same geographic place at the same time.

población: (pág. 36) grupo de organismos de la misma especie que viven en la misma localidad geográfica al mismo tiempo

postzygotic isolating mechanism: (p. 437) factor that prevents a hybrid zygote from developing, or prevents hybrid offspring from reproducing; operates after fertilization.

mecanismo de aislamiento postcigótico: (pág. 437) factor que impide el desarrollo de un cigoto hibrido o que impide que la progenie híbrida se reproduzca; opera después de la fecundación.

predation (prih DAY shun): (p. 38) act of one organism feeding on another organism.

depredación: (pág. 38) modo de nutrición de un organismo al alimentarse de otro.

prehensile tail: (p. 456) functions like a fifth limb, provides the ability to grasp tree limbs or other objects and can support the body weight of some animals.

cola prensil: (pág. 456) funciona como una quinta extremidad y permite que algunos animales se agarren de las ramas de los árboles u otros objetos y la cual puede sostener el peso de algunos animales.

prezygotic isolating mechanism: (p. 437) factor that prevents individuals from different species from mating; operates before fertilization.

mecanismo de aislamiento precigótico: (pág. 437) factor que imposibilita el apareamiento de individuos de diferentes especies; opera antes de la fecundación.

primary succession: (p. 62) establishment of a community in an area of bare rock or bare sand, where no topsoil is present.

sucesión primaria: (pág. 62) colonización en un área de roca o arena desnudas, sin mantillo (capa vegetal superior).

product: (p. 157) substance formed by a chemical reaction; located on the right side of the arrow in a chemical equation.

producto: (pág. 157) sustancia formada por una reacción química; localizada en el lado derecho de la flecha en una ecuación química.

profundal zone: (p. 77) deepest, coldest area of a large lake with little light and limited biodiversity.

zona profunda: (pág. 77) el área más fría y profunda de un lago grande, con poca luz y una biodiversidad limitada.

prokaryotic cell: (p. 186) microscopic, unicellular organism without a nucleus or other membrane-bound organelles.

célula procariótica: (pág. 186) organismo unicelular, microscópico, sin núcleo u otros organelos limitados por membranas.

prophase: (p. 248) first stage of mitosis, during which the cell's chromatin condenses into chromosomes.

profase: (pág. 248) primera etapa de la mitosis, durante la cual la cromatina celular se condensa para formar cromosomas.

protein: (p. 170) organic compound made of amino acids joined by peptide bonds; primary building block of organisms.

proteína: (pág. 170) compuesto orgánico formado por aminoácidos unidos por enlaces pépticos; piedra angular de los organismos.

proteomics: (p. 379) study of the structure and function of proteins in the human body.

proteómica: (pág. 379) estudio de la estructura y función de proteínas en el cuerpo humano.

protist: (p. 501) unicellular, multicellular, or colonial eukaryote whose cell walls may contain cellulose; can be plantlike, animal-like, or funguslike.

protista: (pág. 501) eucariota unicelular, multicelular o colonial cuyas paredes celulares pueden contener celulosa; pueden tener forma vegetal, animal o fungosa.

proton: (p. 148) positively charged particle in an atom's nucleus.

protón: (pág. 148) particular cargada positivamente en el núcleo de un átomo.

puberty: (p. 639) growth period during which sexual maturity is reached.

pubertad: (pág. 639) período durante el cual se llega a la madurez sexual.

punctuated equilibrium: (p. 440) theory that evolution occurs with relatively sudden periods of speciation followed by long periods of stability.

equilibrio puntuado: (pág. 440) teoría que sostiene que la evolución ocurre con períodos relativamente súbitos de especiación, seguido de largos períodos de estabilidad.

Glossary • Glosario

R

radiometric dating: (p. 395) method used to determine the age of rocks using the rate of decay of radioactive isotopes.

datación radiométrica: (pág. 395) método utilizado para determinar la edad de las rocas mediante la tasa de desintegración de los isótopos radioactivos.

reactant: (p. 157) substance that exists before a chemical reaction starts; located on the left side of the arrow in a chemical equation.

reactivo: (pág. 157) sustancia que existe antes de empezar una reacción química; localizada al lado izquierdo de la flecha en una ecuación química.

recessive: (p. 256) Mendel's name for a specific trait hidden or masked in the F1 generation.

recesivo: (pág. 256) nombre de Mendel para una rasgo específico oculto o encubierto en la generación F1.

recombinant DNA: (p. 366) newly generated DNA fragment containing exogenous DNA.

DNA recombinante: (pág. 366) fragmento de DNA recién generado que contiene DNA exógeno.

red blood cell: (p. 587) hemoglobin-containing, disc-shaped, short-lived blood cell that lacks a nucleus and that transports oxygen to all the body's cells.

glóbulo rojo: (pág. 587) célula sanguínea de corta vida, esférica, anucleada, que contiene hemoglobina y que transporta oxígeno a todas las células del cuerpo.

red bone marrow: (p. 532) type of marrow that produces red and white blood cells and platelets.

médula roja: (pág. 532) tipo de médula que produce glóbulos rojos, glóbulos blancos y plaquetas.

reflex arc: (p. 553) nerve pathway consisting of a sensory neuron, an interneuron, and a motor neuron.

arco reflejo: (pág. 553) trayecto nervioso que consiste en una neurona sensorial, una interneurona y una neurona motora.

relative dating: (p. 394) method used to determine the age of rocks by comparing the rocks with younger and older rock layers.

datación relativa: (pág. 394) método empleado para determinar la edad de las rocas al compararlas con capas rocosas más recientes y más antiguas.

renewable resource: (p. 130) any resource replaced by natural processes more quickly than it is consumed.

recurso renovable: (pág. 130) cualquier recurso reemplazable por procesos naturales de manera más rápida de lo que se consume.

reproduction: (p. 9) production of offspring.

reproducción: (pág. 9) producción de la progenie.

reservoir: (p. 668) source of a pathogen in the environment.

reservorio: (pág. 668) fuente de un patógeno en el medio ambiente.

response: (p. 9) organism's reaction to a stimulus.

respuesta: (pág. 9) la reacción de un organismo a un estímulo.

restriction enzyme: (p. 364) bacterial protein that cuts DNA into fragments.

enzima restrictiva: (pág. 364) proteína bacterial que corta el DNA en fragmentos.

retina: (p. 564) innermost layer of the eye that contains rods and cones.

retina: (pág. 564) capa más interna del ojo que contiene bastoncillos y conos.

ribosomal RNA (rRNA): (p. 336) type of RNA that associates with proteins to form ribosomes.

RNA ribosomal (rRNA): (pág. 336) tipo de RNA que se asocia con las proteínas para formar ribosomas.

ribosome: (p. 193) simple cell organelle that helps manufacture proteins.

ribosoma: (pág. 193) organelo celular simple que ayuda a elaborar proteínas.

RNA polymerase: (p. 337) enzyme that regulates RNA synthesis.

RNA polimerasa: (pág. 337) enzima que regula la síntesis de RNA.

RNA: (p. 336) ribonucleic acid; guides protein synthesis.

RNA: (pág. 336) ácido ribonucleico; guía la síntesis de proteínas.

rod: (p. 564) one of the light-sensitive cells in the retina that sends action potentials to the brain via neurons in the optic nerve.

bastoncillo: (pág. 564) una de las células de la retina que es sensible a la luz y que envía potenciales de acción al cerebro mediante las neuronas del nervio óptico.

rubisco: (p. 226) enzyme that converts inorganic carbon dioxide molecules into organic molecules during the final step of the Calvin cycle.

rubisco: (pág. 226) enzima que convierte las moléculas inorgánicas de dióxido de carbono en moléculas orgánicas durante la etapa final del ciclo de Calvin.

S

safety symbol: (p. 21) logo representing a specific danger such as radioactivity, electrical or biological hazard, or irritants that may be present in a lab activity or field investigation.

símbolo de seguridad: (pág. 21) logotipo que advierte acerca de algún peligro, como radioactividad, agentes irritantes, riesgos eléctricos o biológicos, que pudieran presentarse en una actividad de laboratorio o investigación de campo.

sarcomere: (p. 538) in skeletal muscle, the functional unit that contracts and is composed of myofibrils.

sarcómero: (pág. 538) en el músculo esquelético, la unidad funcional que se contrae y se compone de miofibrilla muscular.

science: (p. 11) a body of knowledge based on the study of nature.

ciencia: (pág. 11) conjunto de conocimiento basado en el estudio de la naturaleza y su entorno físico.

scientific methods: (p. 16) a series of problem-solving procedures that might include observations, forming a hypothesis, experimenting, gathering and analyzing data, and drawing conclusions.

método científico: (pág. 16) una serie de procedimientos de solución de problemas que pueden incluir observaciones, formulación de una hipótesis, experimentación, recopilación y análisis de datos y sacar conclusiones.

sebaceous gland: (p. 527) oil-producing gland in the dermis that lubricates skin and hair.

glándula sebácea: (pág. 527) glándula productora de aceite en la dermis que lubrica la piel y el cabello.

secondary succession: (p. 63) orderly change that occurs in a place where soil remains after a community of organisms has been removed.

sucesión secundaria: (pág. 63) cambio ordenado que ocurre en el suelo de los lugares que experimentaron la expulsión de una comunidad de organismos.

sediment: (p. 75) material deposited by water, wind, or glaciers.

sedimento: (pág. 75) material depositado por el agua, el viento o los glaciares.

selective breeding: (p. 360) directed breeding to produce plants and animals with desired traits.

criaza selectiva: (pág. 360) crianza dirigida hacia la producción de plantas y animales con rasgos deseados.

selective permeability (pur mee uh BIH luh tee): (p. 187) property of the plasma membrane that allows it to control movement of substances into or out of the cell.

permeabilidad selectiva: (pág. 187) propiedad de la membrana plasmática que le permite controlar el movimiento de las sustancias dentro o fuera de la célula.

semen (SEE mun): (p. 639) fluid that contains sperm, nourishment, and other fluids of the male reproductive system.

semen: (pág. 639) fluido que contiene espermatozoides, nutrientes y otros fluidos del sistema reproductor masculino.

semicircular canal: (p. 565) inner-ear structure that transmits information about body position and balance to the brain.

canal semicircular: (pág. 565) estructura interna del oído que transmite al cerebro información relativa a la posición y equilibrio corporales.

semiconservative replication: (p. 333) method of DNA replication in which parental strands separate, act as templates, and produce molecules of DNA with one parental DNA strand and one new DNA strand.

replicación semiconservadora: (pág. 333) método de replicación del DNA mediante el cual los filamentos paternos se separan, actúan como plantillas y producen moléculas de DNA con un filamento paterno de DNA y otro nuevo de DNA.

seminiferous tubule (se muh NIHF rus • TEW byul): (p. 639) tubule of the testis in which sperm develop.

túbulo seminífero: (pág. 639) túbulo del teste donde se desarrollan los espermatozoides.

serendipity: (p. 18) occurrence of accidental or unexpected but fortunate outcomes.

serendipia: (pág. 18) hecho accidental o inesperado con resultados favorables.

sex chromosome: (p. 305) X or Y chromosome; paired sex chromosomes determine an individual's gender—XX individuals are female and XY individuals are male.

cromosoma sexual: (pág. 305) cromosoma X o Y; los cromosomas sexuales pareados determinan el sexo del individuo: los individuos XX son femeninos y los XY, masculinos.

sex-linked trait: (p. 307) characteristic, such as red-green color blindness, controlled by genes on the X chromosome; also called an X-linked trait.

rasgo ligado al sexo: (pág. 307) característica, como el daltonismo, controlada por los genes en el cromosoma X; también denominado rasgo ligado a la X.

sexual selection: (p. 436) change in the frequency of a trait based on competition for a mate.

selección sexual: (pág. 436) cambio de la frecuencia de un rasgo basado en la rivalidad por una pareja.

SI: (p. 19) system of measurements used by scientists, abbreviation of the International System of Units.

SI: (pág. 19) sistema de medición que usan los científicos, abreviatura del Sistema Internacional de Unidades.

single nucleotide polymorphism: (p. 376) variation in a DNA sequence occurring when a single nucleotide in a genome is altered.

polimorfismo de un nucleótido simple: (pág. 376) variación en una secuencia de DNA que ocurre al alterarse un solo nucleótido en un genoma.

sister chromatid: (p. 248) structure that contains identical DNA copies and is formed during DNA replication.

cromátides hermanas: (pág. 248) estructura formada durante la replicación del DNA, que contiene copias idénticas de DNA.

skeletal muscle: (p. 538) striated muscle that causes movement when contracted and is attached to bones by tendons.

músculo óseo: (pág. 538) músculo estriado que causa movimiento al contraerse, adherido a los huesos por los tendones.

small intestine: (p. 612) longest part of the digestive tract; involved in mechanical and chemical digestion.

intestino delgado: (pág. 612) parte más larga del tracto digestivo; presente en la digestión mecánica y química.

smooth muscle: (p. 537) muscle that lines many hollow internal organs, such as the stomach and uterus.

músculo liso: (pág. 537) músculo que recubre las paredes de muchos órganos internos, como el estómago y el útero.

solute: (p. 163) substance dissolved in a solvent.

soluto: (pág. 163) sustancia disuelta en un disolvente.

solution: (p. 163) homogeneous mixture formed when a substance (the solute) is dissolved in another substance (the solvent).

solución: (pág. 163) mezcla homogénea formada al disolverse una sustancia (el soluto) en otra sustancia (el disolvente).

solvent: (p. 163) substance in which another substance is dissolved.

disolvente: (pág. 163) sustancia en la cual se disuelve otra sustancia.

somatic nervous system: (p. 561) part of the peripheral nervous system that transmits impulses to and from skin and skeletal muscles.

sistema nervioso somático: (pág. 561) porción del sistema nervioso periférico que transmite impulsos hacia y desde la piel a los músculos esqueléticos.

species diversity: (p. 117) in a biological community, the number and abundance of different species.

diversidad de especies: (pág. 117) en una comunidad biológica, el número y la abundancia de diferentes especies.

species: (p. 9) group of organisms that can interbreed and produce fertile offspring.

especie: (pág. 9) grupo de organismos que pueden cruzarse y producir progenies fértiles.

spindle apparatus: (p. 250) structure made of spindle fibers, centrioles, and aster fibers that is involved in moving and organizing chromosomes before the cell divides.

huso: (pág. 250) estructura compuesta por fibras de microtúbulos, centriolos y áster encargada de movilizar y organizar los cromosomas antes de la división celular.

spongy bone: (p. 532) less dense inner-bone layer with many cavities that contain bone marrow.

hueso esponjoso: (pág. 532) capa de hueso interno menos densa con muchos orificios que contienen médula.

spontaneous generation: (p. 401) idea that life arises from nonliving things.

generación espontánea: (pág. 401) idea de que la vida surge de la materia no viva.

stabilizing selection: (p. 434) most common form of natural selection in which organisms with extreme expressions of a trait are removed.

selección estabilizadora: (pág. 434) la selección natural más común, mediante la cual se eliminan los organismos con expresiones extremas de un rasgo.

stem cell: (p. 256) unspecialized cell that can develop into a specialized cell under the right conditions.

célula madre: (pág. 256) célula no especializada capaz de desarrollarse en una célula especializada bajo las condiciones adecuadas.

stimulant: (p. 568) substance/drug that increases alertness and physical activity.

estimulante: (pág. 568) sustancia / droga que aumenta la agudeza y actividad física.

stimulus: (p. 9) any change in an organism's internal or external environment that causes the organism to react.

estímulo: (pág. 9) cualquier cambio en el ambiente interno o externo de un organismo que ocasiona una reacción en el organismo.

stroma: (p. 223) fluid-filled space outside the grana in which light-dependent reactions take place.

estroma: (pág. 223) espacio relleno de fluido fuera de las granas donde suceden reacciones lumino-dependientes.

substrate: (p. 160) reactant to which an enzyme binds.

sustrato: (pág. 160) reactivo al cual se adhiere una enzima.

sustainable use: (p. 130) use of resources at a rate that they can be replaced or recycled.

uso sostenible: (pág. 130) uso de los recursos a una tasa tal que puedan reemplazarse o reciclarse.

symbiosis (sihm bee OH sus): (p. 39) close mutualistic, parasitic, or commensal association between two or more species that live together.

simbiosis: (pág. 39) asociación estrecha mutualista, parasítica o comensal entre dos o más especies que viven juntas.

sympathetic nervous system: (p. 562) branch of the autonomic nervous system that controls organs and is most active during emergencies or stress.

sistema nervioso simpático: (pág. 562) rama del sistema nervioso autónomo que controla los órganos y es muy activo durante las emergencias o el estrés.

sympatric speciation: (p. 438) occurs when a species evolves into a new species in an area without a geographic barrier.

especiación simpátrica: (pág. 438) ocurre cuando una especie evoluciona en una especie nueva dentro de un área sin frontera geográfica.

synapse (SIH naps): (p. 557) gap between one neuron's axon and another nueron's dendrite.

sinapsis: (pág. 557) brecha entre el axón de una neurona y las dendritas de otra.

T

taste bud: (p. 563) one of a number of specialized chemical receptors on the tongue that can detect sweet, sour, salty, and bitter tastes.

gustativa: (pág. 563) una de un número de receptores químicos especializados de la lengua que detectan los sabores dulces, agrios, salados y amargos.

taxon: (p. 487) named group of organisms, such as a phylum, genus, or species.

taxón: (pág. 487) grupo nombrado de organismos, como un filo, un género o una especie.

taxonomy (tak SAH nuh mee): (p. 485) branch of biology that identifies, names, and classifies species based on their natural relationships.

taxonomía: (pág. 485) rama de la biología que identifica, nombra y clasifica las especies en base a su morfología y comportamiento.

technology (tek NAH luh jee): (p. 15) application of knowledge gained from scientific reasearch to solve society's needs and problems and improve the quality of life.

tecnología: (pág. 15) aplicación del conocimiento derivado de la investigación científica a fin de resolver los problemas y necesidades de la sociedad y mejorar la calidad de vida.

telomere: (p. 311) protective cap made of DNA that is found on the ends of a chromosome.

telómero: (pág. 311) capa protectora de DNA que se encuentra en los extremos de un cromosoma.

telophase: (p. 251) last stage of mitosis in which nucleoli reappear. Two new nuclear membranes begin to form, but the cell has not yet completely divided.

telofase: (pág. 251) fase final de la mitosis en que reaparecen los nucléolos. Comienzan a formarse dos nuevas membranas nucleares sin que la célula haya terminado de dividirse.

temperate forest: (p. 69) biome south of the boreal forest characterized by broad-leaved, deciduous trees, well-defined seasons, and average yearly precipitation of 75–150 cm.

bosque templado: (pág. 69) bioma al sur del bosque boreal compuesto por árboles caducifolios de hojas anchas, estaciones bien definidas y entre 70 y 150 cm de precipitación promedio anual.

tendon: (p. 538) tough connective-tissue band that connects muscle to bone.

tendón: (pág. 538) banda dura de tejido conectivo que adhieren los músculos a los huesos.

test cross: (p. 362) breeding that can be used to determine an organism's genotype.

cruzamiento de prueba: (pág. 362) cruce que puede ayudar a determinar el genotipo de un organismo.

theory of biogenesis (bi oh JEN uh sus): (p. 402) states that only living organisms can produce other living organisms.

teoría de la biogénesis: (pág. 402) plantea que sólo los organismos vivos pueden producir otros organismos vivos.

theory: (p. 14) explanation of a natural phenomenon based on many observations and investigations over time.

teoría: (pág. 14) explicación de un fenómeno natural basado en muchas observaciones y experimentos con el correr del tiempo.

thermodynamics: (p. 218) study of the flow and transformation of energy in the universe.

termodinámica: (pág. 218) estudio del flujo y transformación de la energía del universo.

threshold: (p. 554) minimum stimulus needed to produce a nerve impulse.

umbral: (pág. 554) estímulo mínimo requerido para producir un impulso nervioso.

thylakoid: (p. 223) in choroplasts, one of the stacked, flattened, pigment-containing membranes in which light-dependent reactions occur.

tilacoide: (pág. 223) en los cloroplastos, una de las membranas apiladas y aplanadas que contienen pigmento donde ocurren las reacciones lumino-dependientes.

thyroxine: (**p. 624**) thyroid hormone that increases the metabolic rate of cells.

tiroxina: (**pág. 624**) hormona tiroidea que aumenta la tasa metabólica de las células.

tolerance: (**p. 61**) organism's ability to survive biotic and abiotic factors. (**p. 571**) as the body becomes less responsive to a drug, an individual needs larger and more frequent doses to achieve the same effect.

tolerancia: (**pág. 61**) capacidad de un organismo de sobrevivir factores bióticos y abióticos. (pág. 571) a medida que el cuerpo se vuelve menos sensible a una droga, un individuo necesita dosis más frecuentes y mayores para obtener el mismo efecto.

trachea: (**p. 591**) tube that carries air from the larynx to the bronchi.

tráquea: (**pág. 591**) conducto que lleva el aire desde la laringe hasta los bronquios.

transcription (trans KRIHP shun): (**p. 337**) process in which mRNA is synthesized from the template DNA.

transcripción: (**pág. 337**) proceso en que el mRNA se sintetiza del patrón de DNA.

transfer RNA: (**p. 336**) type of RNA that transports amino acids to the ribosome.

RNA de transferencia: (**pág. 336**) tipo de RNA que transporta los aminoácidos a los ribosomas.

transformation: (**p. 367**) process in which bacterial cells take up recombinant plasmid DNA.

transformación: (**pág. 367**) proceso en el cual las células bacterianas recogen el DNA plásmido recombinante.

transgenic organism: (**p. 370**) organism that is genetically engineered by inserting a gene from another organism.

organismo transgénico: (**pág. 370**) organismo generado genéticamente al insertar el gene de un organismo distinto.

translation: (**p. 338**) process in which mRNA attaches to the ribosome and a protein is assembled.

traducción: (**pág. 338**) proceso mediante el cual el mRNA se adhiere al ribosoma y se sintetiza una proteína.

transport protein: (**p. 189**) protein that moves substances or wastes through the plasma membrane.

proteína de transporte: (**pág. 189**) proteína que mueve sustancias o desechos a través de la membrana plasmática.

trophic (TROH fihk) level: (**p. 42**) each step in a food chain or food web.

nivel trófico: (**pág. 42**) cada paso de una cadena o red alimenticia.

tropical rain forest: (**p. 72**) hot, wet biome with year-round humidity; contains Earth's most diverse species of plants and animals.

pluviselva tropical: (**pág. 72**) bioma caliente, lluvioso, con una humedad anual continua; contiene las especies más diversas de plantas y animales terrestres.

tropical savanna: (**p. 71**) biome characterized by grasses and scattered trees, and herd animals such as zebras and antelopes.

sabana tropical: (**pág. 71**) bioma caracterizado por hierbas, árboles dispersos y animales que se agrupan en manadas, como cebras y antílopes.

tropical seasonal forest: (**p. 71**) biome characterized by deciduous and evergreen trees, a dry season, and animal species that include monkeys, elephants, and Bengal tigers.

bosque estacional tropical: (**pág. 71**) bioma caracterizado por árboles caducifolios y siempreverdes, una estación seca y especies de animales que incluyen a los monos, los elefantes y los tigres de Bengala.

tundra: (**p. 68**) treeless biome with permanently frozen soil under the surface and average yearly precipitation of 15–25 cm.

tundra: (**pág. 68**) bioma carente de árboles, con suelo permanentemente congelado bajo la superficie; y una precipitación promedio anual de 15-25 cm.

U

urea: (**p. 596**) nitrogenous waste product of the excretory system.

urea: (**pág. 596**) producto de desecho nitrogenado del sistema excretorio.

urethra (yoo REE thruh): (**p. 639**) tube that conducts semen and urine out of the body through the penis in males and transports urine out of the body in females.

uretra: (**pág. 639**) conducto que conduce el semen y la orina fuera del cuerpo a través del pene en los machos y transporta la orina fuera del cuerpo de las hembras.

vacuole: (**p. 195**) **membrane-bound** vesicle for temporary storage of materials such as food, enzymes, and wastes.

valve: (**p. 584**) one of the tissue flaps in veins that prevents backflow of blood.

van der Waals forces: (**p. 155**) attractive forces between molecules.

vas deferens (VAS • DEF uh runz): (**p. 639**) duct through which sperm move away from the testis and toward the urethra.

vein: (**p. 584**) blood vessel that carries deoxygenated blood back to the heart.

vestigial structure: (**p. 425**) **reduced form** of a functional structure that indicates shared ancestry.

villus (VIH luhs): (**p. 613**) fingerlike structure through which most nutrients are absorbed from within the small intestine.

vitamin: (**p. 618**) fat-soluble or water-soluble organic compound needed in very small amounts for the body's metabolic activities.

voluntary muscle: (**p. 538**) consciously controlled skeletal muscle.

area: (**pág. 195**) espacio encerrado por una membrana para el almacenamiento temporal de materiales como alimento, enzimas y desechos.

válvula: (**pág. 584**) uno de los opérculos de los tejidos en las venas que evita que la sangre fluya hacia atrás.

fuerzas de van der Waals: (**pág. 155**) fuerzas de atracción entre las moléculas.

conducto deferente: (**pág. 639**) ducto por el cual los espermatozoides se alejan de los testículos hacia la uretra.

vena: (**pág. 584**) vaso sanguíneo que devuelve la sangre desoxigenada al corazón.

estructura vestigial: (**pág. 425**) forma reducida de una estructura funcional que indica ascendencia compartida.

vellosidad: (**pág. 613**) estructura en forma de dedos por la cual el intestino delgado absorbe la mayor parte de los nutrientes.

vitamina: (**pág. 618**) compuesto orgánico liposoluble o hidrosoluble, que se necesita en porciones muy pequeñas para las actividades metabólicas del cuerpo.

músculo voluntario: (**pág. 538**) músculo esquelético controlado en forma consciente.

W

weather: (**p. 65**) atmospheric conditions such as temperature and precipitation at a specific place and time.

wetland: (**p. 78**) water-saturated land area that supports aquatic plants.

white blood cell: (**p. 588**) large, nucleated, disease-fighting blood cell produced in the bone marrow.

woodland: (**p. 69**) biome characterized by small trees and mixed shrub communities.

tiempo: (**pág. 65**) condiciones atmosféricas, como la temperatura y la precipitación, en un lugar y tiempo específico.

humedal: (**pág. 78**) terreno saturado de agua que mantiene a las plantas acuáticas.

glóbulo blanco: (**pág. 588**) célula sanguínea gigante y nucleada que combate las enfermedades y se produce en la médula ósea.

zona boscosa: (**pág. 69**) bioma caracterizado por árboles pequeños y comunidades de arbustos mixtas.

yellow bone marrow: (**p. 532**) type of marrow that consists of stored fat.

médula ósea amarilla: (**pág. 532**) tipo de médula que consiste en grasas almacenadas.

Z

zero population growth (ZPG): (**p. 104**) occurs when the birthrate equals the death rate.

crecimiento demográfico nulo (CDN): (**pág. 104**) sucede cuando la tasa de natalidad es igual a la tasa de mortalidad.

INDEX

Index Key
Italic page numbers = illustration/photo **Bold page numbers = vocabulary term**
Italic page numbers + act = activity

A

Index

C

Index

F

Index

H

I

Index

Index

Z

A Biologist's Guide To The Periodic Table

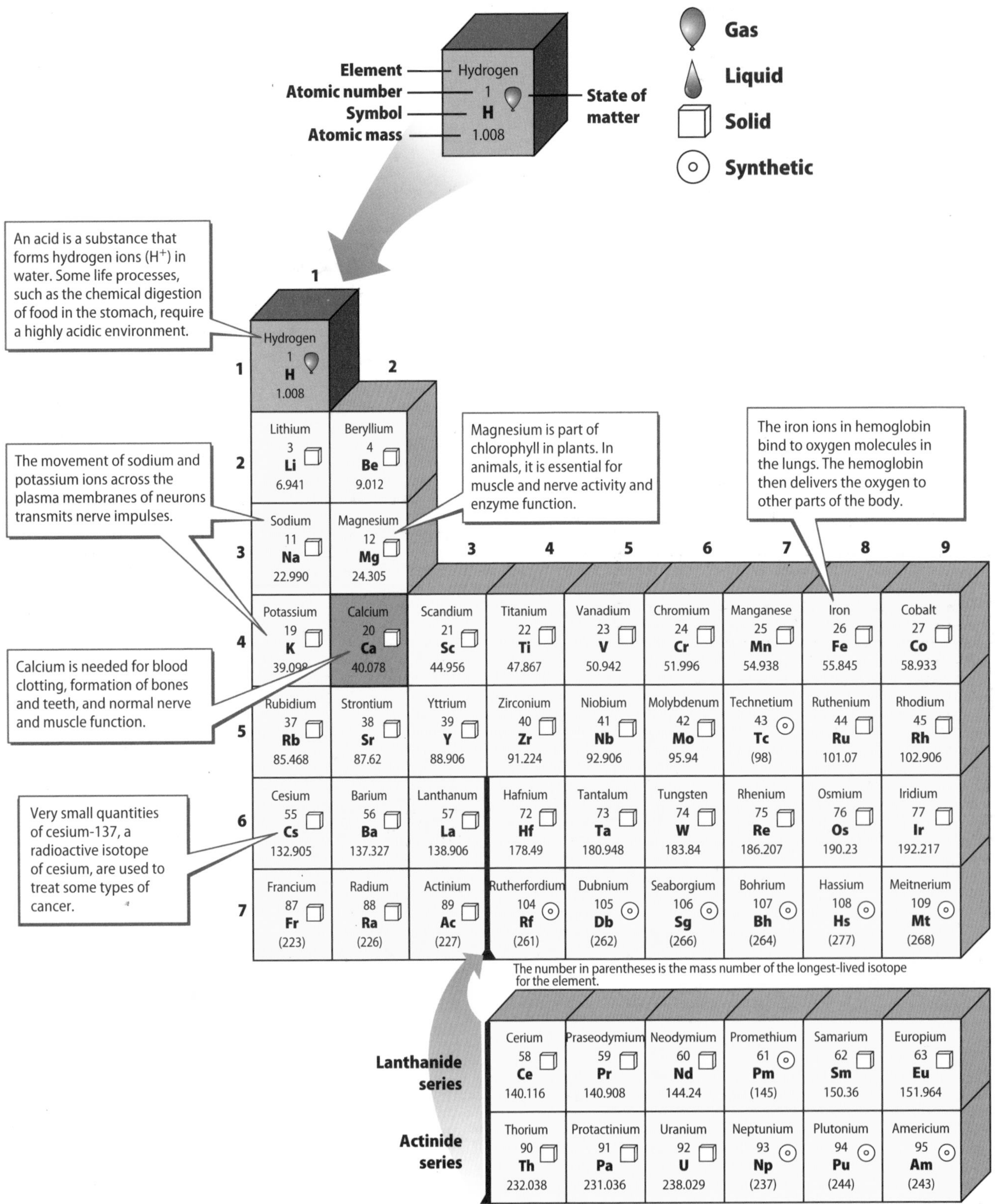